Values of fundamental constants

Quantity	Symbol	Value
Speed of light in vacuum	c_0	3.00×10^8 m/s
Gravitational constant	G	6.6738×10^{-11} N·m^2/kg^2
Avogadro's number	N_A	6.0221413×10^{23} mol^{-1}
Boltzmann's constant	k_B	1.380×10^{-23} J/K
Charge on electron	e	1.60×10^{-19} C
Permittivity constant	ϵ_0	$8.85418782 \times 10^{-12}$ C^2/(N·m^2)
Permeability constant	μ_0	$4\pi \times 10^{-7}$ T·m/A
Planck's constant	h	6.626×10^{-34} J·s
Electron mass	m_e	9.11×10^{-31} kg
Proton mass	m_p	1.6726×10^{-27} kg
Neutron mass	m_n	1.6749×10^{-27} kg
Atomic mass unit	amu	1.6605×10^{-27} kg

Other useful numbers

Number or quantity	Value
π	3.1415927
e	2.7182818
1 radian	57.2957795°
Absolute zero ($T = 0$)	-273.15 °C
Average acceleration g due to gravity near Earth's surface	9.8 m/s^2
Speed of sound in air at 20 °C	343 m/s
Density of dry air at atmospheric pressure and 20 °C	1.29 kg/m^3
Earth's mass	5.97×10^{24} kg
Earth's radius (mean)	6.38×10^6 m
Earth–Moon distance (mean)	3.84×10^8 m

PRINCIPLES & PRACTICE OF
PHYSICS
VOLUME 1

Eric Mazur
Harvard University

With contributions from

Catherine H. Crouch
Swarthmore College

Peter A. Dourmashkin
Massachusetts Institute of Technology

Boston   Columbus   Indianapolis   New York   San Francisco   Upper Saddle River
Amsterdam   Cape Town   Dubai   London   Madrid   Milan   Munich   Paris   Montréal   Toronto
Delhi   Mexico City   São Paulo   Sydney   Hong Kong   Seoul   Singapore   Taipei   Tokyo

Executive Editor: Becky Ruden
Publisher: Jim Smith
Senior Development Editor: Margot Otway
Project Managers: Martha Steele and Beth Collins
Vice-President of Marketing: Christy Lesko
Marketing Manager: Will Moore
Photo Researcher: Eric Schrader
Manufacturing Buyer: Jeff Sargent
Managing Development Editor: Cathy Murphy
Development Editor: Irene Nunes
Program Manager: Katie Conley
Image Lead, Senior Project Manager: Maya Melenchuk
Copyeditor: Carol Reitz
Associate Content Producer: Megan Power
Full-Service Production and Composition: Cenveo® Publisher Services
Illustrators: Rolin Graphics
Senior Market Development Manager: Michelle Cadden
Text Designer: Hespenheide Design
Cover Designer: Tandem Creative, Inc.
Cover Photo Credit: Franklin Kappa

Credits and acknowledgments borrowed from other sources and reproduced, with permission, in this textbook appear on the appropriate page within the text or on p. C-1.

Library of Congress Cataloging-in-Publication Data on file.

ISBN 10: 0-321-95840-3; ISBN 13: 978-0-321-95840-2

2 3 4 5 6 7 8 9 10—DOR—17 16 15 14

www.pearsonhighered.com

Brief Contents

Volume 1 of *Principles of Physics* includes Chapters 1–21. Volume 2 of *Principles of Physics* includes Chapters 22–34.

Chapter 1	Foundations	1
Chapter 2	Motion in One Dimension	28
Chapter 3	Acceleration	53
Chapter 4	Momentum	75
Chapter 5	Energy	101
Chapter 6	Principle of Relativity	121
Chapter 7	Interactions	148
Chapter 8	Force	176
Chapter 9	Work	202
Chapter 10	Motion in a Plane	226
Chapter 11	Motion in a Circle	254
Chapter 12	Torque	281
Chapter 13	Gravity	308
Chapter 14	Special Relativity	337
Chapter 15	Periodic Motion	374
Chapter 16	Waves in One Dimension	400
Chapter 17	Waves in Two and Three Dimensions	432
Chapter 18	Fluids	463
Chapter 19	Entropy	501
Chapter 20	Energy Transferred Thermally	530
Chapter 21	Degradation of Energy	562
Chapter 22	Electric Interactions	
Chapter 23	The Electric Field	
Chapter 24	Gauss's Law	
Chapter 25	Work and Energy in Electrostatics	
Chapter 26	Charge Separation and Storage	
Chapter 27	Magnetic Interactions	
Chapter 28	Magnetic Fields of Charged Particles in Motion	
Chapter 29	Changing Magnetic Fields	
Chapter 30	Changing Electric Fields	
Chapter 31	Electric Circuits	
Chapter 32	Electronics	
Chapter 33	Ray Optics	
Chapter 34	Wave and Particle Optics	

About the Author

Eric Mazur is the Balkanski Professor of Physics and Applied Physics at Harvard University and Area Dean of Applied Physics. Dr. Mazur is a renowned scientist and researcher in optical physics and in education research, and a sought-after author and speaker.

Dr. Mazur joined the faculty at Harvard shortly after obtaining his Ph.D. at the University of Leiden in the Netherlands. In 2012 he was awarded an Honorary Doctorate from the École Polytechnique and the University of Montreal. He is a Member of the Royal Academy of Sciences of the Netherlands and holds honorary professorships at the Institute of Semiconductor Physics of the Chinese Academy of Sciences in Beijing, the Institute of Laser Engineering at the Beijing University of Technology, and the Beijing Normal University.

Dr. Mazur has held appointments as Visiting Professor or Distinguished Lecturer at Carnegie Mellon University, the Ohio State University, the Pennsylvania State University, Princeton University, Vanderbilt University, Hong Kong University, the University of Leuven in Belgium, and National Taiwan University in Taiwan, among others.

In addition to his work in optical physics, Dr. Mazur is interested in education, science policy, outreach, and the public perception of science. In 1990 he began developing peer instruction, a method for teaching large lecture classes interactively. This teaching method has developed a large following, both nationally and internationally, and has been adopted across many science disciplines.

Dr. Mazur is author or co-author of over 250 scientific publications and holds two dozen patents. He has also written on education and is the author of *Peer Instruction: A User's Manual* (Pearson, 1997), a book that explains how to teach large lecture classes interactively. In 2006 he helped produce the award-winning DVD *Interactive Teaching*. He is the co-founder of Learning Catalytics, a platform for promoting interactive problem solving in the classroom, which is available in MasteringPhysics®.

To the Student

Let me tell you a bit about myself.

I always knew exactly what I wanted to do. It just never worked out that way.

When I was seven years old, my grandfather gave me a book about astronomy. Growing up in the Netherlands I became fascinated by the structure of the solar system, the Milky Way, the universe. I remember struggling with the concept of infinite space and asking endless questions without getting satisfactory answers. I developed an early passion for space and space exploration. I knew I was going to be an astronomer. In high school I was good at physics, but when I entered university and had to choose a major, I chose astronomy.

It took only a few months for my romance with the heavens to unravel. Instead of teaching me about the mysteries and structure of the universe, astronomy had been reduced to a mind-numbing web of facts, from declinations and right ascensions to semi-major axes and eccentricities. Disillusioned about astronomy, I switched majors to physics. Physics initially turned out to be no better than astronomy, and I struggled to remain engaged. I managed to make it through my courses, often by rote memorization, but the beauty of science eluded me.

It wasn't until doing research in graduate school that I rediscovered the beauty of science. I knew one thing for sure, though: I was never going to be an academic. I was going to do something useful in my life. Just before obtaining my doctorate, I lined up my dream job working on the development of the compact disc, but I decided to spend one year doing postdoctoral research first.

It was a long year. After my postdoc, I accepted a junior faculty position and started teaching. That's when I discovered that the combination of doing research—uncovering the mysteries of the universe—and teaching—helping others to see the beauty of the universe—is a wonderful combination.

When I started teaching, I did what all teachers did at the time: lecture. It took almost a decade to discover that my award-winning lecturing did for my students exactly what the courses I took in college had done for me: It turned the subject that I was teaching into a collection of facts that my students memorized by rote. Instead of transmitting the beauty of my field, I was essentially regurgitating facts to my students.

When I discovered that my students were not mastering even the most basic principles, I decided to completely change my approach to teaching. Instead of lecturing, I asked students to read my lecture notes at home, and then, in class, I taught by questioning—by asking my students to reflect on concepts, discuss in pairs, and experience their own "aha!" moments.

Over the course of more than twenty years, the lecture notes have evolved into this book. Consider this book to be my best possible "lecturing" to you. But instead of listening to me without having the opportunity to reflect and think, this book will permit you to pause and think; to hopefully experience many "aha!" moments on your own.

I hope this book will help you develop the thinking skills that will make you successful in your career. And remember: your future may be—and likely will be—very different from what you imagine.

I welcome any feedback you have. Feel free to send me email or tweets.

I wrote this book for you.

Eric Mazur
🐦 @eric_mazur
mazur@harvard.edu
Cambridge, MA

To the Instructor

They say that the person who teaches is the one who learns the most in the classroom. Indeed, teaching led me to many unexpected insights. So, also, with the writing of this book, which has been a formidably exciting intellectual journey.

Why write a new physics text?

In May 1993 I was driving to Troy, NY, to speak at a meeting held in honor of Robert Resnick's retirement. In the car with me was a dear friend and colleague, Albert Altman, professor at the University of Massachusetts, Lowell. He asked me if I was familiar with the approach to physics taken by Ernst Mach in his popular lectures. I wasn't. Mach treats conservation of momentum before discussing the laws of motion, and his formulation of mechanics had a profound influence on Einstein.

The idea of using conservation principles derived from experimental observations as the basis for a text—rather than Newton's laws and the concept of force—appealed to me immediately. After all, most physicists never use the concept of force because it relates only to mechanics. It has no role in quantum physics, for example. The conservation principles, however, hold throughout all of physics. In that sense they are much more fundamental than Newton's laws. Furthermore, conservation principles involve only algebra, whereas Newton's second law is a differential equation.

It occurred to me, however, that Mach's approach could be taken further. Wouldn't it be nice to start with conservation of both momentum *and* energy, and only *later* bring in the concept of force? After all, physics education research has shown that the concept of force is fraught with pitfalls. What's more, after tediously deriving many results using kinematics and dynamics, most physics textbooks show that you can derive the same results from conservation principles in just one or two lines. Why not do it the easy way first?

It took me many years to reorganize introductory physics around the conservation principles, but the resulting approach is one that is much more unified and modern—the conservation principles are the theme that runs throughout this entire book.

Additional motives for writing this text came from my own teaching. Most textbooks focus on the acquisition of information and on the development of procedural knowledge. This focus comes at the expense of conceptual understanding or the ability to transfer knowledge to a new context. As explained below, I have structured this text to redress that balance. I also have drawn deeply on the results of physics education research, including that of my own research group.

I have written this text to be accessible and easy for students to understand. My hope is that it can take on the burden of basic teaching, freeing class time for synthesis, discussion, and problem solving.

Setting a new standard

The tenacity of the standard approach in textbooks can be attributed to a combination of inertia and familiarity. Teaching large introductory courses is a major chore, and once a course is developed, changing it is not easy. Furthermore, the standard texts worked for *us*, so it's natural to feel that they should work for our students, too.

The fallacy in the latter line of reasoning is now well-known thanks to education research. Very few of our students are like us at all. Most take physics because they are required to do so; many will take no physics beyond the introductory course. Physics education research makes it clear that the standard approach fails these students.

Because of pressure on physics departments to deliver better education to non-majors, changes are occurring in the way physics is taught. These changes, in turn, create a need for a textbook that embodies a new educational philosophy in both format and presentation.

Organization of this book

As I considered the best way to convey the conceptual framework of mechanics, it became clear that the standard curriculum truly deserved to be rethought. For example, standard texts are forced to redefine certain concepts more than once—a strategy that we know befuddles students. (Examples are *work*, the standard definition of which is incompatible with the first law of thermodynamics, and *energy*, which is redefined when modern physics is discussed.)

Another point that has always bothered me is the arbitrary division between "modern" and "classical" physics. In most texts, the first thirty-odd chapters present physics essentially as it was known at the end of the 19th century; "modern physics" gets tacked on at the end. There's no need for this separation. Our goal should be to explain physics in the way that works best for students, using our full contemporary understanding. *All* physics is modern!

That is why my table of contents departs from the "standard organization" in the following specific ways.

Emphasis on conservation laws. As mentioned earlier, this book introduces the conservation laws early and treats them the way they should be: as the backbone of physics. The advantages of this shift are many. First, it avoids many of the standard pitfalls related to the concept of force, and it leads naturally to the two-body character of forces and the laws of motion. Second, the conservation laws enable students to solve a wide variety of problems without any calculus. Indeed, for complex systems, the conservation laws are often the natural (or only) way to solve problems. Third, the book deduces the conservation laws from observations, helping to make clear their connection with the world around us.

Table 1 Scheduling matrix

Topic	Chapters	Can be inserted after chapter...	Chapters that can be omitted without affecting continuity
Mechanics	1–14		6, 13–14
Waves	15–17	12	16–17
Fluids	18	9	
Thermal Physics	19–21	10	21
Electricity & Magnetism	22–30	12 (but 17 is needed for 29–30)	29–30
Circuits	31–32	26 (but 30 is needed for 32)	32
Optics	33–34	17	34

I and several other instructors have tested this approach extensively in our classes and found markedly improved performance on problems involving momentum and energy, with large gains on assessment instruments like the Force Concept Inventory.

Early emphasis on the concept of system. Fundamental to most physical models is the separation of a system from its environment. This separation is so basic that physicists tend to carry it out unconsciously, and traditional texts largely gloss over it. This text introduces the concept in the context of conservation principles and uses it consistently.

Postponement of vectors. Most introductory physics concerns phenomena that take place along one dimension. Problems that involve more than one dimension can be broken down into one-dimensional problems using vectorial notation. So a solid understanding of physics in one dimension is of fundamental importance. However, by introducing vectors in more than one dimension from the start, standard texts distract the student from the basic concepts of kinematics.

In this book, I develop the complete framework of mechanics for motions and interactions in one dimension. I introduce the second dimension when it is needed, starting with rotational motion. Hence, students are free to concentrate on the actual physics.

Just-in-time introduction of concepts. Wherever possible, I introduce concepts only when they are necessary. This approach allows students to put ideas into immediate practice, leading to better assimilation.

Integration of modern physics. A survey of syllabi shows that less than half the calculus-based courses in the United States cover modern physics. I have therefore integrated selected "modern" topics throughout the text. For example, special relativity is covered in Chapter 14, at the end of mechanics. Chapter 32, Electronics, includes sections on semiconductors and semiconductor devices. Chapter 34, Wave and Particle Optics, contains sections on quantization and photons.

Modularity. I have written the book in a modular fashion so it can accommodate a variety of curricula (See Table 1, "Scheduling matrix").

The book contains two major parts, Mechanics and Electricity and Magnetism, plus five shorter parts. The two major parts by themselves can support an in-depth two-semester or three-quarter course that presents a complete picture of physics embodying the fundamental ideas of modern physics. Additional parts can be added for a longer or faster-paced course. The five shorter parts are more or less self-contained, although they do build on previous material, so their placement is flexible. Within each part or chapter, more advanced or difficult material is placed at the end.

Pedagogy

This text draws on many models and techniques derived from my own teaching and from physics education research. The following are major themes that I have incorporated throughout.

Separation of conceptual and mathematical frameworks. Each chapter is divided into two parts: Concepts and Quantitative Tools. The first part, Concepts, develops the full conceptual framework of the topic and addresses many of the common questions students have. It concentrates on the underlying ideas and paints the big picture, whenever possible without equations. The second part of the chapter, Quantitative Tools, then develops the mathematical framework.

Deductive approach; focus on ideas before names and equations. To the extent possible, this text develops arguments deductively, starting from observations, rather than stating principles and then "deriving" them. This approach makes the material easier to assimilate for students. In the same vein, this text introduces and explains each idea before giving it a formal name or mathematical definition.

Stronger connection to experiment and experience. Physics stems from observations, and this text is structured so that it can do the same. As much as possible, I develop the material from experimental observations (and preferably those that students can make) rather than assertions. Most chapters use actual data in developing ideas, and new notions are always introduced by going from the specific to the general—whenever possible by interpreting everyday examples.

By contrast, standard texts often introduce laws in their most general form and then show that these laws are consistent with specific (and often highly idealized) cases. Consequently the world of physics and the "real" world remain two different things in the minds of students.

Addressing physical complications. I also strongly oppose presenting unnatural situations; real life complications must always be confronted head-on. For example, the use of unphysical words like *frictionless* or *massless* sends a message to the students that physics is unrealistic or, worse, that the world of physics and the *real* world are unrelated entities. This can easily be avoided by pointing out that friction or mass may be neglected under certain circumstances and pointing out *why* this may be done.

Engaging the student. Education is more than just transfer of information. Engaging the student's mind so the information can be assimilated is essential. To this end, the text is written as a dialog between author and reader (often invoking the reader—*you*—in examples) and is punctuated by Checkpoints—questions that require the reader to stop and think. The text following a Checkpoint often refers directly to its conclusions. Students will find complete solutions to all the Checkpoints at the back of the book; these solutions are written to emphasize physical reasoning and discovery.

Visualization. Visual representations are central to physics, so I developed each chapter by designing the figures before writing the text. Many figures use multiple representations to help students make connections (for example, a sketch may be combined with a graph and a bar diagram). Also, in accordance with research, the illustration style is spare and simple, putting the emphasis on the ideas and relationships rather than on irrelevant details. The figures do not use perspective unless it is needed, for instance.

Structure of this text

Division into *Principles* and *Practice* volumes

I've divided this text into a *Principles* volume, which teaches the physics, and a *Practice* volume, which puts the physics into practice and develops problem-solving skills. This division helps address two separate intellectually demanding tasks: understanding the physics and learning to solve problems. When these two tasks are mixed together, as they are in standard texts, students are easily overwhelmed. Consequently many students focus disproportionately on worked examples and procedural knowledge, at the expense of the physics.

Structure of *Principles* chapters

As pointed out earlier, each *Principles* chapter is divided into two parts. The first part (Concepts) develops the conceptual framework in an accessible way, relying primarily on qualitative descriptions and illustrations. In addition to including Checkpoints, each Concepts section ends with a one-page Self-quiz consisting of qualitative questions.

The second part of each chapter (Quantitative Tools) formalizes the ideas developed in the first part in mathematical terms. While concise, it is relatively traditional in nature—teachers should be able to continue to use material developed for earlier courses. To avoid creating the impression that equations are more important than the concepts behind them, no equations are highlighted or boxed.

Both parts of the *Principles* chapters contain worked examples to help students develop problem-solving skills.

Structure of the *Practice* chapters

This volume contains material to put into practice the concepts and principles developed in the corresponding chapters in the *Principles* volume. Each chapter contains the following sections:

1. *Chapter Summary*. This section provides a brief tabular summary of the material presented in the corresponding *Principles* chapter.
2. *Review Questions*. The goal of this section is to allow students to quickly review the corresponding *Principles* chapter. The questions are straightforward one-liners starting with "what" and "how" (rather than "why" or "what if").
3. *Developing a Feel*. The goals of this section are to develop a quantitative feel for the quantities introduced in the chapter; to connect the subject of the chapter to the real world; to train students in making estimates and assumptions; to bolster students' confidence in dealing with unfamiliar material. It can be used for self-study or for a homework or recitation assignment. This section, which has no equivalent in existing books, combines a number of ideas (specifically, Fermi problems and tutoring in the style of the *Princeton Learning Guide*). The idea is to start with simple estimation problems and then build up to Fermi problems (in early chapters Fermi problems are hard to compose because few concepts have been introduced). Because students initially find these questions hard, the section provides many hints, which take the form of questions. A key then provides answers to these "hints."
4. *Worked and Guided Problems*. This section contains complex worked examples whose primary goal is to teach problem solving. The Worked Problems are fully solved; the Guided Problems have a list of questions and suggestions to help the student think about how to solve the problem. Typically, each Worked Problem is followed by a related Guided Problem.
5. *Questions and Problems*. This is the chapter's problem set. The problems 1) offer a range of levels, 2) include problems relating to client disciplines (life sciences, engineering, chemistry, astronomy, etc.), 3) use the second person as much as possible to draw in the student, and 4) do not spoon-feed the students with information and unnecessary diagrams. The problems are classified into three levels as follows: (•) application of single concept; numerical plug-and-chug; (••) nonobvious application of single concept or application of multiple concepts from current chapter; straightforward numerical or algebraic computation; (•••) application of multiple concepts, possibly spanning multiple chapters. Context-rich problems are designated CR.

As I was developing and class-testing this book, my students provided extensive feedback. I have endeavored to incorporate all of their feedback to make the book as useful as possible for future generations of students. In addition, the book was class-tested at a large number of institutions, and many of these institutions have reported significant increases in learning gains after switching to this manuscript. I am confident the book will help increase the learning gains in your class as well. It will help you, as the instructor, coach your students to be the best they can be.

Instructor supplements

The **Instructor Resource DVD** (ISBN 978-0-321-56175-6/0-321-56175-9) includes an Image Library, the Procedure and special topic boxes from *Principles*, and a library of presentation applets from **ActivPhysics**, PhET simulations, and PhET Clicker Questions. **Lecture Outlines** with embedded **Clicker Questions in PowerPoint®** are provided, as well as the *Instructor's Guide* and *Instructor's Solutions Manual*.

The *Instructor's Guide* (ISBN 978-0-321-94993-6/0-321-94993-5) provides chapter-by-chapter ideas for lesson planning using *Principles & Practice of Physics* in class, including strategies for addressing common student difficulties.

The *Instructor's Solutions Manual* (ISBN 978-0-321-95053-6/0-321-95053-4) is a comprehensive solutions manual containing complete answers and solutions to all Developing a Feel questions, Guided Problems, and Questions and Problems from the *Practice* volume. The solutions to the Guided Problems use the book's four-step problem-solving strategy (Getting Started, Devise Plan, Execute Plan, Evaluate Result).

MasteringPhysics® is the leading online homework, tutorial, and assessment product designed to improve results by helping students quickly master concepts. Students benefit from self-paced tutorials that feature specific wrong-answer feedback, hints, and a wide variety of educationally effective content to keep them engaged and on track. Robust diagnostics and unrivalled gradebook reporting allow instructors to pinpoint the weaknesses and misconceptions of a student or class to provide timely intervention.

MasteringPhysics enables instructors to:

- Easily assign **tutorials** that provide individualized coaching.
- Mastering's hallmark **Hints** and **Feedback** offer scaffolded instruction similar to what students would experience in an office hour.

- **Hints** (declarative and Socratic) can provide problem-solving strategies or break the main problem into simpler exercises.
- **Feedback** lets the student know precisely what misconception or misunderstanding is evident from their answer and offers ideas to consider when attempting the problem again.

Learning Catalytics™ is a "bring your own device" student engagement, assessment, and classroom intelligence system available within MasteringPhysics. With Learning Catalytics you can:

- Assess students in real time, using open-ended tasks to probe student understanding.
- Understand immediately where students are and adjust your lecture accordingly.
- Improve your students' critical-thinking skills.
- Access rich analytics to understand student performance.
- Add your own questions to make Learning Catalytics fit your course exactly.
- Manage student interactions with intelligent grouping and timing.

The **Test Bank** (ISBN 978-0-130-64688-0/0-130-64688-1) contains more than 2000 high-quality problems, with a range of multiple-choice, true-false, short-answer, and conceptual questions correlated to *Principles & Practice of Physics* chapters. Test files are provided in both TestGen® and Microsoft® Word for Mac and PC.

Instructor supplements are available on the Instructor Resource DVD, the Instructor Resource Center at www. pearsonhighered.com/irc, and in the Instructor Resource area at www.masteringphysics.com.

Student supplements

MasteringPhysics (www.masteringphysics.com) is designed to provide students with customized coaching and individualized feedback to help improve problem-solving skills. Students complete homework efficiently and effectively with tutorials that provide targeted help.

Interactive eText allows you to highlight text, add your own study notes, and review your instructor's personalized notes, 24/7. The eText is available through MasteringPhysics, www.masteringphysics.com.

Acknowledgments

This book would not exist without the contributions from many people. It was Tim Bozik, currently President, Higher Education at Pearson plc, who first approached me about writing a physics textbook. If it wasn't for his persuasion and his belief in me, I don't think I would have ever undertaken the writing of a textbook. Tim's suggestion to develop the art electronically also had a major impact on my approach to the development of the visual part of this book.

Albert Altman pointed out Ernst Mach's approach to developing mechanics starting with the law of conservation of momentum. Al encouraged me throughout the years as I struggled to reorganize the material around the conservation principles.

I am thankful to Irene Nunes, who served as Development Editor through several iterations of the manuscript. Irene forced me to continuously rethink what I had written and her insights in physics kept surprising me. Her incessant questioning taught me that one doesn't need to be a science major to obtain a deep understanding of how the world around us works and that it is possible to explain physics in a way that makes sense for non-physics majors.

Catherine Crouch helped write the final chapters of electricity and magnetism and the chapters on circuits and optics, permitting me to focus on the overall approach and the art program. Peter Dourmashkin helped me write the chapters on special relativity and thermodynamics. Without his help, I would not have been able to rethink how to introduce the ideas of modern physics in a consistent way.

Many people provided feedback during the development of the manuscript. I am particularly indebted to the late Ronald Newburgh and to Edward Ginsberg, who meticulously checked many of the chapters. I am also grateful to Edwin Taylor for his critical feedback on the special relativity chapter and to my colleague Gary Feldman for his suggestions for improving that chapter.

Lisa Morris provided material for many of the Self-quizzes and my graduate students James Carey, Mark Winkler, and Ben Franta helped with data analysis and the appendices. I would also like to thank my uncle, Erich Lessing, for letting me use some of his beautiful pictures as chapter openers.

Many people helped put together the *Practice* volume. Without Daryl Pedigo's hard work authoring and editing content, as well as coordinating the contributions to that volume, the manuscript would never have taken shape. Along with Daryl, the following people provided the material for the *Practice* volume: Wayne Anderson, Linda Barton, Ronald Bieniek, Michael Boss, Anthony Buffa, Catherine Crouch, Peter Dourmashkin, Paul Draper, Andrew Duffy, Edward Ginsberg, William Hogan, Gerd Kortemeyer, Rafael Lopez-Mobilia, Christopher Porter, David Rosengrant, Gay Stewart, Christopher Watts, Lawrence Weinstein, Fred Wietfeldt, and Michael Wofsey.

I would also like to thank the editorial and production staff at Pearson. Margot Otway helped realize my vision for the art program. Martha Steele and Beth Collins made sure the production stayed on track. In addition, I would like to thank Frank Chmely for his meticulous accuracy checking of the manuscript. I am indebted to Jim Smith and Becky Ruden for supporting me through the final stages of this process and for Alison Reeves of Prentice Hall for keeping me on track during the early stages of the writing of this book. Finally, I am grateful to Will Moore for his enthusiasm in developing the marketing program for this book.

I am also grateful to the participants of the NSF Faculty Development Conference "Teaching Physics Conservation Laws First" held in Cambridge, MA, in 1997. This conference helped validate and cement the approach in this book.

Finally, I am indebted to the hundreds of students in Physics 1, Physics 11, and Applied Physics 50 who used early versions of this text in their course and provided the feedback that ended up turning my manuscript into a text that works not just for instructors but, more importantly, for students.

Reviewers of *Principles & Practice of Physics*

Over the years many people reviewed and class-tested the manuscript. The author and publisher are grateful for all of the feedback the reviewers provided, and we apologize if there are any names on this list that have been inadvertently omitted.

Edward Adelson, *Ohio State University*
Albert Altman, *University of Massachusetts, Lowell*
Susan Amador Kane, *Haverford College*
James Andrews, *Youngstown State University*
Arnold Arons, *University of Washington*
Robert Beichner, *North Carolina State University*
Bruce Birkett, *University of California, Berkeley*
David Branning, *Trinity College*
Bernard Chasan, *Boston University*
Stéphane Coutu, *Pennsylvania State University*
Corbin Covault, *Case Western Reserve University*
Catherine Crouch, *Swarthmore College*
Paul D'Alessandris, *Monroe Community College*
Paul Debevec, *University of Illinois at Urbana-Champaign*
N. John DiNardo, *Drexel University*
Margaret Dobrowolska-Furdyna, *Notre Dame University*
Paul Draper, *University of Texas, Arlington*
David Elmore, *Purdue University*
Robert Endorf, *University of Cincinnati*
Thomas Furtak, *Colorado School of Mines*
Ian Gatland, *Georgia Institute of Technology*
J. David Gavenda, *University of Texas, Austin*
Edward Ginsberg, *University of Massachusetts, Boston*
Gary Gladding, *University of Illinois*
Christopher Gould, *University of Southern California*
Victoria Greene, *Vanderbilt University*
Benjamin Grinstein, *University of California, San Diego*
Kenneth Hardy, *Florida International University*
Gregory Hassold, *Kettering University*
Peter Heller, *Brandeis University*
Laurent Hodges, *Iowa State University*
Mark Holtz, *Texas Tech University*
Zafar Ismail, *Daemen College*
Ramanathan Jambunathan, *University of Wisconsin Oshkosh*
Brad Johnson, *Western Washington University*
Dorina Kosztin, *University of Missouri Columbia*
Arthur Kovacs, *Rochester Institute of Technology* (deceased)
Dale Long, *Virginia Polytechnic Institute* (deceased)

John Lyon, *Dartmouth College*
Trecia Markes, *University of Nebraska, Kearney*
Peter Markowitz, *Florida International University*
Bruce Mason, *University of Oklahoma*
John McCullen, *University of Arizona*
James McGuire, *Tulane University*
Timothy McKay, *University of Michigan*
Carl Michal, *University of British Columbia*
Kimball Milton, *University of Oklahoma*
Charles Misner, *University of Maryland, College Park*
Sudipa Mitra-Kirtley, *Rose-Hulman Institute of Technology*
Delo Mook, *Dartmouth College*
Lisa Morris, *Washington State University*
Edmund Myers, *Florida State University*
Alan Nathan, *University of Illinois*
K.W. Nicholson, *Central Alabama Community College*
Fredrick Olness, *Southern Methodist University*
Dugan O'Neil, *Simon Fraser University*
Patrick Papin, *San Diego State University*
George Parker, *North Carolina State University*
Claude Penchina, *University of Massachusetts, Amherst*
William Pollard, *Valdosta State University*
Amy Pope, *Clemson University*
Joseph Priest, *Miami University* (deceased)
Joel Primack, *University of California, Santa Cruz*
Rex Ramsier, *University of Akron*
Steven Rauseo, *University of Pittsburgh*
Lawrence Rees, *Brigham Young University*
Carl Rotter, *West Virginia University*
Leonard Scarfone, *University of Vermont*
Michael Schatz, *Georgia Institute of Technology*
Cindy Schwarz, *Vassar College*
Hugh Scott, *Illinois Institute of Technology*
Janet Segar, *Creighton University*
Shahid Shaheen, *Florida State University*
David Sokoloff, *University of Oregon*
Gay Stewart, *University of Arkansas*
Roger Stockbauer, *Louisiana State University*
William Sturrus, *Youngstown State University*
Carl Tomizuka, *University of Illinois*
Mani Tripathi, *University of California–Davis*
Rebecca Trousil, *Skidmore College*
Christopher Watts, *Auburn University*
Robert Weidman, *Michigan Technological University*
Ranjith Wijesinghe, *Ball State University*
Augden Windelborn, *Northern Illinois University*

Detailed Contents

About the Author iv
To the Student v
To the Instructor vi
Acknowledgments x

Chapter 1 Foundations 1
1.1 The scientific method 2
1.2 Symmetry 4
1.3 Matter and the universe 6
1.4 Time and change 8
1.5 Representations 9
1.6 Physical quantities and units 14
1.7 Significant digits 17
1.8 Solving problems 20
1.9 Developing a feel 23

Chapter 2 Motion in One Dimension 28
2.1 From reality to model 29
2.2 Position and displacement 30
2.3 Representing motion 32
2.4 Average speed and average velocity 34
2.5 Scalars and vectors 39
2.6 Position and displacement vectors 41
2.7 Velocity as a vector 45
2.8 Motion at constant velocity 46
2.9 Instantaneous velocity 48

Chapter 3 Acceleration 53
3.1 Changes in velocity 54
3.2 Acceleration due to gravity 55
3.3 Projectile motion 57
3.4 Motion diagrams 59
3.5 Motion with constant acceleration 63

3.6 Free-fall equations 66
3.7 Inclined planes 69
3.8 Instantaneous acceleration 70

Chapter 4 Momentum 75
4.1 Friction 76
4.2 Inertia 76
4.3 What determines inertia? 80
4.4 Systems 81
4.5 Inertial standard 86
4.6 Momentum 87
4.7 Isolated systems 89
4.8 Conservation of momentum 94

Chapter 5 Energy 101
5.1 Classification of collisions 102
5.2 Kinetic energy 103
5.3 Internal energy 105
5.4 Closed systems 108
5.5 Elastic collisions 112
5.6 Inelastic collisions 115
5.7 Conservation of energy 116
5.8 Explosive separations 118

Chapter 6 Principle of Relativity 121
6.1 Relativity of motion 122
6.2 Inertial reference frames 124
6.3 Principle of relativity 126
6.4 Zero-momentum reference frame 130
6.5 Galilean relativity 133
6.6 Center of mass 137
6.7 Convertible kinetic energy 142
6.8 Conservation laws and relativity 145

Chapter 7 Interactions 148
7.1 The effects of interactions 149
7.2 Potential energy 152
7.3 Energy dissipation 153
7.4 Source energy 156
7.5 Interaction range 158
7.6 Fundamental interactions 160
7.7 Interactions and accelerations 164
7.8 Nondissipative interactions 165
7.9 Potential energy near Earth's surface 168
7.10 Dissipative interactions 171

Chapter 8 Force 176
8.1 Momentum and force 177
8.2 The reciprocity of forces 178
8.3 Identifying forces 180
8.4 Translational equilibrium 181
8.5 Free-body diagrams 182
8.6 Springs and tension 184
8.7 Equation of motion 188
8.8 Force of gravity 191
8.9 Hooke's law 192
8.10 Impulse 194
8.11 Systems of two interacting objects 196
8.12 Systems of many interacting objects 198

Chapter 9 Work 202
9.1 Force displacement 203
9.2 Positive and negative work 204
9.3 Energy diagrams 206
9.4 Choice of system 208
9.5 Work done on a single particle 213
9.6 Work done on a many-particle system 216
9.7 Variable and distributed forces 220
9.8 Power 223

Chapter 10 Motion in a Plane 226
10.1 *Straight* is a relative term 227
10.2 Vectors in a plane 228
10.3 Decomposition of forces 231
10.4 Friction 234
10.5 Work and friction 235
10.6 Vector algebra 238
10.7 Projectile motion in two dimensions 240
10.8 Collisions and momentum in two dimensions 242

10.9 Work as the product of two vectors 243
10.10 Coefficients of friction 248

Chapter 11 Motion in a Circle 254
11.1 Circular motion at constant speed 255
11.2 Forces and circular motion 259
11.3 Rotational inertia 262
11.4 Rotational kinematics 264
11.5 Angular momentum 269
11.6 Rotational inertia of extended objects 274

Chapter 12 Torque 281
12.1 Torque and angular momentum 282
12.2 Free rotation 285
12.3 Extended free-body diagrams 286
12.4 The vectorial nature of rotation 288
12.5 Conservation of angular momentum 293
12.6 Rolling motion 297
12.7 Torque and energy 302
12.8 The vector product 304

Chapter 13 Gravity 308
13.1 Universal gravity 309
13.2 Gravity and angular momentum 314
13.3 Weight 317
13.4 Principle of equivalence 320
13.5 Gravitational constant 325
13.6 Gravitational potential energy 326
13.7 Celestial mechanics 329
13.8 Gravitational force exerted by a sphere 334

Chapter 14 Special Relativity 337
14.1 Time measurements 338
14.2 *Simultaneous* is a relative term 341
14.3 Space-time 345

14.4   Matter and energy   350
14.5   Time dilation   355
14.6   Length contraction   360
14.7   Conservation of momentum   364
14.8   Conservation of energy   368

Chapter 15 **Periodic Motion**   374

15.1   Periodic motion and energy   375
15.2   Simple harmonic motion   377
15.3   Fourier's theorem   379
15.4   Restoring forces in simple harmonic motion   381
15.5   Energy of a simple harmonic oscillator   385
15.6   Simple harmonic motion and springs   389
15.7   Restoring torques   393
15.8   Damped oscillations   396

Chapter 16 **Waves in One Dimension**   400

16.1   Representing waves graphically   401
16.2   Wave propagation   404
16.3   Superposition of waves   409
16.4   Boundary effects   411
16.5   Wave functions   416
16.6   Standing waves   421
16.7   Wave speed   424
16.8   Energy transport in waves   426
16.9   The wave equation   429

Chapter 17 **Waves in Two and Three Dimensions**   432

17.1   Wavefronts   433
17.2   Sound   436
17.3   Interference   439
17.4   Diffraction   445
17.5   Intensity   448

17.6   Beats   451
17.7   Doppler effect   454
17.8   Shock waves   459

Chapter 18 **Fluids**   463

18.1   Forces in a fluid   464
18.2   Buoyancy   469
18.3   Fluid flow   471
18.4   Surface effects   475
18.5   Pressure and gravity   482
18.6   Working with pressure   487
18.7   Bernoulli's equation   491
18.8   Viscosity and surface tension   494

Chapter 19 **Entropy**   501

19.1   States   502
19.2   Equipartition of energy   505
19.3   Equipartition of space   507
19.4   Evolution toward the most probable macrostate   509
19.5   Dependence of entropy on volume   514
19.6   Dependence of entropy on energy   519
19.7   Properties of a monatomic ideal gas   523
19.8   Entropy of a monatomic ideal gas   526

Chapter 20 **Energy Transferred Thermally**   530

20.1   Thermal interactions   530
20.2   Temperature measurement   534
20.3   Heat capacity   537
20.4   *PV* diagrams and processes   541
20.5   Change in energy and work   547

20.6 Isochoric and isentropic ideal gas processes 549

20.7 Isobaric and isothermal ideal gas processes 551

20.8 Entropy change in ideal gas processes 555

20.9 Entropy change in nonideal gas processes 559

Chapter 21 Degradation of Energy 562

21.1 Converting energy 563

21.2 Quality of energy 566

21.3 Heat engines and heat pumps 570

21.4 Thermodynamic cycles 575

21.5 Entropy constraints on energy transfers 580

21.6 Heat engine performance 583

21.7 Carnot cycle 587

21.8 Brayton cycle 589

Appendix A: Notation A-1

Appendix B: Mathematics Review A-11

Appendix C: Useful Data A-16

Appendix D: The Center of Mass of Extended Objects A-20

Appendix E: Lorentz Transformations A-21

Solutions to Checkpoints A-25

Credits C-1

Index I-1

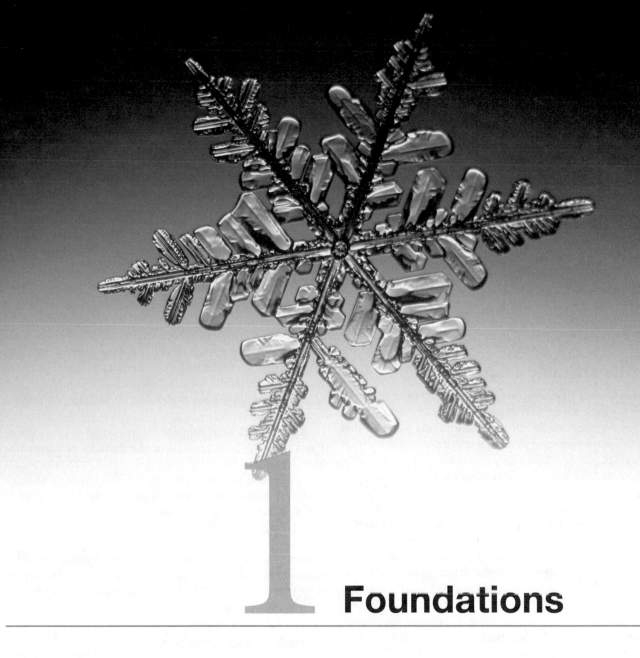

1 Foundations

1.1 The scientific method

1.2 Symmetry

1.3 Matter and the universe

1.4 Time and change

1.5 Representations

1.6 Physical quantities and units

1.7 Significant digits

1.8 Solving problems

1.9 Developing a feel

CONCEPTS

QUANTITATIVE TOOLS

Chances are you are taking this course in physics because someone told you to take it, and it may not be clear to you *why* you should be taking it. One good reason for taking a physics course is that, first and foremost, physics provides a fundamental understanding of the world. Furthermore, whether you are majoring in psychology, engineering, biology, physics, or something else, this course offers you an opportunity to sharpen your reasoning skills. Knowing physics means becoming a better problem solver (and I mean *real* problems, not textbook problems that have already been solved), and becoming a better problem solver is empowering: It allows you to step into unknown territory with more confidence. Before we embark on this exciting journey, let's map out the territory we are going to explore so that you know where we are going.

1.1 The scientific method

Physics, from the Greek word for "nature," is commonly defined as the study of matter and motion. Physics is about discovering the wonderfully simple unifying patterns that underlie absolutely everything that happens around us, from the scale of subatomic particles, to the microscopic world of DNA molecules and cells, to the cosmic scale of stars, galaxies, and planets. Physics deals with atoms and molecules; gases, solids, and liquids; everyday objects, and black holes. Physics explores motion, light, and sound; the creation and annihilation of matter; evaporation and melting; electricity and magnetism. Physics is all around you: in the Sun that provides your daylight, in the structure of your bones, in your computer, in the motion of a ball you throw. In a sense, then, physics is the study of all there is in the universe. Indeed, biology, engineering, chemistry, astronomy, geology, and so many other disciplines you might name all use the principles of physics.

The many remarkable scientific accomplishments of ancient civilizations that survive to this day testify to the fact that curiosity about the world is part of human nature. Physics evolved from *natural philosophy*—a body of knowledge accumulated in ancient times in an attempt to explain the behavior of the universe through philosophical speculation—and became a distinct discipline during the scientific revolution that began in the 16th century. One of the main changes that occurred in that century was the development of the **scientific method,** an iterative process for going from observations to validated theories.

In its simplest form, the scientific method works as follows (**Figure 1.1**): A researcher makes a number of observations concerning either something happening in the natural world (a volcano erupting, for instance) or something happening during a laboratory experiment (a dropped brick and a dropped Styrofoam peanut travel to the floor at different speeds). These observations then lead the researcher to formulate a **hypothesis,** which is a tentative explanation of the observed phenomenon. The hypothesis is used to predict

Figure 1.1 The scientific method is an iterative process in which a hypothesis, which is inferred from observations, is used to make a prediction, which is then tested by making new observations.

the outcome of some related natural occurrence (how a similarly shaped mountain near the erupting volcano will behave) or related laboratory experiment (what happens when a book and a sheet of paper are dropped at the same time). If the predictions prove inaccurate, the hypothesis must be modified. If the predictions prove accurate in test after test, the hypothesis is elevated to the status of either a **law** or a **theory.**

A law tells us *what* happens under certain circumstances. Laws are usually expressed in the form of relationships between observable quantities. A theory tells us *why* something happens and explains phenomena in terms of more basic processes and relationships. A scientific theory is not a mere conjecture or speculation. It is a thoroughly tested explanation of a natural phenomenon, one that is capable of making predictions that can be verified by experiment. The constant testing and retesting are what make the scientific method such a powerful tool for investigating the universe: The results obtained must be repeatable and verifiable by others.

Exercise 1.1 Hypothesis or not?

Which of the following statements are hypotheses? (*a*) Heavier objects fall to Earth faster than lighter ones. (*b*) The planet Mars is inhabited by invisible beings that are able to elude any type of observation. (*c*) Distant planets harbor forms of life. (*d*) Handling toads causes warts.

SOLUTION (*a*), (*c*), and (*d*). A hypothesis must be experimentally verifiable. (*a*) I can verify this statement by dropping a heavy object and a lighter one at the same instant and observing which one hits the ground first. (*b*) This statement asserts that the beings on Mars cannot be observed, which precludes any experimental verification and means this statement is not a valid hypothesis. (*c*) Although we humans currently have no means of exploring or closely observing distant planets, the statement is in principle testable. (*d*) Even though we know this statement is false, it *is* verifiable and therefore is a hypothesis.

Because of the constant reevaluation demanded by the scientific method, science is not a stale collection of facts but rather a living and changing body of knowledge. More important, any theory or law *always* remains tentative, and the testing never ends. In other words, it is not possible to prove any scientific theory or law to be absolutely true (or even absolutely false). Thus the material you will learn in this book does not represent some "ultimate truth"—it is true only to the extent that it has not been proved wrong.

A case in point is *classical mechanics,* a theory developed in the 17th century to describe the motion of everyday objects (and the subject of most of this book). Although this theory produces accurate results for most everyday phenomena, from balls thrown in the air to satellites orbiting Earth, observations made during the last hundred years have revealed that under certain circumstances, significant deviations from this theory occur. It is now clear that classical mechanics is applicable for only a limited (albeit important) range of phenomena, and new branches of physics—*quantum mechanics* and the theory of *special relativity* among them—are needed to describe the phenomena that fall outside the range of classical mechanics.

The formulation of a hypothesis almost always involves developing a **model,** which is a simplified conceptual representation of some phenomenon. You don't have to be trained as a scientist to develop models. Everyone develops mental models of how people behave, how events unfold, and how things work. Without such models, we would not be able to understand our experiences, decide what actions to take, or handle unexpected experiences. Examples of models we use in everyday life are that door handles and door hinges are on opposite sides of doors and that the + button on a TV remote increases the volume or the channel number. In everyday life, we base our models on whatever knowledge we have, real or imagined, complete or incomplete. In science we must build models based on careful observation and determine ways to fill in any missing information.

Let's look at the iterative process of developing models and hypotheses in physics, with an eye toward determining what skills are needed and what pitfalls are to be avoided (**Figure 1.2**). Developing a scientific hypothesis often begins

with recognizing patterns in a series of observations. Sometimes these observations are direct, but sometimes we must settle for indirect observations. (We cannot directly observe the nucleus of an atom, for instance, but a physicist can describe the structure of the nucleus and its behavior with great certainty and accuracy.) As Figure 1.2 indicates, the patterns that emerge from our observations must often be combined with simplifying assumptions to build a model. The combination of model and assumptions is what constitutes a hypothesis.

It may seem like a shaky proposition to build a hypothesis on assumptions that are accepted without proof, but making these assumptions—*consciously*—is a crucial step in making sense of the universe. All that is required is that, when formulating a hypothesis, we must be aware of these assumptions and be ready to revise or drop them if the predictions of our hypothesis are not validated. We should, in particular, watch out for what are called *hidden assumptions*—assumptions we make without being aware of them. As an example, try answering the following question. (Turn to the final section of the *Principles* volume, "Solutions to checkpoints," for the answer.)

☝ 1.1 I have two coins in my pocket, together worth 30 cents. If one of them is not a nickel, what coins are they?

Advertising agencies and magicians are masters at making us fall into the trap of hidden assumptions. Imagine a radio commercial for a new drug in which someone says, "Baroxan lowered my blood pressure tremendously." If you think that sounds good, you have made a number of assumptions without being aware of them—in other words, hidden assumptions. Who says, for instance, that lowering blood pressure "tremendously" is a good thing (dead people have tremendously low blood pressure) or that the speaker's blood pressure was too high to begin with?

Magic, too, involves hidden assumptions. The trick in some magic acts is to make you assume that something happens, often by planting a false assumption in your mind. A magician might ask, "How did I move the ball from here to there?" while in reality he is using two balls. I won't knowingly put false assumptions into *your* mind in this book, but on occasion you and I (or you and your instructor) may unknowingly make different assumptions during a given discussion, a situation that unavoidably leads to confusion and misunderstanding. Therefore it is important that we carefully analyze our thinking and watch for the assumptions that we build into our models.

If the prediction of a hypothesis fails to agree with observations made to test the hypothesis, there are several ways to address the discrepancy. One way is to rerun the test to see if it is reproducible. If the test keeps producing the same result, it becomes necessary to revise the hypothesis, rethink the assumptions that went into it, or reexamine the original observations that led to the hypothesis.

Figure 1.2 Iterative process for developing a scientific hypothesis.

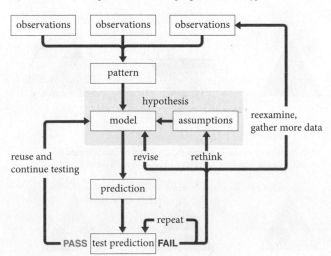

CONCEPTS

Exercise 1.2 Dead music player

A battery-operated portable music player fails to play when it is turned on. Develop a hypothesis explaining why it fails to play, and then make a prediction that permits you to test your hypothesis. Describe two possible outcomes of the test and what you conclude from the outcomes. (*Think* before you peek at the answer below.)

SOLUTION There are many reasons the player might not turn on. Here is one example. Hypothesis: The batteries are dead. Prediction: If I replace the batteries with new ones, the player should work. Possible outcomes: (1) The player works once the new batteries are installed, which means the hypothesis is supported; (2) the player doesn't work after the new batteries are installed, which means the hypothesis is not supported and must be either modified or discarded.

1.2 In Exercise 1.2, each of the conclusions drawn from the two possible outcomes contains a hidden assumption. What are the hidden assumptions?

The development of a scientific hypothesis is often more complicated than suggested by Figures 1.1 and 1.2. Hypotheses do not always start with observations; some are developed from incomplete information, vague ideas, assumptions, or even complete guesses. The refining process also has its limits. Each refinement adds complexity, and at some point the complexity outweighs the benefit of the increased accuracy. Because we like to think that the universe has an underlying simplicity, it might be better to scrap the hypothesis and start anew.

Figure 1.2 gives an idea of the skills that are useful in doing science: interpreting observations, recognizing patterns, making and recognizing assumptions, thinking logically, developing models, and using models to make predictions. It should not come as any surprise to you that many of these skills are useful in just about any context. Learning physics allows you to sharpen these skills in a very rigorous way. So, whether you become a financial analyst, a doctor, an engineer, or a research scientist (to name just a few possibilities), there is a good reason to take physics.

Figure 1.1 also shows that doing science—and physics in particular—involves two types of reasoning: *inductive*, which is arguing from the specific to the general, and *deductive*, arguing from the general to the specific. The most creative part of doing physics involves inductive reasoning, and this fact sheds light on how you might want to learn physics. One way, which is neither very useful nor very satisfying, is for me to simply tell you all the general principles physicists presently agree on and then for you to apply those principles in examples and exercises (**Figure 1.3a**). This approach involves deductive reasoning only and robs you of the opportunity to learn the skill that is the most likely to benefit your career: discovering underlying patterns. Another way is for me to present you with data and observations and make you part of the discovery and refinement of the physics principles (Figure 1.3b). This approach

Figure 1.3

(*a*) Learning science by applying established principles

(*b*) Learning science by discovering those principles for yourself before applying them

is more time-consuming, and sometimes you may wonder why I'm not just *telling* you the final outcome. The reason is that discovery and refinement are at the heart of doing physics!

1.3 After reading this section, reflect on your goals for this course. Write down what you would like to accomplish and why you would like to accomplish this. Once you have done that, turn to the final section of the *Principles* volume, "Solutions to checkpoints," and compare what you have written with what I wrote.

1.2 Symmetry

One of the basic requirements of any law of the universe involves what physicists call *symmetry*, a concept often associated with order, beauty, and harmony. We can define **symmetry** as follows: An object exhibits symmetry when certain operations can be performed on it without changing its appearance. Consider the equilateral triangle in **Figure 1.4a**. If you close your eyes and someone rotates the triangle by 120° while you have your eyes closed, the triangle appears

Figure 1.4

(*a*) Rotational symmetry: Rotating an equilateral triangle by 120° doesn't change how it looks

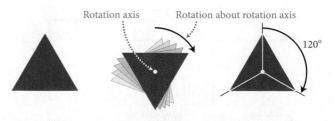

(*b*) Reflection symmetry: Across each reflection axis (labeled R), two sides of the triangle are mirror images of each other

Figure 1.5 The symmetrical arrangement of atoms in a salt crystal gives these crystals their cubic shape.

(*a*) Micrograph of salt crystals

(*b*) Symmetrical arrangement of atoms in a salt crystal

(*c*) Da Vinci's Vitruvian Man shows the reflection symmetry of the human body

Na—
Cl—

the same when you open your eyes, and you can't tell that it has been rotated. The triangle is said to have *rotational symmetry,* one of several types of geometrical symmetry.

Another common type of geometrical symmetry, *reflection symmetry,* occurs when one half of an object is the mirror image of the other half. The equilateral triangle in Figure 1.4 possesses reflection symmetry about the three axes shown in Figure 1.4*b*. If you imagine folding the triangle in half over each axis, you can see that the two halves are identical. Reflection symmetry occurs all around us: in the arrangement of atoms in crystals (**Figure 1.5***a* and *b*) and in the anatomy of most life forms (Figure 1.5*c*), to name just two examples.

The ideas of symmetry—that something appears unchanged under certain operations—apply not only to the shape of objects but also to the more abstract realm of physics. If there are things we can do to an experiment that leave the result of the experiment unchanged, then the phenomenon tested by the experiment is said to possess certain symmetries. Suppose we build an apparatus, carry out a certain measurement in a certain location, then move the apparatus to another location, repeat the measurement, and get the same result in both locations.* By moving the apparatus to a new location (*translating* it) and obtaining the same result, we have shown that the observed phenomenon has *translational symmetry.* Any physical law that describes this phenomenon must therefore mathematically exhibit translational symmetry; that is, the mathematical expression of this law must be independent of the location.

Likewise, we expect any measurements we make with our apparatus to be the same at a later time as at an earlier time; that is, translation in time has no effect on the measurements. The laws describing the phenomenon we are

studying must therefore mathematically exhibit symmetry under translation in time; in other words, the mathematical expression of these laws must be independent of time.

Exercise 1.3 Change is no change

Figure 1.6 shows a snowflake. Does the snowflake have rotational symmetry? If yes, describe the ways in which the flake can be rotated without changing its appearance. Does it have reflection symmetry? If yes, describe the ways in which the flake can be split in two so that one half is the mirror image of the other.

Figure 1.6 Exercise 1.3.

SOLUTION I can rotate the snowflake by 60° or a multiple of 60° (120°, 180°, 240°, 300°, and 360°) in the plane of the photograph without changing its appearance (**Figure 1.7***a*). It therefore has rotational symmetry.

I can also fold the flake in half along any of the three blue axes and along any of the three red axes in Figure 1.7*b*. The flake therefore has reflection symmetry about all six of these axes.

Figure 1.7

(*a*) Rotational symmetry

(*b*) Reflection symmetry

60°

R
R   R
R   R
R
R   R

*In moving our apparatus, we must take care to move any relevant external influences along with it. For example, if Earth's gravity is of importance, then moving the apparatus to a location in space far from Earth does not yield the same result.

A number of such symmetries have been identified, and the basic laws that govern the inner workings of the physical world must reflect these symmetries. Some of these symmetries are familiar to you, such as translational symmetry in space or time. Others, like electrical charge or parity symmetry, are unfamiliar and surprising and go beyond the scope of this course. Whereas symmetry has always implicitly been applied to the description of the universe, it plays an increasingly important role in physics: In a sense the quest of physics in the 21st century is the search for (and test of) symmetries because these symmetries are the most fundamental principles that all physical laws must obey.

✋ **1.4** You always store your pencils in a cylindrical case. One day while traveling in the tropics, you discover that the cap, which you have placed back on the case day in, day out for years, doesn't fit over the case. What do you conclude?

1.3 Matter and the universe

The goal of physics is to describe all that happens in the universe. Simply put, the **universe** is the totality of matter and energy combined with the space and time in which all events happen—everything that is directly or indirectly observable. To describe the universe, we use *concepts,* which are ideas or general notions used to analyze natural phenomena.* To provide a quantitative description, these concepts must be expressed quantitatively, which requires defining a procedure for measuring them. Examples are the length or mass of an object, temperature, and time intervals. Such **physical quantities** are the cornerstones of physics. It is the accurate measurement of physical quantities that has led to the great discoveries of physics. Although many of the fundamental concepts we use in this book are familiar ones, quite a few are difficult to define in words, and we must often resort to defining these concepts in terms of the procedures used to measure them.

The fundamental physical quantity by which we map out the universe is **length**—a distance or an extent in space. The length of a straight or curved line is measured by comparing the length of the line with some standard length. In 1791, the French Academy of Sciences defined the standard unit for length, called the **meter** and abbreviated m, as one ten-millionth of the distance from the equator to the North Pole. For practical reasons, the standard was redefined in 1889 as the distance between two fine lines engraved on a bar of platinum-iridium alloy kept at the International Bureau of Weights and Measures near Paris. With the advent of lasers, however, it became possible to measure the speed of light with extraordinary accuracy, and so the meter was redefined in 1983 as the distance traveled by light in vacuum in a time interval of $1/299{,}792{,}458$ of a second. This number is chosen so as to make the speed of light exactly 299,792,458 meters per second and yield a standard length for the meter that is very close to the length of the original platinum-iridium standard. This laser-based standard is final and will never need to be revised.

✋ **1.5** Based on the early definition of the meter, one ten-millionth of the distance from the equator to the North Pole, what is Earth's radius?

Now that we have defined a standard for length, let us use this standard to discuss the structure and size scales of the universe. Because of the extraordinary range of size scales in the universe, we shall round off any values to the nearest power of ten. Such a value is called an **order of magnitude.** For example, any number between 0.3 and 3 has an order of magnitude of 1 because it is within a factor of 3 of 1; any number greater than 3 and equal to or less than 30 has an order of magnitude of 10. You determine the order of magnitude of any quantity by writing it in scientific notation and rounding the coefficient in front of the power of ten to 1 if it is equal to or less than 3 or to 10 if it is greater than 3.† For example, 3 minutes is 180 s, which can be written as 1.8×10^2 s. The coefficient, 1.8, rounds to 1, and so the order of magnitude is 1×10^2 s $= 10^2$ s. The quantity 680, to take another example, can be written as 6.8×10^2; the coefficient 6.8 rounds to 10, and so the order of magnitude is $10 \times 10^2 = 10^3$. And Earth's circumference is 40,000,000 m, which can be written as 4×10^7 m; the order of magnitude of this number is 10^8 m. You may think that using order-of-magnitude approximations is not very scientific because of the lack of accuracy, but the ability to work effectively with orders of magnitude is a key skill not just in science but also in any other quantitative field of endeavor.

All ordinary matter in the universe is made up of basic building blocks called **atoms** (**Figure 1.8**). Nearly all the matter in an atom is contained in a dense central nucleus, which consists of **protons** and **neutrons,** two types of subatomic particles. A tenuous *cloud* of **electrons,** a third type of subatomic particle, surrounds this nucleus. Atoms are spherical and have a diameter of about 10^{-10} m. Atomic nuclei are also spherical, with a diameter of about 10^{-15} m, making atoms mostly empty space. Atoms attract one another when they are a small distance apart but resist being squeezed into one another. The arrangement of atoms in a material determines the properties of the material.

Figure 1.9 shows the relative size of some representative objects in the universe. The figure reveals a lot about the organization of matter in the universe and serves as a visual model of the structure of the universe. Roughly

---

*When an important concept is introduced in this book, the main word pertaining to the concept is printed in **boldface type.** All important concepts introduced in a chapter are listed at the end of the chapter, in the Chapter Glossary.

†The reason we use 3 in order-of-magnitude rounding, and not 5 as in ordinary rounding, is that orders of magnitude are logarithmic, and on this logarithmic scale $\log 3 = 0.48$ lies nearly halfway between $\log 1 = 0$ and $\log 10 = 1$.

Figure 1.8 Scanning tunneling microscope image showing the individual atoms that make up a silicon surface. The size of each atom is about 1/50,000 the width of a human hair.

Figure 1.9 A survey of the size and structure of the universe.

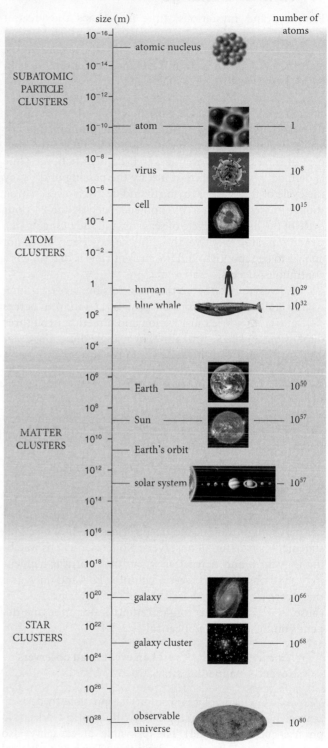

speaking, there is clustering of matter from smaller to larger at four length scales. At the subatomic scale, most of the matter in an atom is compressed into the tiny atomic nucleus, a cluster of subatomic particles. Atoms, in turn, cluster to form the objects and materials that surround us, from viruses to plants, animals, and other everyday objects. The next level is the clustering of matter in stars, some of which, such as the Sun, are surrounded by planets like Earth. Stars, in turn cluster to form galaxies. As we shall discuss in Chapter 7, this clustering of matter reveals a great deal about the way different objects interact with one another.

Exercise 1.4 Tiny universe

If all the matter in the observable universe were squeezed together as tightly as the matter in the nucleus of an atom, what order of magnitude would the diameter of the universe be?

SOLUTION From Figure 1.9 I see that there are about 10^{80} atoms in the universe. I can arrange these atoms in a cube that has 10^{27} atoms on one side because such a cube could accommodate $10^{27} \times 10^{27} \times 10^{27} = 10^{81}$ atoms. Given that the diameter of a nucleus is about 10^{-15} m, the length of a side of this cube would be

$$(10^{27} \text{ atoms})(10^{-15} \text{ m per atom}) = 10^{12} \text{ m},$$

which is a bit larger than the diameter of Earth's orbit around the Sun.

An alternative method for obtaining the answer is to realize that the matter in a single nucleus occupies a cubic volume of about $(10^{-15} \text{ m})^3 = 10^{-45} \text{ m}^3$. If all the matter in the universe were squeezed together just as tightly, it would occupy a volume of about 10^{80} times the volume of an atomic nucleus, or $10^{80} \times 10^{-45} \text{ m}^3 = 10^{35} \text{ m}^3$. The side of a cube of this volume is equal to the cube root of 10^{35} m^3, or 4.6×10^{11} m, which is the same order of magnitude as my first answer.

1.6 Imagine magnifying each atom in an apple to the size of the apple. What would the diameter of the apple then be?

1.4 Time and change

Profound and mysterious, time is perhaps the greatest enigma in physics. We all know what is meant by *time*, but it is difficult, if not impossible, to explain the idea in words. (Put the book down for a minute and try defining *time* in words before reading on.) One way to describe time is that it is the infinite continual progression of events in the past, present, and future, often experienced as a force that moves the world along. This definition is neither illuminating nor scientifically meaningful because it merely relates the concept of time to other, even less well-defined notions. Time is defined by the rhythm of life, by the passing of days, by the cycle of the seasons, by birth and death. However, even though many individual phenomena, such as the 24-hour cycle of the days, the cycle of seasons, and the swinging of a pendulum, are repetitive, the time we experience does not appear to be repetitive, and the current view is that time is a continuous succession of events.

The irreversible flow of time controls our lives, pushing us inexorably forward from the past to the future. Whereas we can freely choose our location and direction in all three dimensions in space, time flows in a single direction, dragging us forward with it. Time thus presents less symmetry than the three dimensions of space: Although opposite directions in space are equivalent, opposite directions in time are not equivalent. The "arrow of time" points only into the future, a direction we define as the one we have no memory of. Curiously, most of the laws of physics have no requirement that time has to flow in one direction only, and it is not until Chapter 19 that we can begin to understand why events in time are irreversible.

The arrow of time allows us to establish a *causal relationship* between events. For example, lightning causes thunder and so lightning has to occur *before* the thunder. This statement is true for all observers: No matter who is watching the storm and no matter where that storm is happening, every observer first sees a lightning bolt and only after that hears the thunder because an effect never precedes its cause. Indeed, the very organization of our thoughts depends on the **principle of causality:**

> **Whenever an event A causes an event B, all observers see event A happening first.**

Without this principle, it wouldn't be possible to develop any scientific understanding of how the world works. (No physics course to take!) The principle of causality also makes it possible to state a definition: **Time** is a physical quantity that allows us to determine the sequence in which related events occur.

To apply the principle of causality and sort out causes and effects, it is necessary to develop devices—clocks—for keeping track of time. All clocks operate on the same principle: They repeatedly return to the same state. The rotation of Earth about its axis can serve as a clock if we note the instant the Sun reaches its highest position in the sky on successive days. A swinging pendulum, which repeatedly returns to the same vertical position, can also serve as a clock. The time interval between two events can be determined by counting the number of pendulum swings between the events. The accuracy of time measurements can be increased by using a clock that has a large number of repetitions in a given time interval.

1.7 (*a*) State a possible cause for the following events: (*i*) The light goes out in your room; (*ii*) you hear a loud, rumbling noise; (*iii*) a check you wrote at the bookstore bounces. (*b*) Could any of the causes you named have occurred after their associated event? (*c*) Describe how you feel when you experience an event but don't know what caused it—you hear a strange noise when camping, for instance, or an unexpected package is sitting on your doorstep.

The familiar standard unit for measuring time is the **second** (abbreviated s), originally defined as $1/86,400$ of a day but currently more accurately defined as the duration of 9,192,631,770 periods of certain radiation emitted by cesium atoms. **Figure 1.10** gives an idea of the vast range of time scales in the universe.

The English physicist Isaac Newton stated, "Absolute, true, and mathematical time, of itself and from its own nature, flows equably without relation to anything external." In other words, the notion of past, present, and future is universal—"now" for you, wherever you are at this instant, is also "now" everywhere else in the universe. Although this notion of the universality of time, which is given the name **absolute time,** is intuitive, experiments described in Chapter 14 have shown this notion to be false. Still, for many experiments and for the material we discuss in most of this book, the notion of absolute time remains an excellent approximation.

Now that we have introduced space and time, we can use these concepts to study events. Throughout this book, we focus on **change,** the transition from one state to another. Examples of change are the melting of an ice cube, motion (a change in location), the expansion of a piece of metal, the flow of a liquid. As you will see, one might well call physics the study of the changes that surround us and convey the passage of time. What is most remarkable about all this is that we shall discover that underneath all the changes we'll look at, certain properties remain *unchanged*. These properties give rise to what are called *conservation laws,* the most fundamental and universal laws of physics.

There is a profound aesthetic appeal in knowing that symmetry and conservation are the cornerstones of the laws that govern the universe. It is reassuring to know that an elegant simplicity underlies the structure of the universe and the relationship between space and time.

1.8 A single chemical reaction takes about 10^{-13} s. What order of magnitude is the number of sequential chemical reactions that could take place during a physics class?

Figure 1.10 A survey of the time scales on which events in the universe take place.

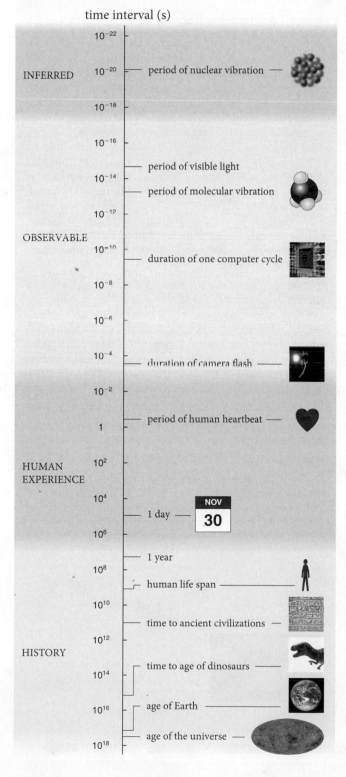

1.5 Representations

Of all our senses, it is vision that most informs our mind. For this reason, expert problem solvers rarely start working on a problem without first making some sort of visual representation of the available information, and you should always do the same. Such a drawing helps you establish a clear mental image of the situation, interpret the problem in light of your own knowledge and experience, develop a qualitative understanding of the problem, and organize the information in a meaningful way. Without the drawing, you have to juggle all the information in your head. The drawing frees your brain to deal with the solution. As an example, consider the situation described in Checkpoint 1.9. First try solving the problem without a piece of paper and note the mental effort it takes; then make a sketch and work out the solution.

1.9 You and your spouse are working out a seating arrangement around a circular table for dinner with John and Mary Jones, Mike and Sylvia Masters, and Bob and Cyndi Ahlers. Mike is not fond of the Ahlers, and Sylvia asked that she not be seated next to John. You would like to alternate men and women and avoid seating spouses next to each other. Determine an arrangement that satisfies all the constraints.

Were you able to solve the problem without a sketch? Doing so would be difficult because there is more information than most people can comfortably keep in mind at once. When you represent the information visually, however, it is relatively easy to solve this problem (see the solution in the back of this book). The drawing breaks the problem down into small steps and helps you articulate in your mind what you are trying to accomplish.

Visual representations are not helpful only for making seating arrangements. They work just as well for solving physics problems, although it may not immediately be clear *how* to represent the available information. For this reason we shall develop a number of different ways—pictures, sketches, diagrams, graphs—and a number of different context-specific procedures to represent information visually in our study of physics. As you will see, these visual representations are an integral part of getting a grip on a problem and developing a model (**Figure 1.11**).

As we discussed in Section 1.1, descriptions of the physical world always begin with simplified representations. When you solve physics problems, elaborate drawings clutter your mind with irrelevant information and prevent you from getting a clear view of the important features. One of the most basic skills in physics, therefore, is to decide what to leave out of your drawings. If you leave out essential features, the representation is useless, but if you put in too many details, it becomes impossible to analyze the situation. Sometimes it is necessary to begin with an oversimplification in order to develop a feel for a given situation. Once this initial understanding has been gained, however,

Figure 1.11 Multiple representations help you solve problems. (*a*) Many problems start with a verbal representation. (*b*) Turning the words into a sketch helps you to grasp the problem. (*c*) The sketch can then give meaning to a mathematical representation of the problem.

(*a*)

Two collisions are carried out to crash-test a 1000-kg car: (*a*) While moving at 15 mph, the car strikes an identical car initially at rest. (*b*) While moving at 15 mph, the car strikes an identical car moving toward it and also traveling at 15 mph. For each collision, what is the amount of kinetic energy that can be converted to another form in the collision, and what fraction of the total initial (*a*) kinetic energy of the two-car system does this represent?

(*b*)

(*c*)

$$\Delta v_x = v_{x,f} - v_{x,i} = \int_{t_i}^{t_f} a_x\, dt = a_x \int_{t_i}^{t_f} dt = a_x (t_f - t_i).$$

$$\Delta v_x = \lim_{\Delta t \to 0} \sum_{n}^{f} a_x(t_n)\, \Delta t \equiv \int_{t_i}^{t_f} a_x(t)\, dt$$

◄ ABSTRACT   CONCRETE ►

it becomes possible to construct less idealized models, with each successive model being a more realistic representation of the real-world situation.

In any drawings you make, therefore, you should treat everyday objects as simplifications that can be characterized by a minimum number of features or quantities. Some joke that physicists hold a grossly oversimplified view of the world, thinking in such terms as, for instance, "Consider a spherical cow...." The world around us, cows included, contains infinitely many details that may play a role in the grand scheme of things, but to get a grip on any problem it is important to begin by leaving out as much detail as possible. If the resulting model reproduces the main features of the real world, you know you have taken the essential

attributes into account. As an example, **Figure 1.12** shows a progression from a photograph of a cow to an abstract rendition of it. To study the pattern on the cow's hide, you need the photograph. If you are interested in only the position of a certain cow in a certain pasture, however, a simple dot suffices (Figure 1.12*d*). By reducing the cow to a dot, you have discarded any information about its size and shape, but as you will see as you continue with your study of physics, this information is often not relevant.

Exercise 1.5 Stretching a spring

For a physics laboratory assignment, one end of a spring is attached to a horizontal rod so that the spring hangs vertically, and a ruler is hung vertically alongside the spring. The stretching properties of the spring are to be measured by attaching eight identical beads to the spring's free end. With no beads attached, the free end of the spring is at a ruler reading of 23.4 mm. With one bead attached, the end of the spring drops to 25.2 mm. When the second, third, and fourth beads are attached one at a time, the end drops to ruler readings of 26.5 mm, 29.1 mm, and 30.8 mm, respectively. Adding the fifth and sixth beads together moves the spring end to 34.3 mm, and adding the last two beads moves the end to 38.2 mm. (*a*) Make a pictorial representation of this setup. (*b*) Tabulate the data. (*c*) Plot the data on a graph, showing the ruler readings on the vertical axis and the numbers of beads on the horizontal axis. (*d*) Describe what can be inferred from the data.

SOLUTION (*a*) The important items that should appear in my drawing are the spring, the rod from which it is suspended, the ruler, and at least one bead. My drawing should also indicate how the ruler readings are obtained. I can illustrate this procedure with just one bead, as **Figure 1.13*a*** shows. By drawing the spring first with no beads attached and then with one bead attached and showing the two ruler readings, I've represented the general procedure of adding beads one (or two) at a time and paying attention to how each addition changes the position of the spring end.

(*b*) See Figure 1.13*b*.

(*c*) See Figure 1.13*c*.

(*d*) The relationship between the ruler readings and the numbers of suspended beads is linear. That is to say, each additional bead stretches the spring by about the same amount.

Figure 1.12 Increasingly simplified and abstract representations of a cow.

(*a*) Photograph   (*b*) Simplified sketch   (*c*) Rectangle: represents cow's position and extent   (*d*) Dot: shows only cow's position

◄ CONCRETE   ABSTRACT ►

Figure 1.13

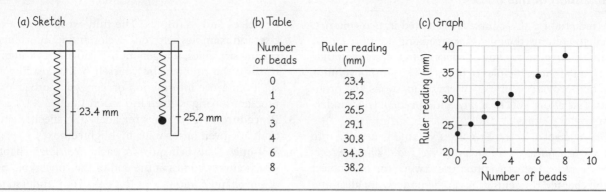

(a) Sketch

23.4 mm

25.2 mm

(b) Table

Number of beads	Ruler reading (mm)
0	23.4
1	25.2
2	26.5
3	29.1
4	30.8
6	34.3
8	38.2

(c) Graph

Exercise 1.5 demonstrates how various ways of representing information help you interpret data. The pictorial representation of Figure 1.13a helps you visualize how the measurements were taken. The table of Figure 1.13b organizes the data, and the graph of Figure 1.13c allows you to recognize the linear relationship between how far the spring stretches and the number of beads suspended from it—something that is not at all obvious from the text or the table.

Like the sketch, the graph is a simplified representation of the stretching of the spring. Each representation involves a loss of information and detail. The sketch is a simplified two-dimensional representation of a three-dimensional setup, and the graph shows only one piece of information for each measurement: the position of the bottom of the spring. All other information is left out in order to reveal one crucial point: How much the spring stretches is proportional to the number of beads suspended from it (something we look at in more detail in Chapter 9).

You may be beginning to wonder what the role of mathematics is in physics, given that we haven't used any thus far. One of the main roles of mathematics in physics is allowing us to express succinctly and unambiguously ideas that if expressed verbally would require a lot of words whose meaning may not be precise. Take this statement, for example:

The magnitude of the acceleration of an object is directly proportional to the magnitude of the vector sum of the forces exerted on the object and inversely proportional to the object's inertia. The direction of the acceleration is the same as the direction of the vector sum of the forces.

(Don't worry about the meaning of this statement for now; just note that it is quite a mouthful.) We can express this statement mathematically as

$$\vec{a} = \frac{\Sigma \vec{F}}{m}.$$

These two expressions—one verbal, the other mathematical—are identical. Neither one is more accurate than the other. Right now the symbols in the equation may make no more sense to you than hieroglyphs. Once you understand their meaning, however, the mathematical expression can be parsed much more quickly than the verbal expression can. In this respect, mathematics plays the same role as visual representations: It relieves the brain of having to keep track of many words. Another important benefit of mathematical representation is that we can use the techniques of mathematics to manipulate the symbols and obtain new insights.

Without an understanding of the meaning of the concepts in any expression (acceleration and force in our example here), however, verbal expressions and mathematical ones are both meaningless, and so it is important to focus first on the meanings of concepts. As you will notice, this book has been designed to develop concepts first and to emphasize the visual representation of these concepts before moving on to a mathematical treatment (see the box "Organization of this book").

1.10 Picture a long, straight corridor running east-west, with a water fountain located somewhere along it. Starting from the west end of the corridor, a woman walks a short distance east along the corridor and stops before reaching the water fountain. The distance from her to the fountain is twice the distance she has walked. She then continues walking east, passes the water fountain, and stops 60 m from her first stop. Now the distance from her to the fountain is twice the distance from her to the east end of the corridor. How long is the corridor?

CONCEPTS

Organization of this book

The material for this course is presented in two volumes. The first volume (the one you are reading now, *Principles*) is aimed at guiding you in developing a solid understanding of the principles of physics. The second volume, *Practice,* provides a broad variety of questions and problems that allow you to apply and sharpen your understanding of physics.

Each chapter in the *Principles* volume is divided into two parts: *Concepts* and *Quantitative Tools*. The *Concepts* part develops the conceptual framework for the subject of the chapter, concentrating on the underlying ideas and helping you develop a mental picture of the subject. The *Quantitative Tools* part develops the mathematical framework, building on the ideas developed in the *Concepts* part. Interspersed in the text of each chapter are several types of learning aids to guide you through the chapter:

1. **Checkpoints** ( ). These questions compel you to test yourself on how well you understand the material you just read. Do not skip them as you read the text. First of all, the answer to a checkpoint may be necessary to understand the text following that checkpoint. Second, and more important, I've put these checkpoints right in the text because working on them means learning the material. The answers to all the checkpoints are at the end of this volume.

2. **Exercises and examples.** The fully-worked-out exercises and examples help you develop and apply problem-solving strategies. It is generally a good idea to attempt to solve the problem by yourself before reading the solution. More information on general approaches to problem solving is given in Section 1.8.

3. **Procedures.** Approaches for analyzing specific situations are given in separate, highlighted boxes.

4. **Self-quiz.** The Self-quiz in each *Principles* chapter, which always comes at the end of the conceptual part of the chapter, allows you to assess your understanding of the concepts before you move on to the quantitative treatment. Complete each Self-quiz before working on the quantitative part of the chapter, even if you are already familiar with most of the material covered. Before tackling the quantitative material, be sure to resolve any difficulties you might have in answering a Self-quiz question, either by rereading the material in the conceptual part of the chapter or by consulting your instructor.

5. **Glossary.** At the end of each chapter is a list defining the important concepts in the chapter (which are the terms printed in bold).

CONCEPTS

Self-quiz

1. Two children in a playground swing on two swings of unequal length. The child on the shorter swing is considerably heavier than the child on the longer swing. You observe that the longer swing swings more slowly. Formulate a hypothesis that could explain your observation. How could you test your hypothesis?

2. What symmetries do you observe in the quilt patterns of **Figure 1.14**?

Figure 1.14

(a)   (b)   (c)   (d)

3. Give the order of magnitude of these quantities in meters or seconds: (a) length of a football field, (b) height of a mature tree, (c) one week, (d) one year.

4. Starting from the first floor, an elevator stops at floors 5, 2, 4, 3, 6, and 4 before returning to the first floor. (a) Represent this motion visually. (b) If the distance between the first and sixth floors is 15 m, what is the total distance traveled by the elevator?

Answers

1. One hypothesis is that longer swings swing more slowly than shorter swings. You can test this hypothesis by adjusting the length of either swing until the two lengths are the same and then asking the children to remount their respective swings and swing again. If the originally longer swing is still the slower one, your hypothesis is not correct. If the two swings now have the same speed, your hypothesis is correct. Another hypothesis is that heavier children swing faster than lighter ones. You can test this hypothesis by asking the children to trade places. If the longer swing now swings faster than the shorter swing, your hypothesis is correct. If the longer swing still swings more slowly, your hypothesis is incorrect.

2. See **Figure 1.15** (a) Reflection symmetry about a horizontal line through the center. (b) Rotational symmetry by multiples of 90°. (c) Rotational symmetry by 180°. (d) Rotational symmetry by multiples of 90° and reflection symmetry about a horizontal, vertical, or diagonal line through the center.

Figure 1.15

(a)   (b)   (c)   (d)

3. (a) 100 yards is about 100 m; the order of magnitude is thus $100 \text{ m} = 10^2 \text{ m}$. (b) An average mature tree is between 5 and 20 m tall, for an average of $12 \text{ m} = 1.2 \times 10^1 \text{ m}$. The coefficient 1.2 rounds to 1, and so the order of magnitude is $1 \times 10^1 \text{ m} = 10 \text{ m}$. (c) 1 week = (1 week)(7 days/week)(24 h/day)(60 min/h)(60 s/min) = $604{,}800 \text{ s} = 6 \times 10^5 \text{ s}$; the coefficient 6 rounds to 10, and so the order of magnitude is $10 \times 10^5 \text{ s} = 10^6 \text{ s}$. (d) 1 year = 52 weeks = (52 weeks)(604,800 s/week) = $31{,}449{,}600 \text{ s} = 3.1 \times 10^7 \text{ s}$; the coefficient 3.1 rounds to 10, and so the order of magnitude is $10 \times 10^7 \text{ s} = 10^8 \text{ s}$.

4. (a) See **Figure 1.16** for one way to represent the motion. Note that the elevator itself is not represented because showing it would add nothing we need to the visual information. The only thing we are interested in is distances traveled, represented by the vertical lines. (b) If the distance between floors 1 and 6 is 15 m, one floor is (15 m)/5 = 3.0 m. From the figure, I see that the numbers of floors traveled between successive stops are 4, 3, 2, 1, 3, 2, and 3, for a total of 18 floors, or 18(3.0 m) = 54 m.

Figure 1.16   floor

Table 1.1 Physical quantities and their symbols

Physical quantity	Symbol
length	ℓ
time	t
mass	m
speed	v
volume	V
energy	E
temperature	T

1.6 Physical quantities and units

Because physics is a quantitative science, statements must be expressed in numbers, which requires either measuring or calculating numerical values for physical quantities. In this section we review some basic rules for dealing with physical quantities, which in this book are represented by italic symbols—typically letters from the Roman or Greek alphabet, such as t for time and σ for electrical conductivity. **Table 1.1** gives the symbols for some of the physical quantities we use throughout the book.

Physical quantities are expressed as the product of a numerical value and a unit of measurement. For example, the length ℓ of an object that is 1.2 m long can be expressed as $\ell = 1.2$ m. The unit system used in science and engineering throughout the world and in everyday life in most countries is the Système International (International System), and the units are collectively called **SI units.** This system consists of seven base units (**Table 1.2**) from which all other units currently in use can be derived. For example, the physical quantity speed, which we discuss in Chapter 2, is defined as the distance traveled divided by the time interval over which the travel takes place. Thus the SI derived unit of speed is meters per second (m/s), the base unit of length divided by the base unit of time. A list of SI derived units and their relationship to the seven base units is given in Appendix C.

Be careful not to confuse abbreviations for units with symbols for physical quantities. Unit abbreviations are printed in roman (upright) type—m for meters, for instance—and symbols for physical quantities are printed in italic (slanted) type—t for time, say. Also, bear in mind that you can add and subtract quantities only if they have the same units; it is meaningless to add, say, 3 m to 4 kg.

To produce multiples of any SI unit and conveniently work with very large or very small numbers, we modify the unit name with prefixes representing integer powers of ten (**Table 1.3**). For example, a billionth of a second is denoted by 1 ns (pronounced "one nanosecond"):

$$1 \text{ ns} = 10^{-9} \text{ s}. \tag{1.1}$$

One thousand meters is denoted by 1 km, "one kilometer." Prefixes are never used without a unit and are never combined into compound prefixes. The unit *kilogram* contains a prefix (*kilo-*) because it is derived from the non-SI unit *gram* (1 kg = 1000 g). Therefore 10^{-6} kg never becomes 1 μkg. Instead, the names and multiples of the kilogram are constructed by adding the appropriate prefix to the word *gram* and the abbreviation g. For example, 10^{-6} kg becomes 1 mg, "one milligram."

The standard practice in engineering is to use only the powers of ten that are multiples of three.

Table 1.2 The seven SI base units

Name of unit	Abbreviation	Physical quantity
meter	m	length
kilogram	kg	mass
second	s	time
ampere	A	electric current
kelvin	K	thermodynamic temperature
mole	mol	amount of substance
candela	cd	luminous intensity

Table 1.3 SI prefixes

10^n	Prefix	Abbreviation	10^n	Prefix	Abbreviation
10^0	—	—			
10^3	kilo-	k	10^{-3}	milli-	m
10^6	mega-	M	10^{-6}	micro-	μ
10^9	giga-	G	10^{-9}	nano-	n
10^{12}	tera-	T	10^{-12}	pico-	p
10^{15}	peta-	P	10^{-15}	femto-	f
10^{18}	exa-	E	10^{-18}	atto-	a
10^{21}	zetta-	Z	10^{-21}	zepto-	z
10^{24}	yotta-	Y	10^{-24}	yocto-	y

1.11 Use prefixes from Table 1.3 to remove either all or almost all of the zeros in each expression. (*a*) $\ell = 150{,}000{,}000$ m, (*b*) $t = 0.000\,000\,000\,012$ s, (*c*) 1200 km/s, (*d*) 2300 kg.

Of the seven SI base units, we have already discussed two, the meter and the second. We discuss the base unit for mass, the kilogram, in Chapter 4, the base unit for electric current, the ampere, in Chapter 27, and the base unit for temperature, the kelvin, in Chapter 20.

The **mole** (abbreviated mol) is the SI base unit that measures the quantity of a given substance. A mole is currently defined as the number of atoms in 12×10^{-3} kg of carbon-12, the most common form of carbon. This number is called **Avogadro's number** N_A, after the 19th-century Italian physicist Amedeo Avogadro. The currently accepted experimental measurement of Avogadro's number is

$$N_A = 6.0221413 \times 10^{23}.$$

Note that the mole is simply a number: Just as *one dozen* means 12 of anything and *one gross* means 144 of anything, *one mole* means 6.022×10^{23} of anything. So 1 mol of helium atoms is 6.022×10^{23} helium atoms, and 1 mol of carbon dioxide molecules is 6.022×10^{23} carbon dioxide molecules.

The final SI base unit, the *candela*, measures luminous intensity. One candela (1 cd) is roughly the amount of light generated by a single candle; the light emitted by a 100-watt light bulb is about 120 cd. The definition of the candela takes into account how the human eye perceives the intensity of various colors and is therefore rather unwieldy. For this reason we do not use the candela in this book in the chapters dealing with light, concentrating instead on the amount of energy carried by light.

An important concept used throughout physics is **density,** the physical quantity that measures how much of some substance there is in a given volume. Depending on the quantity being measured, there are various types of density. For example, *number density* is the number of objects per unit volume. If there are N objects in a volume V, then the number density n of these objects is

$$n \equiv \frac{N}{V}. \tag{1.3}$$

(The symbol $\equiv$ means that the equality is either a definition or a convention.) If the objects in a given volume are packed together more tightly, the number density is higher (**Figure 1.17**). *Mass density* ρ (Greek rho) is the amount of mass *m* per unit volume:

$$\rho \equiv \frac{m}{V}. \tag{1.4}$$

Figure 1.17 Number density.

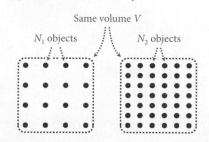

Same volume V

N_1 objects N_2 objects

The greater the number N of objects in a given space V, the higher the number density $n = N/V$. In this case $N_2 > N_1$, so $n_2 > n_1$.

QUANTITATIVE TOOLS

Exercise 1.6 Helium density

At room temperature and atmospheric pressure, 1 mol of helium gas has a volume of $24.5 \times 10^{-3}\,\text{m}^3$. The same amount of *liquid* helium has a volume of $32.0 \times 10^{-6}\,\text{m}^3$. What are the number and mass densities of (*a*) the gaseous helium and (*b*) the liquid helium? The mass of one helium atom is $6.647 \times 10^{-27}\,\text{kg}$.

SOLUTION (*a*) I know from Eq. 1.2 that 1 mol of helium contains 6.022×10^{23} atoms, and I can use this information in Eq. 1.3 to get the number density:

$$n = \frac{6.022 \times 10^{23}\,\text{atoms}}{24.5 \times 10^{-3}\,\text{m}^3} = 2.46 \times 10^{25}\,\text{atoms/m}^3.$$

For the mass density, I must know the mass of 1 mol of helium atoms, and so I multiply the mass of one helium atom by the number of atoms in 1 mol:

$$m = (6.647 \times 10^{-27}\,\text{kg/atom})(6.022 \times 10^{23}\,\text{atoms/mol})$$

$$= 4.003 \times 10^{-3}\,\text{kg/mol}.$$

Equation 1.4 then yields

$$\rho = \frac{4.003 \times 10^{-3}\,\text{kg}}{24.5 \times 10^{-3}\,\text{m}^3} = 0.163\,\text{kg/m}^3.$$

(*b*) For the liquid helium, the same reasoning gives me

$$n = \frac{6.022 \times 10^{23}\,\text{atoms}}{32.0 \times 10^{-6}\,\text{m}^3} = 1.88 \times 10^{28}\,\text{atoms/m}^3$$

$$\rho = \frac{4.003 \times 10^{-3}\,\text{kg}}{32.0 \times 10^{-6}\,\text{m}^3} = 125\,\text{kg/m}^3.$$

Examples of non-SI units accepted for use along with SI units are the minute (1 min = 60 s), the hour (1 h = 3600 s), the liter ($1\,\text{L} = 10^{-3}\,\text{m}^3$), and the metric ton ($1\,\text{t} = 10^3\,\text{kg}$).

A number of traditional, non-SI units are used in engineering; in various businesses, industries, sports, and trades; and in everyday life in the United States. Examples are inches, feet, yards, miles, acres, ounces, pints, gallons, and fluid ounces. These units are nondecimal, which makes it hard to interconvert them. When solving problems in this course, always begin by converting any quantities given in non-SI units to the SI equivalents. A conversion table is given in Appendix C.

The simplest way to convert from one unit to another is to write the conversion factor for the two units as a ratio. For, example, in Appendix C, we see that 1 in. = 25.4 mm. By bringing the 25.4 mm to the left side of the equals sign, we can write this as either

$$\frac{1\,\text{in.}}{25.4\,\text{mm}} = 1 \quad \text{or} \quad \frac{25.4\,\text{mm}}{1\,\text{in.}} = 1 \tag{1.5}$$

Note that you *must* write the units in these expressions because without them you obtain the incorrect expressions $\frac{1}{25.4} = 1$ and $\frac{25.4}{1} = 1$. Because multiplying any number by 1 doesn't change the number, you can use these ratios to convert units. For example, to express 4.5 in. in millimeters, you multiply by the ratio on the right in Eq. 1.5 and cancel out the inches:

$$4.5 \text{ in.} = (4.5 \text{ in.})\left(\frac{25.4 \text{ mm}}{1 \text{ in.}}\right) = 4.5 \times 25.4 \text{ mm} = 1.1 \times 10^2 \text{ mm}. \quad (1.6)$$

✋ **1.12** Why is the ratio on the left in Eq. 1.5 not suitable for converting inches to millimeters?

Exercise 1.7 Unit conversions

Convert each quantity to a quantity expressed either in meters or in meters raised to some power: (*a*) 4.5 in., (*b*) 3.2 acres, (*c*) 32 mi, (*d*) 3.0 pints.

SOLUTION I obtain my conversions factors from Appendix C.

(*a*) $$(4.5 \text{ in.})\left(\frac{2.54 \times 10^{-2} \text{ m}}{1 \text{ in.}}\right) = 1.1 \times 10^{-1} \text{ m}.$$

(*b*) $$(3.2 \text{ acres})\left(\frac{4.047 \times 10^3 \text{ m}^2}{1 \text{ acre}}\right) = 1.3 \times 10^4 \text{ m}^2.$$

(*c*) $$(32 \text{ mi})\left(\frac{1.609 \times 10^3 \text{ m}}{1 \text{ mi}}\right) = 5.1 \times 10^4 \text{ m}.$$

(*d*) $$(3.0 \text{ pints})\left(\frac{4.732 \times 10^{-4} \text{ m}^3}{1 \text{ pint}}\right) = 1.4 \times 10^{-3} \text{ m}^3.$$

✋ **1.13** (*a*) Using what you know about the diameters of atoms from Section 1.3, estimate the length of one side of a cube made up of 1 mol of closely packed carbon atoms. (*b*) The mass density of graphite (a form of carbon) is $2.2 \times 10^3 \text{ kg/m}^3$. By how much does the length you calculated in part *a* change when you do your calculation with this mass density value? Remember that 1 mol is the number of atoms in 12×10^{-3} kg of carbon.

1.7 Significant digits

The numbers we deal with in physics fall into two categories: exact numbers that are known with complete certainty (integers, such as the 14 in "I have 14 books on my desk") and inexact numbers that result from measurements and are known to only within some finite precision. Consider, for example, using a ruler to measure the width of a piece of paper (**Figure 1.18**). The width falls between the ruler marks for 21 mm and 22 mm and is closer to 21 mm than 22 mm. We might guess that the width is about 21.3 mm, but we cannot be sure about the last digit without a better measurement method. By recording the width as 21 mm, we are indicating that the actual value lies between 20.5 mm and 21.5 mm. The value 21 mm is said to have two **significant digits**—digits that are known reliably.

By expressing a value with the proper number of significant digits, we can convey the precision to which that value is known. For numbers that don't contain any zeros, all digits shown are significant, which means that 21 has two significant digits, as just noted, and 21.3 has three significant digits (implying that the actual value lies between 21.25 and 21.35).

With numbers that contain zeros, the situation is more complicated. *Leading zeros,* which means any that come before the first nonzero digit, are never significant: 0.037 has two significant digits. Zeros that come between two nonzero digits,

Figure 1.18 If you measure the width of a sticky note with the ruler shown, you can reliably read off two digits.

as in 0.602, are always significant. *Trailing zeros* are those that come after the last nonzero digit in a number, as in 3.500 and 20. Trailing zeros to the right of the decimal point are always significant: 25.10 has four significant digits. However, trailing zeros in numbers that do not contain a decimal point are ambiguous. For example, in the number 7900, it is not clear whether the trailing zeros are significant or not. The number of significant digits is at least two but could be three or four. To accurately convey the precision for such numbers, we use scientific notation, which lets us place significant zeros to the right of the decimal point: 7.900×10^3 has four significant digits, 7.90×10^3 has three, and 7.9×10^3 has two.

Important note: To simplify the notation in this book, we consider all trailing zeros in numbers that do not contain a decimal point to be significant: four significant digits for 3400, for instance, and two significant digits for 30.

Do not confuse significant digits with the number of decimal places or the number of digits: 0.000584 has three significant digits, six decimal places, and seven digits; 58.4 has three significant digits, one decimal place, and three digits. With the exception of fundamental constants such as the speed of light, most values in this book are given to two or three significant digits.

When you use a calculator for the math involved in solving physics problems, the calculator display usually shows many more digits than the number of significant digits allowed by the problem data. In such cases, you need to round your answer to the correct number of significant digits. If the digit just to the right of the last significant digit you are allowed is less than 5, report your last significant digit as it appears on the calculator display. If the digit just to the right of the last significant digit is 5 or greater, increase your last significant digit by 1. For example, if you are allowed two significant digits, 1.356 rounds to 1.4, 2.5199 rounds to 2.5, and 7.95 rounds to 8.0.

Multiple roundings can yield an accumulation of errors, and therefore it is best to wait until you have obtained the final result in a multistep calculation before rounding. In intermediate results, therefore, retain a few more digits than what your input quantities have and then round off to the correct number of significant digits only in your final result.

Exercise 1.8 Significant digits

(*a*) How many significant digits are there in 403.54 kg, 3.010×10^{57} m, 2.43×10^{-3} s, 14.00 μm, 0.0140 s, 5300 kg? (*b*) Round 12,300 kg and 0.0125 s to two significant digits.

SOLUTION (*a*) 403.54 kg has five, 3.010×10^{57} m has four, 2.43×10^{-3} s has three, 14.00 μm has four, 0.0140 s has three, 5300 kg has four in this book (but is considered ambiguous in general).

(*b*) 1.2×10^4 kg (or 12 Mg); 0.013 s (or 1.3×10^{-3} s or 1.3 ms).

Suppose you measure the mass and volume of some object to be $m = 1.2$ kg and $V = 0.123$ m^3, and you wish to use these values to compute the object's mass density. If you substitute the measured values into Eq. 1.4 and carry out the division on your calculator, you get

$$\rho \equiv \frac{m}{V} = \frac{1.2 \text{ kg}}{0.123 \text{ m}^3} = 9.756\,097\,56 \text{ kg/m}^3. \tag{1.7}$$

You measured the mass to two significant digits and the volume to three significant digits, but your calculator suggests you have determined the density to a precision of better than one part in a billion! The rigorous way to deal with uncertainties in measurements is to recalculate any computed value by using the high and low uncertainties for each value in the calculation, which is a time-consuming task. For this reason, we shall use two shortcuts. The first deals with multiplication and division:

> When multiplying or dividing quantities, the number of significant digits in the result is the same as the number of significant digits in the input quantity that has the fewest significant digits.

In your calculation of the mass density in Eq. 1.7, the input quantity that has the fewest significant digits is the mass (two significant digits), and so the answer should be rounded to two significant digits:

$$\rho \equiv \frac{m}{V} = \frac{1.2 \text{ kg}}{0.123 \text{ m}^3} = 9.8 \text{ kg/m}^3. \tag{1.8}$$

Now suppose you determine the mass of two parts of an object and obtain 105 kg for one part and 0.01 kg for the other (three and one significant digit, respectively). Adding the two measured values yields a value containing five significant digits:

$$105 \text{ kg} + 0.01 \text{ kg} = 105.01 \text{ kg}. \tag{1.9}$$

Given that the precision in the value 105 kg is $+0.5$ kg, it makes no sense to report the final result to five significant digits. Rounding so that the number of significant digits in the sum is the same as the number of significant digits in the input value that has the fewest significant digits would yield 100 kg, which deviates from the actual value (around 105 kg) by significantly more than the precision in the individual measurements (± 0.5 kg and ± 0.005 kg). To solve this problem, whenever we add or subtract numerical values, we focus on the number of *decimal places*:

> When adding or subtracting quantities, the number of decimal places in the result is the same as the number of decimal places in the input quantity that has the fewest decimal places.

For the addition in Eq. 1.9, the input quantity that has the fewest decimal places is 105 kg (zero decimal places), and so

$$105 \text{ kg} + 0.01 \text{ kg} = 105 \text{ kg}. \tag{1.10}$$

Bear in mind that *counting numbers* (that is, integers) are exact and so have an infinite number of significant digits. For example, the product of the width of two buttons each 15.7 mm wide is $2 \times 15.7 \text{ mm} = 31.4 \text{ mm}$ (not 3×10^1 mm because the 2 is a counting number).

Exercise 1.9 Significant digits and calculations

Calculate: (a) $f = a/(bc)$, where $a = 2.34 \text{ mm}^2$, $b = 54.26$ m, and $c = 0.14 \ \mu\text{m}$; (b) $g = kt^3$, where $k = 1.208 \times 10^{-2} \text{ s}^{-3}$ and $t = 2.84$ s; (c) $f + g$; (d) the sum of $b = 54.26$ m and $c = 1.4$ mm; (e) $h = k(m - n)$, where $k = 1.252$, $m = 32.21$, and $n = 32.1$.

SOLUTION (a) I first need to convert the millimeters-squared in $a = 2.34 \text{ mm}^2$ to meters-squared and the micrometers in $c = 0.14 \ \mu\text{m}$ to meters:

$$2.34 \text{ mm}^2\left(\frac{1 \text{ m}}{1 \times 10^3 \text{ mm}}\right)^2 = 2.34 \text{ mm}^2\left(\frac{1 \text{ m}^2}{1 \times 10^6 \text{ mm}^2}\right) = 2.34 \times 10^{-6} \text{ m}^2$$

$$0.14 \ \mu\text{m}\left(\frac{1 \text{ m}}{1 \times 10^6 \ \mu\text{m}}\right) = 0.14 \times 10^{-6} \text{ m}.$$

(Continued)

Substituting the values given, I get

$$f = \frac{2.34 \times 10^{-6}\ \mathrm{m}^2}{(54.26\ \mathrm{m})(0.14 \times 10^{-6}\ \mathrm{m})} = 0.30804,$$

which I must round to two significant digits, 0.31, because that is the number of significant digits in the value given for c.

(b) $g = (1.208 \times 10^{-2}\ \mathrm{s}^{-3})(2.84\ \mathrm{s})^3 = 0.2767$, which I must round to three significant digits, 0.277, because of t.

(c) $f + g = 0.30804 + 0.2767 = 0.58474$, which I round to 0.58 because I must report only two decimal places, limited by $c = 0.14\ \mu\mathrm{m}$. Note that if I had added the rounded values for f and g, my result reported to two significant digits would not be 0.58: $f + g = 0.31 + 0.277 = 0.587$, which rounds to 0.59. Be careful—reporting the correct number of significant digits can be tricky.

(d) $b + c = 54.26\ \mathrm{m} + 0.0014\ \mathrm{m} = 54.26\ \mathrm{m}$ (reported to two decimal places, limited by the 54.26 value).

(e) $h = 1.252(32.21 - 32.1) = 0.1$ (reported to one significant digit, limited by the 32.1 value).

The number zero requires special consideration. When some physical quantity is exactly zero, we denote this quantity by a zero *without units*. The speed of an object that is not moving is exactly zero and is therefore denoted by $v = 0$ (no units). However, if we measure a speed as zero to two significant digits, we write $v = 0.0\ \mathrm{m/s}$ (note the units), implying that the actual value is zero to within $0.05\ \mathrm{m/s}$.

✋ **1.14** (a) Express the circumference of a circle of radius $R = 27.3\ \mathrm{mm}$ with the correct number of significant digits. (b) Let $a = 12.3$, $b = 3.241$, and $c = 55.74$. Compute $a + b + c$. (c) Let $m = 4.00$, $n = 3.00$, and $k = 7$ (exact). Compute $f = m^2/k$, $g = n^2/k$, and $f + g$.

1.8 Solving problems

You encounter problems every day. You are in a rush to get somewhere but can't find your car keys. You run out of flour while baking a birthday cake, and the supermarket is closed. Your flight is canceled on your way to a job interview. You want to buy those great new shoes, but there's no money in the bank. There is no formula for solving these or any other types of problems (if there were a formula, you wouldn't have a problem!). Because real-world problems defy one-shot solutions, we must break them down into smaller parts and solve them in steps. In this section we develop a four-step problem-solving strategy that will help you tackle a broad variety of problems (the procedure is summarized in the box "Solving problems").

Most physics problems are formulated in words. This is true not only of the problems in this book but also of questions you might have about the world around you. Standing on the rim of the Grand Canyon, you might wonder, If I drop a stone, how long does it take to hit the bottom?, or while watching the Olympics, you might wonder, Is there a physical limit to how high an athlete can jump?

❶ GETTING STARTED

Because it's not clear which road leads you most efficiently to the answer to a given problem, the first step of our problem-solving strategy, *getting started*, is the most difficult one. It is therefore useful to begin with something you *can* do: Organize the information given and be sure you are clear on exactly what is asked for in the problem. To clarify the goal of the problem in your mind, it is crucial to begin by visualizing the situation: Sketch, describe in your own words, list, and/or tabulate the main features of the problem to relieve yourself from having to hold all this information in memory. In making a sketch, be sure to follow the guidelines given in Section 1.5: Make your rendering as simple as possible and show all relevant numerical information in the sketch. Recasting your problem visually or verbally forces you to spell out what you want to accomplish and often automatically leads to ideas on how to solve the problem.

Once you have the information organized, ask yourself which concepts and principles apply. Throughout this book, we develop principle-specific procedures for solving problems. By determining which principles apply to a problem you are working on, you can identify which problem-solving procedures apply to your problem.

Finally, you must determine whether or not you have all the information necessary to solve the problem. Sometimes you may have to supplement the information provided with things you know about the situation at hand. Furthermore, because no problem can be formulated with absolute precision, you will often need to make a number of simplifying assumptions. This lack of precision is often a source of frustration for anyone beginning to solve physics problems. How do you know which assumptions are valid for a given problem? Do not let this question trouble you—as long as you are aware of the assumptions you make, you can always reexamine them once you have obtained an answer and then refine the assumptions and the solution.

❷ DEVISE PLAN

Next you must *devise a plan* for solving your problem, which means spelling out what you must do to solve the problem. Are there any physical relationships or equations that you can apply to determine the information you are trying to obtain? A good plan is to outline the steps you need to take to obtain a solution. For some (but certainly not all) problems, these steps are carried out mathematically.

❸ EXECUTE PLAN

In the third step, you *execute your plan* by following the steps you have outlined, substituting the information given and carrying out any mathematical operations necessary to isolate the quantity you wish to determine. In problems involving numerical values, you should solve for an algebraic answer first, waiting until the final step to substitute numerical values and obtain a numerical answer. The only exception to this algebraic-answer-first approach is that, in order to simplify your algebraic expressions, you should eliminate any quantities that are zero from them as soon as possible.

In the final step, substituting numerical values into your algebraic expression, do not forget to show the correct units on all numerical values and to carry these units through the calculation.

Once you have obtained an answer, you should check your work for these five important points (which you can remember via the acronym *VENUS*):

1. **V**ectors/scalars used correctly? As you will see in Chapter 2, the quantities we deal with in this book fall into two classes, vectors and scalars. Make sure you have expressed your answer in the appropriate form. (In this chapter all quantities are scalars.)

2. **E**very question asked in problem statement answered? Reread the problem statement to make sure you have completely answered every question.

3. **N**o unknown quantities in answers? If your answer is an algebraic expression, be sure that every variable appearing in terms to the right of the equals sign has been given as a known quantity in the problem statement. Example: "A car moving at speed v . . . " means that v in this problem is a known quantity.

4. **Units correct?** Each numerical answer should be expressed as a number with the appropriate units for that quantity (Section 1.6). When your answer is an algebraic expression, be sure that the combined units of all terms to the right of the equals sign work out to be equivalent to the unit of the quantity to the left of the equals sign.

5. **Significant digits justified?** The number of significant digits reported in your answer should reflect the number of significant digits of the quantities given in the problem statement (Section 1.7).

As a reminder to yourself, put a checkmark beside each answer to indicate that you checked these five points.

❹ EVALUATE RESULT

You may think you are done, but there is one final—and very important—step left: *Evaluate your answer*. In this step, you should reflect on your work, examine the result, and determine whether your answer is reasonable (or, if you can't tell whether or not it is reasonable, at least make sure that it is not unreasonable). The first thing you might try is seeing whether your answer conforms to what you expect based on your situation sketch, diagram, or other information given. If any part of your answer is unexpected, go back and check your math and any assumptions you made.

If your result is an algebraic expression or if your numerical answer comes directly from an algebraic expression, check whether or not that expression behaves as you expect with changes in physical quantities. For example, say you obtain the expression $v = k/t$ for the speed of an object and you know from experience that for this object the speed is zero for large values of t. If you let t go to infinity, your expression should indeed give the right answer: $v = k/\infty = 0$. If it didn't, you must go back and check your math and any assumptions you made.

Some problems can be solved in more than one way. If you solve your problem in two ways and obtain the same answer, you can be pretty sure your answer is correct. If you don't get the same answer from the two ways, you'd better go back and check your work!

Procedure: Solving problems

Although there is no set approach when solving problems, it helps to break things down into several steps whenever you are working a physics problem. Throughout this book, we use the four-step procedure summarized here to solve problems. For a more detailed description of each step, see Section 1.8.

1. **Getting started.** Begin by carefully analyzing the information given and determining in your own words what question or task is being asked of you. Organize the information by making a sketch of the situation or putting data in tabular form. Determine which physics concepts apply, and note any assumptions you are making.

2. **Devise plan.** Decide what you must do to solve the problem. First determine which physical relationships or equations you need, and then determine the order in which you will use them. Make sure you have a sufficient number of equations to solve for all unknowns.

3. **Execute plan.** Execute your plan, and then check your work for the following five important points:

   Vectors/scalars used correctly?
   Every question asked in problem statement answered?
   No unknown quantities in answers?
   Units correct?
   Significant digits justified?

   As a reminder to yourself, put a checkmark beside each answer to indicate that you checked these five points.

4. **Evaluate result.** There are several ways to check whether an answer is reasonable. One way is to make sure your answer conforms to what you expect based on your sketch and the information given. If your answer is an algebraic expression, check to be sure the expression gives the correct trend or answer for special (limiting) cases for which you already know the answer. Sometimes there may be an alternative approach to solving the problem; if so, use it to see whether or not you get the same answer. If any of these tests yields an unexpected result, go back and check your math and any assumptions you made. If none of these checks can be applied to your problem, check the algebraic signs and order of magnitude.

If none of the evaluation methods can be applied to your answer, you should at least verify that there is nothing obviously wrong with it by checking that the algebraic signs you obtain make sense and that any numerical value has the correct order of magnitude. For example, if the algebraic sign of your solution tells you that an object moves to the left when you know it should move to the right, you know your answer can't be right. You can find some techniques for estimating orders of magnitude in the next section. Using these techniques, you should be able to obtain reasonable upper and lower bounds for your answer. Provided your answer does not lie outside this range, you know there is not something obviously wrong with it.

With the exception of one-step exercises that are applications of procedures, the examples in this book follow this four-step procedure.

Example 1.10 Length of string

A certain cylinder is 15 in. long and has a circumference of 4.0 in. When one end of a piece of string is attached to the left end of the cylinder and the string is then wound exactly five times around, the string just reaches to the cylinder's right end. What is the length of the string?

❶ GETTING STARTED I begin by making a sketch of the situation (**Figure 1.19a**). The shortest length is going to be obtained when the string is wound uniformly, with each of the five windings running one-fifth of the length of the cylinder. I need to find a way to determine the length of this spiraling string. This appears to be a geometry problem, but the surface of the cylinder is curved, not flat.

Figure 1.19

(a)

(b)

❷ DEVISE PLAN If I imagine drawing a straight line between the endpoints of the string, cutting the cylinder surface along that line, and then flattening the cylinder out, I obtain the situation shown in Figure 1.19b. Now the solution is clear: The total length of the string is the sum of the hypotenuses of five identical triangles.

❸ EXECUTE PLAN The width of each triangle is equal to one-fifth of the length of the cylinder: (15 in.)/5 = 3.0 in. The height of each triangle is equal to the circumference of the cylinder (4.0 in.). With these values, I can now use the Pythagorean theorem to determine the length ℓ of the hypotenuse of each triangle:

$$\ell = \sqrt{(3.0 \text{ in.})^2 + (4.0 \text{ in.})^2} = 5.0 \text{ in.}$$

The length of the string is equal to five times this value, or 25 in. ✔*

❹ EVALUATE RESULT The answer I obtain should be larger than the string length I would obtain if the string were wound around the cylinder in one place, which would give a string length of five times the circumference: 5 × 4.0 in. = 20 in. My answer should be smaller than what I would get if the string were wound five times around the cylinder at one end and then run along the cylinder length to the other end, which would give a string length of five times the circumference plus the length of the cylinder: (5 × 4.0 in.) + 15 in. = 35 in. The answer I obtained does indeed lie between these values, giving me confidence that it is correct.

---

*The checkmark shows that I checked my answer regarding the five important details listed on page 21: Vector/scalar: all quantities scalar; Every question answered: yes; No unknown quantities in answers: no; Units correct: yes, inches; Significant digits: everything given to two significant digits.

1.9 Developing a feel

Making order-of-magnitude estimates is possibly the most important skill to retain from a physics course because this is a skill you will use long after you leave your last classroom, no matter what you plan for a career. Economists, for instance, carry out order-of-magnitude estimates to predict market trends, and business owners might carry out such estimates to validate a business plan, to name just two possibilities.

Here in this physics course, to get back to the present, order-of-magnitude estimates allow you to develop a feel for a problem before you try to solve it. They also allow you to validate your answer: If your order-of-magnitude estimate and your answer disagree, you know to go back and reevaluate your work.

Order-of-magnitude estimates involve determining relationships between known and unknown quantities, making gross oversimplifications, combining assumptions and ideas, and even outright guessing. In general, there are multiple ways to obtain such estimates. The uncertainty in how to carry out an estimate is intimidating at first, and the lack of accuracy may appear unscientific to you. It isn't—estimation is an important aspect of science, and it is a great way to obtain physical insight and at the same time train your analytical and outside-the-box thinking skills.

For example, suppose we need to determine the number of cells in the human body. That we can't see individual cells tells us they must be very small, and therefore the number is probably very large. We could *guess* the number of cells, but the answer would probably be meaningless because we have no way of assessing its accuracy without looking it up somewhere. A billion? Ten billion? Hundred billion? What do you think?

To obtain an order-of-magnitude estimate, the first thing to do is to think of a strategy. For the number of cells in the human body, for example, if we knew the volume of a typical human body and the volume of a typical cell, we could divide the former by the latter to obtain our answer. Knowing neither volume, however, we need to estimate both.

There are several ways to estimate the volume of the human body. One way is to model the body as a cylinder (**Figure 1.20**). For the height of the cylinder, we take the height of a typical human, say $h_{human} \approx 1.7$ m. The symbol $\approx$ indicates that this value is an approximation. For the diameter, we take $d_{human} \approx 0.2$ m. That makes the diameter less than the left-to-right thickness of the body but greater than the front-to-back thickness, which should be in the right ballpark. This gives a volume of

$$V_{human} = \left(\frac{1}{4}\pi d_{human}^2\right) h_{human} \approx 0.05 \text{ m}^3.$$

Another way is to realize that the human body has roughly the same mass density as water—about 1 kg/L, which is

$$1 \text{ kg/L}\left(\frac{1 \text{ L}}{1 \times 10^{-3} \text{ m}^3}\right) = 1000 \text{ kg/m}^3.$$

The average human has a mass of about 70 kg, which corresponds to 70 L of water, and thus $V_{human} \approx (70 \text{ L})(1 \times 10^{-3} \text{ m}^3/1 \text{ L}) = 0.07 \text{ m}^3$, which is in the same ballpark as the estimate we got using the body-as-cylinder approach.

You may feel that there is too big a difference between 0.05 m³ and 0.07 m³. Indeed, if you were shopping for clothing, you'd want your clothing to fit your body better than that. However, here we are interested in only the order of magnitude. Either estimate is good enough for this purpose because for both the order of magnitude is the same: $0.05 \text{ m}^3 = 5 \times 10^{-2} \text{ m}^3$, which rounds to $10 \times 10^{-2} \text{ m}^3$, and so the order of magnitude is 10^{-1} m^3; $0.07 \text{ m}^3 = 7 \times 10^{-2} \text{ m}^3$, which also rounds to $10 \times 10^{-2} \text{ m}^3$, giving the same order of magnitude: 10^{-1} m^3.

Next we need to estimate the volume of a typical human cell. You may remember from biology class that the diameter of a typical cell is around $20 \ \mu\text{m} = 20 \times 10^{-6}$ m. Or, if you never learned cell sizes, you may recall that you can clearly see cells under a microscope and that a microscope can see objects as small as 10^{-6} m. To see the structure of a cell clearly under a microscope, the cell would need to be, say, at least 50 times the minimum size the microscope

Figure 1.20 To determine the volume of the human body, we approximate the body as a cylinder.

can handle, making our cell-diameter estimate 50×10^{-6} m. Although you may think there is a big difference between 20×10^{-6} m and 50×10^{-6} m, these two numbers are only a factor of 2.5 apart, which is much less than a factor of 10 ("one order of magnitude").

Cells viewed under a microscope tend to spread out on the glass and are thus less high than they are wide. Let's for simplicity assume they are disk-shaped and that their height is about one-quarter of their diameter. That means they have a diameter of 20×10^{-6} m and a height of 5×10^{-6} m, and so $V_{cell} = (\frac{1}{4}\pi d_{cell}^2)h_{cell} \approx 1.6 \times 10^{-15}$ m^3. The number of cells is thus $V_{human}/V_{cell} \approx (0.05 \text{ m}^3)/(1.6 \times 10^{-15} \text{ m}^3) \approx 3.1 \times 10^{13}$. Given the roughness of the estimates and assumptions, I give the final answer as an order of magnitude: 10^{14} (about 100 trillion cells).

I can be quite confident that the number of cells is somewhere between 10^{13} (10 trillion) and 10^{15} (1000 trillion), both substantially greater than the largest guess I offered earlier (100 billion = 10^{11}). The difference between that largest guess and the order-of-magnitude estimate is that I have no idea how much confidence to place in the guess, whereas I can feel reasonably certain about the result of my order-of-magnitude estimate.

You may think that this exercise is outrageous and that it is impossible to have faith in any order-of-magnitude value because it requires so many assumptions and estimates. However, the fact that we combine so many assumptions and estimates is precisely why the method works: We are unlikely to be either too high on every estimate or too low on every estimate. Instead, we unwittingly overestimate some values and underestimate others, and the over- and underestimates tend to cancel out. The result is that the final answer very likely is in the right ballpark. What is more important is that, in the process of obtaining an order-of-magnitude value, we develop insights and some feeling for the quantities involved.

Figure 1.21 shows in graphical form the process by which we obtained our estimate of the number of cells N_{cell} in the human body. We got to our answer through a combination of *devising a strategy* (using a ratio of volumes to determine the number of cells), *simplifying* (treating the human body as a cylinder and the cell as a disk), *estimating* (the diameter of the human body), and using snippets of *knowledge*. Figure 1.21 also shows why this approach can be intimidating at first: To determine a single target unknown, N_{cell}, we have to divide the problem into a larger number of questions, an approach that makes the number of unknowns increase initially! The point of this dividing, of course, is to arrive at values we know (or can guess).

The diagram in Figure 1.21*a* reduces the problem of obtaining N_{cell} to one of obtaining another value, d_{cell}. If you know the value of d_{cell} from your biology course, you are done. If you don't know the value, you can *translate* the problem into another one, as illustrated in Figure 1.21*b*. If you get stuck, guess upper and lower bounds for your unknowns, use the middle value to obtain an answer, and then reevaluate to see how your *guesstimate* affects the final answer.

Making order-of-magnitude estimates requires practice. As you go through the exercise more often, you'll gain confidence, and the process will come more naturally. An important point is not to worry too much about accuracy when working out orders of magnitude: A factor of ten doesn't matter. You'll be surprised how far you can get with this technique, some resourcefulness, and commonly available knowledge.

✋ **1.15** To work an order-of-magnitude problem, you need the value of the mass density of water, but you don't know what that value is. Design either a translation strategy (Figure 1.21*b*) or a division strategy (Figure 1.21*a*) for making an order-of-magnitude estimate of this mass density.

Figure 1.21 The process by which we estimated the number of cells in the human body.

(*a*) A division strategy

(*b*) A translation strategy

Exercise 1.11 Selling books

Consider writing a book for high-school graduates in the United States who are planning to take a year off—sometimes called a gap year—before enrolling in college. There are currently no similar books. Estimate how many such books might be purchased annually.

SOLUTION I can estimate the number of books sold by estimating the percentage of college-bound high-school graduates who take a gap year. I know two things: (1) Not all graduates do this, and (2) there is a rising interest in doing it. I estimate that 5% of high-school graduates take a gap year before going to college, but I still have to estimate the number of college-bound high-school students in the United States. I know that approximately 50% of high-school graduates go on to college, but how many high-school graduates are there each year?

If I assume every person in the country graduates from high school when she or he is 18, I've reduced this part of the problem to determining the number of 18-year-olds in the country. I know that the total population is 300 million and that the average life span is about 75 years. If I assume that age is uniformly distributed, then 1/75 of the U.S. population should be 18 years old at any given instant (this is an oversimplification but is good enough for an order-of-magnitude estimate). So the number of high-school graduates in a given year is $(1/75)(3 \times 10^8) = 4 \times 10^6$, and 5% of this is 2×10^5. Thus the number of students taking a gap year each year is approximately 200,000, which strikes me as a reasonable number. If 5% of these students buy the proposed book, about 10,000 copies will be purchased each year.

1.16 Make an order-of-magnitude estimate of the mass of Earth in kilograms.

Chapter Glossary

SI units of physical quantities are given in parentheses.

Absolute time The notion that time is the same for all observers in the universe, regardless of their location or motion.

Atom A basic building block of matter.

Avogadro's number The number of atoms or molecules in 1 mol:

$$N_A = 6.022 \times 10^{23}. \tag{1.2}$$

See also *mole*.

Change The transition from one state to another.

Density A measure of how much of some substance there is in a given volume. The *number density* (m^{-3}) is the number of objects per volume:

$$n \equiv \frac{N}{V}. \tag{1.3}$$

The *mass density* (kg/m^3) is the amount of mass per volume:

$$\rho \equiv \frac{m}{V}. \tag{1.4}$$

Electron A subatomic particle manifesting itself in a cloud around atomic nuclei.

Hypothesis A tentative explanation of observations to be used as a starting point for further investigation.

Law A description of a relationship between observable quantities that manifests itself in recurring patterns of events.

Length ℓ (m) A distance or extent in space.

Meter (m) The SI base unit of length, defined as the distance traveled by light in vacuum in $1/299{,}792{,}458$ of a second.

Model A simplified conceptual representation of a phenomenon.

Mole (mol) The SI base unit for measuring the quantity of a given substance, defined as the number of atoms in 12×10^{-3} kg of carbon-12, which is measured to be 6.022×10^{23}. See also *Avogadro's number*.

Order of magnitude A value rounded off to the nearest power of ten.

Physical quantity A physical property that can be measured and that is expressed as the product of a numerical value and a physical unit.

Principle of causality Whenever an event A causes an event B, all observers see event A happening first.

Proton, neutron Subatomic particles residing in atomic nuclei.

Scientific method An iterative process for going from observations to theories validated by experiments.

Second (s) The SI base unit of time, defined as the duration of $9{,}192{,}631{,}770$ periods of certain radiation emitted by cesium atoms.

SI units Units of measure in the International System, used in science and engineering.

Significant digits Digits in a numerical value that are reliably known.

Symmetry An object exhibits symmetry when certain operations can be performed on it without changing its appearance.

Theory A well-tested explanation of a natural phenomenon in terms of more basic processes and relationships.

Time t (s) A physical quantity that allows us to determine the sequence of related events.

Universe The totality of matter and energy combined with the space and time in which all events happen.

2 Motion in One Dimension

CONCEPTS

2.1 From reality to model

2.2 Position and displacement

2.3 Representing motion

2.4 Average speed and average velocity

QUANTITATIVE TOOLS

2.5 Scalars and vectors

2.6 Position and displacement vectors

2.7 Velocity as a vector

2.8 Motion at constant velocity

2.9 Instantaneous velocity

The branch of physics that deals with the quantitative representation of motion is called *kinematics*. Kinematics does not consider the causes and effects of motion; its goal is simply to provide a mathematical description of motion. In this chapter, we follow a kinematics approach; that is, we represent motion on a graph and quantify that motion without worrying about what causes it. In Chapter 8 we shall begin to look at the causes of motion, but for now all we care about is the motion while it is happening.

By describing the motion represented in a film clip, we begin to develop the most basic skill in physics: making simplified representations of real-world situations. You'll see how to use tables, graphs, and mathematical functions to represent quantitative data on motion. Finally, you'll learn the distinction between the terms *position* and *displacement* as well as the distinction between *speed* and *velocity*.

2.1 From reality to model

The opening picture of this chapter shows the *Shinkansen*—the Japanese bullet train—speeding over a bridge. Although the image conveys the idea of motion, it does not contain any quantitative representation of that motion. If I were to ask, "How fast is the train moving?" you wouldn't be able to answer if all you had to go on was this photograph. In order to answer my question, you need a more quantitative representation of the motion.

To analyze the motion of an object, we need to keep track of the object's position at different instants. If the position changes as time passes, the object is in motion. If the position is not changing, the object is said to be **at rest.** As a first step in measuring position, let's analyze the film clip reproduced in **Figure 2.1**, a record of me walking (and you thought physics was going to be dull!). As you can see from the clip, I first walked forward a certain distance, stood still for a short while, and then walked backward.

The imaginary straight line on the ground along which I took my steps is our *reference axis*. My position is determined by my location along this axis relative to some arbitrarily chosen reference point called the *origin*. Giving my position at different instants in time determines my motion in much the same way the film clip does. Choosing the left edge of the frame as the origin, we can say that in frame 1 the center of my body is 2.5 mm from that point; a few frames later it is 8.5 mm from the edge (frame 5); another few frames and it is 12.0 mm from the edge (frame 8). In other words, we can describe my motion by specifying my position for every frame, which is what **Table 2.1** does.

The same information is shown graphically in **Figure 2.2**, where my position relative to the left edge is plotted along the vertical axis and the horizontal axis represents the frame number. The formal way of describing this graph is to say that it shows my position (information on the vertical axis) *as a function of* the frame number

Figure 2.1 Film clip showing me walking to the right, pausing, then walking back to the left. The camera recorded this event at 30 frames per second; only one frame in ten is reproduced here. Using a ruler, you can determine the position of the center of my body in each frame. For instance, in frame 5, this position is 8.5 mm from the left edge of the frame; in frame 10, it is 12.0 mm from the left edge.

frame number
(three frames per second)

walking forward

frame 5

8.5 mm

pausing

frame 10

12.0 mm

walking backward

Figure 2.2 My distance from the left edge of each frame in Figure 2.1 versus frame number. We see that I start, in frame 1, 2.5 mm from the left edge of the frame, walk forward to 12.0 mm from the left edge at frame 8, stay there for five frames, then walk backward to 8.5 mm from the left edge.

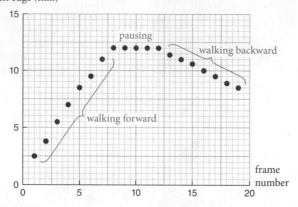

(information on the horizontal axis). The coordinates of the center of each circle correspond to the values listed in the first two columns in Table 2.1. The size of the circle is representative of the accuracy of the measurements. The upward trend of data points between frames 1 and 8 indicates that my distance from the left edge increases with increasing frame number and represents my motion walking from left to right. Then, representing the time

Table 2.1 Position versus frame number from the film sequence in Figure 2.1

Frame number	Distance from left edge (mm)	Position value x (m)	Time t (s)
1	2.5	+1.0	0
2	3.8	+1.5	0.33
3	5.5	+2.2	0.67
4	7.0	+2.8	1.00
5	8.5	+3.4	1.33
6	9.5	+3.8	1.67
7	11.0	+4.4	2.00
8	12.0	+4.8	2.33
9	12.0	+4.8	2.67
10	12.0	+4.8	3.00
11	12.0	+4.8	3.33
12	12.0	+4.8	3.67
13	11.4	+4.6	4.00
14	11.0	+4.4	4.33
15	10.6	+4.2	4.67
16	10.0	+4.0	5.00
17	9.5	+3.8	5.33
18	8.9	+3.6	5.67
19	8.5	+3.4	6.00

interval when I stood still, the data points stay flat from frame 8 to 12. Finally, from frame 12 onward, the data points show a downward trend representing my motion back to the left.

2.1 (*a*) Using a metric ruler, measure the position of the center of my body from the left edge in each frame of Figure 2.1. Compare your list of values with the positions given in Table 2.1. (*b*) Plot the positions you measured as a function of frame number—no need for graph paper, just draw your axes and plot your data by eye.

Taking information from the real world and creating a simplified abstract representation of it—making a model of a real-world happening—is one of the most important skills in physics. You'll be making such models hundreds of times throughout this course, some graphical like Figure 2.2, some in the form of tables as Table 2.1, some in the form of mathematical expressions.

2.2 (*a*) In Figure 2.2 the data points for frames 8–12 are all at position 12.0 mm. Explain what this alignment of data points means in terms of what is happening in the real world. (*b*) The data points for frames 7 and 14 are aligned horizontally. What does this alignment imply about the real-world motion? (*c*) What would it mean if two data points were aligned vertically? Could this happen?

2.2 Position and displacement

Figure 2.2 is of limited value as a model of a real-world happening. It tells us only that, in 19 frames of a certain video camera, my image moved from a position 2.5 mm from the left edge of the frame to a position 8.5 mm from the edge. It would be more useful to have this information in terms of real-world distances and time intervals. To know what distance I traveled and how long the trip took, I should have put markers on the ground at known intervals and a clock in the camera's field of view. Even though I did not do this, we can still determine position and time by *calibrating* the graph, as you can see in the next checkpoint.

2.3 (*a*) Take a reasonable guess at my height and calculate what real-world distance 1 mm in Figure 2.1 corresponds to. (*b*) Using this result, calculate the distance I walked between frames 1 and 10.

This checkpoint gives a procedure for calibrating the vertical axis in Figure 2.2 without taking any new pictures. Using 1.8 m as my height, I obtained the position values listed in the third column of Table 2.1. For motion in one dimension, position can be represented by the x coordinate along a reference axis (also called the x axis), and this coordinate is denoted by the symbol x. Because the x coordinate can be positive or negative, we always explicitly denote its

CONCEPTS

algebraic sign. In frame 4, for example, my position is given by $x = +2.8$ m. Note that by following this procedure, x values increase to the right.

We can do something similar for time. The camera takes 30 frames per second, and so the time interval between successive frames on the original film is $1/30$ s $= 0.033$ s. If we imagine having started a stopwatch at the first frame, that stopwatch would read 0.033 s at the second frame, 0.067 s at the third, 0.100 s at the fourth, and so on. Because only every tenth frame is shown in Figure 2.1, we must multiply these readings by 10. All these clock readings are listed in the fourth column in Table 2.1. Clock readings are represented by the symbol t; each value of t represents an instant in time. In everyday language *instant* can mean different things. For example, when you say, "I'll be back in an instant," the word *instant* refers to a short time interval. In physics, however, an instant has no duration at all; it represents a single value in time.

Figure 2.3 shows the resulting calibrated data in graphical form, with the position given by x on the vertical axis and time t on the horizontal axis. We refer to such a graph as a *position-versus-time graph*.

To obtain the data shown in Figures 2.2 and 2.3, we arbitrarily chose an origin. An origin is always needed in order to specify a position: The statement "the ball's position is $x = +3.2$ m" makes no sense unless we know from where to start measuring these 3.2 meters. The choice of origin is arbitrary. In analyzing Figure 2.1, for instance, I arbitrarily chose the left edge of the frame as the origin. To show that the choice of origin is arbitrary, suppose we re-plot our data, but now take my position in frame 1 to correspond to $x = 0$ and the clock reading at the first frame to be $t = 0.33$ s. Doing so produces the graph shown in **Figure 2.4**. Compare this graph with Figure 2.3 and you see that the change in origin and in the instant at which $t = 0$ changes the x and t values of each data point. However, as the next checkpoint shows, changing the origin and the

Figure 2.3 Position-versus-time graph obtained by calibrating the data points in Figure 2.2. The vertical axis now represents my position, measured in meters, relative to a point on the left edge of the frame. The x and t values are listed also in Table 2.1.

Figure 2.4 Position-versus-time graph for the data plotted in Figure 2.3, but with a different choice of origin.

instant at which $t = 0$ does not affect the relative positions of the data points.

2.4 (*a*) What are the final position values in Figures 2.3 and 2.4? (*b*) What values are obtained by subtracting the initial position value from the final position value in each figure?

We can represent the motion of an object that moves from one position to another by an arrow that points from the initial position to the final position (**Figure 2.5**). This arrow represents a physical quantity called the **displacement** of the object. The displacement does not depend in any way on the choice of reference axis or origin; you don't need any axis to draw the arrow in Figure 2.5. Numerically, we can represent the displacement by subtracting the initial x coordinate from the final x coordinate. The resulting value is called the *x component of the displacement*:

> **The x component of an object's displacement is the change in its x coordinate. The value of the x component of the displacement is obtained by subtracting the initial x coordinate from the final x coordinate and is independent of the choice of origin.**

Figure 2.5 The arrow pointing from my initial position to my final position represents my displacement.

The term *x component* serves to remind us that this quantity is measured along some specific *x* axis. In the second part of this chapter you will see how to specify a displacement like the one in Figure 2.5 by choosing an *x* axis and determining the *x* component of the displacement. Later on, in Chapter 10, when we discuss motion that is not along a straight line, we shall need more than one axis and a correspondingly larger number of components to specify displacements.

Note that the *x* component of the displacement can be either positive or negative: It is positive for displacements in the direction of increasing *x* and negative for displacements in the direction of decreasing *x*. To remind ourselves of this fact, we shall always explicitly denote the algebraic sign of the *x* component of the displacement. The *x* component of the displacement between my initial and final positions in Figure 2.3, for example, is $+2.4$ m, indicating that I end up 2.4 m to the right of my starting position.

Returning to Checkpoint 2.4, we see that because every data point in Figure 2.4 is shifted down and to the right by exactly the same amount, the value obtained by subtracting the initial *x* coordinate from the final *x* coordinate is not affected by the change in origin. If it puzzles you that the *x* component of the displacement is independent of the choice of origin, consider the following: Suppose you tell a friend, "See you at the bakery in thirty minutes." Even if your watch says 3:30 at that instant and your friend's watch says 2:30, you will both arrive at the bakery at the same time: 30 minutes after you made the date. Your reference point is the clock reading 3:30 and your friend's reference point is the clock reading 2:30, but both of you add the same value—30 minutes—to your reference point. Just like the *x* component of the displacement (a *change in* the *x* coordinate), a time interval (a *change in* the clock reading) does not depend on the choice of reference point.

2.5 Suppose you walk in a straight line from a point P to a point Q, 2 m away from P, and then walk back along the same line to P. (*a*) What is the *x* component of your displacement for the round trip? (*b*) What distance did you travel during the round trip? (*c*) Is *distance traveled* the same thing as the *x component of the displacement*?

As this checkpoint shows, it is important to distinguish between the *x* component of the displacement and the *distance traveled*.

The distance traveled is the distance covered by a moving object along the path of its motion.

In contrast to the *x* component of the displacement, which can be either positive or negative, the distance traveled is always positive. Note also that, for an object that turns around, as in Checkpoint 2.5, the distance traveled is

greater than the distance between the endpoints. Only when the motion is always in the same direction is the distance traveled equal to the distance between the endpoints.

2.3 Representing motion

The graphs of Figures 2.3 and 2.4 specify position only at the specific instants represented by the frames in Figure 2.1. What about the positions at intermediate instants? To answer this question, we would need to look at all the frames taken between those shown in Figure 2.1. Doing so would give us ten times as many data points because the camera took ten times the number of frames shown in the figure. If we wanted information more detailed than that, we would need a camera that takes more than 30 frames per second.

As we repeat our measurements over smaller and smaller time intervals, the spacing between data points becomes increasingly smaller, eventually yielding what looks like a continuous curve instead of discrete points. If we assume the motion proceeds smoothly from frame to frame, we can obtain the same result by *interpolating* the data points in Figure 2.3—in other words, by drawing a smooth curve through the points, as in **Figure 2.6**.

2.6 (*a*) From Figure 2.6, how many seconds did it take me to go from $x = +1.0$ m to $x = +4.0$ m? (*b*) From $x = +2.0$ m to $x = +3.0$ m? (*c*) At what instant did I reach $x = +2.5$ m? (*d*) For how long was I at $x = +2.5$ m?

Figure 2.7 shows how the position-versus-time graph of Figure 2.6 relates to Figure 2.1. Figure 2.6 is a further simplification of our representation of the motion in the film clip. In reality, the motion may have been less smooth than the graph suggests. However, the film clip and Figure 2.6 both tell the same story: I moved forward about 3.8 m in 2.3 s, stood still for 1.3 s, and then moved 1.4 m backward in 2.3 s. Even though it gives less detail than the film clip, the simple curve in Figure 2.6 entirely describes the motion.

Figure 2.6 By interpolating the data points in Figure 2.3, we obtain a smooth curve representing my motion.

CONCEPTS

Figure 2.7 If you connect the images in sequential frames by a line, you obtain a curve representing the motion. Turn the page sideways and compare the curve through the images with the curve in Figure 2.6.

position

time

Example 2.1 Graphical representation

The curve in **Figure 2.8** is a graphical representation of the motion of a certain object. (*a*) What was the *x* coordinate of the object at $t = 0.50$ s? (*b*) At what instant(s) did the object reach $x = +0.80$ m? (*c*) What distance did the object travel between $t = 0.80$ s and $t = 1.2$ s? (*d*) How long did it take for the object to move from $x = +1.0$ m to $x = 0$?

Figure 2.8 A position-versus-time graph representing the motion of an object. The curve, which shows the position of the object at any instant between $t = 0$ and $t = 1.2$ s, can be represented by a mathematical function $x(t)$ (Examples 2.1 and 2.2).

x axis in units of meters

x (m)

x(*t*) curve

t axis in units of seconds

t (s)

❶ **GETTING STARTED** This problem requires me to use Figure 2.8 to answer questions about the motion of the object. The problem boils down to reading off values from the graph.

❷ **DEVISE PLAN** To find the object's position *x* at a given instant *t*, I draw (or imagine drawing) a vertical line at the value on the *t* axis corresponding to the given instant in time and read off the value of *x* at which that line intercepts the curve in the graph. Likewise, to find the instant *t* at which the object is at a given position *x*, I draw a horizontal line at the given value of *x* and read off the value of *t* at which that horizontal line intercepts the curve.

❸ **EXECUTE PLAN** (*a*) A vertical line drawn at $t = 0.50$ s in Figure 2.8 intercepts the curve at $x = +1.0$ m. ✔

(*b*) A horizontal line at $x = +0.80$ m intercepts the curve at $t = 0.20$ s and at $t = 0.80$ s. ✔

(*c*) At $t = 0.80$ s the object was at $x = +0.80$ m, and at $t = 1.2$ s it was at $x = 0$. The distance traveled was thus 0.80 m. ✔

(*d*) The object was at $x = +1.0$ m at $t = 0.50$ s and at $x = 0$ at $t = 1.2$ s. Thus it took the object 1.2 s $-$ 0.50 s $= 0.7$ s to move between these points. ✔

✔ The checkmarks show that I carried out the following checks: Vectors and scalars used appropriately; Everything answered; No unknowns left; Units correct; Significant digits justified.

❹ **EVALUATE RESULT** That I obtain two instants in part *b* is OK because the object can return to a certain position. The answers to parts *c* and *d* (0.80 m and 0.7 s) are within the range of the curve (1.0 m and 1.2 s), so my answers are not unreasonable.

A curve in a position-versus-time graph like the one shown in Figures 2.6 and 2.8 is called an $x(t)$ *curve* because it can be represented by a mathematical function $x(t)$.

The curve and the function specify where the object is at any given instant. Note that $x(t)$ is a single symbol that means "x at instant t"; it is not the product of x and t and should not be confused with the label "x (m)" on the x axis, which means "x in units of meters."

To find the position of the object at a specific instant, we can either read off the position from the graph or substitute that instant into the function. For example, "$x(t = 0.2\text{ s})$" gives the position of the object at the instant $t = 0.2$ s; this position can be obtained by substituting 0.2 s for t in the mathematical expression for $x(t)$.

Example 2.2 Mathematical representation

The curve in Figure 2.8 can be mathematically represented by the function $x(t) = a + bt + ct^2$, where $a = 0.50$ m, $b = +2.0$ m/s, and $c = -2.0$ m/s^2. Use this function to answer the four questions in Example 2.1.

❶ **GETTING STARTED** This problem requires me to use a mathematical expression rather than a graph to answer questions about the motion of an object.

❷ **DEVISE PLAN** To find the object's position at a given instant, I substitute that instant for t in the function given in the problem and compute the value of x. To find the instant at which the object is at a given position, I substitute that position for x in the function given in the problem and solve for t.

❸ **EXECUTE PLAN** (a) Substituting $t = 0.50$ s into the function, I find for the position at $t = 0.50$ s: $x(t = 0.50\text{ s}) = 0.50$ m $+ (+2.0\text{ m/s})(0.50\text{ s}) + (-2.0\text{ m/s}^2)(0.50\text{ s})^2 = +1.0$ m. ✔

(b) To find the instants at which the object reached $x = +0.80$ m, I must set x in the mathematical function equal to $+0.80$ m: $+0.80$ m $= 0.50$ m $+ (+2.0\text{ m/s})t + (-2.0\text{ m/s}^2)t^2$ or, simplifying the equation by omitting the units, $(2.0)t^2 - (2.0)t + 0.30 = 0$. This is a quadratic equation in t, which has two solutions: $t = [2.0 \pm \sqrt{4.0 - 4 \times 2.0 \times 0.30}]/(4.0)$. Working out this expression yields $t = 0.18$ s and $t = 0.82$ s. ✔

(c) At $t = 0.80$ s, the object's position is $x(t = 0.80\text{ s}) = 0.50$ m $+ (+2.0\text{ m/s})(0.80\text{ s}) + (-2.0\text{ m/s}^2)(0.80\text{ s})^2 = +0.82$ m. At $t = 1.2$ s, the object is at $x = 0.50$ m $+ (+2.0\text{ m/s})(1.2\text{ s}) + (-2.0\text{ m/s}^2)(1.2\text{ s})^2 = +0.02$ m. The distance it traveled is the difference between these two positions: $x(t = 0.80\text{ s}) - x(t = 1.2\text{ s}) = +0.82$ m $-(+0.02$ m$) = 0.80$ m. ✔

(d) I begin by calculating at what instant the object reached $x = +1.0$ m. Substituting this value into the mathematical expression yields 1.0 m $= 0.50$ m $+ (+2.0\text{ m/s})t + (-2.0\text{ m/s}^2)t^2$ or, simplifying the equation by omitting the units, $-(2.0)t^2 + (2.0)t + 0.50 = 1.0$. Solving this quadratic equation yields $t = 0.50$ s. Next I must find the instant at which the object reached $x = 0$. Following the same procedure, I find two solutions: $t = -0.20$ s and $t = 1.2$ s. The first solution is before the starting point of the motion represented in Figure 2.8, and so I use the second solution to find that the object took 1.2 s $- 0.50$ s $= 0.7$ s to travel this distance. ✔

❹ **EVALUATE RESULT** To check my work, I can compare my answers with the ones I obtained in Example 2.1. Indeed, my answers are the same as (or very close to) the ones I obtained from reading the graph.

2.4 Average speed and average velocity

Now that you know how to represent motion in terms of position and time, let us use this information to calculate first the average speed and then the average velocity of the motion.

First, average speed. The more slowly I move, the larger the time interval I require to travel a given distance. Suppose, for instance, I had walked twice as slowly while the camera was rolling. I would have taken twice as much time to get to, say, the end of the forward part of my walk, which is the point $x = +4.8$ m in Figure 2.6. The distance traveled from my starting point would have been the same as before (4.8 m $-$ 1.0 m $=$ 3.8 m), but it would have taken 4.67 s to reach this point rather than the 2.33 s shown in Figure 2.6. This difference is shown in **Figure 2.9**.

The rate at which an $x(t)$ curve rises with increasing time is called the *slope* of the curve. Notice how the slope becomes less steep when the speed decreases.

✋ **2.7** For each speed in Figure 2.9, what are (*a*) the distance traveled between $t = 0$ and $t = 1.50$ s and (*b*) the ratio of the distance traveled to the corresponding time interval? For each speed, what are (*c*) the time interval required to move from $x = 2.00$ m to $x = 3.50$ m and (*d*) the ratio of the distance traveled to the corresponding time interval?

This checkpoint reveals how to extract speed from an $x(t)$ curve: Divide the distance traveled by the time interval required to travel this distance. The ratios of parts *b* and *d* correspond to the slopes of the lines in Figure 2.9 and bear out what I said before: The steeper the slope (the higher the number you got for your ratios), the higher the speed.

Suppose someone rode a bicycle 20 km in 2 h. Using the above procedure to calculate the cyclist's speed, we get $(20\text{ km})/(2\text{ h}) = 10$ km/h. This doesn't necessarily mean the speed was constant—the person could have, for instance,

Figure 2.9 Forward motion at two speeds. Walking half as fast means taking twice as long to travel the same distance. To get to the arbitrary point $x = 3.5$ m, for example, takes about 3.0 s at half speed but only about 1.5 s at normal speed.

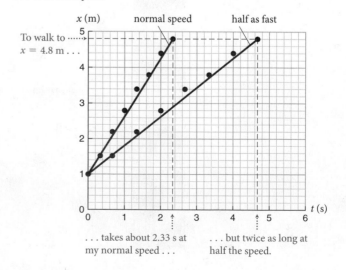

CONCEPTS

gone much faster than 10 km/h and taken a break somewhere in the middle of the trip. From the data provided, we can say only that the person's speed was 10 km/h *on average*. Hence:

An object's average speed is the distance traveled divided by the time interval required to travel that distance.

Note that this definition involves the *distance traveled* and not the *x component of the displacement*. To see why, let us again use the data from my walk. According to Table 2.1, the *x* component of my displacement was (final position) − (initial position) = (+3.4 m) − (+1.0 m) = +2.4 m over the 6.0-s duration of the trip. The distance I traveled, on the other hand, is the sum of my forward and backward distances: 4.8 m − 1.0 m = 3.8 m for the forward part and 4.8 − 3.4 = 1.4 m for the backward part. Thus the distance I traveled in 6 s was 5.2 m, so my average speed was (5.2 m)/(6.0 s) = 0.87 m/s, *not* (2.4 m)/(6.0 s) = 0.40 m/s.

If I had walked at a constant speed of 0.40 m/s for 6 s, my *x*(*t*) curve would be curve 1 in **Figure 2.10**. A constant speed of 0.40 m/s implies that I traveled 0.40 m every second. More generally, a constant speed during a given time interval means that when the time interval is divided into any number of equal-sized subintervals, the distance traveled is the same in all subintervals. A constant speed

Figure 2.10 Two of the infinite number of ways for getting from an initial position x_i to a final position x_f. Curve 1: walking in one direction only; curve 2: walking beyond the endpoint and then backtracking. Both ways result in a displacement of +2.4 m in 6 s.

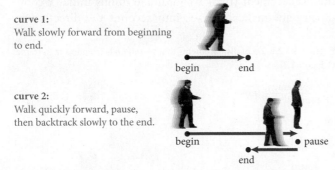

curve 1:
Walk slowly forward from beginning to end.

begin   end

curve 2:
Walk quickly forward, pause, then backtrack slowly to the end.

begin   pause
end

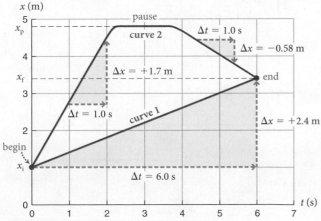

therefore shows up as a straight line in a position-versus-time graph.

Instead of walking at a constant speed from the initial position x_i directly to the final position x_f in Figure 2.10, however, I got to x_f by first walking beyond that point and then walking back, as illustrated by curve 2 in Figure 2.10.

2.8 (*a*) At what instant did I first pass the position $x_f = +3.4$ m (see curve 2 in Figure 2.10)? (*b*) What was my average speed up to that instant?

In Figure 2.10 let us use the symbol x_p to denote the point at which I paused in my walk. Walking forward, I traveled $x_p − x_i = 4.8$ m − 1.0 m = +3.8 m in 2.3 s, and so my average speed was (3.8 m)/(2.3 s) = 1.7 m/s. After pausing for 1.3 s, I traveled the distance $x_p − x_f$ = 4.8 m − 3.4 m = 1.4 m in 6.0 s − 3.6 s = 2.4 s. So the average speed at which I walked backward was (1.4 m)/(2.4 s) = 0.58 m/s. My higher forward speed is shown in Figure 2.10 by the steeper slope of curve 2 between x_i and x_p.

In a graph of position versus time, the steeper the slope of the curve, the higher the speed.

Another point to note about curve 2 in Figure 2.10 is that the curve slopes up from x_i to x_p and down from x_p to x_f. The reason is that I moved in the direction of increasing *x* from x_i to x_p and in the direction of decreasing *x* from x_p to x_f. Average speed, as we defined it, tells us only how fast something moves without indicating the direction in which the motion takes place. In contrast, the slope of an *x*(*t*) curve tells us both how fast and in what direction an object is moving. Motion in the positive *x* direction gives a rising *x*(*t*) curve and positive slope; motion in the negative *x* direction gives a falling *x*(*t*) curve and a negative slope.

The quantity that gives us both the speed and the direction of travel is **velocity**. Like displacement, velocity can be represented by an arrow (more on these arrows and their representation in the second part of this chapter). For now, we define the *x component of the average velocity* as follows:

The *x* component of an object's average velocity is the *x* component of its displacement divided by the length of the time interval taken to travel that displacement.

As before, the term *x component* serves to remind us that this quantity depends on the choice of axis and that it can be both positive and negative (in contrast to *average speed*, which is always positive). For motion in the positive *x* direction, the *x* component of the average velocity is positive; for motion in the negative *x* direction, it is negative. Just as we are doing for the *x* component of the displacement, we indicate the direction of motion along the *x* axis by using an algebraic sign. For example, in going from x_i to x_p along curve 2 in Figure 2.10, the *x* component of my average velocity is $+1.7$ m/s, meaning the motion is in the positive x direction; from x_p to x_f it is -0.58 m/s. (My *speed*, however, was 1.7 m/s between x_i and x_p and -0.58 m/s between x_p and x_f. Speed has no direction and therefore carries no algebraic sign.)

Example 2.3 Speed and velocity

With about 20 min to spare, you walk leisurely from your dorm to class, which is 1.0 km away. Halfway there, you realize you have forgotten your notebook and run back to your dorm. You walked 6.0 min before turning around, and you travel three times as far per unit of time running as you do when walking. What are (a) the x component of your average velocity and (b) your average speed over the entire trip?

❶ GETTING STARTED To begin this problem, it helps to make a sketch to visualize the situation (**Figure 2.11**).

Figure 2.11

❷ DEVISE PLAN To find the x component of your average velocity, I need to divide the x component of your displacement by the time interval over which this displacement took place. To find your average speed, I must divide the distance traveled by the time interval.

❸ EXECUTE PLAN (a) When you are back at the dorm, the x component of your displacement is zero because your initial and final positions are the same. Therefore the x component of your average velocity, (x component of the displacement)/(time interval), is zero too. ✔

(b) Because you traveled halfway to class and back, and the distance between your dorm and the classroom is 1 km, the distance you traveled by the time you returned to your dorm is 1.0 km. You walked for 6.0 min before turning around. Because you run three times as fast as you walk, it takes you only 2.0 min to return to your dorm, and so the total round-trip time is 8.0 min, or 480 s. Your average speed therefore is (distance traveled)/(time interval) = (1000 m)/(480 s) = 2.1 m/s. ✔

❹ EVALUATE RESULT If you start and end at the same place, your displacement is zero and so your average velocity is zero, regardless of how fast you move. The answer I obtained in part b means that you would cover about $(2.1\ \text{m/s})(3600\ \text{s}) = 7600\ \text{m} = 7.6$ km in one hour. This speed—$(7.6\ \text{km/h})/(1.6\ \text{km/mi}) = 4.7$ mi/h—is in the right ballpark for a person doing a combination of walking and running.

✋ 2.9 In Example 2.3, what was your average speed during the time interval that you walked (a) away from and (b) back toward your dorm? (c) Is the average of your answers to parts a and b the same as the average speed calculated in Example 2.3? Why or why not?

Let us now return to the motion illustrated in the film clip. In Figure 2.10 we determined the x component of the average velocity for my motion in each direction: $+1.7$ m/s walking forward, zero standing still, and -0.58 m/s walking backward. We can obtain more detailed information by calculating the x component of the average velocity from one frame to the next. We can do this by calculating the x components of the displacements between successive frames from the values of x in Table 2.1. The change in the value of x from one frame to the next gives the x component of the displacements between frames. If we then divide these displacement values by the time interval between frames (0.33 s), we get values for the x component of my average velocity that are averaged over much smaller time intervals than before. The result of this computation is shown in **Figure 2.12**.

The first thing that stands out in this graph is that the x component of the average velocity obtained from one frame to another varies quite a bit around the x component of the average velocity we calculated before. This variation is due to variations in my speed as I walked and to limits in the accuracy of determining the relatively small displacement values from one frame to the next.

Another striking feature in Figure 2.12 is that the x component of the average velocity is *negative* for $t \geq 4$ s. This is because the calculation for the x component of the displacement (final x coordinate minus initial x coordinate) automatically takes into account the direction in

Figure 2.12 Ratio of displacements to time intervals from frame to frame in Figure 2.1.

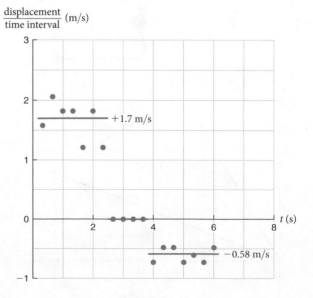

which the motion takes place. Between $t = 5.0$ s and 5.3 s, for instance, I moved from $x = +4.0$ m to $+3.8$ m (see Table 2.1), and so the x component of my displacement was $+3.8$ m $- (+4.0$ m$) = -0.2$ m. Whenever x decreases, the x component of the displacement is *negative*. The time intervals, on the other hand, are always positive because time runs forward only. Therefore the ratio of the x component of the displacement to the time interval has the same algebraic sign as the x component of the displacement.

Figure 2.13 shows how the x component of the average velocity, denoted by v_x, changes as a function of time. The curve in this figure (which we'll refer to as a $v_x(t)$ *curve*) contains the same information as the $x(t)$ curve in Figure 2.6. Both are simplified representations of the motion shown in Figure 2.1.

2.10 (*a*) Suppose an object moves from an initial position $x_i = -1.2$ m to a final position $x_f = -2.3$ m without reversing its direction of travel. Is the x component of its average velocity positive or negative? (*b*) Repeat for an object moving from $x_i = +1.2$ m to $x_f = -1.2$ m. (*c*) Do your answers agree with the above statement about the algebraic sign of the x component of the average velocity being the same as the sign of the x component of the displacement?

Figure 2.13 Velocity-versus-time graph for the data shown in Figure 2.12.

Self-quiz

1. Describe the motion represented by each graph in **Figure 2.14**.

Figure 2.14

(a)

(b)

(c)

(d)

2. One or more of the graphs in **Figure 2.15** represent an impossible motion. Identify which ones and explain why the motion is not possible.

Figure 2.15

(a)

(b)

(c)

(d)

3. Two cars start from some point P, drive 10 km to a point Q, and then return to P. Car 1 completes the trip in 10 min; car 2 takes 11 min. For each car, what are (a) the x component of the average velocity and (b) the average speed?

4. Suppose you travel 10 km from P to Q at 10 km/h and another 10 km from Q to R at 20 km/h. What is your average speed during the entire trip from P to R?

5. (a) Which of the numbered lines 1–8 in the graphs in Figure 2.14 represents the greatest average speed? (b) For which of the numbered lines is the x component of the average velocity negative?

Answers

1. (a) An object moving away from the origin at constant speed; (b) an object at rest a certain distance from the origin; (c) an object moving toward the origin, then pausing halfway between its starting point and the origin, then continuing (more slowly) toward the origin; (d) an object moving away from the origin at constant speed for one-third of the time, then continuing in the same direction at a slower constant speed for another third of the time, and finally moving toward the origin at some intermediate constant speed.

2. (a) and (d). Put the left edge of a ruler along the x axis and slowly slide the ruler to the right. The point where this edge intersects the curve shows the position of the object at the instant indicated by the horizontal axis. For both (a) and (d) there are instants at which the ruler edge intersects the curve at more than one place for the same value of t. This tells you that these curves are meaningless because no object can be in two places at the same instant.

3. The x component of the displacement of both cars is zero because they end where they began. So the x component of their average velocities is zero. The distance they travel, however, is 20 km. So the average speed of car 1 is (20 km)/(10 min) = 2.0 km/min, and the average speed of car 2 is (20 km)/(11 min) = 1.8 km/min.

4. If you answered 15 km/h, think again—you cannot simply average the two speeds! To calculate the average speed, you need to know how long the entire trip from P to R took and the distance traveled. The 10 km from P to Q takes (10 km)/(10 km/h) = 1 h; the 10 km from Q to R takes (10 km)/(20 km/h) = 0.5 h, and so the total duration of the trip is 1.5 h. The average speed for the 20-km trip from P to R is thus (20 km)/(1.5 h) = 13 km/h.

5. (a) Line 3 because its slope is steepest. (b) Lines 3, 5, and 8 because the x(t) curves slope downward with increasing time.

2.5 Scalars and vectors

The physical quantities we use in this book fall into two categories. The first type, called **scalars,** are completely specified by a number, which can be positive or negative, and a unit of measure. An example is temperature, a quantity that is specified completely by a number and a unit (as in 21 °C or 70 °F). The second type, called **vectors,** require, in order to be completely specified, both a magnitude (the "how much" and "of what," specified by a number and a unit) and a direction in space.

Exercise 2.4 Scalar or vector?

(*a*) Is the statement *Yesterday the car was parked 3 m from the telephone pole* sufficient to determine the position of the car? Is position a scalar or a vector? (*b*) Is the statement *New York is 200 miles from Boston* sufficient to determine the distance between the two cities? Is distance a vector or a scalar? (*c*) Is the statement *My friend walked 3 m due north from the telephone pole* sufficient to determine your friend's position at the end of her short walk? Is displacement a vector or a scalar?

SOLUTION (*a*) No. The car could have been anywhere on the perimeter of a circle of radius 3 m centered on the telephone pole. A direction is required in addition to a distance, and so position is a vector. ✔

(*b*) Yes. All that is required to specify distance is a number (200) and a unit of length (miles). Because distance does not depend on a direction in space, it is a scalar. ✔

(*c*) Yes. *3 m north* completely specifies your friend's displacement from the telephone pole because it gives both a distance (3 m) and a direction (north). Because it requires a direction, displacement is a vector. ✔

2.11 Are the following quantities vectors or scalars: (*i*) the price of a movie ticket, (*ii*) the average velocity of a ball launched vertically upward, (*iii*) the position of the corner of a rectangle, (*iv*) the length of a side of that rectangle?

Scalars follow the ordinary arithmetic laws of addition, subtraction, multiplication, and division. For example, 2 m + 3 m = 5 m and 2 × 5 s = 10 s. Vectors, on the other hand, obey special laws of addition, subtraction, and multiplication that we begin to discuss in the following sections and then learn about in more detail in Chapter 10.

The only type of motion we study through Chapter 9 is motion in one dimension, which means it occurs either forward or backward along a straight line. For now, therefore, the difference between scalars and vectors is not a major issue because in one dimension the direction of any vector can be specified by an algebraic sign. The difference between scalars and vectors becomes important when we discuss motion in more than one dimension in Chapter 10. It is therefore important that we be able to distinguish vectors from scalars, and so in this book we use arrows to denote vectors:*

$$\vec{a} \quad \text{vector}$$
$$b \quad \text{scalar.}$$

The arrow is a reminder that vectors have a direction in space and that they obey rules that are different from those for scalars. Throughout this book, we graphically represent vectors by thick arrows of appropriate length and direction and label these arrows with the corresponding symbol (see, for example, Figures 2.16 and 2.17).

---

*Note that the direction of the arrow used in the vector notation (that is, the → in $\vec{a}$) does not represent the direction of the vector. In particular, it does not reverse direction when we multiply a vector by −1.

The **magnitude of a vector** tells us how much there is of that vector. In Exercise 2.4c, for instance, the magnitude of your friend's displacement is 3 m. When we draw one vector arrow longer than another in a diagram, we are saying that the vector represented by the longer arrow has a magnitude that is greater than the magnitude of the vector represented by the shorter arrow. A magnitude never has a sign associated with it.

There are two common ways of designating the magnitude of a vector symbolically: by drawing vertical lines on either side of its symbol or by removing the overarrow. Thus the magnitude of vector $\vec{b}$ is denoted by either $|\vec{b}|$ or b. In this book, we usually use b for simplicity.

To specify vectors mathematically, we introduce a **unit vector**—a vector whose sole purpose is to define a direction in space. Unit vectors have no units, and the number associated with them (their *magnitude*) is one. They are denoted by a caret or "hat" (^) to distinguish them from ordinary vectors, whose magnitude can have any value; for example, the unit vector pointing in the direction of increasing x along the x axis is denoted by $\hat{i}$ (pronounced *i-hat*). In **Figure 2.16a** this unit vector is represented by a black arrow that points in the direction of increasing x along the axis. Because unit vectors have a magnitude of 1 and no units, we have

Figure 2.16 The product of a unit vector $\hat{i}$ and a scalar b_x yields a vector $\vec{b} = b_x\hat{i}$.

(a)   Unit vector $\hat{i}$ defines axis.

(b)   Multiplying $\hat{i}$ by $b_x = +2.0$ m gives $\vec{b}$.

(c)   Multiplying $\hat{i}$ by $c_x = -1.5$ m gives $\vec{c}$.

$$|\hat{i}| \equiv 1. \tag{2.1}$$

Any vector along the x axis can be written in **unit vector notation** as the product of a scalar and this unit vector:

$$\vec{b} \equiv b_x\hat{i} \quad \text{(one dimension)} \tag{2.2}$$

where b_x is a scalar called the *x component of the vector* $\vec{b}$. The subscript x indicates that the quantity refers to the x axis and reminds you that the sign of b_x depends on our choice of axis direction. If the vector $\vec{b}$ points in the positive x direction (that is, in the direction of $\hat{i}$, the direction of increasing x), the scalar b_x is positive. If the vector $\vec{b}$ points in the negative x direction (that is, opposite the direction of $\hat{i}$, the direction of decreasing x), the scalar b_x is negative.

If we take the absolute value of Eq. 2.2 and substitute Eq. 2.1, we see that, for vectors in one dimension, the magnitude of the vector $\vec{b}$ is equal to the absolute value of b_x:

$$b \equiv |\vec{b}| = |b_x\hat{i}| = |b_x||\hat{i}| = |b_x| \quad \text{(one dimension).} \tag{2.3}$$

For practice, let us determine the x components of the vectors in Figure 2.16 and also write the vectors in unit vector notation. In Figure 2.16b, the vector $\vec{b}$ points in the positive x direction, which means that the scalar b_x (which is the x component of $\vec{b}$) is a positive number. The length of the arrow in Figure 2.16b tells us that the magnitude of $\vec{b}$ is 2.0 m (no sign; never a sign for a *magnitude*). From Eq. 2.3, therefore, the absolute value of b_x is 2.0 m. Consequently, the x component of $\vec{b}$ is $b_x = +2.0$ m. In unit vector notation, we write $(+2.0$ m$)\hat{i}$ for our vector $\vec{b}$.

In Figure 2.16c, the vector $\vec{c}$ points in the negative x direction, and so the scalar c_x (the x component of $\vec{c}$) is a negative number. The magnitude of $\vec{c}$ along the x axis is 1.5 m, which means the absolute value of c_x is 1.5 m. The x component of $\vec{c}$ is thus $c_x = -1.5$ m. In unit vector notation, we write $(-1.5$ m$)\hat{i}$ for our vector $\vec{c}$.

Figure 2.17 summarizes how a vector $\vec{b}$ is represented graphically and mathematically. To remind ourselves that x components are signed numbers, we always show the algebraic sign of a component, even if it is positive (for instance, $b_x = +2.0$ m). Note also that the x component of a vector always has the same units as the quantity represented by that vector.

Figure 2.17 Graphical and mathematical representation of a vector.

symbolic representation of vector	x component of vector	unit vector defining direction of increasing x

$$\vec{b} = b_x\hat{i}$$

→ x axis

graphical representation of vector

• magnitude of vector: $b = |b_x|$
• If $b_x > 0$: $\vec{b}$ is in same direction as $\hat{i}$
• If $b_x < 0$: $\vec{b}$ is in opposite direction to $\hat{i}$

In Chapter 10 you'll learn how to mathematically describe vectors that do not lie along the x axis. For motion in one dimension, however, we can always align the axis along the line of motion, and so all vectors can be written in the form given by Eq. 2.2. Because x components are sufficient to completely specify vectors in one dimension, we shall for now work with mostly components rather than vectors.

✋ **2.12** Consider the axis and unit vector shown in **Figure 2.18**. Let the vector $\vec{r}$ have its tail at the origin and its tip at my feet. (*a*) What is the x component of that vector? (*b*) Write the vector $\vec{r}$ in terms of its x component and the unit vector. (*c*) What does the vector $\vec{r}$ represent? (*d*) Does $r_x = +2.5$ m unambiguously determine a vector in Figure 2.18? If so, draw the vector, and state what it might represent.

Figure 2.18 The unit vector $\hat{\imath}$ completely specifies a reference axis. The unit vector's direction determines the direction of increasing x along the axis. The tail of the vector locates the origin, and its length defines the unit.

2.6 Position and displacement vectors

The most fundamental vector is displacement, which, as noted in Section 2.2, can be represented graphically by an arrow that points from an object's initial position to its final position. **Figure 2.19**, for example, shows the displacement from my position in frame 3 in Figure 2.1 to my position in frame 10. This vector has a magnitude that is equal to the distance between my initial and final positions (2.6 m), and its direction is toward increasing values of x along the reference axis.

Figure 2.19 Superposition of frames 3 and 10 of Figure 2.1. The arrow is my displacement.

Mathematically we denote displacement by $\Delta \vec{r}$, where the Greek letter Δ (delta) means "the change in" and $\vec{r}$ is a vector specifying position (more on this vector in a bit). The change in a quantity is always taken to be the final value minus the initial value. If your height h increases from 1.75 m to 1.78 m, for instance, the change in your height is $\Delta h = 1.78$ m $- 1.75$ m $= +0.03$ m. If the number n of cookies in a jar is down to 10 from an initial 12, the change is $\Delta n = 10 - 12 = -2$ cookies.

As we saw in Section 2.2, the x component of the displacement is equal to the change in the x coordinate: $\Delta r_x \equiv \Delta x$. Because of this identity, which is specific to position and displacement, we henceforth denote the x component of the displacement by Δx rather than by Δr_x. So, if the x coordinate of an object changes from some initial value x_i at instant t_i to some final value x_f at some later instant t_f, the x component of the object's displacement is given by

$$\Delta x \equiv x_f - x_i. \qquad (2.4)$$

As we saw in Section 2.2, the *x component of the displacement* and the *distance traveled* are not necessarily the same. In particular, if an object turns around during its motion, we need to add the distances between successive turning points (including the initial and final positions) in order to calculate the distance traveled. The **distance** d between two points is equal to the absolute value of the difference in the x coordinates of those two points:

$$d \equiv |x_1 - x_2| \quad \text{(one dimension)}. \qquad (2.5)$$

Because distance is obtained by taking the absolute value of a quantity, it is always positive. Likewise, the distance traveled, which is the sum of the distances between successive points, is always positive.

Example 2.5 Displacement as a vector

On the reference axis shown in **Figure 2.20**, draw vectors representing my displacements between the following frames in Figure 2.1: (*a*) 4 and 8, (*b*) 11 and 19, (*c*) 6 and 17. Use the values listed in Table 2.1 to describe each vector in terms of its magnitude and direction.

Figure 2.20 Example 2.5.

❶ **GETTING STARTED** The pairs of frames given in each part of this example define the initial and final positions. For each pair, I need to determine the displacement vector.

❷ **DEVISE PLAN** I know that a displacement vector points from the initial position to the final position, and so I must draw the tail of the vector at the initial x coordinate and its head at the final x coordinate. Then I can use Eq. 2.3 to determine the magnitude of the displacement vector.

❸ **EXECUTE PLAN** (*a*) The displacement points from my initial position at $x_i = +2.8$ m to my final position at $x_f = +4.8$ m (see Table 2.1). The x component of the displacement is $\Delta x = x_f - x_i = +4.8\ \text{m} - (+2.8\ \text{m}) = +2.0\ \text{m}$. The magnitude of this vector is $|\Delta \vec{r}| = |\Delta x| = 2.0$ m; its direction is to the right because the x component is positive (**Figure 2.21**). ✔

Figure 2.21

(*b*) The displacement points from $x_i = +4.8$ m to $x_f = +3.4$ m. The x component of the displacement is $\Delta x = x_f - x_i = +3.4\ \text{m} - (+4.8\ \text{m}) = -1.4\ \text{m}$. The magnitude of this vector is $|\Delta \vec{r}| = |\Delta x| = |-1.4\ \text{m}| = 1.4$ m; its direction is to the left because the x component is negative (**Figure 2.22**). ✔

Figure 2.22

(*c*) The displacement points from $x_i = +3.8$ m to $x_f = +3.8$ m, and thus it has zero magnitude (and no direction, of course; see **Figure 2.23**). ✔

Figure 2.23

❹ **EVALUATE RESULT** The arrow in part *a* points right, as I would expect because I moved forward (that is, to the right). In part *b* the arrow points left because I moved backward. Even though I moved between frames 6 and 17, I end at my initial position and so the displacement is zero.

When a vector has zero magnitude as in Example 2.5*c*, we say that it is equal to the *zero vector*, denoted by a zero with an arrow: $\Delta \vec{r} = \vec{0}$. In diagrams, we denote the zero vector by a dot (see Figure 2.23).

✋ **2.13** (*a*) What is the x component of the displacement shown in Figure 2.19? (*b*) Write the displacement in terms of its x component and the unit vector.

Rearranging Eq. 2.4, I get an expression for the x coordinate of the final position in terms of the x coordinate of the initial position and the x component of the displacement:

$$x_f = x_i + \Delta x. \tag{2.6}$$

This expression tells you that you can determine the x coordinate of an object's final position by adding the x coordinate of the object's initial position and the x component of its displacement.

Example 2.6 Working with displacements

(*a*) An object moves from an initial position at $x_i = +3.1$ m to a final position at $x_f = +1.4$ m. What is the x component of the object's displacement? (*b*) The x component of an object's displacement is $+2.3$ m. If the object's initial position is at $x_i = +1.6$ m, what is the x coordinate of its final position? (*c*) After undergoing a displacement of -1.3 m, an object is at $x_f = -0.4$ m. What is the x coordinate of the object's initial position?

❶ **GETTING STARTED** To visualize what is happening, I begin by making a sketch showing what is given for each situation and which quantities I need to determine (**Figure 2.24**).

❷ **DEVISE PLAN** The relationship among the initial x coordinate, the final x coordinate, and the x component of the

Figure 2.24 (*a*)

$\Delta x = ?$

$x_f = +1.4$ m $x_i = +3.1$ m

(*b*)

$\Delta x = +2.3$ m

$x_i = +1.6$ m $x_f = ?$

(*c*)

$\Delta x = -1.3$ m

$x_f = -0.4$ m $x_i = ?$

displacement is given by Eqs. 2.4 and 2.6. For each part of the problem, I know two of the three terms in each of these equations, and so I can use them to find the unknown quantity.

❸ EXECUTE PLAN (*a*) The *x* component of the displacement is given by Eq. 2.4:

$$\Delta x = x_f - x_i = +1.4 \text{ m} - (+3.1 \text{ m}) = -1.7 \text{ m}. ✔$$

(*b*) Using Eq. 2.6, I get

$$x_f = x_i + \Delta x = +1.6 \text{ m} + (+2.3 \text{ m}) = +3.9 \text{ m}. ✔$$

(*c*) Rearranging terms in Eq. 2.4, I have

$$x_i = x_f - \Delta x = -0.4 \text{ m} - (-1.3 \text{ m}) = +0.9 \text{ m}. ✔$$

❹ EVALUATE RESULT In the sketch I made, the displacement in part *a* points to the left, so the *x* component of the displacement should indeed be negative. In part *b* the displacement is to the right, so the final *x* coordinate should be larger than the initial *x* coordinate. For part *c* I expect the initial *x* coordinate to be positive because the 1.3-m displacement is larger than the distance from the final *x* coordinate to the origin (0.4 m).

Example 2.7 Displacement, distance, distance traveled

An object moves from point P at $x = +2.3$ m to point Q at $x = +4.1$ m and then to point R at $x = +1.5$ m. (*a*) What is the *x* component of the object's displacement after traveling from P to R? (*b*) What is the distance between the object's initial and final positions? (*c*) What is the distance traveled by the object?

❶ GETTING STARTED A simple sketch helps me visualize the motion and the relative locations of P, Q, and R (**Figure 2.25**).

Figure 2.25

R ———— P ———— Q ——→ x (m)
+1.5   +2.3   +4.1

❷ DEVISE PLAN For part *a*, I can use Eq. 2.4 to calculate the *x* component of the object's displacement given x_i and x_f. In parts *b* and *c*, I need to calculate distances, which are given by Eq. 2.5.

❸ EXECUTE PLAN (*a*) The object's initial position is at $x_i = +2.3$ m and its final position is at $x_f = +1.5$ m, so the *x* component of its displacement is (see Eq. 2.4)

$$\Delta x = x_f - x_i = +1.5 \text{ m} - (+2.3 \text{ m}) = -0.8 \text{ m}. ✔$$

(*b*) The distance between the initial and final positions is $d = |x_P - x_R| = |+2.3 \text{ m} - (+1.5 \text{ m})| = 0.8$ m (see Eq. 2.5). ✔

(*c*) The distance between P and Q is $d = |x_P - x_Q| = |+2.3 \text{ m} - (+4.1 \text{ m})| = 1.8$ m; the distance between Q and R is $d = |x_Q - x_R| = |+4.1 \text{ m} - (+1.5 \text{ m})| = 2.6$ m. The distance traveled is thus 1.8 m + 2.6 m = 4.4 m. ✔

❹ EVALUATE RESULT The sketch shows that the displacement from P to R is in the negative *x* direction, and so my answer to part *a* should be negative. The distance between P and R is the absolute value of the displacement, and my answer to part *b* is indeed the absolute value of my answer to part *a*. In part *c*, the total distance traveled (4.4 m) is greater than the distance between P and R. The sketch I made readily confirms that this should be the case.

✋ **2.14** (*a*) Consider an *x* axis on which positive values of *x* are to the right of the origin. For an object initially located to the left of the origin, is the *x* component of a displacement to the right positive or negative? (*b*) Does the answer to part *a* depend on whether or not the object crosses the origin?

If displacement is a vector, then the position of an object can also be represented by a vector. To see this, multiply Eq. 2.4 through by $\hat{\imath}$:

$$\Delta x \, \hat{\imath} = (x_f - x_i)\hat{\imath} = x_f \, \hat{\imath} - x_i \, \hat{\imath}. \tag{2.7}$$

The left side represents the displacement

$$\Delta x \, \hat{\imath} = \Delta r_x \, \hat{\imath} = \Delta \vec{r}. \tag{2.8}$$

The vector $x_i \, \hat{\imath}$ in Eq. 2.7 is represented in **Figure 2.26** by an arrow running from the origin to my initial position. This arrow represents the *position vector* (or simply the **position**)—a vector that lets us determine the position of a point in space relative to some chosen origin. Mathematically, position is represented by the symbol $\vec{r}$. For one-dimensional motion we have

$$\vec{r} \equiv x \, \hat{\imath} \quad \text{(one dimension)}, \tag{2.9}$$

and so we see that the *x* component of position is equal to the *x* coordinate: $r_x \equiv x$.

Figure 2.26 Superposition of frames 3 and 10 of Figure 2.1. The arrows show my initial and final positions, $\vec{r}_i$ and $\vec{r}_f$, and the relationship of these vectors to the displacement $\Delta \vec{r}$.

My initial position can be thus written as $x_i \hat{\imath} = \vec{r}_i$; my final position is $\vec{r}_f = x_f \hat{\imath}$, and so Eq. 2.7 becomes

$$\Delta \vec{r} = \vec{r}_f - \vec{r}_i. \tag{2.10}$$

This equation states that the displacement (the change in position) is equal to the final position minus the initial position. Figure 2.26 graphically shows the relationship between displacement $\Delta \vec{r}$ and the initial and final positions.

Exercise 2.8 Displacement and position vectors

(a) Write each displacement in Example 2.5 in terms of the unit vector $\hat{\imath}$ shown in Figure 2.18. (b) What is the magnitude of each displacement vector in part a? (c) Write my final position in Figure 2.26 in terms of the unit vector.

SOLUTION

(a) $\Delta \vec{r} = (+2.0\text{ m})\hat{\imath}$

      $\Delta \vec{r} = (-1.4\text{ m})\hat{\imath}$

      $\Delta \vec{r} = (0)\hat{\imath} = \vec{0}.$ ✔

(b) $|(+2.0\text{ m})| = 2.0\text{ m}$

      $|(-1.4\text{ m})| = 1.4\text{ m}$

      $|0| = 0.$ ✔

(c) $\vec{r}_f = (+4.8\text{ m})\hat{\imath}.$ ✔

Rearranging Eq. 2.10, we get

$$\vec{r}_f = \vec{r}_i + \Delta \vec{r}, \tag{2.11}$$

which tells us that the final position is equal to the sum of the initial position and the displacement. Together with Figure 2.26, Eq. 2.11 gives a graphical prescription for adding two vectors:

> **To add two vectors, place the tail of the second vector in the sum at the tip of the first vector; the vector representing the sum runs from the tail of the first vector to the tip of the second.**

Figure 2.27a shows this procedure for two arbitrary vectors $\vec{a}$ and $\vec{b}$.

Equation 2.10 also gives us a prescription for subtracting vectors:

$$\Delta \vec{r} = \vec{r}_f - \vec{r}_i = \vec{r}_f + (-1)\vec{r}_i. \tag{2.12}$$

This equation states that we can find the displacement $\Delta \vec{r}$ by subtracting the initial position $\vec{r}_i$ from the final position $\vec{r}_f$ or, alternatively, by adding the vector $(-1)\vec{r}_i$ to $\vec{r}_f$. The vector $(-1)\vec{r}_i$ has the same magnitude as $\vec{r}_i$ but points in the opposite direction. So the graphical prescription for subtracting two vectors is:

> **To subtract a vector from another vector, reverse the direction of the vector being subtracted and add the reversed vector to the vector from which you are subtracting.**

Figure 2.27b shows this procedure for two arbitrary vectors $\vec{a}$ and $\vec{b}$.

Figure 2.26 suggests another way of finding the difference between two vectors: The vectors $\vec{r}_i$ and $\vec{r}_f$ both have their tails at the origin, and the vector $\vec{r}_f - \vec{r}_i$ points from the tip of $\vec{r}_i$ to the tip of $\vec{r}_f$. So an alternative graphical prescription for subtracting two vectors is:

Figure 2.27 (a) Adding two vectors. (b, c) Two ways to subtract one vector from another.

To subtract a vector from another vector, place their tails at the same point
and then draw a vector from the tip of the vector being subtracted to the
tip of the vector from which you are subtracting.

or

The vector $\vec{a} - \vec{b}$ representing the difference between two vectors $\vec{a}$ and $\vec{b}$
points from the tip of $\vec{b}$ (the vector being subtracted) to the tip of $\vec{a}$.

This approach is illustrated in Figure 2.27c.

In later chapters we discuss rules for multiplying vectors. For now it suffices
to know how to multiply a vector by a scalar. The effect of such a multiplication
is the same as that of multiplying the unit vector by a scalar (see Figure 2.16):
Multiplying a vector $\vec{a}$ by a scalar c yields a vector whose length equals the length
of the original vector times the scalar:

$$c\,\vec{a} = c(a_x \hat{\imath}) = (ca_x)\hat{\imath}. \tag{2.13}$$

If the scalar c is positive, then the product vector points in the same direction as
the original vector $\vec{a}$; if c is negative, the product vector points in the direction
opposite that of $\vec{a}$.

Although our current treatment of vectors is limited to one dimension, we
shall be able to use the same methods when dealing with vectors in more than
one dimension in Chapter 10.

✋ **2.15** Consider the three vectors illustrated in **Figure 2.28**. (a) Make a sketch rep-
resenting the vectors $\vec{a} + \vec{c}$, $\vec{a} - \vec{b}$, and $\vec{c}\ \ \vec{b}$. (b) Are the vectors $\vec{a} + \vec{c}$ and $\vec{c} + \vec{a}$
identical? (c) Are the vectors $\vec{c} - \vec{b}$ and $\vec{b} - \vec{c}$ identical?

Figure 2.28 Checkpoint 2.15.

2.7 Velocity as a vector

Like displacement, average velocity is a vector. As we saw in Section 2.4, by dividing the x component of the displacement by the time interval required for
that displacement, we obtain the x component of the average velocity during that
time interval. Consider, for example, an object for which the x component of the
displacement in the time interval between clock readings t_i and t_f is Δx. We can
write the time interval as the change in the clock reading, $\Delta t = t_f - t_i$, and so
the x component of the average velocity is

$$v_{x,\text{av}} \equiv \frac{\Delta x}{\Delta t} = \frac{x_f - x_i}{t_f - t_i}. \tag{2.14}$$

As before, the subscript x reminds us that this component is measured relative to
our reference axis and that it can be either positive or negative, depending on the
sign of Δx (Δt is always positive because $t_f > t_i$).

Equation 2.14 gives us the x component of the vector $\vec{v}_{\text{av}} = v_{x,\text{av}}\,\hat{\imath}$. Multiplying the first and middle terms of Eq. 2.14 by $\hat{\imath}$ and substituting $\Delta\vec{r} = \Delta x\,\hat{\imath}$
(Eq. 2.8), we see that average velocity can be written as

$$\vec{v}_{\text{av}} \equiv v_{x,\text{av}}\,\hat{\imath} = \frac{\Delta\vec{r}}{\Delta t}. \tag{2.15}$$

Because Δt is always positive ($t_f > t_i$), Eq. 2.15 shows that for motion in one
dimension, the average velocity $\vec{v}_{\text{av}}$ always points in the same direction as the
displacement.

QUANTITATIVE TOOLS

Example 2.9 Average velocity and average speed

Consider my motion between frames 1 and 8 in Figure 2.1. Use the values listed in Table 2.1 to determine the answers to these questions: (a) What is my average speed over this time interval? (b) What is the x component of my average velocity over this time interval? (c) Write the average velocity in terms of the unit vector $\hat{\imath}$.

❶ **GETTING STARTED** Frames 1 through 8 correspond to my forward motion. To determine my average speed and velocity, I need to know both my displacement between these frames and the time interval between them.

❷ **DEVISE PLAN** I can get the average speed from its definition: the distance traveled divided by the time interval. Because I travel in only one direction between frames 1 and 8, the distance traveled is equal to the distance between my initial and final positions. For part b, I can use Eq. 2.14 to get the x component of the average velocity, and Eq. 2.15 shows me how to write the average velocity in unit vector form.

❸ **EXECUTE PLAN** (a) From Table 2.1, $|x_f - x_i| = |+4.8 \text{ m} - (+1.0 \text{ m})| = 3.8 \text{ m}$. I traveled from x_i to x_f in time interval $\Delta t = 2.3$ s. My average speed was thus $(3.8 \text{ m})/(2.3 \text{ s}) = 1.7$ m/s. ✔

(b) The x component of my displacement is $\Delta x = x_f - x_i = +4.8 \text{ m} - (+1.0 \text{ m}) = +3.8 \text{ m}$. Using Eq. 2.14, I find for the x component of average velocity $v_{x,av} = \Delta x/\Delta t = (+3.8 \text{ m})/(2.3 \text{ s}) = +1.7$ m/s. ✔

(c) $\vec{v}_{av} = \Delta \vec{r}/\Delta t = (+3.8 \text{ m})\hat{\imath}/(2.3 \text{ s}) = (+1.7 \text{ m/s})\hat{\imath}$. ✔

❹ **EVALUATE RESULT** The answer to part a shows that I cover a distance roughly equal to my height each second, which is reasonable for a person walking. Because I walk in one direction only, the answer to part b has the same value as the answer to part a. The positive sign indicates that my motion is in the positive x direction, as I expect. My answer to part c expresses this result in unit vector form.

✋ **2.16** (a) Consider my motion between frames 6 and 17 in Figure 2.1. Use the values in Table 2.1 to determine the answers to these questions: What is my average speed over this time interval? What is the x component of my average velocity? What is the average velocity? (b) Repeat for the motion between frames 1 and 17.

2.8 Motion at constant velocity

If an object moves at constant velocity, we can drop the term *average* when referring to velocity. When we do so, the x component of the average velocity is simply v_x. According to Eq. 2.14, we thus have

$$\Delta x = v_x \, \Delta t \quad \text{(constant velocity).} \tag{2.16}$$

To give just one example, a car going at a constant velocity of $+10$ m/s in the x direction travels a distance of 10 m during each second of its motion. A plot of position versus time is therefore a straight line, as indicated in **Figure 2.29a**. Recall from Checkpoint 2.7 and the text immediately following it that the ratio $\Delta x/\Delta t$ is the slope of the $x(t)$ curve. Looking at Figure 2.29a, you can see that this ratio $\Delta x/\Delta t$ is the tangent of the angle that the $x(t)$ curve makes with any horizontal line drawn through the curve. So we see that for motion at constant velocity, the slope of the $x(t)$ curve is numerically equal to the x component of the velocity:

$$\frac{\Delta x}{\Delta t} = v_x \quad \text{(constant velocity).} \tag{2.17}$$

Another useful fact can be obtained by looking at the $v_x(t)$ curve for an object moving at constant velocity. Because the x component of the velocity always has the same value when the velocity is constant, this curve is a horizontal line, as shown in Figure 2.29b. Notice that the area $v_x \, \Delta t$ (height times width) of the shaded rectangle of width Δt under this line is, from Eq. 2.16, equal to the x component of the displacement, Δx, during the time interval.* This is true for any time interval Δt, and so:

Figure 2.29 Graphs of position and velocity as a function of time for an object moving at constant velocity.

(a) Position versus time: straight line with nonzero slope

(b) Velocity versus time: horizontal line

---

*The word *area* requires some caution here: The height of the rectangle represents the x component of a velocity (in meters per second), and the width represents a time interval (in seconds), and so the product—the "area"—has units of (m/s) × s = m, not m² as would a surface area in the traditional sense. This is so because the area of the rectangle, $v_x \, \Delta t = \Delta x$, represents the x component of a displacement, which has units of meters.

The *x* component of the displacement during any time interval is given by the area under the $v_x(t)$ curve between the beginning and the end of the time interval.

Because the *x* component of the velocity can be positive or negative, the area can also be positive or negative, as it should given that it represents the *x* component of a displacement. As we shall see in Chapter 3, this correspondence between the *x* component of the displacement and the area under the $v_x(t)$ curve holds not just for motion at constant velocity but for any type of motion.

For an object moving at constant velocity, Eq. 2.16 gives us a way of determining the *x* coordinate of the position of the object at any time. Remembering that $\Delta x = x_f - x_i$, we can write Eq. 2.16 in the form

$$x_f - x_i = v_x \Delta t \quad \text{(constant velocity)}, \qquad (2.18)$$

or, solving for x_f,

$$x_f = x_i + v_x \Delta t \quad \text{(constant velocity)}. \qquad (2.19)$$

This expression allows us to determine, at any time t_f, the *x* coordinate of the position of an object moving at constant velocity, provided we know the object's initial position coordinate x_i at time t_i.

Example 2.10 Motion at constant velocity

Figure 2.30 shows the position versus-time graph for part of the motion of an object moving at constant velocity. (*a*) What is the *x* component of the object's velocity? (*b*) Write an expression for $x(t)$, the *x* coordinate of the position of the object at an arbitrary time *t*. (*c*) What is the *x* coordinate of the object's position at $t = 25$ s?

Figure 2.30 Example 2.10.

x (m)

① **GETTING STARTED** The $x(t)$ curve in Figure 2.30 is a straight line, as it should be for a motion at constant velocity. To answer the question, I have to read off information from the graph.

② **DEVISE PLAN** The *x* component of the object's velocity is given by Eq. 2.14. Once I have found this value, I can use Eq. 2.19 to answer part *b*. Although the graph doesn't show the position of the object at $t = 25$ s, I can use my solution to part *b* to find the position by substituting $t = 25$ s.

③ **EXECUTE PLAN** (*a*) From the graph I see that the object's position changes from $x_i = +1.6$ m to $x_f = +5.2$ m in the time interval between $t_i = 0$ and $t_f = 6.0$ s. Substituting these values into Eq. 2.14, I find for the *x* component of the velocity:

$$v_x = \frac{x_f - x_i}{t_f - t_i} = \frac{+5.2\text{ m} - (+1.6\text{ m})}{6.0\text{ s} - 0} = \frac{+3.6\text{ m}}{6.0\text{ s}}$$
$$= +0.60\text{ m/s.} \checkmark$$

(*b*) I take the object's position at $t = 0$ as the initial position. Substituting $t_i = 0$, $x_i = +1.6$ m, and $v_x = +0.60$ m/s from part *a* into Eq. 2.19, I get

$$x_f = +1.6\text{ m} + (+0.60\text{ m/s})(t_f - 0)$$
$$= +1.6\text{ m} + (+0.60\text{ m/s})t_f.$$

Because the choice of t_f is arbitrary, I may just as well write, for the *x* coordinate of the position at any instant of time *t*:

$$x(t) = +1.6\text{ m} + (+0.60\text{ m/s})t. \checkmark$$

(*c*) Substituting $t = 25$ s into the expression I obtained in part *b* yields

$$x(t = 25\text{ s}) = +1.6\text{ m} + (+0.60\text{ m/s})(25\text{ s})$$
$$= +1.6\text{ m} + 15\text{ m} = +17\text{ m.} \checkmark$$

④ **EVALUATE RESULT** The *x* component of the object's velocity is positive, as I would expect from the positive slope of the $x(t)$ curve. I can double-check the value (0.60 m/s) by reading off the increase in *x* over a 1-s interval in the graph. The result is indeed about 0.6 m. I cannot read off the value for *x* for $t = 25$ s from the graph because the graph extends to only $t = 6$ s. However, from the graph I see that the object starts near $x = 2$ m and the *x* coordinate increases by 3 m every 5 s. In 25 s, the object displacement should therefore be 5(3 m) = 15 m, and so the object's final position should be near (2 m) + (15 m) = 17 m, which is what I got.

QUANTITATIVE TOOLS

2.17 In Example 2.10, suppose I had taken x_i to be the x coordinate of the object's position not at $t = 0$ but at $t = 2.0$ s. Show that the expression for the x coordinate of the position is the same as the one I obtained in Example 2.10b.

2.9 Instantaneous velocity

If you are driving and wonder How fast am I going *now*?, the answer to your question is provided by the speedometer. This gauge gives your *instantaneous speed,* which is generally not equal to your average speed during the entire trip. Likewise, if you drop a ball from a certain height, the ball speeds up as it falls, and so its velocity changes over time. In addition to being able to calculate the ball's average velocity as it falls over a certain distance, you might be interested in knowing its velocity at any given instant—its **instantaneous velocity.**

Figure 2.31 shows successive positions of a falling ball at 0.0300-s time intervals. Such a picture can be obtained using a strobe light to illuminate the ball at fixed intervals and thus record its position at fixed intervals. As the ball falls, the positions at which it is photographed get farther and farther apart. In other words, the magnitude of the ball's displacement per time interval (the magnitude of its average velocity, from Eq. 2.15) increases. Suppose we want to find the ball's velocity at position 2: We want to answer the question How fast is the ball moving at the instant it passes position 2? Using the ruler in the picture, we can measure how long the ball takes to fall a certain distance after position 2, but doing that gives the ball's *average* velocity over that distance. To get a value closer to the ball's instantaneous velocity at position 2, we have to make the time interval over which we measure the distance shorter and shorter.

From here on, the word *velocity* without any adjective is used to designate the instantaneous value of the velocity. When we are interested in the average value over a certain time interval, we shall always use the adjective *average.* In equations we drop the subscript av when we mean the instantaneous value—by convention, $\vec{v}_{av}$ = average velocity, $\vec{v}$ = instantaneous velocity. Likewise, *speed* always means *instantaneous speed.*

2.18 (*a*) Determine the x component of the ball's average velocity between positions 2 and 9 in Figure 2.31. (*b*) Repeat between positions 2 and 8. (*c*) Repeat for increasingly smaller time intervals. (*d*) As the time interval decreases, does the x component of the average velocity increase, decrease, or stay the same? Explain. (*e*) Plot the x components of the average velocity you obtained in parts *a*–*c* versus the length of the time interval. (*f*) Do you expect the x component of the average velocity to become zero as the time interval approaches zero?

Figure 2.32 shows the position of the ball as a function of time, as obtained from Figure 2.31. The x component of the average velocity measured over an interval Δt is given by Eq. 2.14, and in Checkpoint 2.18 you used that equation to evaluate the x component of the average velocity between positions 2 and 9:

$$v_{x,29} = \frac{x_9 - x_2}{t_9 - t_2}. \tag{2.20}$$

(I substituted 29 for the subscript av to indicate that we are averaging over the time interval between t_2 and t_9.) This calculation yields the slope of the hypotenuse of the right triangle between positions 2 and 9 in Figure 2.32a. As you reduced the size of Δt, you got closer and closer to the value of the velocity at position 2. As the checkpoint shows, the x component of the displacement gets smaller as Δt gets smaller, but the ratio of the two (the slope of the hypotenuse)

Figure 2.31 Successive positions of a falling ball recorded at 0.0300-s intervals.

Figure 2.32 Procedure for finding the x component of the velocity of the ball in Figure 2.31 from its $x(t)$ curve. (*a*) As we reduce the time interval $\Delta t = t_f - t_2$ over which the x component of the velocity is averaged, Δx shrinks and the straight line between (x_2, t_2) and (x_f, t_f) approaches the tangent to the curve at (x_2, t_2). (*b*) The slope of the tangent at (x_2, t_2) gives the x component of the velocity at that point.

never becomes zero. This is not surprising because the x component of the ball's average velocity had some positive value while passing position 2. Thus that component should also be nonzero at position 2.

Letting the interval Δt approach zero, we obtain the x component of the velocity at instant t:

$$v_x \equiv \lim_{\Delta t \to 0} \frac{\Delta x}{\Delta t}. \tag{2.21}$$

The right side of this equation is the definition of the *derivative* of x with respect to time:

$$v_x \equiv \frac{dx}{dt}. \tag{2.22}$$

As you can see from Figure 2.32, the hypotenuse of the triangle spanned by the time interval Δt approaches the tangent to the $x(t)$ curve at time t_2, when Δt goes to zero. The x component of the velocity at instant t is thus equal to the slope of the tangent to the $x(t)$ curve at instant t.

The velocity (which is a vector) is then

$$\vec{v} = v_x \,\hat{\imath} = \left(\lim_{\Delta t \to 0} \frac{\Delta x}{\Delta t} \right)\hat{\imath}. \tag{2.23}$$

Because the unit vector is constant, we can pull it inside the parentheses and write

$$\left(\lim_{\Delta t \to 0} \frac{\Delta x}{\Delta t} \right)\hat{\imath} = \lim_{\Delta t \to 0} \frac{\Delta x\,\hat{\imath}}{\Delta t} = \lim_{\Delta t \to 0} \frac{\Delta \vec{r}}{\Delta t}, \tag{2.24}$$

where I have used the relationship $\Delta \vec{r} = \Delta x\,\hat{\imath}$ from Eq. 2.8. The term on the right in Eq. 2.24 is the derivative of the position vector, and so we can write

$$\vec{v} = \frac{d\vec{r}}{dt}. \tag{2.25}$$

The magnitude of this vector is the **speed** $v = |\vec{v}|$.

Table 2.2 Symbols and their meaning

Symbol	Meaning
t	clock reading = instant in time
$\Delta t \equiv t_f - t_i$	change in clock reading = interval of time
x	x coordinate
$d \equiv \lvert x_1 - x_2 \rvert$	straight-line distance between two points (never has sign)
$\hat{\imath}$	unit vector defining direction of x axis (vector magnitude 1)
$\vec{b} \equiv b_x \hat{\imath}$	vector and unit vector notation (see examples below)
b_x	x component of vector $\vec{b}$ (can be positive or negative)
$b \equiv \lvert \vec{b} \rvert = \lvert b_x \rvert$	magnitude of vector $\vec{b}$ (always positive)

Vector	Meaning	Component	Meaning
$\Delta \vec{r} = \Delta r_x \hat{\imath}$	displacement	$\Delta r_x \equiv \Delta x$	x component of displacement = change in x coordinate
$\vec{r} = r_x \hat{\imath}$	position	$r_x \equiv x$	x component of position = x coordinate
$\vec{v}_{av} = v_{x,av} \hat{\imath}$	average velocity	$v_{x,av} \equiv \dfrac{\Delta x}{\Delta t}$	x component of average velocity
$\vec{v} = v_x \hat{\imath}$	(instantaneous) velocity	$v_x \equiv \lim\limits_{\Delta t \to 0} \dfrac{\Delta x}{\Delta t} \equiv \dfrac{dx}{dt}$	x component of (instantaneous) velocity

Table 2.2 summarizes the various symbols we have introduced in this chapter and their meaning.

Example 2.11 Time intervals and derivatives

Suppose the x coordinate of the position of an object moving along the x axis varies in time according to the expression $x(t) = ct^3$, where c is a constant. Derive an expression for the x component of the velocity as a function of time.

❶ **GETTING STARTED** There are two ways to obtain the answer to this problem. One is to use differential calculus: The x component of the velocity is the derivative of the function $x(t)$ with respect to time. The other way is to evaluate the x component of the velocity over a finite time interval Δt and then let that interval go to zero. If I use both methods, I can easily verify my answer.

❷ **DEVISE PLAN** I'll use the (harder) second method first. To do so, I have to determine the change in the x coordinates between two instants t_i and $t_f = t_i + \Delta t$. The x component of the average velocity is then the ratio of this change in the x coordinate and Δt. Equation 2.21 then allows me to find the x component of the (instantaneous) velocity at any instant by taking the limit of this result as Δt goes to zero.

❸ **EXECUTE PLAN** The x coordinate of the object's initial position at time t_i is $x_i = ct_i^3$. At a later time $t_f = t_i + \Delta t$, the x coordinate of the position is

$$x_f = ct_f^3 = c(t_i + \Delta t)^3$$

$$= ct_i^3 + 3ct_i^2 \Delta t + 3ct_i(\Delta t)^2 + c(\Delta t)^3.$$

Therefore the x component of the displacement in the time interval Δt is

$$\Delta x = x_f - x_i$$

$$= \left[ct_i^3 + 3ct_i^2 \Delta t + 3ct_i(\Delta t)^2 + c(\Delta t)^3 \right] - ct_i^3$$

$$= 3ct_i^2 \Delta t + 3ct_i(\Delta t)^2 + c(\Delta t)^3.$$

The x component of the average velocity is thus

$$v_{x,av} = \frac{\Delta x}{\Delta t} = 3ct_i^2 + 3ct_i \Delta t + c(\Delta t)^2.$$

If I let Δt approach zero, the second and third terms on the right go to zero, so that I have

$$v_x = \lim_{\Delta t \to 0} \frac{\Delta x}{\Delta t} = 3ct^2, ✔$$

where I have dropped the subscript i because the result holds for any instant t. This equation gives the velocity at any time t. It tells me that v_x changes as the square of t.

❹ **EVALUATE RESULT** I can verify my result using differential calculus:

$$v_x(t) = \frac{d}{dt}x(t) = \frac{d}{dt}(ct^3) = 3ct^2.$$

Example 2.12 The limiting process

Consider again an object moving along the x axis according to the expression $x(t) = ct^3$, with $c = +0.12$ m/s^3. (a) Determine the x component of the object's average velocity during the interval from $t_i = 1.0$ s to $t_f = 2.0$ s. (b) Repeat for the interval from $t_i = 1.0$ s to $t_f = 1.1$ s. (c) Show that your result approaches the x component of the velocity at $t = 1.0$ s if you continue to reduce the interval by factors of ten. Ignore the significant digits rules taught in Chapter 1. Instead, use all the digits your calculator shows in every step.

❶ GETTING STARTED I have to use a fixed initial instant ($t_i = 1.0$ s) and evaluate the change in the function $x(t)$ over increasingly smaller time intervals Δt, starting with $\Delta t = 1.0$ s.

❷ DEVISE PLAN Evaluating the change in $x(t)$ is just a matter of doing it, and so my plan is to roll up my sleeves and dig in!

❸ EXECUTE PLAN (a) At $t_i = 1.0$ s, the object is at $x_i = (+0.12$ m/s$^3)(1.0$ s$)^3 = +0.12$ m. At $t_f = 2.0$ s, it is at $x_f = (+0.12$ m/s$^3)(2.0$ s$)^3 = +0.96$ m, and so $\Delta x = +0.96$ m $- (+0.12$ m$) = +0.84$ m. The x component of the average velocity therefore is $(\Delta x)/(\Delta t) = (+0.84$ m$)/(1.0$ s$) = +0.84$ m/s. ✔

(b) Between $t_i = 1.0$ s and $t_f = 1.1$ s, I have $\Delta x = (+0.12$ m/s$^3)(1.1$ s$)^3 - (+0.12$ m$) = +0.03972$ m, and $v_{x,av} = (+0.03972$ m$)/(0.10$ s$) = +0.3972$ m/s. ✔

Table 2.3 Example 2.12

Δt (s)	Δx (m)	$v_{x,av} = \Delta x/\Delta t$ (m/s)
1	+0.84	+0.84
0.1	+0.03972	+0.3972
0.01	+0.00363612	+0.363612
0.001	+0.00036036012	+0.36036012
0.0001	+0.000036003600 12	+0.360036 0012
0.00001	+0.000003600036 00	+0.360003 6000
0.000001	+0.000000360000 36	+0.360000 3600
0.0000001	+0.000000036000 00	+0.360000 0360

(c) Table 2.3 shows what happens as I continue to shorten the time interval by factors of ten. As Δt becomes smaller and smaller, $v_{x,av}$ approaches 0.36 m/s. ✔

❹ EVALUATE RESULT If I substitute $c = +0.12$ m/s^3 and $t = 1.0$ s into the expression for the x component of the velocity obtained in Example 2.11, I should obtain the same answer as the limiting value for small intervals Δt. Indeed, I find

$$v_x(t) = 3ct^2 = 3(+0.12 \text{ m/s}^3)(1.0 \text{ s})^2 = +0.36 \text{ m/s}.$$

2.19 (a) Suppose the position for a certain object is constant. Determine the x component of its velocity by using Eq. 2.22 and by evaluating the limit in Eq. 2.21 of the ratio of the x component of the displacement over a finite time interval. (b) Repeat for the case where the x coordinate of the position changes with time according to the expression $x = ct$, where c is a constant. Explain your answer.

Chapter Glossary

SI units of physical quantities are given in parentheses.

At rest The condition of an object whose position is not changing.

Component of a vector The scalar by which the unit vector must be multiplied to generate a given vector along the axis defined by the unit vector. See also *unit vector notation*.

Displacement $\Delta \vec{r}$ (m) A vector pointing from an object's initial position to its final position:

$$\Delta \vec{r} = \vec{r}_{\mathrm{f}} - \vec{r}_{\mathrm{i}}. \tag{2.10}$$

Distance d (m) A distance d between two points is a scalar equal to the absolute value of the difference in the x coordinates of those two points:

$$d \equiv |x_1 - x_2| \quad \text{(one dimension)}. \tag{2.5}$$

Magnitude of a vector A positive scalar associated with a vector. The magnitude of a vector in one dimension is equal to the absolute value of the x component of the vector:

$$b \equiv |\vec{b}| = |b_x| \quad \text{(one dimension)}. \tag{2.3}$$

Position $\vec{r}$ (m) A vector that specifies the location of an object along a reference axis. The vector runs from the origin to the location of the object and can be written as the product of the x coordinate of the object's position and the unit vector $\hat{\imath}$:

$$\vec{r} \equiv x\,\hat{\imath} \quad \text{(one dimension)}. \tag{2.9}$$

Scalar A quantity that is entirely specified by a number and a unit of measure.

Speed v (m/s) The *average speed* v_{av} is a scalar equal to the distance traveled divided by the time interval it took to travel that distance. The *instantaneous speed* (or simply *speed*) is a scalar equal to the magnitude of the velocity: $v = |\vec{v}|$.

Unit vector A vector of magnitude one with no units used to specify a direction in space.

Unit vector notation A mathematical representation of a vector, the product of a scalar and a unit vector:

$$\vec{b} \equiv b_x\,\hat{\imath} \quad \text{(one dimension)}. \tag{2.2}$$

The scalar b_x is called the x component of vector $\vec{b}$. The subscript x reminds you that b_x is a signed number whose value depends on the choice of the unit vector.

Vector A quantity that requires a number, a unit, and a direction in space to be completely specified.

Velocity $\vec{v}$ (m/s) A vector that gives the time rate of change in the position of an object. The *average velocity* over any interval is obtained by dividing the displacement during that time interval by the duration of the interval:

$$\vec{v}_{\mathrm{av}} \equiv \frac{\Delta \vec{r}}{\Delta t}. \tag{2.15}$$

The *instantaneous velocity* (or simply *velocity*) is the limit of the average velocity as the time interval goes to zero:

$$\vec{v} = \lim_{\Delta t \to 0} \frac{\Delta \vec{r}}{\Delta t} \equiv \frac{d\vec{r}}{dt}. \tag{2.25}$$

3 Acceleration

3.1 Changes in velocity

3.2 Acceleration due to gravity

3.3 Projectile motion

3.4 Motion diagrams

3.5 Motion with constant acceleration

3.6 Free-fall equations

3.7 Inclined planes

3.8 Instantaneous acceleration

CONCEPTS

QUANTITATIVE TOOLS

In Section 2.8 we considered objects moving at constant velocity—unchanging speed and unchanging direction. Most motions, however, are not at constant velocity because things speed up and slow down and change direction all the time. Any change in velocity is caused by *acceleration*, the subject of this chapter.

3.1 Changes in velocity

Consider a car at rest at a traffic light. The light turns green, and the driver puts the car in motion. As long as the car's velocity is changing, the car is *accelerating*:

> **If an object's velocity is changing, the object is accelerating.**

An object's velocity can change quickly or slowly: A sports car takes off much more quickly than a heavily loaded truck. Starting from rest, a sports car can reach a speed of 30 m/s in as little as 5 s; a truck might take minutes to reach the same speed. The difference between the two motions is the *rate* at which the speeds change. For example, if a sports car's speed increases from 0 to 10 m/s in 2.5 s, the rate at which the speed changes is $(10 \text{ m/s} - 0)/(2.5 \text{ s}) = 4.0 \text{ m/s}^2$. This rate, which is typically greater for a sports car than for a truck, is the magnitude of a quantity we call *acceleration*. Like velocity, acceleration is a vector, and so we need not only a magnitude but also a direction to specify it completely. We represent acceleration by the symbol $\vec{a}$.

For now, let's return to the example of the sports car and choose the x axis along its direction of travel. The rate at which the x component of the car's velocity changes is called the x component of its **average acceleration:**

> **The x component of the average acceleration of an object is the change in the x component of the velocity divided by the time interval during which this change took place.**

I deliberately use the word *average* here because nothing prevents the x component of the car's velocity from increasing at different rates. For example, the x component of its velocity could increase from 0 to $+5.0 \text{ m/s}$ in 1.0 s, and then from $+5.0 \text{ m/s}$ to $+10 \text{ m/s}$ in 1.5 s.

The SI unit of acceleration, m/s^2 (meters per second squared), is a shorthand way of writing $(\text{m/s})/\text{s}$ (meters per second, per second). If something accelerates at $+1 \text{ m/s}^2$, the x component of its velocity increases by $+1 \text{ m/s}$ each second. One of the units of time in the s^2 comes from the change in velocity; the other comes from the time interval during which this change occurs.

🖐 **3.1** The x component of a car's velocity increases from 0 to $+5.0 \text{ m/s}$ in 1.0 s, and then from $+5.0 \text{ m/s}$ to $+10 \text{ m/s}$ in the next 2.0 s. What is the x component of its average acceleration (*a*) during the first second, (*b*) during the last 2 seconds, and (*c*) during the entire 3.0-s interval?

Figure 3.1 The direction of the car's acceleration depends on the direction of the x axis and on whether the car is speeding up or slowing down.

(*a*) Car speeds up in positive x direction

(*b*) Car slows down in positive x direction

(*c*) Car slows down in negative x direction

To see how the direction of acceleration relates to the motion, consider **Figure 3.1**. In Figure 3.1*a* a car traveling in the positive x direction (which means that its velocity points in the positive x direction) speeds up. The magnitude of the car's final velocity $\vec{v}_\text{f}$ is greater than the magnitude of the car's initial velocity $\vec{v}_\text{i}$, and so the change in the car's velocity $\Delta\vec{v} \equiv \vec{v}_\text{f} - \vec{v}_\text{i}$, which points from the tip of $\vec{v}_\text{i}$ to the tip of $\vec{v}_\text{f}$ (see Figure 2.27*a*), is in the positive x direction. By definition the acceleration $\vec{a}$ always points in the same direction as $\Delta\vec{v}$, and so here $\vec{a}$ points in the positive x direction. Consequently, the x component of the car's acceleration is positive: $a_x > 0$.

The car in Figure 3.1*b* also travels in the positive x direction, but this car slows down, and so $\Delta\vec{v}$ now points in the negative x direction—opposite the velocity vector. The acceleration vector, again pointing in the same direction as $\Delta\vec{v}$, also points in the negative x direction, giving a negative x component of the car's acceleration: $a_x < 0$.

Because its velocity is decreasing, you may be tempted to say that the car in Figure 3.1*b* is "decelerating"—an everyday expression used to indicate that something is slowing down. In physics, however, the word *deceleration* is not necessary and therefore best avoided; *acceleration* refers to *any* change in velocity, regardless of whether the object is speeding up or slowing down.

Figure 3.1*c* shows a surprising fact: A positive a_x does not have to mean speeding up. As you can see from the figure, the car slows down while traveling in the negative x direction. Because of the direction of travel, the car's velocity $\vec{v}$ now points in the negative x direction. The vector $\Delta\vec{v}$, however, points in the positive x direction (still from the tip of $\vec{v}_i$ to the tip of $\vec{v}_f$). The acceleration therefore also points in the positive x direction, and so the x component of the car's acceleration is *positive* even though the car slows down!

> **Whenever an object's velocity and acceleration vectors point in the same direction, the object speeds up. When they point in opposite directions, the object slows down.**

3.2 The x component of the velocity of a car changes from -10 m/s to -2.0 m/s in 10 s. (*a*) Is the car traveling in the positive or negative x direction? (*b*) Does $\Delta\vec{v}$ point in the positive or negative x direction? (*c*) Is the x component of the car's acceleration positive or negative? (*d*) Is the car speeding up or slowing down?

When working with objects traveling in the negative x direction, don't confuse "positive x component of acceleration" with "speeding up." The x component of velocity in Figure 3.1*c*, for example, is increasing (it gets less negative), and so a_x is positive even though the car is slowing down. Something *speeds up* when the *magnitude* of its velocity (which, remember from Chapter 2, is called its *speed*) increases, regardless of which way the object is moving. Whether or not the x component of an object's acceleration is positive, however, depends on the direction in which the object is moving.

As mentioned in Section 2.8, the $x(t)$ curve for an object moving at constant velocity is a straight line (see Figure 2.29*a*). When the velocity is not constant, the $x(t)$ curve is not straight. In **Figure 3.2*a***, the x component of displacement Δx_2 during a certain time interval Δt beginning at t_2 is larger than the x component of displacement Δx_1 during the same time interval beginning at t_1. This means that the x component of the object's velocity is increasing. In Figure 3.2*b*, where the $x(t)$ curve bends downward, the x component of displacement Δx_2 beginning at t_2 is smaller than the x component of displacement Δx_1 beginning at t_1, telling us that the x component of the velocity is decreasing.

Figure 3.2 Position-versus-time graphs for objects accelerating along the positive x axis.

Figure 3.3 Position-versus-time graphs for objects accelerating along the positive x axis.

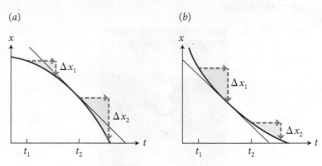

3.3 (*a*) In **Figure 3.3**, are the x components of the velocity represented by the $x(t)$ curves positive or negative? (*b*) Are the speeds increasing or decreasing? (*c*) Are the x components of $\Delta\vec{v}$ positive or negative? (*d*) Are the x components of the acceleration positive or negative?

If you answered Checkpoint 3.3 correctly, you are to be congratulated. Getting this right the first time around is not easy.

An interesting point to note is the following: In Figures 3.2*a* and 3.3*b*, the curves lie above the tangent to any point on them (they are said to *curve up* because they bend upward from the tangent), and the corresponding x components of acceleration are positive. The curves in Figures 3.2*b* and 3.3*a* lie below the tangent to any point; they are said to *curve down*, and the corresponding x components of acceleration are negative. So the sign of the x component of the acceleration is directly related to the curvature of an $x(t)$ curve:

> **The curvature of an $x(t)$ curve is a measure of the x component of acceleration. An upward curvature corresponds to a positive x component of acceleration. A downward curvature corresponds to a negative x component of acceleration.**

3.4 (*a*) A car is speeding up in the negative x direction. In what direction do $\vec{a}$ and $\vec{v}$ point? (*b*) To which of the four graphs in Figures 3.2 and 3.3 does the situation represented in Figure 3.1*c* correspond?

3.2 Acceleration due to gravity

As an example of accelerated motion, think of an object falling in a straight line toward Earth's surface. We attribute the falling to *gravity* and say that there is a gravitational attraction between Earth and the object. Even though we don't know the ultimate cause of gravitational attraction, we can describe its effects.

CONCEPTS

Figure 3.4 Multiple-flash picture of a ball falling. The time interval between successive flashes is 0.05 s. Note how the distance traveled increases from one time interval to the next.

Figure 3.5 (*a*) Feathers and stones released from a certain height inside and outside an evacuated tube. (*b*) In air, the feather soon lags behind the stone; in vacuum, the two fall at the same speed.

Figure 3.4 shows the positions of a falling ball recorded at equal time intervals of 0.05 s. Note how the spacing between successive positions increases as the ball drops. The picture tells us that the ball covers increasingly large distances in successive equal time intervals, and so we know that its speed increases as it falls. In other words, the ball accelerates. Two questions come to mind: *What is the magnitude of the acceleration as an object falls?* and *Does the acceleration depend on the physical characteristics of the object?*

Let us begin with the second question. If you drop a feather and a stone from the same height, there is no denying that the stone hits the ground first. This observation suggests that heavier objects fall faster than lighter ones—a common thought until the Italian mathematician, astronomer, and physicist Galileo Galilei (1564–1642) began to question its validity. Galileo observed that there is no difference between the amount of time taken by two stones to fall the same distance, even if the difference in weight is substantial and the stones are dropped from a considerable height. He argued that any observed difference in the amount of time it takes two objects to fall is a consequence of air resistance, which has a tendency to slow down lighter objects more than heavier ones.

3.5 Hold a book and a sheet of paper, cut to the same size as the book, side by side 1 m above the floor. Hold the paper parallel to the floor and the book with its covers parallel to the floor, and release them at the same instant. Which hits the floor first? Now put the paper on top of the book and repeat the experiment. What do you notice?

Figure 3.5 shows the effect of air resistance on a falling stone and a falling feather. One stone and one feather are dropped inside a glass tube from which the air has been pumped out. An identical stone and feather are released in air next to the tube. Figure 3.5*a* shows the situation at the simultaneous release of both pairs; Figure 3.5*b* shows the situation 0.3 s after release. In air, the feather lags behind the stone. Inside the tube, however, both the stone and the feather fall the same distance. In vacuum, in other words, the feather "falls like a rock." Repeating this experiment with many different objects, we discover that, in the absence of air resistance, the acceleration due to gravity does not depend on the physical characteristics of the falling object.

The motion of objects moving under the influence of gravity only is called **free fall.** The feather inside the evacuated tube is in free fall, but the feather outside the tube is not because its motion is influenced not just by gravity but by air resistance, too.

Notice that the effect of air resistance on the stone outside the tube is hardly noticeable—it falls just as fast as the stone in vacuum. This is true for many objects as long as they are not too light and as long as they are not dropped from too great a height. So, unless you drop a light object from any height or a heavy one from the top of the Eiffel Tower, you can ignore air resistance and consider all dropped objects to be in free fall.

Let us now turn to the first question we posed earlier: What is the magnitude of the acceleration due to gravity? In **Figure 3.6***a* I have plotted the positions of the ball in Figure 3.4; for each image of the ball, I measured the position from the center of the ball to the center of the topmost ball. Figure 3.6*b* shows the *x* component of the displacement between successive exposures; note how the magnitude of the displacement increases from one exposure to the next, telling us that the ball is accelerating.

3.6 What does Figure 3.6*b* tell you about the velocity of the ball from one exposure to the next?

Checkpoint 3.6 is tricky not because I wanted to mislead you but because it is important to see the difference

Figure 3.6 (a) Position-versus-time graph of the freely falling ball in Figure 3.4 for successive flashes $n = 1, 2, \ldots, 10$. (b) The change in the ball's x coordinate during the 10 exposures.

(a)

(b)

between plotting position versus time and plotting displacement (*change* in position) versus time.*

The ball's position at a given instant is simply its distance from the starting position, which is what Figure 3.6a shows. What Figure 3.6b shows is the x component of the *displacement* $\Delta x = x_f - x_i$ from one exposure to the next. Because the motion is not at constant velocity, the displacement changes from one exposure to the next. I include this graph to show the following remarkable fact: The data points lie on a straight line, which means that the magnitude of the

_____

*If you skipped the checkpoint, please do it now before I give you the answers. When you read a thriller, do you skip to the last page to find out how it ends? If you are puzzled by my questions, don't be discouraged and don't give up too soon. I wrote these questions precisely to arouse your curiosity. Discovering the answers to them is part of the learning process. Once you figure out the answers, you are unlikely to forget them. Taking the time to answer each checkpoint gives you something of lasting value. And if you like challenges, figuring out these checkpoints is without any doubt the easiest and most enjoyable way to learn physics. So take my advice to heart: Don't spoil the puzzle. You can do it—and you won't regret it!

Figure 3.7 Gravity map of Earth's oceans compiled from Seasat satellite data. The coloration shows variations in the value of the acceleration due to gravity of a few tenths of a percent.

displacement increases at a constant rate. Because velocity is proportional to displacement, this graph tells us that the velocity of the ball increases at a constant rate; in other words, the ball's acceleration is constant. So, for an object in free fall, the acceleration remains *constant* throughout the object's fall toward Earth.

Experiments show that, near Earth's surface in the absence of air resistance, the magnitude of the acceleration of all objects due to gravity for all objects in free fall is 9.8 m/s².

In the absence of air resistance, the magnitude of the acceleration of all falling objects is 9.8 m/s², and consequently the amount of time it takes to fall from a certain height is the same for all falling objects.

So, each second an object falls, its speed increases by about 10 m/s. After 1 s, an object released from rest near Earth's surface has a speed of about 10 m/s. After 2 s, its speed is about 20 m/s, and so on. The value of the acceleration due to gravity varies a few tenths of a percent over Earth's surface (**Figure 3.7**).

✋ **3.7** (a) Does the speed of a falling object increase or decrease? (b) If the positive x axis points up, does v_x increase or decrease as the object falls? (c) Is the x component of the acceleration positive or negative?

3.3 Projectile motion

So far we have considered only the motion of freely falling objects released from rest. Let us now see what happens when we *launch* an object upward, so that it is already moving when we release it. An object that is launched but not self-propelled is called a *projectile,* and its motion is called **projectile motion.** The path the object follows is called its **trajectory.** The motion of an object in free fall is a special case of projectile motion.

Figure 3.8 A ball launched vertically upward travels to its highest position and then retraces its path; the vertical "ruler" in each frame allows us to determine the position of the ball as a function of time.

(a)

⋯Ball's downward path offset for clarity—ball actually falls straight down.

(b) Film clip of ball's motion; frames are taken at 30 frames per second

(c) $x(t)$ curve for ball

(d) $v_x(t)$ curve for ball

Consider a ball launched straight up, as in **Figure 3.8a**. The ball first moves up and then reverses its direction of travel; its trajectory therefore is a straight line. Figure 3.8*b* shows a film clip of the motion of the ball; between frames 1 and 9 the ball moves vertically upward, and between frames 9 and 16 it moves vertically downward.

Figure 3.8*c* shows the ball's position for each frame in the film clip, and in Figure 3.8*d* I have plotted the ball's average velocity in each frame, obtained by dividing the displacement from one frame to the next by the 33-ms time interval between frames. As you can see, the velocity gets smaller and smaller as the ball nears the top of the trajectory. The ball then reverses direction, and so its velocity becomes negative. Beyond frame 9, the ball's speed—the magnitude of its velocity—increases again.

Because the ball slows down as it moves upward, its acceleration $\vec{a}$ and velocity $\vec{v}$ must point in opposite directions. Thus, because the velocity points upward, the acceleration points downward while the ball is moving upward. As the ball moves downward, it speeds up, and so now its acceleration and velocity both point downward. In other words, the ball's acceleration points downward both on the way up and on the way down.

Figure 3.8*d* shows that the ball's velocity changes *linearly*—it changes by equal amounts in equal time intervals—and so the acceleration is constant. The slope of the straight line in Figure 3.8*d* is about -10 m/s^2, which is the acceleration due to gravity. Therefore we see that, both on the way up and on the way down, the acceleration of a projectile is equal *both in magnitude and in direction* to that of a freely falling object.

If you throw a stone vertically upward and it has a velocity of $+20$ m/s right after leaving your hand, it slows down to $+10$ m/s after 1 s and reverses direction after 2 s. After 3 s, the stone is moving downward with a velocity of -10 m/s. Each second, gravity reduces the stone's velocity by another 10 m/s regardless of whether the stone is moving upward, moving downward, or instantaneously has zero velocity at the top. If you throw the stone harder, it leaves your hand with a higher speed, but once it leaves your hand, its motion is determined *solely* by gravity! In other words:

If an object is launched upward, the launch affects only the initial velocity. Once the object is released, the rest of its motion is determined by gravity alone (free fall).

✋ **3.8** Imagine throwing a ball downward so that it has an initial speed of 10 m/s. What is its speed 1 s after you release it? 2 s after?

What happens at the very top of the trajectory of a ball launched upward? Because the x component of the ball's velocity goes from positive to negative at the top, there must be an instant at which the x component of the velocity is zero. The x component of the acceleration, however, is *not* zero at the top. To see why, consider the motion over a small time interval Δt during which the ball reaches its highest position. Just before the ball reaches the top, its velocity $\vec{v}$ points upward; just after the ball reaches the top, the velocity points downward. The vector $\Delta\vec{v}$ therefore points downward, and so does the acceleration $\vec{a}$. This holds true regardless of the size of the time interval: As we make Δt smaller, Δv_x becomes smaller, too, but the ratio $\Delta v_x/\Delta t$ remains equal to the slope of the $v_x(t)$ curve in Figure 3.8d. So the acceleration of the ball is the same *everywhere*: on the way up, on the way down, and at the top.

If it seems odd that the acceleration at the top is nonzero, remember that the velocity must change there from up to down, and any change in velocity—be it a change in magnitude or a change in direction—means a nonzero acceleration. That the x component of the velocity is zero doesn't matter: The x component of the velocity doesn't remain zero for any finite time interval; it is only *instantaneously* zero, and in order for it to change, there must be an acceleration. Note, also, that even though the x component of the velocity is instantaneously zero, it is not correct to say that the ball is "instantaneously at rest"; *at rest* means that the position of the ball is not changing (see Section 2.1), which is not the case at any position along the ball's trajectory, including the very top.

3.4 Motion diagrams

To help us visualize the motion of an object described in a problem, we make a **motion diagram** representing the position of the moving object at equally spaced time intervals. Motion diagrams look very similar to the multiple-flash picture shown in Figure 3.4 and provide a visual overview of all you know about the motion. The procedure for making such diagrams is explained in the box on page 60.

Suppose a bicycle rider going 8.0 m/s applies the brake and slows down to a stop over a distance of 20 m in 5.2 s. The motion diagram in **Figure 3.9** shows that same information in graphical form. Note how the diagram shows all

Figure 3.9 Motion diagram for bicycle rider slowing down to a stop.

we know about the motion: the initial velocity, the distance it takes to come to a stop, and the time interval over which the stopping takes place. The spacing of the dots shows that the object of interest is slowing down. The question mark shows what information is missing. Making such a diagram helps you visualize the problem, organize the information given, and choose a convenient reference axis.

Nearly all problems in physics—and motion diagrams in particular—involve considering changes that occur over a certain time interval. Throughout this book we shall use clocks as in Figure 3.9 to mark the beginning and end of the time interval of interest. An important part of any physics problem is to record the parameters that characterize the situation under consideration at the beginning and end of that time interval (the *initial* and *final conditions*). When drawing motion diagrams, for example, we record an object's initial and final positions as well as its initial and final velocities. We begin applying this procedure in the next two examples.

Exercise 3.1 Accelerating car

Starting from rest, a car accelerates for 7.0 s at 3.0 m/s² and then travels at constant velocity for another 4.0 s. Make a motion diagram representing this motion.

SOLUTION The motion consists of two parts: constant acceleration during the first 7.0 s and constant velocity (zero acceleration) during the last 4.0 s. In my motion diagram (**Figure 3.10**) I show both parts of the motion: On the left the spacing between the dots increases to show the acceleration; on the right the spacing is constant to show motion at constant velocity.

Figure 3.10

I chose a positive x axis pointing in the direction of travel and with the origin at the car's starting position. The initial conditions are $t_i = 0$, $x_i = 0$, and $v_{x,i} = 0$.

Before specifying the final conditions, I must consider the instant where the car stops accelerating. This instant, which I denote by t_1, occurs 7.0 s after the car begins to accelerate. Neither the car's position nor its velocity at that instant is known, so I denote these values by question marks in the diagram.

The car then moves at constant velocity for 4.0 s, so the final conditions are $t_f = 11.0$ s, $x_f = ?$, and $v_{x,f} = v_{x,1}$. I complete the diagram by indicating that the x component of the car's acceleration is +3.0 m/s² between t_i and t_1 and zero between t_1 and t_f. ✔

✔ The checkmark shows that I carried out the following checks: **Vectors and scalars used appropriately; Everything answered; No unknowns left; Units correct; Significant digits justified.**

Procedure: Analyzing motion using motion diagrams

When you solve motion problems, it is important to begin by making a diagram that summarizes what you know about the motion.

1. Use dots to represent the moving object at equally spaced time intervals. If the object moves at constant speed, the dots are evenly spaced; if the object speeds up, the spacing between the dots increases; if the object slows down, the spacing decreases.
2. Choose an *x* (position) axis that is convenient for the problem. Most often this is an axis that (*a*) has its origin at the initial or final position of the object and (*b*) is oriented in the direction of motion or acceleration.
3. Specify the position and velocity at all relevant instants. In particular, specify the *initial conditions*—position

and velocity at the beginning of the time interval of interest—and the *final conditions*—position and velocity at the end of that time interval. Also specify all positions where the velocity reverses direction or the acceleration changes. Label any unknown parameters with a question mark.
4. Indicate the acceleration of the object between all the instants specified in step 3.
5. To consider the motion of more than one object, draw separate diagrams side by side, one for each object, using one common *x* axis.
6. If the object reverses direction, separate the motion diagram into two parts, one for each direction of travel.

Example 3.2 Can this be?

A newspaper article you read claims that by the time it reaches the ground, a stone dropped from the top of the Empire State Building (which has approximately 100 floors) "travels the length of a window faster than you can say *Watch out! A stone!*" Estimate whether this is true.

❶ **GETTING STARTED** At first this problem appears ill-defined. What am I supposed to calculate? Where to begin? If the answer to the first question is not immediately clear, the answer to the second is: with a motion diagram. I therefore begin by organizing the information following the procedure in the Procedure box "Analyzing motion using motion diagrams". I show the motion represented by a series of dots of increasing spacing to represent the acceleration due to gravity (**Figure 3.11**). I chose an *x* axis having its origin at the top of the building (the stone's initial position) and pointing downward (in the direction of the motion). This choice of axis means that

Figure 3.11

$$t_i = 0$$
$$x_i = 0$$
$$v_{x,i} = 0$$

$$a_x = +9.8 \text{ m/s}^2 \qquad \vec{a}$$

$$t_f = ?$$
$$x_f \approx +300 \text{ m}$$
$$v_{x,f} = ? \qquad \vec{v}_f$$

$$x$$

downward corresponds to the *positive x* direction—*x* increases as the stone falls. The initial conditions are then

$$t_i = 0, \quad x_i = 0, \quad v_{x,i} = 0.$$

The clock reading t_i and position x_i are zero because of my arbitrary choice of reference point. I could have chosen any other values, but the choice I made simplifies things later on. That the *x* component of the initial velocity is zero is an assumption because the problem doesn't specify this detail. All I know is that the stone is dropped, and it seems reasonable to assume it is not thrown downward or upward, but simply released from rest.

Because I am interested in the stone's speed just as it reaches the ground, I choose that instant as the final instant. To estimate the distance between the initial and final positions, I assume that each floor is about 3 m high, making the building about 300 m high.* So the final conditions are

$$t_f = ?, \quad x_f = +300 \text{ m}, \quad v_{x,f} = ?$$

Between $x_i = 0$ and $x_f = +300$ m, the stone accelerates downward because of gravity. I make a simplifying assumption that air resistance doesn't affect the acceleration of the stone very much, so I write "$a_x = +9.8 \text{ m/s}^2$" between the initial and final positions.†

❷ **DEVISE PLAN** To complete the estimating task given in the problem statement, I need to compare the speed of the stone at the bottom of its fall to the speed it would have to have if it traveled the length of a window in the same time interval it takes to say "Watch out! A stone!" Because no values are given, I'll have to use estimates and then evaluate the speed using the relation among speed, distance traveled, and acceleration.

---

* The Empire State Building is 381 m high, and so my estimate is off by about 30%, but you will soon see that this error is irrelevant.

† Note that a_x is positive because both the acceleration and the *x* axis point downward. This assumption is almost certainly an oversimplification because air resistance cannot be ignored for a fall from about 300 m. However, we have not yet developed the tools to include air resistance, and so I have no other choice.

❸ **EXECUTE PLAN** I estimate that it takes roughly 2 s to say those words and a window is about 2 m tall. So, as long as the stone is traveling faster than $(2\text{ m})/(2\text{ s}) = 1$ m/s just before it hits the ground, it passes by a window before the four words can be uttered. I also know that the acceleration in free fall is about 10 m/s^2, so the speed of the stone increases by 10 m/s each second. That means that the stone's speed is 10 m/s 1 s after it is released. I know from experience that it takes far longer than 1 s for an object to fall such a great distance, and so, even without further calculation, I see that the statement must be true. ✔

❹ **EVALUATE RESULT** Even if I account for some slowing down due to air resistance, I know from experience that a stone dropped from even a much smaller height travels more than 1 m in 1 s just before it reaches the ground. (In the second part of this chapter, you will be able to use the motion diagram to calculate how fast the stone moves just before hitting the ground.)

✋ **3.9** Make a motion diagram for the following situation: A seaside cliff rises 30 m above the ocean surface, and a person standing at the edge of the cliff launches a rock vertically upward at a speed of 15 m/s. After reaching the top of its trajectory, the rock falls into the water.

CONCEPTS

Self-quiz

1. Two stones are released from rest at a certain height, one 1 s after the other. (*a*) Once the second stone is released, does the difference in their speeds increase, decrease, or stay the same? (*b*) Does their separation increase, decrease, or stay the same? (*c*) Is the time interval between the instants at which they hit the ground less than, equal to, or greater than 1 s? (Use $x(t)$ curves to help you visualize this problem.)

2. Which of the graphs in **Figure 3.12** depict(s) an object that starts from rest at the origin and then speeds up in the positive x direction?

Figure 3.12

3. Which of the graphs in **Figure 3.13** depict(s) an object that starts from a positive position with a positive x component of velocity and accelerates in the negative x direction?

Figure 3.13

(*a*)   (*b*)   (*c*)   (*d*)

4. Draw a motion diagram for an object that initially has a negative x component of velocity but has a positive x component of acceleration.

Answers

1. (*a*) Both stones accelerate at about 10 m/s^2, and so the speed of each increases about 10 m/s each second. Because the speeds increase at the same rate, the difference in the speeds remains the same. (*b*) As indicated by the vertical lines between the $x(t)$ curves for both stones in **Figure 3.14**, the separation increases because the speed of the first stone is always greater. (*c*) Both stones execute the same motion—they start from rest and have the same acceleration and travel the same distance. So the second stone always remains 1 s behind (the $x(t)$ curves are separated horizontally by 1 s at all instants; see the horizontal lines separating the curves in Figure 3.14). Therefore the second stone hits the ground 1 s after the first one hits.

2. Choice *b* is the correct answer because its initial position is zero and the slope is initially zero but then increasing, indicating that the object speeds up. Choice *a* depicts a motion that does not begin at the origin and has the object speeding up in the negative x direction. Choice *c* depicts an object slowing down while moving in the positive x direction. Choice *d* depicts an object that is initially not at the origin and that moves at constant velocity in the positive x direction.

3. Choice *d*. Choice *a* does not have a positive initial position. Choice *b* represents zero acceleration. Choice *c* represents zero initial velocity.

4. An object that has a negative x component of velocity must slow down in order to have a positive x component of acceleration. **Figure 3.15** shows what a motion diagram for this situation looks like.

Figure 3.14

Figure 3.15

3.5 Motion with constant acceleration

As we saw in Section 3.1, the x component of the average acceleration is the change in the x component of the velocity divided by the time interval during which this change took place:

$$a_{x,\text{av}} \equiv \frac{\Delta v_x}{\Delta t} = \frac{v_{x,\text{f}} - v_{x,\text{i}}}{t_\text{f} - t_\text{i}}. \qquad (3.1)$$

Notice the similarity between this definition and the definition of average velocity (Eq. 2.14):

$$v_{x,\text{av}} \equiv \frac{\Delta x}{\Delta t} = \frac{x_\text{f} - x_\text{i}}{t_\text{f} - t_\text{i}}. \qquad (3.2)$$

Velocity is the rate of change in position, and acceleration is the rate of change in velocity.

Let us begin by analyzing motion with constant acceleration. The x component of the velocity of an object whose acceleration is constant increases by equal amounts Δv_x during equal time intervals Δt. For example, the x component of the velocity of an object that has a constant acceleration $a_x = +5 \text{ m/s}^2$ increases by 5 m/s each second. If we plot the object's x component of velocity versus time, we therefore get a straight line with a nonzero slope, as in **Figure 3.16**.

To obtain an expression that allows us to determine the x component of the final velocity $v_{x,\text{f}}$ at some final instant t_f, we rewrite Eq. 3.1 in the form*

$$\Delta v_x \equiv v_{x,\text{f}} - v_{x,\text{i}} = a_x \Delta t \quad \text{(constant acceleration)} \qquad (3.3)$$

or $\qquad v_{x,\text{f}} = v_{x,\text{i}} + a_x \Delta t \quad$ (constant acceleration). $\qquad (3.4)$

So, if we know the x component of the initial velocity $v_{x,\text{i}}$ at some initial instant t_i for an object moving with constant acceleration, we add $a_x \Delta t$ to this x component of the velocity to obtain the x component of the final velocity $v_{x,\text{f}}$ at a later instant $t_\text{f} = t_\text{i} + \Delta t$.

How do we determine the displacement Δx for an accelerating object? In Section 2.8 we learned that the displacement of an object moving at constant velocity is equal to the area under the $v_x(t)$ curve. The motion we are considering now is not at constant velocity because acceleration is involved, but we can still apply what we know. We begin by approximating the $v_x(t)$ curve of Figure 3.16 by the stepped curve shown at the top of the shaded area in **Figure 3.17a**. The shaded area consists of many small rectangles of equal width δt adjusted in height to fit under the stepped $v_x(t)$ curve. (We use a lowercase Greek delta, δ, instead of an uppercase delta, Δ, to indicate that the time interval is small.) The area of each rectangle gives the displacement δx during an interval δt, and this area is the x component of the velocity at the beginning of the time interval multiplied by δt. The total displacement $\Delta x = x_\text{f} - x_\text{i}$ in the time interval from t_i to t_f is approximately equal to the sum of the areas of all the rectangles. The smaller the width of the rectangles, the more accurate the approximation.

Figure 3.16 For an object moving with constant acceleration, the $v_x(t)$ curve is a straight line.

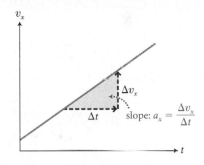

Figure 3.17 Determining the displacement for an object with constant acceleration.

(a)

(b)

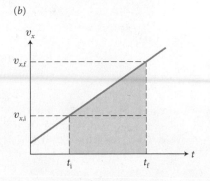

---

*Because the acceleration is constant, it always has the same (average) value, and so we can drop the subscript av.

In the limit that Δt approaches zero, the displacement $\Delta x = x_f - x_i$ is given exactly by the trapezoidal area under the $v_x(t)$ curve between t_i and t_f in Figure 3.17b. This area is equal to the sum of the areas of the shaded triangle and rectangle in Figure 3.17b. The area of the triangle is

$$\tfrac{1}{2}(v_{x,f} - v_{x,i})(t_f - t_i) = \tfrac{1}{2}\Delta v_x \Delta t = \tfrac{1}{2}a_x(\Delta t)^2, \tag{3.5}$$

where I have used Eq. 3.3 to substitute $a_x \Delta t$ for Δv_x. The area of the rectangle is

$$(v_{x,i} - 0)(t_f - t_i) = v_{x,i}\Delta t. \tag{3.6}$$

The displacement is thus the sum of Eqs. 3.5 and 3.6:

$$x_f - x_i = v_{x,i}\Delta t + \tfrac{1}{2}a_x(\Delta t)^2 \quad \text{(constant acceleration)}, \tag{3.7}$$

and the object's final position is

$$x_f = x_i + v_{x,i}\Delta t + \tfrac{1}{2}a_x(\Delta t)^2 \quad \text{(constant acceleration)}. \tag{3.8}$$

Equations 3.4 and 3.8 can be written without the delta notation when we reset our clock to zero at the beginning of a motion segment, so that $t_i = 0$ and $\Delta t = t_f - t_i = t_f$. Equations 3.8 and 3.4 then become, respectively,

$$x_f = x_i + v_{x,i}t_f + \tfrac{1}{2}a_x t_f^2 \quad \text{(constant acceleration)} \tag{3.9}$$

and

$$v_{x,f} = v_{x,i} + a_x t_f \quad \text{(constant acceleration)}, \tag{3.10}$$

giving us the position and the x component of the velocity of an object at any instant t_f.

Equations 3.9 and 3.10 are the basic equations for motion at constant acceleration when the initial conditions at $t_i = 0$ are known. Note that when $a_x = 0$, these equations become identical to the equations for motion at constant velocity: Eq. 3.10 yields an x component of the velocity v_x that is constant, and Eq. 3.9 becomes identical to Eq. 2.19.

Equation 3.9 gives the final position of an object at instant t_f. Because this instant is arbitrary, we can drop the subscript f to obtain an expression for the $x(t)$ curve of an object moving at constant acceleration:

$$x(t) = x_i + v_{x,i}t + \tfrac{1}{2}a_x t^2 \quad \text{(constant acceleration)}. \tag{3.11}$$

This expression shows that, for motion with constant acceleration, position depends on the square of t, and the $x(t)$ curve is thus a parabola. If a_x is positive, the parabola curves upward; if it is negative, the parabola curves downward (for an example, see Figure 3.8c). Likewise, from Eq. 3.10 we see that the $v_x(t)$ curve for motion at constant acceleration is a straight line:

$$v_x(t) = v_{x,i} + a_x t \quad \text{(constant acceleration)}. \tag{3.12}$$

For motion at constant velocity, we can set $a_x = 0$ in Eqs. 3.11 and 3.12, yielding straight lines for both $x(t)$ and $v_x(t)$. **Table 3.1** summarizes the three basic types of motions we have studied so far: at rest, constant velocity, and constant acceleration.

Table 3.1 Kinematics graphs for three basic types of motion

	Motion diagram	Position versus time	Velocity versus time	Acceleration versus time
At rest		$x = $ constant	$v_x = 0$	$a_x = 0$
Constant velocity		$x(t) = x_i + v_x t$ slope $= v_x$	$v_x = $ constant	$a_x = 0$
Constant acceleration		$x(t) = x_i + v_{x,i} t + \frac{1}{2} a_x t^2$ slope $= v_x(t)$	$v_x(t) = v_{x,i} + a_x t$ slope $= a_x$	$a_x = $ constant

Example 3.3 Accelerating car, again

Use Eqs. 3.11 and 3.12 to determine how far the car in Exercise 3.1 travels.

❶ **GETTING STARTED** To quantitatively analyze the situation in Exercise 3.1, I begin by separating the motion diagram in Figure 3.10 into two parts: one representing the acceleration of the car (**Figure 3.18a**) and one representing its motion at constant speed (Figure 3.18b). Note that the initial position and velocity in Figure 3.18b are not labeled with a question mark; even though they are not given, they are identical to the final position and velocity in Figure 3.18a, and so their values can be determined by solving the first part of the problem. The only unknown in the second part is the final position of the car.

❷ **DEVISE PLAN** Equation 3.11 allows me to determine the position of the accelerating car during the first part of the motion. To calculate the distance traveled during the second part of the motion, I need to know the velocity of the car. I can obtain this velocity from Eq. 3.12. From Eq. 2.18, I know that the distance traveled is then the product of this constant velocity and the duration of the time interval (4.0 s). Adding this distance to the position of the car at the end of the first part of the motion then gives me the total distance traveled by the car.

Figure 3.18

(a)

$t_i = 0 \quad a_x = +3.0 \text{ m/s}^2 \quad t_1 = 7.0 \text{ s}$
$x_i = 0 \qquad\qquad\qquad\qquad x_1 = ?$
$v_{x,i} = 0 \qquad\qquad\qquad\quad v_{x,1} = ?$

(b)

$\qquad\qquad t_1 = 7.0 \text{ s} \qquad\qquad t_f = 11.0 \text{ s}$
$\qquad\qquad x_1 \qquad a_x = 0 \qquad x_f = ?$
$\qquad\qquad v_{x,1} \qquad\qquad\qquad v_{x,f} = v_{x,1}$

(Continued)

❸ **EXECUTE PLAN** Given that $x_i = 0$ and $v_{x,i} = 0$, Eq. 3.11 reduces to $x_1 = x(t_1) = \frac{1}{2}a_x t_1^2$. Substituting $a_x = +3.0 \text{ m/s}^2$ and $t_1 = 7.0 \text{ s}$, I obtain for the position of the car at the end of the first part of the motion:

$$x_1 = \tfrac{1}{2}(+3.0 \text{ m/s}^2)(7.0 \text{ s})^2 = +74 \text{ m}.$$

From Eq. 3.12, I obtain the velocity at the beginning of the second interval:

$$v_1 = 0 + (+3.0 \text{ m/s}^2)(7.0 \text{ s}) = +21 \text{ m/s}.$$

At this constant velocity, the car's displacement during the 4.0 s of the second interval is

$$\Delta x = v_{x,1}\Delta t = (+21 \text{ m/s})(11.0 \text{ s} - 7.0 \text{ s}) = +84 \text{ m},$$

and so the x component of the car's total displacement is $(+74 \text{ m}) + (+84 \text{ m}) = +158 \text{ m}$. The car in Exercise 3.1 thus traveled a distance of 158 m. ✔

❹ **EVALUATE RESULT** With an acceleration of 3.0 m/s² (about one-third of the acceleration due to gravity), the car reaches a speed of

$$\frac{21 \text{ m}}{1 \text{ s}} \times \frac{1 \text{ mi}}{1609 \text{ m}} \times \frac{3600 \text{ s}}{1 \text{ h}} = 47 \text{ mi/h}$$

over the 7.0 s of the first interval and travels a distance of 74 m or about the length of a sports field. Both the car's final speed and the distance traveled are in line with what I would expect. During the second part of the motion, the car travels roughly the same distance in 4.0 s, which is also reasonable.

Example 3.4 Collision or not?

You are bicycling at a steady 6.0 m/s when someone suddenly walks into your path 2.5 m ahead. You immediately apply the brakes, which slow you down at 6.0 m/s². Do you stop in time to avoid a collision?

❶ **GETTING STARTED** In order to avoid a collision, you must come to a stop in less than 2.5 m. The problem therefore boils down to calculating the distance traveled under the given conditions and comparing this distance to 2.5 m.

❷ **DEVISE PLAN** Equation 3.7 gives me the displacement, but I don't know the time interval Δt. I can obtain this time interval from Eq. 3.4: $\Delta t = (v_{x,f} - v_{x,i})/a_x$, which contains no unknowns on the right side.

❸ **EXECUTE PLAN** Substituting the expression for the time interval from Eq. 3.4 into Eq. 3.7 gives the x component of the displacement necessary to stop:

$$\Delta x = v_{x,i}\frac{v_{x,f} - v_{x,i}}{a_x} + \tfrac{1}{2}a_x\left(\frac{v_{x,f} - v_{x,i}}{a_x}\right)^2 = \frac{v_{x,f}^2 - v_{x,i}^2}{2a_x}. \quad (1)$$

When I let the x axis point in the direction of the motion, the x component of the initial velocity is $v_{x,i} = +6.0 \text{ m/s}$, the x component of the final velocity is zero, $v_{x,f} = 0$, and the x component of the acceleration is $a_x = -6.0 \text{ m/s}^2$. Substituting these values into Eq. 1, I get

$$\Delta x = \frac{0 - (+6.0 \text{ m/s})^2}{2(-6.0 \text{ m/s}^2)} = +3.0 \text{ m},$$

which is more than the 2.5 m separating you from the person walking into your path. You will not be able to stop in time to avoid a collision. ✔

❹ **EVALUATE RESULT** Because $a_x = -6.0 \text{ m/s}^2$, your speed decreases by 6.0 m/s each 1 s, and so it takes 1 s to come to a stop from your initial speed of 6.0 m/s. Because your speed is decreasing, you travel less than 6.0 m, but without carrying out the calculation, I can't tell whether or not that distance is less than 2.5 m. All I can really say is that my answer should be less than 6.0 m, which it is.

Equation 3.4 allows us to determine the x component of the final velocity of an object undergoing constant acceleration after a certain time interval Δt. By multiplying both sides of Eq. 1 in Example 3.4 by $2a_x$ and rearranging terms, I get an expression for the x component of the final velocity of an object undergoing constant acceleration over a certain displacement Δx:

$$v_{x,f}^2 = v_{x,i}^2 + 2a_x\Delta x \quad \text{(constant acceleration)}. \tag{3.13}$$

✋ **3.10** Determine the velocity of the stone dropped from the top of the Empire State Building in Example 3.2 just before the stone hits the ground.

3.6 Free-fall equations

The magnitude of the **acceleration due to gravity** is designated by the letter g:

$$g \equiv |\vec{a}_{\text{free fall}}|. \tag{3.14}$$

As noted in Section 3.2, near Earth's surface the magnitude of the acceleration due to gravity is $g = 9.8 \text{ m/s}^2$. The direction of this acceleration is always downward, and so if we choose a positive x axis that points upward, the x component of the acceleration due to gravity is given by $a_x = -g$, where the minus sign takes into account that the acceleration vector points downward.

If an object is dropped from a certain height with zero initial velocity along an upward-pointing x axis, then, according to Eqs. 3.9 and 3.10,

$$x_f = x_i - \tfrac{1}{2}gt_f^2 \tag{3.15}$$

and

$$v_{x,f} = -gt_f. \tag{3.16}$$

Example 3.5 Dropping the ball

Suppose a ball is dropped from height $h = 20$ m above the ground. How long does it take to hit the ground, and what is its velocity just before it hits?

❶ GETTING STARTED I begin by drawing a motion diagram, arbitrarily choosing an x axis that points upward and has its origin at the initial position of the ball (**Figure 3.19**). I make two simplifying assumptions: that the ball is released from rest ($v_{x,i} = 0$ at $t_i = 0$) and that I may ignore air resistance (so that the ball is in free fall).

Figure 3.19

When the ball is released from rest at the origin, the initial conditions are

$$t_i = 0, \quad x_i = 0, \quad v_{x,i} = 0.$$

The final position x_f at instant t_f is a distance h below the initial position, and so, just before impact at instant t_f, the final conditions are

$$t_f = ?, \quad x_f = -h, \quad v_{x,f} = ?.$$

As the ball falls, its acceleration is negative (because $\vec{a}$ points toward increasingly negative values of x), and so $a_x = -g$.

❷ DEVISE PLAN Because the acceleration of the ball is constant, I can use Eqs. 3.9 and 3.10. Doing so gives me two equations to determine the two unknowns t_f and $v_{x,f}$.

❸ EXECUTE PLAN Substituting the initial and final conditions into Eq. 3.9 yields

$$-h = 0 + 0 - \tfrac{1}{2}gt_f^2 = -\tfrac{1}{2}gt_f^2,$$

and so

$$t_f = \sqrt{\frac{2h}{g}}.$$

Substituting $h = 20$ m and $g = 9.8$ m/s^2, I obtain for the amount of time the ball takes to fall 20 m

$$\Delta t = t_f - t_i = \sqrt{\frac{2h}{g}} - 0 = \sqrt{\frac{2(20\text{ m})}{9.8\text{ m/s}^2}} = \sqrt{4.0\text{ s}^2} = 2.0\text{ s.} ✔ \tag{1}$$

Next I use Eq. 3.10. Because the ball starts from rest, I have

$$v_{x,f} = 0 - gt_f = -gt_f = -(9.8\text{ m/s}^2)(2.0\text{ s})$$

$$= -20\text{ m/s.} ✔$$

❹ EVALUATE RESULT The 2.0 s I obtained for the time interval it takes the ball to fall is not unreasonable: 20 m corresponds approximately to the height of a six-story building, and from experience I know that something dropped from such a height takes a few seconds to reach the ground. My answer for the final velocity $v_{x,f} = -20$ m/s also makes sense: The x component of the velocity is negative because it points in the negative x direction, and if the ball were moving always at a constant speed of 20 m/s, it would cover the 20-m distance in 1 s. Because it moves at that speed only at the end of the drop, it takes longer to fall, as Eq. 1 shows.

3.11 Repeat Example 3.5 for an x axis that points downward (leaving the origin at the ball's initial position).

Example 3.6 A stone launched up

A stone is launched straight up from ground level at a speed of 8.0 m/s. (*a*) How high does it rise? (*b*) How many seconds does it take for the stone to hit the ground?

❶ **GETTING STARTED** I am asked to consider two parts of the trajectory: part *a* from the launch position to the top of the trajectory and part *b* from the launch position to the top and back down to the launch position. I begin therefore by drawing two motion diagrams: one for the upward motion and the other for the downward motion. I (arbitrarily) choose an *x* axis pointing upward, put the origin at the launching position, and start the clock at $t_i = 0$ at the instant the stone is launched (**Figure 3.20**).

Figure 3.20

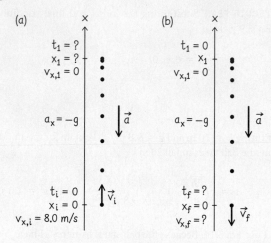

For the upward motion (Figure 3.20*a*), the initial conditions are $t_i = 0$, $x_i = 0$, and $v_{x,i} = +8.0$ m/s. The hard part of this problem is specifying the final conditions, and here is where the motion diagram helps. I know neither the instant t_1 at which the highest position is reached nor the location x_1 of that position. I do, however, know *something* about the stone at the highest position. (Put the book down and think for a second—you know it, too.)

The key is the word *highest*: The stone reverses direction at the highest position, and so its velocity must be zero there. So, for the upward part of the motion, the stone's final conditions are $t_f = t_1 = ?$, $x_f = x_1 = ?$ and $v_{x,f} = v_{x,1} = 0$.

For the downward motion, I reset the clock to zero at the top, as indicated by $t_1 = 0$ in Figure 3.20*b*. Doing this simplifies the calculation because it makes this part of the problem nearly identical to Example 3.5. I should not forget, however, that $\Delta t = t_f - t_1 = t_f - 0 = t_f$ now represents the duration of the downward motion only, not the total duration for the upward and downward travel.

❷ **DEVISE PLAN** To determine the height reached by the stone, I need to obtain a value for x_1. The stone is undergoing constant acceleration, so its position and velocity are given by Eqs. 3.8 and 3.4. For the upward part of the motion I see from my

motion diagram that there are two unknowns (x_1 and t_1), and so the number of unknowns is equal to the number of equations. After I obtain x_1 and t_1, the downward part of the motion also contains two unknowns ($v_{x,f}$ and t_f), which I can calculate using the same two equations.

❸ **EXECUTE PLAN** (*a*) For the upward portion of the motion I can use Eqs. 3.9 and 3.10 instead of Eqs. 3.8 and 3.4 because the clock reads zero at the beginning of the motion. With the *x* axis pointing upward, the acceleration of the stone is $a_x = -g$, and so these equations become

$$x_1 = 0 + v_{x,i}t_f - \tfrac{1}{2}gt_f^2 \tag{1}$$

and

$$0 = v_{x,i} - gt_f. \tag{2}$$

Solving Eq. 2 for t_f, I get

$$t_f = \frac{v_{x,i}}{g} = \frac{+8.0 \text{ m/s}}{9.8 \text{ m/s}^2} = 0.82 \text{ s}. \tag{3}$$

Substituting this result into Eq. 1, I determine the height to which the stone rises

$$x_1 = v_{x,i}\left(\frac{v_{x,i}}{g}\right) - \tfrac{1}{2}g\left(\frac{v_{x,i}}{g}\right)^2 = \frac{v_{x,i}^2}{g} - \frac{v_{x,i}^2}{2g} = \frac{v_{x,i}^2}{2g}, \tag{4}$$

and so

$$x_1 = \frac{(+8.0 \text{ m/s})^2}{2(9.8 \text{ m/s}^2)} = +3.3 \text{ m}. ✔$$

(*b*) For the downward part of the motion, Eq. 3.7 becomes

$$0 - x_1 = 0 - \tfrac{1}{2}g(t_f - t_1)^2.$$

Rearranging terms and substituting Eq. 4 for x_1, I have

$$(t_f - t_1)^2 = \frac{2x_1}{g} = \frac{2v_{x,i}^2}{2g^2} = \left(\frac{v_{x,i}}{g}\right)^2,$$

which shows that the amount of time it takes for the stone to fall back to the ground, $\Delta t = t_f - t_1 = v_{x,i}/g$, is identical to the amount of time it takes for the stone to reach its highest position (see Eq. 3).

The amount of time it takes for the round trip is

$$t_f = 2\left(\frac{v_{x,i}}{g}\right) = 2\left(\frac{8.0 \text{ m/s}}{9.8 \text{ m/s}^2}\right) = 1.6 \text{ s}. ✔$$

❹ **EVALUATE RESULT** That it takes as much time to travel up as it takes to fall back down makes sense if you look at the position-versus-time graph for a projectile in Figure 3.8*c*. The parabola is symmetrical about the maximum, meaning that the acceleration is the same in both directions, and so both parts of the motion must take the same amount of time. The stone's initial velocity is 8.0 m/s, so at an acceleration of about 10 m/s², it should take 0.8 s to slow down to zero and reach its highest position. The downward part of the motion is similar to the upward part, with the motion reversed, and so the total time should be twice as long. At a constant 8.0 m/s, the stone would travel (0.8 s)(8.0 m/s) = 6.4 m, but because it slows it travels only half that distance. My answers appear to make sense!

3.12 In Example 3.6, what is the x component of the velocity of the stone just before it hits the ground?

3.7 Inclined planes

Galileo concluded that the acceleration due to gravity is constant even though he was unable to study falling objects using high-speed video or multiple-flash photography. Instead, he used inclined planes at shallow angles of incline to reduce the acceleration. By rolling balls along such inclined planes, he came to the following remarkable conclusion:

> **When a ball rolls down an incline starting from rest, the ratio of the distance traveled to the square of the amount of time needed to travel that distance is constant.**

For instance, if a ball released from position $x_i = 0$ at $t_i = 0$ reaches position x_1 at instant t_1, x_2 at t_2, and x_3 at t_3 (**Figure 3.21**), Galileo found experimentally that

$$\frac{x_1}{t_1^2} = \frac{x_2}{t_2^2} = \frac{x_3}{t_3^2}. \tag{3.17}$$

Figure 3.21 Galileo measured how long it takes a ball to roll down planes inclined at different angles and concluded that the acceleration due to gravity is constant.

Note that for an object moving with constant acceleration and starting from rest at $x_i = 0$ and $t_i = 0$, we have, from Eq. 3.9,

$$x_f = \tfrac{1}{2} a_x t_f^2, \tag{3.18}$$

so that

$$\frac{x_f}{t_f^2} = \tfrac{1}{2} a_x, \tag{3.19}$$

which tells us that Galileo's ratio (Eq. 3.17) is directly proportional to the x component of the acceleration. The fact that the ratio doesn't change as the ball rolls down the incline demonstrates that the acceleration is constant.

When Galileo increased the angle of the incline, the ratio x_f/t_f^2 increased, too, although for any fixed angle it remained constant regardless of the distance covered by the ball. Galileo was able to study only a limited range of angles, but he conjectured that for a given angle of incline the ratio x_f/t_f^2 would remain constant. For a vertical incline, he reasoned, the ball would be in free fall and still have a constant acceleration.

We saw in Section 3.2 that Galileo's conjecture was correct. **Figure 3.22a** shows a low-friction cart rolling down inclines of different angles. For each angle, the component of the velocity along the incline increases linearly with time, indicating that the component of the acceleration along the incline is constant for that angle. Moreover, the component of the acceleration along the incline (the slope of the lines in Figure 3.22b) becomes larger as the angle is increased. Figure 3.22c

Figure 3.22 The acceleration of a low-friction cart rolling down an incline increases as the angle of incline increases.

(a)

(b) Component of cart's velocity along incline as function of time

(c) Component of acceleration along incline as function of angle of incline

shows how the component of the acceleration along the incline varies with the angle of incline θ. Experimentally we determine that the component of the acceleration along the incline obeys the relationship

$$a_x = +g \sin \theta \tag{3.20}$$

when the x axis points downward along the incline. For a vertical incline, $\theta = 90°$ and Eq. 3.20 correctly yields the x component of the acceleration of a freely falling object.

3.13 As the angle θ of the incline used to collect the data of Figure 3.22 is increased beyond 90°, what happens to the acceleration? Does this result make sense (provided you always put the cart on the top side of the track)?

3.8 Instantaneous acceleration

So far, we have discussed only motion that has constant acceleration, but not all acceleration is constant. For example, when a car accelerates, the acceleration levels off as the car approaches top speed. This is illustrated in **Figure 3.23**. If the car's acceleration were constant, the $v_x(t)$ curve would be the dashed straight line in Figure 3.23a; instead, the x component of the velocity levels off at about $+50$ m/s.

To determine the car's acceleration at a given instant, we follow the procedure of successive approximations we used in Section 2.9 to determine instantaneous velocity. Suppose we are interested in the x component of the car's acceleration 10 s after it begins accelerating. The x component of the *average* acceleration is obtained by dividing the change in the x component of the velocity during a certain time interval by the duration of that time interval (Eq. 3.1). For example, the x component of the car's average acceleration during the 25-s time interval following the instant we are interested in is given by the slope of the straight line segment PQ_1 in Figure 3.23a. To obtain the x component of the acceleration at $t = 10$ s, we make the time interval Δt over which we evaluate Δv_x successively shorter. As Δt approaches zero, the straight line segment PQ becomes tangent to the $v_x(t)$ curve at P, and the ratio $\Delta v_x/\Delta t$ approaches the x component of the **instantaneous acceleration** (or simply **acceleration**)* at point P:

$$a_x \equiv \lim_{\Delta t \to 0} \frac{\Delta v_x}{\Delta t}. \tag{3.21}$$

The right side of Eq. 3.21 is the definition of the derivative of v_x with respect to t, and so

$$a_x = \frac{dv_x}{dt}. \tag{3.22}$$

Note that the result is again a function of time. The acceleration-versus-time graph for the accelerating car of Figure 3.23 is shown in **Figure 3.24**. The slope of the $v_x(t)$ curve at a given point along the curve of Figure 3.23b gives the x component of the acceleration at that instant. For example, the value of the x component of the acceleration 10 s after the car begins accelerating is equal to the slope of the tangent to the $v_x(t)$ curve at point P (of Figure 3.23b).

In Section 2.9 we saw that the slope of the $x(t)$ curve for an object gives the x component of the object's velocity. Now we see that the slope of the $v_x(t)$ curve gives the x component of the object's acceleration:

$$
\begin{array}{ccccc}
& \text{slope of} & & \text{slope of} & \\
& x(t)\ curve & x \text{ component of } v_x(t)\ curve & x \text{ component of} \\
\text{position } x & \longrightarrow & \text{instantaneous} & \longrightarrow & \text{instantaneous} \\
& & \text{velocity } \vec{v} & & \text{acceleration } \vec{a}
\end{array}
$$

Mathematically this can be expressed as

$$a_x = \frac{dv_x}{dt} = \frac{d}{dt}\left(\frac{dx}{dt}\right) \equiv \frac{d^2x}{dt^2}, \tag{3.23}$$

where the expression on the right side represents the *second derivative* (the "derivative of the derivative") of x with respect to t.

Equation 3.23 allows us to obtain the x component of the acceleration of an object from its position. Often we are interested in the inverse procedure, however: What is the displacement during a given time interval for, say, the varying

---

* As with velocity, the word *instantaneous* is implied whenever we say "acceleration." Only when we want to speak of *average* acceleration will we use the adjective.

Figure 3.23 Velocity-versus-time graphs for an accelerating car. (*a*) As the time interval Δt over which the x component of the acceleration is averaged gets smaller, Δv_x gets smaller and the straight-line segment PQ approaches the tangent to the curve at P. (*b*) The slope of the tangent to the curve at P gives the x component of the instantaneous acceleration at that instant.

(*a*)

(*b*)

Figure 3.24 Determining the change in the x component of the velocity for an accelerating object.

(a) To find change in velocity over time interval, we approximate acceleration curve by steps of constant acceleration.

During this step, velocity changes by $a_x(t_4)\delta t$.

(b) Velocity change over entire interval is sum of velocity changes over steps.

Velocity change during step 4 equals $a_x(t_4)\delta t$ (area of rectangle).

$a_x(t_4)$

(c) As we make δt smaller, approximation improves and sum of rectangular areas approaches area under curve.

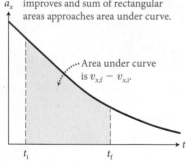

Area under curve is $v_{x,f} - v_{x,i}$.

acceleration shown in Figure 3.24? The trick is to apply what we know about constant-acceleration motion over time intervals small enough to make the acceleration approximately constant over that time interval.

Suppose we want to know the displacement during the time interval between t_i and t_f. We first obtain the change in velocity during that time interval and then calculate the displacement.

We begin by dividing up the time interval between t_i and t_f into a number of equal shorter intervals δt and approximating the acceleration by the stepped series of short segments of constant acceleration as shown in Figure 3.24a. Applying Eq. 3.3 to each shorter interval δt, we can write the x component of the change in velocity during each segment as

$$(\Delta v_x)_n = a_x(t_n)\delta t, \tag{3.24}$$

where $n = 1, 2, \ldots, 7$ and $a_x(t_n)$ is the x component of the acceleration at t_n (this instant is at the middle of each short interval, as shown in Figure 3.24a). The product $a_x(t_n)\delta t$ is the area of the dark shaded rectangle in Figure 3.24b. The x component of the velocity change during the entire interval from t_i to t_f is then approximately equal to the sum of the $(\Delta v_x)_n$ for all the short intervals δt between t_i and t_f:

$$\Delta v_x \approx \sum_n (\Delta v_x)_n = \sum_n a_x(t_n)\delta t, \tag{3.25}$$

where $\sum a_x(t_n)\delta t$ represents the sum of all the rectangular areas under the steps between t_i and t_f (the light shaded area in Figure 3.24b).

To get a better approximation, we can divide the time interval $t_f - t_i$ into a larger number of smaller intervals δt, so that the variation of the acceleration over each interval becomes even smaller and the red stepped curve is closer to the actual (light red) $a_x(t)$ curve.

An exact result is obtained if we let δt approach zero (and the number of small intervals approaches infinity), as in Figure 3.24c:

$$\Delta v_x = \lim_{\delta t \to 0} \sum_n a_x(t_n)\delta t, \tag{3.26}$$

which is precisely the definition of the *integral* of the x component of the acceleration with respect to t from t_i to t_f:

$$\Delta v_x = \int_{t_i}^{t_f} a_x(t)dt, \tag{3.27}$$

This integral represents the area under the $a_x(t)$ curve between t_i and t_f in Figure 3.24c. Integrals, like derivatives, can be evaluated mathematically, providing us with a convenient method for calculating the right side of Eq. 3.27 and allowing us to determine velocity from acceleration.

Once we know the velocity, we can use the same approach to obtain the displacement from the velocity. **Figure 3.25** graphically shows how to determine the x component of the displacement by evaluating the area under the $v_x(t)$ curve. In analogy to Eq. 3.27 we can thus write

$$\Delta x = \int_{t_i}^{t_f} v_x(t)dt. \tag{3.28}$$

This expression allows us to mathematically determine the x component of the displacement from a $v_x(t)$ curve. The x component of the velocity, in turn, can be obtained from the $a_x(t)$ curve (Eq. 3.27).

In Section 2.8, I showed that for motion at constant velocity the area under a $v_x(t)$ curve is equal to the x component of the object's displacement. Now we see that this holds true for accelerated motion as well. The geometrical relationship among acceleration, velocity change, and displacement is thus

$$\text{acceleration } a_x \xrightarrow{\substack{\text{area under} \\ a_x(t) \text{ curve}}} \substack{\text{velocity} \\ \text{change } \Delta v_x \\ \text{from } t_i \text{ to } t_f} \xrightarrow{\substack{\text{area under} \\ v_x(t) \text{ curve}}} \substack{\text{displacement } \Delta x \\ \text{from } t_i \text{ to } t_f}$$

Exercise 3.7 Using calculus to determine displacement

Suppose an object initially at x_i at $t_i = 0$ has a constant acceleration whose x component is a_x. Use calculus to show that the x component of the velocity and the x coordinate at some final instant t_f are given by Eqs. 3.10 and Eq. 3.9, respectively.

SOLUTION Because the acceleration is constant, I can pull a_x out of the integration in Eq. 3.27:

$$\Delta v_x = v_{x,f} - v_{x,i} = \int_{t_i}^{t_f} a_x dt = a_x \int_{t_i}^{t_f} dt = a_x(t_f - t_i).$$

Substituting $t_i = 0$ and rearranging terms, I obtain Eq. 3.10:

$$v_{x,f} = v_{x,i} + a_x t_f. \checkmark$$

For an arbitrary final instant t, I can drop the subscript f. Substituting this expression into Eq. 3.28, I get

$$\Delta x = \int_{t_i}^{t_f} (v_{x,i} + a_x t) dt$$

or, pulling constant terms out of the integration and then carrying out the integration,

$$\Delta x = x_f - x_i = v_{x,i} \int_{t_i}^{t_f} dt + a_x \int_{t_i}^{t_f} t\, dt = v_{x,i} t_f + a_x \left[\tfrac{1}{2} t^2 \right]_{t_i}^{t_f},$$

which yields Eq. 3.9:

$$x_f = x_i + v_{x,i} t_f + \tfrac{1}{2} a_x t_f^2. \checkmark$$

3.14 Take the first and second time derivatives of x_f in Eq. 3.9. What do you notice?

Figure 3.25 (*a*) To determine the x component of the displacement, we approximate the $v_x(t)$ curve by short segments of constant velocity. (*b*) When the segments are made infinitesimally small, the x component of the displacement becomes equal to the area under the $v_x(t)$ curve.

(*a*)

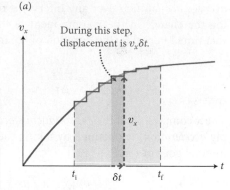

During this step, displacement is $v_x \delta t$.

(*b*)

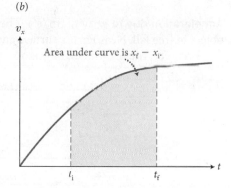

Area under curve is $x_f - x_i$.

Chapter Glossary

SI units of physical quantities are given in parentheses.

Acceleration $\vec{a}$ (m/s²) A vector that gives the time rate of change in the velocity of an object. The *x* component of the *average acceleration* over any interval is obtained by dividing the change in the *x* component of the velocity during that time interval by the duration of the interval:

$$a_x \equiv \frac{\Delta v_x}{\Delta t}. \tag{3.1}$$

The *x* component of the *instantaneous acceleration* (or simply *acceleration*) is obtained by taking the limit as the time interval goes to zero:

$$a_x = \lim_{\Delta t \to 0} \frac{\Delta v_x}{\Delta t} \equiv \frac{dv_x}{dt} = \frac{d}{dt}\left(\frac{dx}{dt}\right) = \frac{d^2 x}{dt^2}. \tag{3.23}$$

Acceleration due to gravity (m/s²) The acceleration of an object in free fall. Near Earth's surface and in the absence of air resistance, the magnitude of this acceleration is

$$g \equiv |\vec{a}_{\text{free fall}}| = 9.8 \text{ m/s}^2 \quad \text{(near Earth's surface)}.$$

Free fall The motion of an object subject to only the influence of gravity.

Motion diagram A diagram that shows the position of a moving object at equally spaced time intervals and summarizes what is known about the object's initial and final conditions (its position, velocity, and acceleration). See the procedure on page 60.

Projectile motion The motion of an object that is launched but not self-propelled. (Such an object is called a *projectile*.) The launch affects only the object's initial velocity. Once the object is launched, its motion is determined by gravity only, and hence the object is in free fall on the way up as well as on the way down.

Trajectory The path taken by a projectile. For motion at constant acceleration, the *x* coordinate and the *x* component of the velocity of an object are given by

$$x_{\text{f}} = x_{\text{i}} + v_{x,\text{i}}\Delta t + \tfrac{1}{2} a_x (\Delta t)^2 \text{ (constant acceleration)} \tag{3.8}$$

$$v_{x,\text{f}} = v_{x,\text{i}} + a_x \Delta t \qquad \text{(constant acceleration)}. \tag{3.4}$$

4 Momentum

4.1 Friction
4.2 Inertia
4.3 What determines inertia?
4.4 Systems

4.5 Inertial standard
4.6 Momentum
4.7 Isolated systems
4.8 Conservation of momentum

CONCEPTS

QUANTITATIVE TOOLS

In the preceding two chapters, we developed a mathematical framework for describing motion along a straight line. In this chapter, we continue our study of motion by investigating inertia, a property of objects that affects their motion. The experiments we carry out in studying inertia lead us to discover one of the most fundamental laws in physics—conservation of momentum.

4.1 Friction

Picture a block of wood sitting motionless on a smooth wooden surface. If you give the block a shove, it slides some distance but eventually comes to rest. Depending on the smoothness of the block and the smoothness of the wooden surface, this stopping may happen sooner or it may happen later. If the two surfaces in contact are very smooth and slippery, the block slides for a longer time interval than if the surfaces are rough or sticky. This you know from everyday experience: A hockey puck slides easily on ice but not on a rough road.

Figure 4.1 shows how the velocity of a wooden block decreases on three different surfaces. The slowing down is due to *friction*—the resistance to motion that one surface or object encounters when moving over another. Notice that, during the interval covered by the velocity-versus-time graph, the velocity decrease as the block slides over ice is hardly observable. The block slides easily over ice because there is very little friction between the two surfaces. The effect of friction is to bring two objects to rest with respect to each other—in this case the wooden block and the surface it is sliding on. The less friction there is, the longer it takes for the block to come to rest.

Figure 4.1 Velocity-versus-time graph for a wooden block sliding on three different surfaces. The rougher the surface, the more quickly the velocity decreases.

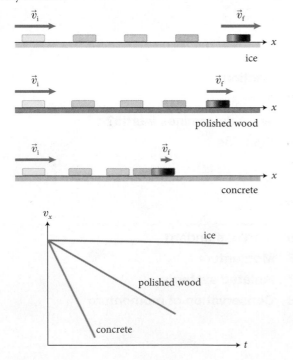

Figure 4.2 Low-friction track and carts used in the experiments described in this chapter.

You may wonder whether it is possible to make surfaces that have no friction at all, such that an object, once given a shove, continues to glide forever. There is no totally frictionless surface over which objects slide forever, but there are ways to minimize friction. You can, for instance, float an object on a cushion of air. This is most easily accomplished with a low-friction track—a track whose surface is dotted with little holes through which pressurized air blows. The air serves as a cushion on which a conveniently shaped object can float, with friction between the object and the track all but eliminated. Alternatively, one can use wheeled carts with low-friction bearings on an ordinary track. **Figure 4.2** shows low-friction carts you may have encountered in your lab or class. Although there is still some friction both for low-friction tracks and for the track shown in Figure 4.2, this friction is so small that it can be ignored during an experiment. For example, if the track in Figure 4.2 is horizontal, carts move along its length without slowing down appreciably. In other words:

In the absence of friction, objects moving along a horizontal track keep moving without slowing down.

Another advantage of using such carts is that the track constrains the motion to being along a straight line. We can then use a high-speed camera to record the cart's position at various instants, and from that information determine its speed and acceleration.

4.1 (*a*) Are the accelerations of the motions shown in Figure 4.1 constant? (*b*) For which surface is the acceleration largest in magnitude?

4.2 Inertia

We can discover one of the most fundamental principles of physics by studying how the velocities of two low-friction carts change when the carts collide. Let's first see what happens with two identical carts. We call these *standard carts* because we'll use them as a standard against which to compare the motion of other carts. First we put one standard cart on the low-friction track and make sure it doesn't move. Next we place the second cart on the track some distance from the first one and give the second cart a shove toward the first. The two carts collide, and the collision alters the velocities of both.

Figure 4.3 shows a high-speed film sequence of such a collision. Cart 1 is initially at rest, and consequently its position doesn't change in the first seven frames. Cart 2 approaches cart 1 from the left and collides with it 60 ms after

Figure 4.3 (*a*) Two identical carts collide on a low-friction track. The length of track visible in each frame is 0.40 m. Cart 1 is initially at rest; cart 2 collides with it in the middle of the sequence. (*b*) Two curves, one marking the position of the rear of cart 1 and the other marking the position of the front of cart 2, superimposed on the film clip.

Figure 4.4 Position-versus-time graph for the two carts in Figure 4.3. The curves correspond to the curves of Figure 4.3*b*. All 120 original frames in the sequence were used to obtain this graph.

the beginning of the film sequence. The collision causes cart 1 to move to the right and cart 2 to stop dead in its tracks (or, rather, track).

Measuring the positions of the two carts at various instants gives us the $x(t)$ curves shown in **Figure 4.4**, where the shaded region shows the time interval during which the collision took place. Although the collision appears "instantaneous" to any observer, it takes about 10 ms for the motion of the carts to adjust.

Figure 4.5, which shows the velocities of the two carts, tells us that initially the velocities are constant: 0 for cart 1 and about $+0.58$ m/s (the plus sign indicating motion to the right) for cart 2. After the collision, the velocities are

Figure 4.5 Velocity-versus-time graph for the carts of Figure 4.3 before and after the collision. Before the collision, cart 1 is at rest; after the collision, cart 2 is at rest and cart 1 moves at the initial velocity of cart 2.

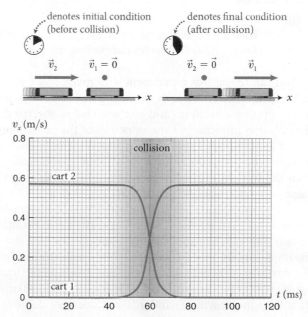

Figure 4.6 Velocity-versus-time graph for two identical carts before and after a collision on a low-friction track. Both carts are initially moving in the same direction.

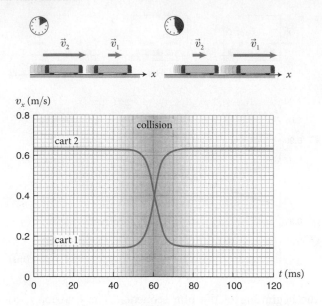

Figure 4.7 Velocity-versus-time graph for a standard cart and a double cart before and after the two collide on a low-friction track. The collision sets the double cart into motion and reverses the direction of travel of the standard cart.

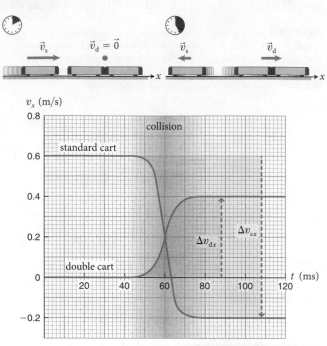

interchanged: Cart 1 now moves to the right at $+0.58$ m/s, and cart 2 has come to a complete stop. We can also see this interchanging of velocities in Figures 4.3 and 4.4, where the slopes of the two $x(t)$ curves are interchanged after the collision.

We can repeat the experiment, this time giving cart 2 a harder shove, and then repeat it again, this third time giving cart 2 just a gentle nudge. What we discover is that, *no matter what the initial velocity of cart 2 is,* the collision always interchanges the two velocities.

Further experiments show that it is not necessary that cart 1 be initially at rest. **Figure 4.6** shows what happens when both carts are moving in the same direction at the instant of collision: Once again the collision interchanges the two velocities.

✋ **4.2** What is the change in velocity of (*a*) cart 1 and (*b*) cart 2 in Figure 4.6? (*c*) What do you notice about your two answers?

You can repeat this experiment with many different initial velocities, with the carts moving in the same direction or in opposite directions, and you will always observe that the collision interchanges the velocities of the carts. Moreover, Checkpoint 4.2 shows that, if the velocity of one cart increases by a certain amount as a result of the collision, then the velocity of the other cart decreases by exactly the same amount.

To determine whether the amount of material that makes up each cart affects the motion, let's fasten two standard carts together so that the size of this unit is twice the size of the other cart we are going to use, which we continue to call the standard cart. With this double cart at rest on the track, we shove the standard cart toward it at a speed of 0.60 m/s. This time the moving (standard) cart does not come to a

complete stop; instead, the collision reverses its direction of travel, so that after the collision it moves to the left with a speed of 0.2 m/s, as **Figure 4.7** shows. After the collision, the initially stationary double cart, being more difficult to set in motion than the single standard cart, moves to the right, as before, but now its speed is lower than in the earlier experiments (0.40 m/s versus about 0.60 m/s). This result makes sense because we already know from experience that more massive objects are harder to set into motion than less massive ones—it's easier to throw a small stone than a large boulder.

The x component of the velocity of the double cart changed by $\Delta v_{\mathrm{d}x} = +0.40$ m/s $- 0 = +0.40$ m/s, and the x component of the velocity of the standard cart changed by $\Delta v_{\mathrm{s}x} = -0.20$ m/s $- (+0.60$ m/s$) = -0.80$ m/s.* The magnitude of the double cart's velocity change, $|\Delta v_{\mathrm{d}x}| = 0.40$ m/s, is half that of the standard cart, $|\Delta v_{\mathrm{s}x}| = 0.80$ m/s.

We can repeat this experiment and vary the initial speeds and directions of motion, but we would continue to observe that *no matter how the carts move (or do not move) initially, the magnitude of the velocity change of the double cart is always half that of the standard cart.* Also, the two velocity

---

*Because we must keep track of the changes in velocity of two colliding objects, we need an additional subscript. For example, $\Delta v_{\mathrm{d}x} = v_{\mathrm{d}x,\mathrm{f}} - v_{\mathrm{d}x,\mathrm{i}}$ is the change in velocity for the double cart. The final subscript, separated by a comma, designates the instant: f for final and i for initial. The middle subscript indicates that we are dealing with the x component. The first subscript designates the object (d for double cart).

Figure 4.8 Velocity-versus-time graph for a standard cart and a half cart before and after the two collide on a low-friction track.

An oil supertanker has an enormous inertia. Even at full throttle it can take as long as 10 min to bring a large ship to a halt, which explains why ships like the *Titanic* and the *Exxon Valdez* could not avoid a collision in spite of seeing the danger well ahead of time.

changes are always in opposite directions, which means the *x* component of the velocity of one cart increases and that of the other cart decreases.

Now let us repeat the collision once again, this time with the original cart 1 cut in half so that it is half the size of the other cart we'll be using. With the half cart at rest on the track, we push a standard cart toward it. As **Figure 4.8** shows, the magnitude of the velocity change of the half cart is twice the magnitude of the velocity change of the standard cart: $|\Delta v_{hx}| = 0.58$ m/s and $|\Delta v_{sx}| = 0.29$ m/s.

A pattern is developing here: For a group of objects all made of the same material, the motion of larger objects is harder to change than the motion of smaller objects. The larger objects put up more resistance when we try to change their velocity. This tendency of an object to resist a change in its velocity is called **inertia.**

Inertia is a measure of an object's tendency to resist any change in its velocity.

The results of our experiments are summarized in **Table 4.1.** As you can see, the *ratio of the inertias* of the two carts is equal to the inverse of the ratio of their velocity changes. In experiment 2, the double cart inertia is twice the standard cart inertia, and the ratio $|\Delta v_{dx}| : |\Delta v_{sx}|$ is 0.5. In experiment 3, the half cart inertia is half that of the standard cart, and the ratio $|\Delta v_{hx}| : |\Delta v_{sx}|$ is 2.

The data in Table 4.1 suggest that we could now take a new cart of unknown inertia, let a standard cart collide with it, and then *determine* from the changes in velocity the inertia of the new cart relative to that of the standard cart.

4.3 The *x* component of the final velocity of the standard cart in Figure 4.8 is positive. Can you make it negative by adjusting this cart's initial speed while still keeping the half cart initially at rest?

Figure 4.9 is a graph of the collision between some unknown cart and a standard cart—both solid and made of the same material. The magnitude of the unknown cart's change in velocity is one-third that of the standard cart (Checkpoint 4.4). We conclude from this result that the unknown cart's inertia is three times that of the standard cart. In other words, the amount of material in the unknown cart is three times that in the standard cart.

4.4 Verify that $|\Delta v_{ux}| / |\Delta v_{sx}| \approx 1/3$ for the two carts in Figure 4.9.

Figure 4.9 Velocity-versus-time graph for a standard cart and a cart of unknown inertia before and after the two collide on a low-friction track. The unknown inertia can be determined from the ratio of the carts' velocity changes.

Table 4.1 Ratio of Velocity Changes in Collisions Between Two Carts

Experiment	Cart 1	Cart 2	$|\Delta v_{1x}| : |\Delta v_{2x}|$
1	standard	standard	1
2	double	standard	0.5
3	half	standard	2

4.3 What determines inertia?

Having established that an object's inertia (its resistance to a change in velocity) is proportional to the amount of material in the object, we now come to the next important question: Is it only the amount of material that determines inertia? So far, all the carts we've been studying have been made of the same material. Would our results in experiment 1 be the same if we replaced one of the standard carts with a cart of the same volume of material but made of a different material—plastic instead of metal, say? As you probably know from experience, the answer is *no*: For example, a lead ball is more difficult to set in motion than a rubber ball of equal volume.

So let's make two carts of identical amounts of material, one of plastic and the other of metal, and see what happens when the two collide. The result, shown in **Figure 4.10**, is very different from the result for two identical carts (Figure 4.5).

4.5 What is the ratio of the x components of the change in velocity for the plastic and metal carts, $\Delta v_{px}/\Delta v_{mx}$, in Figure 4.10?

As we expect, the x component of the velocity of the plastic cart changes by a much larger amount than that of the metal cart (but it is still opposite in sign). In other words, it is easier to change the motion of the plastic cart than the motion of the metal cart. Given that inertia is a measure of an object's tendency to resist any change in its velocity, we conclude that an object's inertia is determined not just by the volume of material it contains but also by what that material is.

What about other physical properties—shape, say, or the smoothness of an object's surface? Experiments show that inertia does not depend on any of these other properties:

The inertia of an object is determined entirely by the type of material of which the object is made and by the amount of that material contained in the object.

Figure 4.10 Velocity-versus-time graph for two colliding carts that have the same volume but are made of different materials.

Once we have chosen one object as the standard for inertia, we can determine the inertia of any other object—whatever its size, shape, or composition—by letting it collide with our standard and measuring the ratio of the changes in the velocity of the two objects.

4.6 Is the inertia of the cart of unknown inertia in Figure 4.9 greater or less than that of the standard cart?

Example 4.1 Friction and collisions

Figure 4.11 shows the $v_x(t)$ curves for a collision between two identical carts moving not on a low-friction track but rather on a rough surface, so that friction affects their motion. Are the changes in the velocity of the carts caused by the collision still equal in magnitude?

Figure 4.11 Example 4.1.

❶ **GETTING STARTED** Looking at the graph, I'm tempted to say yes because if I tilt Figure 4.11 a bit, it looks very similar to Figure 4.6. Determining the change in velocity due to the collision, however, is not as straightforward because friction also affects the velocities. So, because the velocities of the carts before the collision decrease due to friction, it is not possible to read off a well-defined "initial" value of the velocity. The shape of the graph suggests that friction continues to decrease the velocities in the same way during and after the collision, so I have to determine a way to separate the change in velocity due to friction from the change due to the collision.

❷ **DEVISE PLAN** Because the effect of friction is a steady decrease in velocity, I can extrapolate the $v_x(t)$ curve for cart 1 to calculate what its velocity would have been at $t = 80$ ms if the collision had not taken place. To determine the change in velocity due to the collision, I then read off the actual value of the velocity of cart 1 at $t = 80$ ms and subtract the two velocities. Then I repeat the procedure for cart 2 and compare the changes in velocity.

❸ **EXECUTE PLAN** By placing a ruler along the first part of the $v_x(t)$ curve for cart 1, I observe that the curve lies in line with the second part of the $v_x(t)$ curve for cart 2. Reading off the value of the curve at $t = 80$ ms gives a value of $+0.15$ m/s. Repeating this procedure for cart 2, I obtain a value of $+0.60$ m/s. Now I can determine the velocities the carts would have had at $t = 80$ ms if the collision had not taken place. As the graph shows, however, the carts do collide and their velocities at $t = 80$ ms are interchanged. The magnitudes of the changes in velocity caused by the collision are thus 0.45 m/s and 0.45 m/s. These velocity changes are equal in magnitude. ✔

❹ **EVALUATE RESULT** Extrapolation of the velocity curves in Figure 4.11 shows that the collision interchanges the velocities of the two carts, just as in a collision between identical carts in the absence of friction. The interchanging means that the changes in velocity must be of equal magnitude, as I found numerically.

As this example shows, the magnitude of the changes in velocity in a collision is the same even in the presence of friction. This means that even in the presence of friction, we can determine an object's inertia from the magnitude of the velocity changes in a collision.

4.4 Systems

In the preceding chapters we were always concerned with just a single object—a puck, a car, and so on. Starting with this chapter, however, most situations we encounter deal with any number of objects that interact with one another. To analyze such situations, we shall usually focus on one or more principal objects—a person climbing a mountain, two carts colliding, gas atoms in a container. The first step in any analysis therefore is to separate the object(s) of interest from the rest of the universe:

> **Any object or group of objects that we can separate, in our minds, from the surrounding environment is a system.**

For example, when considering a collision between two carts on a low-friction track, we might consider both carts together as the system. When someone throws a ball and we are interested in only the motion of the ball, a logical choice of system might be just the ball by itself. Once we have chosen the ball as our system, everything else—the thrower, the air around the ball, Earth—is outside the system and constitutes its **environment**. This imaginary separation of the universe into two parts—objects within the system and everything in the rest of the universe—makes it possible to develop simple but powerful accounting procedures.

When solving problems, you should imagine a boundary enclosing the objects of interest. What is inside this well-defined boundary constitutes your system and what is outside is the environment. The region of space enclosed in the system boundary may be quite large and contain within it a great many processes or activities, or it may be very small and contain an inert piece of material undergoing no change. The precise shape of the system boundary

Figure 4.12 Two choices of system for carts colliding on a track.

(a) Choice 1: system consists of both carts

(b) Choice 2: system consists of one cart

is unimportant; what counts is that it clearly separates the objects inside the system from those outside. To make this separation explicit, it will generally be helpful to make a pictorial representation of the objects within the system. In your sketch, you should draw a boundary around the objects that constitute your system.

There may be more than one way to separate the system and the environment in any given situation. For two carts colliding on a low-friction track, as illustrated in **Figure 4.12**, we can define our system as containing both carts (in which case the track is part of the environment) or just one cart (in which case the track and the other cart are part of the environment). Deciding what to include in the system will be dictated by the information you wish to learn. Often the choice is obvious; sometimes you will need to rely on experience to make this decision. More important, once you decide to include a certain object in the system, *it must stay that way throughout the analysis.* Failing to make a consistent choice of system is a frequent source of error.

Exercise 4.2 Choosing a system

Indicate at least two possible choices of system in each of the following two situations. For each choice, make a sketch showing the system boundary and state which objects are inside the system and which are outside. (a) After you throw a ball upward, it accelerates downward toward Earth. (b) A battery is connected to a light bulb that illuminates a room.

SOLUTION (a) The description of the situation mentions three objects: the ball, Earth, and you. One option is to include all three of them in the system (**Figure 4.13a**). As a second choice, I include you and the ball in the system (Figure 4.13b). ✔

Figure 4.13

(b) Again I have three objects: the battery, the light bulb, and the room. I can choose just one of them—the battery—as my system (**Figure 4.14a**) or two of them—the battery and the light bulb (Figure 4.14b). ✔

Figure 4.14

(a)   (b)

Note that my choices of system are arbitrary. Nothing in the problem prescribes the choice of system. If you tried this problem on your own before looking at my solution and you made different choices, then your answer is just as "correct" as mine!

Defining a system tells us nothing whatsoever about what is happening within it. It is simply a tool to help us set up an accounting scheme. Once we have chosen a system, we can study how certain quantities associated with the system change over time by determining the value of these quantities at the beginning and end of a time interval.

We shall in particular be interested in **extensive quantities**—that is, quantities whose value is proportional to the size or "extent" of the system. More specifically, if we divide the system into a number of pieces, then the sum of an extensive quantity for all the separate pieces is equal to the value of that quantity for the entire system. The number of trees in a park, for example, is extensive: If we divide the park into two parts and add the number of trees in each part, then we obtain the number of trees in the park. The price per gallon of gasoline is not an extensive quantity: If we divide a tankful of gas into two parts and add the price per gallon for the two parts, then we obtain twice the price per gallon for the entire tank. Quantities that do not depend on the extent of the system are **intensive quantities.**

✋ **4.7** Are the following quantities extensive or intensive: (a) inertia, (b) velocity, (c) the product of inertia and velocity?

Only four processes can change the value of an extensive quantity: input, output, creation, and destruction. To see this, consider **Figure 4.15**, which schematically represents a park's initial and final conditions over a certain time interval. The edge of the park is the system boundary, and

Figure 4.15 System diagram of a park. The number of trees in the park is an extensive quantity.

the park itself—trees and all—is the system. Diagrams that show a system's initial and final conditions are called **system diagrams;** we shall use such diagrams throughout this book. The change in the number of trees over the time interval is given by

change = final tree count − initial tree count.

The number of trees can change because new trees grow (creation) and old trees die or are taken down (destruction). Alternatively, new trees can be brought into the park (input) and some trees can be moved out of the park (output):

change = input − output + creation − destruction.

This equation is illustrated graphically in **Figure 4.16a**. If we understand how these four processes affect the trees, we can explain (or predict) any change in their number.

The accounting is often simplified by constraints put on the system. For example, if we build a fence around the park so that no trees can be transported into or out of the park, then the number of trees can change only because of creation and destruction. If there is no transfer of the extensive quantity under consideration across the boundary of the system, the change in that property can be due to only creation and destruction (Figure 4.16b):

change = creation − destruction.

Under certain circumstances we can also exclude creation and destruction. Suppose, for example, that we are counting the number of indestructible benches in the park rather than trees. The number of these benches changes only when benches are transported into or out of the park across the park boundary (unless there is a factory making indestructible benches in the park—an unlikely assumption). Any extensive quantity that cannot be created or destroyed is said to be **conserved.** The value of a

Figure 4.16 The effect of input, output, creation, and destruction on the extensive quantities of a system.

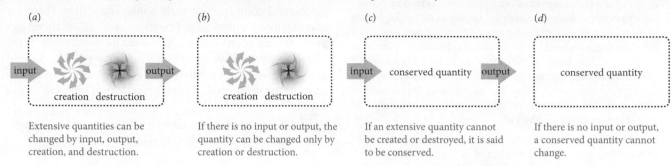

(a)

Extensive quantities can be changed by input, output, creation, and destruction.

(b)

If there is no input or output, the quantity can be changed only by creation or destruction.

(c)

If an extensive quantity cannot be created or destroyed, it is said to be conserved.

(d)

If there is no input or output, a conserved quantity cannot change.

conserved quantity can change only due to transfer of that quantity across the system boundary (Figure 4.16c):

$$\text{change} = \text{input} - \text{output}.$$

For a conserved quantity in a system for which there is no transfer, things are even more simple: Its value cannot change at all (Figure 4.16d). Conserved quantities play an important role in physics because their accounting is greatly simplified. In systems for which there is no transfer of a conserved quantity across the system boundary, this quantity does not change *regardless of the processes occurring inside or outside the system* (see the box "Conservation").

Conservation

Imagine a sheet of paper of width a and length b. The circumference of this sheet is $2a + 2b$, and the surface area of one side is ab. Suppose we cut the sheet lengthwise into two equal parts. Are there any quantities that are unchanged by the cutting?

Circumference is not a conserved quantity: The sum of the circumferences of the two parts is not equal to the circumference of the single sheet. The circumference of each cut piece is $2(\frac{1}{2}a) + 2b$, and the combined circumference of the two pieces is $2(a + 2b)$, whereas the original circumference was $2(a + b)$.

Surface area is conserved: The surface area of each cut piece is $\frac{1}{2}ab$, and so the sum of the surface areas of the two pieces is ab, exactly as it was before we cut up the sheet.

Trivial? Well, suppose that instead of cutting the sheet in two, we cut it into 148 equal pieces. Can we say anything about the sum of the circumferences? Not without some brainwork! Conservation of surface area, on the other hand, allows us to state—with no calculations whatsoever—that the sum of the surface areas of all the pieces is still ab.

We have found a conserved quantity: surface area! No matter in how many pieces a sheet of paper is cut, the sum of the surface areas of the pieces is equal to the surface area of the original sheet.

If you are a skeptic (and in science you should always be skeptical), you could calculate the surface area of one of the 148 pieces and verify that the sum of the surface areas of all the pieces is indeed ab. To convince yourself that conservation of surface area is a general law, you might also want to repeat this procedure for a few more cases—say, 79 and 237 pieces.

Once you are convinced, however, it is easy to see the value of the conservation law. Suppose that instead of cutting the sheet neatly into equal pieces, someone tears it into ragged pieces, hands them to you, and asks, "What is the combined surface area of all of these pieces?" Even though an actual determination of the surface area would be difficult at best, you would answer, without hesitation, "ab"!

The idea that certain quantities are unaffected by events is appealing, not only because the notion of conservation intuitively makes sense (*some* things must remain unchanged) but also because it provides simple constraints on the behavior of a system.

Is surface area truly conserved? The answer is *no*: you can burn the sheet and make the entire surface area disappear. As we shall see, only a few quantities are truly conserved.

Exercise 4.3 Accounting principles

(a) Classify and give examples of the kinds of processes that can change (i) the number of loaves of bread in a bakery, (ii) the number of Lego pieces inside a house, and (iii) the number of coins in a safe that remains locked. (b) For each of these three cases, what is the system? Is the transfer of the quantity of interest across the system boundary possible? Is the quantity of interest conserved?

SOLUTION (a) (i) Input: a delivery of loaves of bread to the bakery; output: customers leaving the bakery with loaves they purchased; creation: the baking of a batch of loaves; destruction: the eating of loaves by patrons (inside the bakery; destruction outside the bakery falls under "output" because the loaves first leave the bakery). (ii) Input: Lego pieces are brought into the house;

CONCEPTS

output: Lego pieces are taken out of the house; creation: assuming there is no manufacturing of Lego pieces in the house, there is no creation; destruction: for all practical purposes, I can consider the Lego pieces to be indestructible and so there is no destruction. (*iii*) Input: if the safe is locked it's impossible to add coins, so the input is zero; output: zero, too; creation: zero; destruction: zero. (Everything is zero, meaning the number of coins can't change inside a locked safe—which is precisely why people put valuables in safes!) ✔

(*b*) (*i*) The bakery and its contents make up the system. Loaves of bread can be taken into and out of the bakery, so transfer is possible. The number of loaves of bread is not conserved because loaves can be created and destroyed. (*ii*) The house and its contents are the system. Lego pieces can be taken into and out of it, so transfer is possible. Assuming that the Lego pieces cannot be fabricated or destroyed, I can consider their number to be conserved in this problem. (*iii*) The safe and its contents are the system. The safe remains locked so nothing can be put into it or taken out, and so transfer is not possible. Coins cannot be made or destroyed, so their number is conserved. ✔

Strictly speaking, indestructible benches in a park, Lego pieces, and coins are not truly conserved—all of them are manufactured somewhere (creation) and all of them can be destroyed (destruction). You may be wondering, then, whether *anything* is conserved. The answer is yes: Several quantities we shall encounter are conserved, giving rise to some of the most fundamental principles in physics.

4.8 Which of these quantities is extensive? (*a*) money, (*b*) temperature, (*c*) humidity, (*d*) volume.

Self-quiz

1. Two carts give the same velocity-versus-time graphs when they collide with the same standard cart. Can you conclude from this information that the two carts are identical?

2. The graphs in **Figures 4.17a** and 4.17b show the effects of carts A and B colliding (separately) with a standard cart S. List the three carts in order of increasing inertia.

Figure 4.17

3. The graphs in Figures 4.17c and 4.17d show the effects of carts A and B colliding (separately) with a standard cart S. Which has greater inertia, A or B?

4. You do not know whether or not carts A and B of question 3 are made of the same material. Can you tell from the graphs which cart contains a larger quantity of material?

5. Imagine accounting for the number of cattle on a ranch. What do you choose as your system? What are the processes corresponding to input, output, creation, and destruction? Is transfer into and out of the system possible? Is the accountable quantity conserved?

Answers

1. No. Although the identical graphs tell you that the two carts have identical inertias, they need not be identical physically. A large plastic cart, for instance, can have the same inertia as a much smaller metal cart.

2. A and B (identical and less), S (greater). Because the magnitude of the velocity change for S is smaller than that for either A or B, cart S must have greater inertia. The *ratio* of the magnitudes of the velocity changes is about the same in both graphs, however, indicating that A and B have about the same inertias.

3. B. Don't be fooled by the bigger velocity change for S in part *c*; you must first consider each graph separately. Graph *c* tells you that A has less inertia than S because the magnitude of the velocity change for A is *larger* than that for S. Graph *d* tells you that B has greater inertia than S because the magnitude of the velocity change for B is *smaller* than that for S. Hence B must have greater inertia than A.

4. No. Although B has greater inertia, you cannot conclude anything about the quantity of material in it relative to A because you don't know from what materials the two carts are made.

5. The ranch is the system. Input: cattle transported into the ranch; output: cattle transported out of the ranch; creation: cattle born on the ranch; destruction: cattle expiring on the ranch. Transfer is possible because there is input and output, and the number of cattle is not conserved because cattle can be created and destroyed.

This replica of the standard kilogram is kept under two evacuated glass jars at the National Research Laboratory of Metrology in Japan. It is compared once every thirty years against the original international standard kept in France.

4.5 Inertial standard

The inertia of an object is represented by the symbol m (m is for *mass*, a concept that is related to inertia and that we shall examine later on). We shall use the term *inertia* rather than *mass* to underscore the physical meaning of this concept: An object's resistance to a change in its velocity. Inertia is a scalar, which means it does not depend on the orientation of any axis in space. By international agreement, the inertial standard is a platinum-iridium cylinder stored at the International Bureau of Weights and Measures in Sèvres, France. The inertia of this standard is defined as one **kilogram,** the basic SI unit of inertia ($m_s \equiv 1$ kg).*

Armed with a replica of this inertial standard and the knowledge gained in Sections 4.1 through 4.3, we can determine the inertia m of any other object. To do so, we make the object we are studying collide with the inertial standard and then measure the changes in velocity. In Section 4.2, we defined the ratio of the inertias of two colliding objects as the inverse of the ratio of the magnitude of their velocity changes, and so we can use this ratio for our inertial standard and our object of unknown inertia:

$$\frac{m_u}{m_s} \equiv -\frac{\Delta v_{sx}}{\Delta v_{ux}} \tag{4.1}$$

or

$$m_u \equiv -\frac{\Delta v_{sx}}{\Delta v_{ux}} m_s. \tag{4.2}$$

Why the minus sign? Well, suppose the object of unknown inertia is a replica of the standard. The left side of Eq. 4.1 then becomes $m_s/m_s = 1$. From the collision in Figure 4.5, we know, however, that the velocity of one of the carts increases (positive Δv_x) while that of the other decreases by the same amount (negative Δv_x). Without the minus sign, Eq. 4.1 would therefore become $1 = -1$. Notice that in all collisions we considered (Figures 4.5 through 4.9), the x components of the velocity change for the two colliding objects have opposite signs. Because this is true for *all* collisions, the minus sign in Eq. 4.1, the defining equation for inertia, means inertia is always a *positive* quantity.

In principle, this simple procedure makes it possible to determine the inertia of any object. Substituting the value $m_s \equiv 1$ kg in Eq. 4.2 allows us to determine the inertia of any other object in kilograms. In practice, it may not be a good idea to let objects collide in order to determine their inertia. (I don't recommend determining the inertia of a Ming vase in this way!) In Chapter 13 we shall discuss equivalent but more practical ways to determine the inertia of objects.

Example 4.4 Determining the inertia of a stone

A small stone is fastened to the top of a standard cart of inertia 1 kg to form a combination of unknown inertia m_u. A second standard cart is then launched with an initial velocity given by $v_{sx,i} = +0.46$ m/s toward the combination that is initially at rest. After the collision, the x component of the velocity of the cart with the stone is $v_{ux,f} = +0.38$ m/s and that of the standard cart is $v_{sx,f} = -0.08$ m/s. What is the inertia of the stone?

❶ **GETTING STARTED** This collision is much like the one depicted in Figure 4.7 with a standard cart moving toward a cart

of greater inertia that is initially at rest. The ratio of the carts' inertias follows from the ratio of the magnitude of their velocity changes.

❷ **DEVISE PLAN** To calculate the unknown inertia m_u, I can use Eq. 4.2. I know the x components of the two carts' initial and final velocities, so all the quantities on the right side of the equation are known.

---

*You may associate the unit kilogram with *weight,* a physical property that has to do with gravitation rather than inertia. More about the concept of weight in Chapter 13.

③ **EXECUTE PLAN** I begin by determining the changes in the x components of the velocity for each cart. For the cart with the stone, $\Delta v_{ux} = v_{ux,f} - v_{ux,i} = +0.38 \text{ m/s} - 0 = +0.38 \text{ m/s}$; for the standard cart $\Delta v_{sx} = v_{sx,f} - v_{sx,i} = -0.08 \text{ m/s} - 0.46 \text{ m/s} = -0.54 \text{ m/s}$. Substituting these values into Eq. 4.2, I get

$$m_u = -\frac{\Delta v_{sx}}{\Delta v_{ux}} m_s = -\frac{-0.54 \text{ m/s}}{+0.38 \text{ m/s}} (1 \text{ kg}) = 1.4 \text{ kg}.$$

This represents the inertia of the stone and the cart as one unit. Given that the inertia of the standard cart is 1 kg, the inertia of the stone must be 0.4 kg. ✔

④ **EVALUATE RESULT** The inertia of the cart-and-stone combination is greater than 1 kg, as I would expect. If the magnitude of the velocity change of this combination were half that of the standard cart ($\frac{1}{2}(0.54 \text{ m/s}) = 0.27 \text{ m/s}$), then the inertia of the cart-and-stone combination would be twice that of a standard cart, and so the inertia of the stone would be 1.0 kg. The magnitude of the velocity change is more than half, so I should expect the stone's inertia to be less than 1.0 kg, which agrees with the answer I found.

✋ **4.9** (*a*) Suppose that instead of a replica of the platinum-iridium cylinder kept in France, we had chosen another object as our inertial standard and defined the inertia of that object as being exactly equal to 1 kg. Would the inertia of our unknown object as measured against the new standard be different from that object's inertia measured against the French standard? (*b*) Would the outcome of a collision between two arbitrary objects be different?

4.6 Momentum

Our definition of inertia leads to the definition of another important physical quantity: *momentum*. Let's rewrite Eq. 4.2 in a slightly different form by multiplying both sides by Δv_{ux} and then bringing all terms to the left side:

$$m_u \Delta v_{ux} + m_s \Delta v_{sx} = 0. \tag{4.3}$$

Because the changes in velocity Δv_x can be written in the form $v_{x,f} - v_{x,i}$, we can rewrite this equation as

$$m_u(v_{ux,f} - v_{ux,i}) + m_s(v_{sx,f} - v_{sx,i}) = 0 \tag{4.4}$$

or

$$m_u v_{ux,f} - m_u v_{ux,i} + m_s v_{sx,f} - m_s v_{sx,i} = 0. \tag{4.5}$$

This form of Eq. 4.3, which contains nothing but products of inertias and velocities, is important because it suggests something new. The product of the inertia and the velocity of an object is called the **momentum** (plural: *momenta*) of that object. The conventional symbol for momentum is p, and so we can write

$$\vec{p} \equiv m\vec{v}. \tag{4.6}$$

As you learned in Section 2.6, the product of a vector and a scalar is a vector. Because inertia is a scalar and velocity is a vector, momentum is a vector. The direction of the momentum vector for any object is the same as the direction of the object's velocity vector. The x component of the momentum is the product of the inertia and the x component of the velocity:

$$p_x \equiv m v_x. \tag{4.7}$$

The SI units of momentum are the units of the product mv: $\text{kg} \cdot \text{m/s}$. For example, the magnitude of the momentum of an object of inertia 1 kg moving at a speed of 1 m/s is $1 \text{ kg} \cdot \text{m/s}$. Inertia is an intrinsic property of an object (you can't change it without changing the object), but the value of the momentum of that object, like its velocity, can change.

Example 4.5 Bullet and bowling ball

Compare the magnitude of the momenta of a 0.010-kg bullet fired from a rifle at 1300 m/s and a 6.5-kg bowling ball lumbering across the floor at 4.0 m/s.

❶ GETTING STARTED Momentum is the product of inertia and velocity. I have to calculate this quantity for both the bullet and the bowling ball and then compare the resulting values.

❷ DEVISE PLAN Equation 4.6 gives the momentum of an object. To determine the magnitude of the momentum of an object, I must take the product of the inertia m and the speed v: $p = mv$.

❸ EXECUTE PLAN Substituting the values given in the problem statement, I get

$$p_{bullet} = (0.010 \text{ kg})(1300 \text{ m/s}) = 13 \text{ kg} \cdot \text{m/s} \checkmark$$

$$p_{bowling} = (6.5 \text{ kg})(4.0 \text{ m/s}) = 26 \text{ kg} \cdot \text{m/s}. \checkmark$$

❹ EVALUATE RESULT Surprisingly, the magnitudes of the momenta are very close! I have no way of evaluating momenta because I don't have much experience yet with this quantity. However, the bullet has less inertia and a high speed and the bowling ball has greater inertia and a low speed, so it is not unreasonable that the product of these quantities is similar.

Momentum is a quantitative measure of "matter in motion" and depends on both the amount of matter in motion and how fast that matter is moving. Momentum is very different from inertia. A truck, for example, has greater inertia than a fly (it has a higher resistance to a change in its velocity), but if the truck is at rest and the fly is in motion, then the magnitude of the fly's momentum is larger than that of the truck, which is zero. In Example 4.5, the inertias of the bullet and the bowling ball are very different, yet their momenta are similar. Conceptually you can think of an object's momentum as its capacity to affect the motion of other objects in a collision.

With the definition of momentum, we can rewrite Eq. 4.5 in the form

$$p_{ux,f} - p_{ux,i} + p_{sx,f} - p_{sx,i} = 0. \tag{4.8}$$

If we write $\Delta p_{ux} \equiv p_{ux,f} - p_{ux,i}$ and $\Delta p_{sx} \equiv p_{sx,f} - p_{sx,i}$, Eq. 4.8 takes on the beautifully simple form

$$\Delta p_{ux} + \Delta p_{sx} = 0. \tag{4.9}$$

This equation means that, whenever an object of unknown inertia collides with the inertial standard, the changes in the x components of the momenta of the two objects add up to zero. In other words, the change in the x component of the momentum for one object is always the negative of the change for the other.

Example 4.6 Collisions and momentum changes

(a) A red cart with an initial speed of 0.35 m/s collides with a stationary standard cart ($m_s = 1.0$ kg). After the collision, the standard cart moves away at a speed of 0.38 m/s. What is the momentum change for each cart? (b) The experiment is repeated with a blue cart, and now the final speed of the standard cart is 0.31 m/s. What is the momentum change for each cart in this second collision? (c) If in the collisions $v_{rx,f} = +0.032$ m/s and $v_{bx,f} = -0.039$ m/s, what are the inertias of the red and the blue carts?

❶ GETTING STARTED I begin organizing the information given in the problem in a picture by showing the initial and final conditions for each of the two collisions (**Figure 4.18**).

Figure 4.18

(a)

(b)

❷ **DEVISE PLAN** In each collision, I know the inertia and the x components of the initial and final velocities of the standard cart, so I can readily determine the change in the x component of its momentum. To determine the change in momentum for the other carts, I can then use Eq. 4.9, which tells me that for each collision the changes in the x components of the momenta of the two carts must add up to zero. For part c, I can use Eq. 4.7 together with the values for the red and blue carts' initial and final velocities and their changes in momenta calculated in parts a and b to determine the inertias.

❸ **EXECUTE PLAN** (a) Because it initially is at rest, the standard cart's initial momentum is zero. The x component of its final momentum is $p_{sx,f} = (1.0\ \text{kg})(+0.38\ \text{m/s}) = +0.38\ \text{kg}\cdot\text{m/s}$, and so the x component of its change in momentum is

$$\Delta p_{sx} = +0.38\ \text{kg}\cdot\text{m/s} - 0 = +0.38\ \text{kg}\cdot\text{m/s}. ✔$$

Because the x components of the momentum changes of the two carts must add up to zero (Eq. 4.9), the corresponding x component of the red cart's momentum change is $\Delta p_{rx} = -0.38\ \text{kg}\cdot\text{m/s}. ✔$

(b) Applying the same procedure for this second collision, I get

$$\Delta p_{sx} = (1.0\ \text{kg})(+0.31\ \text{m/s}) - 0 = +0.31\ \text{kg}\cdot\text{m/s};$$

$$\Delta p_{bx} = -0.31\ \text{kg}\cdot\text{m/s}. ✔$$

(c) The change in momentum for the red cart is $\Delta p_{rx} = p_{rx,f} - p_{rx,i}$. Using Eq. 4.7, I can write this change in momentum as

$$\Delta p_{rx} = m_r v_{rx,f} - m_r v_{rx,i} = m_r(v_{rx,f} - v_{rx,i})$$

and so

$$m_r = \frac{\Delta p_{rx}}{v_{rx,f} - v_{rx,i}} = \frac{-0.38\ \text{kg}\cdot\text{m/s}}{+0.032\ \text{m/s} - 0.35\ \text{m/s}}$$

$$= 1.2\ \text{kg}. ✔$$

Likewise, for the blue cart:

$$m_b = \frac{\Delta p_{b,x}}{v_{bx,f} - v_{bx,i}} = \frac{-0.31\ \text{kg}\cdot\text{m/s}}{-0.039\ \text{m/s} - 0.35\ \text{m/s}}$$

$$= 0.80\ \text{kg}. ✔$$

❹ **EVALUATE RESULT** If either the red or the blue cart had an inertia of 1.0 kg, then the cart would come to rest in the collision. My work shows that the inertia of the red cart is greater than that of a standard cart. Indeed, after the collision it still moves in the same direction it initially moved, as it should for a cart of greater inertia colliding with one of lesser inertia (see, for example, Figure 4.8). In contrast, the inertia of the blue cart is less than that of the standard cart. After the collision it bounces back and travels in the opposite direction, as I would expect (see Figure 4.7).

Equation 4.9 can be written in vectorial form:

$$\Delta \vec{p}_u + \Delta \vec{p}_s = \vec{0} \tag{4.10}$$

and so, in a collision between an object of unknown inertia and the inertial standard, the changes in the momenta of the two objects add to zero.

✋ **4.10** In part a of Example 4.6, what are the directions of the changes in momentum, $\Delta \vec{p}_s$ and $\Delta \vec{p}_r$, of the two carts?

4.7 Isolated systems

As we saw in Checkpoint 4.7, momentum is an extensive property—you can add up the momenta of all the objects in a system to obtain the *momentum of the system*. In particular, the momentum of a system of two moving carts is the sum of the momenta of the two individual carts:

$$\vec{p} \equiv \vec{p}_1 + \vec{p}_2. \tag{4.11}$$

With this definition we can begin to develop an accounting scheme for the momentum of a system. In particular, we shall be interested in determining what causes the momentum of a system to change. Let us begin by reexamining a number of situations we have encountered. In **Figure 4.19a** a puck slides to a stop on a wood floor. In Figure 4.19b a cart moves at constant velocity on a low-friction track. In Figure 4.19c a standard cart collides with another cart on a low-friction track, and in Figure 4.19d someone gives a cart moving at constant

Figure 4.19 Velocity-versus-time and acceleration-versus-time graphs for four situations. The shading indicates nonzero acceleration.

(a) Puck slows to a halt

(b) Cart moves at constant velocity

(c) Standard cart collides with cart of unknown inertia

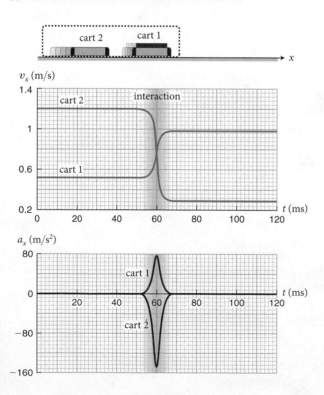

(d) Cart moving at constant velocity is given a shove

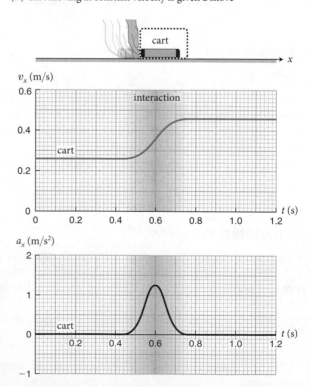

Table 4.2 Interactions and momentum changes in Checkpoint 4.11

Situation	Interacting objects	System	System interacting?	$\Delta\vec{p}$
a	floor ↔ puck	puck	yes	nonzero
b	none	cart	no	$\vec{0}$
c	cart 1 ↔ cart 2	cart 1	yes	nonzero
d	cart 1 ↔ cart 2	carts 1 & 2	no	$\vec{0}$
e	hand ↔ cart	cart	yes	nonzero

velocity on a low-friction track a shove. In some cases the velocity (and therefore the momentum) remains constant; in others it changes.

4.11 Is the change in the momentum $\Delta\vec{p}$ zero or nonzero for the following choices of system over the 120-ms time interval in Figure 4.19: (*a*) puck in Figure 4.19*a*, (*b*) cart in Figure 4.19*b*, (*c*) cart 1 in Figure 4.19*c*, (*d*) both carts in Figure 4.19*c*, (*e*) cart in Figure 4.19*d*?

In the graphs, I have highlighted the time intervals during which the acceleration of objects within the system is nonzero—that is, the time interval when the velocity and therefore the momentum of objects within the system change. Notice that this time interval always coincides with the time interval during which the object under consideration *interacts* with something else. In Figure 4.19*a* the puck slows down because the puck and the floor rub against (interact with) each other, in Figure 4.19*c* the two carts collide with (interact with) each other, and in Figure 4.19*d* the cart and the hand interact with each other. Conversely, in Figure 4.19*b* the interaction between the track and the cart has been virtually eliminated by reducing friction, and so the acceleration is zero.

In these examples, *interaction* refers to objects touching or rubbing against each other. Interactions are the subject in Chapter 7. For now, we'll use the word *interaction* to mean two objects acting on each other in such a way that one or both are accelerated.

Table 4.2 summarizes the observations from Checkpoint 4.11. Note that whenever the system interacts with something outside the system, the momentum of the system changes. Interactions across the boundary of a system are called *external interactions*. Interactions between two objects inside the system are called *internal interactions*. Looking at Figure 4.19 and Table 4.2, we see that external interactions transfer momentum into or out of the system.

A system for which there are no external interactions is said to be **isolated**. For such a system there is no input or output of momentum, and so the momentum of the system does not change: $\Delta\vec{p} = \vec{0}$. In Figure 4.19*b*, the cart's motion is not influenced by the track, and so the cart constitutes an isolated system. In Figure 4.19*c*, the two carts interact with each other but not with anything outside the system, and so the two carts together constitute a system that is isolated (but either cart by itself does not; see **Table 4.3**). In Figures 4.19*a* and 4.19*d*, where

Table 4.3 Two choices of system for carts colliding

	Choice 1	Choice 2
System:	carts 1 & 2	cart 1
Environment:	track	cart 2 & track
Interactions:	internal	external
System isolated?	yes	no
Momentum changing?	no	yes

Figure 4.20 The choice of system determines whether the interactions in question are internal or external and hence whether the system is isolated or not. We use the symbol ⓟ to denote an isolated system, indicating that no momentum crosses the system's boundary.

(*a*) Choice 1: system = both carts

Interaction is *internal* to system . . .

. . . so system is isolated.

(*b*) Choice 2: system = cart 1

Interaction is *external* (crosses system boundary), so system is not isolated.

$\Delta \vec{p} \neq \vec{0}$, the system is not isolated. In Figure 4.19*a* the only object in the system (the puck) interacts with the floor, which is outside the system. In Figure 4.19*d*, the only object in the system (the cart) interacts with the hand, which is outside the system.

Figure 4.20 and Table 4.3 illustrate two system choices for studying a collision. The system containing both carts is isolated (the interaction between the two carts takes place inside the system; it is an internal interaction), and the momentum of the system is constant. The system containing just cart 1 is not isolated because it interacts with cart 2, which is now part of the environment, and the momentum of the system is not constant.

In isolated systems the analysis of momentum is simplified because we can concentrate on what happens inside the system. The procedure for choosing an isolated system is shown in the Procedure box on the next page and illustrated for a collision between two carts on a low-friction track in **Figure 4.21**. We begin by separating from one another all the objects that could play a role: the carts, the track, and the air. Next we identify all possible interactions: the collision between the two carts, the interaction between the air and the carts, and any possible interaction between the track and the carts. We know that each cart by itself rolls without slowing down on the track, so the interaction between the track and the carts and between the air and the carts does not have any significant effect on the carts' velocity. We therefore eliminate these and retain only the collision between the carts, which does change their velocities.*

Having eliminated all but the interaction between the carts, we can choose an isolated system by enclosing the two carts so that this interaction becomes internal. Finally, we complete the procedure by making a system diagram, showing the initial and final conditions of the isolated system (before and after the collision). In general, the interaction between two colliding objects affects their motion much more strongly than any other interaction, and so we can for all practical purposes always consider the system of two colliding objects to be isolated.

Figure 4.21 Applying the procedure for choosing an isolated system (see the Procedure box) to the collision between two carts on a low-friction track.

*Leaving out the air-cart and track-cart interactions is a simplification, because both *do* have a small effect on the carts' acceleration. However, you can ignore the effects of the these interactions because they are so much smaller than the effects of the collision. Never be afraid to make a simplifying assumption; you can always return to the beginning of a problem and refine your assumptions.

Procedure: Choosing an isolated system

When you analyze momentum changes in a problem, it is convenient to choose a system for which no momentum is transferred into or out of the system (an isolated system). To do so, follow these steps:

1. Separate all objects named in the problem from one another.
2. Identify all possible interactions among these objects and between these objects and their environment (the air, Earth, etc.).
3. Consider each interaction individually and determine whether it causes the interacting objects to accelerate. Eliminate any interaction that does not affect (or has only a negligible effect on) the objects' accelerations during the time interval of interest.
4. Choose a system that includes the object or objects that are the subject of the problem (for example, a cart whose momentum you are interested in) in such a way that none of the remaining interactions cross the system boundary. Draw a dashed line around the objects in your choice of system to represent the system boundary. None of the remaining interactions should cross this line.
5. Make a system diagram showing the initial and final states of the system and its environment.

Exercise 4.7 Who's pulling whom?

A person standing on a skateboard on horizontal ground pulls on a rope fastened to a cart. Both the person and the cart are initially at rest. Use the Procedure box to identify an isolated system and make a system diagram.

SOLUTION See **Figure 4.22**. I begin by separating the objects in the problem: the person, the cart, and Earth. (I could always go into more detail—include the air, the rope, and the skateboard—but it pays to keep things as simple as possible. For that reason, I consider the skateboard to be part of the person and the rope to be part of the cart.) The cart interacts with Earth and the person; the person interacts with the cart and Earth. Ignoring friction in the wheels of the cart, I know that the interaction between the cart and Earth has no effect on any motion, and so I can eliminate it from the analysis. The same holds for the interaction between the person (the skateboard) and Earth. I then draw a boundary around the person and the cart, making the interaction between the two internal. Because there are no external interactions, this system is isolated. Finally I draw a system diagram showing the initial and final conditions of the system with the person and cart initially at rest and then moving. ✔

Figure 4.22

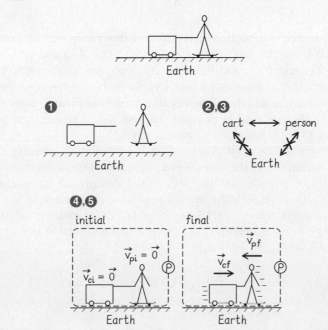

4.12 Imagine sitting on a sled on the slippery surface of a frozen lake. To reposition yourself closer to the back of the sled, you push with your legs against the front end. (*a*) Do you constitute an isolated system? (*b*) How about you and the sled? Ignore the interaction between sled and ice.

4.8 Conservation of momentum

In Section 4.4 we saw that the change in an extensive property can be due to transport into or out of the system and to creation or destruction. In Section 4.7 we saw that whenever we consider a system that is isolated, the momentum of the system is not changing:

$$\Delta \vec{p} = \vec{0} \quad \text{(isolated system)}. \tag{4.12}$$

You may be tempted to conclude from this observation that momentum is conserved. All we can conclude, however, is that there is no creation or destruction of momentum *inside the systems we considered*—not that it is impossible to create or destroy momentum under any circumstances.

Because it is a direct consequence of the definition of momentum, Eq. 4.10 must—by definition—hold for *any* object that collides with the inertial standard. So if we take any two objects 1 and 2 and let each collide with the inertial standard on a level, low-friction track, we *always* obtain—no matter how we vary the initial velocities and no matter what the values of inertias m_1 and m_2 are—that

$$\Delta \vec{p}_1 + \Delta \vec{p}_s = \vec{0} \quad \text{(by definition)} \tag{4.13}$$

and

$$\Delta \vec{p}_2 + \Delta \vec{p}_s = \vec{0} \quad \text{(by definition)}. \tag{4.14}$$

Suppose now that, instead of making objects 1 and 2 collide with the inertial standard, we make them collide with each other. Should we expect to obtain

$$\Delta \vec{p}_1 + \Delta \vec{p}_2 = \vec{0}? \tag{4.15}$$

You may be tempted to think that this equation follows from our earlier observations, but that is not the case. The value of $\Delta \vec{p}_s$ in Eqs. 4.13 and 4.14 need not be the same because Δv_{sx}, and therefore $\Delta \vec{p}_s$, vary from collision to collision (compare, for instance, Figures 4.8 and 4.9). So each of these equations holds for a separate collision and therefore we cannot combine them to draw any conclusions about the relationship between $\Delta \vec{p}_1$ and $\Delta \vec{p}_2$. The only way to verify whether Eq. 4.15 holds is to do the measurement.

Figure 4.23 shows the graphs for a collision between two arbitrary carts. To get the momentum values shown in Figure 4.23*b*, I multiplied the *x* component of the velocity of each cart by the cart's inertia determined by *independently* letting each cart collide with the inertial standard. The change in the *x* component of the momentum of cart 1 can be obtained by multiplying its inertia ($m_1 = 0.36$ kg) with the *x* components of the initial and final velocities read off from Figure 4.23*a* ($v_{1x,i} = 0$ and $v_{1x,f} = +0.17$ m/s):

$$\Delta p_{1x} = m_1(v_{1x,f} - v_{1x,i}) = (0.36 \text{ kg})(+0.17 \text{ m/s} - 0)$$

$$= 0.061 \text{ kg} \cdot \text{m/s}.$$

Figure 4.23 (*a*) Velocity-versus-time graph and (*b*) momentum-versus-time graph of two carts before and after the two collide on a low-friction track. The sum of the momenta is the same before and after the collision. The inertias are $m_1 = 0.36$ kg and $m_2 = 0.12$ kg.

For cart 2 we have $v_{2x,\text{i}} = +0.34$ m/s, $v_{2x,\text{f}} = -0.17$ m/s, and $m_2 = 0.12$ kg, so

$$\Delta p_{2x} = m_2(v_{2x,\text{f}} - v_{2x,\text{i}}) = (0.12 \text{ kg})(-0.17 \text{ m/s} - 0.34 \text{ m/s})$$

$$= -0.061 \text{ kg} \cdot \text{m/s}.$$

Because the two changes in momentum are equal in magnitude and of opposite sign, they add up to zero: $\Delta p_{1x} + \Delta p_{2x} = 0$. Consequently the momentum of the system comprising the two carts does not change:

$$\Delta \vec{p} \equiv \Delta \vec{p}_1 + \Delta \vec{p}_2 = \vec{0}. \tag{4.16}$$

Repeating the experiment with another pair of carts or changing the initial velocities always yields the same result: The momentum of the system comprising any two colliding objects is not changed by the collision. The collision merely transfers some momentum from one cart to the other—one gains a certain amount of momentum, and the other loses the same amount.

4.13 (*a*) How much momentum is transferred in the collisions in Figure 4.23? (*b*) Is this momentum transferred from cart 1 to cart 2, or in the opposite direction?

Experiments show that *any* interaction between two objects—not just collisions—transfers momentum from one object to the other. The sum of the momenta of the interacting objects, however, never changes. No interactions or other phenomena have ever been observed where momentum is created out of nothing or destroyed. We must therefore conclude that momentum is conserved:

Momentum can be transferred from one object to another, but it cannot be created or destroyed.

This statement is one of the most fundamental principles of physics and is often referred to as the **conservation of momentum.**

For an isolated system, conservation of momentum means

$$\Delta \vec{p} = \vec{0} \quad \text{(isolated system).} \tag{4.17}$$

For a system that is not isolated, we have

$$\Delta \vec{p} = \vec{J}, \qquad (4.18)$$

where $\vec{J}$ represents the transfer of momentum from the environment to the system. The quantity $\vec{J}$ is called the **impulse** delivered to the system. Like momentum, impulse is a vector and has SI units of kg $\cdot$ m/s. Depending on its direction relative to the momentum, the impulse can increase or decrease the magnitude of the momentum of the system. $\vec{J}$ therefore represents what we called "input" and "output" in Section 4.4.

✋ **4.14** (a) What is the magnitude of the impulse delivered to cart 1 in Figure 4.23? (b) Write the impulse delivered to cart 1 in vector form. (c) Does the fact that the change in the momentum of cart 1 is nonzero mean that momentum is not conserved?

Equation 4.18, which we shall use extensively throughout this book, is called the **momentum law.** This equation embodies conservation of momentum because it tells us that the momentum of a system can change only due to a transfer of momentum to the system ($\vec{J}$). If momentum were not conserved, then the right side of this equation would need to contain an additional term to account for changes in momentum due to the creation or destruction of momentum. For an isolated system the impulse is zero, $\vec{J} = \vec{0}$, and the momentum law takes on the form of Eq. 4.17.

Example 4.8 Bounce

A 0.20-kg rubber ball is dropped from a height of 1.0 m onto a hard floor and bounces straight up. Assuming the speed with which the ball rebounds from the floor is the same as the speed it has just before hitting the floor, determine the impulse delivered by the floor to the rubber ball.

❶ **GETTING STARTED** I define the ball to be my system in this problem. The impulse delivered to the ball is then given by the change in its momentum (Eq. 4.18). I need to develop a way to determine this change in momentum.

❷ **DEVISE PLAN** To solve this problem I need to first determine the velocity of the ball just before it hits the floor. I therefore break the problem into two parts: the downward fall of the ball and its collision with the floor. I can use Eq. 3.15 to determine the time interval it takes the ball to fall from its initial height (assuming the ball is initially at rest). As it falls, the ball undergoes constant acceleration, so I can use Eq. 3.10 to calculate its velocity just before it hits the floor and, because its speed is not changing as it rebounds, I also know its velocity after it bounces up. Knowing the velocities, I can calculate the ball's momentum before and after the bounce using Eq. 4.7. The change in momentum then gives the impulse according to Eq. 4.18.

❸ **EXECUTE PLAN** From Eq. 3.15 I see that it takes an object $t = \sqrt{2h/g} = \sqrt{2(1.0 \text{ m})/(9.8 \text{ m/s}^2)} = 0.45$ s to fall from a height of 1.0 m. Choosing the positive x axis pointing upward and substituting this result into Eq. 3.10, I obtain for the x component of the velocity of the ball just before it hits the floor:

$$v_{x,\mathrm{f}} = 0 + (-9.8 \text{ m/s}^2)(0.45 \text{ s})^2 = -2.0 \text{ m/s}.$$

Now that I know the ball's velocity just before it hits the ground I can obtain the x component of the momentum of the ball just

before it hits the ground by multiplying the ball's velocity by its inertia: $p_{x,\mathrm{i}} = (0.20 \text{ kg})(-2.0 \text{ m/s}) = -0.40$ kg $\cdot$ m/s. (I use the subscript i to indicate that this is the initial momentum of the ball before the collision with the floor.) If the ball rebounds with the same speed, then the x component of the momentum after the collision with the floor has the same magnitude but opposite sign: $p_{x,\mathrm{f}} = +0.40$ kg $\cdot$ m/s. The change in the ball's momentum is thus

$$\Delta p_x = p_{x,\mathrm{f}} - p_{x,\mathrm{i}} = +0.40 \text{ kg} \cdot \text{m/s} - (-0.40 \text{ kg} \cdot \text{m/s})$$

$$= +0.80 \text{ kg} \cdot \text{m/s}.$$

The interaction with the ground changes the momentum of the ball, making it rebound. The ball does not constitute an isolated system, and the change in its momentum is due to an impulse delivered by Earth to the ball. To determine the impulse, I substitute the change in momentum of the ball into Eq. 4.18:

$$\vec{J} = \Delta \vec{p} = \Delta p_x \hat{\imath} = (+0.80 \text{ kg} \cdot \text{m/s})\hat{\imath}. ✔$$

❹ **EVALUATE RESULT** The x component of the velocity of the ball just before it hits the floor is negative because the ball moves downward, in the negative x direction. After the collision it moves in the opposite direction, and consequently the x components of the changes in velocity and momentum are both positive, as I calculated. Because the x component of the change in the ball's momentum is positive, the impulse is directed upward (in the positive x direction). This makes sense because this impulse changes the direction of travel of the ball from downward to upward.

Because the momentum law takes on the simplest form for an isolated system, we shall usually try to choose an isolated system (unlike the above example). In such a case, we can write out the $\Delta \vec{p}$ term in Eq. 4.17:

$$\vec{p}_{\mathrm{f}} = \vec{p}_{\mathrm{i}} \quad \text{(isolated system)}. \tag{4.19}$$

In this form, the momentum law states that the initial and final values of the momentum of an isolated system are equal. For two colliding (or otherwise interacting) objects moving along the x axis, Eqs. 4.17 and 4.19 become

$$\Delta p_{1x} + \Delta p_{2x} = 0 \quad \text{(isolated system)} \tag{4.20}$$

and $\qquad\qquad p_{1x,\mathrm{f}} + p_{2x,\mathrm{f}} = p_{1x,\mathrm{i}} + p_{2x,\mathrm{i}} \quad \text{(isolated system)}. \tag{4.21}$

Equations 4.20 and 4.21 are equivalent: Eq. 4.20 states that any change in momentum in one object is made up by a change of the same magnitude but in the opposite direction in the other object; Eq. 4.21 states that the sum of the momenta is the same before and after the collision. Which of these two equations you use in solving a problem is a matter of convenience.

✋ **4.15** (*a*) Are the changes in velocity in Figure 4.23*a* equal in magnitude? Why or why not? (*b*) Determine the velocity changes of the carts and verify that $m_1/m_2 = -\Delta v_{2x}/\Delta v_{1x}$ in Figure 4.23*a*. (*c*) Determine the initial and final momenta of the two carts. (*d*) What is the momentum of the system before the collision? (*e*) After the collision? (*f*) Are the momentum changes equal in magnitude and opposite in direction? Why or why not?

To convince you of the fundamental importance of the conservation of momentum, let me show you something else. Suppose we let carts 1 and 2 of Figure 4.23 collide with the same initial velocities as before, but this time we put something sticky between them, so that they remain locked together once they hit each other, as in **Figure 4.24** (next page). The velocities of the two carts *after* the collision must now be identical.

✋ **4.16** (*a*) Do the two carts in Figure 4.24 still constitute an isolated system like the carts in Figure 4.23? (*b*) What does your answer to part *a* imply about the momentum of the system comprising the two carts after the collision?

As you saw in the preceding checkpoint, the system of the two carts is isolated and so the momentum of the system should not change. **Figure 4.25a** on page 99 shows graphically that the final velocity of the combined carts is somewhere between the values of the two initial velocities. Before the collision, cart 1 is at rest and the x component of the velocity of cart 2 is $+0.34$ m/s; after the collision, both carts move at $v_{x,\mathrm{f}} = +0.085$ m/s. The x component of the momentum of the system before the collision is thus $p_{1x,\mathrm{i}} + p_{2x,\mathrm{i}} = 0 + (0.12\ \mathrm{kg})(0.34\ \mathrm{m/s}) = 0.041\ \mathrm{kg \cdot m/s}$. After the collision, the x component of the momentum of the system is $p_{1x,\mathrm{f}} + p_{2x,\mathrm{f}} = (0.36\ \mathrm{kg})(0.085\ \mathrm{m/s}) + (0.12\ \mathrm{kg})(0.085\ \mathrm{m/s}) = 0.031\ \mathrm{kg \cdot m/s} + 0.010\ \mathrm{kg \cdot m/s} = 0.041\ \mathrm{kg \cdot m/s}$. The data indeed confirm that the momentum of the system does not change.

Note that the before-collision parts of Figures 4.23*a* and 4.25*a* are identical. The after-collision parts of these two figures are quite different from each other, however. Yet even with these two entirely different outcomes—the carts in Figure 4.23 flying off in opposite directions after colliding and those in Figure 4.25 sticking together—the momentum of the system does not change in both cases:

$$\vec{p}_{\mathrm{i}} = \vec{p}_{\mathrm{f}} \quad \text{(isolated system)}. \tag{4.22}$$

Figure 4.24 (*a*) Two identical carts collide and stick together on a low-friction track. (*b*) High-speed film sequence of such a collision. The length of track visible in each frame is 0.40 m. (*c*) Curves indicating the positions of the rear of cart 1 and the front of cart 2 superimposed on the sequence.

Figure 4.25 (*a*) Velocity-versus-time graph and (*b*) momentum-versus-time graph for the carts of Figure 4.24. Notice that the sum of the momenta is again the same before and after the collision. The inertia of cart 1 is 0.36 kg, and that of cart 2 is 0.12 kg.

The momentum law is not confined to two objects. Suppose we put *three* objects in motion on a low-friction track such that they all end up colliding with one another. Let 1 first collide with 2 and then 2 with 3 (you can pick whatever sequence you like). In the first collision, $\vec{p}_1$ and $\vec{p}_2$ change but their sum remains unchanged. In addition, the sum of all three momenta remains unchanged because nothing has happened to $\vec{p}_3$ yet. When 2 and 3 collide, $\vec{p}_2$ and $\vec{p}_3$ change but the sum $\vec{p}_2 + \vec{p}_3$ does not change. So again, the momentum of the system comprising all three remains constant. In other words, throughout the two collisions, the momentum of the system comprising all three objects, $\vec{p}$, remains unchanged:

$$\vec{p}_i = \vec{p}_{1,i} + \vec{p}_{2,i} + \vec{p}_{3,i} = \vec{p}_{1,f} + \vec{p}_{2,f} + \vec{p}_{3,f} = \vec{p}_f \quad \text{(isolated system).} \quad (4.23)$$

This argument can be extended to any number of objects and any number of collisions or interactions.

That we can apply conservation of momentum to predict the final momentum of carts colliding on a low-friction track may seem like nothing special because you are indeed unlikely to encounter this situation outside the physics classroom. Conservation of momentum has much broader applications, however, because it governs *everything that happens in the universe*. Conservation of momentum applies to atoms and elementary particles at the subatomic scale, to stars and galaxies at the cosmic scale, and to everything in between. Next time you fly in an airplane consider this: you are moving forward because of conservation of momentum. The aircraft engines "throw air backward" so the airplane and the passengers move forward. Conservation of momentum is used to solve many science and engineering problems: from calculating the forces of impact during vehicle collisions, to the trajectories of satellites, to the load-carrying capabilities of artificial limbs.

4.17 A railroad car moves at velocity v_i on a track toward three other railroad cars at rest on the track. All the cars are identical, and each stationary car is some distance from the others. The moving car hits the first stationary car and locks onto it. Then the two hit the second stationary car, lock onto that one, and so on. When all four cars have locked onto one another, what is the velocity v_f of the four-car train?

Chapter Glossary

SI units of physical quantities are given in parentheses.

Conservation of momentum Momentum can be transferred from one object to another, but it cannot be created or destroyed. The momentum of an isolated system therefore cannot change:

$$\Delta \vec{p} = \vec{0} \quad \text{(isolated system).} \tag{4.17}$$

Conserved quantity A quantity that cannot be created or destroyed.

Environment Everything that is not part of the system.

Extensive quantity If the value of a quantity for a system is equal to the sum of the values of that quantity for each part of the system, then the quantity is extensive.

Impulse $\vec{J}$ (kg·m/s) A vector defined as the transfer of momentum from the environment to the system due to an interaction between the two. For an isolated system, the impulse is zero: $\vec{J} = \vec{0}$.

Inertia m (kg) A scalar that is a measure of an object's tendency to resist any change in its velocity. The inertia m_u of any object can be found by letting that object collide with the inertial standard $m_s = 1$ kg along the x axis and taking the negative of the ratio of the changes in the x components of the velocities:

$$m_u \equiv -\frac{\Delta v_{sx}}{\Delta v_{ux}} m_s. \tag{4.2}$$

Intensive quantity If the value of a quantity for a system is equal to the value of that quantity for any part of that system, then that quantity is intensive.

Isolated system A system for which there are no external interactions. For such a system there is no transfer of momentum into or out of the system. See the Procedure box on page 93.

Kilogram (kg) The SI base unit of inertia, defined as being equal to the inertia of a platinum-iridium cylinder stored in Sèvres, France.

Momentum $\vec{p}$ (kg·m/s) A vector that is the product of the inertia and the velocity of an object:

$$\vec{p} \equiv m\vec{v}. \tag{4.6}$$

Momentum law The law that accounts for the change in the momentum of a system or object. Because momentum is conserved, the momentum of a system can change only due to a transfer of momentum between the environment and the system:

$$\Delta \vec{p} = \vec{J}. \tag{4.18}$$

System Any object or group of objects that we can separate, in our minds, from the surrounding environment.

System diagram A schematic diagram that shows a system's initial and final conditions.

5
Energy

5.1 Classification of collisions
5.2 Kinetic energy
5.3 Internal energy
5.4 Closed systems

5.5 Elastic collisions
5.6 Inelastic collisions
5.7 Conservation of energy
5.8 Explosive separations

CONCEPTS

QUANTITATIVE TOOLS

Now that we know about conservation of momentum, can we determine the final velocities of two colliding objects if the only things we know are the initial velocities and the fact that the momentum is conserved? The answer is *no* if our only tool is the momentum law. In the collisions represented in Figures 4.23 and 4.25, for instance, momentum is unchanged in both cases, and yet the two outcomes are definitely not the same. So knowing only that momentum remains constant isn't enough. We need additional information in order to predict future positions and velocities. In the process of looking for this additional information, we shall develop another conservation law—the law of conservation of *energy*.

5.1 Classification of collisions

If you look at the velocity-versus-time graphs in Chapter 4, you will notice that the velocity difference in the two carts, $\vec{v}_2 - \vec{v}_1$, in most cases has the same magnitude before and after the collision. **Figure 5.1** shows two graphs of collisions we considered in Chapter 4 and highlights the velocity difference before and after the collision. This difference is the **relative velocity** of the carts: $\vec{v}_{12} \equiv \vec{v}_2 - \vec{v}_1$ is the velocity of cart 2 relative to cart 1 and $\vec{v}_{21} \equiv \vec{v}_1 - \vec{v}_2$ is the velocity of cart 1 relative to cart 2. The subscript in the relative velocity symbol is always shown with the object we are studying printed last: v_{12} is the velocity *of cart 2* and v_{21} is the velocity *of cart 1*. (We cannot use Δ here because we reserve that symbol to denote the change in a *single* quantity; now we are dealing with the difference between the same quantity for two different objects.)

The magnitude of the relative velocity is called the **relative speed.** Thus $v_{12} \equiv |\vec{v}_2 - \vec{v}_1|$ is the speed of cart 2 (last subscript in v_{12}) relative to cart 1. For motion along the *x* axis, the relative speed is the absolute value of the difference in the *x* components of the velocities: $v_{12} \equiv |v_{2x} - v_{1x}|$.

Note that the sequence of the subscripts for relative speeds does not matter: $v_{12} \equiv |v_{2x} - v_{1x}| = |v_{1x} - v_{2x}| = v_{21}$ (the speed of cart 2 relative to cart 1 is equal to the speed of cart 1 relative to cart 2).

A collision in which the relative speed before the collision is the same as the relative speed after the collision is called an **elastic collision.** Collisions between hard objects are generally elastic collisions. For instance, a superball bouncing off a hard floor bounces up with nearly the same speed with which it came down. Thus the relative speed of floor and ball does not change, and the collision is elastic.

5.1 Two cars are moving along a highway with neither one accelerating. Is their relative speed equal to the difference between their speeds? Why or why not?

Any collision for which the relative speed after the collision is lower than that before the collision is called an **inelastic collision.** If you drop a tennis ball to the floor, it rebounds with a lower speed than it had when it hit the floor. The relative speed is reduced, and the collision is inelastic.

A special type of inelastic collision is one in which the two objects move together after the collision so that their relative speed is reduced to zero. We call this special case a **totally inelastic collision.** Imagine dropping a ball of dough to the floor. Splat! The dough sticks to the floor, and the relative speed of dough and floor is reduced to zero. The collision in Figure 4.25 is another example of an inelastic collision.

As you might imagine, whether a collision is elastic, inelastic, or totally inelastic depends on the properties of the objects involved. However, if we know what happens to the relative speed in a collision, we can use that knowledge together with conservation of momentum to determine the final velocities.

Figure 5.1 Velocity-versus-time graphs of (*a*) two identical carts colliding on a low-friction track, with one of the carts initially at rest, and (*b*) a standard cart colliding with a cart of unknown inertia that is initially at rest. Notice that for both collisions the relative speeds of the two carts are the same before and after the collision.

(*a*) Moving cart collides with identical cart at rest

(*b*) Standard cart collides with cart of unknown inertia at rest

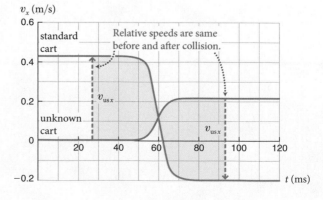

Exercise 5.1 Classifying collisions

Are the following collisions elastic, inelastic, or totally inelastic? (a) A red billiard ball moving at $v_{rx,i} = +2.2$ m/s hits a white billiard ball initially at rest. After the collision, the red ball is at rest and the white ball moves at $v_{wx,f} = +1.9$ m/s. (b) Cart 1 moving along a track at $v_{1x,i} = +1.2$ m/s hits cart 2 initially at rest. After the collision, the two carts move at $v_{1x,f} = +0.4$ m/s and $v_{2x,f} = +1.6$ m/s. (c) A piece of putty moving at $v_{px,i} = +22$ m/s hits a wooden block moving at $v_{bx,i} = +1.0$ m/s. After the collision, the two move at $v_{x,f} = +1.7$ m/s.

SOLUTION (a) The initial relative speed is $v_{wr,i} = |v_{rx,i} - v_{wx,i}| = |+2.2$ m/s $- 0| = 2.2$ m/s; the final relative speed is $v_{wr,f} = |v_{rx,f} - v_{wx,f}| = |0 - 1.9$ m/s$| = 1.9$ m/s, lower than the initial relative speed, which means the collision is inelastic. ✔

(b) $v_{12i} = |v_{2x,i} - v_{1x,i}| = |0 - (+1.2$ m/s$)| = 1.2$ m/s; $v_{12f} = |v_{2x,f} - v_{1x,f}| = |+1.6$ m/s $- (+0.4$ m/s$)| = 1.2$ m/s. Because the relative speeds are the same, the collision is elastic. ✔

(c) After the collision, both the putty and the block travel at the same velocity, making their relative speed zero. The collision is totally inelastic. ✔

5.2 (a) An outfielder catches a baseball. Is the collision between ball and glove elastic, inelastic, or totally inelastic? (b) When a moving steel ball 1 collides head-on with a steel ball 2 at rest, ball 1 comes to rest and ball 2 moves away at the initial speed of ball 1. Which type of collision is this? (c) Is the sum of the momenta of the two colliding objects constant in part a? In part b?

5.2 Kinetic energy

Relative speed is not an extensive quantity, and so we cannot develop an accounting scheme for it as we did for momentum in Chapter 4. The trick in studying elastic collisions therefore is to obtain a quantity that allows us to express the fact that the relative speed doesn't change in the form: (something of object 1) + (something of object 2) doesn't change. As I shall show you in Section 5.5, for an object of inertia m moving at speed v this something is the quantity $K = \frac{1}{2}mv^2$, called the object's **kinetic energy** (literally "energy* associated with motion"). Unlike relative speed, which refers to two objects, kinetic energy is associated with a single object. Furthermore, kinetic energy is always positive and independent of the direction of motion (which means that it is a scalar). A ball moving at speed v to the left has exactly the same kinetic energy as the same ball moving at speed v to the right (or any other direction in space). Whenever the speed of an object changes, the kinetic energy changes.

5.3 Is kinetic energy an extensive quantity?

To develop some feel for this new quantity and its relationship to relative speed, let us calculate the kinetic energies of the carts before and after the collisions shown in **Figure 5.2**. The two collisions have identical initial conditions, but one is elastic (Figure 5.2a) and the other is totally inelastic (Figure 5.2b).

Table 5.1 gives the initial and final kinetic energies of the carts, obtained by reading off the x components of the velocities from the figure. For the elastic collision, where the relative speed doesn't change, the sum of the two kinetic energies before the collision is equal to the sum after the collision: $(0.12 + 0)$ kg·m²/s² $= (0.086 + 0.029)$ kg·m²/s². For the totally inelastic collision, both the relative speed and the sum of the two kinetic energies change.

In general we observe:

In an elastic collision, the sum of the kinetic energies of the objects before the collision is the same as the sum of the kinetic energies after the collision.

---

*For now think of "energy" as the capacity to do things like accelerating and heating objects. We shall develop a more complete picture of what energy is in later sections and chapters.

CONCEPTS

Figure 5.2 Velocities for elastic and inelastic collisions between two carts. Cart 1 has inertia 0.12 kg, and cart 2 has inertia 0.36 kg.

(a) Elastic collision

(b) Totally inelastic collision

Table 5.1 Kinetic energy in elastic and totally inelastic collisions

| | Inertia m (kg) | Velocity v_x (m/s) | | Kinetic energy $\frac{1}{2}mv^2$ (kg · m²/s²) | | Velocity v_x (m/s) | | Kinetic energy $\frac{1}{2}mv^2$ (kg · m²/s²) | |
| | | ELASTIC | | | | TOTALLY INELASTIC | | | |
		before	*after*	*before*	*after*	*before*	*after*	*before*	*after*
Cart 1	0.12	0	+1.2	0	0.086	0	+0.60	0	0.022
Cart 2	0.36	+0.80	+0.40	0.12	0.029	+0.80	+0.60	0.12	0.065
Relative speed		0.80	0.80			0.80	0		
Kinetic energy of system				**0.12**	**0.12**			**0.12**	**0.087**

In Section 5.5 we'll see that this statement is equivalent to the requirement that the relative speed remains the same.

For problems involving elastic collisions, we now have two tools: the momentum conservation law, which tells us that the momentum of an isolated system doesn't change, and the fact that the relative speed of the colliding objects doesn't change (or, alternatively, the fact that the kinetic energy of the system doesn't change). Let's now use both tools in an example.

Example 5.2 Carts colliding

(a) Is the collision in Figure 4.23 elastic, inelastic, or totally inelastic? How can you tell? (b) Verify your answer by comparing the initial kinetic energy of the two-cart system with the final kinetic energy.

❶ **GETTING STARTED** In Figure 4.23, it looks as if the initial and final relative speeds are the same, which makes the collision elastic. The problem asks me to confirm this fact by calculating the initial and final kinetic energies of the system.

❷ **DEVISE PLAN** To answer part *a*, I need to determine the initial and final relative speeds of the carts from the velocities, which I get from Figure 4.23a: $v_{1x,i} = 0$; $v_{2x,i} = +0.34$ m/s; $v_{1x,f} = +0.17$ m/s; $v_{2x,f} = -0.17$ m/s. To answer part *b*, I use $K = \frac{1}{2}mv^2$. The inertias of the carts are given in the figure caption: $m_1 = 0.36$ kg and $m_2 = 0.12$ kg.

❸ **EXECUTE PLAN** (a) $v_{12i} = |v_{2x,i} - v_{1x,i}| = |(+0.34\text{ m/s}) - 0|$ = 0.34 m/s; $v_{12f} = |v_{2x,f} - v_{1x,f}| = |(-0.17\text{ m/s}) - (+0.17\text{ m/s})|$ = 0.34 m/s. The relative speed is unchanged, and thus the collision is elastic. ✔

(b) The initial values are

$$K_{1i} = \tfrac{1}{2}m_1 v_{1i}^2 = \tfrac{1}{2}(0.36\text{ kg})(0)^2 = 0$$

$$K_{2i} = \tfrac{1}{2}m_2 v_{2i}^2 = \tfrac{1}{2}(0.12\text{ kg})(0.34\text{ m/s})^2 = 0.0069\text{ kg} \cdot \text{m}^2/\text{s}^2$$

so $\quad K_i = K_{1i} + K_{2i} = 0.0069\text{ kg} \cdot \text{m}^2/\text{s}^2.$

The final values are

$$K_{1f} = \tfrac{1}{2}m_1 v_{1f}^2 = \tfrac{1}{2}(0.36\text{ kg})(0.17\text{ m/s})^2 = 0.0052\text{ kg} \cdot \text{m}^2/\text{s}^2$$

$$K_{2f} = \tfrac{1}{2}m_2 v_{2f}^2 = \tfrac{1}{2}(0.12\text{ kg})(-0.17\text{ m/s})^2 = 0.0017\text{ kg} \cdot \text{m}^2/\text{s}^2$$

so $\quad K_f = (0.0052\text{ kg} \cdot \text{m}^2/\text{s}^2) + (0.0017\text{ kg} \cdot \text{m}^2/\text{s}^2)$

$$= 0.0069\text{ kg} \cdot \text{m}^2/\text{s}^2,$$

which is the same as before the collision, as it should be for an elastic collision. ✔

❹ **EVALUATE RESULT** Because I've reached the same conclusion—the collision is elastic—using two approaches, I can be pretty confident that my solution is correct.

Because kinetic energy is a scalar extensive quantity, bar diagrams are a good way to visually represent changes in this quantity. **Figure 5.3**, for example, shows the initial and final kinetic energies of the carts in the two collisions of Figure 5.2. Before the collision, only cart 2 has kinetic energy; after the collision, both carts have kinetic energy. For the elastic collision (Figure 5.3a), the sum of the kinetic

Figure 5.3 Bar diagrams representing the initial and final kinetic energies of the carts for the collisions shown in Figure 5.2. (a) The sum of the kinetic energies does not change for the elastic collision because the changes are equal and opposite. (b) The sum of the kinetic energies changes for the totally inelastic collision: The change in K_1 is smaller than the change in K_2.

(a) Elastic collision

(b) Totally inelastic collision

energies after the collision is the same as the sum before the collision because the change in the kinetic energy of cart 1 is the negative of that of cart 2. For the totally inelastic collision (Figure 5.3b), the changes in the kinetic energies do not cancel, and so the system's kinetic energy after the collision is not equal to the system's kinetic energy before the collision.

5.4 A moving cart collides with an identical cart initially at rest on a low-friction track, and the two lock together. What fraction of the initial kinetic energy of the system remains in this totally inelastic collision?

5.3 Internal energy

In both inelastic and totally inelastic collisions, the relative speed changes and therefore the kinetic energy of the system changes. For example, the decrease in the kinetic energy of cart 2 in Figure 5.2b, represented by the downward pointing arrow labeled ΔK_2 in Figure 5.3b, is larger than the increase in the kinetic energy K_1 of cart 1, resulting in a decrease in the kinetic energy of the stuck-together carts. Where does this kinetic energy go? Does it simply vanish, or does it go elsewhere?

We can determine the answer to this question by looking more closely at inelastic collisions between objects and noticing that changes occur in the **state** of one or both objects. What I mean by *state* is the condition of the object as specified by some complete set of physical parameters: shape, temperature, whatever—*every possible physical variable that defines the object.* In inelastic collisions, objects deform (their shape changes) and heat up (their temperature changes). A ball of dough changes shape as it hits the ground, two cars deform as they collide, hands vigorously clapped together heat up and make sound.

The transformation of a system from an initial state to a final state is called a **process.** Processes cause change (see Section 1.4), and so in physics we aim to understand processes. Collisions that change either the motion or the state of objects are an example of a process. Other examples are the melting of an ice cube, the burning of fuel, the flow of a liquid, and an explosive separation. Initially we focus on collisions because they are easily visualized and we can study what happens in collisions using carts on tracks. As we gain experience, we shall replace collisions with other processes.

In inelastic collisions, the state of the objects after the collision is different from the state before the collision. If I were to make a movie of the ball of dough hitting the ground and then play the movie in reverse, you'd have no trouble telling that the movie was being played in the wrong direction. This is because this inelastic collision involves changes that cannot undo themselves—the dough is flat and at rest after the collision and round and moving before (and never the other way around). The same is true for a collision between two cars: The cars are damaged after the collision and not before, and it is not possible to repair

Figure 5.4 Before or after? (*a*) Inelastic collisions are an irreversible process. There is no question that the picture was taken *after* the accident because the state of the two cars has changed. (*b*) Elastic collisions are a reversible process. Can you tell whether this picture was taken before or after the ball collided with the racquet?

(*a*)   (*b*)

them simply by pulling them apart (**Figure 5.4a**). After the clapping, your hands are warmer than before, and you cannot cool your hands by "unclapping" them. All these inelastic collisions are **irreversible processes,** which means that the changes that occur in the state of the colliding objects cannot spontaneously undo themselves.

In contrast, viewing a movie of a superball bouncing off the floor or two carts colliding on a low-friction track (without sticking together), you'd be hard pressed to tell whether the movie is playing forward or in reverse. This is because elastic collisions are a **reversible process,** which means there are no permanent changes in the state of the colliding objects. The objects look the same before and after the collision (Figure 5.4b).

I have summarized these facts in **Table 5.2.** Notice how a change in the relative speed (and therefore a change in the sum of the kinetic energies) goes hand in hand with a change in the state: The sum of the kinetic energies of two colliding objects doesn't change unless their states change. Let us look at this connection with an eye to formulating a new conservation law.

Suppose we could associate some quantity having the same units as kinetic energy ($\mathrm{kg \cdot m^2/s^2}$) with the state of an object—let's call this quantity the object's **internal energy** (denoted by E_{int}). Suppose further that we could arrange things in such a way that in an inelastic collision the increase in the sum of the internal energies of the colliding objects is equal to the decrease in their kinetic energies. This would mean that in an inelastic collision one form of energy is converted to another form (kinetic to internal) but the sum of the kinetic and internal energies—collectively called the **energy** of the system—doesn't change.

Table 5.2 Elastic and inelastic collisions

Collision type	Relative speed	State
elastic	unchanged	unchanged
inelastic	changed	changed
totally inelastic	changed (becomes zero)	changed

Figure 5.5 (a) Elastic collision. Because the relative speed of the carts does not change, the sum of the kinetic energies is also unchanged. The carts' states do not change, and so their internal energies are also unchanged. (b) Inelastic collision. Because the relative speed changes as a result of the collision, the kinetic energy changes. The cars' states also change, and so the internal energy changes too. For both collisions the sum of the kinetic and internal energies is constant.

(a) Elastic collision

(b) Totally inelastic collision

In Chapter 7 we'll learn how to specify the state of an object and how to calculate the corresponding internal energy. For now, all we need to do is account for the missing kinetic energy in an inelastic collision by saying:

In any inelastic collision, the states of the colliding objects change, and the sum of their internal energies increases by an amount equal to the decrease in the sum of their kinetic energies.

Whenever some kinetic energy disappears in a collision, we can *always* determine changes in state to account for that loss. The big appeal of the relationship between state and internal energy is that we can now say:

The energy of a system of two colliding objects does not change during the collision.

This statement holds for all types of collisions: elastic, inelastic, and totally inelastic. In the elastic collision shown in **Figure 5.5a**, the collision alters the velocities and thus the kinetic energies of both carts. However, the sum of the kinetic energies before and after the collision remains unchanged, as shown by the kinetic energy bars. Because the collision is elastic, there are no changes in the states of the carts, which means their internal energies also remain unchanged, as shown by the internal energy bars. So the energy of the two-cart system does not change.

In the totally inelastic collision of Figure 5.5b, the sum of the kinetic energies decreases. Because changes occur in the states—the cars change shape—the internal energies of the carts change as well. The changes in motion and state are such that the energy of the system is the same before and after the collision. We account for the lost kinetic energy by saying that it has been converted to internal energy.

Note that in making the bar diagrams in Figure 5.5, I had to choose some initial value for the internal energies of the colliding objects. As we have no way (yet) of calculating internal energies, the values I chose are arbitrary. At present we are interested only in *changes* in energy, however, and so the initial value is not important.

✋ **5.5** A piece of dough is thrown at a wall and sticks to it. Does the internal energy of the dough-wall system increase, decrease, or stay the same?

Example 5.3 Internal energy change

A 0.2-kg cart 1 initially at rest is struck by an identical cart 2 traveling at $v_{2x,i} = +0.5$ m/s along a low-friction track. After the collision, the velocity of cart 2 is reduced to $v_{2x,f} = +0.2$ m/s. (a) Is the collision elastic, inelastic, or totally inelastic? (b) By what amount does the internal energy of the two-cart system change? (c) Make a bar diagram showing the initial and final kinetic and internal energies of the two carts.

❶ **GETTING STARTED** I begin by organizing the information given in the problem in a sketch (**Figure 5.6**). To classify the collision, I need to determine the final relative speed, but the final velocity of cart 1 is not given.

Figure 5.6

❷ **DEVISE PLAN** The two-cart system is isolated, and so the momentum of the system does not change, regardless of the type of collision. I can use this information to determine the final velocity of cart 1 and the final relative speed of the carts. By comparing the final and initial relative speeds, I can determine the type of collision. Once I know the initial and final velocities, I can calculate the kinetic energies using $K = \frac{1}{2}mv^2$ and determine what fraction of the initial kinetic energy has been converted to internal energy.

❸ EXECUTE PLAN (*a*) The initial relative speed is

$$|v_{2x,i} - v_{1x,i}| = |(+0.5 \text{ m/s}) - 0| = 0.5 \text{ m/s}.$$

To determine $v_{1x,f}$, I apply conservation of momentum to the system. The initial momentum of the system is

$$(0.2 \text{ kg})(+0.5 \text{ m/s}) + (0.2 \text{ kg})(0) = (0.2 \text{ kg})(+0.5 \text{ m/s})$$

and its final momentum is

$$(0.2 \text{ kg})(+0.2 \text{ m/s}) + (0.2 \text{ kg})(v_{1x,f}).$$

Conservation of momentum requires these two momenta to be equal:

$$(0.2 \text{ kg})(+0.5 \text{ m/s}) = (0.2 \text{ kg})(+0.2 \text{ m/s}) + (0.2 \text{ kg})(v_{1x,f})$$

$$(+0.5 \text{ m/s}) = (+0.2 \text{ m/s}) + v_{1x,f}$$

$$v_{1x,f} = +0.3 \text{ m/s}.$$

The final relative speed is thus

$$|v_{2x,f} - v_{1x,f}| = |(+0.2 \text{ m/s}) - (+0.3 \text{ m/s})| = 0.1 \text{ m/s},$$

which is different from the initial value. Thus the collision is inelastic. (I know that the collision is not *totally* inelastic because the relative speed has not been reduced to zero.) ✔

(*b*) The initial kinetic energies are

$$K_{1i} = 0$$

$$K_{2i} = \tfrac{1}{2}(0.2 \text{ kg})(0.5 \text{ m/s})^2 = 0.025 \text{ kg} \cdot \text{m}^2/\text{s}^2$$

so $K_i = K_{1i} + K_{2i} = 0.025 \text{ kg} \cdot \text{m}^2/\text{s}^2.$

The final kinetic energies are

$$K_{1f} = \tfrac{1}{2}(0.2 \text{ kg})(0.3 \text{ m/s})^2 = 0.009 \text{ kg} \cdot \text{m}^2/\text{s}^2$$

$$K_{2f} = \tfrac{1}{2}(0.2 \text{ kg})(0.2 \text{ m/s})^2 = 0.004 \text{ kg} \cdot \text{m}^2/\text{s}^2$$

so $K_f = K_{1f} + K_{2f} = 0.013 \text{ kg} \cdot \text{m}^2/\text{s}^2.$

The kinetic energy of the system has changed by an amount $(0.013 \text{ kg} \cdot \text{m}^2/\text{s}^2) - (0.025 \text{ kg} \cdot \text{m}^2/\text{s}^2) = -0.012 \text{ kg} \cdot \text{m}^2/\text{s}^2$. To keep the energy of the system (the sum of its kinetic and internal energies) unchanged, the decrease in kinetic energy must be made up by an increase in internal energy. This tells me that the internal energy of the system increases by $0.012 \text{ kg} \cdot \text{m}^2/\text{s}^2$. ✔

(*c*) My bar diagram is shown in **Figure 5.7**. The final kinetic energy bar is about half of the initial kinetic energy bar. Because I don't know the value of the initial internal energy, I set it to zero and make the final internal energy bar equal in height to the difference in the kinetic energy bars. ✔

Figure 5.7

❹ EVALUATE RESULT If the collision were elastic, the velocities of the carts would be interchanged and cart 2 would come to a stop (see Figure 4.5). So the collision must be inelastic. Indeed, I found that both the relative speed and the sum of the kinetic energies change in the collision, as expected for an inelastic collision.

We are now in a position to extend the idea of internal energy to other interactions. Consider, for example, a cart initially at rest on a low-friction track set in motion by an expanding spring that is held fixed at one end, as shown in **Figure 5.8a**. As the cart is accelerated by the spring, the cart's kinetic energy increases but its state doesn't change, and so its energy increases (Figure 5.8b). Where did this energy come from? The spring sets the cart in motion, and so it makes sense to assume that the spring transfers energy to the cart. Indeed, the spring expands—its state changes— and so its internal energy changes. If we include the spring

Figure 5.8 Initial and final energies for two choices of system.

(*a*) Expanding spring accelerates cart from rest

(*b*) Initial and final energies: system = cart only

(*c*) Initial and final energies: system = cart + spring

in the system and attribute the increase in the cart's kinetic energy to a decrease in the spring's internal energy, we can again arrange things in such a way that the energy of the cart-spring system remains unchanged (Figure 5.8c).

If we replace the cart in Figure 5.8 with a cart with a different inertia, compress the spring to the same initial state, and then let that cart go, we discover that its final kinetic energy is exactly the same as that of the first cart. So the spring always transfers the same amount of energy as it expands from a given compressed state to its relaxed state *regardless* of the object to which it transfers that energy.

5.6 Think of a few other ways to put the cart of Figure 5.8 in motion. In each case, can you account for the increase in the cart's kinetic energy by either a change in state or a change in motion of another object?

Checkpoint 5.6 suggests that a change in the cart's kinetic energy can always be attributed to either a change in state (and therefore a change in the internal energy) or a change in the motion of another object. Because the states of objects can change in many different ways, we associate different forms of internal energy with different kinds of state change. For example, the internal energy associated with a change in chemical state is called *chemical energy* and the internal energy associated with a change in the temperature of an object is called *thermal energy*. **Table 5.3** lists additional forms of internal energy.

Absolutely everything happening around us entails changes in state and therefore changes in internal energy. Rivers flowing, air masses moving, machines lifting things, people walking, and atoms emitting light can all be expressed in terms of changes in state (and therefore changes in internal energy). More important, we discover that any change in state or motion is always accompanied by a compensating change in state or motion, and we can always attribute energy to these changes in such a way that the energy of the system remains unchanged. In other words, energy cannot be destroyed or created, and energy, like momentum, is a conserved quantity. Indeed, no observation has ever been found to violate the law of **conservation of energy:**

Energy can be transferred from one object to another or converted from one form to another, but it cannot be destroyed or created.

Table 5.3 Various state changes and their associated internal energy

State change	Internal energy
temperature change	thermal energy
chemical change	chemical energy
reversible change in shape	elastic energy
phase transformation	transformation energy

Kinetic energy and all forms of internal energy are thus different manifestations of the same conserved quantity: *energy*.

5.7 (a) Is the momentum of the cart-spring system in Figure 5.8 constant? (b) Is the system isolated?

5.4 Closed systems

As Checkpoint 5.7 shows, the system comprising the spring and cart in Figure 5.8 is not isolated. However, no energy is transferred to it, and therefore the energy of the system is constant.* Any system to or from which no energy is transferred is called a **closed system.** An important point to keep in mind is that a closed system need not be isolated (and likewise an isolated system is not necessarily closed). The procedure for choosing a closed system is described in the Procedure box. To see how this procedure works, let's look at the setup in **Figure 5.9**—some fuel (gasoline, say) being burned in a container open to the air.

I begin by making a sketch of the canister with the fuel before and after the combustion (Figure 5.9a). The combustion involves two changes in state: a change in the chemical state of the fuel and the air, and a change in the

Figure 5.9 (a) The burning of fuel involves a change in chemical composition and in temperature. (b) If we choose a closed system, the change in chemical energy must be compensated by a change in thermal energy.

(a) Sketch initial and final conditions, identify changes, choose system

change in motion: none
changes in state: • chemical state of fuel and air changes
• temperature rises

(b) Draw energy bar diagrams for initial and final conditions

---

*How do I know that no energy is transferred to the cart-spring system? The expanding spring and the accelerating cart do not cause any changes in the state or motion of the environment (the track, Earth, and so on). Consequently the energy of the environment doesn't change, which means that no energy has been transferred from the environment to the system.

Procedure: Choosing a closed system

When we analyze energy changes, it is convenient to choose a system for which no energy is transferred to or from the system (a closed system). To do so, follow this procedure:

1. Make a sketch showing the initial and final conditions of the objects under consideration.
2. Identify all the changes in state or motion that occur during the time interval of interest.
3. Choose a system that includes all the objects undergoing these changes in state or motion. Draw a dashed line around the objects in your chosen system to represent the system boundary. Write "closed" near the system boundary to remind yourself that no energy is transferred to or from the system.
4. Verify that nothing in the surroundings of the system undergoes a change in motion or state that is related to what happens inside the system.

Once you have selected a closed system, you know that its energy remains constant.

temperature. The fuel and the air immediately surrounding it are what undergo these changes in state, and so I include them in my system. Because there are no other related changes in state, I know that my system is closed and its energy remains constant.

I can now make a bar diagram to represent the changes in energy that take place inside the system (Figure 5.9*b*). The change in the chemical state corresponds to a change in chemical energy, and the change in the temperature corresponds to a change in thermal energy. I therefore draw two bars. The combustion raises the temperature, and so the thermal energy increases. Because the system is closed and its energy remains constant, there must be a decrease in chemical energy that compensates for the increase in thermal energy.

Given that the energy of a closed system remains constant, we can focus on the energy conversions and transfers that happen inside the system. We speak of an *energy conversion* when energy is converted from one form to another. In the combustion illustrated in Figure 5.9, for example, an amount ΔE_{chem} of chemical energy is converted to an equal amount ΔE_{th} of thermal energy. When energy is transferred from one object to another, we speak of an *energy transfer*. An example is shown in Figure 5.3*a*, where energy is transferred from cart 2 to cart 1.

Because we are still lacking the quantitative tools, let me illustrate the transfer and conversion of energy qualitatively with a few examples. By converting some form of internal energy to kinetic energy, we can put objects in motion. For example, a car burns gasoline as it accelerates from rest. If we ignore the effects of air resistance, this situation represents a change in the chemical state of the gasoline and a change in the motion of the car. Chemical energy (a form of internal energy associated with the chemical state) stored in the gasoline is converted to kinetic energy of the car (**Figure 5.10**).

🖐 **5.8** In describing what's going on in Figure 5.10, I ignored the change in temperature of the engine that accompanies the combustion of the fuel. Make a bar diagram that includes this change in temperature.

Figure 5.10 (*a*) An accelerating car constitutes a closed system because no changes occur in its environment. (*b*) The increase in the car's kinetic energy can be attributed to a decrease in chemical energy (due to the combustion of fuel).

(*a*) Initial and final conditions, changes in state and motion, system

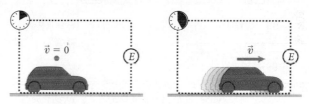

change in motion: car accelerates
change in state: chemical state of fuel changes

(*b*) Energy bar diagrams for initial and final conditions

The generation and consumption of electrical power provide many other examples of energy conversions and transfers. In a coal-burning electrical power plant, coal is burned in a boiler to heat water and convert it to steam. The two complementary changes in state (a change in the chemical state of the coal and a change in the temperature and state of the water) correspond to a conversion of chemical energy to thermal energy. The steam drives a turbine, where the steam cools and a turbine blade spins, and so thermal energy is converted to kinetic energy. The moving turbine drives a generator, which converts the kinetic energy to electrical energy. Power lines transfer energy from the plant to our homes, where it is converted to many forms. Lamps convert electrical energy to light (a form of energy) and thermal energy (lamps get hot), a stereo converts electrical energy to sound energy, and on and on.

CONCEPTS

Exercise 5.4 State changes and internal energy

Choose an appropriate closed system and make a bar diagram representing the energy conversions and transfers that occur when (*a*) a pan of water is heated on a propane burner, (*b*) a cyclist accelerates from rest, and (*c*) a spring-loaded gun fires a ball of putty.

SOLUTION For each case, I apply the steps of the Procedure box on page 109. My sketches are shown in the figures.

(*a*) Changes in motion: none. Changes in state: the temperature of the water increases, and the chemical states of the propane and the air change. The bar diagram shows an increase in thermal energy and an equal decrease in chemical energy (**Figure 5.11**). Chemical energy is converted to thermal energy, and in the process energy is transferred from the propane to the water.

Figure 5.11

(*b*) Changes in motion: the bicycle and the cyclist accelerate. Changes in state: the chemical state of the cyclist changes because setting the bicycle in motion requires muscles to contract, a physiological process that involves a complex series of chemical reactions. The bar diagram shows an increase in kinetic energy and an equal decrease in chemical energy (**Figure 5.12**). Chemical energy is converted to kinetic energy of the bicycle and cyclist.

Figure 5.12

(*c*) Changes in motion: the putty is accelerated. Changes in state: the spring expands. The bar diagram shows a decrease in the elastic energy of the spring and an increase in the kinetic energy of the putty (**Figure 5.13**). As the spring expands, elastic energy is converted to kinetic energy of the putty.

Figure 5.13

We started our study of physics by describing motion in terms of velocities, accelerations, and inertias. Now we have two new quantities, *momentum* and *energy*, and we have found two fundamental conservation laws that allow us to use simple accounting principles to describe changes in motion.

5.9 (*a*) Can the magnitude of the momentum of an object change without a change in the object's kinetic energy? (*b*) Without a change in the object's energy? (*c*) What are your answers to parts *a* and *b* for a system consisting of more than one object?

CONCEPTS

Self-quiz

1. Consider an isolated object at rest in space. The object contains internal energy in some form or another. Is it—in principle—possible to convert the internal energy to kinetic energy so that the object starts to move?

2. Imagine squeezing a piece of foam with your hands. Choose an appropriate closed system and make a bar diagram representing the energy conversions and transfers that occur during the squeezing.

3. When you heat a pot of water on a gas stove, the water temperature increases until the water begins to boil. This change in thermal state from cool water to hot water is due to chemical energy from the burning gas being converted to thermal energy of the water. Once boiling starts, the water temperature stays constant until all the water has turned to steam, even though the burning gas continues to transfer energy to the water. While the water is boiling off and becoming steam, what becomes of the energy released by the burning gas?

4. An electric fan turns electrical energy into wind energy (a form of kinetic energy because it involves moving air). Suppose a blowing fan is suddenly unplugged. Even though the fan no longer receives electrical energy, it continues to blow air while the blades slowly come to a stop. What type of energy is converted to wind energy after the fan is unplugged?

Answers

1. No. Getting the object to move would violate the law of conservation of momentum because the object would start with zero momentum ($\vec{p} = m\vec{v} = m\vec{0} = \vec{0}$) and end with nonzero momentum ($\vec{p} = m\vec{v}$).

2. Draw the foam before and after the squeezing. Two changes in state occur: The shape of the foam changes, and the chemical state of your muscles changes. These two changes in state correspond to changes in the foam's elastic energy and in chemical energy. In your closed system, include the foam and yourself (Figure 5.14).

Figure 5.14

3. It goes into changing the phase of the water from liquid to steam.

4. The kinetic energy of the fan blades is converted to wind energy.

5.5 Elastic collisions

As we saw in Section 5.1, we can classify collisions according to what happens to the relative velocity of the two colliding objects. The **relative velocity** of cart 2 relative to cart 1 is defined as

$$\vec{v}_{12} \equiv \vec{v}_2 - \vec{v}_1. \tag{5.1}$$

The relative velocity of cart 1 relative to cart 2 is the negative of this vector:

$$\vec{v}_{21} \equiv \vec{v}_1 - \vec{v}_2 = -\vec{v}_{12}. \tag{5.2}$$

If the magnitude of this relative velocity (the objects' **relative speed** $v_{12} \equiv |\vec{v}_2 - \vec{v}_1|$) is the same before and after the collision, the collision is elastic:

$$v_{12i} = v_{12f} \quad \text{(elastic collision).} \tag{5.3}$$

For two objects moving along the x axis, we can write this as

$$v_{2x,i} - v_{1x,i} = -(v_{2x,f} - v_{1x,f}) \quad \text{(elastic collision),} \tag{5.4}$$

where I have added a minus sign on the right because if object 2 initially moves faster than object 1, object 1 must move faster after the collision (**Figure 5.15**). In other words, in an elastic collision, if $v_{2x,i} > v_{1x,i}$, we must have $v_{2x,f} < v_{1x,f}$. The relative velocity in an elastic collision always changes sign after the collision: $v_{12x,i} = -v_{12x,f}$.

Because we can consider a system made up of two colliding objects to be isolated during the collision, conservation of momentum requires that the momentum of the colliding objects remains unchanged in the collision:

$$m_1 v_{1x,i} + m_2 v_{2x,i} = m_1 v_{1x,f} + m_2 v_{2x,f} \quad \text{(isolated system).} \tag{5.5}$$

Equations 5.4 and 5.5 allow us to determine the final velocities of the objects, given their initial velocities.

Figure 5.15 A collision between two objects moving in the same direction at different speeds.

If object 2 initially moves faster than object 1 . . .

. . . then after the collision, object 1 must move faster than object 2.

Example 5.5 Elastic collision

Two carts, one of inertia $m_1 = 0.25$ kg and the other of inertia $m_2 = 0.40$ kg, travel along a straight horizontal track with velocities $v_{1x,i} = +0.20$ m/s and $v_{2x,i} = -0.050$ m/s. What are the carts' velocities after they collide elastically?

❶ **GETTING STARTED** I begin by organizing the information in a sketch to help visualize the situation (**Figure 5.16**). I need to determine the velocities after the collision from the information given, knowing that the collision is elastic.

Figure 5.16

$v_{1x,i} = +0.20$ m/s
$m_1 = 0.25$ kg

$v_{2x,i} = -0.050$ m/s
$m_2 = 0.40$ kg

❷ **DEVISE PLAN** To determine the two unknowns $v_{1x,f}$ and $v_{2x,f}$, I need two equations. Because the collision is elastic, I can use Eqs. 5.4 and 5.5.

❸ **EXECUTE PLAN** I begin by solving Eq. 5.4 for $v_{2x,f}$:

$$v_{2x,f} = v_{1x,i} - v_{2x,i} + v_{1x,f}$$

so that I can eliminate $v_{2x,f}$ from Eq. 5.5:

$$m_1 v_{1x,i} + m_2 v_{2x,i} = m_1 v_{1x,f} + m_2(v_{1x,i} - v_{2x,i} + v_{1x,f}).$$

Solving this expression for $v_{1x,f}$ yields

$$v_{1x,f} = \frac{m_1 - m_2}{m_1 + m_2} v_{1x,i} + \frac{2m_2}{m_1 + m_2} v_{2x,i}. \tag{1}$$

Repeating this procedure, I can eliminate $v_{1x,f}$ and solve for $v_{2x,f}$:

$$v_{2x,f} = \frac{2m_1}{m_1 + m_2} v_{1x,i} - \frac{m_1 - m_2}{m_1 + m_2} v_{2x,i}. \qquad (2)$$

Substituting the given values into Eqs. 1 and 2 yields $v_{1x,f} = -0.11$ m/s and $v_{2x,f} = +0.14$ m/s. ✔

4 EVALUATE RESULT The final velocities yield the final relative speed $v_{12f} = |(+0.14 \text{ m/s}) - (-0.11 \text{ m/s})| = 0.25$ m/s. This value is the same as the initial relative speed $v_{12i} = |(-0.05 \text{ m/s}) - (+0.20 \text{ m/s})| = 0.25$ m/s, as required for an elastic collision.

Let me now show how Eqs. 5.4 and 5.5 lead to an expression that shows that the kinetic energy of two colliding objects doesn't change in an elastic collision. Rearranging the terms in Eq. 5.5, I get

$$m_1(v_{1x,i} - v_{1x,f}) = m_2(v_{2x,f} - v_{2x,i}), \qquad (5.6)$$

while Eq. 5.4 yields

$$v_{1x,i} + v_{1x,f} = v_{2x,i} + v_{2x,f}. \qquad (5.7)$$

Now I multiply the left side of Eq. 5.6 by the left side of Eq. 5.7 and likewise for the right sides to get

$$m_1(v_{1x,i} - v_{1x,f})(v_{1x,i} + v_{1x,f}) = m_2(v_{2x,f} - v_{2x,i})(v_{2x,i} + v_{2x,f}), \qquad (5.8)$$

which multiplies out to

$$m_1 v_{1x,i}^2 - m_1 v_{1x,f}^2 = m_2 v_{2x,f}^2 - m_2 v_{2x,i}^2. \qquad (5.9)$$

For motion along the x axis, the square of the x component of a velocity is the same as the square of the speed, $v_x^2 = v^2$, and so I can drop all the subscripts x. If I put all the v_i terms on the left and all the v_f terms on the right, I get

$$m_1 v_{1i}^2 + m_2 v_{2i}^2 = m_1 v_{1f}^2 + m_2 v_{2f}^2. \qquad (5.10)$$

I now divide both sides by 2 to get

$$\tfrac{1}{2} m_1 v_{1i}^2 + \tfrac{1}{2} m_2 v_{2i}^2 = \tfrac{1}{2} m_1 v_{1f}^2 + \tfrac{1}{2} m_2 v_{2f}^2. \qquad (5.11)$$

As you saw in Section 5.2, the quantity $\tfrac{1}{2} mv^2$ is the **kinetic energy**, which we denote by K:*

$$K \equiv \tfrac{1}{2} mv^2. \qquad (5.12)$$

With this definition, Eq. 5.11 simplifies to

$$K_{1i} + K_{2i} = K_{1f} + K_{2f} \quad \text{(elastic collision)}, \qquad (5.13)$$

where $K_{1i} = \tfrac{1}{2} m_1 v_{1i}^2$ is the initial kinetic energy of object 1, and so on. In words, in an elastic collision the sum of the initial kinetic energies is the same as the sum of the final kinetic energies.

*The factor $\tfrac{1}{2}$ in Eq. 5.12 is there for convenience. We could have defined kinetic energy as simply mv^2, but the definition given in Eq. 5.12 simplifies matters later on.

Note that there is no new physics in Eqs. 5.11 and 5.13—both express the same fact as Eq. 5.3. The great advantage of writing this information in the form of Eq. 5.13 is that this form expresses Eq. 5.3 in terms of an extensive quantity. Because kinetic energy is an extensive quantity, the kinetic energy of a system comprising two objects is the sum of the kinetic energies of the individual objects: $K = K_1 + K_2$. Equation 5.13 thus tells us that the kinetic energy K of a system of objects undergoing an elastic collision does not change:

$$K_i = K_f \quad \text{(elastic collision).} \tag{5.14}$$

This result can also be written in the form

$$\Delta K = 0 \quad \text{(elastic collision).} \tag{5.15}$$

As you know from studying Table 5.1, the SI unit for kinetic energy is $\text{kg} \cdot \text{m}^2/\text{s}^2$. Because energy is such an important quantity, we give this combination of units the name **joule** (rhymes with *pool*), after the British physicist James Prescott Joule (1818–1889), who studied energy:

$$1 \text{ kg} \cdot \text{m}^2/\text{s}^2 \equiv 1 \text{ J}.$$

Example 5.6 Collision and kinetic energy

A rubber ball of inertia $m_b = 0.050$ kg is fired along a track toward a stationary cart of inertia $m_c = 0.25$ kg. The kinetic energy of the system after the two collide elastically is 2.5 J. (*a*) What is the initial velocity of the ball? (*b*) What are the final velocities of the ball and the cart?

❶ **GETTING STARTED** I organize the problem graphically (**Figure 5.17**). I choose my x axis in the direction of the incoming rubber ball. Only one initial velocity is given. I need to determine the other initial velocity and both final velocities.

Figure 5.17

$$\vec{v}_{b,i}$$

ball
$m_b = 0.050$ kg

$$\vec{v}_{c,i} = \vec{0}$$

cart
$m_c = 0.25$ kg

$K_f = 2.5$ J

❷ **DEVISE PLAN** Because the collision is elastic, I know that the kinetic energy of the system doesn't change, which means that the final value (2.5 J) is the same as the initial value. Because the cart is initially at rest, all of this kinetic energy belongs initially to the ball, and so I can use Eq. 5.12 to determine the initial velocity

of the ball. Once I have this information, I know the initial velocities of both colliding objects and I can use Eqs. 1 and 2 from Example 5.5 to calculate the final velocities.

❸ **EXECUTE PLAN** (*a*) From Eq. 5.12, I obtain the initial speed of the ball:

$$v_{b,i} = \sqrt{\frac{2K_{b,i}}{m_b}} = \sqrt{\frac{2(2.5 \text{ J})}{0.05 \text{ kg}}} = 10 \text{ m/s}.$$

Because the ball is initially moving in the positive x direction, its initial velocity is given by $v_{bx,i} = +10$ m/s. ✔

(*b*) I can now substitute the two initial velocities and the inertias into Eqs. 1 and 2 of Example 5.5, which gives me $v_{bx,f} = -6.7$ m/s and $v_{cx,f} = +3.3$ m/s. ✔

❹ **EVALUATE RESULT** It makes sense that the velocity of the ball is reversed by the collision because the inertia of the cart is so much greater than that of the ball. Now that I know both the initial and final velocities, I can also check to make sure that the relative speed remains the same. Because the cart is initially at rest, the initial relative speed is 10 m/s; the final relative speed is $v_{bc,f} = |(+3.3 \text{ m/s}) - (-6.7 \text{ m/s})| = 10$ m/s, which is the same, as required for an elastic collision.

5.10 Conservation of momentum tells us that mv_x doesn't change for an isolated system. Now we see that in an elastic collision mv_x^2 also doesn't change. Does this mean that mv_x^3 remains unchanged, too?

5.6 Inelastic collisions

In a totally inelastic collision between two objects, the objects move together after the collision and so the two final velocities are identical. This means that the final relative speed is zero:

$$v_{12f} = 0 \quad \text{(totally inelastic collision)}. \qquad (5.16)$$

Therefore if you know the inertias m_1 and m_2 of the objects and the x components of their initial velocities $v_{1x,i}$ and $v_{2x,i}$, you can obtain the final velocities from Eq. 5.5 by setting

$$v_{1x,f} = v_{2x,f} \quad \text{(totally inelastic collision)}. \qquad (5.17)$$

The majority of collisions, however, fall somewhere between the two extremes of elastic and totally inelastic. For these collisions, the final relative speed is between zero and the value of the initial relative speed. For these cases, it is convenient to define the ratio of relative speeds as

$$e \equiv \frac{v_{12f}}{v_{12i}}. \qquad (5.18)$$

The unitless quantity e is called the **coefficient of restitution** of the collision. It tells us how much of the initial relative speed is restituted (restored) after the collision. Because it is a ratio of speeds (which are always positive), e is always positive.

In general, it is more convenient to write Eq. 5.18 in terms of components:

$$e = -\frac{v_{2x,f} - v_{1x,f}}{v_{2x,i} - v_{1x,i}} = -\frac{v_{12x,f}}{v_{12x,i}}, \qquad (5.19)$$

where the minus sign appears because the relative velocity changes sign after the collision (see Figure 5.15).

When $e = 1$, Eq. 5.19 is equal to Eq. 5.4 and the collision is elastic (all of the initial relative speed is restored). A value of $e = 0$ means that v_{12f} must be zero, and so the collision is totally inelastic. For values of e between 0 and 1, the collision is inelastic. This information is summarized in **Table 5.4**.

In an inelastic collision, therefore, we again have two equations—Eqs. 5.1 and 5.19—but we need to know the value of e to be able to calculate the final velocities. The details of how the states of the objects change in the collision (these state changes depend on the material and structural properties of the objects) are hidden in this coefficient e.

Table 5.4 Coefficient of restitution for various processes

Process	Relative speed	Coefficient of restitution
totally inelastic collision	$v_{12f} = 0$	$e = 0$
inelastic collision	$0 < v_{12f} < v_{12i}$	$0 < e < 1$
elastic collision	$v_{12f} = v_{12i}$	$e = 1$
explosive separation*	$v_{12f} > v_{12i}$	$e > 1$

*See Section 5.8.

Example 5.7 Restitution

A white car of inertia 1200 kg that is moving at a speed of 7.2 m/s rear-ends a blue car of inertia 1000 kg that is initially at rest. Immediately after the collision, the white car has a speed of 3.6 m/s. What is the coefficient of restitution for this collision?

❶ GETTING STARTED By putting all the information in graphical form (**Figure 5.18**), I see that I do not have a value for the final velocity of the blue car, which I need in order to calculate the coefficient of restitution.

Figure 5.18

initial   final

$v_{wx,i} = +7.2$ m/s $v_{bx,i} = 0$ $v_{wx,f} = +3.6$ m/s $v_{bx,f} = ?$

❷ DEVISE PLAN Because the system of the two colliding cars is isolated, I can use conservation of momentum (Eq. 5.5) to obtain the final velocity of the blue car, $v_{bx,f}$.

❸ EXECUTE PLAN I begin by writing Eq. 5.5 with subscripts appropriate to this particular collision:

$$m_w v_{wx,i} + m_b v_{bx,i} = m_w v_{wx,f} + m_b v_{bx,f}$$

or

$$m_w v_{wx,i} + 0 = m_w v_{wx,f} + m_b v_{bx,f}.$$

Solving for $v_{bx,f}$ and substituting the values given, I get

$$v_{bx,f} = \frac{m_w}{m_b}(v_{wx,i} - v_{wx,f})$$

$$= \frac{1200 \text{ kg}}{1000 \text{ kg}}(7.2 \text{ m/s} - 3.6 \text{ m/s}) = 4.3 \text{ m/s}.$$

Now I can substitute the initial and final velocities into Eq. 5.19 to obtain the coefficient of restitution:

$$e = -\frac{v_{wx,f} - v_{bx,f}}{v_{wx,i} - v_{bx,i}}$$

$$= -\frac{(+3.6 \text{ m/s}) - (+4.3 \text{ m/s})}{(7.2 \text{ m/s}) - 0} = 0.097. \checkmark$$

❹ EVALUATE RESULT The coefficient of restitution is rather small, but that is to be expected because cars don't bounce like superballs. Indeed, the blue car moves just a little bit faster than the white car after the collision (4.3 m/s versus 3.6 m/s), as I expect.

5.11 In a totally inelastic collision between two objects in an isolated system with one of the objects initially at rest, is it possible to lose *all* of the system's initial kinetic energy?

5.7 Conservation of energy

Because no energy is transferred to or from a closed system, conservation of energy requires that any change in the kinetic energy of a closed system be compensated by an equal change in the internal energy so that the sum of the kinetic and internal energies of the system does not change:

$$K_i + E_{int,i} = K_f + E_{int,f} \quad \text{(closed system).} \tag{5.20}$$

In contrast to Eq. 5.14, which holds for only an elastic collision, Eq. 5.20 holds for any closed system. If we write the sum of the kinetic and internal energies of an object or system as the **energy** of the object or system,

$$E \equiv K + E_{int}, \tag{5.21}$$

then we can rewrite Eq. 5.20 as

$$E_i = E_f \quad \text{(closed system)} \tag{5.22}$$

or

$$\Delta E = 0 \quad \text{(closed system).} \tag{5.23}$$

Note the parallel between Eq. 4.17, $\Delta \vec{p} = \vec{0}$, and Eq. 5.23. Equation 4.17 embodies conservation of momentum and states that the momentum of an isolated system cannot change. Equation 5.23 embodies conservation of energy: It states

Figure 5.19 Two examples of energy conservation in a closed system. (*a*) The ball's kinetic energy is converted to internal energy in the deformed mattress. (*b*) Chemical energy stored in the battery is converted to thermal energy (the battery gets hot). In both cases, as the bar graphs show, the system's energy remains the same.

(*a*) Dropping a ball onto a mattress

Collision converts kinetic energy to internal energy; sum of K and E_{int} does not change.

(*b*) Draining a battery by shorting it

Short converts chemical energy to thermal energy; sum of E_{chem} and E_{th} does not change.

that the energy of a closed system cannot change; that is, energy cannot be created or destroyed.

Even though we cannot yet calculate the internal energy E_{int}, Eq. 5.23 allows us to draw a number of important conclusions. First, if the kinetic energy of a closed system changes, then the state of the system must change in such a way that its internal energy changes by an amount

$$\Delta E_{int} = -\Delta K \quad \text{(closed system)}. \tag{5.24}$$

As an example, consider **Figure 5.19a**. A ball is dropped onto a mattress, where it comes to rest. During the time interval from the instant just before the ball hits the mattress to the instant at which the ball comes to rest, the motion of the ball changes and the shape of the mattress changes. The ball and mattress constitute a closed system, and so the decrease in kinetic energy must be accompanied by an increase in internal energy. Equation 5.24 requires the loss in kinetic energy to be equal to the gain in internal energy.

The second conclusion we can draw from Eq. 5.23 is that if the kinetic energy of a closed system does not change ($\Delta K = 0$), neither does the internal energy of the system ($\Delta E_{int} = 0$). Because E_{int} is the sum of the internal energies of all the parts that make up the system, however, $\Delta E_{int} = 0$ does *not* mean that no changes in state take place. For instance, E_{int} remains constant when internal energy is transferred from one part of a closed system to another:

$$\Delta E_{int,1} = -\Delta E_{int,2} \Rightarrow \Delta E_{int} = 0 \quad \text{(closed system, } \Delta K = 0) \tag{5.25}$$

or when one form of internal energy is converted to another:

$$\Delta E_{form\,1} = -\Delta E_{form\,2} \Rightarrow \Delta E_{int} = 0 \text{ (closed system, } \Delta K = 0). \tag{5.26}$$

As an example, consider Figure 5.19b. When the battery is drained rapidly, it becomes very hot. Because there is no motion before and after the draining, no change in kinetic energy occurs, but the chemical energy in the battery is converted to thermal energy. Equation 5.26 requires the loss in chemical energy to be equal to the gain in thermal energy:

$$\Delta E_{chem} + \Delta E_{th} = 0. \tag{5.27}$$

QUANTITATIVE TOOLS

In practice there are often more than two simultaneous changes of state in a system (see Checkpoint 5.8, for instance), but regardless of how many energy conversions and transfers take place, the law of conservation of energy requires that the *amount of energy* in a closed system never changes.

Example 5.8 Making light

A 0.20-kg steel ball is dropped into a ball of dough, striking the dough at a speed of 2.3 m/s and coming to rest inside the dough. If it were possible to turn all of the energy converted in this totally inelastic collision into light, how long could you light a desk lamp? It takes 25 J to light a desk lamp for 1.0 s.

❶ GETTING STARTED I begin by applying the procedure for choosing a closed system. Although the problem doesn't specify it explicitly, I'm assuming the dough is at rest both before and after the steel ball is dropped in it; it could, for example, be at rest on a countertop. Only the steel ball has kinetic energy initially, and all of this energy is converted to internal energy as the ball comes to rest in the dough (**Figure 5.20**). So I have to calculate the initial kinetic energy of the ball and determine how long that amount of energy could light a lamp, given that 25 J lights a lamp for 1.0 s.

Figure 5.20

❷ DEVISE PLAN To determine the initial kinetic energy of the ball, I use Eq. 5.12. Then I divide this result by 25 J to determine how many seconds I can light a lamp.

❸ EXECUTE PLAN The initial kinetic energy of the ball is

$$K_{b,i} = \tfrac{1}{2} m_b v_{b,i}^2 = \tfrac{1}{2}(0.20 \text{ kg})(2.3 \text{ m/s})^2 = 0.53 \text{ J}.$$

Given that a desk lamp requires 25 J per second, this 0.53 J lights a lamp for

$$\frac{\text{energy available}}{\text{energy needed per second}} = \frac{0.53 \text{ J}}{25 \text{ J/s}} = 0.021 \text{ s.} ✔$$

❹ EVALUATE RESULT The length of time I obtained, two hundredths of a second, is not very much! However, a 0.20-kg steel ball moving at 2.3 m/s does not have much kinetic energy: I know from experience that a small steel ball's ability to induce state changes—to crumple or deform objects, for example—is very limited. So it makes sense that one can't light a desk lamp for very long.

5.12 A gallon of gasoline contains approximately 1.2×10^8 J of energy. If all of this energy were converted to kinetic energy in a 1200-kg car, how fast would the car go?

5.8 Explosive separations

Is it possible to have a process in which kinetic energy is *gained* at the expense of internal energy? Yes, in an *explosion*, or any other type of **explosive separation**, where objects separate or break apart from each other, kinetic energy increases and internal energy decreases. The firing of a cannon is one example (**Figure 5.21**). Initially the cannon and cannonball are at rest. When the cannon is fired, the cannonball flies out of the barrel, and the cannon *recoils* in the opposite direction. (If it didn't recoil, the momentum of the system would not remain zero.) Both the cannon and cannonball therefore gain kinetic energy at the expense of chemical energy in the gun powder. This situation is the inverse of a totally inelastic collision: In this explosive separation, we start with the two objects together ($v_{12} = 0$) and end with them moving apart ($v_{12} > 0$).

Figure 5.22a shows an explosive separation that can be carried out on a low-friction track. Two carts, of inertias m and $3m$, are held against a compressed spring. When the carts are released, they move apart as the spring expands. As it expands, the spring's state changes and so does its internal energy; the decrease

Figure 5.21 When a cannon is fired, internal (chemical) energy is converted to kinetic energy.

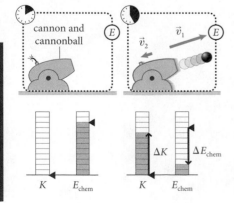

Figure 5.22 Another example of an explosive separation.

(a) When carts are released, spring pushes them apart

(c) Velocity-versus-time graph for the motion

(b) Initial and final energies of system

in internal energy of the spring causes an increase in the kinetic energy of the carts (Figure 5.22b). Notice how the velocity-versus-time graph for this explosive separation (Figure 5.22c) is the inverse of the one in Figure 5.2b.

To determine the final speeds in Figure 5.22, we need to know how much energy E_{int} the spring releases, a topic not covered until Chapter 9. Once we know ΔE_{int}, we have two equations that allow us to obtain the two final velocities, one a consequence of conservation of momentum:

$$0 = m_1 v_{1x,f} + m_2 v_{2x,f} \qquad (5.28)$$

(because $v_{1x,i} = v_{2x,i} = 0$) and the other a consequence of conservation of energy:

$$\Delta K + \Delta E_{int} = \tfrac{1}{2} m_1 v_{1f}^2 + \tfrac{1}{2} m_2 v_{2f}^2 + \Delta E_{int} = 0. \qquad (5.29)$$

Note that in this example the *initial* relative speed is zero, making e in Eq. 5.19 infinite. There is no restitution because there is no initial relative speed to be restituted. In the more general case where the two objects have a nonzero initial relative speed, $e > 1$.

Example 5.9 Spring energy

A 0.25-kg cart is held at rest against a compressed spring as in Figure 5.8a and then released. The cart's speed after it separates from the spring is 2.5 m/s. The spring is then compressed by the same amount between a 0.25-kg cart and a 0.50-kg cart, as shown in Figure 5.22a, and the carts are released from rest. What are the carts' speeds after separating from the spring?

❶ **GETTING STARTED** The key point in this problem is the identical compression of the spring in the two cases: The initial state of the spring is therefore the same before both releases. Because the spring ends in the same uncompressed state in both cases, the change in its internal energy must be the same in both cases. In the first case, all of this energy is transferred to the 0.25-kg cart. In the second case, the same amount of energy is distributed between the two carts.

❷ **DEVISE PLAN** To calculate the kinetic energy of the single cart in the first release, I use Eq. 5.12. This gives me the amount of energy stored in the compressed spring. The final velocities of the two carts in the second case are then given by Eqs. 5.28 and 5.29.

❸ **EXECUTE PLAN** From Eq. 5.12, I get

$$K = \tfrac{1}{2} m v^2 = \tfrac{1}{2} (0.25 \text{ kg})(2.5 \text{ m/s})^2 = 0.78 \text{ J}$$

and so the change in the spring's internal energy is $\Delta E_{int} = -0.78$ J. Next I rewrite Eq. 5.28 as $v_{1x,f} = -(m_2/m_1)v_{2x,f}$. Substituting this result in Eq. 5.29, I get

$$\tfrac{1}{2} m_1 \left(\frac{m_2}{m_1} \right)^2 v_{2x,f}^2 + \tfrac{1}{2} m_2 v_{2x,f}^2 = -\Delta E_{int}.$$

(Continued)

Solving for the final velocity of cart 2 gives

$$v_{2xf} = \sqrt{\frac{-2m_1 \Delta E_{int}}{m_2(m_1 + m_2)}}$$

$$v_{2xf} = \sqrt{\frac{-2(0.25 \text{ kg})(-0.78 \text{ J})}{(0.50 \text{ kg})(0.25 \text{ kg} + 0.50 \text{ kg})}} = 1.0 \text{ m/s.} ✔$$

Substituting this result into my rewritten Eq. 5.28, $v_{1x,f} = -(m_2/m_1)v_{2x,f}$, I get $v_{1x,f} = -2.0$ m/s. ✔

❹ EVALUATE RESULT The carts move in opposite directions, as expected. I also note that cart 1 moves at twice the speed of cart 2, as it should to keep the final momentum of the system zero. Finally, because my assignment of m_1 and m_2 is arbitrary, I verify that I get the same result when I substitute $m_1 = 0.50$ kg and $m_2 = 0.25$ kg. (You may want to check this yourself. When you reverse the inertias, why does the velocity of cart 1 reverse to positive and the velocity of cart 2 reverse to negative?)

✋ **5.13** Does each cart in Example 5.9 get half of the spring's energy? Why or why not?

Chapter Glossary

SI units of physical quantities are given in parentheses.

Closed system A system to or from which no energy is transferred. See the Procedure box on page 109.

Coefficient of restitution e (unitless) A scalar equal to the ratio of relative speeds after and before a collision of two objects:

$$e \equiv \frac{v_{12f}}{v_{12i}} \tag{5.18}$$

Conservation of energy Energy can be transferred from one object to another or converted from one form to another, but it cannot be created or destroyed. The energy of a closed system cannot change:

$$\Delta E = 0 \quad \text{(closed system)}. \tag{5.23}$$

Elastic, inelastic, totally inelastic collision Collisions between two objects are classified according to what happens to the relative speed $v_{12} = |\vec{v}_2 - \vec{v}_1|$ of the two objects, as summarized in Table 5.4.

Energy E (J) A scalar that provides a quantitative measure of the state or motion of an object or system. Energy appears in many different forms. The energy of an object or system always refers to the sum of all forms of energy in that object or system.

Explosive separation A process in which objects break apart from one another and the relative speed of the objects increases.

Internal energy E_{int} (J) Any energy not associated with the motion of an object or system. Internal energy is a quantitative measure of the state of the object or system.

Irreversible process A process involving changes that cannot undo themselves spontaneously.

Joule (J) The derived SI unit of energy, defined as $1 \text{ J} \equiv 1 \text{ kg} \cdot \text{m}^2/\text{s}^2$.

Kinetic energy K (J) Energy associated with the motion of an object. The kinetic energy K of an object of inertia m moving at speed v is

$$K \equiv \tfrac{1}{2}mv^2. \tag{5.12}$$

Process The transformation of a system from an initial state to a final state.

Relative velocity $\vec{v}_{12}$ (m/s) The velocity of one object relative to another:

$$\vec{v}_{12} \equiv \vec{v}_2 - \vec{v}_1. \tag{5.1}$$

The magnitude of this velocity is called the *relative speed* $v_{12} \equiv |\vec{v}_2 - \vec{v}_1|$.

Reversible process A process that can run backward so that the initial state is restored.

State The condition of an object (or a system) as specified by a complete set of variables.

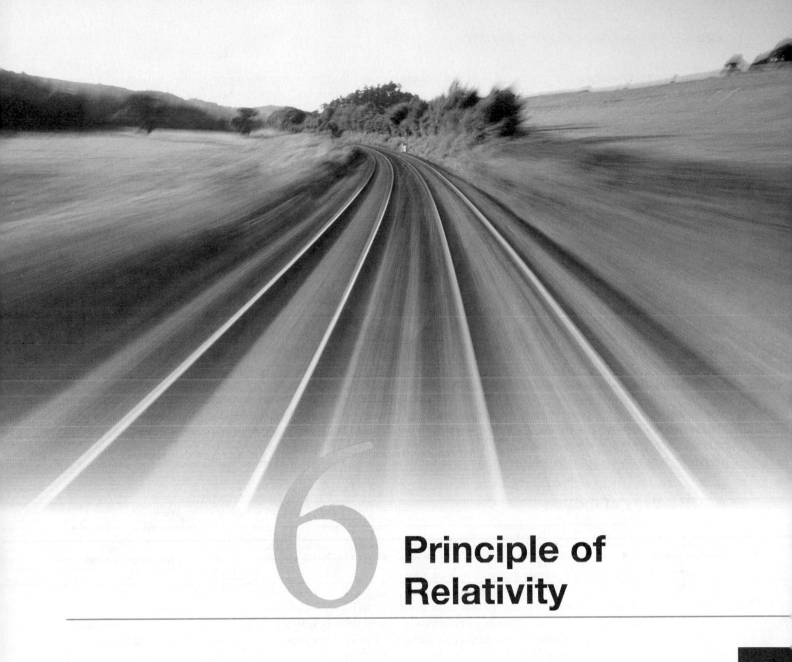

6 Principle of Relativity

6.1 Relativity of motion

6.2 Inertial reference frames

6.3 Principle of relativity

6.4 Zero-momentum reference frame

6.5 Galilean relativity

6.6 Center of mass

6.7 Convertible kinetic energy

6.8 Conservation laws and relativity

CONCEPTS

QUANTITATIVE TOOLS

Did you ever, sitting in a car at a red light and looking at the car next to you, slam on the brakes because you thought you were starting to roll but it turned out your car never moved? If you did, you experienced the relativity of motion, first described quantitatively by Galileo. You may have heard the term *relativity* in the context of Albert Einstein's famous theories of general relativity and special relativity. We'll touch upon one basic aspect of general relativity in Chapter 13 and discuss special relativity in Chapter 14. Underlying all of relativity is something we have so far ignored in our discussion of motion: the fact that the velocity measured for any object depends on the motion of the **observer** (the person doing the measuring). For example, to a person sitting in a moving train, a suitcase on the overhead rack is at rest, but to a person standing on a station platform watching the train speed by, the suitcase is not at rest. According to the person in the train, the suitcase has zero momentum ($m\vec{v}$) and zero kinetic energy ($\frac{1}{2}mv^2$). According to the person on the platform, the suitcase has nonzero momentum and nonzero kinetic energy. In this chapter we investigate whether or not the laws of conservation of momentum and conservation of energy depend on the velocity of the observer. In other words, if these laws are valid for one observer, are they also valid for an observer who is moving relative to the first observer?

6.1 Relativity of motion

Remember from Chapter 2 that whenever we talk about motion, we must specify a reference axis along which the motion occurs and an origin. Together, the axis and origin are called a **reference frame.** In our study of motion thus far, we have considered the motion of carts along a low-friction track, collecting our data using a ruler affixed to the track; that is to say, we collected our data while standing in a reference frame at rest relative to the surface of Earth (this is called an **Earth reference frame**).

What happens to the data if we are moving as we collect them—in other words, if we are in a reference frame that is moving relative to Earth? Imagine that we are moving alongside the track and want to describe a collision between two carts. Do the conservation laws hold in a reference

frame that is moving relative to Earth? Or, to put the question another way, does the behavior of the carts change if we are in motion as we study that behavior?

Consider, for example, the situation depicted in **Figure 6.1a**: two observers watching the motions of two cars. Car 1 is moving at constant velocity $\vec{v}_1$, and car 2 is at rest relative to Earth. Observer E is at rest relative to Earth, while observer M is inside car 1. The velocity $\vec{v}_M$ of observer M is the same as the velocity of car 1: $\vec{v}_M = \vec{v}_1$.

Relative to observer M, the position of car 1 is not changing; that is, car 1 is at rest relative to observer M. The distance to car 2, however, is steadily increasing, and so relative to observer M, car 2, observer E, and all the surroundings move to the left (Figure 6.1b). To distinguish quantities measured by different observers, we add a capital letter subscript to denote the observer. For instance, $\vec{v}_{M2}$ represents observer M's measurement of the velocity of car 2, also called the velocity of car 2 *relative to* observer M. When we are comparing quantities in various reference frames, quantities measured relative to Earth are given the subscript E. For example, relative to Earth the velocity of car 1 is represented by $\vec{v}_{E1}$ (When the Earth reference frame is the only reference frame, we drop the subscript E, recovering the notation we have used before: $\vec{v}_{E1} = \vec{v}_1$.)

To determine a relationship between the quantities measured by two observers moving relative to each other, let's start with a simple example. **Figure 6.2** shows five frames of a film of two carts on a low-friction track. In Figure 6.2a the positions of the two carts are measured with ruler A, which is affixed to the track (that is, in the Earth reference frame). Relative to ruler A, cart 1 is at rest and its position remains fixed at 22.5 mm. Cart 2 is moving to the right, and its position on ruler A changes from 0 to 14.4 mm.

In Figure 6.2b the positions of the two carts are measured with ruler B, which moves along with cart 2: The zero mark on ruler B remains aligned with the front of cart 2. The position of cart 2 therefore remains fixed at a ruler reading of 0, and so, relative to ruler B, cart 2 is at rest. On this ruler, the position of cart 1 does *not* remain fixed, however—the reading for this cart's position decreases from 22.5 mm to 8.1 mm over the five frames. That is to say, cart 1 moves 22.5 mm − 8.1 mm = 14.4 mm *to the left* along ruler B.

Figure 6.1 The motion you perceive depends on your reference frame.

(a) **Earth reference frame (observer E)**

$\vec{v}_2 = \vec{0}$ $\vec{v}_M$ $\vec{v}_1$

car 2   car 1

Relative to observer E, car 2 is at rest and car 1 moves to the right.

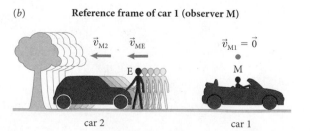

(b) **Reference frame of car 1 (observer M)**

$\vec{v}_{M2}$ $\vec{v}_{ME}$ $\vec{v}_{M1} = \vec{0}$

car 2   car 1

But relative to observer M, car 1 is at rest while car 2, observer E, and Earth move to the left.

Figure 6.2 Two identical carts on a low-friction track. The positions of the carts are measured with (*a*) a ruler affixed to the track and (*b*) a ruler moving along with cart 2. In the Earth reference frame, cart 1 is at rest and cart 2 is moving to the right.

(*a*) Ruler is fixed to track

(*b*) Ruler moves with cart 2

Figure 6.3*a* shows a position-versus-frame graph for the two carts drawn from the readings on ruler A in Figure 6.2*a*. What is shown in the graph corresponds to what an observer at rest alongside the track sees: cart 1 at rest and the *x* component of the velocity of cart 2 a constant $+3.6$ mm/frame. These are the observations taken in the Earth reference frame.

Figure 6.3*b* is the position-versus-frame graph for the two carts drawn from the readings on ruler B in Figure 6.2*b*. What is shown in the graph corresponds to what an observer M sitting on top of cart 2 sees: cart 2 at rest and the *x* component of the velocity of cart 1 a constant -3.6 mm/frame (the negative sign indicates that the cart moves to the left in the figure).

Example 6.1 Moving at my own speed

Suppose that in the situation shown in Figure 6.2, a third ruler is affixed to some device (not shown) that moves to the right along the track at a speed of 2.0 mm/frame. If in the Earth reference frame cart 2 again moves at $+3.6$ mm/frame and cart 1 is again at rest, what are the cart velocities according to an observer moving along with ruler C?

❶ **GETTING STARTED** If I arbitrarily let ruler C start in the position shown in frame 1 of Figure 6.2*b*—the zero mark on ruler C aligned with the front of cart 2—this ruler is shifted 2.0 mm to the right in the second frame and another 2.0 mm to the right in each successive frame. I have to use the readings from this ruler to determine the cart velocities.

❷ **DEVISE PLAN** I begin by making a table showing the position of each cart in each frame according to an observer moving along with ruler C. Because the ruler moves 2.0 mm to the right in each frame, I can obtain the readings on this ruler by subtracting 2.0 mm from each cart position in frame 2 of Figure 6.2*a*, subtracting 4.0 mm from each cart position in frame 3, subtracting 6.0 mm from each cart position in frame 4, and so on. I can then use these positions to make a position-versus-frame graph like the ones in Figure 6.3 and determine the velocities of the carts from the slopes of the curves.

Figure 6.3 Position-versus-frame graphs for the carts of Figure 6.2 as determined from readings on (*a*) ruler A and (*b*) ruler B.

❸ EXECUTE PLAN My table of the cart positions measured with ruler C is shown in **Figure 6.4**. By plotting these data, I see that the x component of the velocity of cart 1 is -2.0 mm/frame and that of cart 2 is $+1.6$ mm/frame. ✔

Figure 6.4

x_{M2} (mm)	x_{M1} (mm)
0	22.5
1.6	20.5
3.2	18.5
4.8	16.5
6.4	14.5

❹ EVALUATE RESULT The observer moving with ruler C sees cart 1 moving to the left, meaning that the x component of its velocity should be negative, as I found. This observer and cart 2 both move in the positive x direction in the Earth reference frame, but the speed of cart 2 is higher than that of ruler C, and so cart 2 moves to the right relative to the observer. Therefore the x component of its velocity should be positive, in agreement with what I found. Because the velocity of ruler C is different from the velocity of either cart, neither cart is at rest relative to ruler C.

This example and the text preceding it show that motion is a relative concept. In the Earth reference frame, cart 1 is at rest and cart 2 is moving. Relative to the moving ruler in Figure 6.2b, cart 1 is moving and cart 2 is at rest. And relative to the ruler of Example 6.1, both carts are moving. In all three reference frames, however, we discover that the carts move at constant velocity. We could just as well have used a ruler moving at $+1.0$ mm/frame, $+4.0$ mm/frame, -0.1 mm/frame, or any other constant velocity. In each case, we would reach the same conclusion: The carts move at constant velocity. So, if an object moves at constant velocity in the Earth reference frame, its motion observed from *any reference frame moving at constant velocity relative to Earth* is also at constant velocity.

Comparing Figures 6.3a and 6.3b, we see that the x component of each cart's velocity according to ruler A (Figure 6.3a) is 3.6 mm/frame higher than the velocity

according to ruler B (Figure 6.3b). So, an object's velocity $\vec{v}_{Ao}$ determined from the readings on ruler A is equal to the sum of the velocity $\vec{v}_{AB}$ of ruler B relative to ruler A and the velocity $\vec{v}_{Bo}$ of the object relative to ruler B: $\vec{v}_{Ao} = \vec{v}_{AB} + \vec{v}_{Bo}$. For cart 1, we have $0 = +3.6$ mm/frame $+ (-3.6$ mm/frame$)$; for cart 2, $+3.6$ mm/frame $= +3.6$ mm/frame $+ 0$. You can readily verify that the same is true for the velocities determined with ruler C in Example 6.1.

✋ 6.1 What is the velocity of each cart in Figure 6.2 measured by an observer moving at -3.0 mm/frame in the Earth reference frame?

6.2 Inertial reference frames

How does the choice of reference frame affect our accounting methods for momentum and energy? To answer this question, let's consider the two carts of Figure 6.2 from the point of view of two observers. To an observer E, who is at rest relative to Earth, cart 1 is at rest and cart 2 is moving at constant velocity (**Figure 6.5a**). To an observer M, who is moving along with cart 2, cart 2 is at rest and cart 1 is moving at constant velocity (Figure 6.5b). Even though the observers obtain different values for the carts' velocities, these values are constant, and therefore both observers conclude that the momentum of each cart is constant. Both observers also agree that the two carts are isolated, which means that conservation of momentum yields $\Delta\vec{p} = \vec{0}$ (Eq. 4.17) for each cart, in agreement with their observations.

✋ 6.2 From the point of view of each observer in Figure 6.5, (a) is the energy of each cart constant? (b) Is the isolated system containing cart 1 closed? (c) Is the isolated system containing cart 2 closed?

Although we checked for only the simple case of carts moving at constant velocity on a low-friction track, Figure 6.5 and Checkpoint 6.2 suggest that the accounting procedures and principles we introduced in the preceding two chapters can be applied in any reference frame moving at constant velocity relative to Earth. Indeed, when we are moving at constant velocity relative to Earth, things around us behave the same way they behave when we are at rest on the ground. For example, imagine being in a plane flying at a constant speed of 260 m/s in a straight line. The surface of the coffee in the cup in front of you looks no different

Figure 6.5 The carts of Figure 6.2 seen by (a) an observer in the Earth reference frame and (b) an observer moving along with cart 2.

(a) **Earth reference frame (observer E)**   (b) **Reference frame of cart 2 (observer M)**

Observers E and M see both carts as isolated and as having constant momentum.

Figure 6.6 Motion of a marble in an accelerating car viewed from (*a*) the Earth reference frame and (*b*) a reference frame affixed to the car. $\vec{a}_{Ec}$ is the **E**arth observer's measurement of the **c**ar's acceleration, $\vec{a}_{ME}$ is the **m**oving observer's measurement of **E**arth's acceleration, and $\vec{a}_{Mc}$ is the **m**oving observer's measurement of the **c**ar's acceleration.

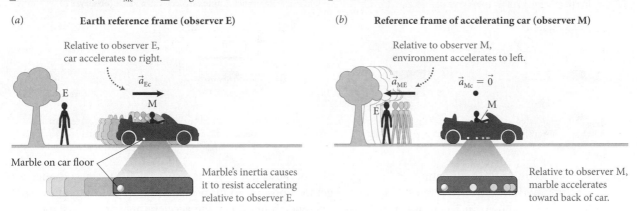

(*a*) **Earth reference frame (observer E)**

Relative to observer E, car accelerates to right.

$\vec{a}_{Ec}$

E
M

Marble on car floor

Marble's inertia causes it to resist accelerating relative to observer E.

(*b*) **Reference frame of accelerating car (observer M)**

Relative to observer M, environment accelerates to left.

$\vec{a}_{ME}$ $\vec{a}_{Mc} = \vec{0}$

E
M

Relative to observer M, marble accelerates toward back of car.

from the way it looks at home. If you drop your keys, they fall straight down just as they would if the plane were at rest on the ground. And when the flight attendant pours coffee into your cup while you all move at 260 m/s, you don't expect him to spill it on you any more than you do when a waiter pours your coffee in a restaurant.

In fact, if the engines are very quiet, the ride is smooth, and the window shades are down, it is impossible for you to determine whether or not the plane is moving. Here is the simplest possible experiment: Put a marble on the floor of the plane. Provided the floor is level relative to the ground, the marble remains at rest where you placed it. This is true whether the plane is at rest or cruising at a constant 260 m/s. When the plane is sitting at the gate, inertia keeps the marble at rest relative to the floor (which is at rest relative to the ground), and so $\vec{a} = \vec{0}$. In the air, inertia keeps the marble moving along with the plane at a constant velocity relative to the ground (or, put differently, inertia keeps the marble at rest relative to the floor), and so again $\vec{a} = \vec{0}$.

The Earth reference frame or any reference frame moving at constant velocity relative to Earth is called an **inertial reference frame.** We can tell whether or not a reference frame is inertial by testing whether or not the **law of inertia** holds:

In an inertial reference frame, any isolated object that is at rest remains at rest, and any isolated object in motion keeps moving at a constant velocity.

The law of inertia does not hold in a reference frame that is accelerating relative to Earth. For example, imagine sitting in the passenger seat of a car moving at constant velocity with a marble on the floor near your feet. As long as the car is on a horizontal surface and keeps going straight at a constant speed, the marble remains at rest. When the driver suddenly accelerates forward, however, everything in the car lurches backward, with the marble probably ending up somewhere in the back of the car. According to an observer at rest in the Earth reference frame (**Figure 6.6a**), the marble resists being accelerated forward because of its inertia, and unless you have glued it to the floor or restrained it in some other way, it fails to keep up with the accelerating car. Seen

from inside the car, the isolated marble suddenly accelerates backward, and so the law of inertia does not hold in the reference frame of the accelerating car (Figure 6.6*b*). Reference frames in which the law of inertia does not hold are called *noninertial reference frames.*

We have singled out the Earth reference frame as the basic inertial reference frame. There is nothing fundamentally special about the Earth reference frame, however, other than that we perform most experiments in this frame. Strictly speaking, Earth is not an inertial reference frame because it revolves around a north-south axis and orbits the Sun in a nearly circular orbit. Because motion on a curved path means that the direction of the velocity is changing and so the velocity is not constant, Earth is accelerating and therefore is a noninertial reference frame. For most cases, the acceleration is too small to be noticeable, and so we may, for most practical purposes, consider the Earth reference frame to be inertial.

Exercise 6.2 Inertial or not?

Which of these reference frames are inertial: one affixed to (*a*) a merry-go-round, (*b*) the space shuttle orbiting Earth, (*c*) an airplane taking off, (*d*) a train moving at constant speed along a straight track?

SOLUTION (*b*) and (*d*). If I imagine placing a marble at rest in each reference frame and then observing the marble's motion, I can tell whether the law of inertia holds in that reference frame. From experience, I know that a marble remains at rest on the floor of a train moving at constant speed along a straight track, and so the train's reference frame is inertial. I also know that a marble moves away from where I place it on a merry-go-round and in an airplane taking off, so those reference frames are noninertial. Having never been on the space shuttle, I have no direct experience with such a reference frame. However, I have seen astronauts and objects floating in the space shuttle, and this motion suggests that objects stay at rest or keep moving as the law of inertia states, suggesting that the reference frame of the shuttle is inertial.* ✔

---

*Just like the Earth reference frame, the shuttle reference frame is only approximately inertial.

Figure 6.7 A stationary cart and an accelerating cart viewed from (*a*) the Earth reference frame and (*b*) a reference frame affixed to the accelerating cart.

(*a*) **Earth reference frame (observer E)**

Observer E: says cart 2 is isolated and has (constant) zero momentum . . .   . . . and cart 1 is not isolated and has changing momentum.

(*b*) **Reference frame of accelerating cart (observer M)**

Observer M: agrees cart 2 is isolated but says its momentum is changing, ... and agrees cart 1 is not isolated, but says it remains at rest.

Our accounting procedures for momentum and energy cannot be used in noninertial reference frames. Consider, for example, the two carts shown in **Figure 6.7**. Cart 1 is being accelerated by a spring, and cart 2 is at rest in the Earth reference frame. Cart 2 constitutes an isolated system, but cart 1 is not isolated because it interacts with the spring. To observer E in the Earth reference frame (Figure 6.7*a*), the behavior of both carts is in agreement with the momentum law: The momentum of the nonisolated cart 1 changes, while the momentum of the isolated cart 2 is constant. For observer M, however, who is accelerating along with cart 1 (Figure 6.7*b*), things don't quite add up. From this observer's perspective, cart 1 remains at rest even though it interacts with the spring, and the momentum of cart 2 changes even though that cart is isolated. Equations 4.17 ($\Delta \vec{p} = \vec{0}$) and 5.23 ($\Delta E = 0$), which embody the laws of conservation of momentum and energy, do not hold in the noninertial reference frame of observer M in Figure 6.7*b*.

Are we going to run into problems because the laws of the universe are different in noninertial reference frames?

No, because nothing prescribes the reference frame; we get to choose it. So for now we just avoid using noninertial reference frames. For the accelerating car, for instance, we would choose not a reference frame affixed to the car but the Earth reference frame.

✋ **6.3** From the point of view of each observer in Figure 6.7, (*a*) is the energy of each cart constant? (*b*) Is the isolated system containing cart 1 closed? (*c*) Is the isolated system containing cart 2 closed? (*d*) Do the observations made by each observer agree with the conservation of energy law?

6.3 Principle of relativity

In the preceding section, we saw that the conservation laws apply for single objects in inertial reference frames. Let us now test the conservation laws for interacting objects.

Figure 6.8 shows velocity-versus-time graphs for two-cart collisions. The values in Figure 6.8*a* were measured by an observer in the Earth reference frame. As you saw in

Figure 6.8 Velocity-versus-time graphs for two carts colliding on a low-friction track as seen (*a*) from the Earth reference frame and (*b*) from a reference frame moving along the track at $v_{EMx} = -0.20$ m/s relative to Earth. The inertias are 0.36 kg for cart 1 and 0.12 kg for cart 2.

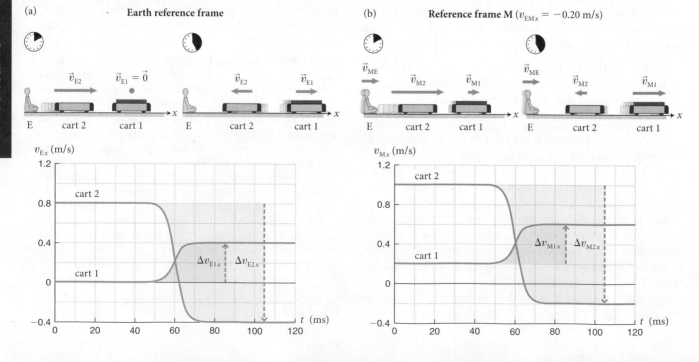

Checkpoint 6.1, we can obtain the velocities of the carts in reference frame M of Figure 6.8b by subtracting the velocities in reference frame M from the velocities in the Earth reference frame. Because reference frame M in Figure 6.8b moves at a constant -0.20 m/s relative to Earth, we must subtract -0.20 m/s (that is, add 0.20 m/s) from the x component of each velocity in the Earth reference frame to obtain the corresponding velocity in reference frame M.

The only difference between Figures 6.8a and 6.8b is that the curves in Figure 6.8b are shifted upward by 0.20 m/s, the relative speed of the two reference frames. However, the *changes* in the x components of the cart's velocities, Δv_{1x} and Δv_{2x}, are not affected by the velocity of reference frame M. Because the inertia of any object is not affected by the motion of an observer studying the object, we observe that the changes in the x component of the carts' momenta, $\Delta p_{1x} = m_1 \Delta v_{1x}$ and $\Delta p_{2x} = m_2 \Delta v_{2x}$, are the same in both reference frames. So, because conservation of momentum requires that $\Delta \vec{p} = 0$ in the Earth reference frame, we also obtain $\Delta \vec{p} = 0$ in reference frame M.

If reference frame M in Figure 6.8b had moved at any other constant velocity relative to Earth, the vertical shift of the curves would be different but the shape of the curves would be the same. Again we would obtain the same momentum changes for the two carts, and again we would conclude that the collision does not change the momentum of the system. So, if the change in the system momentum is zero in the Earth reference frame, it must be zero in all reference frames moving at a constant velocity relative to Earth. Experiments show that this statement can be extended to any inertial reference frame, not just the Earth reference frame.

Example 6.3 Momentum shove

A 0.12-kg cart moving on a straight, low-friction track gets a shove so that its speed changes. Its initial and final speeds measured in the Earth reference frame are 0.40 m/s and 0.80 m/s (**Figure 6.9**). Determine the change in the cart's momentum as seen from (a) the Earth reference frame and (b) a reference frame M moving in the same direction as the cart at a speed of 0.60 m/s relative to the track.

Figure 6.9 Example 6.3.

❶ **GETTING STARTED** To determine the momentum change in either case, I need to know the cart's initial and final velocities in the two reference frames. In the Earth reference frame, $v_{Ecx,i} = +0.40$ m/s and $v_{Ecx,f} = +0.80$ m/s. In reference frame M, which moves at $v_{MEx} = +0.60$ m/s relative to Earth, these values are 0.60 m/s lower: $v_{Mcx,i} = -0.20$ m/s and $v_{Mcx,f} = +0.20$ m/s. I then make a velocity-versus-time graph for the cart as viewed from reference frame M (**Figure 6.10**).

Figure 6.10

❷ **DEVISE PLAN** Now that I have the x components of the initial and final velocities in both reference frames, I can calculate the x components of the initial and final momenta and determine the change in momentum.

❸ **EXECUTE PLAN** (a) In the Earth reference frame, the x components of the initial and final momenta are $p_{Ecx,i} = mv_{Ecx,i} = (0.12$ kg$)(+0.40$ m/s$) = +0.048$ kg·m/s and $p_{Ecx,f} = mv_{Ecx,f} = (0.12$ kg$)(+0.80$ m/s$) = +0.096$ kg·m/s. So the x component of the change in momentum is $\Delta p_{Ecx} = (+0.096$ kg·m/s$) - (+0.048$ kg·m/s$) = +0.048$ kg·m/s. ✔

(b) In reference frame M, $p_{Mcx,i} = mv_{Mcx,i} = (0.12$ kg$) \times (-0.20$ m/s$) = -0.024$ kg·m/s and $p_{Mcx,f} = mv_{Mcx,f} = (0.12$ kg$)(+0.20$ m/s$) = +0.024$ kg·m/s. So $\Delta p_{Mcx} = (+0.024$ kg·m/s$) - (-0.024$ kg·m/s$) = +0.048$ kg·m/s. ✔

❹ **EVALUATE RESULT** The momentum change is the same in the two reference frames, as I expect. In reference frame M, the $v_x(t)$ curve shifts up or down, but its shape does not change, and therefore the values of $\Delta \vec{v}$ and $\Delta \vec{p}$ must also remain the same.

Example 6.3 reaffirms what we have already seen:

The change in a system's momentum is the same in any inertial reference frame.

✋ **6.4** In Example 6.3, what is the change in the cart's kinetic energy due to the shove (a) in the Earth reference frame, (b) in a reference frame moving in the same direction as the cart at 0.60 m/s relative to Earth, and (c) in a reference frame moving in the same direction as the cart at 0.80 m/s relative to Earth?

Unlike changes in momentum, changes in kinetic energy are not the same in two reference frames moving relative to each other. As Checkpoint 6.4 shows, the cart's kinetic energy increases, decreases, or stays the same depending on the reference frame.

The observation that changes in kinetic energy depend on the reference frame is disturbing. What does this result imply about conservation of energy? To begin addressing this question, let's look first at an elastic collision, such as

CONCEPTS

Table 6.1 An elastic collision seen from two reference frames

Cart	Inertia (kg)	v_x (m/s) before	after	Δv_x	Kinetic energy (10^{-3} J) before	after	ΔK
Earth reference frame							
1	0.36	0	+0.40	+0.40	0	29	+29
2	0.12	+0.80	−0.40	−1.2	38	9	−29
				K	$\overline{38}\,+$	$\overline{38}\,+$	$\overline{0}\,+$
Reference frame moving at −0.20 m/s relative to Earth							
1	0.36	+0.20	+0.60	+0.40	7	65	+58
2	0.12	+1.0	−0.20	−1.2	60	2	−58
				K	$\overline{67}\,+$	$\overline{67}\,+$	$\overline{0}\,+$

the one in Figure 6.8. In **Table 6.1** I have listed the velocities and kinetic energy of both carts. Note that even though the change in velocity Δv_x for each cart is the same in the two reference frames, the change in kinetic energy ΔK for each cart is not. In a given reference frame, however, the absolute value of ΔK is the same for both carts, and so the change in the kinetic energy K of the two-cart system is zero in each frame.

A simple way of arguing that the kinetic energy of the two-cart system *has* to remain unchanged in elastic collisions in any inertial reference frame is to look at how we formulated kinetic energy in Chapter 5 in terms of the relative velocities of two objects in a collision. As we saw earlier, differences in velocity do not depend on the velocity of the reference frame (**Figure 6.11**). In particular, our experimental observation that the relative speed of two colliding objects is unchanged in an elastic collision holds when we measure that relative speed in a reference frame that is moving at constant velocity. More generally, we observe:

> **The kinetic energy of a system of two elastically colliding objects does not change in any inertial reference frame.**

Even though K does not change in elastic collisions, the fact that the individual ΔK values depend on the reference frame could be a big problem for conservation of energy

in inelastic collisions. This reference-frame dependence for the individual ΔK values could mean that ΔK for the system also depends on the reference frame. Recall from Section 5.3 that in inelastic collisions some kinetic energy is converted to internal energy, which is a measure of the state of the system. Because changes in kinetic energy are reference-frame-dependent, the amount that gets converted could be reference-frame-dependent as well and that would mean that the final state of the system would depend on the reference frame! To determine whether or not this is the case, we examine an inelastic collision in the next example.

Example 6.4 Energy conversion

Consider a collision between the two carts of Table 6.1, starting from the same initial velocities, but with $v_{\mathrm{E1x,f}} = +0.30$ m/s. Make a table like Table 6.1 for this situation, and compare the amount of kinetic energy converted to internal energy in the Earth reference frame and in a reference frame M moving at −0.20 m/s relative to the track.

❶ **GETTING STARTED** Because all the initial values are the same, I can copy all the "before" values from Table 6.1. I am given the final velocity of cart 1, and so I need to determine the final velocity of cart 2 in the Earth reference frame, then determine the final velocities in reference frame M, calculate the corresponding kinetic energies, and determine the change in kinetic energy in each reference frame.

Figure 6.11 The relative velocity of the two colliding carts of Figure 6.8 is the same in (*a*) the Earth reference frame and (*b*) a reference frame moving along the track at $v_{\mathrm{EMx}} = -0.20$ m/s relative to Earth.

❷ DEVISE PLAN To determine $v_{E2x,f}$, I apply conservation of momentum to the isolated system of the two carts, which tells me that $\Delta \vec{p} = \vec{0}$. To calculate the two final velocities in reference frame M, I subtract the velocity of this reference frame from the carts' velocities in the Earth reference frame. Then I determine the kinetic energies from $K = \frac{1}{2}mv^2$ and complete the table by determining the changes in kinetic energy.

❸ EXECUTE PLAN Because $\vec{p}_i = \vec{p}_f$, I have

$$m_1 v_{E1x,i} + m_2 v_{E2x,i} = m_1 v_{E1x,f} + m_2 v_{E2x,f}.$$

Substituting $v_{E1x,i} = 0$ and solving for $v_{E2x,f}$, I get

$$v_{E2x,f} = \frac{m_2 v_{E2x,i} - m_1 v_{E1x,f}}{m_2}.$$

Substituting the given values into this expression, I obtain $v_{E2x,f} = -0.10 \text{ m/s}$.

Because $v_{EMx} = -0.20$ m/s, I must add 0.20 m/s to the x components of the carts' velocities in the Earth reference frame to determine the corresponding values in reference frame M:

$$v_{M1x,i} = 0 + (+0.20 \text{ m/s}) = +0.20 \text{ m/s}$$

$$v_{M2x,i} = (+0.80 \text{ m/s}) + (+0.20 \text{ m/s}) = +1.00 \text{ m/s}$$

$$v_{M1x,f} = (+0.30 \text{ m/s}) + (+0.20 \text{ m/s}) = +0.50 \text{ m/s}$$

$$v_{M2x,f} = (-0.10 \text{ m/s}) + (+0.20 \text{ m/s}) = +0.10 \text{ m/s}.$$

Now I can calculate all the kinetic energies and complete the table (**Table 6.2**). ✔

❹ EVALUATE RESULT Each cart's kinetic energy change is different in the two reference frames because, as just noted in the text, changes in kinetic energy are reference-frame-dependent. However, the change in the *system*'s kinetic energy is the same in the two reference frames: −21 mJ in both cases. This tells me that the amount of kinetic energy converted to internal energy—and therefore the final state of the two carts—does not depend on the reference frame, as I expect.

✋ **6.5** Repeat Example 6.4 but let the collision be totally inelastic.

The results of Example 6.4 and Checkpoint 6.5 are reassuring. Imagine that the converted kinetic energy becomes thermal energy, with the result that the temperature of each cart increases. You wouldn't expect these temperature changes to be different when you view the collision from reference frames that are moving at constant speed relative to each other. Likewise, in a collision between two cars, where the converted kinetic energy goes into crushing the fenders, you wouldn't expect the bending of the metal to depend on the reference frame. The amount of kinetic energy converted to internal energy during an inelastic collision does not depend on the velocity of the reference frame relative to the colliding objects.

These observations, together with the results we obtained in the examples in this section, tell us that the same laws and principles we discussed in Chapters 4 and 5 hold in any inertial reference frame. In particular, the momentum and energy laws can be used in any inertial reference frame. Earlier we saw that it is not possible to tell the difference between various inertial reference frames—that is, reference frames in which the law of inertia holds. It is an experimental fact that things behave the same way in all inertial reference frames. We should therefore expect the laws that describe that behavior to be the same too. This leads us to formulate the **principle of relativity:**

The laws of the universe are the same in all inertial reference frames moving at constant velocity relative to each other.

The principle of relativity provides a criterion for judging theories: For a theory to be valid, it must prescribe the same behavior in all inertial reference frames. Although observers in different inertial reference frames record different values for the velocities of carts involved in a collision and therefore different momenta and kinetic energies, they agree that the momentum and energy of the two-cart system do not change.

It follows from the principle of relativity that no experiment carried out entirely in one inertial reference frame can tell what the motion of that reference frame is relative to another reference frame. Returning to the example of Section 6.2: Sitting in a very quiet airplane during a smooth, turbulence-free ride, it is impossible to tell if you are flying

CONCEPTS

Table 6.2 An inelastic collision seen from two reference frames

Cart	Inertia (kg)	v_x (m/s) before	v_x (m/s) after	Δv_x	Kinetic energy (10^{-3} J) before	Kinetic energy (10^{-3} J) after	ΔK
Earth reference frame							
1	0.36	0	+0.30	+0.30	0	16	+16
2	0.12	+0.80	−0.10	−0.90	38	1	−37
				K	$-\dfrac{38}{38} +$	$-\dfrac{1}{17} +$	$-\dfrac{-37}{-21} +$
Reference frame moving at −0.20 m/s relative to Earth							
1	0.36	+0.20	+0.50	+0.30	7	45	+38
2	0.12	+1.0	+0.10	−0.90	60	1	−59
				K	$-\dfrac{60}{67} +$	$-\dfrac{1}{46} +$	$-\dfrac{-59}{-21} +$

or if the airplane is sitting on the runway with its engines running. Of course, you can tell you are moving relative to Earth's surface by peeking out of the window and observing the landscape move by. By timing the motion of some reference points on Earth, you could even determine the velocity of the airplane relative to Earth. By peeking out of the window, however, your observations are no longer confined to a single reference frame. To determine your velocity relative to Earth's surface, you need to take measurements in two reference frames.

A consequence of the principle of relativity is that it is not possible to deduce from measurements taken entirely in one reference frame the motion of that reference frame relative to other reference frames.

This statement also means that no inertial reference frame is preferred over any other; it is not possible to determine the *absolute* velocity of any reference frame or object. The laws of the universe are the same in all inertial reference frames, and there is no reference frame that is "at rest" in some absolute sense.

When you are standing on Earth's surface, are you "at rest" or moving at 30 km/s (the speed of Earth in its orbit around the Sun), or is your speed higher still—say, the speed of the Sun in its galactic orbit? None of these statements is meaningful because no experiments can be done to determine your speed in empty space. You can only speak of your velocity or speed *relative to something else*.

When specifying the velocity of an object, we must therefore always state relative to what we measure that velocity. For simplicity, when the Earth reference frame is the only reference frame of interest, we will omit this relative statement and the subscript E. The phrase "his velocity was $\vec{v}$" will be understood to mean the velocity is measured relative to Earth.

✋ **6.6** Is the coefficient of restitution *e* different in two inertial reference frames that are moving at constant velocity relative to each other? (See Eq. 5.18 if you have forgotten the definition of *e*.)

6.4 Zero-momentum reference frame

Let me end this first part of the chapter by addressing a practical question. If you can choose whichever inertial reference frame you wish, is any choice better than another? The reference frame you are in (usually one at rest relative to Earth) is a logical choice. By choosing some other reference frame, however, you could adjust the value of the momentum of a system up or down by some fixed amount without violating the conservation laws. You could, for instance, adjust the velocity of your reference frame in such a way that the momentum of the system you are observing becomes zero. Such a reference frame is called the system's **zero-momentum reference frame.**

To distinguish the zero-momentum reference frame from other reference frames, we'll refer to quantities measured in that reference frame with the capital letter Z. As we shall see, examining collisions from this reference frame often simplifies things.

The prescription for calculating the velocity of the zero-momentum reference frame is as follows:

The velocity $\vec{v}_{EZ}$ of a system's zero-momentum reference frame relative to Earth is equal to the momentum of the system in the Earth reference frame divided by the inertia of the system.

Example 6.5 Zeroing out the momentum

For the colliding carts in Figure 6.8, (*a*) determine the velocity of the zero-momentum reference frame relative to Earth and (*b*) show that the system momentum measured in the zero-momentum reference frame is zero both before and after the collision.

❶ **GETTING STARTED** This example requires me to apply the prescription for calculating the velocity of the zero-momentum reference frame and then verify that the system momentum is indeed zero in that reference frame.

❷ **DEVISE PLAN** To determine the velocity of the zero-momentum reference frame relative to Earth, I calculate the momentum of the two-cart system in the Earth reference frame and then divide this result by the sum of the inertias of the two carts.

Once I have determined the velocity of the zero-momentum reference frame, I subtract it from the carts' velocities in the Earth reference frame to obtain their velocities in the zero-momentum reference frame. I then use these velocities to calculate the carts' initial and final momenta.

❸ **EXECUTE PLAN** (*a*) In the Earth reference frame, cart 1 (inertia 0.36 kg) is initially at rest and cart 2 (inertia 0.12 kg) is moving at +0.80 m/s. The *x* component of the combined momentum of the two carts is therefore (0.12 kg)(+0.80 m/s) = +0.096 kg·m/s. The *x* component of the velocity of the zero-momentum reference frame is thus

$$\frac{0.096 \text{ kg} \cdot \text{m/s}}{0.36 \text{ kg} + 0.12 \text{ kg}} = +0.20 \text{ m/s.} \checkmark$$

(*b*) To obtain the *x* component of the velocities of the carts in the zero-momentum reference frame, I must subtract 0.20 m/s from their values in the Earth reference frame: $v_{Z1x,i} = -0.20$ m/s and $v_{Z2x,i} = +0.60$ m/s. Then $p_{Z1x,i} = -0.072$ kg·m/s and $p_{Z2x,i} = +0.072$ kg·m/s, making the initial momentum of the system measured from this reference frame zero. ✔

For the *x* component of the final velocities in the zero-momentum reference frame, I get $v_{Z1x,f} = +0.20$ m/s and $v_{Z2x,f} = -0.60$ m/s. So $p_{Z1x,f} = +0.072$ kg·m/s and $p_{Z2x,f} = -0.072$ kg·m/s, making the system's final momentum measured from this reference frame zero. ✔

❹ **EVALUATE RESULT** In the zero-momentum reference frame, the momentum of the two-cart system before the collision is zero, as it must be from the definition of the zero-momentum frame. I also observe that it is zero after the collision, as I expect given that the system is isolated.

Figure 6.12 Collision between two carts as seen (*a*) from the Earth reference frame and (*b*) from the zero-momentum reference frame. The inertias of the carts are $m_1 = 0.36$ kg and $m_2 = 0.12$ kg and the *x* axis points to the right in the diagrams.

Figure 6.12 and Table 6.3 summarize the results of Example 6.5. Note how the shift from the Earth reference frame to the zero-momentum reference frame increases symmetry in the momentum-versus-time graph. In the zero-momentum reference frame, the velocity and momentum of each cart simply change sign in the collision. In this frame, the system as a whole is at rest, allowing us to concentrate on the motion of the objects within the system.

6.7 Is the kinetic energy of the two-cart system in Figure 6.12 in the zero-momentum reference frame less than, equal to, or greater than the system's kinetic energy in the Earth reference frame?

Table 6.3 Symmetry in a zero-momentum reference frame

Cart	Velocity change (m/s)		Momentum change (kg · m/s)	
	Earth reference frame	Zero-momentum reference frame	Earth reference frame	Zero-momentum reference frame
1	$0 \rightarrow +0.40$	$-0.20 \rightarrow +0.20$	$0 \rightarrow +0.14$	$-0.072 \rightarrow +0.072$
2	$+0.80 \rightarrow -0.40$	$+0.60 \rightarrow -0.60$	$+0.096 \rightarrow -0.048$	$+0.072 \rightarrow -0.072$

Self-quiz

1. A space traveler discovers an object that accelerates in her reference frame. Which conclusion is correct? (*a*) Her reference frame is noninertial. (*b*) The object is not isolated. (*c*) You cannot tell.

2. A jogger starts from rest along a straight track. Consider the jogger-Earth system to be isolated. As the jogger's speed increases, does the speed of Earth change or remain constant?

3. A driver slams on the brakes of a car in which a marble is glued to the dashboard. To an observer standing by the side of the road, the marble slows down and has a nonzero acceleration. This happens because (*a*) the observer is in a noninertial reference frame, (*b*) the marble is not isolated, (*c*) some other reason.

4. Is it always possible to choose a zero-momentum reference frame for an isolated system that contains more than two objects?

5. On a low-friction track, two carts with unequal inertias move toward each other. After the collision, the two stick together and are at rest relative to the track. Before the collision, a zero-momentum reference frame would (*a*) move in the direction of the cart that has the greater inertia, (*b*) move in the direction of the faster cart, (*c*) not move relative to the track. (*d*) Can't tell—you need to know the carts' inertias and velocities.

Answers

1. (*c*). To claim that her reference frame is inertial, you need to know whether or not an *isolated* object remains at rest in that reference frame. From the information given, you don't know whether the object is accelerating because it is not isolated or because the reference frame is noninertial.

2. It changes. Strange as it sounds, Earth's velocity does change every time you start moving! Otherwise, conservation of momentum would not hold. Can you verify this statement experimentally? Not for the jogger-Earth case, because the ratio $\Delta v_{jogger}/\Delta v_{Earth}$ is equal to the inverse ratio of the inertias. Because Earth's inertia is enormous, its velocity change is infinitesimally small. This being so, how can you be sure you have the correct answer? Certainty comes from knowing that the law of conservation of momentum has been found to hold everywhere it has ever been tested—including on a cosmic scale.

3. (*b*). From the point of view of the observer, if the marble were not glued to the dashboard, the inertia of the marble would keep it moving at the velocity it had before the driver hit the brakes. The marble slows down only because the car's dashboard holds it in place. In other words, the dashboard and the marble interact with each other, and therefore the marble is not isolated.

4. Yes. The momentum of any system of objects is the sum of the individual momenta. To obtain the momentum of an object of inertia m_o in a reference frame moving at velocity $\vec{v}_{EM}$ relative to Earth, we must subtract $m_o\vec{v}_{EM}$ from the momentum of that object in the Earth reference frame. The system's momentum in that reference frame is then equal to the momentum of the system in the Earth reference frame minus the product $(m_1 + m_2 + m_3 + \cdots)\vec{v}_{EM}$. We can always choose a velocity $\vec{v}_{EM}$ such that the magnitude of this product is equal to the magnitude of the momentum of the system in the Earth reference frame and the algebraic signs are opposites.

5. (*c*). After the collision, both carts come to rest in the reference frame of the track, which means that the momentum of the two-cart system after the collision is zero. This means that the system's momentum before the collision was also zero. Therefore the reference frame of the track is a zero-momentum reference frame.

6.5 Galilean relativity

Consider two observers, A and B, moving at constant velocity relative to each other. Suppose they observe the same event and describe it relative to their respective reference frames and clocks (**Figure 6.13**). Let the origins of the two observers' reference frames coincide at $t = 0$ (Figure 6.13a). Observer A sees the event as happening at position $\vec{r}_{Ae}$ at clock reading t_{Ae} (Figure 6.13b).* Observer B sees the event at position $\vec{r}_{Be}$ at clock reading t_{Be}. What is the relationship between these clock readings and positions?

If, as we discussed in Chapter 1, we assume time is absolute—the same everywhere—and if the two observers have synchronized their (identical) clocks, they both observe the event at the same clock readings, which means

$$t_{Ae} = t_{Be}. \tag{6.1}$$

Because the clock readings of the two observers always agree, we can omit the subscripts referring to the reference frames:

$$t_A = t_B = t. \tag{6.2}$$

From Figure 6.13 we see that the position $\vec{r}_{AB}$ of observer B in reference frame A at instant t_e is equal to B's displacement over the time interval $\Delta t - t_e - 0 = t_e$, and so $\vec{r}_{AB} = \vec{v}_{AB} t_e$ because B moves at constant velocity $\vec{v}_{AB}$. Therefore

$$\vec{r}_{Ae} = \vec{r}_{AB} + \vec{r}_{Be} = \vec{v}_{AB} t_e + \vec{r}_{Be}. \tag{6.3}$$

Equations 6.2 and 6.3 allow us to relate event data collected in one reference frame to data on the same event e collected in a reference frame that moves at constant velocity relative to the first one (neither of these has to be at rest relative to Earth, but their origins must coincide at $t = 0$). To this end we rewrite these equations so that they give the values of time and position in reference frame B

Figure 6.13 Two observers moving relative to each other observe the same event. Observer B moves at constant velocity $\vec{v}_{AB}$ relative to observer A. (a) The origins O of the two reference frames overlap at instant $t = 0$. (b) At instant t_e, when the event occurs, the origin of observer B's reference frame has a displacement $\vec{v}_{AB} t_e$ relative to reference frame A.

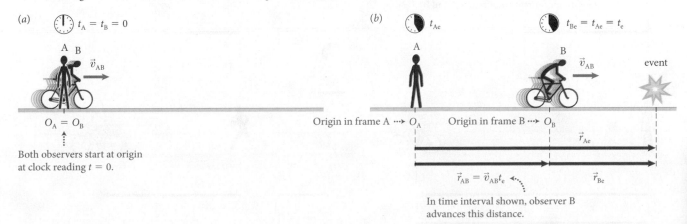

(a) $t_A = t_B = 0$

A B

$\vec{v}_{AB}$

$O_A = O_B$

Both observers start at origin at clock reading $t = 0$.

(b) t_{Ae} $t_{Be} = t_{Ae} = t_e$

A   B

$\vec{v}_{AB}$ event

Origin in frame A ⟶ O_A Origin in frame B ⟶ O_B

$\vec{r}_{Ae}$

$\vec{r}_{Be}$

$\vec{r}_{AB} = \vec{v}_{AB} t_e$

In time interval shown, observer B advances this distance.

*Remember our subscript form: The capital letter refers to the reference frame; the lowercase e is for "event." Thus the vector $\vec{r}_{Ae}$ represents observer **A**'s measurement of the position at which the **e**vent occurs.

in terms of quantities measured in reference frame A:

$$t_B = t_A = t \tag{6.4}$$

$$\vec{r}_{Be} = \vec{r}_{Ae} - \vec{v}_{AB} t_e. \tag{6.5}$$

These two equations, called the **Galilean transformation equations,** form the basis for *Galilean relativity*; they allow us to relate observations made in different reference frames. The Galilean transformation equations are predicated on the assumption that measurements of time intervals and lengths are not affected by motion. Even though this assumption sounds reasonable, it has been invalidated by experimental confirmation of the theory of special relativity (see Chapter 14). For most everyday phenomena, however, when speeds are much lower than the speed of light (about 3.0×10^8 m/s, see Section 1.3), Eqs. 6.4 and 6.5 remain excellent approximations.

6.8 A jogger runs in place on a treadmill whose belt moves at $v_{EBx} = +2.0$ m/s relative to Earth. Let the origins of the Earth reference frame and the reference frame B moving along with the top surface of the belt coincide at $t = 0$. (*a*) What is the jogger's position in the reference frame of the belt at $t = 10$ s? (*b*) Use Eq. 6.3 to show that an Earth observer's measurement of the jogger's position is $r_{Ejx} = 0$ at all instants.

Now that we have determined the relationship between positions in two reference frames, let us examine the relationship between the velocities of a cyclist relative to two observers, A and B, who are moving at constant velocity $\vec{v}_{AB}$ relative to each other (**Figure 6.14**). Each observer determines the velocity of the cyclist by measuring the cyclist's displacement during a certain time interval Δt.

Figure 6.14 The cyclist's displacement $\Delta \vec{r}_{Ac}$ measured by observer A is different from the displacement $\Delta \vec{r}_{Bc}$ measured by observer B, who is moving relative to observer A.

According to observer A, the bicycle undergoes a displacement $\Delta\vec{r}_{\text{Ac}}$ in the time interval Δt (Figure 6.14a). The bicycle's displacement $\Delta\vec{r}_{\text{Bc}}$ measured by observer B, however, is different because B undergoes a displacement $\Delta\vec{r}_{\text{AB}}$ relative to A (Figure 6.14b). Comparing the displacements, we obtain (Figure 6.14c)

$$\vec{r}_{\text{Ac,f}} - \vec{r}_{\text{Ac,i}} = \Delta\vec{r}_{\text{Ac}} = \Delta\vec{r}_{\text{AB}} + \Delta\vec{r}_{\text{Bc}}. \tag{6.6}$$

If we divide the two sides of this equation by the time interval Δt, we obtain

$$\frac{\Delta\vec{r}_{\text{Ac}}}{\Delta t} = \frac{\Delta\vec{r}_{\text{AB}}}{\Delta t} + \frac{\Delta\vec{r}_{\text{Bc}}}{\Delta t}, \tag{6.7}$$

and if we let Δt approach zero, we get

$$\vec{v}_{\text{Ac}} = \vec{v}_{\text{AB}} + \vec{v}_{\text{Bc}}. \tag{6.8}$$

Rewriting this equation so that it gives the velocity of an object o in reference frame B in terms of quantities measured in reference frame A, we get

$$\vec{v}_{\text{Bo}} = \vec{v}_{\text{Ao}} - \vec{v}_{\text{AB}}. \tag{6.9}$$

Equation 6.8 tells us that velocities obtained in different reference frames are additive. If an object moves at a velocity $\vec{v}_{\text{Bo}}$ in a reference frame that is moving at a velocity $\vec{v}_{\text{AB}}$ relative to some observer A, then the velocity $\vec{v}_{\text{Ao}}$ of that object in A's reference frame is the sum $\vec{v}_{\text{AB}} + \vec{v}_{\text{Bo}}$.

As an example, imagine walking in a train that moves along a straight track at 25 m/s relative to Earth. If you are walking forward at 1.0 m/s relative to the train, what is your velocity relative to Earth? In 1.0 s, the train moves 25 m relative to Earth, and in that same time interval you move that same 25 m plus an additional 1.0 m. Because you move (25 m) + (1.0 m) = 26 m each second, your velocity relative to Earth is 26 m/s.

To determine the relationship between an object's acceleration in the two reference frames, we begin by writing what a change in the object's velocity in reference frame B corresponds to in reference frame A. Using Eq. 6.8 and keeping in mind that the relative velocity $\vec{v}_{\text{AB}}$ of the two reference frames is constant, we get

$$\Delta\vec{v}_{\text{Ao}} = \vec{v}_{\text{Ao,f}} - \vec{v}_{\text{Ao,i}} = (\vec{v}_{\text{AB}} + \vec{v}_{\text{Bo,f}}) - (\vec{v}_{\text{AB}} + \vec{v}_{\text{Bo,i}})$$

$$= \vec{v}_{\text{Bo,f}} - \vec{v}_{\text{Bo,i}} = \Delta\vec{v}_{\text{Bo}}. \tag{6.10}$$

In words, *changes in velocity are the same in any two reference frames moving at constant relative velocity*—a conclusion we reached in Section 6.3.

Dividing both sides of Eq. 6.10 by Δt and taking the limit as Δt approaches zero, we determine that the accelerations in the two reference frames are identical, too:

$$\vec{a}_{\text{Ao}} \equiv \lim_{\Delta t \to 0} \frac{\Delta\vec{v}_{\text{Ao}}}{\Delta t} = \lim_{\Delta t \to 0} \frac{\Delta\vec{v}_{\text{Bo}}}{\Delta t} \equiv \vec{a}_{\text{Bo}}. \tag{6.11}$$

In particular, if an object moves at constant velocity in the Earth reference frame ($\vec{a}_{\text{Eo}} = \vec{0}$), then it moves at constant velocity ($\vec{a}_{\text{Mo}} = \vec{0}$) in any reference frame M that moves at constant velocity relative to Earth, confirming what we concluded in Section 6.1.

Two bullet trains passing each other. If each train has a speed of 50 m/s relative to the track, at what speed does the oncoming train approach the one from which the photo is taken?

Answer: 100 m/s.

To simplify working with quantities in various reference frames, note from Figure 6.13*b* that

$$\vec{r}_{Ae} = \vec{r}_{AB} + \vec{r}_{Be} \tag{6.12}$$

The first and last subscripts on either side of this equation are the same, as indicated by the arrows. Moreover, if you imagine canceling the two identical subscripts B that follow each other on the right side and contracting the two vectors $\vec{r}$ into one, you get

$$\vec{r}_{A\cancel{B}} + \vec{r}_{\cancel{B}e} = \vec{r}_{Ae}, \tag{6.13}$$

which is the same as Eq. 6.12. This "subscript cancellation" works with any relative quantity. For example, observer A's measurement of the velocity of an object is equal to observer A's measurement of the velocity of observer B plus observer B's measurement of the velocity of the object:

$$\vec{v}_{Ao} = \vec{v}_{A\cancel{B}} + \vec{v}_{\cancel{B}o}, \tag{6.14}$$

which is the same as Eq. 6.8.

Figure 6.15 shows another useful subscript operation: Reversing the order of the subscripts reverses the direction of a relative vector $\vec{r}_{AB}$. The vector describing the position of observer B relative to A has the same magnitude as the vector $\vec{r}_{BA}$ describing the position of observer A relative to B, but it points in the opposite direction:

$$\vec{r}_{AB} = -\vec{r}_{BA}, \tag{6.15}$$

and by taking the derivative with respect to time of this equation, we obtain a similar expression for the velocity:

$$\vec{v}_{AB} = -\vec{v}_{BA}. \tag{6.16}$$

Figure 6.15 The position vectors of two observers relative to each other are of equal magnitude and point in opposite directions.

Position vectors are each other's opposites.

Procedure: Applying Galilean relativity

In problems dealing with more than one reference frame, you need to keep track not only of objects, but also of reference frames. For this reason, each quantity is labeled with two subscripts. The first subscript denotes the observer; the second denotes the object of interest. For example, if we have an observer on a train and also a car somewhere on the ground but in sight of the train, then $\vec{a}_{Tc}$ is the train observer's measurement of the acceleration of the car. Once you understand this notation and a few basic operations, working with relative quantities is easy and straightforward.

observer A's measurement of velocity of car:

$$\vec{v}_{Ac}$$

observer ·····┊┊····· object of interest

1. Begin by listing the quantities given in the problem, using this double-subscript notation.
2. Write the quantities you need to determine in the same notation.

3. Use subscript cancellation (Eq. 6.13) to write an equation for each quantity you need to determine, keeping the first and the last subscripts on each side the same. For example, in a problem where you need to determine $\vec{v}_{Tc}$ involving a moving observer B, write

$$\vec{v}_{Tc} = \vec{v}_{TB} + \vec{v}_{Bc}\,.$$

4. If needed, use subscript reversal (Eq. 6.15) to eliminate any unknowns.
5. Use the kinematics relationships from Chapters 2 and 3 to solve for any remaining unknowns, making sure you stay in one reference frame.

You can use this procedure and the subscript operations for any of the three basic kinematic quantities (position, velocity, and acceleration).

Example 6.6 Who is moving?

You are driving at 25 m/s on a straight, horizontal road when a truck going 30 m/s in the same direction overtakes you. Let the positive x direction point in the direction of travel, and let the origins of the reference frames affixed to your car and the truck coincide at the instant the truck overtakes you. (*a*) What is your car's velocity as measured by someone in the truck? (*b*) What is the velocity of the truck relative to your car? (*c*) What is your car's position as measured by someone in the truck 60 s after overtaking you?

❶ GETTING STARTED This example involves two reference frames: the Earth reference frame (E) and the reference frame moving along with the truck (T). The velocities of the car and the truck are given in the Earth reference frame: $v_{Ecx} = +25$ m/s and $v_{ETx} = +30$ m/s. I need to determine the velocity of my car $\vec{v}_{Tc}$ relative to the truck, the velocity of the truck $\vec{v}_{cT}$ relative to my car, and my car's position $\vec{r}_{Tc}$ relative to the truck 60 s after the overtaking.

❷ DEVISE PLAN I begin by using subscript cancellation to write an equation that gives the velocity $\vec{v}_{Tc}$ of my car relative to the truck in terms of velocities involving the Earth reference frame: $\vec{v}_{Tc} = \vec{v}_{TE} + \vec{v}_{Ec}$. The value of $\vec{v}_{Ec}$ is given ($+25$ m/s), but I don't have a value for $\vec{v}_{TE}$. However, I can use subscript reversal to write $v_{TEx} = -v_{ETx} = -30$ m/s. Once I have $\vec{v}_{Tc}$, I can

use subscript reversal once more to determine $\vec{v}_{cT}$. The product of $\vec{v}_{Tc}$ and the 60-s time interval gives me $\vec{r}_{Tc}$ (from Eq. 2.16 $\Delta x = v_x \Delta t$).

❸ EXECUTE PLAN (*a*) Using subscript cancellation and reversal, I get $\vec{v}_{Tc} = \vec{v}_{TE} + \vec{v}_{Ec} = -\vec{v}_{ET} + \vec{v}_{Ec}$ or, in terms of x components,

$$v_{Tcx} = -v_{ETx} + v_{Ecx} = -(+30 \text{ m/s}) + (+25 \text{ m/s})$$

$$= -5.0 \text{ m/s.} ✔$$

(*b*) $v_{cTx} = -v_{Tcx} = +5.0$ m/s ✔

(*c*) My displacement in the truck's reference frame is $\Delta x_{Tc} = (-5.0 \text{ m/s})(60 \text{ s}) = -300$ m. Thus 60 s after the truck passes you, a person in the truck measures your position as $r_{Tcx} = 300$ m behind the truck. ✔

❹ EVALUATE RESULT The truck is moving faster than my car, and so relative to the truck my car moves in the negative x direction, confirming the minus sign on my answers to parts *a* and *c*. Relative to me, the truck moves in the positive x direction, in agreement with the plus sign of my answer to part *b*.

✋ **6.9** In a train moving due north at 3.1 m/s relative to Earth, a passenger carrying a suitcase walks forward down the aisle at 1.2 m/s relative to the train. A spider crawls along the bottom of the suitcase at 0.5 m/s southward relative to the suitcase. What is the velocity of the spider relative to Earth?

6.6 Center of mass

To relate momentum in two reference frames moving relative to each other, we must examine inertia. Equation 4.2 told us how to obtain the inertia m_o of an object by letting the object collide with the standard inertia:

$$m_o \equiv -\frac{\Delta v_{sx}}{\Delta v_{ox}} m_s. \tag{6.17}$$

Suppose this inertia m_o is measured by two observers, A and B, who are moving at constant velocity $\vec{v}_{AB}$ relative to each other. Even though the velocity values measured by the two observers differ, Eq. 6.10 tells us that the moving observer obtains the same velocity changes Δv_{sx} and Δv_{ox} as those measured in the Earth reference frame. This means that we can omit the subscript referring to the reference frame and write

$$m_{Ao} = m_{Bo} = m_o. \tag{6.18}$$

Therefore the momenta of an object measured in two reference frames A and B are related by

$$\vec{p}_{Ao} \equiv m_o\vec{v}_{Ao} = m_o(\vec{v}_{AB} + \vec{v}_{Bo}) \equiv m_o\vec{v}_{AB} + \vec{p}_{Bo}, \tag{6.19}$$

where we have used Eq. 6.8 to relate the velocities in the two reference frames. Equation 6.19 shows that the momentum measured in reference frame B is different from the momentum measured in reference frame A. In particular, if the velocity of reference frame B relative to reference frame A is $\vec{v}_{AB} = \vec{p}_{Ao}/m_o$, the momentum measured in reference frame B is zero: $\vec{p}_{Bo} = \vec{0}$ (and so reference frame B is a zero-momentum reference frame for that object).

We can make the momentum of a system of objects zero in the same way. Suppose we have a system made up of objects that have inertias $m_1, m_2, \ldots$, and we let the momentum of the system in reference frame A be $\vec{p}_{A\,sys}$. Using Eq. 6.19, we can write for the momentum of the system

$$\vec{p}_{A\,sys} = \vec{p}_{A1} + \vec{p}_{A2} + \cdots$$

$$= (m_1\vec{v}_{AB} + \vec{p}_{B1}) + (m_2\vec{v}_{AB} + \vec{p}_{B2}) + \cdots$$

$$= (m_1 + m_2 + \cdots)\vec{v}_{AB} + (\vec{p}_{B1} + \vec{p}_{B2} + \cdots) = m\vec{v}_{AB} + \vec{p}_{B\,sys}, \quad (6.20)$$

where $m = m_1 + m_2 + \cdots$ is the inertia of the system. If we adjust the velocity $\vec{v}_{AB}$ of reference frame B relative to reference frame A such that

$$\vec{v}_{AB} = \frac{\vec{p}_{A\,sys}}{m}, \quad (6.21)$$

then, according to Eq. 6.20, reference frame B is a zero-momentum reference frame:

$$\vec{p}_{B\,sys} = \vec{p}_{A\,sys} - m\vec{v}_{AB} = \vec{p}_{A\,sys} - m\frac{\vec{p}_{A\,sys}}{m} = \vec{0}. \quad (6.22)$$

Equations 6.21 and 6.22 show that relative to Earth the velocity of the zero-momentum reference frame Z for a system of objects is equal to the system's momentum measured in the Earth reference frame divided by the inertia of the system (as we stated in Section 6.4):

$$\vec{v}_{EZ} = \frac{\vec{p}_{E\,sys}}{m} = \frac{m_1\vec{v}_{E1} + m_2\vec{v}_{E2} + \cdots}{m_1 + m_2 + \cdots}. \quad \begin{array}{l}\text{(zero-momentum} \\ \text{reference frame)}\end{array} \quad (6.23)$$

The velocity of the zero-momentum reference frame is related to the position of the **center of mass** of a system. This position is defined as

$$\vec{r}_{cm} \equiv \frac{m_1\vec{r}_1 + m_2\vec{r}_2 + \cdots}{m_1 + m_2 + \cdots}, \quad (6.24)$$

where $\vec{r}_1, \vec{r}_2, \ldots$ represent the positions of the objects of inertia $m_1, m_2, \ldots$ in the system.* Equation 6.24 applies to the values of the positions measured in *any* reference frame (and for this reason we can omit the reference-frame subscripts). To show the relationship between the velocity of the zero-momentum reference frame and the position of the center of mass, we take the derivative of the left and right sides of Eq. 6.24 with respect to time:

$$\frac{d\vec{r}_{cm}}{dt} = \frac{m_1(d\vec{r}_1/dt) + m_2(d\vec{r}_2/dt) + \cdots}{m_1 + m_2 + \cdots}. \quad (6.25)$$

---

*Even though I pointed out in Chapter 5 that *mass* and *inertia* are synonyms, we should—to be consistent with our use of the word *inertia* for the quantity m—call $\vec{r}_{cm}$ the position of the *center of inertia*. Historically, however, $\vec{r}_{cm}$ has always been called the position of the *center of mass*, a tradition we shall follow.

Because $d\vec{r}/dt = \vec{v}$ (Eq. 2.25), we can rewrite Eq. 6.25 in the form

$$\vec{v}_{cm} \equiv \frac{d\vec{r}_{cm}}{dt} = \frac{m_1\vec{v}_1 + m_2\vec{v}_2 + \cdots}{m_1 + m_2 + \cdots}, \qquad (6.26)$$

where $\vec{v}_{cm}$ is the system's **center-of-mass velocity.** Note that this velocity is precisely the velocity of the zero-momentum reference frame in Eq. 6.23. Thus we conclude that, when measured from a reference frame moving at the same velocity as the center of mass of a system, the system's momentum is automatically zero. (In other words, such a reference frame is a zero-momentum reference frame.) In figures we shall denote the center of mass by a circle with a cross in it: $\otimes$.

Example 6.7 Two-cart center of mass

The positions of two identical carts at rest on a low-friction track are measured relative to two axes oriented in the same direction along the track. On axis A, cart 1 is at x_{A1} and cart 2 is at x_{A2}. On axis B, cart 1 is at the origin and cart 2 is at x_{B2}. (a) Determine the position of the center of mass of the two-cart system relative to each axis. (b) If instead of identical carts you have $m_1 - 2m_2$, what is the position of the center of mass on each axis?

❶ GETTING STARTED I begin by making a sketch of the situation (**Figure 6.16**). Each axis corresponds to a reference frame that is at rest relative to Earth. Because the origins of the two axes don't coincide, the x components of the cart positions on axis A are different from those on axis B. I have to use these x components to determine the position of the system's center of mass on each axis for two cases: when the cart inertias are identical and when they are not.

Figure 6.16

(a)

(b)

❷ DEVISE PLAN The position of the center of mass of a system of objects is given by Eq. 6.24. To use this equation in this problem, I must write it in terms of components. For axis A, I have

$$x_{Acm} = \frac{m_1 x_{A1} + m_2 x_{A2}}{m_1 + m_2}, \qquad (1)$$

and for axis B I replace the subscripts A with B. To solve this problem, I substitute the given values into this equation.

❸ EXECUTE PLAN (a) Substituting $m_1 = m_2 = m$ into Eq. 1, I get for axis A

$$x_{Acm} = \frac{m x_{A1} + m x_{A2}}{m + m} = \frac{m(x_{A1} + x_{A2})}{2m} = \frac{x_{A1} + x_{A2}}{2}. \checkmark$$

This position is halfway between the the two carts (see Figure 6.16). For axis B, I get

$$x_{Bcm} = \frac{m x_{B1} + m x_{B2}}{m + m} = \frac{m(0 + x_{B2})}{2m} = \frac{x_{B2}}{2}, \checkmark$$

which is again the position midway between the two carts.

(b) Now I have $m_1 = 2m_2 = 2m$, and so for axis A,

$$x_{Acm} = \frac{2m x_{A1} + m x_{A2}}{2m + m} = \frac{2x_{A1} + x_{A2}}{3}. \checkmark$$

This position is one third of the way from x_{A1} to x_{A2} on axis A because $(2x_{A1} + x_{A2})/3 = x_{A1} + (x_{A2} - x_{A1})/3$. For axis B,

$$x_{Bcm} = \frac{2m \cdot (0) + m x_{B2}}{2m + m} = \frac{x_{B2}}{3}, \checkmark$$

which is one-third of the way between the origin of axis B and cart 2. If you go back to the carts in Figure 6.16b and mark the center-of-mass position on both axes, you'll see that the position $x_{Bcm} = x_{B2}/3$ is aligned with the position $x_{Acm} = (2x_{A1} + x_{A2})/3$, as it must be. The center of mass of any given system can be at one position only, regardless of which reference frame is used to locate that position.

❹ EVALUATE RESULT When $m_1 = m_2$, the center of mass lies at the center of the system (midway between the carts) regardless of the choice of axis, which makes sense. When $m_1 = 2m_2$, the center of mass lies twice as close to cart 1 as to cart 2. This makes sense because I expect the center of mass to shift toward the object with the larger inertia. If, for example, the inertia of cart 1 were so large that the inertia of cart 2 was negligible, I could drop the second term in the numerator and denominator of Eq. 1, which would make the position of the center of mass be that of cart 1.

6.10 In Example 6.7, let $m_1 = 3m_2$. (*a*) Where on axis A is the center of mass of the two-cart system? (*b*) Where on axis A would you need to place a third cart of inertia $m_3 = m_1$ so that the center of mass of the three-cart system is at the position of cart 2?

Example 6.7 demonstrates an important point: The position of the center of mass of a system is a property of the system that is independent of the choice of reference frame. Equation 6.24 suggests that the center of mass represents a sort of "average" position of a system, but the center of mass is more important than that. Back in Chapter 2 we began our study of motion by specifying the position of an object at each instant by the position vector $\vec{r}$. Real objects, however, are *extended* rather than *pointlike,* and so to say "the position" of a system or of a real object is not a precise statement unless we specify a fixed reference point in the system or on the object. For example, the statement "I parked my car 3 m from the fire hydrant" could mean that the front end of the car is 3 m away from the hydrant, or the midpoint of the car is 3 m from the hydrant, or any other point on the car is 3 m from the hydrant. The center of mass allows us to specify a fixed position in a system according to an exact prescription given by Eq. 6.24.

For extended objects, we can apply Eq. 6.24 by dividing the object into small pieces and substituting the position and inertia of each piece into the equation. This method is described in Appendix D. For symmetrical objects that have a uniformly distributed inertia, however, we don't need to carry out the calculation because the center of mass lies on an axis of symmetry and on any plane of symmetry. For example, the center of mass of a uniform rod lies at the center of the rod, midway between its ends, and the center of mass of a uniform sphere or cube lies at the geometric center of the sphere or cube.

Center of mass is also an important tool in our quest for simplification: It allows us to be precise even for systems where the motion is complex. To take a specific example, consider the motions shown in **Figure 6.17**. Because the two carts are identical, the center of mass of the two-cart system is always halfway between them. Notice that the center-of-mass motion is unaffected by the collision in Figure 6.17*a*. This is so because the momentum of the system doesn't change, and so the motion of the system must be constant. The center of mass of the system moves at velocity $\vec{v}_{cm}$ both before and after the collision.

The importance of the center of mass becomes even more evident in Figure 6.17*b*. Now the carts bounce back and forth because of the action of the spring while the two-cart system as a whole moves to the right. The motion of the center of mass of the system is entirely independent of the motion of the carts relative to each other and independent of the interactions between the carts. Even though the system continuously changes shape (the distance between the carts keeps changing), the center of mass provides a fixed reference point that moves at constant velocity.

6.11 (*a*) Determine the center-of-mass velocity of the two carts in Figure 6.8*a* before and after the collision, and verify that it is equal to the velocity of the carts at the point where the two $v_x(t)$ curves intersect. (*b*) Is the velocity of the carts at the point where the two $v_x(t)$ curves intersect always equal to the center-of-mass velocity? (*c*) Determine the velocities of the two carts in the zero-momentum reference frame, before and after the collision, and show that in this reference frame the momentum of the system is always zero.

Figure 6.17 Two identical carts moving on a low-friction track. (*a*) The carts collide elastically. (*b*) The carts are connected by a spring and bounce back and forth about the center of mass. In both cases, the center of mass moves at constant velocity, so that the $x(t)$ curve for the center of mass is always a straight line.

6.7 Convertible kinetic energy

We can derive some additional useful expressions involving the center-of-mass velocity. Keeping in mind that $\vec{v}_{Eo} = \vec{v}_{EZ} + \vec{v}_{Zo}$ (Eq. 6.8) and that for the zero-momentum reference frame $\vec{v}_{EZ} = \vec{v}_{cm}$ (Eqs. 6.23 and 6.26), we can derive an expression that gives, for a system of objects, the kinetic energy $K_{E\,sys}$ measured in the Earth reference frame in terms of the corresponding kinetic energy $K_{Z\,sys}$ measured in the zero-momentum reference frame:

$$K_{E\,sys} = \tfrac{1}{2}m_1 v_{E1x}^2 + \tfrac{1}{2}m_2 v_{E2x}^2 + \cdots$$

$$= \tfrac{1}{2}m_1(v_{cmx} + v_{Z1x})^2 + \tfrac{1}{2}m_2(v_{cmx} + v_{Z2x})^2 + \cdots. \qquad (6.27)$$

Working out the first term on the right gives

$$\tfrac{1}{2}m_1(v_{cmx} + v_{Z1x})^2 = \tfrac{1}{2}m_1 v_{cm}^2 + m_1 v_{cmx}v_{Z1x} + \tfrac{1}{2}m_1 v_{Z1}^2, \qquad (6.28)$$

where I dropped the subscripts x on the terms that contain squares of the x component of the velocity because $v_x^2 = v^2$. Working out the other terms in Eq. 6.27 and gathering terms that contain equal powers of v_{cmx}, we obtain

$$K_{E\,sys} = \tfrac{1}{2}(m_1 + m_2 + \cdots)v_{cm}^2 + (m_1 v_{Z1x} + m_2 v_{Z2x} + \cdots)v_{cmx}$$

$$+ (\tfrac{1}{2}m_1 v_{Z1}^2 + \tfrac{1}{2}m_2 v_{Z2}^2 + \cdots). \qquad (6.29)$$

From the definition of the zero-momentum reference frame, we have

$$m_1 v_{Z1x} + m_2 v_{Z2x} + \cdots = p_{Z1x} + p_{Z2x} + \cdots = (p_{Z\,sys})_x = 0, \qquad (6.30)$$

so that the middle term on the right in Eq. 6.29 disappears. The last term in Eq. 6.29 is the kinetic energy $K_{Z\,sys}$ of the system measured in the zero-momentum reference frame, and so substituting $m = m_1 + m_2 + \cdots$, we have

$$K_{E\,sys} = \tfrac{1}{2}mv_{cm}^2 + K_{Z\,sys}. \qquad (6.31)$$

The first term on the right in this equation, called the system's **translational kinetic energy,** is the kinetic energy associated with the motion of the center of mass of the system:

$$K_{cm} \equiv \tfrac{1}{2}mv_{cm}^2. \qquad (6.32)$$

This term has the form of the kinetic energy of an object of inertia m moving at speed v_{cm}.

For an isolated system, the translational kinetic energy K_{cm} is *nonconvertible,* which means that it cannot be converted to internal energy. To see why this is true, note that this kinetic energy is a function of the system's center-of-mass velocity, which cannot change for an isolated system (see Section 6.8).

The remainder of the kinetic energy—the $K_{Z\,sys}$ term in Eq. 6.31—is the system's **convertible kinetic energy,** the amount that can be converted to internal energy without changing the momentum of the system. It is equal to the system's kinetic energy minus the (nonconvertible) translational kinetic energy:

$$K_{conv} \equiv K_{Z\,sys} = K_{E\,sys} - \tfrac{1}{2}mv_{cm}^2$$

$$= (\tfrac{1}{2}m_1v_{E1}^2 + \tfrac{1}{2}m_2v_{E2}^2 + \cdots) - \tfrac{1}{2}(m_1 + m_2 + \cdots)v_{cm}^2. \qquad (6.33)$$

With this last equation, we can eliminate any reference to the zero-momentum reference frame in Eq. 6.31, leaving only quantities measured in the Earth reference frame:

$$K_{E\,sys} = K_{cm} + K_{conv}. \qquad (6.34)$$

If we had started not from an expression for the kinetic energy in the Earth reference frame (Eq. 6.27) but from the corresponding expression in any other inertial reference frame A, we would have obtained the same results, with A substituted for all the subscripts E. For this reason, we can omit the subscript E and rewrite Eqs. 6.31–6.34 in a form that holds in any inertial reference frame:

$$K = K_{cm} + K_{conv}, \qquad (6.35)$$

where
$$K_{conv} = (\tfrac{1}{2}m_1v_1^2 + \tfrac{1}{2}m_2v_2^2 + \cdots) - \tfrac{1}{2}mv_{cm}^2. \qquad (6.36)$$

The kinetic energy of a system can be split into a convertible part and a nonconvertible part. The nonconvertible part is the system's translational kinetic energy $K_{cm} = \tfrac{1}{2}mv_{cm}^2$. The remainder of the kinetic energy is convertible.

For a system of two colliding objects, the convertible kinetic energy is

$$K_{conv} = K - \tfrac{1}{2}mv_{cm}^2 = (\tfrac{1}{2}m_1v_1^2 + \tfrac{1}{2}m_2v_2^2) - \tfrac{1}{2}(m_1 + m_2)v_{cm}^2. \qquad (6.37)$$

With some algebra (see Checkpoint 6.12), substituting the Eq. 6.26 form of v_{cm} into this expression yields

$$K_{conv} = \tfrac{1}{2}\left(\frac{m_1m_2}{m_1 + m_2}\right)v_{12}^2 \quad \text{(two-object system)}. \qquad (6.38)$$

If I now write
$$\mu \equiv \frac{m_1m_2}{m_1 + m_2}, \qquad (6.39)$$

then the convertible kinetic energy for two objects takes the simple form

$$K_{conv} = \tfrac{1}{2}\mu v_{12}^2 \quad \text{(two-object system)}, \qquad (6.40)$$

where $\vec{v}_{12} = \vec{v}_2 - \vec{v}_1$ is the relative velocity of the two objects (see Eq. 5.1). The right side of this expression has the form of the kinetic energy of an object of inertia μ moving at a speed v_{12}. The quantity represented by the Greek letter μ (mu), which we introduced to simplify our notation, thus has the same units as inertia. It is called the **reduced inertia**, or *reduced mass*, because it is less than the inertia of either of the two colliding objects.

QUANTITATIVE TOOLS

✋ **6.12** Verify that Eq. 6.38 is valid by substituting Eq. 6.26 for v_{cm} into Eq. 6.37 and working through the algebra.

Example 6.8 Crash test

Two collisions are carried out to crash-test a 1000-kg car. (*a*) While moving at 15 mi/h, the car strikes an identical car initially at rest. (*b*) While moving at 15 mi/h, the car strikes an identical car moving toward it and also traveling at 15 mi/h. For each collision, how much kinetic energy can be converted to internal energy, and what fraction of the initial kinetic energy of the two-car system does this represent?

❶ **GETTING STARTED** I am given the inertias of two cars and their initial velocities in two collisions. I must calculate two values for each collision: the amount of kinetic energy converted during the collision and what fraction of the system's energy this converted amount is. I begin by making a sketch of the situation before each collision (**Figure 6.18**). I assume that the car that is initially at rest is free to roll (its parking brake is not on), and I ignore any friction so that I can consider the two-car system to be isolated. I also convert the speed from miles per hour to meters per second:

$$\frac{15 \text{ mile}}{1 \text{ hour}} \times \frac{1 \text{ hour}}{3600 \text{ s}} \times \frac{1609 \text{ m}}{1 \text{ mile}} = 6.7 \text{ m/s}.$$

Figure 6.18

❷ **DEVISE PLAN** The amount of energy that can be converted is given by Eq. 6.40, which requires me to calculate the reduced inertia of the two-car system (Eq. 6.39) and the relative speed of the two cars (Eq. 5.1). To determine the fraction of the initial kinetic energy that this converted amount of energy represents, I divide the converted amount by the sum of the initial kinetic energies $\frac{1}{2}mv^2$ of the two cars.

❸ **EXECUTE PLAN** (*a*) Substituting $m_1 = m_2 = 1000$ kg into Eq. 6.39, I obtain the reduced inertia of the two-car system: $\mu = 500$ kg. The initial relative speed of the two cars is

$$v_{12} = |v_{2x} - v_{1x}| = |0 - (+6.7 \text{ m/s})| = 6.7 \text{ m/s}$$

and so

$$K_{conv} = \frac{1}{2}(500 \text{ kg})(6.7 \text{ m/s})^2 = 11 \text{ kJ}. ✔$$

The initial kinetic energy of the system is $K_i = K_{1,i} = \frac{1}{2}(1000 \text{ kg})(6.7 \text{ m/s})^2 = 22$ kJ, and so the fraction of energy converted is $K_{conv}/K_i = (11 \text{ kJ})/(22 \text{ kJ}) = 0.50$. ✔

(*b*) The initial relative speed of the two cars is

$$v_{12} = |v_{2x} - v_{1x}| = |6.7 \text{ m/s} - (-6.7 \text{ m/s})| = 13.4 \text{ m/s}$$

and so $\quad K_{conv} = \frac{1}{2}(500 \text{ kg})(13.4 \text{ m/s})^2 = 45 \text{ kJ}.$ ✔

The initial kinetic energy of the system is $K_i = K_{1,i} + K_{2,i} = \frac{1}{2}(1000 \text{ kg})(6.7 \text{ m/s})^2 + \frac{1}{2}(1000 \text{ kg})(6.7 \text{ m/s})^2 = 45$ kJ, and so all of the initial kinetic energy is convertible: $K_{conv}/K_i = (45 \text{ kJ})/(45 \text{ kJ}) = 1.0.$ ✔

❹ **EVALUATE RESULT** When both cars move at 15 mi/h, the system has twice as much kinetic energy as when only one car moves at that speed, which makes sense. When only one car moves, however, the momentum of the system is nonzero, which means that not all the kinetic energy can be converted, as I found. In the second collision, the momentum of the system is zero, and so all of the kinetic energy can be converted, in agreement with my answer.

For an inelastic collision, v_{12} changes and so K changes, too. Using Eq. 6.35, we can write for the change in the kinetic energy of the system:

$$\Delta K = \Delta K_{cm} + \Delta K_{conv}. \tag{6.41}$$

The first term on the right is zero because the system is isolated, and so its translational kinetic energy cannot change. Substituting Eq. 6.40 into the last term, we have

$$\Delta K = \frac{1}{2}\mu v_{12f}^2 - \frac{1}{2}\mu v_{12i}^2 = \frac{1}{2}\mu(v_{12f}^2 - v_{12i}^2). \tag{6.42}$$

If we pull v_{12i}^2 out of the parentheses, we can write this expression in terms of the coefficient of restitution e (see Eq. 5.18):

$$\Delta K = \frac{1}{2}\mu v_{12i}^2 \left(\frac{v_{12f}^2}{v_{12i}^2} - 1\right) = \frac{1}{2}\mu v_{12i}^2(e^2 - 1). \tag{6.43}$$

This value represents the amount of kinetic energy converted to internal energy during the inelastic collision. The maximum change in the system's kinetic energy occurs in a totally inelastic collision ($e = 0$):

$$\Delta K = -\tfrac{1}{2}\mu v_{12i}^2 \quad \text{(totally inelastic collision).} \tag{6.44}$$

So, when two colliding objects stick together, their relative velocity becomes zero and all of the convertible kinetic energy is converted to internal energy (compare Eqs. 6.40 and 6.44). Even though the collision is totally inelastic, however, the two-object system still has some kinetic energy because the nonconvertible part of the system's kinetic energy ($\tfrac{1}{2}mv_{cm}^2$) is unaffected by the collision.

For an elastic collision, $e = 1$, and so Eq. 6.43 becomes $\Delta K = 0$: The kinetic energy is the same before and after the collision, as expected.

6.13 A moving object that has inertia m strikes a stationary object that has inertia $0.5m$. (*a*) What fraction of the initial kinetic energy of the system is convertible? (*b*) Why can't the rest be converted?

6.8 Conservation laws and relativity

In Section 6.3 we introduced the principle of relativity, which states that the laws of the universe are the same in any inertial reference frame. In this section we prove this statement for the momentum and energy laws, which embody the laws of conservation of momentum and energy.

Let us consider a system from two reference frames, A and B, that are moving at velocity $\vec{v}_{AB}$ relative to each other. In Section 6.6 we saw that the momentum of an object is different in two reference frames that are moving relative to each other (Eq. 6.19), but now we are interested in *changes* in momentum. For an object of inertia m_o, we can write

$$\Delta \vec{p}_{Ao} = m_o \Delta \vec{v}_{Ao}. \tag{6.45}$$

Because a change in velocity in reference frame A is the same as a change in reference frame B (Eq. 6.10), we have

$$\Delta \vec{p}_{Ao} = m_o \Delta \vec{v}_{Ao} = m_o \Delta \vec{v}_{Bo} = \Delta \vec{p}_{Bo}, \tag{6.46}$$

which tells us that the change in momentum of an object is the same in reference frames A and B. So, for the momentum of a system of objects, we have

$$\Delta \vec{p}_{A\,\text{sys}} = \Delta \vec{p}_{B\,\text{sys}}. \tag{6.47}$$

In words, *changes in the momentum of a system are the same in any two reference frames moving at constant velocity relative to each other.*

Equation 6.47 tells us that if the change in momentum of a system is zero in reference frame A, then it is also zero in reference frame B. So, if a system is isolated in reference frame A, it is also isolated in reference frame B, as required by the principle of relativity (**Figure 6.19**).

Next we examine changes in the energy of a system. Let us first consider a change in the system's internal energy. In Section 5.3 we introduced internal energy as a quantitative measure of a change in state. Given that the state of any object or system cannot depend on the motion of the observer, we must conclude that any change in internal energy must be independent of the reference frame:

$$\Delta E_{A\,\text{int}} = \Delta E_{B\,\text{int}}. \tag{6.48}$$

Figure 6.19 Whether or not a system is isolated does not depend on the motion of the observer, as long as the reference frames are inertial relative to each other.

QUANTITATIVE TOOLS

Unfortunately, the situation is not so simple for a change in kinetic energy, as we saw in Section 6.3. If an object's velocity in reference frame A increases to $v_{Aox,i} + \Delta v_{Aox}$ from an initial value $v_{Aox,i}$, its kinetic energy increases by an amount

$$\Delta K_{Ao} = \tfrac{1}{2}m_o\big[(v_{Aox,i} + \Delta v_{Aox})^2 - (v_{Aox,i})^2\big]$$

$$= m_o v_{Aox,i}\Delta v_{Aox} + \tfrac{1}{2}m_o(\Delta v_{Aox})^2. \tag{6.49}$$

Substituting Eqs. 6.8 and 6.10 into the right side, we get

$$\Delta K_{Ao} = m_o(v_{ABx} + v_{Box,i})\Delta v_{Box} + \tfrac{1}{2}m_o(\Delta v_{Box})^2. \tag{6.50}$$

Applying Eq. 6.49 to reference frame B, we have

$$\Delta K_{Bo} = m_o v_{Box,i}\Delta v_{Box} + \tfrac{1}{2}m_o(\Delta v_{Box})^2. \tag{6.51}$$

When we expand Eq. 6.50, we get

$$\Delta K_{Ao} = m_o v_{ABx}\Delta v_{Box} + m_o v_{Box,i}\Delta v_{Box} + \tfrac{1}{2}m_o(\Delta v_{Box})^2. \tag{6.52}$$

Because the second and third terms on the right are exactly what we have on the right in Eq. 6.51, we see that

$$\Delta K_{Ao} = m_o v_{ABx}\Delta v_{Box} + \Delta K_{Bo} \neq \Delta K_{Bo} \quad \text{(single object)}, \tag{6.53}$$

which means that the change in an object's kinetic energy depends on the reference frame in which that change is measured.

To investigate whether or not ΔK, the change in the kinetic energy of a system made up of two colliding objects, is independent of the reference frame in which the energy is measured, let us examine the kinetic energy converted to internal energy, given by Eq. 6.42. In reference frame A we have

$$\Delta K_A = \tfrac{1}{2}\mu(v_{A12,f}^2 - v_{A12,i}^2) \quad \text{(two-object system)}. \tag{6.54}$$

Because the relative velocities are *differences* in velocities, Eq. 6.10 tells us that $v_{B12} = v_{A12}$, and so the change in the system's kinetic energy must also be the same in any two inertial reference frames:

$$\Delta K_B = \Delta K_A \tag{6.55}$$

(in spite of the fact that the changes in kinetic energy are different for the individual objects!). Combining Eqs. 6.55 and 6.48 and generalizing the result to a system of more than two objects, we obtain

$$\Delta K_B + \Delta E_{Bint} = \Delta K_A + \Delta E_{Aint} \tag{6.56}$$

or

$$\Delta E_{Asys} = \Delta E_{Bsys}. \tag{6.57}$$

In words, *changes in the energy of a system are the same in any two reference frames moving at constant velocity relative to each other.*

Equation 6.57 tells us that if the change in energy of a system is zero in reference frame A, then it is also zero in reference frame B. So, if a system is closed in reference frame A, it is also closed in reference frame B, as required by the principle of relativity.

✋ **6.14** Objects 1 ($m_1 = 1.0$ kg) and 2 ($m_2 = 3.0$ kg) collide inelastically. The velocities are $v_{1x,i} = +4.0$ m/s, $v_{2x,i} = 0$, $v_{1x,f} = -0.50$ m/s, and $v_{2x,f} = +1.5$ m/s. (*a*) What is the coefficient of restitution *e*? (*b*) Make a table like Table 6.1 showing the kinetic energy converted to internal energy both in the Earth reference frame and in a reference frame moving at $v_{EMx} = -1.0$ m/s relative to Earth.

Chapter Glossary

SI units of physical quantities are given in parentheses.

Center of mass A reference-frame-independent reference point on a system of objects, whose position is given by

$$\vec{r}_{cm} \equiv \frac{m_1\vec{r}_1 + m_2\vec{r}_2 + \cdots}{m_1 + m_2 + \cdots}. \tag{6.24}$$

Center-of-mass velocity $\vec{v}_{cm}$ (m/s) Velocity of the center of mass of a system of objects:

$$\vec{v}_{cm} \equiv \frac{m_1\vec{v}_1 + m_2\vec{v}_2 + \cdots}{m_1 + m_2 + \cdots}. \tag{6.26}$$

Convertible kinetic energy K_{conv} (J) The portion of the kinetic energy of a system that can be converted to internal energy:

$$K_{conv} \equiv K - \tfrac{1}{2}mv_{cm}^2. \tag{6.36}$$

The convertible kinetic energy measured for a system is the same in any inertial reference frame.

Earth reference frame A reference frame at rest relative to Earth.

Galilean transformation equations The relationships between the coordinates in time and space of an event in two reference frames A and B moving at constant velocity $\vec{v}_{AB}$ relative to each other:

$$t_B = t_A = t \tag{6.4}$$

$$\vec{r}_{Be} = \vec{r}_{Ae} - \vec{v}_{AB}t_e. \tag{6.5}$$

See also the Procedure box on page 136.

Inertial reference frame A reference frame in which the law of inertia holds.

Law of inertia In an inertial reference frame, any isolated object that is at rest remains at rest, and any isolated object that is in motion keeps moving at a constant velocity.

Observer A person (real or imaginary) carrying out measurements or observations in a reference frame.

Principle of relativity The laws of the universe are the same in any inertial reference frame.

Reduced inertia μ (kg) A scalar defined as

$$\mu \equiv \frac{m_1 m_2}{m_1 + m_2}. \tag{6.39}$$

Reference frame An axis and an origin that define a direction in space and a unit of length relative to which one can observe and measure motion.

Translational (nonconvertible) kinetic energy K_{cm} (J) The kinetic energy associated with the motion of the center of mass of a system:

$$K_{cm} \equiv \tfrac{1}{2}mv_{cm}^2. \tag{6.32}$$

The translational kinetic energy of an isolated system cannot be converted to internal energy because if it were, the system's momentum would not be constant.

Zero-momentum reference frame A reference frame in which the momentum of the system is zero. The velocity of this reference frame relative to another reference frame is equal to the system's center-of-mass velocity relative to that reference frame.

7 Interactions

CONCEPTS

7.1 The effects of interactions
7.2 Potential energy
7.3 Energy dissipation
7.4 Source energy
7.5 Interaction range
7.6 Fundamental interactions

QUANTITATIVE TOOLS

7.7 Interactions and accelerations
7.8 Nondissipative interactions
7.9 Potential energy near Earth's surface
7.10 Dissipative interactions

In past chapters we saw how interactions can change the kinetic energy of objects as well as their internal energy. Every event that happens in this universe is the result of some interaction between objects. Interactions determine the structure of the universe, from the subatomic scale to the cosmological scale. In this chapter we study how interactions convert energy from one form to another. In the process we learn more about the concept of internal energy introduced in Chapter 5.

7.1 The effects of interactions

In the broadest sense, **interactions** are mutual influences between two objects that produce change (either physical change or a change in motion). As an example, consider a cart at rest on a horizontal track. The only way to get the cart to move is to make it *interact* with something else. We could, for instance, give it a shove or make it collide with another cart or fasten a magnet to it and push or pull it with another magnet.

Note that in each case we make the cart interact with something else. We can't make it change its state of motion without that something else: a hand, another cart, a magnet. If you look at Figure 4.19, you'll see that in each case where there is an interaction (*a*, *c*, and *d*), the interaction takes place between *two* objects: puck and floor, cart and cart, hand and cart.

An interaction that causes objects to accelerate can be either repulsive or attractive. A *repulsive interaction* is one in which the interacting bodies accelerate away from each other; an *attractive interaction* is one in which the interacting bodies accelerate toward each other. Some interactions are repulsive under some conditions and attractive under others, as illustrated in **Figure 7.1**.

✋ **7.1** (*a*) Imagine holding a ball a certain height above the ground. If you let the ball go, it accelerates downward. An interaction between the ball and what other object causes this acceleration? Is this interaction attractive or repulsive? (*b*) Once the ball hits the ground, its direction of travel reverses. Is this reversal the result of an attractive interaction or a repulsive one?

Figure 7.1 An interaction between two carts linked by a spring. When the spring is stretched, the interaction is attractive; when the spring is compressed, the interaction is repulsive.

Stretched spring: attractive interaction

Relaxed spring: no interaction

Compressed spring: repulsive interaction

Figure 7.2 shows the x components of the velocities, momenta, and accelerations as well as the kinetic energies of two carts before and after an interaction. Cart 1, of inertia $m_1 = 0.12$ kg and initially at rest, is hit by cart 2, of inertia $m_2 = 0.24$ kg and initially moving at 0.55 m/s. The collision is elastic.

Figure 7.2*a* shows the x components of the velocities of the two carts. We've seen similar graphs before (Figure 4.8, for example). The x components of the final velocities are +0.73 m/s for cart 1 and +0.18 m/s for cart 2, and their relative speed remains 0.55 m/s, as it must for an elastic collision.

Figure 7.2*b* shows what happens to the x components of the momenta: One cart undergoes a momentum change in one direction, and the other cart undergoes an equal momentum change in the opposite direction. This is true at every instant: Even *during* the interaction, the momentum of the two-cart system is constant.

✋ **7.2** (*a*) Use Figure 7.2*a* to calculate the x components of the momenta of the two carts at $t = 30, 60,$ and 90 ms. (*b*) What is the x component of the momentum of the system at each of these three instants?

Notice in Figure 7.2 that the interaction that causes the changes in velocity and momentum is not instantaneous; instead, it takes place over a certain time interval (represented by the shaded area in the graphs). The x component of the average acceleration of each cart during the interaction is equal to the change in the x component of the velocity for that cart divided by the duration of the interaction. Because the change in speed for cart 1 is twice as big as that for cart 2 (Figure 7.2*a*) and because the time interval over which the interaction takes place is the same for both carts, the magnitude of the average acceleration of cart 1 is twice that of cart 2. This result is a direct consequence of conservation of momentum.

As we shall see in Section 7.7, this relationship between the average accelerations of colliding bodies is true for the instantaneous accelerations as well. So, whenever two objects interact, the ratio of the x components of their accelerations is equal to the negative inverse of the ratio of their inertias.

Example 7.1 Crash

A small car and a heavy truck moving at equal speeds in opposite directions collide head-on in a totally inelastic collision. Compare the magnitudes of (*a*) the changes in momentum and (*b*) the average accelerations of the car and the truck.

❶ **GETTING STARTED** I begin by making a sketch of the situation before and after the collision (**Figure 7.3**). Before the collision, the truck and car both move at the same speed. After the totally inelastic collision, the two move as one unit with zero relative velocity. Because the inertia m_t of the truck is greater than the inertia m_c of the car, the momentum of the system points in the same direction as the direction of travel of the truck. The combined wreck must therefore move in the same direction after the collision.

Figure 7.2 Conservation of momentum and kinetic energy in an elastic collision between two carts on a low-friction track. The inertia of cart 1 is 0.12 kg, and that of cart 2 is 0.24 kg.

(a) Velocity

(b) Momentum

(c) Acceleration

(d) Kinetic energy

❷ **DEVISE PLAN** To compare the changes in momentum, I can apply conservation of momentum to the isolated truck-car system. I can obtain the change in velocity by dividing the change in momentum by the inertia. Because the changes in velocity occur over the same time interval for both car and truck, and because the magnitude of the average acceleration is given by $\Delta v/\Delta t$, the ratio of the accelerations is the same as the ratio of the changes in velocity.

Figure 7.3 Example 7.1.

initial   final

❸ **EXECUTE PLAN** (a) The momentum of the isolated truck-car system does not change in the collision, and so the magnitudes of the changes in momentum for the car and the truck are the same. ✔

(b) The change in the x component of the velocity of the truck is $\Delta p_{tx}/m_t$, and the change in the x component of the velocity of the car is $\Delta p_{cx}/m_c$. Because $m_t > m_c$ and because the magnitudes of the changes in momentum are equal, I conclude that the magnitude of the velocity change of the car is larger than that of the truck. ✔

❹ **EVALUATE RESULT** In any collision the magnitudes of the changes in momentum are the same for the two colliding objects, and so the answer to part a does not surprise me. That the magnitude of the velocity change for the car is larger also makes sense: As my sketch shows, the velocity of the car reverses, whereas the truck slows down somewhat but keeps traveling in the same direction.

Figure 7.2*d* shows the kinetic energy of the two carts. Just like the momentum, the kinetic energy of each cart changes, but because the collision is elastic, the kinetic energy of the system before the interaction is the same as the kinetic energy of the system afterward. Note, however, that the kinetic energy of the system does not remain constant *during* the collision! Unlike momentum, the kinetic energy of a system of colliding objects changes during the interaction—even when the interaction is an elastic collision.

To see why, remember from Section 5.5 that kinetic energy's being constant is mathematically equivalent to saying that the relative speed of two objects is the same before and after an interaction. Whenever two objects collide, however, their relative speed has to change during the interaction. If the objects were to maintain a constant relative speed during the interaction, changing their velocities would change the momentum of the system, and this can't happen if the system is isolated. Consequently the kinetic energy of any system of colliding objects has to change during the interaction, regardless of the type of collision—elastic, inelastic, or totally inelastic.

Figure 7.4 illustrates the instant of zero relative velocity for the elastic collision shown in Figure 7.2. At the instant at which the two $v(t)$ curves intersect ($t = 60$ ms), the velocities are equal, and hence the relative velocity is zero at that instant. If you cover up the rightmost diagram at the top of Figure 7.2 (representing the carts' motion after the collision), you have no way of distinguishing this elastic collision from a *totally inelastic* one. In other words, in an elastic collision and a totally inelastic collision that have the

same initial conditions, the same amount of kinetic energy is converted. The difference is that in the elastic collision any kinetic energy in the system before the collision that is converted to internal energy during the collision is all converted back to kinetic energy after the collision, whereas in the totally inelastic collision all of the initial kinetic energy converted to internal energy during the collision stays as internal energy and is not converted back to kinetic energy. The important point here is that, whenever two objects interact, their relative speed has to change, and therefore the kinetic energy of the system must change during the interaction.

7.3 (*a*) Use Figure 7.2*a* to calculate the kinetic energies of the two carts at $t = 30$, 60, and 90 ms. (*b*) What is the kinetic energy of the system at each instant?

This disappearance of kinetic energy doesn't jeopardize conservation of energy. The kinetic energy "missing" during the interaction has merely been temporarily converted to internal energy. Consider, for instance, a rubber ball thrown against a wall and bouncing off, as in **Figure 7.5**. At the instant of impact, the ball has zero velocity and has lost all the kinetic energy it had while moving toward the wall. Where has all this kinetic energy gone? It has gone into changing the shape of the ball. **Figure 7.6** shows a golf club striking a golf ball. The deformation of the ball at the instant of impact is clearly visible. After impact, both the rubber ball of Figure 7.5 and the golf ball of Figure 7.6 regain their original shape, and the kinetic energy converted to

Figure 7.4 Even in an elastic collision between two carts, there is an instant at which the carts have the same velocity, which means that at that instant their relative velocity is zero.

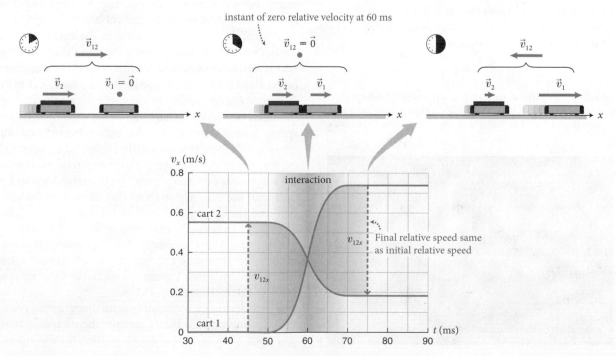

Figure 7.5 At the instant the ball in this elastic collision has zero velocity, all its kinetic energy has been used to deform the ball (and, to a lesser extent, the wall). Thus, this energy is stored temporarily as elastic potential energy.

kinetic energy

internal energy during the interaction reappears as kinetic energy. Because the system (ball and wall in Figure 7.5, ball and club in Figure 7.6) is closed, the energy of the system remains constant throughout the collision. In the elastic collision in Figure 7.4, similar changes in shape take place in the carts, but these changes occur too fast and are too small to be observed easily.

In inelastic collisions, the system's kinetic energy is not the same before and after the collision. As in an elastic collision, there is an instant at which the relative speed of the colliding objects is zero, but unlike in an elastic collision, not all of the kinetic energy converted to internal energy during the interaction reappears as kinetic energy after the collision. Some of the kinetic energy is converted irreversibly to internal energy (see Section 5.3).

Figure 7.6 At the instant of impact, a golf club and golf ball have zero relative speed, and much of the system's initial kinetic energy has gone into severe deformation of the ball (plus some deformation of the elastic club).

We can summarize the characteristics of an interaction:

1. *Two objects* are needed.
2. The *momentum* of a system of interacting objects is the same before, during, and after the interaction (provided the system is isolated).

Moreover, for interactions that affect the motion of objects:

1. The ratio of the *x* components of the accelerations of the interacting objects is the negative inverse ratio of their inertias. Because the velocities of both objects change in an interaction, the *individual* momenta and kinetic energies change.
2. The system's *kinetic energy changes during the interaction.* Part of it is converted to (or from) some internal energy. In an elastic collision, all of the converted energy reappears as kinetic energy *after* the collision. In an inelastic collision, some of the converted kinetic energy reappears as kinetic energy; in a totally inelastic collision, none of the converted kinetic energy reappears.

7.4 (*a*) In Figure 7.5, what is the momentum of the ball during the collision? (*b*) Is the momentum of the ball constant before, during, and after the collision? If so, why? If not, why not, and for what system is the momentum constant?

7.2 Potential energy

In any collision or interaction, the part of the converted kinetic energy that is temporarily stored in reversible changes in physical state and is then converted back to kinetic energy after the interaction is called **potential energy,** represented by *U.* Potential energy is a form of internal energy. The term *potential* refers to the fact that the energy has the potential to be converted back to kinetic energy—it is only temporarily stored. Just think of the rubber ball in Figure 7.5. At the instant it has zero velocity, all the energy that before impact was kinetic energy has gone into deforming the ball and is therefore now stored inside the ball. Because rubber is elastic, the stored energy has the potential to revert to kinetic energy. Similarly, if a cart on a track hits a spring mounted on a post (**Figure 7.7**), the cart compresses the spring, and all the energy that before impact was kinetic energy of the cart is temporarily converted to potential energy stored in the spring. As the spring returns to its original shape, this potential energy is converted back to kinetic energy of the cart. Throughout the interaction between the cart and the spring, the sum of the kinetic and potential energies of the closed cart-spring system is constant.

How and where is energy stored as potential energy? It is stored in reversible changes in the *configuration state* of the system, by which I mean the spatial arrangement of the system's interacting components.

There are many forms of potential energy, all related to the way interacting objects arrange themselves spatially. If you hoist a boulder up through a third-floor window, you

Figure 7.7 Energy conversion during the compression of a spring by a moving cart.

Exercise 7.2 Launch

A ball is pressed down on a spring and then released from rest. The spring launches the ball upward. Identify the energy conversions that occur between the instant the ball is released and the instant it reaches the highest point of its trajectory.

SOLUTION As the spring expands, elastic potential energy stored in the spring is converted to kinetic energy of the ball. As the ball travels upward, it slows down and the kinetic energy is converted to gravitational potential energy of the ball-Earth system. ✔

7.5 In Figure 7.7, the initial speed of the cart is v_i. Assuming no potential energy is initially stored in the spring, how much potential energy is stored in the spring at the instant depicted in the middle drawing and at the instant depicted in the bottom drawing? Give your answers in terms of m, v_i, and v.

7.3 Energy dissipation

The part of the converted kinetic energy that does not reappear after an inelastic collision is said to be *dissipated* (in other words, irreversibly converted). To understand what happens to energy that is dissipated, try the following simple experiment with a crisp sheet of paper lying flat on a horizontal surface. Without making any folds, bend one end of the sheet over the other, as illustrated in **Figure 7.8a**. If you remove your hand, the sheet straightens itself out. If you crumple up the sheet, however, as in Figure 7.8b, and then remove your hand, the crumpled sheet may expand a little, but it doesn't regain its original shape. There is an important difference between the two changes in shape. In Figure 7.8a the deformation takes place in a *coherent* manner, which means that at the atomic level, there is a pattern in the displacements of the atoms: They move orderly in rows, with each successive row experiencing a small displacement in the same direction as adjacent rows. As you bend the sheet in this fashion, you store potential energy in it. When you release the sheet, this potential energy appears as kinetic energy. In Figure 7.8b, the change in shape

change the configuration state of the boulder-Earth system. As the boulder is hoisted upward, the form of potential energy called **gravitational potential energy** is stored in the Earth-boulder system. To see that the stored energy is potential energy, imagine cutting the rope that holds the boulder in place: The boulder accelerates as it tumbles back to Earth because of the gravitational interaction between it and Earth. As the boulder gains speed, its kinetic energy increases. Because energy is conserved and because the ball-Earth system is closed, the gain in kinetic energy has to be compensated by a loss of potential energy associated with the changed configuration state.

Moving to the atomic level, whenever you squeeze a ball or a spring, you change the configuration state of the atoms that make up the ball or spring. Reversible deformations correspond to changes in **elastic potential energy**. In Figure 7.7, for instance, the kinetic energy of the cart is temporarily converted to elastic potential energy in the spring.

> Potential energy is the form of internal energy associated with reversible changes in the configuration state of an object or system. Potential energy can be converted entirely to kinetic energy.

Figure 7.8 Reversible and irreversible deformations of a sheet of paper. If the sheet is simply bent (*a*), it returns spontaneously to its original shape; if it is crumpled (*b*), it does not.

(*a*) Coherent deformation: reversible

(*b*) Incoherent deformation: irreversible

is *incoherent* because the atoms are displaced in random directions. The sheet can't straighten itself out because the randomly displaced atoms are in one another's way. Some of the smaller, less random deformations can restore themselves when you let go, but in general the energy used to do the crumpling has been irreversibly converted, producing a permanent deformation.

In addition to being dissipated to incoherent deformations, energy can be dissipated to incoherent motion, as shown in **Figure 7.9**. In Figure 7.9*a* a cart with a metal bar on top collides with a post that is anchored to the track. The collision is elastic, and so the cart's final kinetic energy is equal to the initial kinetic energy. In Figure 7.9*b* the metal bar has been replaced by a frame from which a large number of little balls are suspended. When this cart hits the post, the cart comes to a dead stop but the balls—initially at rest relative to the cart—chaotically jiggle back and forth in random directions. What has happened is that the initial kinetic energy of the cart has been converted to kinetic energy associated with the incoherent motion of the balls. We still have exactly the same amount of kinetic energy, but it has all become "internal." The initially coherent kinetic energy of the moving cart has been dissipated to the incoherent kinetic energy of the balls.

The experiment illustrated in Figure 7.9*b* is a large-scale model of what happens at the atomic scale in inelastic collisions. When a tennis ball bounces off a hard surface, part of the ball's kinetic energy is converted to incoherent energy of the atoms that make up the ball. (Imagine the atoms in the ball jiggling incoherently like the balls in Figure 7.9*b*.) Consequently the ball's kinetic energy after the bounce is

Figure 7.9 Reversible and irreversible collisions. In the totally inelastic collision in (*b*), the cart's coherent kinetic energy is converted completely to random energy of motion in the suspended balls.

(*a*) Cart rebounds elastically from barrier

Energy remains coherent: Cart's initial and final kinetic energies are equal.

(*b*) Barrier stops cart, putting balls in random motion

Cart's coherent kinetic energy is converted to incoherent energy of balls' motion.

less than that before the bounce, and so the rebound height is below the original height.

We can now give a complete classification of energy (**Figure 7.10**). All energy can be divided into two fundamental classes: energy associated with motion and energy associated with the configuration of interacting objects. Each class of energy comes in two forms: coherent and incoherent.

When all the atoms in an object move in a coherent fashion in the same direction—which means the entire object moves in that direction—the energy of motion is called

Figure 7.10 Classification of energy.

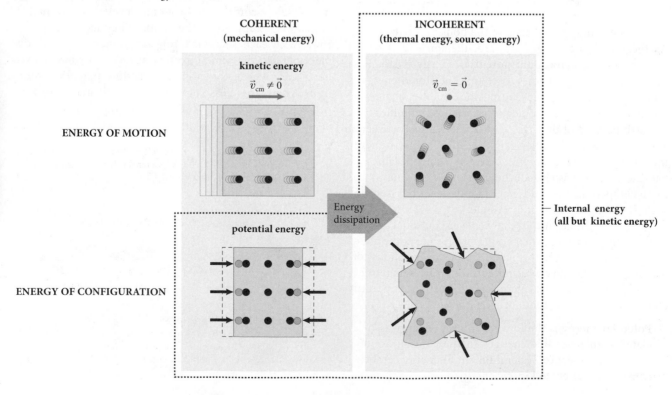

kinetic energy. Energy stored in coherent changes in configuration is called *potential energy.* The sum of a system's kinetic energy and potential energy is called the system's **mechanical energy** or **coherent energy.**

In addition to this coherent energy, a system can have **incoherent energy** associated with the incoherent motion and configuration of its parts. An important part of a system's incoherent energy is its **thermal energy.** (As we shall see in Checkpoint 7.7, not all incoherent energy is thermal energy.) The higher the thermal energy of an object, the higher its temperature—a concept we shall return to in Chapter 20. A rubber ball that has been squeezed repeatedly becomes noticeably hotter because the incoherent energy of the atoms that make up the ball has increased.

Here is a quick experiment you should try. Unfold a metal paper clip so that it takes on an S-shape. Holding the two ends, touch your lips with the central part of the clip—it should feel cold. Then vigorously bend the clip back and forth until it snaps in the middle and hold the two broken ends against your lips—the ends feel *hot.* The coherent energy you put into the back-and-forth bending has been converted to incoherent energy of the atoms in the metal (and some has gone into the breaking of the metal). When you hold the broken ends against your lips, you "feel" the atoms in the metal jiggling back and forth—they bounce against the atoms in your lips, transferring some of their energy to the atoms in your lips, thereby warming up your lips.

The sum of the system's incoherent energy and its potential energy is the system's *internal energy.*

Energy dissipation corresponds to the conversion of coherent energy into incoherent energy. This process is irreversible because incoherent energy cannot revert by itself to a coherent form. Consider the cart in Figure 7.9b, for example. If you shake it so that all the balls jiggle back and forth wildly, you are storing a certain amount of incoherent energy in the cart. If you then place the cart with the jiggling balls on the track against the post, this incoherent energy doesn't spontaneously turn into coherent kinetic energy of the cart as a whole—the cart does not suddenly start moving away from the post. What does happen, if you wait, is that the motion of the balls eventually stops. The kinetic energy of each ball gets dissipated, too—broken down into the incoherent jiggling of the individual atoms that make up each ball. (Because of the increased jiggling, the temperature of the balls increases but, as we shall see later, the temperature rise is imperceptibly small.)

This breaking down of the coherent energy of a large object into smaller units of incoherent thermal energy raises an interesting question: What happens to the energy once it has become thermal energy? Except for the motion of the Sun, the Moon, and other celestial objects, *all* motion we are familiar with comes to a stop unless something keeps it going. The stopping occurs because dissipation causes the coherent energy of the moving object to turn into incoherent energy. Does the energy of motion of the object's atoms dissipate, too? The answer to this question is *no*; at the

Figure 7.11 (*a*) Bouncing balls come to rest because their kinetic energy is converted to internal kinetic energy of the atoms (thermal energy). (*b*) Atoms have no internal structure to which kinetic energy can be dissipated, so they keep moving.

(*a*) Rubber balls bouncing in a box

atoms in ball

Atoms share ball's coherent kinetic energy.

Kinetic energy is converted to incoherent atomic motion (thermal energy).

(*b*) Gas atoms moving in a container

Atoms do not have internal structure to which their kinetic energy can dissipate . . .

. . . so they continue to move.

atomic level, there simply is no way to further break down and randomize the energy.

To see that this is so, suppose we throw a bunch of rubber balls into a box (**Figure 7.11a**). The balls initially bounce around, but if we look into the box a minute or so later, all of them are lying motionless on the bottom. All the energy is still there, but now it is inside the individual balls in the form of thermal energy. (The balls don't feel any warmer to you because the increase in thermal energy is so small as to be imperceptible.) Now suppose we observe a number of gas atoms randomly flying around in a container (Figure 7.11b). Provided the atoms do not interact with their environment, they keep flying around in the container *forever* because there are no smaller parts inside the atoms to which their kinetic energy can be dissipated.* And, because there is no dissipation at the atomic scale, nothing is required to keep atoms moving.

Friction, which occurs whenever two solid objects rub against each other or when an object moves through any fluid (air or water, say), is one of the causes of energy dissipation. Friction also causes wear and tear by removing microscopic pieces of material. This removal of material

---

*What about the particles that make up the atoms—electrons, protons, neutrons? As we shall see in Chapter 20, these parts can store energy only in certain minimum increments that are larger than the typical kinetic energy of an atom, and so the kinetic energy of an atom cannot be further dissipated inside the atom.

involves breaking the chemical bonds that hold atoms together. The incoherent configuration energy associated with the breaking of chemical bonds by friction or by crumpling, however, is many orders of magnitude smaller than the thermal energy generated in these processes (see the box "Coherent versus incoherent energy" on page 158). In general, we assume that the only type of dissipation caused by friction and crumpling is dissipation of mechanical energy into thermal energy. In Chapter 19 we shall examine energy dissipation and the accompanying conversion of coherent energy to incoherent energy in more detail.

7.6 Because of friction, a 0.10-kg hockey puck initially sliding over ice at 8.0 m/s slows down at a constant rate of 1.0 m/s² until it comes to a halt. (*a*) On separate graphs, sketch the puck's speed and its kinetic energy as functions of time. (*b*) To what form of energy is the kinetic energy of the puck converted?

7.4 Source energy

Because of the inexorable dissipation of mechanical energy, we need a source of energy—fuel, food, and so on—to either generate or maintain the mechanical energy of a system. For instance, the energy of gasoline is required to keep a car moving. Without this supply of energy, the car slows down as its kinetic energy dissipates because of friction. Likewise, to walk around the block, to send a message across the continent, to lift a basket, or to squeeze a spring, we need some source of energy.

Our current needs for mechanical energy are met using energy from a variety of sources—fossil and mineral fuels (oil, coal, natural gas), nuclear fuel, biomass fuel (food, wood, organic waste), water reservoirs, solar radiation, and wind. We refer to the energy obtained from these sources collectively as **source energy.** Broadly speaking, there are four kinds of source energy: *chemical energy* (energy associated with the configuration of atoms inside molecules) released in such chemical reactions as the burning of oil, coal, gas, and wood and the metabolizing of food; *nuclear energy* (energy

associated with the configuration of the nuclei of atoms) released in nuclear reactions; *solar energy* delivered by radiation from the Sun; and *stored solar energy* in the form of wind and hydroelectric energy.

Nearly all source energy can be traced back to energy delivered by the Sun. Nuclear reactions in the Sun create the solar radiation responsible for the energy content of biomass—the food we eat, the wood we burn. Fossil and mineral fuels were formed from the buried remains of plants and animals that lived and stored energy from the Sun millions of years ago. Wind energy results from the uneven heating of Earth's surface and atmosphere by solar radiation. Solar radiation evaporates the water that forms the clouds that deposit water in reservoirs behind dams.

7.7 How should chemical energy be classified in Figure 7.10?

To facilitate our accounting of energy in the rest of this book, we divide all energy into four categories: kinetic energy K, potential energy U, source energy E_s, and thermal energy E_{th} (**Figure 7.12a**). Interactions convert energy from one category to another, but conservation of energy requires that, for a closed system, the energy E of the system remains unchanged (Figure 7.12b).

Figure 7.13 illustrates the various types of energy conversions that can occur. Figure 7.13a shows the reversible conversion between the two forms of mechanical energy. Examples of this conversion are the (reversible) conversion between gravitational potential energy and kinetic energy for a ball thrown vertically upward and the (reversible) conversion between elastic potential energy and kinetic energy for a cart hitting a spring.

Figure 7.13b shows the (irreversible) dissipation of mechanical energy: Friction converts mechanical energy to thermal energy. Because of this dissipation, we need to convert source energy to maintain or generate mechanical energy (Figure 7.13c). For example, in a chemical reaction, the spatial arrangement of atoms inside molecules changes, and chemical energy is converted to kinetic energy of the

Figure 7.12 Energy accounting.

(*a*) The four categories of energy used for energy accounting

potential energy: coherent energy associated with configuration of interacting objects (gravitational and elastic potential energy go here)

source energy: incoherent energy used to produce other forms of energy (chemical, nuclear, solar, and stored solar energy go here)

kinetic energy: coherent energy associated with motion of objects

thermal energy: incoherent energy associated with chaotic motion of atoms making up objects

K U E_s E_{th}

mechanical energy (all coherent energy)

(*b*) In any closed system, the sum of the four categories is constant

K U E_s E_{th} (E)

$$E = K + U + E_s + E_{th}$$
is constant (does not change)

Figure 7.13 Energy conversion processes.

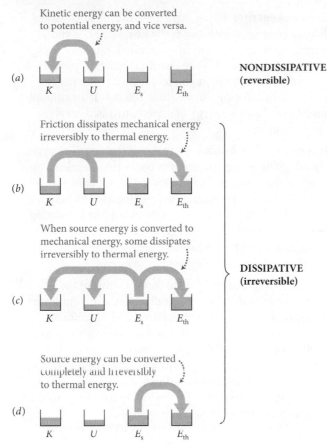

Kinetic energy can be converted to potential energy, and vice versa.

(a) K U E_s E_{th} **NONDISSIPATIVE (reversible)**

Friction dissipates mechanical energy irreversibly to thermal energy.

(b) K U E_s E_{th}

When source energy is converted to mechanical energy, some dissipates irreversibly to thermal energy.

(c) K U E_s E_{th} **DISSIPATIVE (irreversible)**

Source energy can be converted completely and irreversibly to thermal energy.

(d) K U E_s E_{th}

Figure 7.14 In the combustion of methane, each molecule of methane (CH_4) reacts with two oxygen molecules (O_2). The reaction rearranges the constituent atoms to form two water molecules (H_2O) and one molecule of carbon dioxide (CO_2). In the reaction, chemical energy originally in the reactant molecules is converted to kinetic energy of the products.

reactant molecules E

CH_4 O_2 O_2

product molecules E

H_2O H_2O CO_2

K E_{chem}

K E_{chem} ΔK ΔE_{chem}

reaction products (**Figure 7.14**). In the combustion of fuel in an engine, some of the kinetic energy of the combustion products can be converted to mechanical energy, but a large portion of it is converted to thermal energy (a car engine gets so hot that part of the mechanical energy generated by the engine must be used to turn a fan to *cool* the engine). Friction in the engine converts even more energy to thermal energy. Most of this thermal energy ends up either in the atmosphere or in the ground and cannot be easily recovered. We shall examine the generation of mechanical energy by *engines* in more detail in Chapter 21. For now, remember that the generation of mechanical energy from source energy is always accompanied by the generation of thermal energy, as illustrated in Figure 7.13c.

Figure 7.13d shows the conversion of source energy to thermal energy. An example of this process is the burning of gas or oil to heat our homes. The conversion of source energy to either mechanical or thermal energy is *irreversible*. The combustion of a methane-oxygen gas mixture, for example, causes permanent changes in the physical state of the gas mixture; it becomes a mixture of water and carbon dioxide. The reverse—obtaining methane from a mixture of water and carbon dioxide—is inconceivable even if energy is added to the system. Because of this irreversibility, the conversion of source energy to mechanical energy for transportation, heating, and so on—what we call *energy consumption*—decreases the available amount of source energy stored on Earth.

Because of dissipation, all forms of energy eventually are converted to thermal energy. As we shall see in Chapter 21, our ability to recover mechanical energy from thermal energy is very limited, however, making thermal energy not as useful as other forms of energy. Although some energy sources are renewable (solar, wind, water, biomass), they are not likely to meet our future demands for energy. Consequently the supply of source energy is limited, and a number of sources, such as oil and gas, are likely to run out during the 21st century.

7.8 Whenever you leave your room, you diligently turn off the lights to "conserve energy." Your friend tells you that energy is conserved regardless of whether or not your lights are off. Which of you is right?

As we have seen, interactions that convert source energy to either mechanical or thermal energy and interactions that convert mechanical energy to thermal energy are irreversible. Irreversible interactions change the thermal energy in a system and are called **dissipative interactions;** reversible interactions do not change the thermal energy in a system and are called **nondissipative interactions.**

To determine whether or not an interaction is dissipative, all you need to do is ask yourself whether the interaction is reversible:

Interactions that cause reversible changes are nondissipative; those that cause irreversible changes are dissipative.

Consider a puck sliding to a stop on a rough surface. If you were to make a movie of this action and then play the movie in reverse, you would immediately notice that something is not correct: A puck lying on a rough surface doesn't spontaneously start moving. So the interaction between the rough surface and the puck is irreversible and therefore dissipative.

CONCEPTS

Coherent versus incoherent energy

To get a feel for the different types of energy, let's look at a very ordinary object—a pencil. How many types of energy are (or can be) stored in a pencil?

Coherent (mechanical) energy

Kinetic energy: If the pencil is at rest on your desk, its kinetic energy is zero. If, however, you throw it across the room, you give it a kinetic energy of about **1 J.**

Potential energy: To store potential energy in the pencil, you must change its configuration by squeezing or bending it. The pencil, being stiff, does not bend or squeeze easily, and so, if you are lucky, you might be able to store **0.1 J** of elastic potential energy in it before it snaps.

Incoherent energy

Thermal energy: Thermal energy is the energy associated with the random jiggling of atoms. It is impossible to convert all of this energy to another form, and so instead let's imagine you take the pencil out of a drawer and carry it around in your pocket so that its temperature rises from room temperature to body temperature. This rise in temperature increases its thermal energy by **100 J.** If you could convert this 100 J of thermal energy to kinetic energy, your pencil would be moving at the speed of an airplane!

Chemical energy: Being made of wood, a pencil stores chemical energy, which can easily be released. If you burn the pencil, the wood turns to ashes, and the configuration energy stored in the chemical bonds is converted to thermal energy, which you feel as heat. The energy converted by burning the pencil is **100,000 J,** an amount equal to the kinetic energy of a medium-sized car moving at 35 mi/h.

Broken chemical bonds: If you bend the pencil enough, it breaks. The energy required to break the chemical bonds in the pencil is about **0.001 J.** This amount is only 1% of that 0.1 J of potential energy you added by bending the pencil to just before its breaking point; the remaining 99% ends up as thermal energy: When the pencil snaps, the stress created by the bending is relieved, and the snapping increases the jiggling of the atoms.

This comparison of energies makes two important points that are valid more generally. First, coherent forms of energy are insignificant compared with incoherent forms—most of the energy around us is in the form of incoherent energy. Second, when energy is dissipated, virtually all of it becomes thermal energy; the incoherent configuration energy associated with deformation, breaking, and abrasion is generally negligible compared to the energies required to cause these changes.

Exercise 7.3 Converting energy

For each of the following scenarios, choose a closed system, identify the energy conversions that take place, and classify each conversion according to the four processes shown in Figure 7.13. (*a*) A person lifts a suitcase. (*b*) A toy suspended from a spring bobs up and down. (*c*) A pan of water is brought to a boil on a propane burner. (*d*) A cyclist brakes and comes to a stop.

SOLUTION (*a*) Closed system: person, suitcase, and Earth. During the lifting, the potential energy of the Earth-suitcase system increases and the kinetic energy of the suitcase increases. The source energy is supplied by the person doing the lifting, who converts chemical (source) energy from food. In the process of converting this source energy, thermal energy is generated (the person gets hot). This process is represented in Figure 7.13*c*. ✔

(*b*) Closed system: toy, spring, and Earth. As the toy bobs, its height relative to the ground changes, its velocity changes, and the configuration of the spring changes. The bobbing thus involves conversions of gravitational and elastic potential energy and kinetic energy. This reversible process is represented in Figure 7.13*a*. ✔

(*c*) Closed system: pan of water and propane tank. As chemical (source) energy is released by burning the propane, the water is heated and its thermal energy increases. This process is represented in Figure 7.13*d*. ✔

(*d*) Closed system: Earth and cyclist. During the braking, the bicycle's kinetic energy is converted to thermal energy by friction (I'm ignoring the muscle source energy required to pull the brakes). This process is represented in Figure 7.13*b*. ✔

7.9 For each of the following processes, determine what energy conversion takes place and classify the interaction as dissipative or nondissipative. (Hint: Imagine what you would see if you played each situation in reverse.) (*a*) The launching of a ball by the expanding of a compressed spring, (*b*) the fall of a ball released a certain height above the ground, (*c*) the slowing down of a coasting bicycle, (*d*) the acceleration of a car.

7.5 Interaction range

The underlying mechanisms of interactions are still poorly understood, and as a result no one can answer the question, How do objects interact? From experience we know that not all objects interact with one another, but what determines when and why certain things do interact? It appears that each type of interaction occurs only between certain kinds of objects. So we assign to these objects certain *attributes* (magnetic strength, color, and so on) that are responsible for the interaction.

Note that it is the interaction that defines these attributes; we have no independent way of determining them. Consider a magnet, for instance. Is it a magnet because it behaves like one, or does it behave like a magnet because it *is* a magnet? In other words, do we say it has the attributes of a magnet because it interacts with other magnets? Or does it interact with other magnets because it has the attributes of a magnet?

Figure 7.15 Long-range interactions are perceptible over macroscopic distances; short-range ones, only over distances at the atomic scale or smaller. For instance, the contact interaction between two billiard balls is noticeable only when they are within nanometers of each other.

(*a*) Long-range interaction (magnetic)

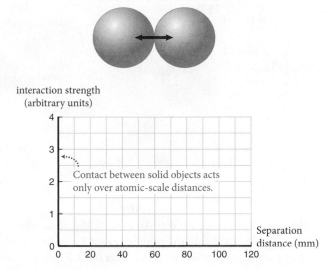

(*b*) Short-range interaction (contact)

What all this boils down to is that we *define* the properties of matter (whether something is magnetic or nonmagnetic, heavy or light, red or green) according to the interactions the matter takes part in (it interacts with iron or doesn't, Earth pulls on it strongly or not, it interacts with green light or with red). Matter can therefore be classified according to its interactions, and the attributes we give to various types of matter are just a convenient way of indicating the types of interactions they take part in.

We are used to thinking of interactions as "things touching." You know, however, that a bar magnet can attract or repel another magnet located some distance away. The gravitational interaction works that way, too: Without any physical contact, Earth pulls downward on an object thrown up in the air. And so does electricity: On a day when the humidity is low, a plastic comb held near your head can attract your hair without physical contact.

To help us understand how things can interact without touching, we need to examine what we mean by *physical contact*. On the macroscopic level, *physical contact* means just that—two surfaces touching each other. On the atomic level, however, two atoms attract or repel each other even when they are separated by distances several times their size. Because all things are made up of atoms, there is no such thing as "touching" on the atomic level and therefore no such thing as physical contact. Your feet resting on the floor, for example, are supported by countless interactions between the atoms of your feet and those in the floor. So, on the atomic level, because atoms interact without physical contact, even feet "touching" floor is really an interaction without physical contact!

The strength of any interaction between two objects (in this context, think of *strength* in the sense of the magnitude of the acceleration caused by the interaction) is a function of the distance separating the objects. **Figure 7.15** shows how this strength varies with distance for magnets and for billiard balls. Because the magnets "feel" each other over quite a large distance, their interaction is said to be a *long range* interaction. The repulsion (or, depending on the orientation of the magnets, attraction) is greatest at small separation distances but continues to be felt even at relatively large distances. In contrast, there is no noticeable interaction between the billiard balls even when they are separated by as little as the width of a hair. The two balls interact only when they are brought sufficiently close for the individual atoms to "feel" one another (which we call "touching"). The physical contact between two objects is thus a *short-range* interaction.

As these examples illustrate, our notion of physical contact has to do with how rapidly the effects of an interaction change with distance. The difference between the magnets and billiard balls in Figure 7.15 is their **interaction range**—the distance over which the interaction is appreciable.

One model widely used to picture long-range interactions is the **field** (**Figure 7.16a**). In this model, every object is surrounded by a field, the properties of which are determined

Figure 7.16 (*a*) The field of a stationary spherical object occupies the space around the object. The shading indicates the strength of the field—a measure of how strongly the object interacts with other objects. The field shown here rapidly decreases in strength with distance. (*b*) An outward traveling ripple in the field created by shaking the object.

(*a*)   (*b*)

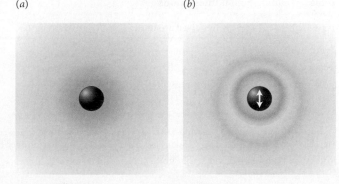

Figure 7.17 Protons and neutrons (the particles that make up the atomic nucleus) can interconvert by exchanging a particle called a pion. As a result of this pion exchange, an example of which is shown schematically below, protons and neutrons exchange places continually as though "pulled through each other." The effect is that of an attractive interaction between protons and neutrons.

by the attributes of the object. An electrically charged object has an electric field, a magnetic object has a magnetic field, any object with what is called mass has a gravitational field, and so on. (We shall discuss mass in Chapter 13; for now just think of the mass of an object as a measure of how heavy that object is.) Interactions between objects are mediated by these fields.

Fields have an existence that is separate from the objects that create them. If I shake an object, the shaking creates a disturbance in the field that travels outward much like ripples on the surface of water (Figure 7.16b). The field of any object therefore contains information on the entire history of the object. As an example, think of watching the stars on a clear, moonless night. The light that reaches your eyes from some of the stars you are looking at was emitted as long as a million years ago. Some of the stars you see may not even exist anymore. Yet, via the ripples they once created in their fields—manifested as the light they once emitted—they are still interacting with you.

An alternative model explains interactions in terms of an exchange of fundamental particles called *gauge particles* (**Figure 7.17** and Checkpoint 7.10). Physicists now believe that every interaction is caused by corresponding exchange of gauge particles. The existence of many of these particles has indeed been confirmed experimentally.

7.10 As an example of an interaction mediated by a "particle," imagine tossing a ball back and forth with a friend. You are both standing on an icy surface so slippery that friction is negligible. (*a*) Describe the effect the throwing and catching have on your momentum and your friend's momentum. (*b*) Is this an attractive or repulsive interaction? (*c*) Could you change the interaction into the other type?

7.6 Fundamental interactions

An interaction is **fundamental** if it cannot be explained in terms of other interactions. The interaction between, say, two colliding carts is not fundamental because it can be explained as being the result of the interactions between the atoms that make up the carts. Nor are the atomic interactions fundamental because they are the result of the interactions between the electrons and atomic nuclei that make up the atoms. And inside each atomic nucleus we observe yet another interaction responsible for holding the components of the nucleus together. This last interaction, the *strong interaction*, is today classified as fundamental because it cannot (yet) be explained in terms of other interactions.

All known interactions can be traced to just four fundamental interactions, two of them familiar from everyday life and two not (**Table 7.1**). The two familiar ones are the

Table 7.1 Fundamental Interactions

Type	Required attribute	Relative strength	Range	Gauge particle	Propagation speed
gravitational	mass	1	∞	graviton?	c?
weak	weak charge	10^{25}	10^{-18} m	vector bosons	varies
electromagnetic	electrical charge	10^{36}	∞	photon	c
strong	color charge	10^{38}	10^{-15} m	gluon	c

The relative strength is a measure of the magnitude of the effects of these interactions on two protons separated by about 10^{-15} m. The question marks in the last two columns indicate that the information provided has not yet been verified experimentally. The symbol c represents the speed at which lights travels.

gravitational and electromagnetic interactions. We know of the gravitational interaction as Earth pulling on objects. A nylon sock interacts with a silk blouse in the clothes dryer via the electric part of the electromagnetic interaction; a magnet interacts with a refrigerator door via the magnetic part. The two unfamiliar fundamental interactions are those that take place inside the nuclei of atoms: the weak interaction and the strong interaction. A brief overview of the four fundamental interactions follows.

1. Gravitational interaction. This long-range interaction manifests itself as an attraction between all objects that have *mass,* and it is mediated by a still undetected gauge particle called the *graviton.* It is the weakest fundamental interaction, as manifested by the observation that you can't feel it acting between your body and any nearby object even though both of you possess mass. Only for very massive objects does this interaction become appreciable: The gravitational interaction between Earth and your body, for instance, *is* noticeable.

Even though it is weak and decreases with increasing distance between the interacting objects, the gravitational interaction is what determines the structure of the universe on the cosmic scale. All other interactions cease to play a role on this scale. The existence of planetary systems and the shape of galaxies, such as the one shown in **Figure 7.18**, indicate the enormous range of the gravitational interaction.

2. Electromagnetic interaction. It is no exaggeration to say that this long-range interaction is responsible for most of what happens around us. It is responsible for the structure of atoms and molecules, for all chemical and biological processes, for the cohesion of matter into liquids and solids, for the repulsive interaction between objects such as a bat and ball, as well as for light and other electromagnetic radiation. The attribute of matter responsible for this interaction is called *electrical charge,* which comes in two varieties: *positive* and *negative,* each appearing in equal numbers in the universe. The gauge particle associated with the electromagnetic interaction is the *photon* (discussed in Chapter 34).

Figure 7.18 The matter in a galaxy is held together by the gravitational interaction—an indication of the tremendous range of this interaction.

Figure 7.19 Residual interaction. Even though a single magnet interacts strongly with a piece of iron, a pair of magnets joined together interacts only weakly with it.

For moving charged particles, the electromagnetic interaction is complex (we'll treat it later in this book). For charged particles at rest, the interaction is either attractive or repulsive, depending on the combination of charged particles involved. Like the gravitational interaction, the strength of the electromagnetic interaction decreases rapidly with increasing distance between the interacting objects. However, the electromagnetic interaction is 36 orders of magnitude (that is, 10^{36} times) stronger than the gravitational interaction. To get a feel for just how large this difference in magnitude is, consider that the inertia of a grain of sand is "only" 33 orders of magnitude less than the inertia of Earth.

Because of the perfect balance in the amount of positive and negative charge in the universe and because the electromagnetic interaction is so strong, all matter tends to arrange itself in such a way that it is electrically neutral (which means it contains just as much positive as negative charge, and as a result most electromagnetic interactions cancel out). Consequently the electromagnetic interaction is most noticeable at the atomic scale. As noted in Section 7.5, what we call physical contact between objects is the result of the electromagnetic interactions between the individual charged parts of the atoms—interactions that average out at greater distances. The situation is much the same as when you let two horseshoe magnets attract each other until they stick together, as in **Figure 7.19**. The magnetic interaction between the pair and a piece of iron is considerably weaker than the interaction between that piece of iron and just one of the magnets. This is so because, in the pair, most of the effect of, say, the north pole of one magnet is canceled by the south pole of the other magnet. At short range, the canceling of the magnetic effect is not complete, and so there is some magnetic interaction—a *residual electromagnetic interaction*—left over, to interact weakly with the piece of iron.

3. Weak interaction. This repulsive interaction is responsible for some radioactive decay processes and for the conversion of hydrogen to helium in stars. The weak interaction acts inside the nucleus between subatomic particles that possess an attribute called *weak charge* and causes most subatomic particles to be unstable. The gauge particles associated with the weak interaction are called *vector bosons.*

CONCEPTS

Figure 7.20 A neutron that is not part of an atomic nucleus disintegrates into a proton, an electron, and a subatomic particle called the antineutrino. This disintegration, called beta decay, is caused by the weak interaction.

An isolated neutron . . .

. . . decays into a proton, an electron, and a neutrino, plus kinetic energy.

neutron

electron

proton

antineutrino

K E_{nuclear}

ΔK $\Delta E_{\text{nuclear}}$

K E_{nuclear}

There is a strong parallel between the role of the electromagnetic interaction in chemical reactions and the role of the weak interaction in the decay of subatomic particles. Chemical reactions are caused by the rearrangement of electrons among atoms or groups of atoms (Figure 7.14). In the process, chemical energy is converted to (or from) kinetic energy of the reaction products. Likewise, when the weak interaction causes a subatomic particle to decay, internal energy of the original particle is converted to kinetic energy of the decay products (**Figure 7.20**).

There is a strong connection between the electromagnetic and weak interactions. Both can be considered manifestations of a single interaction called the *electroweak interaction*.

4. Strong interaction. The strong interaction acts between *quarks*, which are the building blocks of protons, neutrons, and other particles. This interaction, which can be either attractive or repulsive, is so strong that it completely overwhelms all other interactions among particles. The attribute required for this interaction is *color charge*, and the gauge particles are called *gluons*.

Quarks, like electrically charged particles and magnets, always arrange themselves in such a way that the effects of the strong interaction cancel. Only at very short range does some of the strong interaction remain. This *residual strong interaction* is responsible for holding the nucleus of an atom together.

In Table 7.1 note that the gravitational interaction—the fundamental interaction we are most directly aware of in our daily life—is orders of magnitude weaker than the other fundamental interactions. This is so because the stronger the interaction, the smaller the scale on which it affects the structure of the universe (**Figure 7.21**).

Figure 7.21 The fundamental interactions determine the structure of the universe at different scales. At the subatomic scale, the strong interaction is responsible for fusing quarks into the protons and neutrons that make up the atomic nucleus. The residual strong interaction and the weak interaction, along with electromagnetic repulsion between protons, are responsible for the formation and stability of atomic nuclei. Outside the atomic nucleus all effects of the strong interaction cancel, and weaker interactions become noticeable. Electromagnetic interactions between the positively charged atomic nucleus and negatively charged electrons are responsible for the structure of atoms. Interactions between atoms are due to residual electromagnetic interactions. At the human scale, the picture is dominated by the short-range residual electromagnetic interactions involved in contact between objects and by gravitational interactions. At the cosmic scale, the gravitational interaction plays the main role.

Size scale

10^{26} m

Gravitational interactions organize matter at planetary to cosmic scales.

Residual electromagnetic interactions assemble atoms into molecules and substances; these interactions are also responsible for contact interactions between objects.

electron cloud

nucleus

Electromagnetic interactions assemble electrons and nuclei into atoms.

Residual strong interactions assemble protons and neutrons into nuclei; **electromagnetic interactions** between protons limit nuclear size.

The **strong interaction** assembles quarks to form protons and neutrons.

10^{-15} m

Self-quiz

1. Two carts are about to collide head-on on a track. The inertia of cart 1 is greater than the inertia of cart 2, and the collision is elastic. The speed of cart 1 before the collision is higher than the speed of cart 2 before the collision. (*a*) Which cart experiences the greater acceleration during the collision? (*b*) Which cart has the greater change in momentum due to the collision? (*c*) Which cart has the greater change in kinetic energy during the collision?

2. Which of the following deformations are reversible and which are irreversible: (*a*) the deformation of a tennis ball against a racquet, (*b*) the deformation of a car fender during a traffic accident, (*c*) the deformation of a balloon as it is blown up, (*d*) the deformation of fresh snow as you walk through it?

3. Translate the kinetic energy graph in Figure 7.2 into three sets of energy bars: before the collision, during the collision, and after the collision. In each set, include a bar for K_1, a bar for K_2, and a bar for the internal energy of the system, and assume that the system is closed.

4. Describe a scenario to fit the energy bars shown in **Figure 7.22**. What happens during the interaction?

Figure 7.22

Figure 7.23

5. Describe a scenario to fit the velocity-versus-time curves for two colliding objects shown in **Figure 7.23**. What happens to the initial energy of the system of colliding objects during the interaction?

Answers

1. (*a*) The cart with the smaller inertia experiences the greater acceleration (see Figure 7.2). (*b*) The magnitude of $\Delta \vec{p}_1$ is the same as the magnitude of $\Delta \vec{p}_2$, but the changes are in opposite directions because the momentum of the system does not change during the collision. (*c*) $|\Delta K_1| = |\Delta K_2|$, but the changes are opposite in sign because the kinetic energy of the system before the elastic collision has to be the same as the kinetic energy of the system afterward.

2. (*a*) Reversible. The ball returns to its original shape. (*b*) Irreversible. The fender remains crumpled. (*c*) Irreversible. The balloon does not completely return to its original shape after deflation. (*d*) Irreversible. Your footprints remain.

3. See **Figure 7.24**. Before the collision $K_1 = 0$, K_2 is maximal, and $E_{int} = 0$; during the collision K_1, K_2, and E_{int} are all about one-third of the initial value of K_1; after the collision K_1 is about $7/8$ of the initial value of K_1, K_2 is about $1/8$ of the initial value of K_1, and $E_{int} = 0$. Because the system is closed, its energy is constant, which means the sum of the three bars is always the same.

Figure 7.24

4. During the interaction, eight units of source energy is converted to two units of kinetic energy, two units of potential energy, and four units of thermal energy. One possible scenario is the vertical launching of a ball. Consider the system comprising you, the ball, and Earth from just before the ball is launched until after it has traveled some distance upward: The source energy goes down (you exert some effort), thermal energy goes up (in the process of exerting effort you heat up), kinetic energy goes up (the ball was at rest before the launch), and so does potential energy (the distance between the ground and the ball increases).

5. The graph represents an inelastic collision because the relative velocity of the two objects decreases to about half its initial value. In order for the momentum of the system to remain constant, the inertia of object 1 must be twice that of object 2. Possible scenario: Object 2, inertia m, collides inelastically with object 1, inertia $2m$. The collision brings object 2 to rest and sets object 1 in motion. The interaction converts the initial kinetic energy of object 2 to kinetic energy of cart 1 and to thermal energy and/or incoherent configuration energy of both carts.

7.7 Interactions and accelerations

Let us now prove a statement made in Section 7.1: For interactions that affect the motion of objects, the ratio of the x components of the accelerations of the interacting objects is equal to the negative inverse of the ratio of their inertias.

Whenever two objects interact, they exchange momentum and energy. If we consider the two-object system to be isolated during the interaction, conservation of momentum requires that, at any instant during the interaction, the momentum changes of the two objects be equal in magnitude and opposite in direction:

$$\Delta \vec{p}_1 = -\Delta \vec{p}_2. \tag{7.1}$$

Because the change in momentum for each object is caused by the interaction with the other object, the time interval over which the momenta change—the duration of the interaction—is the same for both objects. If we denote this time interval by Δt, we can write

$$\frac{\Delta \vec{p}_1}{\Delta t} = -\frac{\Delta \vec{p}_2}{\Delta t}. \tag{7.2}$$

If the inertias m_1 and m_2 of the two objects are not changed by the interaction, we have, from the definition $\vec{p} \equiv m\vec{v}$,

$$\frac{m_1 \Delta \vec{v}_1}{\Delta t} = -\frac{m_2 \Delta \vec{v}_2}{\Delta t}. \tag{7.3}$$

Using the definition of acceleration given as Eq. 3.21,

$$\lim_{\Delta t \to 0} \frac{\Delta v_x}{\Delta t} \equiv a_x, \tag{7.4}$$

we take the limit of both sides of Eq. 7.3 as Δt goes to zero and get for the x components of the accelerations:

$$m_1 a_{1x} = -m_2 a_{2x}. \tag{7.5}$$

Hence, both objects accelerate during the interaction, and the ratio of the x components of their accelerations is equal to the negative inverse of the ratio of their inertias:

$$\frac{a_{1x}}{a_{2x}} = -\frac{m_2}{m_1}. \tag{7.6}$$

This relationship between the accelerations of two interacting objects of constant inertia holds for all interactions in an isolated two-object system, regardless of what happens to the energy during the interaction.

7.11 A 1000-kg compact car and a 2000-kg van, each traveling at 25 m/s, collide head-on and remain locked together after the collision, which lasts 0.20 s. (*a*) According to Eq. 7.6, their accelerations during the collision are unequal. How can this be if both initially have the same speed and the time interval during which the collision takes place is the same amount of time for both? (*b*) Calculate the average acceleration in the direction of travel experienced by each vehicle during the collision.

7.8 Nondissipative interactions

Conservation of energy requires that the energy of any closed system remain unchanged. Using the four categories of energy introduced in Section 7.4, we can write this in the form

$$\Delta E = \Delta K + \Delta U + \Delta E_s + \Delta E_{th} = 0 \quad \text{(closed system).} \qquad (7.7)$$

For nondissipative interactions, there are no changes in either the source energy or the thermal energy of the system: $\Delta E_s = 0$ and $\Delta E_{th} = 0$. Thus the only energy conversions allowed in nondissipative interactions are reversible transformations between kinetic energy K and potential energy U. For these types of interactions Eq. 7.7 simplifies to

$$\Delta E = \Delta K + \Delta U = 0 \quad \text{(closed system, nondissipative interaction).} \quad (7.8)$$

If we introduce the mechanical energy of a system

$$E_{mech} = K + U, \qquad (7.9)$$

we can write Eq. 7.8 as

$$\Delta E_{mech} = 0 \quad \text{(closed system, nondissipative interaction).} \qquad (7.10)$$

In words, in a closed system in which only nondissipative interactions take place, the mechanical energy (the sum of the kinetic and potential energies) is constant.

We can deduce an important property of potential energy from the reversibility of nondissipative interactions. Consider the nondissipative interaction shown in **Figure 7.25a**. A cart, initially traveling to the right, bounces off a spring. The cart interacts with the spring, which is anchored to Earth. The system comprising the cart, spring, track, and Earth is closed. The interaction between the cart and Earth (which we'll consider to include the track and the spring) is nondissipative because it is reversible: Reversing the sequence yields the same result. From the motion of the cart, you cannot tell if time runs from t_1 to t_5 or the other way around (Figure 7.25b).

This reversibility means that the cart's kinetic energy at some given position x must be the same on the way in and on the way out. For example, K_{cart} at t_2—when the front end of the cart is at x_2—must be the same as K_{cart} at t_4—when the front end returns to x_2. Because K_{Earth} doesn't change (see Checkpoint 7.12), Eq. 7.8 yields

$$\Delta K_{cart} = -\Delta U_{spring}, \qquad (7.11)$$

where U_{spring} is the elastic potential energy associated with the shape of the spring. Consequently, the potential energy in the spring must also have the same value at any given position on the way in and on the way out. In other words, the potential energy stored in the spring must be a unique function of position: U_{spring} has a definite value at each position x of the end of the spring. More generally, the potential energy of any system (that is, the portion of the system's internal energy that is associated with reversible configuration changes) can be written in the form

$$U = U(x), \qquad (7.12)$$

where $U(x)$ is a unique function of a position variable x that quantifies the configuration of the system.

Figure 7.25 Reversible interaction between a cart and a spring anchored to a post.

(a) Forward

We know this interaction is reversible . . .

(b) Reverse

. . . because it could run in reverse—the reverse process is possible.

A direct consequence of this dependence of potential energy on position is that the change in the kinetic energy of an object that moves from a position x_1 to a position x_2 during some nondissipative interaction depends *only* on those positions, not on the path taken by the object. Example 7.4 shows how this applies to the specific case of a cart bouncing off a spring.

7.12 Use the conservation laws to show that, when the spring in Figure 7.25 expands, the change in the kinetic energy of Earth is negligible and we are therefore justified in using Eq. 7.11.

Example 7.4 Path independence of change in potential energy

Figure 7.26 shows a cart striking a spring. In Figure 7.26a, consider the motion of the cart along the direct path from the initial position x_1, which is the position at which the cart makes initial contact with the free end of the spring, to the position x_2 (path A). In Figure 7.26b, consider the motion along the path from x_1 to the position of maximum compression x_3 and then back to x_2 (path B). Show that the change in the cart's kinetic energy is the same for both paths if the interaction caused by the spring is reversible.

❶ **GETTING STARTED** As the cart moves from x_1 to x_2 along path A, the spring is compressed and the cart's kinetic energy steadily decreases. Along path B, the spring is first compressed and the cart comes to a stop at x_3. The spring then expands, accelerating the cart back to x_2. To solve this problem, I'll consider the closed system made up of the cart, the spring, and Earth.

❷ **DEVISE PLAN** The change in the cart's kinetic energy is given by Eq. 7.11. Therefore if the change in the elastic potential energy

Figure 7.26 Example 7.4.

(a) Cart moves directly from x_1 to x_2

→ path A

(b) Cart moves from x_1 to x_2 via x_3

path B

of the spring is the same along both paths, then the change in the kinetic energy of the cart must also be the same along both paths. I'll first determine the change in potential energy between the initial and final positions of path A, then do the same between the initial and final positions of the two parts of path B.

❸ **EXECUTE PLAN** Because the potential energy associated with a reversible interaction is a function of x only (Eq. 7.12), the change in elastic potential energy along path A is

$$\Delta U_{\text{path A}} = U_f - U_i = U(x_2) - U(x_1).$$

Along path B I have two contributions to ΔU_{spring}: an increase in U from x_1 to x_3 and a decrease from x_3 to x_2:

$$\Delta U_{\text{path B}} = \Delta U_{13} + \Delta U_{32}$$

$$= \left[U(x_3) - U(x_1) \right] + \left[U(x_2) - U(x_3) \right]$$

$$= U(x_2) - U(x_1) = \Delta U_{\text{path A}}. ✔$$

So, the change in the cart's kinetic energy is the same for both paths.

❹ **EVALUATE RESULT** The change in the cart's kinetic energy is independent of the path joining x_1 and x_2 even though the cart ends up moving in opposite directions along the two paths. This is because the change in potential energy ΔU_{12} depends only on the coordinates of the initial and final positions x_1 and x_2.

Another way to see that this must be true is to consider only the motion from x_2 to x_3 and back. From x_2 to x_3 all the kinetic energy of the cart is converted to elastic potential energy of the spring. From x_3 to x_2 the elastic potential energy is converted back to kinetic energy, and so the motion from x_2 to x_3 and back to x_2 doesn't change the cart's kinetic energy. (Remember that kinetic energy is always positive and independent of the direction of travel.)

✋ **7.13** Show that, in Figure 7.26, the change in potential energy along a round trip from position x_1 to position x_2 and then back to x_1 is zero.

We can deduce a very important point from the fact that potential energy is a unique function of position. Consider, for example, a closed system with the potential energy function $U(x)$ shown in **Figure 7.27a**. If there is no dissipation, the sum of the kinetic and potential energies of this closed system is constant. Therefore, because the potential energy increases with increasing x, the kinetic energy must decrease with increasing x. So, if we consider two positions x_1 and $x_2 > x_1$, we see that the kinetic energy must be smaller at x_2 than at x_1. If the object whose kinetic energy is represented in the graph moves toward increasing x, as shown in Figure 7.27b, it slows down, and so its acceleration must point to the left. If, on the other hand, the object moves toward smaller x, as shown in Figure 7.27c, it speeds up, and so its acceleration again points to the left. This means that the object tends to be accelerated in the direction of lower potential energy, regardless of its original direction of motion. Quite generally we can state:

The parts of any closed system always tend to accelerate in the direction that lowers the system's potential energy.

In Figure 7.26, for example, the potential energy increases as the free end of the spring moves to the right. The free end therefore accelerates the cart to the left. This acceleration slows the cart down as it moves to the right and speeds it up as it moves to the left.

Figure 7.27 Acceleration in a closed system that has no energy dissipation.

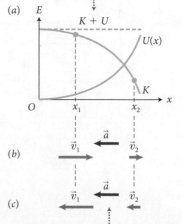

Acceleration always points toward positions of lower potential energy, regardless of direction of motion.

7.14 Consider a ball launched upward. Verify that its acceleration points in the direction that lowers the gravitational potential energy of the Earth-ball system.

7.9 Potential energy near Earth's surface

As a first example of how to determine the potential energy for a nondissipative interaction, consider a familiar interaction: the gravitational interaction near Earth's surface. As we discussed in Chapter 3, it is an experimental fact that, in the absence of air resistance, all objects near the ground fall with constant acceleration $g = 9.8 \text{ m/s}^2$. If we ignore friction, this interaction is nondissipative because free fall is reversible (see Checkpoint 7.9b).

If we release a ball from a certain height above the ground, the ball gains kinetic energy as it accelerates downward. As the ball falls, the distance between it and the ground decreases so that the (gravitational) configuration of the Earth-ball system and hence the potential energy associated with this configuration change. Because the ball and Earth constitute a closed system and because the gravitational interaction is nondissipative, we can use Eq. 7.8 to relate the change in the ball's kinetic energy to a change in the gravitational potential energy U^G (as we found in Checkpoint 7.12, Earth's kinetic energy doesn't change):*

$$\Delta U^G + \Delta K_b = 0, \tag{7.13}$$

where ΔU^G is the change in the gravitational potential energy of the Earth-ball system and ΔK_b is the change in the ball's kinetic energy.

Equation 7.13 allows us to obtain ΔU^G if we know ΔK_b. Using some of the kinematics from Chapter 3, we can obtain an expression that gives ΔU^G in terms of physical quantities other than the kinetic energy. Let's begin by looking at our ball as it falls from x_i to x_f in a time interval $\Delta t = t_f - t_i$. As illustrated in **Figure 7.28**, at t_i the ball is at a height x_i above the ground and the x component of its velocity is $v_{x,i}$; at t_f the ball is at x_f and the x component of its velocity is $v_{x,f}$. In that time interval, the ball accelerates with a constant acceleration given by Eqs. 3.1 and 3.14:

$$a_x = \frac{\Delta v_x}{\Delta t} = -g. \tag{7.14}$$

Next we turn to Eq. 3.7, which when we substitute $-g$ for a_x is

$$\Delta x = v_{x,i}\Delta t - \tfrac{1}{2}g(\Delta t)^2. \tag{7.15}$$

Rearranging Eq. 7.14 gives $\Delta t = -\Delta v_x/g$, and substituting this expression for Δt into Eq. 7.15 gives us

$$\Delta x = -v_{x,i}\frac{\Delta v_x}{g} - \tfrac{1}{2}g\left(\frac{\Delta v_x}{-g}\right)^2. \tag{7.16}$$

Figure 7.28 A freely falling ball gains kinetic energy at the expense of the gravitational potential energy of the (closed) Earth-ball system.

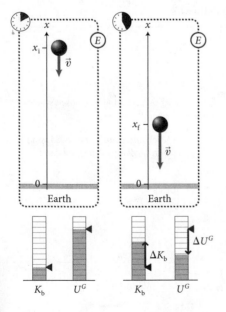

---

*We use superscripts to indicate the type of interaction associated with the potential energy: G for gravitational, E for electric, and so on.

Expanding the delta notations and working through the algebra, we get

$$x_f - x_i = -\frac{2v_{x,i}(v_{x,f} - v_{x,i}) + v_{x,f}^2 - 2v_{x,i}v_{x,f} + v_{x,i}^2}{2g} = -\frac{v_f^2 - v_i^2}{2g}, \quad (7.17)$$

where we have used the fact that $v_x^2 = v^2$. Multiplying through by g and by the inertia m_b of the ball, we get

$$m_b g(x_f - x_i) + \tfrac{1}{2}m_b(v_f^2 - v_i^2) = 0. \quad (7.18)$$

The second term on the left is precisely the change in the ball's kinetic energy, and so comparison with Eq. 7.13 tells us that the first term must be ΔU^G, the change in gravitational potential energy we are looking for. When the distance between the ball and the ground changes by an amount Δx, the gravitational potential energy changes by an amount $m_b g \Delta x$.

Because *all* objects falling near Earth's surface experience the same acceleration, this reasoning holds for any object. So, if the vertical coordinate of any object of inertia m changes by Δx, the change in the gravitational potential energy of the Earth-object system is

$$\Delta U^G = mg\Delta x \quad \text{(near Earth's surface).} \quad (7.19)$$

✋ **7.15** Suppose you raise this book (inertia $m = 3.4\,\text{kg}$) from the floor to your desk, 1.0 m above the floor. (*a*) Does the gravitational potential energy of the Earth-book system increase or decrease? (*b*) By how much? (*c*) Conservation of energy requires that this change in potential energy be compensated for by a change in energy somewhere in the universe. Where?

Equation 7.19 gives the change in gravitational potential energy between two positions:

$$\Delta U^G = U_f^G - U_i^G = mg(x_f - x_i) = mgx_f - mgx_i, \quad (7.20)$$

from which we deduce that the gravitational potential energy of the Earth-object system is given by

$$U^G(x) = mgx \quad \text{(near Earth's surface),} \quad (7.21)$$

where x is the object's vertical coordinate with the x axis pointing up.

Implicit in this expression is that $U^G = 0$ at $x = 0$. Note, however, that if we write $U^G = mg(x + c)$, with c some arbitrary constant, Eq. 7.20 remains the same because the constant c, which appears in both terms, cancels out. This arbitrariness in the reference point for zero gravitational potential energy is no different from the arbitrariness in the reference point for measuring elevations or from the reference frame dependence of kinetic energy—physically, only *changes* in energy are relevant. Because of this arbitrariness, you can choose whichever reference point you like as the position where the gravitational potential energy is zero (for example, the ground at $x = 0$, as in Eq. 7.21).

QUANTITATIVE TOOLS

Example 7.5 Path independence of gravitational potential energy

Ball A is released from rest at a height h above the ground. Ball B is launched upward from the same height at initial speed $v_{B,i}$. The two balls have the same inertia m. Consider this motion from the instant they are released to the instant they hit the ground. (a) Using kinematics, show that the change in kinetic energy is the same for both balls. (b) Show that this change in kinetic energy is equal to the negative of the change in the gravitational potential energy of the Earth-ball system between positions $x = +h$ and $x = 0$.

❶ **GETTING STARTED** I begin by representing these two motions graphically (**Figure 7.29**). Ball A drops straight down; ball B first rises a distance d above the launch position h and then falls from a height $h + d$.

Figure 7.29

❷ **DEVISE PLAN** I can obtain the initial kinetic energies from the initial speeds, which are given. So all I need to do is calculate the final speeds using the kinematics equations for motion at constant acceleration from Chapter 3. From my sketch, I see that the x component of the acceleration of the balls is given by $a_x = -g$. For part b I can use Eq. 7.20 to calculate the change in gravitational potential energy.

❸ **EXECUTE PLAN** (a) The time interval ball A takes to fall to the ground can be obtained from Eq. 3.7:

$$\Delta x = x_f - x_i = 0 - h = v_{Ax,i}\Delta t - \tfrac{1}{2}g(\Delta t)^2$$

$$= -\tfrac{1}{2}g(\Delta t)^2$$

$$(\Delta t)^2 = \frac{2h}{g}. \qquad (1)$$

The x component of the ball's final velocity is, from Eq. 7.14, $v_{Ax,f} = v_{Ax,i} - g\Delta t = -g\Delta t$, and so, using Eq. 1, I calculate that the kinetic energy of ball A just before it strikes the ground is

$$K_{A,f} = \tfrac{1}{2}mv_{A,f}^2 = \tfrac{1}{2}m[-g\Delta t]^2 = \tfrac{1}{2}mg^2\left(\frac{2h}{g}\right) = mgh. \qquad (2)$$

Because the ball begins at rest, $K_{A,i} = 0$, and so the change in kinetic energy is $\Delta K_A = K_{A,f} - K_{A,i} = mgh$.

Equation 2 holds for any value of h. After reaching its highest position, ball B falls a distance $h + d$ to the ground, and so, substituting $h + d$ for h in Eq. 2, I obtain the final kinetic energy of ball B: $K_{B,f} = mg(h + d)$. To determine d, I examine ball B's motion from its initial position $x_i = h$ to the top of its path, where $x_f = h + d$, and again use Eq. 3.7:

$$\Delta x = (h + d) - h = d = v_{Bx,i}\Delta t_{top} - \tfrac{1}{2}g(\Delta t_{top})^2, \qquad (3)$$

but the time interval Δt_{top} required to reach the top of the trajectory is not known. I do know, however, that the ball's velocity at the top is zero, and so I can say, again using Eq. 7.14, that $v_{Bx,top} = 0 = v_{Bx,i} - g\Delta t_{top}$, or $\Delta t_{top} = v_{Bx,i}/g$. Equation 3 then becomes

$$d = v_{Bx,i}\left(\frac{v_{Bx,i}}{g}\right) - \tfrac{1}{2}g\left(\frac{v_{Bx,i}}{g}\right)^2 = \frac{v_{B,i}^2}{g} - \tfrac{1}{2}\frac{v_{B,i}^2}{g} = \tfrac{1}{2}\frac{v_{B,i}^2}{g}.$$

The final kinetic energy of ball B is thus

$$K_{B,f} = mg(h + d) = mgh + mg\left(\tfrac{1}{2}\frac{v_{B,i}^2}{g}\right) = mgh + \tfrac{1}{2}mv_{B,i}^2.$$

Because $K_{B,i} = \tfrac{1}{2}mv_{B,i}^2$ is the initial kinetic energy of ball B, the gain in kinetic energy for ball B is $\Delta K_B = K_{B,f} - K_{B,i} = mgh$, which is indeed equal to that of ball A (Eq. 2). ✔

(b) According to Eq. 7.20, the change in gravitational potential energy is

$$\Delta U^G = mg(x_f - x_i) = mg(0 - h) = -mgh. ✔$$

This result is equal in magnitude to the gains in the balls' kinetic energies I found in part a.

❹ **EVALUATE RESULT** Because I obtained the same result in two ways, I can be quite confident of my answer. My result further confirms that the change in potential energy is independent of the path taken and depends on only the endpoints of the path.

QUANTITATIVE TOOLS

🖐 **7.16** Suppose that instead of choosing Earth and the ball as our system in the discussion leading up to Eq. 7.21, we had chosen to consider just the ball. Does it make sense to speak about the gravitational potential energy of the ball (the way we speak of its kinetic energy)?

7.10 Dissipative interactions

As noted in Section 7.3, a dissipative interaction is one in which there are changes in thermal energy. These interactions are *irreversible*. As an example of such an interaction consider **Figure 7.30a**, which shows a puck sliding along a wooden board and slowing to a stop. The friction between the board and the puck is dissipative: If we play the sequence in reverse, we obtain an impossible situation (Figure 7.30b). The friction acting on the puck in Figure 7.30a causes its kinetic energy to be converted to thermal energy—to be dissipated. The system comprising the puck, the board, and Earth (which holds the board in place) is closed, and so Eq. 7.7, $\Delta E = \Delta K + \Delta U + \Delta E_s + \Delta E_{th} = 0$, holds. We know that ΔU is zero because there is no change in the puck's height relative to Earth and there are no springs involved. The source energy has to be zero because no nuclear or chemical reactions are involved, and so Eq. 7.7 simplifies to

$$\Delta K + \Delta E_{th} = 0. \tag{7.22}$$

Because the only kinetic energy that changes is that of the puck (the changes in the kinetic energies of the board and Earth are negligible, see Checkpoint 7.12), we can say

$$\Delta K_{puck} = -\Delta E_{th}. \tag{7.23}$$

Figure 7.30 A puck that slides to a halt (*a*) dissipates energy through friction. Because this interaction is dissipative, the process is irreversible; the sequence shown in (*b*) cannot occur.

(*a*) Forward

This interaction is *not reversible* . . .

(*b*) Reverse

. . . because we could never observe a puck start to move on its own, spontaneously converting incoherent thermal energy to coherent kinetic energy.

QUANTITATIVE TOOLS

Although this expression looks similar to Eq. 7.11, the right side is very different conceptually. In particular, thermal energy is not a function of position the way U is. The motion shown in Figure 7.30 can take place *anywhere* along the board (unlike the motion shown in Figure 7.25, which can take place only when the cart is at the spring).

Another way to see that the interaction between the puck and the board is dissipative is to look at what happens during a round trip. Imagine putting the puck down at some position x_A and then moving it back and forth between x_A and some other position x_B a dozen times. When the puck eventually returns to x_A, its state is changed: It is hotter because of the friction (and some wear has taken place). This means that energy has been dissipated irreversibly, and so $\Delta E_{th} \neq 0$ even though the puck is back at its starting position. Moving the cart of Figure 7.25 back and forth a dozen times, on the other hand, yields no change in the spring's potential energy: $\Delta U_{spring} = 0$ whenever the cart is back at its starting position.

Equation 7.7 also describes the changes in energy that take place during inelastic collisions. We know that ΔU is zero because any reversible configuration changes that occur during the first half of the collision are undone during the second half. Provided no source energy is converted during the collision, conservation of energy applied to the closed system of the colliding objects requires that the changes in kinetic energy and thermal energy add up to zero, as stated in Eq. 7.22, which we can restate in the form

$$\Delta K = - \Delta E_{th}. \tag{7.24}$$

This equation is applicable to elastic, inelastic, and totally inelastic collisions. In elastic collisions, no energy is dissipated. Thus $\Delta E_{th} = 0$ and so Eq. 7.24 reduces to

$$\Delta K = 0 \quad \text{(elastic collision)}, \tag{7.25}$$

which means that the kinetic energy of the system does not change, as we already know from Eq. 5.15. For inelastic collisions, we can compare Eq. 7.24 and Eq. 6.43, $\Delta K = \frac{1}{2}\mu v_{12i}^2(e^2-1)$, where the reduced inertia μ is $m_1 m_2/(m_1 + m_2)$ and the coefficient of restitution e (Eq. 5.18) is v_{12f}/v_{12i}. This comparison tells us that the amount of kinetic energy converted to thermal energy is determined by the coefficient of restitution:

$$\Delta E_{th} = -\Delta K = \frac{1}{2}\mu v_{12i}^2(1 - e^2). \tag{7.26}$$

The smaller the value of e, the larger the amount of energy dissipated from coherent energy to incoherent energy.

Example 7.6 Fender bender

A 1000-kg car traveling at 10 m/s collides with and attaches to an identical car that is initially at rest. (*a*) How much energy is dissipated in the collision? (*b*) Use Eq. 7.26 to verify your result.

❶ **GETTING STARTED** The collision is totally inelastic, and so the kinetic energy of the two-car system after the collision is less than it was before the collision. (It has to be nonzero, however, to maintain the momentum of the isolated two-car system.) Because the system can be considered closed during the collision and because no energy is stored reversibly ($\Delta U = 0$), the kinetic energy that disappears is converted to thermal energy (the crumpling heats the metal). I make the sketch in **Figure 7.31** to represent the energy changes in the system.

Figure 7.31

❷ **DEVISE PLAN** Equation 7.24 tells me that the increase in thermal energy in the system is equal to the decrease in kinetic energy. I can determine the initial kinetic energy from the data given. To obtain the final kinetic energy, I first use conservation of momentum to calculate the velocity of the two cars immediately after impact and then calculate the kinetic energy of the combined cars.

❸ **EXECUTE PLAN** (a) The initial kinetic energy is $\frac{1}{2}(1000 \text{ kg}) \times (10 \text{ m/s})^2 = 50 \text{ kJ}$. After the collision, the cars, locked together and forming an object of inertia 2000 kg, must have the same combined momentum as the single car before the collision, and so

$$(2000 \text{ kg})v_{x,f} = (1000 \text{ kg})(+10 \text{ m/s})$$

$$v_{x,f} = +5.0 \text{ m/s}.$$

The final kinetic energy is thus

$$\tfrac{1}{2}(2000 \text{ kg})(5.0 \text{ m/s})^2 = 25 \text{ kJ}$$

so

$$\Delta K = 25 \text{ kJ} - 50 \text{ kJ} = -25 \text{ kJ}.$$

The amount of energy dissipated is 25 kJ. ✔

(b) For a totally inelastic collision, $e = 0$ and Eq. 7.26 becomes

$$\Delta E_{th} = \tfrac{1}{2}\mu v_{12i}^2 = \tfrac{1}{2}\left(\frac{m_1 m_2}{m_1 + m_2}\right)v_{12i}^2 = \frac{m^2}{4m}v_{12i}^2 = \tfrac{1}{4}mv_{12i}^2,$$

where I have used the fact that the two cars have the same inertia m. The initial relative speed v_{12i} is equal to the initial speed of car 1, and so $E_{th} = \tfrac{1}{4}(1000 \text{ kg})(10 \text{ m/s})^2 = 25 \text{ kJ}$, as I found before. ✔

❹ **EVALUATE RESULT** The two methods yield the same result, which is reassuring. The energy dissipated is equal to the chemical energy stored in just one-fourth of a wooden pencil (see the box on page 158), and yet both cars are likely to be wrecked beyond repair. Although it is surprising that one could wreck two cars with the chemical energy stored in one pencil, the box on page 158 states that coherent forms of energy are insignificant compared with incoherent forms, leading me to believe that the answer I obtained is not unreasonable.

As we saw in Section 5.8, a system's kinetic energy increases in an explosive separation. **Figure 7.32** shows two explosive separations. In Figure 7.32*a* the increase in kinetic energy is due to energy stored in a spring: One form of coherent energy (the elastic potential energy in the spring) is converted to another form of coherent energy (the kinetic energy of the moving carts). Because the compression of the spring is reversible, this interaction is nondissipative, and so this type of explosive separation is described by Eq. 7.8, $\Delta K + \Delta U = 0$.

The situation in Figure 7.32*b* is irreversible. Two carts are placed back to back against a firecracker, and when the firecracker is ignited, the explosive separation accelerates the carts away from each other. There is no change in potential energy because there is no change in the cart's height relative to Earth and there are no springs involved. There is, however, a change in source energy: During the explosive separation, chemical energy is converted partly to (coherent) kinetic energy of the carts and partly to (incoherent) thermal energy (things get hot during an explosion). For this dissipative interaction, we have, with $\Delta E_s = \Delta E_{chem}$,

$$\Delta K + \Delta E_{chem} + \Delta E_{th} = 0. \tag{7.27}$$

Figure 7.32 Interactions that increase the kinetic energy of a system (*a*) nondissipatively and (*b*) dissipatively.

(*a*) Compressed spring pushes carts apart

(*b*) Exploding firecracker pushes carts apart

Elastic potential energy converted nondissipatively to kinetic energy

Source energy converted dissipatively to kinetic and thermal energy

QUANTITATIVE TOOLS

More generally, for any interaction involving a rise in temperature, or a permanent deformation in one or more of the interacting objects, or the conversion of source energy—in short, for any dissipative interaction—we have

$$\Delta K + \Delta U + \Delta E_s + \Delta E_{th} = 0 \quad \text{(closed system, dissipative interaction). (7.28)}$$

In general $\Delta E_s < 0$ because source energy is converted to another form of energy and $\Delta E_{th} > 0$ because dissipation increases the amount of thermal energy.

Exercise 7.7 Skateboard

Standing a few meters from a skateboard, a boarder begins running and then jumps onto the board. Make bar diagrams like the ones in Figure 7.32 to illustrate the energy conversions (*a*) while he accelerates and (*b*) while he jumps onto the board. Are the interactions dissipative or nondissipative?

SOLUTION (*a*) I choose a closed system consisting of the boarder, the skateboard, and Earth. The boarder's initial kinetic energy is zero. As he accelerates during his run, he gains kinetic energy while the kinetic energy of Earth and the board remain zero. As he accelerates, he converts source energy (chemical energy extracted from food) to kinetic energy (he speeds up) and thermal energy (he gets warmer). This conversion is irreversible and therefore dissipative. There are no reversible changes in potential energy, and therefore I draw the energy bars shown in **Figure 7.33**.

Figure 7.33

(*b*) The jump onto the skateboard is a totally inelastic collision. Initially the boarder moves while the skateboard is at rest; after he lands on the board, both move at the same velocity. During this "collision," there is no conversion of source energy and no change of potential energy. As in any other totally inelastic collision, however, part of the initial kinetic energy is dissipated to thermal energy between the boarder's feet and the board and between the wheels and the ground. My bar diagram is shown in **Figure 7.34**.

Figure 7.34

7.17 How much energy is dissipated in the collision of Checkpoint 7.11?

Chapter Glossary

SI units of physical quantities are given in parentheses.

Coherent energy The sum of the coherent forms of energy (kinetic and potential energy), also called *mechanical energy*.

Dissipative interactions Interactions that involve changes in thermal energy. Such interactions are irreversible.

Elastic potential energy $U(\text{J})$ The potential energy associated with the reversible deformation of objects.

Field A way of describing the interaction of two objects that have a particular attribute, where each object produces in the space surrounding it a field that mediates the interaction.

Fundamental interaction An interaction that cannot (yet) be explained in terms of other interactions.

Gravitational potential energy $U^G(\text{J})$ The potential energy associated with the relative position of objects that are interacting gravitationally. Near Earth's surface, if the vertical coordinate of an object of inertia m is changed by an amount Δx, the gravitational potential energy changes by

$$\Delta U^G = mg\Delta x \quad \text{(near Earth's surface).} \qquad (7.19)$$

Incoherent energy The internal energy associated with the incoherent motion and configuration of the parts of a system.

Interaction An event that produces physical change or a change in motion. An interaction that causes the interacting bodies to accelerate away from each other is *repulsive*. When the interacting bodies accelerate toward each other, the interaction is *attractive*. The ratio of the x components of the accelerations of two interacting objects is given by

$$\frac{a_{1x}}{a_{2x}} = -\frac{m_2}{m_1}. \qquad (7.6)$$

Interaction range The distance over which the interaction between two objects is appreciable. The gravitational and electromagnetic interactions extend to infinite distances and are *long range*. The weak and strong nuclear interactions are *short range*.

Mechanical energy $E_{\text{mech}}(\text{J})$ The sum of the coherent forms of energy (kinetic and potential energy):

$$E_{\text{mech}} = K + U. \qquad (7.9)$$

Nondissipative interactions Interactions that convert kinetic energy to potential energy, and vice versa. For these reversible interactions, the mechanical energy of a closed system does not change:

$$\Delta E_{\text{mech}} = \Delta K + \Delta U = 0 \quad \text{(nondissipative).} \qquad (7.8)$$

Potential energy $U(\text{J})$ A coherent form of internal energy associated with reversible changes in the *configuration* of an object or system. Potential energy can be converted entirely to kinetic energy. The potential energy of a system of two interacting objects can always be written in the form

$$U = U(x), \qquad (7.12)$$

where $U(x)$ is a unique function of a position variable x that quantifies the configuration of the system.

Source energy $E_s(\text{J})$ An incoherent form of internal energy associated with the random configuration of atoms. Source energy can be readily, but never entirely, converted to the two coherent forms of energy.

Thermal energy $E_{\text{th}}(\text{J})$ An incoherent form of internal energy associated with the random internal motion of the atoms that make up objects. Thermal energy cannot be entirely converted to coherent forms of energy.

8 Force

CONCEPTS

8.1 Momentum and force
8.2 The reciprocity of forces
8.3 Identifying forces
8.4 Translational equilibrium
8.5 Free-body diagrams
8.6 Springs and tension

QUANTITATIVE TOOLS

8.7 Equation of motion
8.8 Force of gravity
8.9 Hooke's law
8.10 Impulse
8.11 Systems of two interacting objects
8.12 Systems of many interacting objects

At this point in your study of physics, you can already solve a wide range of problems using just the conservation laws. Up to now we have applied these laws in only isolated or closed systems, however, and it is not always possible to identify such a system when working on problems. For this reason, you also need to know an approach to problem solving that is valid in systems that are interacting with their surroundings. If you look back at the material in earlier chapters, you will notice that many of the interactions we discussed involve pushing, pulling, or rubbing—all actions related to the everyday notion of *force*. So, in order to be able to deal with systems that are not isolated, you must know about the concept of force.

The term *force* is a familiar one—usually associated with the capacity to either move objects (for example, pushing a chair along the floor) or cause physical change (say, crushing an empty can). To which of the physical quantities I have defined so far does this notion of force best correspond, however, and how can we quantify it?

8.1 Momentum and force

To relate the intuitive concept of force to the quantities we have encountered so far, consider the following scenario. You are on a bicycle coming down a steep hill and approaching a sharp turn at 30 km/h. Suddenly you discover that your brakes are not working, leaving you no option but to slam into a concrete wall. The force of impact will be considerable, and if you were going faster—say, 40 km/h—it would be even greater. Conversely, if you were going at a mere 3 km/h, the impact might not be that bad. And it is not just your speed that matters. When you are carrying a backpack full of bricks and traveling at 30 km/h, the force of impact is greater than when you are traveling at the same speed but carrying nothing on your back.

Realizing that both your speed and your inertia govern the force of the impact you make with the wall, you may be tempted to believe that force is related solely to change in momentum, but things are not that simple. To see why, imagine that part of the concrete wall is padded with mattresses. Which part do you head for? You don't need any physics to realize that the mattresses offer you protection. When you hit a mattress, the force of impact is smaller than when you hit the concrete. In terms of momentum change and energy change, however, it doesn't make any difference which one you choose. In either case, your speed decreases by the same amount, 30 km/h, and so the decreases in your momentum and kinetic energy are the same no matter how you come to a stop.

The difference between hitting a mattress and hitting the concrete is that the mattress changes your momentum over a longer time interval. The momentum change therefore occurs at a slower rate. Evidently, the longer the interaction time interval, the smaller the force of impact. In other words, what determines the magnitude of the force of impact is not the absolute value of your momentum change but rather the rate at which this change happens. The faster your momentum changes, the larger the force of the impact on you.

This scenario illustrates two important points about forces. First, forces are manifestations of interactions—the force exerted by the mattress on you, for example, is one part of the interaction between you and the mattress (another part is the force exerted by you on the mattress). Second, for an object that is participating in one interaction only, we can quantitatively define **force:**

The force exerted on the object is the time rate of change in the object's momentum.

Because it is related to a change in momentum, force is a vector and so has direction as well as magnitude. The direction of any given force is the same as the direction of the momentum change the force causes. When you hit the wall in our bicycling example, for instance, the direction of the force exerted by the wall on you is opposite your direction of travel because the direction of your momentum change is opposite your direction of travel.

Even though the arguments leading up to the relationship between force and time rate of change in momentum all sound very plausible, I should warn you that the consequences of this relationship differ from your intuitive notions about forces in a number of ways.

8.1 Imagine pushing a crate in a straight line along a surface at a steady speed of 1 m/s. What is the time rate of change in the momentum of the crate?

The answer to this checkpoint should surprise you. After all, you *are* pushing the crate. So how can the time rate of change in the momentum of the crate be zero? The problem here is that the crate is interacting not just with you but also with the surface because there is friction between it and the surface. The directions and magnitudes of these two interactions (between the crate and your hands and between the crate and the surface) are such that their combined action causes no change in the momentum of the crate, and so it continues to move at constant speed in the direction of your push. In each interaction, there is a force exerted on the crate—exerted by you in one case and by the surface in the other case. The force exerted by your hands on the crate tends to move the crate forward, while the force exerted in the horizontal direction by the surface on the crate (the *force of friction* or *frictional force*) tends to resist the forward motion of the crate. If the two opposing forces exerted on the crate are equal in magnitude, their vector sum (sometimes called the *net force*) is zero. In other words, if the surface pushes on the crate just as hard as you push on it in the opposite direction, the acceleration effects of the

Figure 8.1 When you push a crate along a surface, two opposing forces are exerted on the crate: one by you (the push), the other by the surface (friction). If these forces are equal in magnitude, the crate moves at constant velocity.

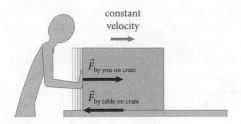

constant velocity

$\vec{F}_{\text{by you on crate}}$

$\vec{F}_{\text{by table on crate}}$

two opposing forces cancel and the crate moves at constant velocity (**Figure 8.1**). If the force exerted by the surface on the crate is smaller than the force you exert on it, the crate speeds up; if the force exerted by the surface is larger, the crate slows down.

For an object A interacting with more than one other object (such as a crate interacting both with you and with the surface), the resulting effect on A's momentum is due to the combined action of a number of forces, one for each interaction. Experimentally, we discover that forces obey the *principle of superposition*: The vector sum of the forces exerted on A is equal to the vector sum of the rate of change caused in A's momentum by the individual forces. Consequently:

The vector sum of all forces exerted on an object equals the time rate of change in the momentum of the object.

For an object of fixed inertia, a change in momentum implies a change in velocity. So, when the vector sum of the forces exerted on an object is not zero, the object has a nonzero acceleration. The vector sum of the forces exerted on an object points in the same direction as the object's acceleration.

8.2 Imagine pushing on a crate initially at rest so that it begins to move along a floor. (*a*) While you are setting the crate in motion, increasing its speed in the desired direction of travel, what is the direction of the vector sum of the forces exerted on it? (*b*) Suppose you suddenly stop pushing and the crate slows to a stop. While the crate slows down, what is the direction of the vector sum of the forces exerted on it? (*c*) What is the direction of the vector sum of the forces once the crate comes to rest?

8.2 The reciprocity of forces

Another surprising aspect of the definition of force is that, because of the reciprocal nature of interactions, forces always come in pairs: When two objects interact, each exerts a force on the other. To see this, consider **Figure 8.2**, which illustrates two elastic collisions. In both collisions, cart 1 of inertia $m_1 = 0.12$ kg is initially at rest and cart 2 of inertia $m_2 = 0.24$ kg is initially moving at 0.60 m/s. For both

collisions, the final velocity of cart 1 is 0.80 m/s and that of cart 2 is 0.20 m/s. The only difference between the two collisions is that in Figure 8.2*a* the impact is softened by a spring, much like the cushioning of a fall by a mattress. As we did before, during the collision, we can ignore all interactions except that between the two carts.

8.3 (*a*) Verify that for both collisions in Figure 8.2 the momentum of the two-cart system remains constant. (*b*) Verify that both collisions are elastic.

As this checkpoint shows, in both collisions the momentum change of cart 1 is compensated for by an opposite change in the momentum of cart 2. Let's now relate these momentum changes to forces. For the soft collision, the changes in momentum take place during a time interval Δt_{soft} (about 10 ms). During this time interval, the *x* component of the momentum of cart 1 changes by an amount $\Delta p_{1x} = +0.096$ kg $\cdot$ m/s. Because force equals time rate of change in momentum, the *x* component of the average force exerted by cart 2 on cart 1 during the time interval Δt_{soft} is $(F_{\text{by 2 on 1}})_x = \Delta p_{1x}/\Delta t_{\text{soft}} = (+0.096$ kg $\cdot$ m/s)/(0.010 s) $= +9.6$ kg $\cdot$ m/s^2.

Because the two-cart system is isolated, the change in the momentum of cart 2 must be equal in magnitude to that of cart 1 and in the opposite direction, and so $\Delta p_{2x} = -0.096$ kg $\cdot$ m/s. Because the time interval it takes for this change to occur is also Δt_{soft}, we calculate for the *x* component of the time rate of change in the momentum of cart 2, $(F_{\text{by 1 on 2}})_x = \Delta p_{2x}/\Delta t_{\text{soft}} = -9.6$ kg $\cdot$ m/s^2. In words, the force exerted by cart 1 on cart 2 is equal in magnitude to the force exerted by cart 2 on cart 1 and in the opposite direction.

For the hard collision in Figure 8.2*b*, the momentum changes are the same as for the soft collision, but now the time interval during which these changes take place is much shorter, $\Delta t_{\text{hard}} \approx 1.0$ ms. As you might expect, the forces are much larger: For cart 1, we now have $(F_{\text{by 2 on 1}})_x = \Delta p_{1x}/\Delta t_{\text{hard}} = (+0.096$ kg $\cdot$ m/s)/(0.0010 s) $= +96$ kg $\cdot$ m/s^2. The force exerted by cart 2 on cart 1 is again equal in magnitude to the force exerted by cart 1 on cart 2 and in the opposite direction because the two-cart system is isolated: $\Delta p_{1x} = -\Delta p_{2x}$. Now $(F_{\text{by 1 on 2}})_x = \Delta p_{2x}/\Delta t_{\text{hard}} = -96$ kg $\cdot$ m/s^2. So we conclude:

Whenever two objects interact, they exert on each other forces that are equal in magnitude but opposite in direction.

The pair of forces that two interacting objects exert on each other is called an **interaction pair**.

8.4 Does the conclusion just stated apply to inelastic collisions?

Figure 8.2 (*a*) Soft and (*b*) hard collisions between two carts on a low-friction track. The inertias are $m_1 = 0.12$ kg and $m_2 = 0.24$ kg.

(*a*)   **Soft collision**

(*b*)   **Hard collision**

8.5 If you drop a book from a certain height, it falls (accelerating all the while) because of the gravitational force exerted by Earth on it. Because forces always come in interaction pairs, the book must exert a force on Earth. (*a*) How does the magnitude of $F_{\text{by book on Earth}}$ compare with the magnitude of $F_{\text{by Earth on book}}$? (*b*) Is Earth accelerating during the interaction? Why or why not?

The conclusion that interacting objects exert equal forces in opposite directions on each other is a direct result of the law of conservation of momentum and of our definition of force. This reciprocity of forces means, for instance, that if you push a crate along the floor, the crate pushes back on you with a force of equal magnitude. Can an inanimate object like a crate exert a force, and, if so, how do we know this force exists?

Let's settle the first question first, using the concrete wall of our earlier example. Even though the wall is inanimate,

there is no denying it exerts a force on you when you slam into it. I don't recommend trying it, but you can imagine feeling this force. So inanimate objects can exert forces.

Now for the second question: How do we know the crate exerts a force on you when you push it? To see that objects push back when you push on them, imagine leaning against a door when someone suddenly opens it away from you—you tumble into the door opening precisely because the force exerted by the door on you (a force that was keeping you upright) is suddenly removed. The force exerted by you on the door and the force exerted by the door on you form an *interaction pair*.

Here is another example: Imagine tipping over a chair by kicking it with your bare foot. The chair is tipped over by the force exerted by your foot on it. Your foot hurts because of the other half of the interaction pair—the force exerted by the chair on your foot.

Example 8.1 Splat!

A mosquito splatters onto the windshield of a moving bus and sticks to the glass. (a) During the collision, is the magnitude of the change in the mosquito's momentum smaller than, larger than, or equal to the magnitude of the change in the bus's momentum? (b) During the collision, is the magnitude of the average force exerted by the bus on the mosquito smaller than, larger than, or equal to the magnitude of the average force exerted by the mosquito on the bus?

❶ GETTING STARTED Because the mosquito sticks to the windshield, the bus and mosquito move together after impact and so this event is a totally inelastic collision. I therefore choose the mosquito plus the bus as my system.

❷ DEVISE PLAN During the collision, the system is isolated, and so its momentum doesn't change. I can use this fact to compare the magnitudes of the changes in momentum. The average forces exerted on the mosquito and the bus are each equal to the corresponding momentum change divided by the time interval over which that momentum change takes place. I also know that this time interval is the same for the mosquito and the bus.

❸ EXECUTE PLAN (a) Because the system's momentum is unchanged, I know that $\Delta \vec{p}_{mos} = -\Delta \vec{p}_{bus}$ and so $|\Delta \vec{p}_{mos}| = |\Delta \vec{p}_{bus}|$. ✔

(b) Because the changes in momentum are equal in magnitude and because the time interval over which the change takes place is the same for both objects, the magnitudes of the average forces must also be equal: $|\vec{F}_{\text{by mos on bus, av}}| = |\vec{F}_{\text{by bus on mos, av}}|$. ✔

❹ EVALUATE RESULT Although the answer to part a conforms to what I've seen before, the answer to part b is surprising. Intuitively I expect the magnitude of the average force exerted by the bus to be much larger than the magnitude of the average force exerted by the mosquito because the mosquito is crushed while nothing happens to the bus. However, I know that the force magnitude required to crush the mosquito is very small, and such a small force magnitude would have no effect on the bus. It therefore makes sense that the two forces are of equal magnitude.

🖐 **8.6** In Example 8.1, the mosquito has an inertia of 0.1 g and is initially at rest, while the bus, with an inertia of 10,000 kg, has an initial speed of 25 m/s. The collision lasts 5 ms. (a) Calculate the final speeds of the mosquito and the bus. (b) What is the average acceleration of each during the collision? (c) By how much does the momentum of each change? (d) During the collision, how large is the average force exerted by the bus on the mosquito? (e) How large is the average force exerted by the mosquito on the bus?

8.3 Identifying forces

To identify the forces exerted on an object, it is convenient to distinguish between contact forces and field forces:

- **Contact forces** are forces that arise when objects physically touch each other. This category of forces includes forces due to pushing, pulling, and rubbing.
- **Field forces** are forces associated with what is called "action at a distance." In this case, the objects exerting forces

on each other do not need to be physically touching. For any object larger than atoms, gravitational and electromagnetic forces are the only field forces.

Identifying contact forces is easy: Whenever the surfaces of two objects touch, the objects exert contact forces on each other. Nearly all familiar forces fall into this category: the pull of a rope, the traction of a tire on a road, the force that keeps an airplane in the air, the push of a bumper, the hit of a hammer, the force that keeps you afloat when you are swimming, the drag caused by air resistance, and so on.

To determine which field forces to include in a given situation, gravitational and electromagnetic interactions must be considered. Gravitational interactions take place between any two objects. In our daily life, for instance, we each interact with Earth via the gravitational force, as does any other object—this book,* an apple, a house, and so on. The gravitational interaction we have with one another and with all other objects except Earth, however, is negligibly small. If you hold this book with your arms stretched out in front of you and let it go, it accelerates toward Earth, not toward you.

Because ordinary objects tend to be both electrically neutral and nonmagnetic, we usually do not need to consider field forces due to magnetic and electric interactions, unless a problem specifically mentions these types of interactions. We will treat electric and magnetic forces in detail in later chapters.

So, in most cases the only field force we need to consider is the gravitational force exerted by Earth. Only if a problem specifically mentions magnetic or electric interactions must we also take the field forces due to these interactions into account.

Exercise 8.2 What forces?

Identify all the forces exerted on the italicized object in each situation: (a) A *book* is lying on top of a magazine on a table. (b) A *ball* moves along a trajectory through the air. (c) A person is sitting on a *chair* on the floor of a room. (d) A *magnet* floats above another magnet that is lying on a table.

SOLUTION Because the interaction with the air is usually very small, I'm ignoring this interaction in this problem.

(a) Contact forces: The book is in contact with the magazine only, and so the magazine exerts a contact force on the book. Field forces: Earth exerts a gravitational force on the book. ✔

(b) Contact forces: The ball is not in contact with anything during its flight, and so there are no contact forces. Field forces: There is a gravitational interaction between Earth and the ball, so Earth exerts a gravitational force on the ball. ✔

(c) Contact forces: The chair is in contact with the floor and the person, and so both the floor and the person exert a force on the chair. Field forces: Earth exerts a gravitational force on the chair. ✔

---

*Hold a book with your arms stretched out in front of you and move it up and down. Do you feel the gravitational force exerted by Earth on the book? You can visualize this interaction as an invisible stretched spring reaching from the center of Earth to the book. Imagine stretching and relaxing this "gravitational spring" as you move the book up and down.

(*d*) Contact forces: The magnet floats, so it is not in contact with anything and thus there are no contact forces. Field forces: Both gravitational and magnetic forces occur in this problem: a gravitational force exerted by Earth on the magnet and a magnetic force exerted by the second magnet. ✔

✋ **8.7** A magnet lies on a table. You place a second magnet near the first one so that the two repel each other. Identify all the forces exerted on the first magnet.

8.4 Translational equilibrium

An object or system whose motion or state is not changing is said to be in **equilibrium.** For example, an object at rest or moving at constant velocity—in other words, its momentum is constant and its acceleration is zero—is said to be in **translational equilibrium.** According to the definition of force given in Section 8.1, constant momentum implies that the vector sum of the forces exerted on the object must be zero. Note that being in translational equilibrium doesn't necessarily mean that no forces are exerted on the object. It means only that all the force vectors add up to zero and therefore do not change the object's momentum.

As **Figure 8.3** illustrates, however, forces can also cause an object to rotate or to deform. Which combination of these effects occurs depends on where and how forces are exerted on the object. For now we consider only the acceleration caused by forces. Deformation is discussed in Chapters 7 and 8 and rotation in Chapter 11.

A book at rest on the floor is in translational equilibrium. So, too, is the crate pushed at constant velocity in Figure 8.1. In both of these cases, as with a coil spring squeezed between your hands, forces are exerted even though the object is in translational equilibrium.

> Whenever an object is at rest or moving at constant velocity, the vector sum of the forces exerted on the object is zero, and the object is said to be in translational equilibrium.

Figure 8.3 Forces can have various effects on an object.

Acceleration

Rotation

Deformation

As an example of an object in translational equilibrium, consider a book lying on a table, as in **Figure 8.4a**. The book's momentum isn't changing, and therefore the vector sum of the forces exerted on it must be zero. What forces are exerted on the book? The only field force we need to consider is gravity. Even though the book is at rest, we know it is subject to gravity because if we suddenly remove the table from under it, the book accelerates downward (Figure 8.4b). Because the book is touching the table, we know there is a contact force exerted by the table on the book—the force that holds the book up and prevents it from falling through the table.

These are the only two forces exerted on the book. Because the vector sum of these forces must be zero, we conclude that the contact force exerted by the table on the book must be of the same magnitude as the gravitational force exerted by Earth on the book but in the opposite direction.

An object is also in translational equilibrium when it is moving at constant velocity. An example is the crate of Figure 8.1. Constant velocity means no change in momentum, and therefore the vector sum of the forces exerted on the crate must be zero. Considering only forces in the direction of motion, we determine two contact forces exerted on the crate: one by you pushing and one by the floor rubbing. In order for the vector sum of these forces to be zero, the frictional force exerted by the floor on the crate must be of the same magnitude as the force exerted by you on the crate but in the opposite direction.

CONCEPTS

Figure 8.4

(*a*) Book at rest on table (vector sum of forces exerted on book is zero)

Gravitational interaction pair

Contact interaction pair

Book is at rest because the two forces exerted on it balance each other exactly.

$\vec{F}_{\text{by table on book}}$

$\vec{F}_{\text{by Earth on book}}$

$\vec{F}_{\text{by book on Earth}}$

$\vec{F}_{\text{by book on table}}$

Earth

Earth

(*b*) Book in free fall (vector sum of forces exerted on book is not zero)

Gravitational interaction pair

If table is removed, gravitational interaction causes book to fall.

$\vec{F}_{\text{by Earth on book}}$

$\vec{F}_{\text{by book on Earth}}$

Earth

8.8 In Figure 8.4, are the contact force exerted by the table on the book and the gravitational force exerted by Earth on the book an interaction pair?

8.5 Free-body diagrams

Knowing about forces gives you a powerful tool for analyzing physical situations:

> If the vector sum of the forces exerted on an object is known, the time rate of change in the object's momentum is also known, and so the object's subsequent motion can be calculated.

Note the condition: To calculate the object's motion you need to know the vector sum of the forces exerted **on** the object only. The forces exerted **by** the object on its surroundings do not enter into the picture because they do not contribute to the change in the object's momentum. So, if you are considering an accelerating car and you need to calculate the time rate of change of its momentum, then you need to determine the vector sum of the forces exerted *on* the car (by the road, by the air, by gravity, and so on). The forces exerted *by* the car (on the road, on the air, . . .) determine what happens to those objects and not what happens to the car.

Whenever you are interested in one object in a collection of interacting objects, you must separate that one object and the forces exerted on it from the rest of the collection of objects and ignore the forces exerted by that object on anything else. To facilitate this separation, you should use what is called a **free-body diagram.** The procedure for drawing such diagrams is explained in "Drawing free-body diagrams." It is often also helpful to make a small sketch to identify the objects of interest. Be sure, however, to keep this "situation sketch" and your free-body diagram separate.

Until we begin to treat motion in more than one dimension in Chapter 10, we shall consider only the forces that are exerted in the direction of motion. For example, when

Procedure: Drawing free-body diagrams

1. Draw a center-of-mass symbol (a circle with a cross) to indicate the object you wish to consider*—this object is your system. Pretend the object is by itself in empty space (hence the name *free body*). If you need to consider more than one object in order to solve a problem, draw a separate free-body diagram for each.

2. List all the items in the object's environment that are in contact with the object. These are the items that exert *contact forces* on the object. *Do not add these items to your drawing!* If you do, you run the risk of confusing the forces exerted *on* the object with those exerted *by* the object.

3. Identify all the forces exerted *on* the object by objects in its environment. (For now, omit from consideration any force not exerted along the object's line of motion.) In general, you should consider (*a*) the *gravitational field force* exerted by Earth on the object and (*b*) the *contact force* exerted by each item listed in step 2.

4. Draw an arrow to represent each force identified in step 3. Point the arrow in the direction in which the force is exerted and place the tail at the center of mass. If possible, draw the lengths of the arrows so that they reflect the relative magnitudes of the forces. Finally, label each arrow in the form

$$\vec{F}^{\text{type}}_{\text{by on}},$$

where "type" is a single letter identifying the origin of the force (c for contact force, G for gravitational force), "by" is a single letter identifying the object exerting the force, and "on" is a single letter identifying the object subjected to that force (this object is the one represented by the center of mass you drew in step 1).

5. Verify that all forces you have drawn are exerted **on** and not **by** the object under consideration. Because the first letter of the subscript on $\vec{F}$ represents the object exerting the force and the second letter represents the object on which the force is exerted, every force label in your free-body diagram should have the same second letter in its subscript.

6. Draw a vector representing the object's acceleration *next to* the center of mass that represents the object. Check that the vector sum of your force vectors points in the direction of the acceleration. If you cannot make your forces add up to give you an acceleration in the correct direction, verify that you drew the correct forces in step 4. If the object is not accelerating (that is, if it is in translational equilibrium), write $\vec{a} = \vec{0}$ and make sure your force arrows add up to zero. If you do not know the direction of acceleration, choose a tentative direction for the acceleration.

7. Draw a reference axis. If the object is accelerating, it is often convenient to point the positive *x* axis in the direction of the object's acceleration.

When your diagram is complete it should contain only the center-of-mass symbol, the forces exerted *on* the object (with their tails at the center of mass), an axis, and an indication of the acceleration of the object. Do not add anything else to your diagram.

---

*Representing, say, a car by a single point might seem like an oversimplification, but because we are interested only in the motion of the car as a whole, any details (like its shape or orientation) do not matter. Any unnecessary details you add to your drawing only distract from the issue at hand.

pushing a cart on a horizontal track, you need only draw the forces along the horizontal direction. The forces along the vertical direction—an upward contact force exerted by the track on the cart and a downward gravitational force exerted by Earth on the cart—add up to zero and have no effect on the cart's motion.

The importance of free-body diagrams can hardly be exaggerated: Without a good free-body diagram, it is very difficult to analyze correctly any problem involving forces. In Section 4.4, I pointed out that separating a system from its environment is the most fundamental step in analyzing physical problems. Free-body diagrams help make this separation explicit. Let's therefore put the procedure into practice in a few examples.

Exercise 8.3 A book on the floor

Draw a free-body diagram for a book lying motionless on the floor.

SOLUTION I begin by drawing a small sketch of the situation. Next to it I draw a circle with a cross to represent the center of mass of the book—no line to represent the floor, just the center-of-mass symbol representing the book as if it were by itself in space (**Figure 8.5**). Of the objects in the book's environment, the only one I need to consider is the floor because that is the only thing in contact with the book.

Figure 8.5

Next I name the forces exerted on the book. First there is a downward gravitational force exerted by Earth on the book. In addition, there is the one contact force exerted by the floor on the book. This force, which prevents the book from falling down through the floor, is directed upward.

Then I add arrows to the sketch to represent the forces I have identified. To represent the gravitational force, I draw an arrow pointing vertically downward with its tail at the center of mass. I label this force with a superscript G (for *gravity*) and the subscript Eb to indicate that it is a force exerted *by* Earth (E) *on* the book (b). For the contact force, I draw an upward-pointing arrow with its tail at the center of mass. I label this force with a superscript c (for *contact*) and the subscript fb to indicate that it is a force exerted *by* the floor (f) *on* the book (b). Finally, I verify that all forces in the diagram have subscripts ending in b because my diagram should contain only forces exerted *on* the book.

Because the book is at rest, its acceleration is zero, and therefore I write $\vec{a} = \vec{0}$ near the center of mass. From this information, I conclude that the vector sum of the forces exerted on the book (the sum of the two force vectors I have drawn) must be zero. I therefore adjust the lengths of the two arrows in the diagram so that they are of equal length, as shown in Figure 8.5. I complete the diagram by drawing an upward-pointing *x* axis. ✔

8.9 If Exercise 8.3 had asked about a book in free fall rather than one on the floor, what would the free-body diagram look like?

Exercise 8.4 Hanging around

Consider a person hanging motionless from a ring suspended from a cable, with the person's feet not touching the floor. Draw a free-body diagram for the ring.

SOLUTION I begin by drawing a sketch of the situation and then a center-of-mass symbol representing the ring (**Figure 8.6**). The things in the environment in contact with the ring are the cable and the person.

Figure 8.6

The next step is to identify all the forces exerted on the ring. As in the preceding example—and in *all* other examples concerning situations at or near Earth's surface—a vertically downward gravitational force is exerted by Earth (E) on the ring (r). I therefore draw an arrow from the center of mass down and label it $\vec{F}^G_{Er}$.

Next there are the contact forces: contact with the cable (c) and contact with the person (p). I represent the latter with a second arrow pointing downward. Because I don't know how this force compares in magnitude with the force of gravity, I choose its length arbitrarily. The other contact force is exerted by the cable on the ring. Because this force holds the ring up, I add an arrow pointing upward. Finally, I verify that the subscripts for each force end in r for ring because my diagram should contain only forces exerted *on* the ring.

Because the ring remains at rest, its acceleration is zero, and so I write $\vec{a} = \vec{0}$ near the center of mass. This tells me that the upward and downward forces exerted on the ring must add up to zero. I therefore adjust the length of the upward arrow so that it is equal to the sum of the lengths of the two downward arrows. I complete the diagram by adding an upward-pointing *x* axis. ✔

8.10 Draw a free-body diagram for the person in Exercise 8.4.

CONCEPTS

Exercise 8.5 Elevator woman

A woman stands in an elevator that is accelerating upward. Draw a free-body diagram for her.

SOLUTION After making a situation sketch, I draw a center-of-mass symbol to represent the woman (**Figure 8.7**). The only thing she is in contact with is the elevator floor—it is the floor that pushes her upward.

Figure 8.7

The forces exerted on the woman are a downward gravitational force exerted by Earth and an upward contact force exerted by the floor. I add arrows to the diagram to represent these forces, label them as shown in Figure 8.7, and verify that they all have subscripts ending in w for woman.*

What is the woman's acceleration? Even though she is at rest in the elevator, her acceleration is not zero because the elevator and she are both accelerating upward. I indicate this acceleration with an arrow pointing upward.

The upward acceleration means that the vector sum of the forces exerted on the woman is nonzero and directed upward. This can happen only if the upward force exerted by the elevator floor is larger than the gravitational force exerted by Earth. Therefore I adjust the lengths of the arrows as shown in Figure 8.7. Because the elevator has an upward acceleration, I add an upward-pointing x axis to my drawing. ✔

Warning: When drawing a free-body diagram, you may be tempted to add an arrow to show the vector sum of the forces (the "net force"), but this is not good practice. First, by drawing a vector showing the acceleration of the object, you have already indicated the direction of the vector sum of the forces. Second, this vector sum is the result of all the forces you have already drawn, not a separate force exerted by something on the object in your free-body diagram.

✋ **8.11** You throw a ball straight up. Draw a free-body diagram for the ball (*a*) while it is still touching your hand and is accelerating upward, (*b*) at its highest point, and (*c*) on the way back down.

---

*If all the subscripts in a free-body diagram do not end in the same letter, do not merely change the subscripts! Repeat the identification of the forces and ask yourself if each force you drew points in the correct direction. For example, does the floor push up on the woman? Or did you draw the force that her feet exert *on the elevator floor*? Correct your diagram if necessary.

8.6 Springs and tension

To better understand the origin of contact forces like the upward push of a floor or the pull of a rope, let us examine the behavior of a spring. When a spring is neither stretched nor compressed, we say it is at its *relaxed length*. If you position a spring vertically and put a brick on top of it, as shown in **Figure 8.8*a***, the brick *compresses* the spring and comes to rest in a position below the relaxed length of the spring. Figure 8.8 also shows the free-body diagram for the brick, which is subject to a downward force of gravity and an upward contact force—a *push*—exerted by the spring. Because the brick is at rest, the vector sum of the forces exerted on it must be zero. So the push by the spring and the gravitational force exerted by Earth are equal in magnitude and point in opposite directions. In general, whenever a spring holds an object in place, the spring must exert on the object an upward force, called a *support force*, that is equal in magnitude to the downward gravitational force exerted by Earth on the object.

Similarly, if we suspend the spring from a ceiling and fasten the brick at the bottom, the spring stretches, exerting on the brick an upward force—a *pull*—that counteracts the downward force of gravity (Figure 8.8*b*). The free-body diagram for this situation is identical to the one for the compressed spring; in both cases there is an upward force exerted by the spring on the brick. For the purpose of drawing a free-body diagram, it makes no difference at all whether it is a push or a pull that keeps the brick in place.

The force exerted by the spring always tends to return the spring to its relaxed length. When the spring is stretched, it exerts a pull (back toward the spring); when it is compressed, it exerts a push (away from the spring). Forces exerted by springs are therefore called *restoring forces*.

Now imagine adding additional identical bricks on top of the one shown in Figure 8.8*a*. Each additional brick increases the force exerted on the spring and further compresses it. If we repeat this experiment with the spring suspended from a ceiling, the spring stretches increasingly as the force exerted on the spring increases.

Over a certain range, called the *elastic range*, the compression or stretching of the spring is reversible; that is, when the force causing the compression or stretching is removed,

Figure 8.8 The free-body diagram for the brick is the same whether the spring (*a*) pushes or (*b*) pulls on it.

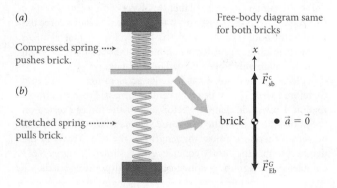

Figure 8.9 A soft spring exerts the same force on a given load as a stiff spring or a post or a rope, even though it deforms much more. In fact, the post and rope behave like very stiff springs, compressing and stretching very slightly in response to the load.

(a) Support pushes on brick

(b) Support pulls on brick

the spring returns to its original shape.* If stretched beyond a certain point, called the *elastic limit*, the spring no longer reverts to its original length when the load is removed. Additional load stretches the spring further until it eventually reaches the breaking point.

The amount of compression or stretching of a spring depends not only on the force exerted on the spring but also on the *stiffness* of the spring. A soft spring compresses or stretches more than a stiffer spring does under the same load (that is, when the same force is exerted on it). As **Figure 8.9** shows, however, the soft and stiff springs *exert exactly the same support force on the load.*

Now imagine putting a brick on a very stiff spring—one meant to support, say, a truck. You are unlikely to be able to see the spring compress (although you can measure the compression), but as with any other spring, compression is necessary in order to generate the upward force that holds the brick in place. With a very stiff spring, you need only a tiny compression to generate this support force. Even a solid object compresses a tiny bit when it supports another

---

*As you might have noticed, the word *elastic* is associated with reversible phenomena: Elastic collisions are reversible, elastic potential energy is associated with reversible deformations, and so on.

object, and as with a spring, the more load you pile on top of a solid object, the more it compresses in order to generate the force necessary to support its load.

Everything around you behaves this way: the chair you sit on, the bed you lie on, the floor you walk on, the road you drive on, and so on. Like a soft spring, an upholstered chair compresses noticeably when you sit on it. Sit on a table, though, and it "gives" a lot less. Even a concrete floor or a steel chair must compress ever so slightly to support you. The upholstered chair, the table, the concrete floor, and the steel chair all exert on you a support force that is equal in magnitude to the force of gravity exerted on you.

The same arguments can be applied to stretched objects (Figure 8.9b). In particular, the pull of a rope is like the pull of a stretched spring because the rope, like a very stiff spring, stretches ever so slightly while providing the support force that holds the object in place. As long as the deformation is reversible, the force exerted by a compressed or stretched material is called an **elastic force.**

Let us now turn our attention to the forces exerted *on* the object being compressed or stretched. **Figure 8.10a** shows a free-body diagram for a spring suspended from a ceiling and stretched by a brick. In addition to the two contact forces exerted by the ceiling and the brick on the spring, the spring is subject to a downward gravitational force. Because the spring is at rest, the upward force must be equal in magnitude to the sum of the downward forces exerted by gravity and the brick.

8.12 In Figure 8.10a, how does the magnitude of the downward force exerted *by the spring on the ceiling* compare with the magnitudes of the downward gravitational forces exerted by Earth on the spring and on the brick?

Be sure to check your answer to Checkpoint 8.12 before proceeding!

Figures 8.10b and 8.10c show free-body diagrams for a rope and a thread stretched by the same brick as in Figure 8.10a. The lower the inertia of the object being stretched, the smaller the force of gravity exerted on it. For objects of very low inertia, the magnitude of the gravitational force approaches zero, and the magnitudes of the two contact forces (exerted by the ceiling and the brick) become equal, as Figure 8.10c shows.

Because of the reciprocity of forces, the force exerted *by the thread on the ceiling* (not shown in the diagram) is equal

Figure 8.10 Free-body diagrams for a spring, rope, and thread that suspend a brick from the ceiling.

Figure 8.11 Transmission of a force by a rope to a box. Free-body diagrams for (a) the rope and (b) the box. (We assume that the force of gravity on the rope is much smaller than the forces exerted by the person and the box, so we can ignore it.)

If force of gravity on rope is negligible . . .

$\vec{v} = \vec{0}$

$\vec{F}^c_{pr}$ rope $\vec{F}^c_{br}$

$\vec{a} = \vec{0}$

$\vec{v} = \vec{0}$

$\vec{F}^c_{rb}$ box $\vec{F}^c_{tb}$

$\vec{a} = \vec{0}$

. . . then force exerted by person on rope is transmitted undiminished to box.

in magnitude to the force exerted by the brick on the thread. Because these two forces point in the same direction, the thread simply transmits the pulling force of the brick to the ceiling.

Of course, we don't usually use thread to pull on objects, but in situations in which a rope—or even a lightweight chain—is used to pull, we can generally ignore the gravitational force exerted on the rope or chain. The only requirement is that the pulling force be much greater than the gravitational force exerted on the rope or chain. So, if we ignore the gravitational force, the same transmission of forces described for our thread is seen when we use a rope. If you fasten a rope to a boat and pull on one end of the rope, the rope stretches a little and the opposite end of the rope transmits your force to the boat. In general, if the force of gravity exerted on any object being stretched—rope, spring, thread—is much smaller than the forces that cause the stretching, you can ignore the force of gravity. This is usually true when ropes, springs, or threads are used to pull or push on objects. Therefore:

> **The force exerted on one end of a rope, spring, or thread is transmitted undiminished to the other end, provided the force of gravity on the rope, spring, or thread is much smaller than the forces that cause the stretching.**

A rope being used to pull an object is subject to two equal outward forces, one on each end (**Figure 8.11**). The stress caused by this pair of forces is called the **tension** in the rope, and the forces causing the tension are called *tensile forces*. Tension is a scalar and is represented by $\mathcal{T}$. In an object subject to two equal tensile forces of magnitude F, one on each end of the object, the tension is $\mathcal{T} = F$.

Example 8.6 Tug of war

If two people, A and B, pull on opposite ends of a rope that is at rest, each exerting a horizontal tensile force of magnitude F, the tension in the rope is $\mathcal{T} = F$. Suppose instead that one end of the rope is tied to a tree and A pulls on the other end by himself with the same force magnitude F. Is the tension in the rope larger than, equal to, or smaller than the tension when A and B pull on opposite ends?

❶ **GETTING STARTED** To determine the tension in each case, I need to know the magnitude of the tensile force exerted on each end of the rope. I begin by making a sketch of the two situations (**Figure 8.12**).

Figure 8.12

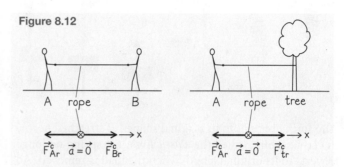

A rope B

$\vec{F}^c_{Ar}$ $\vec{a} = \vec{0}$ $\vec{F}^c_{Br}$

A rope tree

$\vec{F}^c_{Ar}$ $\vec{a} = \vec{0}$ $\vec{F}^c_{tr}$

❷ **DEVISE PLAN** Because I must analyze various forces exerted on the rope, it is best to begin with a free-body diagram for the rope. In a tug of war only the horizontal forces matter, so I ignore the effect of the vertical gravitational force exerted by Earth and consider only the horizontal forces (Figure 8.12). Because the rope is always at rest, I know that the vector sum of the forces exerted on the rope must be zero. The magnitudes of the tensile forces exerted on either end are therefore equal to each other, and the tension in the rope is equal to the magnitude of the tensile force exerted on either end.

❸ **EXECUTE PLAN** The rope tied to the tree is subject to two contact forces, one exerted by A and the other exerted by the tree. Because the vector sum of the forces exerted on the rope must be zero, I make the two force arrows of equal length, as shown in my free-body diagram.

Because A pulls on the rope with a force of magnitude F, the tree must pull with a force of magnitude F in the opposite direction, and so the tension in the rope is $\mathcal{T} = F$. which is the same as when A and B pull on opposite ends. ✔

❹ **EVALUATE RESULT** The magnitude of the force exerted by A is F in both cases. Because the rope has zero acceleration in both cases, the magnitude of the force exerted by the tree must be the same as the magnitude of the force exerted by B when A and B pull. Therefore it makes sense that the tension in the rope is the same in the two cases.

✋ **8.13** In Example 8.6, suppose both people pull on the same end of the rope, each exerting a force F, while the other end is still tied to the tree. Is the tension in the rope larger than, equal to, or smaller than the tension when the two people pull on opposite ends?

Self-quiz

1. (*a*) Two forces, one twice the magnitude of the other, are exerted on identical objects during the same time interval. Which force causes the greater change in momentum? (*b*) Two identical forces are exerted on identical objects, one during a time interval twice as long as the other. Which force causes the greater change in momentum?

2. The free-body diagram of a box subjected to forces is shown in **Figure 8.13**. Because we are concerned about only the horizontal motion, the forces in the vertical direction have been omitted. (*a*) What is the direction of the change in the momentum of the box? (*b*) If the box is at rest before the forces shown in the diagram are exerted on it, what is the direction of its momentum once the forces are exerted?

Figure 8.13

e = elephant
p = person
b = box

3. For the free-body diagram in question 2, list the objects in the environment of the box.

4. A block of wood rests on a shelf, and a second block of wood rests on top of the first. (*a*) List the objects in the environment of the top block. (*b*) List the objects in the environment of the bottom block. (*c*) Draw a free-body diagram for each block.

5. Complete the following sentences, applying the reciprocity of forces. (Example: If I push down on the seat of my chair, *the seat of my chair pushes up on me.*)

   If I push to the right on the wall, . . .
   If I pull to the right on a spring, . . .
   If the floor pushes up on my feet, . . .
   If Earth pulls down on me, . . .

Answers

1. (*a*) The larger force causes the greater change in momentum because force and change in momentum are proportional to each other over a given time interval. (*b*) The force exerted over the longer time interval causes the greater change in momentum because time interval and change in momentum are proportional to each other for a constant force.

2. (*a*) The vector sum of the forces exerted on the box points to the left because the force exerted on the box by the elephant is larger than the force exerted on the box by the person. The change in momentum is to the left, in the same direction as the vector sum of the forces. (*b*) The change in momentum is equal to the final momentum minus the initial momentum of zero. Therefore, the final momentum of the box must be to the left.

3. The objects in the environment of the box are an elephant and a person. If you also consider the vertical direction, you need to include the ground and Earth as being in the environment of the box.

4. (*a*) The objects in the environment of the top block are the bottom block and Earth. The shelf is not in contact with the top block and so is not part of the top block's environment. (*b*) The objects in the environment of the bottom block are the shelf, the top block, and Earth. (*c*) See **Figure 8.14**. Earth pulls downward on each block. The surface below each block pushes upward. If the bottom block pushes upward on the top block, the top block must push down on the bottom block.

Figure 8.14

5. For each, swap the nouns and reverse the given direction.

   If I push to the right on the wall, *the wall pushes to the left on me.*
   If I pull to the right on a spring, *the spring pulls to the left on me.*
   If the floor pushes up on my feet, *my feet push down on the floor.*
   If Earth pulls down on me, *I pull up on Earth.**

---

*Many people find this last statement difficult to accept and are inclined to answer: If Earth pulls down on me, the ground pushes up on me. This statement, however, includes three objects (ground, Earth, me), not just the two required by the reciprocity of forces.

8.7 Equation of Motion

In the first part of this chapter, we determined that the vector sum of the forces exerted on an object is equal to the time rate of change in the object's momentum. If an object's momentum changes by an amount $\Delta \vec{p}_{object}$ in a time interval Δt, the *average* time rate of change in the object's momentum is

$$\frac{\Delta \vec{p}_{object}}{\Delta t}. \tag{8.1}$$

The *instantaneous* time rate of change in momentum is obtained by letting the time interval approach zero:

$$\lim_{\Delta t \to 0} \frac{\Delta \vec{p}_{object}}{\Delta t} = \frac{d\vec{p}_{object}}{dt} \equiv \sum \vec{F}_{object}, \tag{8.2}$$

where $\sum \vec{F}_{object}$ represents the vector sum of all the forces exerted on the object:*

$$\sum \vec{F}_{object} = \vec{F}_{1\,object} + \vec{F}_{2\,object} + \vec{F}_{3\,object} + \cdots, \tag{8.3}$$

where $\vec{F}_{1\,object}$ is the force exerted by object 1 on the object under consideration, and so on. Because we are concerned with only one object, we can omit the subscript on the left side of Eq. 8.3, and so Eq. 8.2 becomes

$$\sum \vec{F} \equiv \frac{d\vec{p}}{dt} \tag{8.4}$$

The vector sum of the forces points in the same direction as the change in momentum of the object.

Substituting $\vec{p} \equiv m\vec{v}$ in the term on the right in Eq. 8.4 gives

$$\frac{d\vec{p}}{dt} \equiv \frac{d(m\vec{v})}{dt} = m\frac{d\vec{v}}{dt}, \tag{8.5}$$

where I have used the fact that the inertia m of the object is constant. Because $d\vec{v}/dt$ is the acceleration $\vec{a}$ of the object, substituting Eq. 8.5 into Eq. 8.4 yields

$$\sum \vec{F} = m\vec{a} \tag{8.6}$$

or

$$\vec{a} = \frac{\sum \vec{F}}{m}. \tag{8.7}$$

In terms of components, Eqs. 8.6 and 8.7 become

$$\sum F_x = ma_x \quad \text{and} \quad a_x = \frac{\sum F_x}{m}. \tag{8.8}$$

Equation 8.7 is called the **equation of motion** for the object. For a given vector sum of forces, this equation allows us to obtain the acceleration and therefore to determine the motion of the object. Conversely, if we know the acceleration of an object, Eq. 8.6 allows us to determine the vector sum of the forces exerted on that object.

Because the SI unit of momentum is $kg \cdot m/s$ and the SI unit of time is seconds, the SI unit of force is $kg \cdot m/s^2$. This derived SI unit is given the special name **newton** (N) in honor of the English scientist Isaac Newton:

$$1\,N \equiv 1\,kg \cdot m/s^2. \tag{8.9}$$

---

*We drop the "by" subscript because the sum represents the forces exerted by *all* objects on the object under consideration.

Figure 8.15 Superposition of forces.

Effect of individual forces

Exerted separately, two forces cause corresponding accelerations.

Effect of multiple forces

When exerted together, the two forces cause the same acceleration . . .

. . . as a single force equal to their vector sum.

This definition means that a force of 1 N exerted on an object that has an inertia of 1 kg causes that object to accelerate at 1 m/s².

Note that while several forces can be exerted simultaneously on a single object, that object can have only one acceleration. For example, if a 1-kg object is simultaneously subject to two forces—say, a 3-N force directed to the right and a 1-N force directed to the left—the object accelerates at 2 m/s² to the right, just as if a single force of 2 N directed to the right had been exerted (see **Figure 8.15**). The reason forces can be added vectorially is that the effect of a force is a change in momentum, and momentum is a vector quantity. This property of adding forces vectorially is called the *superposition of forces*.

Example 8.7 Elevator stool

A person is sitting on a stool in an elevator. The forces exerted on the stool are a downward force of magnitude 60 N exerted by Earth, a downward force of magnitude 780 N exerted by the person, and an upward force of magnitude 850 N exerted by the elevator floor. If the inertia of the stool is 5.0 kg, what is the acceleration of the elevator?

❶ GETTING STARTED I know all the forces that are exerted on the stool, and I must determine its acceleration. I therefore begin by drawing a free-body diagram for the stool that includes the three forces mentioned in the problem statement (**Figure 8.16**). I arbitrarily choose an x axis pointing upward.

Figure 8.16

❷ DEVISE PLAN Equation 8.8 gives a relationship between the vector sum of the forces exerted on an object and the acceleration of the object. By substituting the forces given and the inertia of the stool, I can solve for a_x.

❸ EXECUTE PLAN From Eq. 8.8, I have

$$a_x = \frac{\sum F_x}{m} = \frac{1}{m}(F^c_{\mathrm{fs}x} + F^c_{\mathrm{ps}x} + F^G_{\mathrm{Es}x})$$

$$= \frac{1}{5.0 \text{ kg}}\left[(+850 \text{ N}) + (-780 \text{ N}) + (-60 \text{ N})\right]$$

$$= +2.0 \text{ m/s}^2. ✔$$

❹ EVALUATE RESULT The acceleration I obtained is positive, which means that the elevator has an upward acceleration, which is what I expect because the force exerted by the floor on the stool is upward. The magnitude of the acceleration is about one-fifth the acceleration due to gravity, which strikes me as a reasonable value.

8.14 (*a*) You exert a constant force of 200 N on a friend on roller skates. If she starts from rest, estimate how far she moves in 2.0 s. (*b*) When a person jumps off a wall, what is the magnitude of his acceleration? (*c*) Estimate the magnitude of the force exerted by Earth on the person during the jump in part *b*.

As we saw in Section 8.2, forces always come in interaction pairs. To see this quantitatively, consider an isolated system of two colliding carts. As we have seen before, the momentum of the two-cart system is constant, and so the changes in momentum caused by the collision must obey the relationship

$$\Delta \vec{p}_1 + \Delta \vec{p}_2 = \vec{0}, \tag{8.10}$$

where $\Delta \vec{p}_1$ is the change in momentum of cart 1 and $\Delta \vec{p}_2$ is that of cart 2. During an infinitesimal time interval dt, this relationship yields

$$d\vec{p}_1 + d\vec{p}_2 = \vec{0}. \tag{8.11}$$

Because dt is the same for both carts, the time rates of change in momentum must also add to zero:

$$\frac{d\vec{p}_1}{dt} + \frac{d\vec{p}_2}{dt} = \vec{0}. \tag{8.12}$$

According to Eq. 8.4, the time rate of change of momentum of an object is equal to the vector sum of the forces exerted on that object, and so

$$\Sigma \vec{F}_1 + \Sigma \vec{F}_2 = \vec{0}. \tag{8.13}$$

Because the carts are constrained to move in the horizontal direction, the forces in the vertical direction cancel, and so the only forces exerted on the carts we need to consider are those they exert on each other. The vector sum of the forces exerted on cart 1 is thus just the force exerted by cart 2 on cart 1, and the vector sum of the forces exerted on cart 2 is just the force exerted by cart 1 on cart 2:

$$\Sigma \vec{F}_1 = \vec{F}_{21} \quad \text{and} \quad \Sigma \vec{F}_2 = \vec{F}_{12}, \tag{8.14}$$

and thus $\vec{F}_{12} + \vec{F}_{21} = \vec{0}$, or

$$\vec{F}_{12} = -\vec{F}_{21}. \tag{8.15}$$

Newton's laws of motion

In the modern view, the conservation laws are the heart and soul of physics—they best represent the generally held belief that the universe has an underlying simplicity. In the 17th century, however, 200 years before the concept of energy and the conservation laws were formulated, the English scientist Isaac Newton published a work describing his ideas concerning the fundamental principles that govern forces and their effects on the motion of objects. Newton's three laws of motion, as they are known, have been the backbone of physics for more than two centuries.

We have already discussed each of these three laws—albeit under different, and in the current context more appropriate, names.

Newton's first law of motion, first formulated by Galileo Galilei, is what we called the *law of inertia* in Chapter 6:

In an inertial reference frame, any isolated object that is at rest remains at rest, and any isolated object that is in motion keeps moving at a constant velocity.

Newton's second law of motion corresponds to the *definition of force* given in Eq. 8.4:

The vector sum of the forces exerted on an object is equal to the time rate of change in the momentum of that object.

Equation 8.6, $\Sigma \vec{F} = m\vec{a}$, is frequently referred to as Newton's second law even though it holds only when m is constant.

Newton's third law of motion expresses the law of conservation of momentum in terms of forces (Eq. 8.15):

Whenever two objects interact, they exert on each other forces that are equal in magnitude but opposite in direction.

Newton is widely regarded as one of the greatest physicists of all time, not only for his formulation of the laws of motion but also for his law of gravity, for his development of the calculus, and for laying the foundation of modern optics.

QUANTITATIVE TOOLS

In words, whenever two objects interact, they exert forces on each other that are equal in magnitude and opposite in direction. The forces $\vec{F}_{12}$ and $\vec{F}_{21}$ form an **interaction pair.** Because interactions always involve two objects, every force that is exerted *on* an object has associated with it a force of equal magnitude in the opposite direction exerted *by* the object. Note, in Eq. 8.15, that the subscripts on the forces that form an interaction pair are interchanged. For that reason, both forces in an interaction pair can never be part of the same free-body diagram. Equation 8.15 is called **Newton's third law of motion** (see the box "Newton's laws of motion" on page 190); it is a direct consequence of the conservation of momentum expressed in Eq. 8.10.

✋ **8.15** If forces always come in interaction pairs and the forces in such a pair are equal in magnitude and opposite in direction (Eq. 8.15), how can the vector sum of the forces exerted on an object ever be nonzero?

8.8 Force of gravity

We have seen before that, when we ignore air resistance, all objects dropped from a certain height near Earth's surface have a downward acceleration given by $a_x = -g$ when we define up as being the positive x direction (see Chapter 3). For an object in free fall near Earth's surface, the only force exerted on the object is the gravitational force $\vec{F}_{Eo}^{G}$ exerted by Earth on the object. The left side of Eq. 8.8 is thus

$$\sum F_x - F_{Eox}^{G}. \tag{8.16}$$

The right side is $ma_x = -mg$, where m is the inertia of the object, and so the x component of the gravitational force exerted by Earth on the object is

$$F_{Eox}^{G} = -mg \text{ (near Earth's surface, } x \text{ axis vertically upward)}. \tag{8.17}$$

The minus sign reflects the fact that the acceleration due to gravity (and therefore also the force of gravity) is directed downward and the positive x direction points upward. Because the acceleration due to gravity is the same for all objects, Eq. 8.17 holds for all objects in free fall near Earth's surface. Note that when additional forces are exerted on the object, the x component of the gravitational force exerted by Earth on the object is still given by Eq. 8.17, even though the x component of the object's acceleration is no longer equal to $-g$.

Example 8.8 Tennis ball launch

A tennis ball of inertia 0.20 kg is launched straight up in the air by hitting it with a racquet. If the magnitude of the acceleration of the ball while it is in contact with the racquet is $9g$, what are the magnitude and direction of the force exerted by the racquet on the ball?

❶ **GETTING STARTED** I am given the inertia and acceleration magnitude for a tennis ball hit by a racquet, and I must calculate the force—both magnitude and direction—responsible for this acceleration. Because this problem deals with forces exerted on the ball, I begin by drawing a situation sketch and a free-body diagram for the ball (**Figure 8.17**). While it is being hit, the ball is in contact with the racquet and so I include an upward contact force exerted by the racquet as well as a downward force of gravity exerted by Earth. Because the ball accelerates upward, I make the upward force vector longer than the downward force vector and point the positive x axis upward.

Figure 8.17

❷ **DEVISE PLAN** Equation 8.8 relates the ball's acceleration to the vector sum of the two forces exerted on it. I can use Eq. 8.17 to calculate one of the two forces and then solve for the other one in Eq. 8.8.

(Continued)

❸ EXECUTE PLAN Equation 8.8 yields

$$\sum F_x = F^G_{Ebx} + F^c_{rbx} = ma_x.$$

Because I've defined upward as the positive x direction, $a_x = +9g$. Substituting this value and Eq. 8.17 for the gravitational force exerted by Earth on the object, I get

$$(-mg) + F^c_{rbx} = +9mg$$

or $\quad F^c_{rbx} = +10mg = +10(0.20 \text{ kg})(9.8 \text{ m/s}^2)$

$$= +20 \text{ N}. ✔$$

❹ EVALUATE RESULT The plus sign indicates that this force is directed upward, as expected. The magnitude of the force is ten times larger than the gravitational force exerted by Earth, which also makes sense if the ball is to be accelerated upward during the very short time interval that the racquet is in contact with the ball.

8.16 The magnitude of the gravitational force exerted by Earth on an object of inertia m_1 is m_1g. (a) What is the magnitude of the force exerted by the object on Earth (inertia m_E)? (b) What is the acceleration of Earth due to its gravitational interaction with the object?

Equation 8.17 shows that the magnitude of the force of gravity exerted on an object is proportional to the object's inertia, which is an intrinsic property of the object that has nothing to do with the presence of Earth or with gravity. This surprising conclusion is a direct consequence of the fact that, when air resistance is negligible, all objects experience the same acceleration due to gravity. It is more difficult to accelerate a large boulder than a feather, but the gravitational forces exerted by Earth on the boulder and on the feather are such that both have the same acceleration when they fall (ignoring air resistance). Equation 8.17 doesn't tell us much about the mechanism of gravity; it merely tells us what magnitude and direction the force of gravity must have to account properly for the free fall of objects near the surface of Earth. In Chapter 13, we'll return to the subject of gravity and its relationship to inertia. In the meantime, we can use Eq. 8.17 to calculate the magnitude of the force of gravity on any object near the surface of Earth.

8.17 Suppose you are in an elevator that is accelerating upward at 1 m/s^2. (a) Draw a free-body diagram for your body. (b) Determine the magnitude of the force exerted by the elevator floor on you.

8.9 Hooke's law

Now that we have established the relationship between the inertia of an object and the gravitational force exerted on it (Eq. 8.17), we can analyze the behavior of springs quantitatively. We begin by attaching bricks to the free end of a spring that is suspended from a ceiling. Each additional brick increases the force exerted on the spring and the amount by which the spring stretches. We repeat this experiment, but now we support the spring on a solid surface and stack bricks on top of it. Each additional brick increases the force exerted on the spring and further compresses it, up to the point where the spring "bottoms out"—which means its coils get in the way of further compression.

The graph in **Figure. 8.18** shows the x component of the displacement of the free end of the spring from its relaxed position at x_0 versus the x component of the force exerted *on* the spring *by* the bricks. The shaded region indicates the elastic range. The first thing to note is that, within the elastic range, the displacement and the force exerted by the load on the spring are linearly proportional to each other. The second thing to note is that the force exerted on the spring is always in the same direction as the displacement. We can express this quantitatively as

$$(F_{\text{by load on spring}})_x = k(x - x_0) \quad \text{(small displacement)}, \tag{8.18}$$

where k is called the **spring constant.** The spring constant represents the inverse of the slope of the straight line through the data points in Figure 8.18; it tells us

Figure 8.18 The x component of the displacement of the free end of the spring from its relaxed position is proportional to the x component of the force causing the displacement.

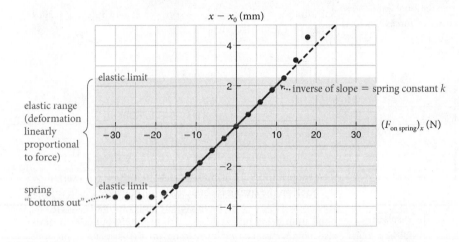

how large a force is required to give the free end of the spring a displacement $x - x_0$. The spring constant is therefore a quantitative measure of the stiffness of the spring discussed in Section 8.6. It is always positive, but different springs have different values of k, depending on how they respond to compression and stretching. The SI unit of the spring constant is N/m.

Often we are interested not in the force exerted *on* the spring, but in the force exerted *by* the spring. We know from Eq. 8.15 that

$$\vec{F}_{\text{by spring on load}} = -\vec{F}_{\text{by load on spring}} \tag{8.19}$$

and so the force exerted by the spring is given by

$$(F_{\text{by spring on load}})_x = -k(x - x_0) \quad \text{(small displacement)}. \tag{8.20}$$

Note that the direction of the force of the spring on the load is opposite to the direction of the displacement. A stretched spring pulls back. A compressed spring pushes out. Equation 8.18 (or its equivalent, Eq. 8.20) is called **Hooke's law** after the British physicist Robert Hooke (1635–1703), who first discovered the linear relationship between a spring's stretching or compression and the force exerted on it.

Unlike the conservation principles, which are of universal validity, Eq. 8.20 is valid for only small displacement. As Figure 8.18 shows, Hooke's "law" fails if we compress or stretch the spring beyond certain limits. Still, Hooke's law is of great use because, for small deformations, many materials—from steel to foam—show a linear relationship between force and displacement when compressed or stretched. For this reason, the force that tends to return a stretched or compressed spring or material to its relaxed position is referred to as a *linear restoring force*.

Example 8.9 Spring compression

A book of inertia 1.2 kg is placed on top of the spring in Figure 8.18. What is the displacement of the top end of the spring from the relaxed position when the book is at rest on top of the spring?

❶ **GETTING STARTED** My task is to determine how much the top end of a spring is displaced when a 1.2-kg book is placed on the spring. Hooke's law tells me that this displacement is proportional to the force exerted by the spring on the book, so after making a sketch of the situation, I draw a free-body diagram for the book. The book is subject to a downward gravitational force exerted by Earth and an upward contact force exerted by the spring (**Figure 8.19**). Because the book is in translational equilibrium, the book's acceleration is zero and so the two forces are equal in magnitude. I arbitrarily point the x axis upward.

Figure 8.19

❷ **DEVISE PLAN** I can use Eq. 8.20 to determine the displacement, but in order to do so I need to know the spring constant k and the x component F_{sbx}^c of the force exerted by the spring on the book. The spring constant is given by the slope of the curve in Figure 8.18. From my free-body diagram I know that $\vec{F}_{sb}^c$ is equal to the negative of the force of gravity $\vec{F}_{Eb}^G$ exerted by Earth on the book.

❸ **EXECUTE PLAN** From the graph in Figure 8.18, I arbitrarily choose 25 N as my force value and see that it causes a displacement of 5.0 mm. The spring constant is thus, from Eq. 8.18:

$$k = \frac{(F_{\text{by load on spring}})_x}{x - x_0} = \frac{+25\text{ N}}{+5.0 \times 10^{-3}\text{ m}}$$

$$= 5.0 \times 10^3\text{ N/m}.$$

Because the book is at rest, I know that $\vec{F}_{sb}^c + \vec{F}_{Eb}^G = \vec{0}$, and so $\vec{F}_{Eb}^G = -\vec{F}_{sb}^c$. The force of gravity is given by Eq. 8.17, and so I get for the force exerted by the spring on the book

$$F_{sbx}^c = -F_{Ebx}^G$$

$$= -(-mg)$$

$$= (1.2\text{ kg})(9.8\text{ m/s}^2)$$

$$= +12\text{ N}.$$

Substituting this value and the spring constant into Eq. 8.20, I obtain for the displacement:

$$x - x_0 = \frac{-F_{sbx}^c}{k}$$

$$= \frac{-12\text{ N}}{5.0 \times 10^3\text{ N/m}}$$

$$= -2.4 \times 10^{-3}\text{ m}. \checkmark$$

❹ **EVALUATE RESULT** It makes sense that the force exerted by the book on the spring is equal to the force exerted by Earth on the book ($\vec{F}_{Eb}^G = \vec{F}_{bs}^c$) because the spring has to keep the book from being pulled downward into the ground. I can thus also obtain my answer by reading off the displacement from Figure 8.18 for a force of magnitude 12 N (the magnitude of the force of gravity exerted on the book). This procedure yields a value that is very close to the result I obtained. The negative sign in my answer indicates that the top end of the spring is displaced downward, as I expect.

✋ **8.18** (a) Is a spring that has a large spring constant k stiffer or softer than a spring that has a small spring constant? (b) Which has a larger spring constant: steel or foam rubber?

8.10 Impulse

Back in Chapter 4 we defined the change in momentum of a system or object as the impulse delivered to it. In this section we determine a relationship between force and impulse, which permits us to determine the effect forces have on momentum.

We begin by considering a simple case: a single object subject to constant forces. To calculate what happens to the momentum of the object, we consider its motion during a time interval $\Delta t = t_f - t_i$. The constant forces exerted on the object give it a constant acceleration $\vec{a}$ given by Eq. 8.7. Because the acceleration is constant, we can write

$$\vec{a} = \frac{\Delta \vec{v}}{\Delta t}. \tag{8.21}$$

Multiplying both sides by the inertia m of the object, we get

$$m\vec{a} = m\frac{\Delta \vec{v}}{\Delta t} = \frac{\Delta \vec{p}}{\Delta t} \tag{8.22}$$

or

$$\Delta \vec{p} = m\vec{a}\,\Delta t. \tag{8.23}$$

From Eq. 8.6 we know that $\sum \vec{F} = m\vec{a}$, and so Eq. 8.23 becomes

$$\Delta \vec{p} = \left(\sum \vec{F}\right) \Delta t \qquad \text{(constant force).} \tag{8.24}$$

If we compare this to the momentum law ($\Delta \vec{p} = \vec{J}$, Eq. 4.18), we see that the impulse delivered by the forces to the object is

$$\vec{J} = \left(\sum \vec{F}\right) \Delta t \qquad \text{(constant force).} \tag{8.25}$$

This equation, called the **impulse equation**, states that the impulse delivered to an object—the change in an object's momentum—during a time interval Δt is equal to the product of the vector sum of the forces exerted on the object and the duration of the time interval. Equation 8.24 shows that the longer a force is exerted, the smaller it has to be to accomplish a given change in the momentum of the object. This is why, in the bicycling example discussed in Section 8.1, the force of impact is less when you hit the mattress instead of the concrete wall. Likewise, it hurts less to catch a ball (that is to say, bring the ball to rest) with a padded glove than without one. And, by holding out your hand in front of you and then drawing it back just as the ball strikes your glove, you can further increase Δt and thus reduce the force required to slow the ball to a stop.

Figure 8.20a shows a force-versus-time graph for an object subject to constant forces whose vector sum is equal to F_0. The impulse delivered during a time interval Δt is equal to the shaded rectangular area under the $F_x(t)$ curve—the width Δt times the height F_0.

So far in this discussion, the impulse-delivering forces we've looked at have been *constant* forces. However, the relationship between impulse and area under the $F_x(t)$ curve holds not only when $\sum \vec{F}$ is constant. Just as we found, in Section 3.8, that the area under the $a_x(t)$ curve of an object yields the change in velocity (Eq. 3.27, $\Delta v_x = \int_{t_i}^{t_f} a_x(t)dt$), we calculate for the impulse delivered by an arbitrary force $\sum \vec{F}$ that varies with time

$$\Delta \vec{p} = \vec{J} = \int_{t_i}^{t_f} \sum \vec{F}(t)\, dt \qquad \text{(time-varying force).} \tag{8.26}$$

You can obtain this equation by integrating Eq. 8.4. You can also convince yourself of this result either by applying to force the procedure we applied to acceleration in Section 3.8 or by multiplying the left and right sides of Eq. 3.27 by the inertia m of the object.

Figure 8.20b shows the momentum of a cart getting a shove. The impulse delivered by the hand to the cart is equal to the change in momentum $\Delta \vec{p}$ shown in the figure. The force exerted by the hand on the cart is also shown in Figure 8.20b. This curve is obtained by applying what we know from Eq. 8.4 and taking the

Figure 8.20 The impulse delivered by a force is equal to the area under the $F_x(t)$ curve, as shown here for (a) a constant force and (b) a force that varies with time.

(a) Impulse delivered by constant force exerted on object

(b) Hand shoves cart, exerting force that varies with time

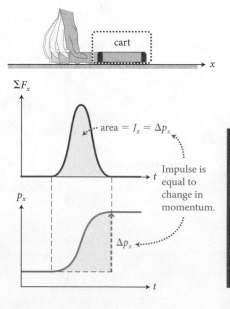

Figure 8.21 As a bat strikes a ball, the magnitude of the force exerted by the bat on the ball increases as the ball deforms, peaks at the instant the ball and bat have zero relative velocity, and finally decreases back to zero as the ball regains its shape and leaves the bat.

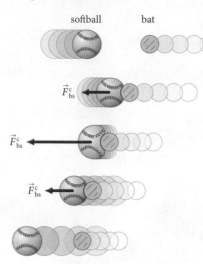

softball   bat

$\vec{F}^c_{bs}$

$\vec{F}^c_{bs}$

$\vec{F}^c_{bs}$

derivative of the $p_x(t)$ curve in Figure 8.20b. As the hand begins pushing, the force increases and peaks. Then, as the hand stops pushing, the force decreases to zero. The impact of a bat on a ball varies in a similar way with time, albeit much more rapidly (**Figure 8.21**). In general, the impulse delivered by a time-varying force during a given time interval is equal to the area under the $F_x(t)$ curve during that time interval (Eq. 8.26 and Figure 8.20b).

If the vector sum of the forces exerted on the object is zero, $\sum \vec{F} = \vec{0}$, the object is in translational equilibrium. Equation 8.26 then tells us that the momentum of the object does not change

$$\Delta \vec{p} = \vec{0} \qquad \text{(translational equilibrium).} \qquad (8.27)$$

In words, the momentum of an object in translational equilibrium does not change.

8.19 (a) A feather and a brick are falling freely in an evacuated tube. Is the magnitude of the gravitational force exerted by Earth on the feather larger than, smaller than, or equal to that exerted by Earth on the brick? (b) Suppose equal forces of 10 N are exerted on both objects for 2 s. Which object gains more momentum? (*Evacuated* means all the air has been sucked out of the tube, so that there is no air resistance to hinder the motion.)

8.11 Systems of two interacting objects

So far we have considered only the very simple case of a single object subject to a force. In this section we look at a system of two interacting objects. For such systems, it is useful to make a distinction between forces exerted from inside the system and forces exerted on the system from outside. The former are called *internal forces,* the latter *external forces*. In **Figure 8.22**, two carts equipped with repelling magnets move on a track while cart 1 gets a push. Because of the magnetic repulsion, the carts never touch each other; instead, cart 2 accelerates to the right when cart 1 approaches. If we choose the two carts as our system, the forces the carts exert on each other are internal, and the push exerted on cart 1 is external.

Figure 8.22 Two carts with repelling magnets moving under the influence of an external force exerted on cart 1.

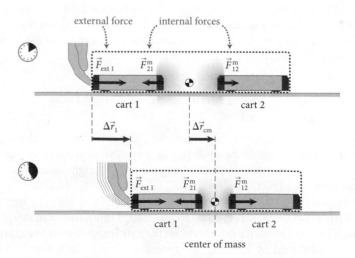

external force   internal forces

$\vec{F}_{ext\,1}$ $\vec{F}^m_{21}$ $\vec{F}^m_{12}$

cart 1   cart 2

$\Delta \vec{r}_1$ $\Delta \vec{r}_{cm}$

$\vec{F}_{ext\,1}$ $\vec{F}^m_{21}$ $\vec{F}^m_{12}$

cart 1   cart 2

center of mass

The momentum of the two-cart system is

$$\vec{p} = \vec{p}_1 + \vec{p}_2. \tag{8.28}$$

Differentiating this equation with respect to time and substituting the vector sum of the forces for each dp/dt term (Eq. 8.4) give

$$\frac{d\vec{p}}{dt} = \frac{d\vec{p}_1}{dt} + \frac{d\vec{p}_2}{dt} = \sum \vec{F}_1 + \sum \vec{F}_2. \tag{8.29}$$

The vector sum of the forces exerted on cart 1 consists of two parts: the external force exerted on cart 1 and an internal force exerted by cart 2 on cart 1 (due to the magnetic repulsion):

$$\sum \vec{F}_1 = \vec{F}_{\text{ext 1}} + \vec{F}_{21}^{\text{m}}. \tag{8.30}$$

Because no external force is exerted on cart 2, the vector sum of the forces exerted on it is

$$\sum \vec{F}_2 = \vec{F}_{12}^{\text{m}}. \tag{8.31}$$

Substituting Eqs. 8.30 and 8.31 into the right side of Eq. 8.29 gives

$$\frac{d\vec{p}}{dt} = \vec{F}_{\text{ext 1}} + \vec{F}_{21}^{\text{m}} + \vec{F}_{12}^{\text{m}}. \tag{8.32}$$

Because $\vec{F}_{12}^{\text{m}}$ and $\vec{F}_{21}^{\text{m}}$ form an interaction pair, we have $\vec{F}_{12}^{\text{m}} = -\vec{F}_{21}^{\text{m}}$, and so

$$\frac{d\vec{p}}{dt} = \vec{F}_{\text{ext 1}}. \tag{8.33}$$

Equation 8.33 shows that only the external force exerted on cart 1 changes the momentum of the system. The internal forces do not have any effect on the momentum of the system.

Using the definition of center-of-mass velocity from Section 6.6, we have $\vec{p} = m\vec{v}_{\text{cm}}$, with $m = m_1 + m_2$. Because the inertia m of the system remains constant in the interaction, we have

$$\frac{d\vec{p}}{dt} = \frac{d(m\vec{v}_{\text{cm}})}{dt} = m\frac{d\vec{v}_{\text{cm}}}{dt} \equiv m\vec{a}_{\text{cm}} \tag{8.34}$$

and hence we can rewrite Eq. 8.33 as simply

$$\vec{F}_{\text{ext 1}} = m\vec{a}_{\text{cm}} \tag{8.35}$$

or

$$\vec{a}_{\text{cm}} = \frac{\vec{F}_{\text{ext 1}}}{m}. \tag{8.36}$$

Equation 8.36 is the equation of motion for the center of mass of the system. In words:

> **The center of mass of a two-object system accelerates as though both objects were located at the center of mass and the external force were exerted at that point.**

You can now begin to see the power of the center-of-mass concept. Although we cannot determine the acceleration of the individual carts without knowing more about the magnetic interaction, Eq. 8.36 allows us to calculate the motion of their center of mass *regardless* of the details of the magnetic interaction. As you will see in the next section, this is true not just for a system of two carts subject to a single external force, but even for a system of many interacting objects subject to many external forces, regardless of the interactions within the system and regardless of where on the system the external forces are exerted.

8.12 Systems of many interacting objects

With the analysis of a system comprising two objects under our belt, we are ready to look at the more complicated case of a system in which there are more than two objects. As in the preceding section, we begin by differentiating the momentum of the system with respect to time:

$$\frac{d\vec{p}}{dt} = \frac{d\vec{p}_1}{dt} + \frac{d\vec{p}_2}{dt} + \cdots = \Sigma \vec{F}_1 + \Sigma \vec{F}_2 + \cdots, \tag{8.37}$$

where $\vec{p}_1, \vec{p}_2, \cdots$ are the momenta of the individual objects in the system and $\Sigma \vec{F}_1, \Sigma \vec{F}_2, \cdots$ are the vector sums of the forces exerted on each of them. Each of these sums has two parts: one due to internal interactions and one due to external interactions. For object 1, for example, we have a sum of internal forces and a sum of external forces exerted on it:

$$\Sigma \vec{F}_1 = \Sigma \vec{F}_{\text{ext }1} + \Sigma \vec{F}_{\text{int }1} \tag{8.38}$$

and we can write similar expressions for all the other objects. Therefore the right side of Eq. 8.37 consists of a sum of external and internal forces:

$$\frac{d\vec{p}}{dt} = \Sigma(\vec{F}_{\text{ext }1} + \vec{F}_{\text{ext }2} + \cdots) + \Sigma(\vec{F}_{\text{int }1} + \vec{F}_{\text{int }2} + \cdots). \tag{8.39}$$

All internal forces drop out of Eq. 8.39, however. To see why, consider the case in which there are no external forces. Then the right side of Eq. 8.39 reduces to the sum of all internal forces:

$$\frac{d\vec{p}}{dt} = \Sigma(\vec{F}_{\text{int }1} + \vec{F}_{\text{int }2} + \cdots). \tag{8.40}$$

In this case, however, the system is isolated (because no external forces are exerted on it), and so we know that its momentum does not change. Therefore $d\vec{p}/dt = \vec{0}$ and Eq. 8.40 becomes

$$\vec{0} = \Sigma(\vec{F}_{\text{int }1} + \vec{F}_{\text{int }2} + \cdots). \tag{8.41}$$

In words, all the internal forces add up to zero! Therefore all of them drop out of the right side of Eq. 8.39, and the time rate of change of the momentum of the system is the sum of the external forces:

$$\frac{d\vec{p}}{dt} = \Sigma(\vec{F}_{\text{ext }1} + \vec{F}_{\text{ext }2} + \cdots) \equiv \Sigma \vec{F}_{\text{ext}}, \tag{8.42}$$

where $\Sigma \vec{F}_{\text{ext}}$ is the vector sum of all of the external forces exerted on the system. (See also the box "Cancellation of internal forces" on page 199.)

Cancellation of internal forces

There is another way to see that internal forces always add to zero. We consider here a system consisting of three particles, but the proof can be extended to any number of particles.

Each particle is subject to forces from the other two particles and to an external force:

$$\Sigma \vec{F}_1 = \Sigma \vec{F}_{\text{ext 1}} + \vec{F}_{21} + \vec{F}_{31}$$

$$\Sigma \vec{F}_2 = \Sigma \vec{F}_{\text{ext 2}} + \vec{F}_{12} + \vec{F}_{32}$$

$$\Sigma \vec{F}_3 = \Sigma \vec{F}_{\text{ext 3}} + \vec{F}_{13} + \vec{F}_{23}.$$

Summing up all the forces, we get

$$\Sigma \vec{F}_1 + \Sigma \vec{F}_2 + \Sigma \vec{F}_3$$
$$= \Sigma \vec{F}_{\text{ext 1}} + \Sigma \vec{F}_{\text{ext 2}} + \Sigma \vec{F}_{\text{ext 3}} + (\vec{F}_{12} + \vec{F}_{21})$$
$$+ (\vec{F}_{13} + \vec{F}_{31}) + (\vec{F}_{32} + \vec{F}_{23}). \qquad (1)$$

Remember, however, that two interacting particles exert on each other forces that are equal in magnitude but opposite in direction (Eq. 8.15). This means that the following equalities must hold:

$$\vec{F}_{12} = -\vec{F}_{21}$$

$$\vec{F}_{13} = -\vec{F}_{31}$$

$$\vec{F}_{32} = -\vec{F}_{23}.$$

So each term in parentheses in Eq. 1 vanishes, and only the external forces remain:

$$\Sigma \vec{F}_1 + \Sigma \vec{F}_2 + \Sigma \vec{F}_3$$
$$= \Sigma \vec{F}_{\text{ext 1}} + \Sigma \vec{F}_{\text{ext 2}} + \Sigma \vec{F}_{\text{ext 3}}.$$

Using the definition of center-of-mass velocity again, we have $\vec{p} = m\vec{v}_{\text{cm}}$, where $m = m_1 + m_2 + \cdots$, so that

$$\frac{d\vec{p}}{dt} = \frac{d(m\vec{v}_{\text{cm}})}{dt} = m\frac{d\vec{v}_{\text{cm}}}{dt} \equiv m\vec{a}_{\text{cm}}. \qquad (8.43)$$

After substituting Eq. 8.43 into Eq. 8.42, we obtain the same result as for the two-object nonisolated system:

$$\Sigma \vec{F}_{\text{ext}} = m\vec{a}_{\text{cm}}. \qquad (8.44)$$

Now, however, this expression applies to many objects and many external forces.* What this result means is the following: If external forces are exerted on the objects in a many-object system, the system's center of mass moves as though all the objects in the system were concentrated at the center of mass and all external forces were exerted at that point.

The equation of motion for the center of mass of a nonisolated system is thus

$$\vec{a}_{\text{cm}} = \frac{\Sigma \vec{F}_{\text{ext}}}{m}. \qquad (8.45)$$

Note the surprising similarities between the equations for a single object (Eqs. 8.4 and 8.6),

$$\frac{d\vec{p}}{dt} = \Sigma \vec{F} \quad \text{and} \quad \Sigma \vec{F} = m\vec{a}, \qquad (8.46)$$

and those for the center of mass of a system of interacting objects (Eqs. 8.42 and 8.44),

$$\frac{d\vec{p}}{dt} = \Sigma \vec{F}_{\text{ext}} \quad \text{and} \quad \Sigma \vec{F}_{\text{ext}} = m\vec{a}_{\text{cm}}. \qquad (8.47)$$

---

*Equation 8.44 is less general than Eq. 8.42. The latter is always true, but the former holds only if the inertia m of the system is not changing. Equation 8.44 cannot be used, for instance, to calculate the acceleration of a rocket where the burning and high-speed ejection of fuel result in an appreciable change in the rocket's inertia.

The most significant difference between Eqs. 8.6 and 8.44 is that instead of the acceleration $\vec{a}$ of a single object, Eq. 8.44 contains the center-of-mass acceleration $\vec{a}_{cm}$ of the system. This subtle but very important difference is what makes it possible to apply this analysis to everyday objects. Any object can be regarded as a system of interacting particles; after all, objects are made up of many interacting atoms. Thus all the relationships we just derived apply to macro-sized objects.

One interesting application is to macro-sized objects that deform easily. For example, imagine pushing a down pillow (**Figure 8.23**). When you begin pushing on one edge of the pillow, your hand deforms the side it touches, meaning that part of the pillow is accelerating. While your hand is accelerating that side of the pillow, the other side of the pillow doesn't move at all. In other words, different parts of the pillow have different instantaneous velocities and different instantaneous accelerations. It therefore makes no sense, while deformation is taking place, to speak of *the* acceleration $\vec{a}$ of the pillow, and Eqs. 8.46 cannot be applied. On the other hand, we can always use Eqs. 8.47 to describe the motion of the pillow's center of mass. In other words, the momentum $\vec{p}$ of the pillow, the acceleration $\vec{a}_{cm}$ of its center of mass, and the vector sum of the forces exerted on it are still well-defined quantities.

Perhaps the most remarkable aspect of this result is that we can always apply Eqs. 8.42 and 8.44 regardless of the internal interactions in a system. Even without any knowledge of these interactions, we can determine the motion of the center of mass of the pillow. What we give up by not considering the internal interactions is the ability to determine how the system deforms or what the motions of the different parts of the system are when the external force is exerted. In Figures 8.22 and 8.23, for example, we can determine only the displacement $\Delta\vec{r}_{cm}$ of the center of mass, not the displacement $\Delta\vec{r}_1$ of the point where the external force is exerted on the system, or the displacement of any other point.

The difference between Eqs. 8.46 and 8.47 vanishes when we consider a single object and ignore any deformation in it—that is to say, if we consider a **rigid object.** Although I argued in Section 8.6 that no object is truly rigid, most objects can be treated as being rigid for the purpose of describing their motion. For example, imagine pushing a stalled car toward the side of the road. For motion in one dimension, the front of the car moves the same way the back does—the minute compression of the car while your hands are pushing it is negligible. If you displace the back of the car by, say, 10 m, you can be pretty sure that the front of the car is also displaced by 10 m (give or take a fraction of the width of a hair). *All* parts of the car get displaced by 10 m in the same direction, and so the velocity and acceleration are the same for all parts of the car. For rigid objects we do not need to take into account any internal interactions or any difference in the displacement of various parts of the object.

Only for *deformable objects* (or for systems consisting of two or more rigid objects that can move relative to one another, like the two magnetically repelling carts in Figure 8.22) do you have to use the results derived in the last two sections.

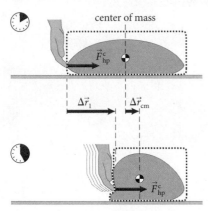

Figure 8.23 As the external force exerted by the hand displaces a down pillow, the pillow deforms, and so different parts of the pillow are displaced by different amounts. For objects that deform, it makes no sense to speak of "the displacement" or "the acceleration" of the object. However, it does makes sense to speak of the displacement or the acceleration of the center of mass.

8.20 (*a*) Show that Eqs. 8.47 reduce to Eqs. 8.46 when you consider a system of just one object. (*b*) Follow the procedure used to get from Eq. 8.21 to Eq. 8.24 for a system of many interacting objects.

Chapter Glossary

SI units of physical quantities are given in parentheses.

Contact force The force that an object exerts on a second object when the two are in physical contact with each other.

Elastic force The force caused by the reversible compression or stretching of an object.

Equation of motion The equation that relates the acceleration of an object to the vector sum of the forces exerted on it:

$$\vec{a} = \frac{\sum \vec{F}}{m}. \qquad (8.7)$$

For a system of more than one object, the equation of motion of the center of mass is

$$\vec{a}_{cm} = \frac{\sum \vec{F}_{ext}}{m}. \qquad (8.45)$$

Equilibrium Any object or system whose motion or state is not changing is in equilibrium.

Field force The force that an object exerts on a second object without the two being in physical contact with each other. The three types of field forces we consider are gravitational, electric, and magnetic forces.

Force $\vec{F}$ (N) When an object participates in an interaction, the force exerted on the object is given by the time rate of change caused in the object's momentum by that interaction. Forces obey the *principle of superposition:* The vector sum of the forces exerted on an object is equal to the vector sum of the rate of change caused in the object's momentum by the individual forces, and so

$$\sum \vec{F} \equiv \frac{d\vec{p}}{dt}. \qquad (8.4)$$

Free-body diagram A sketch showing a single object represented by its center of mass and all forces exerted *on* it. See the box on page 182.

Hooke's law The relationship between the force exerted on a spring (or other elastic object) and the displacement of the end of the spring from its relaxed value x_0 caused by that force:

$$(F_{\text{by load on spring}})_x = k(x - x_0) \quad \text{(small displacement)}, \qquad (8.18)$$

The constant k is the *spring constant.*

Impulse equation The equation that allows us to calculate the change in a system's momentum caused by forces exerted on the system during a time interval Δt. For a constant force,

$$\vec{J} = \left(\sum \vec{F} \right) \Delta t \quad \text{(constant force)}. \qquad (8.25)$$

For a time-varying force,

$$\vec{J} = \int_{t_i}^{t_f} \sum \vec{F}(t) \, dt \quad \text{(time-varying force)}. \qquad (8.26)$$

Interaction pair The forces that two interacting objects exert on each other. Conservation of momentum requires these two forces to be equal in magnitude and to point in opposite directions:

$$\vec{F}_{12} = -\vec{F}_{21}. \qquad (8.15)$$

Newton (N) A derived SI unit of force, defined as $1 \text{ N} = 1 \text{ kg} \cdot \text{m/s}^2$.

Newton's laws of motion Three fundamental principles that govern forces and their effects on the motion of objects.

Rigid object An object whose deformation can be ignored when one or more forces are exerted on it. For such an object the distance between any two points on the object remains fixed.

Spring constant k (N/m) A scalar defined as the ratio of the magnitude of the force exerted on a spring (or other elastic object) and the displacement of the end of the spring from its relaxed value x_0 caused by that force. See also *Hooke's law.*

Tension $\mathcal{T}$ (N) A scalar representing the stress caused in an object subject to a pair of forces, called *tensile forces*, exerted so that they stretch the object. In an object subject to two equal tensile forces of magnitude F, one on each end of the object, the value of the tension is $\mathcal{T} = F$.

Translational equilibrium Any object whose momentum is not changing is in translational equilibrium.

9 Work

CONCEPTS

9.1 Force displacement

9.2 Positive and negative work

9.3 Energy diagrams

9.4 Choice of system

QUANTITATIVE TOOLS

9.5 Work done on a single particle

9.6 Work done on a many-particle system

9.7 Variable and distributed forces

9.8 Power

As you learned in Chapter 8, a system subject to external forces—that is to say, forces exerted by objects outside the system on objects inside the system—is not isolated. The relationship between the momentum of a nonisolated system and the vector sum of the forces exerted on that system is simple: The vector sum of the forces is equal to the time rate of change in the system's momentum (Eq. 8.4). In addition to affecting a system's momentum, external forces can change the energy of the system. In the simplest case, a single force exerted on a system consisting of a single object causes that object to accelerate, and so the force changes the object's kinetic energy. Forces can also change the physical state of objects (think of compressing or stretching a spring or crumpling a piece of paper by exerting a force on it). Because the physical state of an object is related to the object's internal energy, we see that forces can change not only an object's kinetic energy but its internal energy as well.

To describe these changes in energy, physicists use the concept of **work**:

> **Work is the change in the energy of a system due to external forces.**

When an external force $\vec{F}_{ext}$ causes a change in the energy of a system, physicists refer to this change either as "the *work done by* the force $\vec{F}_{ext}$ on the system" or as "the *work done by* the object or person exerting force $\vec{F}_{ext}$ on the system."

Because work is a change in energy, the unit for work is the same as that for energy—the joule.

Note that this definition of work is much more limited than the meaning of the word *work* in ordinary language, which refers to any physical or mental effort or activity. You may be "doing work" for your physics class while reading this book, but there is no work involved in the physics sense.

9.1 Force displacement

Work amounts to a mechanical transfer of energy either from a system to its environment or from the environment to the system. For instance, if you (part of the "environment") push a friend on a bicycle (system is rider plus bicycle) and your friend accelerates, the force exerted by you on your friend transfers energy from your body to hers,

increasing her kinetic energy. If you compress a spring, you transfer energy from your body to the spring, where it is stored in the form of elastic potential energy. In each case, the change in the system's energy is caused by an external force—a force exerted by you on the system.

If you wonder why a force has to be external to do work on a system—that is, to change the energy of the system—remember that forces represent interactions between objects. Any interaction between objects within the system rearranges the energy between these objects but doesn't change the overall amount of energy in the system. Only an interaction between an object inside the system and an object outside it—an external interaction—can transfer energy across the system boundary.

Do external forces *always* cause a change in the energy of a system? To answer this question, it is helpful to consider an example.

9.1 Imagine pushing against a brick wall as shown in Figure 9.1a. (a) Considering the wall as the system, is the force you exert on it internal or external? (b) Does this force accelerate the wall? Change its shape? Raise its temperature? (c) Does the energy of the wall change as a result of the force you exert on it? (d) Does the force you exert on the wall do work on the wall?

As this checkpoint illustrates, external forces exerted on a system do not always do work on the system. The other two examples in **Figure 9.1**, however, do involve changes in energy, and hence in these cases work is done by your external force on the system. If, as shown in Figure 9.1b, you push against something that has wheels and so can accelerate it, its kinetic energy changes. If you push against a deformable object, the object changes shape and so its potential energy changes (Figure 9.1c).

Why is the work zero in Figure 9.1a but nonzero in parts b and c? The key to answering this question lies in looking at the *point of application* of each force (the point at which the force is exerted on the system, as indicated by the black dots in Figure 9.1). When you push against the brick wall, it neither moves nor deforms, and so the point of application of the force does not move. When you push the cart, you must move along with the cart to accelerate it; in other words, the

Figure 9.1 An external force does work on a system only if it causes the point at which it is applied (represented by a black dot) to move.

(a) $\Delta \vec{r}_F = \vec{0}$

Point of application of force

$\vec{F}^c_{pw}$

Point of application does not move, so force does no work on wall.

(b) Force displacement

$\Delta \vec{r}_F$

$\vec{F}^c_{pc}$ $\vec{F}^c_{pc}$

Point of application moves, so force does work on cart.

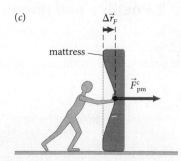

(c) $\Delta \vec{r}_F$

mattress

$\vec{F}^c_{pm}$

Point of application moves, so force does work on mattress.

CONCEPTS

point of application of the force is displaced. Similarly, when your force changes the shape of the deformable mattress in Figure 9.1c, the point of application of the force is displaced.

> **In order for a force to do work, the point of application of the force must undergo a displacement.**

Whenever an external force is exerted on a system and the displacement of the point of application of the force is zero, no work is done by the force on the system. Conversely, in one dimension, when the **force displacement** (shorthand for "the displacement of the point of application of the force") is nonzero, the external force does work on the system, and so the energy of the system changes. (In more than one dimension, the angle between the force and the force displacement also plays a role. We shall discuss this point in Chapter 10.)* To distinguish the force displacement from other displacements, we add a subscript F to the symbol for displacement: $\Delta \vec{r}_F$.

Exercise 9.1 Displaced forces

For which of the following forces is the force displacement nonzero: (a) the force exerted by a hand compressing a spring, (b) the force exerted by Earth on a ball thrown upward, (c) the force exerted by the ground on you at the instant you jump upward, (d) the force exerted by the floor of an elevator on you as the elevator moves downward at constant speed?

SOLUTION (a), (b), and (d).

(a) The point of application of the force is at the hand, which moves to compress the spring.

(b) The point of application of the force of gravity exerted by Earth on the ball is at the ball, which moves.

(c) The point of application is on the ground, which doesn't move.

(d) The point of application is on the floor of the elevator, which moves. ✔

9.2 You throw a ball straight up in the air. Which of the following forces do work on the ball while you throw it? Consider the interval from the instant the ball is at rest in your hand to the instant it leaves your hand at speed v. (a) The force of gravity exerted by Earth on the ball. (b) The contact force exerted by your hand on the ball.

9.2 Positive and negative work

When the energy of a system increases as a result of an external force exerted on the system, the change in energy is positive, and so the work done by that external force on

the system is said to be positive. An external force can also decrease the energy of a system, however. For instance, imagine slowing down a friend who is coasting on a bicycle. In this case, the kinetic energy of the system decreases, the change in energy is negative, and so the work done by the external force (that is, by you on your friend) on the system is said to be negative.

9.3 A ball is thrown vertically upward. (a) As it moves upward, it slows down under the influence of gravity. Considering the changes in energy of the ball, is the work done by Earth on the ball positive or negative? (b) After reaching its highest position, the ball moves downward, gaining speed. Is the work done by the gravitational force exerted on the ball during this motion positive or negative?

Examples of positive and negative work are illustrated in **Figure 9.2**. In both cases the person exerts a force $\vec{F}_{pc}^c$ on the cart. What, then, is the difference between these two situations? The difference lies in the direction in which the force is applied. To speed the cart up, the person must push in the direction of travel of the cart; the force vector $\vec{F}_{pc}^c$ and the force displacement $\Delta \vec{r}_F$ point in the same direction. To slow the cart down, the force must be applied in the direction opposite the cart's direction of travel; the force $\vec{F}_{pc}^c$ and the force displacement $\Delta \vec{r}_F$ point in opposite directions.

> **The work done by a force on a system is positive when the force and the force displacement point in the same direction and negative when they point in opposite directions.**

Figure 9.2 The work done on a system is positive if the system gains kinetic energy and negative if the system loses kinetic energy.

(a) Cart speeds up, so positive work is done on it

Force and force displacement point in same direction.

(b) Cart slows down, so negative work is done on it

Force and force displacement point in opposite directions.

---

*Two additional external forces are exerted on the cart in Figure 9.1b that have nonzero force displacements: the force of gravity and the contact force exerted by the ground. However, these two forces are equal in magnitude and opposite in direction and so they "cancel out": Their net effect is the same as that of no force. Therefore no work is done by these forces on the cart.

Figure 9.3 Only forces that are *external* to a system can do work on the system and change the system's energy.

(a)
Moving blocks compress spring

(b)
Spring expands, pushing blocks apart

System = spring + blocks

Forces are internal to system, so they do no work on system, and system's energy does not change.

System = spring

Forces are external to system, so work they do on system changes system's energy.

Force and force displacement in *same* direction: work done on system is *positive*, system's energy increases.

Force and force displacement in *opposite* directions: work done on system is *negative*, system's energy decreases.

9.4 Go back to Checkpoint 9.3 and answer the same two questions in terms of the directions of the applied forces and the force displacements. Do your answers agree with those you gave in Checkpoint 9.3?

Let us next consider a situation involving changes in potential energy. **Figure 9.3a** shows a spring being compressed by two moving blocks. There are two ways to look at this problem. We can consider the spring and the blocks as a closed system whose energy must remain constant, or we can consider just the spring as a system on which the blocks do work.

For the closed blocks-spring system in Figure 9.3a, the potential energy of the spring increases during the compression by an amount equal to the decrease in the blocks' kinetic energy. Because no external forces are exerted on the system, no work is involved.

Considering just the spring as our system in Figure 9.3a, we note that the increase in the spring's potential energy results from the work done by the blocks on it. Because the spring's potential energy increases, the work done on the system must be positive. Indeed, the forces exerted by the blocks on the spring point in the same direction as the force displacements.

Figure 9.3b shows the reverse situation: Two blocks are held against a compressed spring and then released, so that they accelerate away from each other. For the closed blocks-spring system, the energy doesn't change, and we can account for the increase in kinetic energy of the blocks by a decrease in the potential energy of the expanding spring. If, however, we consider the spring by itself as our system, the decrease in energy of the system implies that the work done by the blocks on the spring is negative.

Let us see if we reach the same conclusion for the sign of the work in Figure 9.3b when we look at the directions of the forces and the force displacements. Because we are interested in the work done *on the spring*, we need to consider the forces exerted by the blocks on it. These forces still point toward the spring, as shown in Figure 9.3b.* The force displacements, however, now point in the opposite direction, away from the spring. Because each force and its force displacement point in opposite directions, the work done by the blocks on the spring is negative. Everything is consistent: Both energy considerations and the directions of the forces and force displacements tell us that the work done by the blocks on the spring is negative as the spring expands.

Exercise 9.2 Positive and negative work

Is the work done by the following forces considered in Exercise 9.1 positive, negative, or zero? In each case the system is the object on which the force is exerted. (a) The force exerted by a hand compressing a spring, (b) the force exerted by Earth on a ball thrown upward, (c) the force exerted by the ground on you at the instant you jump upward, (d) the force exerted by the floor of an elevator on you as the elevator moves downward at constant speed.

---

*Careful! You may think the spring exerts a force on the blocks and not the other way around. Don't forget, however, that the force exerted by the spring on each block is just one part of an interaction pair. If you are having trouble picturing the force exerted by the blocks on the spring, imagine the spring expanding without having to push against the blocks: The expansion would be easier because there would be no resistance from the blocks. So, in a sense, the force exerted by the blocks on the spring slows down the expansion of the spring.

CONCEPTS

SOLUTION (*a*) Positive. To compress a spring, I must move my hand in the same direction as I push. ✔

(*b*) Negative. The force exerted by Earth points downward; the point of application moves upward. ✔

(*c*) Zero, because the point of application is on the ground, which doesn't move. ✔

(*d*) Negative. The force exerted by the elevator floor points upward; the point of application moves downward. ✔

9.5 Suppose that instead of the two moving blocks in Figure 9.3*a*, just one block is used to compress the spring while the other end of the spring is held against a wall. (*a*) Is the system comprising the block and the spring closed? (*b*) When the system is defined as being only the spring, is the work done by the block on the spring positive, negative, or zero? How can you tell? (*c*) Is the work done by the wall on the spring positive, negative, or zero?

9.3 Energy diagrams

In analyzing situations involving work, we extend the bar diagrams introduced in Chapter 5 to include work done on the system. Consider, for example, the situation in **Figure 9.4*a***. The energy of the system represented by this diagram increases from 10 J to 15 J. In order for this 5-J increase to occur, an amount of work equal to 5 J must be done by external forces on the system. The length of the vertical bar representing the final energy is equal to the sum of the lengths of the bars representing the initial energy and the work done by the external forces on the system.

Figure 9.4*b* represents a system whose energy decreases. In order for the energy to decrease, the work done by external forces on the system must be negative, and so the bar representing this work extends below the baseline.

Because any of the four kinds of energy discussed in Chapter 7 (kinetic energy, potential energy, source energy, and thermal energy) can change in situations involving work, our bar diagrams need to include more detail in order to show in what form the energy transferred to a system appears when some external force does work on it. The additional bars make these diagrams more cumbersome to draw, however, and therefore we introduce the following

Figure 9.4 Bar diagrams showing the work done on a system. Positive work adds to the system's energy; negative work subtracts from it.

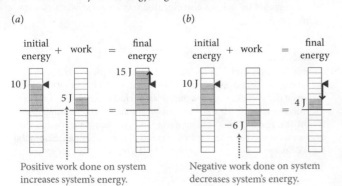

(*a*)

Positive work done on system increases system's energy.

(*b*)

Negative work done on system decreases system's energy.

Figure 9.5 (*a*) Changes in a system's energy can be shown (*b*) by initial and final bar diagrams or, more compactly, (*c*) by a single energy diagram, which shows the *changes* in energy in each category and a column showing work done on the system.

(*a*)

External work by person changes system's kinetic and potential energy.

(*b*)

We can represent the changes in energy by initial and final bar diagrams . . .

(*c*)   . . . or by a single **energy diagram**.

Changes in system's energy . . .   . . . equal work done on system.

simplification. Instead of drawing one set of bars for each of the initial and final individual energies, we draw just one set of bars representing the *change* in each category of energy, and we add a fifth bar, denoted by W, representing the work done by external forces on the system. We call these diagrams **energy diagrams.** Energy diagrams are a graphic representation of conservation of energy: They show that the energy of a system can change only due to the transfer of energy into or out of the system.

Just as with free-body diagrams, the first step in drawing an energy diagram is to define the system. In addition we should show any external force whose point of application undergoes a nonzero displacement; these are the forces that do work on the system. Consider, for example, the situation shown in **Figure 9.5*a***: a person pushing a pair of carts connected by a spring. The pushing accelerates the carts and compresses the spring. Let us choose a system comprising the pair of carts and the spring; Figure 9.5*a* shows its initial and final states.

Procedure: Drawing energy diagrams

1. Specify the **system** under consideration by listing the components inside the system.
2. **Sketch** the system in its initial and final states. (The initial and final states may be defined for you by the problem, or you may have to choose the most helpful states to examine.) Include in your sketch any external forces exerted on the system that undergo a nonzero force displacement, and draw a dot at the point of application of each force.
3. Determine any nonzero **changes in energy** for each of the four categories of energy, taking into account the four basic energy-conversion processes illustrated in Figure 7.13:

   a. Did the speed of any components of the system change? If so, determine whether the system's kinetic energy increased or decreased and draw a bar representing ΔK for the system. For positive ΔK, the bar extends above the baseline; for negative ΔK, it extends below the baseline. (For some problems you may wish to draw separate ΔK bars for different objects in the system; if so, be sure to specify clearly the system component that corresponds to each bar and verify that the entire system is represented by the sum of the components.)

   b. Did the configuration of the system change in a reversible way? If so, draw a bar representing the change in potential energy ΔU for the system. If necessary, draw separate bars for the changes in different types of potential energy, such as changes in elastic and gravitational potential energy.

   c. Was any source energy consumed? If so, draw a bar showing ΔE_s. Source energy usually decreases, making ΔE_s negative, and so the bar extends below the baseline. Keep in mind that conversion of source energy is always accompanied by generation of thermal energy (Figure 7.13c and d).

   d. Does friction occur within the system, or is any source energy consumed? If so, draw a bar showing ΔE_{th}. In nearly all cases we consider, the amount of thermal energy increases, and so ΔE_{th} is positive.

4. Determine whether or not any **work** W is done by external forces on the system. Determine whether this work is negative or positive. Draw a bar representing this work, making the length of the bar equal to the sum of the lengths of the other bars in the diagram.

   If no work is done by external forces on the system, leave the bar for work blank, then go back and adjust the lengths of the other bars so that their sum is zero.

We also draw a vector representing the external force $\vec{F}^c_{pc}$ exerted by the person on the left cart and indicate the position of the point of application of that force with a black dot.

Because the carts speed up, the final kinetic energy of the system is greater than the initial kinetic energy and the change in kinetic energy $\Delta K = K_f - K_i$ is therefore positive. This change in kinetic energy corresponds to the upward-pointing arrow marked ΔK in Figure 9.5b, which is a set of the bar diagrams we used before now (no work values are shown). The compression of the spring causes the elastic potential energy stored in the spring to increase, and so the change in potential energy $\Delta U = U_f - U_i$ is also positive, as shown by the upward-pointing arrow in Figure 9.5b.

To represent this same information in an energy diagram (Figure 9.5c), we draw bars to represent the changes ΔK and ΔU. The heights of the bars, which are equal to the heights of the arrows in Figure 9.5b, now represent the *changes* in each energy category. The ΔE_s and ΔE_{th} bars are empty because there are no changes in these energies.

The change in the system's energy comes from the work done by external forces on the system. The length of the bar representing the work done on the system in Figure 9.5c must therefore equal the sum of the lengths of the ΔK and ΔU bars. Note that these energy arguments tell us that the work done by external forces on the system must be positive. We can verify this sign by checking the directions of the force exerted on the system and its force displacement. From Figure 9.5a, we see that both are to the right, and so the work done by external forces on the system is indeed positive.

The general procedure for making energy diagrams is summarized in the Procedure box "Drawing Energy Diagrams".

Exercise 9.3 Cart launch

A cart is at rest on a low-friction track. A person gives the cart a shove and, after moving down the track, the cart hits a spring, which slows down the cart as the spring compresses. Draw an energy diagram for the system that comprises the person and the cart over the time interval from the instant the cart is at rest until it has begun to slow down.

SOLUTION Following the steps in the Procedure box, I begin by listing the objects that make up the system: cart and person. Then I sketch the system in its initial and final states (**Figure 9.6**). The external forces exerted on the system are the force of gravity on person and cart, the contact force exerted by ground on person, the contact force exerted by track on cart, and the contact force exerted by spring on cart. The vertical forces add up to zero, and so the work done by them on the system is zero. The force exerted by the spring on the cart, however, undergoes a force displacement, so I include that force in my diagram and indicate its point of application, as shown in Figure 9.6.

Figure 9.6

Next I determine whether there are any changes in energy. Kinetic energy: The cart begins at rest and ends with nonzero speed, which means a gain in kinetic energy (**Figure 9.7**). Potential energy: Neither the configuration of the cart nor that of the person changes in a reversible way, so the potential energy does not change. (The configuration of the spring does change in a reversible way, but the spring is not part of the system.) Source energy: The person has to exert effort to give the cart a shove, so source energy is consumed. The source energy of the system therefore decreases. Thermal energy: No friction is involved, but the conversion of source energy is always accompanied by the generation of thermal energy, so the thermal energy increases. (The person's muscles heat up.)

Figure 9.7

In Figure 9.6 the force exerted by the spring on the cart points to the left and the force displacement points to the right. This means that the work done by the spring on the cart is negative, and the W bar of my energy diagram must extend below the baseline. I adjust the lengths of the bars so that the length of the W bar is equal to the sum of the lengths of the other bars, yielding the energy diagram shown in Figure 9.7. ✔

9.6 Draw an energy diagram for the cart in Figure 9.2*b*.

Exercise 9.4 Compressing a spring

A block initially at rest is released on an inclined surface. The block slides down, compressing a spring at the bottom of the incline; there is friction between the surface and the block. Consider the time interval from a little after the release, when the block is moving at some initial speed v, until it comes to rest against the spring. Draw an energy diagram for the system that comprises the block, surface, and Earth.

SOLUTION I begin by listing the objects that make up the system: block, surface, and Earth. Then I sketch the initial and final states of the system (**Figure 9.8**). The spring exerts external forces on the system. The bottom end of the spring exerts a

Figure 9.8

force on the surface edge, but this force has a force displacement of zero. The top end of the spring exerts a force $\vec{F}_{sb}^c$ on the block. Because this force undergoes a nonzero force displacement, I include it in my diagram and show a dot at its point of application.

Next I determine whether there are any energy changes. Kinetic energy: The block's kinetic energy goes to zero, and the kinetic energies of the surface and Earth do not change. Thus the kinetic energy of the system decreases, and ΔK is negative. Potential energy: As the block moves downward, the gravitational potential energy of the block-Earth system decreases, and so ΔU is negative. (Because the spring gets compressed, its elastic potential energy changes, but the spring is not part of the system.) Source energy: none (no fuel, food, or other source of energy is converted in this problem). Thermal energy: As the block slides, energy is dissipated by the friction between the surface and the block, so ΔE_{th} is positive.

To determine the work done on the system, I look at the external forces exerted on it. The point of application of the external force $\vec{F}_{sb}^c$ exerted by the spring on the block undergoes a force displacement opposite the direction of the force, so that force does negative work on the system. Thus the work done on the system by the external forces is negative, and the W bar extends below the baseline (**Figure 9.9**). I adjust the lengths of the bars so that the length of the W bar is equal to the sum of the lengths of the other three bars, yielding the energy diagram shown in Figure 9.9. ✔

Figure 9.9

9.7 Draw an energy diagram for the situation presented in Exercise 9.4, but choose the system that comprises block, spring, surface, and Earth.

9.4 Choice of system

For a given situation, different choices of system yield different energy diagrams, as you just saw if you did Checkpoint 9.7. To examine this point further, consider the situation shown in **Figure 9.10**. Using a long rope, a person lowers a basket from a balcony, smoothly putting the basket down on the ground. The basket initially moves downward at speed v_i, but friction between the person's hands and the rope slows the basket so that it ends up at rest on the ground. For simplicity we assume no source energy is consumed; the person just lets the rope slide, exerting no physical effort.

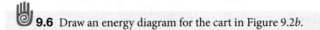

Figure 9.10 Different choices of system yield different energy diagrams.

(*a*)

System = basket + Earth

Negative work done by rope on basket equals decrease in system's kinetic and potential energies.

(*b*)

System = person + rope + basket + Earth

No work done on system; kinetic and potential energies are converted to thermal energy in system.

(*c*)

System = person + rope + basket

Work done by Earth on basket equals decrease in system's kinetic energy plus increase in system's thermal energy.

Let us begin by choosing the basket and Earth as our system, a choice that leads to the energy diagram shown in Figure 9.10*a*. Because the basket comes to rest, its kinetic energy decreases. As the distance between Earth and basket decreases, the potential energy of the Earth-basket system decreases. There is no conversion of source energy nor any dissipation of energy within the system, and so we leave the columns for ΔE_s and ΔE_{th} blank.

Next we examine the external forces exerted on the system. The person exerts forces both on Earth and, via the rope, on the basket. The latter involves a nonzero force displacement (the knot, which is the point of application for the force exerted by the rope on the basket, moves downward), so work is done on the system. This work is negative because the force exerted by the rope on the basket is upward and the force displacement is downward. In order to make the work equal to the change in the system's energy, the length of the bar representing work must be made equal to the sum of the lengths of the ΔK and ΔU bars.

What this energy diagram tells us is that the energy of the basket-Earth system decreases as energy is transferred out of the system. Because energy is transferred out of the system, the work done by the person on the system is negative.

What happens if we include the person and the rope in the system, as is Figure 9.10*b*? The changes in the kinetic and potential energies are the same as before, but now the person no longer exerts external forces and therefore cannot do any work on the system. In fact, because we have included everything in the system, there are no external forces and so there is no work done by external forces on the system—the system is closed.

For this choice of system, we have to take into account the dissipation of energy because of friction between the person's hands and the rope, and so we have a positive ΔE_{th}. The resulting energy diagram tells us that the initial kinetic energy of the basket and the initial potential energy of the system are converted to thermal energy (the rope and the person's hands heat up). No work is done by external forces on the system because the system is closed. This conclusion is entirely consistent with the one we drew on the basis of Figure 9.10*a*, but in the process we've obtained more information on where the energy went.

Finally we consider the same situation for a system that comprises only basket, person, and rope, as in Figure 9.10*c*. The changes in the kinetic and thermal energies are as before. For this choice of system, however, there is no change in gravitational potential energy (remember that gravitational potential energy refers to the configuration of Earth and the basket *together*, and Earth is no longer part of the system). What was counted as gravitational potential energy in Figure 9.10*a* and *b* appears as work done by the gravitational force on the system here. Earth exerts a downward external force on the basket as the basket moves downward, so Earth does positive work on the basket. (Earth also exerts a downward force on the person, but this force involves no force displacement.)

CONCEPTS

In Section 9.5, I shall show that the positive work done by the gravitational force on the system in Figure 9.10c is exactly equal to the negative of the change in the gravitational potential energy in Figure 9.10a and b. As this example shows, in order to avoid double-counting, it is important always to remember the following point:

Gravitational potential energy always refers to the relative position of various parts within a system, never to the relative positions of one component of the system and its environment.

Whenever you are looking at the energy associated with the gravitational interaction between an object inside your system and an object outside the system, do not include that energy in the ΔU bar of your energy diagram. That energy must be accounted for in the W part of the diagram instead.

The energy diagram of Figure 9.10c shows how the initial kinetic energy of the basket and the positive work done by Earth on the system end up as thermal energy.

All three choices of system lead to a valid conclusion. By looking at a situation from various points of view, you gain a better understanding of what energy conversions and transfers take place. Also, by looking at a situation in various ways and verifying that your answers are consistent with one another, you can convince yourself that you have not overlooked something.

9.8 Draw an energy diagram for just the basket in Figure 9.10.

Although you are generally free to choose whichever system suits you best, there are certain choices of system that lead to complications. In particular:

When drawing an energy diagram, do not choose a system for which friction occurs at the boundary of the system.

The reason for this is simple: Wherever friction occurs, thermal energy is generated. The problem is that this thermal energy appears on both sides of the surface where friction occurs. If you pull on a rope to draw a large box toward yourself, as in **Figure 9.11**, friction between floor and box heats up both box and floor. The thermal energy generated ends up partly in the floor and partly in the box. How much ends up where depends, among other things, on the materials that rub against each other and is not something that can be determined easily. So, if you choose just the box as your system, an unknown amount of energy flows out of the system, and it is no longer possible to do the energy accounting for the system.

There is another reason friction at a system boundary leads to problems. Whenever friction occurs at a boundary, the frictional force is *external* to the system (it is exerted by the environment on the system) and hence has to be taken into account in the computation of the work done on the system. The force of friction, however, is not applied at a single, well-defined location. Instead, it is distributed over the surfaces that move relative to each other. Consequently it is not possible to determine the force displacement, which is the other piece of information necessary to determine the work done on the system.

Figure 9.11 If you need to do energy accounting, don't choose a system for which friction occurs at the system boundary.

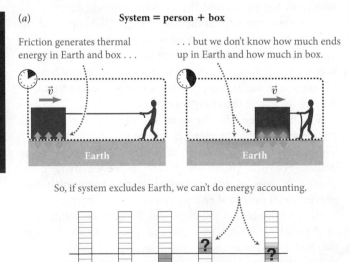

(a) **System = person + box**

Friction generates thermal energy in Earth and box . . .

. . . but we don't know how much ends up in Earth and how much in box.

So, if system excludes Earth, we can't do energy accounting.

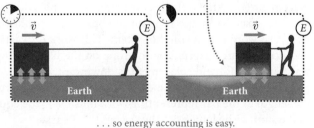

(b) **System = person + box + Earth**

If system also includes Earth, all thermal energy remains in system . . .

. . . so energy accounting is easy.

These problems with friction at a system boundary don't mean we can never treat any situations involving friction. Both our analyses of Figure 9.10 and Exercise 9.4 involve friction, but for all choices of system we considered, the two objects that rub against each other were kept together either inside or outside the system.

Example 9.5 Puck and spring

A puck sliding on a horizontal surface hits the free end of a spring that is held fixed at the other end. There is friction between puck and surface. Consider the interval from the instant before the puck comes in contact with the spring until the instant the puck has zero velocity and the spring reaches maximum compression. Draw an energy diagram for a system that contains the puck and for which the work done on the system is nonzero. (Your system may include objects in addition to the puck if you like.)

❶ GETTING STARTED I begin by making situation sketches at the beginning and end of the time interval of interest. The items in my sketches are the puck, the surface, and the spring (**Figure 9.12**).

Figure 9.12

If I include all three items in my system, the system is closed, so the work done by external forces on the system is zero. Because there is friction between surface and puck, I must keep the two together. Given that the puck must be part of the system, I have no choice but to have my system be the puck plus the surface, so I draw my system boundary around these two objects. The only external force exerted on this system is the contact force exerted by the spring on the puck, so I add that force to my diagram and indicate its point of application.

❷ DEVISE PLAN All I have to do is follow the procedure for drawing an energy diagram for my system.

❸ EXECUTE PLAN My energy diagram is shown in **Figure 9.13**. Because the puck slows to a stop, its kinetic energy decreases. Because there are no reversible changes in the system configuration and because no source energy is consumed, my bars for ΔU and ΔE_s must be zero. The friction causes dissipation of energy, so the ΔE_{th} bar shows an increase.

Figure 9.13

Because the external force exerted by the spring on the system points in the direction opposite the direction of the force displacement, the work done by the spring on the system is negative. I adjust the lengths of the bars so that the length of the W bar is equal to the sum of the lengths of the other bars. ✔

❹ EVALUATE RESULT The puck slows down under the combined action of the frictional force and the force exerted by the spring. So part of the puck's initial kinetic energy is converted to thermal energy, and the rest goes into compressing the spring. Because the spring is not part of the system, that energy leaves the system as (negative) work.

9.9 (a) Draw an energy diagram for the situation shown in Figure 9.11 for the system that comprises Earth and the box. Assume the box keeps moving at constant velocity, and consider the rope to be part of the person. (b) Explain each bar in the energy diagram of Figure 9.11b.

Self-quiz

1. A stunt performer falls from the roof of a two-story building onto a mattress on the ground. The mattress compresses, bringing the performer to rest without his getting hurt. Is the work done by the mattress on the performer positive, negative, or zero? Is the work done by the performer on the mattress positive, negative, or zero?

2. Consider a weightlifter holding a barbell motionless above his head. (*a*) Is the sum of the forces exerted on the barbell zero? (*b*) Is the weightlifter exerting a force on the barbell? (*c*) If the weightlifter exerts a force, does this force do any work on the barbell? (*d*) Does the energy of the barbell change? (*e*) Are your answers to parts *c* and *d* consistent in light of the relationship between work and energy?

3. Do any of the systems in **Figure 9.14** undergo a change in potential energy? If yes, is the change positive or negative? Ignore any friction.

Figure 9.14

4. A person pushes a cart up a small hill, gaining speed along the way. Friction in the cart's wheels is negligible. Name the components of the system depicted in each energy diagram shown in **Figure 9.15**.

Figure 9.15

Answers

1. Because the mattress brings the performer to rest, $\vec{F}^c_{mp}$ must point upward. The point of application of this force moves downward as the mattress compresses, meaning the work done by the mattress on the performer is negative. The work done by the performer on the mattress is positive because $\vec{F}^c_{pm}$ points downward and its point of application moves downward.

2. (*a*) Yes, because the barbell remains motionless. (*b*) Yes. He exerts an upward force to counter the downward gravitational force. (*c*) No, because the point at which the lifter exerts a force on the barbell is not displaced. (*d*) No. (*e*) They are consistent. If no work is done on a system, the energy of the system does not change.

3. Yes. (*a*), (*c*), and (*d*). Because none of the situations involves friction or the conversion of source energy, the only things you need to consider are changes in the kinetic and potential energies and work done by external forces on the system. The system in part *a* is closed, and so the decrease in kinetic energy causes an increase in gravitational potential energy: $\Delta U > 0$. In part *b*, Earth is not included in the system, so there can be no potential energy component of the system's energy. In part *c*, the system is closed, so the increase in kinetic energy must be due to a decrease in gravitational potential energy: $\Delta U < 0$. In part *d*, Earth does negative work on the system, so the energy of the system must decrease. Because the kinetic energy increases, the elastic potential energy of the spring must decrease: $\Delta U < 0$.

4. If there is a change in potential energy, the cart and Earth must be in the system; if there is a change in source energy, the person must be in the system. (*a*) Cart and Earth. The person does positive work on the system. (*b*) Person, cart, and Earth. This system is closed; no work is done by external forces on it. Source energy is converted to increase the kinetic and potential energies (and some of it is dissipated). There is more kinetic and potential energy in this system than in part *a* because the person is included in the system. (*c*) Person and cart. Earth does negative work on the system.

9.5 Work done on a single particle

In the first part of this chapter we defined work as the change in the energy of a system due to external forces, and we represented work by the letter W. The SI unit of work is the same as that of energy, J. When work is done by external forces on a system, the energy of the system changes by an amount

$$\Delta E = W. \tag{9.1}$$

This equation is called the **energy law** and embodies conservation of energy: Because energy cannot be created or destroyed, the energy of a system can change only if energy is transferred into or out of the system.* For a system that is closed, $W = 0$ and so the energy law takes on the form we encountered in Chapter 5: $\Delta E = 0$.

To calculate the work done by an external force on a system, we start by considering a simple case: a single particle of inertia m subject to a constant force $\vec{F}$. The term **particle** refers to any object that has no internal structure and no extent in space. Because it lacks extent and internal structure, a particle cannot change shape and therefore any internal energy is fixed ($\Delta E_{int} = 0$). Only the kinetic energy of a particle can change, so

$$\Delta E = \Delta K \quad \text{(particle)}. \tag{9.2}$$

To calculate what happens to the kinetic energy of a particle subject to a constant force $\vec{F}$, we consider the particle's motion over a time interval $\Delta t = t_f - t_i$ for the case where the particle's velocity at instant t_i is $\vec{v}_i$. The constant force gives the particle a constant acceleration given by the equation of motion (Eq. 8.8):

$$a_x = \frac{\sum F_x}{m} = \frac{F_x}{m}. \tag{9.3}$$

At the end of the time interval, the x component of the particle's velocity is given by Eq. 3.4,

$$v_{x,f} = v_{x,i} + a_x \Delta t, \tag{9.4}$$

and the x component of the particle's displacement is given by Eq. 3.7,

$$\Delta x = v_{x,i} \Delta t + \tfrac{1}{2} a_x (\Delta t)^2. \tag{9.5}$$

Because we are considering a particle, the displacement of the particle is also the force displacement.

Using these expressions, we can evaluate the change in the particle's kinetic energy:

$$\Delta K = K_f - K_i = \tfrac{1}{2} m (v_f^2 - v_i^2). \tag{9.6}$$

---

*For now, we consider only mechanical transfers of energy and ignore any other type of energy transfer. Later we'll also take into account transfer of energy by heating and radiation.

Substituting Eq. 9.4 into Eq. 9.6 and keeping in mind that $v^2 = v_x^2$ and $a^2 = a_x^2$, we get

$$\Delta K = \tfrac{1}{2}m\left[(v_{x,i} + a_x\Delta t)^2 - v_{x,i}^2\right]$$

$$= \tfrac{1}{2}m\left[2v_{x,i}a_x\Delta t + a_x^2(\Delta t)^2\right]$$

$$= ma_x\left[v_{x,i}\Delta t + \tfrac{1}{2}a_x(\Delta t)^2\right]$$

$$= ma_x\Delta x_F = F_x\Delta x_F, \tag{9.7}$$

where the substitution $v_{x,i}\Delta t + \tfrac{1}{2}a_x(\Delta t)^2 = \Delta x_F$ comes from Eq. 9.5, the substitution $ma_x = F_x$ comes from Eq. 9.3, and Δx_F carries a subscript F to remind us that this is the **force displacement** (the displacement of the point of application of the force). Having found this result $\Delta K = F_x\Delta x_F$, we can use Eq. 9.2, $\Delta E = \Delta K$, to say that $\Delta E = F_x\Delta x_F$ and then Eq. 9.1, $\Delta E = W$, to finally say

$$W = F_x\Delta x_F \quad \text{(constant force exerted on particle, one dimension).} \tag{9.8}$$

In words:

> **For motion in one dimension, the work done by a constant force exerted on a particle equals the product of the x components of the force and the force displacement.**

If the external force $\vec{F}$ and the force displacement $\Delta\vec{r}_F$ point in the same direction, F_x and Δx_F are either both positive or both negative, and so the product $F_x\Delta x_F$ is positive. Consequently, the kinetic energy increases. When the force and the particle's displacement point in opposite directions, F_x and Δx_F have opposite algebraic signs. The work done by the force on the particle is then negative, and so the kinetic energy of the particle decreases.

If more than one force is exerted on a particle, the x component of its acceleration is given by Eq. 8.8: $a_x = \Sigma F_x/m$. Substituting this expression for the x component of the acceleration into Eq. 9.7 gives $\Delta K = (\Sigma F_x)\Delta x_F$. Moving on to Eq. 9.8, we obtain the work done by these forces on the particle:

$$W = (\Sigma F_x)\Delta x_F \quad \text{(constant forces exerted on particle, one dimension).} \tag{9.9}$$

Equation 9.9 is what we call the **work equation** for a particle. Together with the energy law (Eq. 9.1), this equation allows us to deal with systems that are not closed.

Notice the parallel between our treatments of momentum/impulse and energy/work (**Figure 9.16**). Conservation of momentum gives rise to the momentum law, Eq. 4.18, $\Delta\vec{p} = \vec{J}$, where $\vec{J}$ is the impulse delivered to the system. For an isolated system, the impulse is zero and so the momentum of the system does not change. If the system is not isolated, we can use the impulse equation, Eq. 8.25, $\vec{J} = (\Sigma\vec{F})\Delta t$, to calculate the change in the momentum of the system. Conservation of energy gives rise to the energy law, Eq. 9.1. The work done on a closed system is zero, and so the energy of the system does not change. If the system is not closed, we can use the work equation, Eq. 9.9, to calculate the change in the energy of the system. When we solve problems, it is possible to choose either a closed system or a system that is not closed. As the next example shows,

Figure 9.16 Energy and momentum changes for systems.

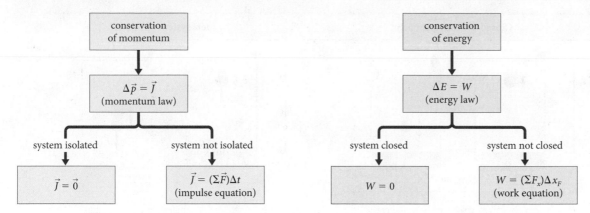

both choices lead to the same answer. If you are unable to obtain a solution with one approach, try the other.

Although we derived Eqs. 9.8 and 9.9 for a particle, they can also be used for any rigid object as long as only the kinetic energy of the object changes. In that case, we can use Eq. 9.2 to calculate the change in the energy of the object. Because all particles that make up the object undergo the same displacement $\Delta \vec{r}$, Eq. 9.8 gives the work done by a constant force exerted on the object.

Example 9.6 Work done by gravity

A ball of inertia m_b is released from rest and falls vertically. What is the ball's final kinetic energy after a displacement $\Delta x = x_f - x_i$?

❶ GETTING STARTED I begin by making a sketch of the initial and final conditions and drawing an energy diagram for the ball (**Figure 9.17**). I choose an x axis pointing upward. Because the ball's internal energy doesn't change as it falls (its shape and temperature do not change), I can treat the ball as a particle. Therefore only its kinetic energy changes. I can also assume air resistance is small enough to be ignored, so that the only

external force exerted on the ball is a constant gravitational force. This force has a nonzero force displacement and so does work on the ball. I therefore include this force in my diagram.

❷ DEVISE PLAN If I treat the ball as a particle, Eqs. 9.1 and 9.2 tell me that the change in the ball's kinetic energy is equal to the work done on it by the constant force of gravity, the x component of which is given by Eq. 8.17: $F_{Eb\,x}^{G} = -m_b g$. (The minus sign means that the force points in the negative x direction.) To calculate the work done by this force on the ball, I use Eq. 9.8.

❸ EXECUTE PLAN Substituting the x component of the gravitational force exerted on the ball and the force displacement $x_f - x_i$ into Eq. 9.8, I get

$$W = F_{Eb\,x}^{G} \Delta x_F = -m_b g (x_f - x_i).$$

Because the work is equal to the change in kinetic energy and the initial kinetic energy is zero, I have $W = \Delta K = K_f - 0 = K_f$, so

$$K_f = -m_b g (x_f - x_i). ✔$$

❹ EVALUATE RESULT Because the ball moves in the negative x direction, $\Delta x = x_f - x_i$ is negative and so the final kinetic energy is positive (as it should be).

An alternative approach is to consider the closed Earth-ball system. For that system, the sum of the gravitational potential energy and kinetic energy does not change, and so, from Eq. 7.13, $\Delta K + \Delta U^G = \frac{1}{2} m_b (v_f^2 - v_i^2) + m_b g (x_f - x_i) = 0$. Because the ball starts at rest, $v_i = 0$, and so I obtain the same result for the final kinetic energy: $\frac{1}{2} m_b v_f^2 = -m_b g (x_f - x_i)$.

Figure 9.17

Figure 9.18 Two ways to determine the change in kinetic energy of a falling ball.

	Closed-system approach	Open-system approach

Energy law

Closed-system approach:
$$\Delta E = 0$$
$$\Delta K + \Delta U^G = 0$$

Open-system approach:
$$\Delta E = \Delta K = W$$
$$W = F^G_{Eb\,x}\Delta x_F$$

Equation to use

Closed-system approach:
$$\Delta U^G = m_b g(x_f - x_i)$$

Open-system approach:
$$F^G_{Eb\,x} = -m_b g$$

Answer

Closed-system approach:
$$\Delta K = -m_b g(x_f - x_i)$$

Open-system approach:
$$\Delta K = -m_b g(x_f - x_i)$$

The two approaches used in Example 9.6 are shown schematically in **Figure 9.18**. In the closed-system approach, the increase in kinetic energy is attributed to a decrease in the gravitational potential energy of the Earth-ball system. In the open-system approach, the increase in kinetic energy is attributed to the work done by the force of gravity on the ball. In this case it is meaningless to talk about gravitational potential energy because gravitational potential energy refers to the configuration of Earth and the ball *together*. Because Earth is not part of the system, it would not be clear whether to attribute this potential energy to Earth or to the ball.

9.10 Verify that in Example 9.6 the momentum transferred to the ball by the gravitational force is $\Delta p_x = m_b(v_{x,f} - v_{x,i})$.

9.6 Work done on a many-particle system

Everyday objects cannot always be treated as either single particles or rigid objects. As we saw in Section 8.12, we must consider such objects as systems of many interacting particles. The acceleration of the center of mass of such a system is given by Eq. 8.45:

$$\vec{a}_{cm} = \frac{\sum \vec{F}_{ext}}{m}, \tag{9.10}$$

where m is the inertia of the system. Using this result, we can now evaluate the work done by external forces on a many-particle system following an approach analogous to that of a single particle in Eqs. 9.4–9.8.

Consider the motion of a two-particle system over a time interval $\Delta t = t_f - t_i$. If the center of mass of the system moves at velocity $\vec{v}_{cm,i}$ at some initial instant t_i and has constant acceleration $\vec{a}_{cm}$, then from Eq. 9.4 the velocity of the center of mass at the end of the time interval is

$$\vec{v}_{cm,f} = \vec{v}_{cm,i} + \vec{a}_{cm}\Delta t \qquad (9.11)$$

and its displacement is (from Eq. 9.5)

$$\Delta\vec{x}_{cm} = \vec{v}_{cm,i}\Delta t + \tfrac{1}{2}\vec{a}_{cm}(\Delta t)^2. \qquad (9.12)$$

Using these expressions, we can evaluate the changes in the translational kinetic energy of the system from Eq. 6.32, $K_{cm} = \tfrac{1}{2}mv_{cm}^2$:

$$\Delta K_{cm} = K_{cm,f} - K_{cm,i} = \tfrac{1}{2}m(v_{cm,f}^2 - v_{cm,i}^2). \qquad (9.13)$$

Following the same derivation used to obtain Eq. 9.7, we calculate for the change in translational kinetic energy of the system

$$\Delta K_{cm} = ma_{cm\,x}\Delta x_{cm} = (\textstyle\sum F_{ext\,x})\Delta x_{cm} \quad \text{(constant forces, one dimension).} \qquad (9.14)$$

Even though this result looks very much like Eq. 9.7, ΔK_{cm} does not represent the work done by the external force on the system. The reasons are that the translational kinetic energy K_{cm} is only part of the kinetic energy of the system (which we know from Eq. 6.35, $K = K_{cm} + K_{conv}$) and for a system of many interacting particles changes can also occur in the other kinds of energy. Therefore $\Delta K_{cm} \neq \Delta E$. Knowing from Eq. 9.1 that $\Delta E = W$, we see that ΔK_{cm} from Eq. 9.14 cannot be equal to the work done by the external force on the many-particle system:

$$\Delta K_{cm} \neq W \quad \text{(many-particle system)} \qquad (9.15)$$

To see this more explicitly, consider the system consisting of two carts connected by a spring, illustrated in **Figure 9.19**. Cart 1 is subject to a single external force $\vec{F}_{ext\,1}$. If we ignore any changes in the carts' internal energies, we can consider the carts to be particles, which means that all of the system's internal energy is stored in the spring. The pushing on cart 1 both accelerates the system and compresses the spring, causing changes in the system's kinetic and internal energies. Unfortunately, we cannot calculate these changes because we don't know how much the spring compresses and we don't know anything about the instantaneous velocities of the carts. Because the work done by external forces on the system is equal to the change in the system's energy E—where E is the sum of all forms of energy—Eq. 9.14 does not provide an expression for the work done on the system.

So, how can we determine the work done by external forces on a many-particle system? Because work is energy transferred, we can use the fact that the work W_{env} done by a system on its environment has the same magnitude as the work W_{sys} done by the environment on the system but carries the opposite sign: $W_{env} = -W_{sys}$. If the system gains, say, 100 J, then conservation of energy dictates that something outside the system must lose 100 J. In **Figure 9.20a**, for example, the external force $\vec{F}_{h1}$ exerted by the hand on cart 1 gives the cart a displacement $\Delta\vec{r}_F$. According to Eq. 8.15, $\vec{F}_{12} = -\vec{F}_{21}$, cart 1 must exert a force $-\vec{F}_{h1}$ on the hand. The work done by cart 1 on the hand over the displacement $\Delta\vec{r}_F$ is, from Eq. 9.8, $-F_{h1\,x}\Delta x_F$ (Figure 9.20b). Because the work done by the two-cart system *on* the hand is $-F_{h1\,x}\Delta x_F$, the work done *by* the hand on the two-cart system must be $+F_{h1\,x}\Delta x_F$. In general, when an external

Figure 9.19 An external force does work on a system of two interacting carts.

Figure 9.20 The work done by its environment on a system has the same magnitude as the work done by the system on its environment, but the two carry opposite signs: $W_{env} = -W_{sys}$.

(*a*) Hand does work on carts

(*b*) Carts do work on hand

force is exerted on one of the particles in a two-particle system, the work equation is*

$$W = F_{\text{ext } 1x}\Delta x_F \quad \text{(constant nondissipative force, one dimension).} \quad (9.16)$$

This work is equal to the product of the external force and Δx_F, the x component of the displacement *of the point of application of this force*, which is different from Δx_{cm}, the x component of the displacement *of the center of mass*, which appears in Eq. 9.14. Although we obtained this result for the specific case of two carts connected by a spring, the result does not depend on any of the specifics of the system and therefore is valid for any system of two interacting particles subject to a single, constant external force.

Example 9.7 Landing on his feet

A 60-kg person jumps off a chair and lands on the floor at a speed of 1.2 m/s. Once his feet touch the floor surface, he slows down with constant acceleration by bending his knees. During the slowing down, his center of mass travels 0.25 m. Determine the magnitude of the force exerted by the floor surface on the person and the work done by this force on him.

❶ GETTING STARTED I begin by making a sketch of the initial and final conditions, choosing my person as the system and assuming the motion to be entirely vertical (**Figure 9.21**). I point the x axis downward in the direction of motion, which means that the x components of both the displacement and the velocity of the center of mass are positive: $\Delta x_{\text{cm}} = +0.25$ m and $v_{\text{cm}x} = +1.2$ m/s. Two external forces are exerted on the person: a downward force of gravity $\vec{F}_{Ep}^{G}$ exerted by Earth and an upward contact force $\vec{F}_{sp}^{c}$ exerted by the floor surface. Only the point of application of the force of gravity undergoes a displacement, and so I need to include only that force in my diagram.

Figure 9.21

❷ DEVISE PLAN Knowing the initial center-of-mass velocity, I can use Eq. 9.13 to calculate the change in the person's translational kinetic energy ΔK_{cm}. To calculate the vector sum of the external forces exerted on the person, I can use the value I obtain for ΔK_{cm} and the displacement $\Delta x_{\text{cm}} = +0.25$ m in Eq. 9.14 to obtain the vector sum of the forces exerted on the person. If I then subtract the force of gravity, I obtain the force

exerted by the floor surface on the person. To determine the work done by this force on the person, I need to multiply it by the force displacement. Because the person slows down as he travels downward, his acceleration is upward and so the vector sum of the forces is upward too. To remind myself of this, I draw a free-body diagram in which the arrow for the upward contact force is longer than the arrow for the downward force of gravity.

❸ EXECUTE PLAN Because the person ends at rest, his final translational kinetic energy is zero, and Eq. 9.13 gives me

$$\Delta K_{\text{cm}} = 0 - \tfrac{1}{2}mv_{\text{cm,i}}^{2} = \tfrac{1}{2}(60 \text{ kg})(1.2 \text{ m/s})^{2} = -43 \text{ J}.$$

Substituting this value and the displacement of the center of mass into Eq. 9.14 yields

$$\sum F_{\text{ext}x} = \frac{\Delta K_{\text{cm}}}{\Delta x_{\text{cm}}} = \frac{-43 \text{ J}}{0.25 \text{ m}} = -170 \text{ N}.$$

To obtain the force exerted by the floor from this vector sum, I add to the sketch a free-body diagram showing the two forces exerted on the person (Figure 9.21).

$$\sum F_{\text{ext}x} = F_{Ep x}^{G} + F_{sp x}^{c}$$

and so $F_{sp x}^{c} = \sum F_{\text{ext}x} - F_{Ep x}^{G}$. The x component of the force of gravity is $F_{Ep x}^{G} = mg = (60 \text{ kg})(9.8 \text{ m/s}^2) = +590$ N and so $F_{sp x}^{c} = -170 \text{ N} - 590 \text{ N} = -760$ N. ✔

To determine the work done by this force on the person, I must multiply the x component of the force by the force displacement. The point of application is at the floor, which doesn't move. This means that the force displacement is zero, and so the work done on the person is zero too: $W = 0$. ✔

❹ EVALUATE RESULT The contact force $F_{sp x}^{c}$ is negative because it is directed upward, as I expect. Its magnitude is larger than that of the force of gravity, as it should be in order to slow the person down.

---

*We can apply this line of reasoning only when the force $\vec{F}_{\text{ext } 1}$ is nondissipative. As we saw in Section 9.4, if the force exerted at the boundary of a system is dissipative, we don't know how much of the dissipated energy ends up inside the system.

✋ **9.11** Compare the rightmost terms of Eqs. 9.14 and Eq. 9.16 to determine whether, in any two-particle system subject to a single, constant external force, ΔE is larger than, equal to, or smaller than ΔK_{cm}. Explain your answer.

We can easily generalize Eq. 9.16 to a many-particle system subject to several constant forces. When more than one external agent interacts with the system, we can follow the same argument to calculate the work done by each external agent on the system. If agent 1 exerts a force $\vec{F}_{ext\,1}$ on a system and the point of application of this force undergoes a displacement $\Delta \vec{r}_{F1}$, then the work done by that agent on the system is $W_1 = F_{ext\,1x}\,\Delta x_{F1}$.* Likewise, the work done by agent 2 is $W_2 = F_{ext\,2x}\,\Delta x_{F2}$. The work done by all the agents in the environment on the system is the sum of the work done by each on the system:

$$W = W_1 + W_2 + \cdots = F_{ext\,1x}\Delta x_{F1} + F_{ext\,2x}\Delta x_{F2} + \cdots \qquad (9.17)$$

or

$$W = \sum_n (F_{ext\,nx}\Delta x_{Fn}) \quad \text{(constant nondissipative forces, one dimension),} \quad (9.18)$$

which is the work equation for a many-particle system subject to constant external forces.

Note that to calculate this work we must take the product of each external force and the force displacement *of that force*. If the system is an object that deforms, these displacement values are different in different parts of the system. For that reason both $F_{ext\,nx}$ and Δx_{Fn} in Eq. 9.18 carry a subscript n.

If the force is dissipative, we cannot use this expression because the dissipated energy is distributed on both sides of the system boundary. Dissipative forces are discussed in the next section. The results for a single particle and a system of particles are summarized in Table 9.1.

✋ **9.12** Show that for a one-particle system, Eqs. 9.14 and 9.18 both reduce to Eq. 9.9.

Table 9.1 Equation of motion and energy accounting for a particle and a system of particles

	Single particle or rigid object	System of particles or deformable object
Equation of motion	$\vec{a} = \dfrac{\sum \vec{F}}{m}$	$\vec{a}_{cm} = \dfrac{\sum \vec{F}_{ext}}{m}$
Energy law	$\Delta E = W$	$\Delta E = W$
Work equation	$W = (\sum F_x)\Delta x_F$	$W = \sum_n (F_{ext\,nx}\Delta x_{Fn})$
Kinetic energy change	$\Delta K = W$	$\Delta K_{cm} = (\sum F_{ext\,x})\Delta x_{cm}$

*When work is done by more than one force on an object or system, the work done by each force individually inherits the subscripts of the corresponding force.

QUANTITATIVE TOOLS

9.7 Variable and distributed forces

The results obtained in the preceding two sections apply only to forces that are constant and that are applied at well-defined locations in a system. If the forces are not constant or if we cannot determine the force displacement, then the results we obtained do not apply. Examples are the force exerted by a spring, which varies with the amount of compression or stretching, and the frictional force, which is distributed over a surface and for which it is not possible to determine the point of application. Let us examine these two cases in more detail.

What should one do if the force exerted on a system isn't constant? (We call such a force a *variable force.*) For this kind of force, the x component can be written as a function of x: $F_x = F_x(x)$. The trick is to apply the constant-force result over a force displacement small enough to make the force approximately constant over that displacement. **Figure 9.22** shows how, for a force that varies with the position at which that force is applied, we can divide the force displacement into small segments.

Suppose we want to know the work done by the variable force on a system while the point of application of the force moves from x_i to x_f in Figure 9.22. We first divide the force displacement $x_f - x_i$ into N equal smaller force displacements δx_F such that the force is approximately constant across each δx_F (Figure 9.22a). Applying Eq. 9.8 to each smaller displacement δx_F, we can write the work done by the variable force on the system during each displacement as

$$W_n = F_x(x_n)\delta x_F, \tag{9.19}$$

where $F_x(x_n)$ is the x component of the force at x_n (this point x_n is located at the center of each interval, as shown in Figure 9.22a). This work is the area of the dark shaded rectangle in Figure 9.22a. The work done over the entire force displacement from x_i to x_f is then approximately equal to the sum of work W_n over all small force displacements δx_F between x_i and x_f:

$$W \approx \sum_n W_n = \sum_n F_x(x_n)\delta x_F, \tag{9.20}$$

where $\sum_n F_x(x_n)\delta x_F$ represents the sum of all the rectangular areas under the steps between x_i and x_f (the light shaded area in Figure 9.22a).

To get a better approximation, we can divide the displacement $x_f - x_i$ into a larger number of smaller force displacements δx_F, so that the variation of the external force over each displacement becomes even smaller and the red stepped curve is closer to the actual (light red) $F_x(x)$ curve.

An exact result is obtained if we let δx_F approach zero (and the number of small displacements approaches infinity), as in Figure 9.22b:

$$W = \lim_{\delta x_F \to 0} \sum_n F_x(x_n)\delta x_F, \tag{9.21}$$

which is precisely the definition of the integral of the x component of the external force with respect to x from x_i to x_f:

$$W = \int_{x_i}^{x_f} F_x(x)dx \quad \text{(nondissipative force, one dimension).} \tag{9.22}$$

✋ **9.13** Show that Eq. 9.22 reduces to Eq. 9.8 when the force is constant.

An example of a force that varies with the position at which it is applied is the force exerted by a spring on a load: $\vec{F}_{sl} = -k(\vec{x} - \vec{x}_0)$ (Eq. 8.20).

Figure 9.22 Evaluating the work done by a variable force $\vec{F}(x)$ on a system.

(*a*) Work approximated by area under steps of constant force

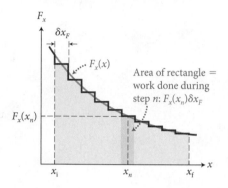

(*b*) As δx_F approaches zero, area under curve approaches work done

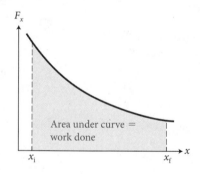

Example 9.8 Spring work

A brick of inertia m compresses a spring of spring constant k so that the free end of the spring is displaced from its relaxed position. What is the work done by the brick on the spring during the compression?

❶ GETTING STARTED I begin by making a sketch of the situation as the free end of the spring is compressed from its relaxed position x_0 to a position x (**Figure 9.23**). Because I need to calculate the work done by the brick on the spring, I choose the spring as my system. Three forces are exerted on the spring: contact forces exerted by the brick and by the floor, and the force of gravity. As usual when dealing with compressed springs, I ignore the force of gravity exerted on the spring (see Section 8.6). Only the force $\vec{F}^c_{bs}$ exerted by the brick on the spring undergoes a nonzero force displacement, so I need to show only that force in my diagram. Because the brick and spring do not exert any forces on each other when the spring is in the relaxed position, I do not draw this force in the initial state.

Figure 9.23

❷ DEVISE PLAN I need to calculate the work done by the brick on the spring. I could use Eq. 9.22 if I knew the force the brick exerts on the spring. That force is not given, but the force exerted

by the brick on the spring and the force exerted by the spring on the brick form an interaction pair: $\vec{F}^c_{bs} = -\vec{F}^c_{sb}$. I can use Eq. 8.20 to determine $\vec{F}^c_{sb}$ and then use it in Eq. 9.22.

❸ EXECUTE PLAN Equation 8.20 tells me that the x component of the force exerted by the spring on the brick varies depending on how far the spring is compressed:

$$F_{sbx} = -k(x - x_0),$$

where x_0 is the coordinate of the relaxed position of the free end of the spring. The x component of the force exerted by the brick on the spring is thus

$$F_{bsx} = +k(x - x_0). \qquad (1)$$

Because $x_0 > x$, F_{bsx} is negative, which means that $\vec{F}^c_{bs}$ points in the same direction as the force displacement. Thus the work done by the brick on the spring is positive. Now I substitute Eq. 1 into Eq. 9.22 and work out the integral to determine the work done by the brick on the spring:

$$W_{bs} = \int_{x_0}^{x} F_{bsx}(x)\,dx = \int_{x_0}^{x} k(x - x_0)\,dx$$

$$= \left[\tfrac{1}{2}kx^2 - kx_0 x \right]_{x_0}^{x} = \tfrac{1}{2}k(x - x_0)^2. \checkmark \qquad (2)$$

❹ EVALUATE RESULT Because the spring constant k is always positive (see Section 8.9 on Hooke's law), the work done by the brick on the spring is also positive. This is what I expect because the work done in compressing the spring is stored as potential energy in the spring.

✋ **9.14** In Example 9.8, consider the situation from the instant the brick is released to the instant at which it has zero velocity (when the spring compression is greatest). Draw an energy diagram for a system that comprises (*a*) the spring alone and (*b*) Earth, spring, and brick.

The energy law tells me that the change in the energy of the spring in Example 9.8 is equal to the work done by the brick on it: $\Delta E = W$. As you saw in part *a* of Checkpoint 9.14, only the potential energy of the spring (corresponding to the configuration of the spring) changes, and so $\Delta E = \Delta U_{spring} = W$. The change in the **potential energy of a spring** as its free end is displaced from its relaxed position x_0 to any position x is thus

$$\Delta U_{spring} = \tfrac{1}{2}k(x - x_0)^2. \qquad (9.23)$$

This expression also describes the change in potential energy when the spring is stretched by some external force. To stretch the spring, the force exerted on it must point upward in Figure 9.23, which means that instead of $\Delta \vec{r}$ and $\vec{F}^c_{bs}$ both pointing downward as they do in compression, these two vectors both point upward. The expression for the work done by the stretching force on the spring (Eq. 2 in Example 9.8) remains the same because the displacement and the force exerted on the spring still both point in the same direction and so Eq. 9.23 also remains the same. Consequently the potential energy of a spring increases both when the spring is compressed and when it is stretched.

✋ **9.15** (Brain twister) As the brick in Example 9.8 moves downward, why is the magnitude of the force it exerts on the spring given by Eq. 1 in Example 9.8 and not by simply the magnitude *mg* of the gravitational force exerted by Earth on the brick? Hint: Draw a free-body diagram for the brick as it moves downward.

Next we turn to the force of friction. As we discussed in Section 9.4, friction poses a problem for two reasons. First, the energy dissipated by friction ends up being divided between two objects. Second, there is no single point of application for frictional forces—the force is distributed over two surfaces that move relative to each other.

Consider a block sliding across a rough surface. The block is initially moving at some speed *v* but eventually comes to rest because of friction between it and the surface. **Figure 9.24** shows an energy diagram for the closed block-surface system. Because there are no reversible changes in configuration and no source energy is used, we know that all of the block's kinetic energy is converted to thermal energy. So, if we know the block's initial kinetic energy, we can determine the thermal energy generated from the energy law:

$$\Delta E = \Delta K + \Delta E_{th} = 0. \tag{9.24}$$

Because the final kinetic energy is zero, we have

$$\Delta E_{th} = -\Delta K = -(K_f - K_i) = K_i. \tag{9.25}$$

How are these energy changes related to the displacement $\Delta \vec{r}_{cm}$ over which the block slides to a stop? Let the force of friction exerted by the surface on the block be $\vec{F}^f_{sb}$. According to Eq. 9.14, the change in the block's translational kinetic energy is equal to the product of the external force exerted on the block and the displacement of its center of mass:

$$\Delta K_{cm} = F^f_{sb\,x}\Delta x_{cm}. \tag{9.26}$$

Because the frictional force and the block's displacement point in opposite directions, the right side of Eq. 9.26 is negative. Because the block is a rigid object, the translational kinetic energy is all of its kinetic energy, and so $\Delta K_{cm} = \Delta K$. Substituting Eq. 9.25, then yields an expression for the energy dissipated by friction:

$$\Delta E_{th} = -F^f_{sb\,x}\Delta x_{cm} \quad \text{(constant dissipative force, one dimension)}. \tag{9.27}$$

When you use this equation, keep in mind that the energy is dissipated on both sides of the surface where the friction occurs. So, even though the right sides of Eqs. 9.26 and 9.27 are the product of a constant force and a displacement, it would not be correct to refer to this product as "the work done by the friction force exerted on the block." Furthermore, Eq. 9.27 holds for travel in only one direction; if the block reverses the direction of travel, you have to apply Eq. 9.26 to each one-way segment separately. If the sum of the distances traveled over all the one-way segments is d_{path}, the change in thermal energy becomes

$$\Delta E_{th} = F^f_{sb}d_{path} \quad \text{(constant dissipative force, one dimension)}, \tag{9.28}$$

where F^f_{sb} is the magnitude of the force of friction and where we have dropped the minus sign of Eq. 9.27 because all quantities are positive.

Figure 9.24 Energy diagram for a system in which friction dissipates kinetic energy to thermal energy.

9.16 A 0.50-kg wood block slides 0.50 m on a horizontal floor before colliding elastically with a wall and reversing its direction of travel. If the block has an initial speed of 1.0 m/s and comes to rest exactly at its starting position, what is the magnitude of the frictional force between block and floor?

9.8 Power

Often we are interested not just in knowing how much energy is converted within a system or transferred to a system but also in knowing *how fast* the energy is converted or transferred. The rate at which energy is transferred or converted is called **power.** If the energy of a system changes by an amount ΔE over a time interval Δt, the average power is defined as

$$P_{av} = \frac{\Delta E}{\Delta t}. \tag{9.29}$$

The SI unit of power is the **watt** (W), which is equal to 1 J of energy per second: $1\ W \equiv 1\ J/s$.* A person in good physical condition can deliver about 75 W of average power over a prolonged time interval. This means a healthy person can do work—shovel snow, accelerate an object, and so on—at the rate of about 75 J/s. An athlete can deliver about 400 W over a sustained time interval and up to about 1000 W during short time intervals.

The instantaneous power is

$$P = \lim_{\Delta t \to 0} \frac{\Delta E}{\Delta t} = \frac{dE}{dt}. \tag{9.30}$$

Equation 9.30 gives the rate at which the energy of a system changes. The concept of power can be applied to the rate at which any type of energy changes. For example, the power at which thermal energy is generated is given by

$$P = \frac{dE_{th}}{dt}. \tag{9.31}$$

Example 9.9 Frictional power

A 0.50-kg wood block initially traveling at 1.0 m/s slides 0.50 m on a horizontal floor before coming to rest. What is the average rate at which thermal energy is generated?

❶ **GETTING STARTED** I begin by making a sketch of the situation, listing all the given quantities and drawing an energy diagram for the closed block-floor system (**Figure 9.25**). I note that as the block slides to a stop, all of its kinetic energy is converted to thermal energy.

❷ **DEVISE PLAN** To calculate the average power at which thermal energy is generated, I need to know the amount ΔE_{th} of thermal energy generated and the time interval Δt over which it is generated. The ratio of these two quantities gives the average power (Eq. 9.29). The amount of thermal energy is equal to the initial kinetic energy of the block. If I assume the block has constant acceleration as it comes to a stop, I can use equations from Chapter 3 to determine Δt from the block's initial speed and the distance over which it comes to a stop.

Figure 9.25

(Continued)

---

*Be careful about distinguishing between italic W, our symbol for work, and nonitalic W, the abbreviation for watt, the SI unit of power.

❸ **EXECUTE PLAN** Because the block ends at rest, I know from Eq. 3.4, $v_{x,f} = v_{x,i} + a_x \Delta t$, that

$$a_x = -\frac{v_{x,i}}{\Delta t}.$$

Substituting this result into Eq. 3.8, $x_f = x_i + v_{x,i}\Delta t + \frac{1}{2}a_x(\Delta t)^2$, gives

$$\Delta x = v_{x,i}\Delta t - \frac{1}{2}\frac{v_{x,i}}{\Delta t}(\Delta t)^2 = \frac{1}{2}v_{x,i}\Delta t$$

or $\qquad \Delta t = \frac{2\Delta x}{v_{x,i}} = \frac{2(0.50\ \text{m})}{1.0\ \text{m/s}} = 1.0\ \text{s}.$

The block's initial kinetic energy is $\frac{1}{2}mv_{x,i}^2 = \frac{1}{2}(0.50\ \text{kg})(1.0\ \text{m/s})^2 = 0.25\ \text{J}$, so the thermal energy generated is $\Delta E_{th} = 0.25\ \text{J}$. From Eq. 9.29, I then obtain for the average power at which this energy is generated: $P_{av} = (0.25\ \text{J})/(1.0\ \text{s}) = 0.25\ \text{W}$. ✔

❹ **EVALUATE RESULT** The value I obtain is rather small—as a gauge, consider that a 25-W light bulb consumes energy at 100 times this rate—but it's unlikely that the energy of a sliding block would be sufficient to generate any light.

Next consider a situation where a system's energy is changed by a constant external force $\vec{F}_{ext}$. One such instance might be when you push a cart. As long as the force you exert on the cart is constant, we can analyze the power being supplied by you to the cart in terms of the x components of the force $F_{ext\,x}$ and the force displacement Δx. We know from Eqs. 9.1 and 9.8 that

$$\Delta E = W = F_{ext\,x}\Delta x. \qquad (9.32)$$

Substituting this expression for ΔE into Eq. 9.29 yields

$$P_{av} = \frac{\Delta E}{\Delta t} = F_{ext\,x}\left(\frac{\Delta x}{\Delta t}\right) \qquad (9.33)$$

or, with the definition of average velocity,

$$P_{av} = F_{ext\,x}\, v_{x,av}, \qquad (9.34)$$

where $v_{x,av}$ is the x component of the average velocity of the point of application of the force (and because the cart is a rigid object it is also the x component of the average velocity of the cart). The power is positive when $\vec{F}_{ext}$ and $\vec{v}_{av}$ point in the same direction, and in this case the energy of the system increases. When $\vec{F}_{ext}$ and $\vec{v}_{av}$ point in opposite directions, the power is negative and the energy of the system decreases.

To obtain the instantaneous power, we take the limit as Δt in Eq. 9.33 goes to zero, yielding

$$P = F_{ext\,x}v_x \quad \text{(one dimension)}. \qquad (9.35)$$

Example 9.10 Car drag

A car requires 300 kJ of energy to overcome air resistance and maintain a constant speed of 20 m/s over a distance of 1.0 km. What is the force of air resistance exerted on the car?

❶ **GETTING STARTED** The air resistance causes dissipation of the car's kinetic energy. The problem statement tells me that 300 kJ is dissipated over a distance of 1.0 km when the car moves at 20 m/s.

❷ **DEVISE PLAN** From the speed and the distance traveled, I can calculate the time interval over which the 300 kJ is required.

I can then use Eq. 9.29 to calculate the rate at which the energy is converted. Knowing the velocity, I can then obtain the force of air resistance from Eq. 9.35.

❸ **EXECUTE PLAN** At 20 m/s it takes the car 50 s to cover 1.0 km. The rate at which energy is converted is thus $P = (300\ \text{kJ})/(50\ \text{s}) = 6.0\ \text{kW}$. From Eq. 9.35, I obtain

$$F_x = \frac{P}{v_x} = \frac{6.0\ \text{kW}}{20\ \text{m/s}} = 300\ \text{N}. ✔$$

❹ **EVALUATE RESULT** The answer I obtain—300 N—is the magnitude of the gravitational force exerted on a 30-kg (65-lb) object and therefore equal in magnitude to the force required to hold up such an object. I know, however, that if I stick my hand out a car window at highway speed, the force exerted by the air on my hand is not much larger than the force required to hold up a small object. The car, being much larger than my hand, intercepts a lot more air, but it is shaped more aerodynamically, and so it is reasonable that the force of air resistance is only 300 N.

✋ **9.17** (*a*) A gallon of gasoline contains about 1.4×10^8 J of chemical energy. A car consumes this amount of gasoline in approximately 30 min when cruising along a highway; a plane consumes the same amount in about 1 s when flying at cruising altitude. What is the average power of the energy release in each case? (*b*) A 10-kg load must be hoisted up the side of a building that is 50 m tall. How quickly can an athlete capable of delivering 500 W of power get the job done? (*c*) A 3-kW engine gets the job done six times faster than the athlete. How does the work done by the engine on the load compare with the work done by the athlete on the load?

Chapter Glossary

SI units of physical quantities are given in parentheses.

Energy diagram A diagram that accounts for changes in the energy of a system. When using such a diagram, avoid choosing a system in which friction occurs at the boundary and remember that potential energy involves an interacting pair of objects. See the Procedure box on page 207.

Energy law The law that accounts for the change in the energy of a system or object. Because energy is conserved, the energy of a system can change only due to a transfer of energy between the environment and the system:

$$\Delta E = W. \tag{9.1}$$

Force displacement $\Delta \vec{r}_F$ (m) The displacement of the point of application of a force.

Particle An object that does not have any internal structure or spatial extent. The internal energy of a particle is fixed: $\Delta E_{\text{int}} = 0$.

Potential energy of a spring U_{spring} (J) The change in the potential energy of a spring as its free end is displaced from its relaxed position x_0 to any position x is

$$\Delta U_{\text{spring}} = \tfrac{1}{2}k(x - x_0)^2. \tag{9.23}$$

Power P (W) A scalar equal to the rate at which energy is transferred or converted:

$$P = \frac{dE}{dt}. \tag{9.30}$$

In one dimension, the power delivered by a constant external force is

$$P = F_{\text{ext}\,x}v_x \quad \text{(one dimension)}, \tag{9.35}$$

where v_x is the velocity of the point of application of the force.

Watt (W) The derived SI unit of power, defined as $1 \text{ W} \equiv 1 \text{ J/s} = 1 \text{ kg} \cdot \text{m}^2/\text{s}^3$.

Work W (J) A scalar equal to the change in the energy of a system due to external forces. If the energy of a system increases, the work done by external forces on the system is positive; if the energy decreases, the work done by external forces on the system is negative.

Work equation The equation that gives the work done by external forces on a particle or system:

$$W = \left(\sum F_x\right)\Delta x_F \quad \begin{array}{l}\text{(constant forces exerted on}\\\text{particle, one dimension)}\end{array} \tag{9.9}$$

and

$$W = \sum_n (F_{\text{ext}\,nx}\Delta x_{Fn}) \quad \begin{array}{l}\text{(constant nondissipative}\\\text{forces, on many-particle}\\\text{system, one dimension).}\end{array} \tag{9.18}$$

When the force and the force displacement point in the same direction, the work done by external forces on the system is positive; when they point in opposite directions, the work done by external forces on the system is negative. The work done by a variable nondissipative force exerted on a system is given by

$$W = \int_{x_i}^{x_f} F_x(x)dx \quad \begin{array}{l}\text{(nondissipative force,}\\\text{one dimension).}\end{array} \tag{9.22}$$

10 Motion in a Plane

CONCEPTS

10.1 *Straight* is a relative term
10.2 Vectors in a plane
10.3 Decomposition of forces
10.4 Friction
10.5 Work and friction

QUANTITATIVE TOOLS

10.6 Vector algebra
10.7 Projectile motion in two dimensions
10.8 Collisions and momentum in two dimensions
10.9 Work as the product of two vectors
10.10 Coefficients of friction

So far, we have restricted our study of physics to events that take place along a straight line—that is, in one dimension. In this chapter we develop the tools that allow us to deal with motion in a plane—in other words, motion that takes place in two dimensions. As you will see, any problem in two dimensions can be reduced to two one-dimensional problems (which you already know how to solve). After discussing the techniques that allow us to deal with vector quantities in two dimensions, we study the decomposition of two-dimensional force vectors. This decomposition allows us to examine more closely the contact forces that arise at the surface between two objects, which leads us to the subject of friction. Finally, we extend the concept of work so that it applies to situations where the force and force displacement vectors are not along the same line.

10.1 *Straight* is a relative term

To begin our discussion of motion in a plane, look at the film clip in **Figure 10.1**, which shows the motion of a ball dropped from the top of a pole attached to a cart that is moving at constant velocity along a horizontal track. You already know the resulting motion of the ball: It accelerates downward because of the force of gravity exerted on it (see Section 8.8). Indeed, the ball falls alongside the pole. As we discussed in Chapter 6, this is the way the motion must be because the laws of physics are the same in all inertial reference frames, regardless of whether the reference frames are at rest or moving at constant velocity with respect to the surface of Earth.

To extend this example to a more common situation, consider what happens when you drop an object inside the cabin of an airplane cruising at constant velocity. That object falls to the cabin floor in a straight line, exactly as it would if the airplane were at rest on the ground. Likewise, in the reference frame of the moving cart of Figure 10.1, the ball drops to the moving cart with a velocity that points vertically downward. In the cart's reference frame, the motion of the ball is free-fall motion, and a camera that moves along with the cart registers the motion shown in **Figure 10.2a**.

The picture is different, however, when observed from a stationary point located somewhere outside the cart—that is, from the Earth reference frame. Because the cart is moving to the right, the trajectory of the ball cannot be a straight vertical line in this reference frame. Figure 10.2*b* shows all the frames of the film clip of Figure 10.1 superimposed on one another. As you can see, in addition to its straight-downward motion relative to the cart, the ball is displaced horizontally from one frame to the next. Note that in spite of the rightward motion of the cart, the distance between ball and pole does not change. This constant distance is precisely what gives the illusion that the ball falls straight down! Your eyes tend to move along with the cart, and so you register only the vertical motion of the ball relative to the cart. The

Figure 10.1 A ball dropped from a pole attached to a cart moving at constant velocity falls straight down *relative to the cart*.

Figure 10.2 Motion of the ball of Figure 10.1 as recorded by a camera that is (*a*) moving along with the cart and (*b*) stationary.

frames of the film clip, however, show that the horizontal displacement of the ball is identical to that of the cart: If the *x* component of the displacement of the cart is Δx from one frame to the next, then the *x* component of the displacement of the ball must also be Δx. So, we see that *straight* is a relative term, one that depends on the reference frame.

The analysis in Figure 10.2 tells us that the motion of the ball in the Earth reference frame can be broken down into two parts: free fall in the vertical direction (called the *vertical component* of the motion) and motion at constant velocity in the horizontal direction (the *horizontal component* of the motion). You already know how to treat each of these motions separately. All that is left to do, therefore, is to develop a way to describe both motions at the same time.

10.1 (*a*) In Figure 10.2, what is the ball's velocity the instant before it is released? (*b*) Is the ball's speed in the reference frame of the cart greater than, equal to, or smaller than its speed in the Earth reference frame?

10.2 Vectors in a plane

To describe the motion of the ball in Figure 10.1, we need to generalize our definition of vectors. First of all, we need not one but two reference axes—one for each component of the motion. **Figure 10.3** shows one possible choice for a set of perpendicular reference axes. To distinguish the two axes, we label the horizontal one *x* and the vertical one *y*. The origins of both axes coincide with the point at which the ball is released.

To specify the position of the ball in each frame, we need two coordinates: an *x coordinate* to specify position along the *x* axis and a *y coordinate* to specify position along the *y* axis. For example, in the coordinate system shown in Figure 10.3, the position of the ball in frame 6 of Figure 10.1 is specified by the coordinates $x = +0.22$ m, $y = -0.42$ m. These coordinates also determine the position vector of the ball (see Section 2.6), which points from the origin to the position of the ball, as shown in Figure 10.3.

Figure 10.3 Position vector for the ball in frame 6 of Figure 10.1, using reference axes in the Earth reference frame.

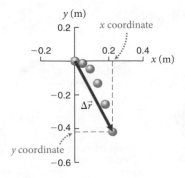

Figure 10.4 Displacement of the ball of Figure 10.1 in the reference frames of the cart and Earth.

(*a*) **Cart's reference frame**　　　(*b*) **Earth reference frame**

"thumbnail axes" indicate coordinate system

Unlike vectors in one dimension (describing motion along a straight line), vectors in two dimensions (describing motion in a plane) do not necessarily point along the axes. Consequently, we need to reexamine the rules for vector addition and subtraction. We'll do this by looking at the vector that represents the ball's displacement between frames 2 and 6 in Figure 10.1. **Figure 10.4a** shows the ball's displacement in the reference frame of the moving cart. This vector is labeled $\Delta \vec{y}$ to reflect the fact that it is parallel to the *y* axis. Figure 10.4*b* shows the corresponding view in the Earth reference frame. The *cart's* displacement is labeled $\Delta \vec{x}$ because it is parallel to the *x* axis. The *ball's* displacement, however, now points diagonally from the ball's initial position P to its final position R. Note that the ball can also go from P to R by two successive displacements: first from P to Q and then from Q to R. Even if the ball follows this path, though, its displacement is still given by the vector pointing from P to R. In other words, the ball's displacement in the Earth reference frame is the *vector sum* of the horizontal displacement $\Delta \vec{x}$ and the vertical displacement $\Delta \vec{y}$.

As with vectors along a straight line (one dimension), the vector sum of two vectors in a plane (two dimensions) is obtained by placing the tail of the second vector at the head of the first vector. There is, however, one important difference between one-dimensional and two-dimensional vector addition (**Figure 10.5**). In one dimension, the sum of two

Figure 10.5 Vector addition in one and two dimensions.

(*a*) Adding vectors in one dimension　　　(*b*) Adding vectors in two dimensions

Figure 10.6 The order in which vectors are added does not affect the final answer. These two imaginary flights starting at LaGuardia airport consist of the same vectors in different orders; both end up at the same destination of John F. Kennedy airport.

Figure 10.7 Vector addition and subtraction in two dimensions.

Vector addition: Vectors may be added in any order: $\vec{a} + \vec{b} = \vec{b} + \vec{a}$

Vector subtraction: Order matters! $\vec{a} - \vec{b} \neq \vec{b} - \vec{a}$

vectors of equal length is either zero (when the vectors point in opposite directions) or a vector twice as long as each original vector (when they point in the same direction). In two dimensions, the length of the vector sum depends on the angle between the vectors being added. As Figure 10.5*b* shows, the length of the sum of two vectors can be smaller than the length of either original vector. When two or more vectors in a plane are added, the order in which the vectors are added is immaterial, as **Figure 10.6** shows.

The procedure for subtracting vectors in a plane is identical to that for subtraction in one dimension (**Figure 10.7**):

> To subtract a vector $\vec{b}$ from a vector $\vec{a}$, reverse the direction of $\vec{b}$ and then add the reversed $\vec{b}$ to $\vec{a}$.

As in one dimension, the vector $\vec{a} - \vec{b}$ points from the tail of vector $\vec{a}$ to the tip of vector $-\vec{b}$. Note that vector addition is commutative but vector subtraction is not: $\vec{a} + \vec{b} = \vec{b} + \vec{a}$ but $\vec{a} - \vec{b} \neq \vec{b} - \vec{a}$.

We can use the principles of vector addition to develop an important procedure: the decomposition of a vector into components. Just as we can add any two vectors to form a new vector, we can decompose (break up) any vector into

two component vectors. For example, any vector $\vec{A}$ can be decomposed into **component vectors** $\vec{A}_x$ and $\vec{A}_y$ along the axes of some conveniently chosen set of mutually perpendicular axes, called a **rectangular coordinate system** (also called a *Cartesian coordinate system*).*

The procedure for decomposing a vector is shown in **Figure 10.8**. Note that if you add the resulting component vectors, you recover the original vector. When you decompose a vector, it is important to cross out the original vector so that you do not take both the original vector and the component vectors into account in any subsequent analysis.

---

*There is no formal requirement that the axes of the coordinate system be perpendicular to each other. Any set of two intersecting axes allows you to decompose and therefore uniquely specify all possible vectors in a plane. Calculations are considerably simpler, however, with axes that are perpendicular to each other.

Figure 10.8 Procedure for decomposing a vector using a set of mutually perpendicular axes.

To decompose a vector . . . **1** Add axes with origin at vector tail. **2** Drop lines from vector tip to axes; these determine lengths of component vectors. **3** Replace original vector with component vectors along axes. Original vector is sum of component vectors.

Figure 10.9 Decomposition of a vector $\vec{A}$ in three coordinate systems. In each coordinate system the component vectors $\vec{A}_x$ and $\vec{A}_y$ completely specify the position of point P relative to the origin. Which coordinate system is most convenient depends on the problem at hand.

Figure 10.9 shows the decomposition of a vector $\vec{A}$ in three coordinate systems. In each coordinate system the component vectors $\vec{A}_x$ and $\vec{A}_y$ completely specify the position of point P relative to the origin O. In Figure 10.9c the coordinate system is such that the vector $\vec{A}$ lines up with the x axis. Now the component vector along the x axis is $\vec{A}$ and the component vector along the y axis is the zero vector. Which choice of coordinate system works best depends on the problem at hand (more on this later).

Exercise 10.1 Decompositions

If each major grid unit in Figure 10.9 corresponds to 1 m, specify the location of point P in terms of its x and y coordinates in each of the three coordinate systems.

SOLUTION (*a*) The vertical line dropped from P intercepts the x axis 4 grid units to the right of the y axis, so $x = +4.0$ m. The horizontal line dropped from P gives $y = +3.0$ m. The location of point P is thus given by $(x, y) = (+4.0 \text{ m}, +3.0 \text{ m})$. ✔

(*b*) $(x, y) = (+4.7 \text{ m}, +1.8 \text{ m})$. ✔

(*c*) $(x, y) = (+5.0 \text{ m}, 0)$. ✔

All the vector quantities we have encountered so far obey the rules for addition and subtraction outlined above, and all can be decomposed into component vectors. There is one significant difference, however, between the way vectors are treated in one-dimensional motion and the way they are treated in two-dimensional motion. As we saw in Section 2.8, the displacement and velocity of an object that moves along a straight line point in the same direction. Section 3.1 taught you that if the object speeds up, the acceleration also points in the same direction as the displacement, and if the object slows down, the acceleration points in the direction opposite that of the displacement and velocity. For motion in a plane, the relationship between the directions of these vectors is more complicated.

The displacement, instantaneous velocity, and acceleration of the ball in Figure 10.1 are shown in **Figure 10.10.** Because the ball's average velocity is its displacement divided by the time interval during which this displacement takes place, the average velocity (not shown in Figure 10.10)

points in the same direction as the displacement. The ball's instantaneous velocity is the average velocity evaluated over infinitesimally small time intervals, and so if the object does not move in a straight line, the instantaneous velocity does not necessarily point in the same direction as the displacement. In Figure 10.10, for instance, $\Delta \vec{r}$ points from the initial to the final position over a certain time interval, while $\vec{v}$ is tangent to the trajectory—that is, in the instantaneous direction of travel.

Let us next consider the acceleration. By definition, the ball's acceleration points in the direction of the change in velocity. Because the horizontal component of the ball's velocity is equal to the velocity of the cart and so is constant, there is no acceleration in the horizontal direction. Only the vertical component of the ball's velocity changes, and so the ball's acceleration points downward rather than in the direction of $\vec{v}$. If you recall the relationship between acceleration and force ($\sum \vec{F} = m\vec{a}$), this makes sense: The ball's acceleration is caused by the downward force of gravity exerted by Earth on the ball. Therefore both the force and the acceleration point straight down.

What does it mean when the instantaneous velocity and acceleration of an object point in different directions? To answer this question, I must decompose the acceleration into two components: one parallel to the instantaneous

Figure 10.10 Displacement, instantaneous velocity, and acceleration for the freely falling ball of Figure 10.1.

Figure 10.11 Velocity and acceleration vectors of the falling ball in frame 2 of Figure 10.1. Decomposition of $\vec{A}$ into component vectors parallel and perpendicular to $\vec{v}$.

Figure 10.13 Change in velocity caused by a perpendicular acceleration.

velocity and one perpendicular to it (**Figure 10.11**). The parallel component causes the length of the instantaneous velocity—in other words, the ball's *speed*—to change. Just as for one-dimensional motion, the speed increases when the parallel component of the acceleration points in the same direction as the instantaneous velocity (as is the case with our ball-and-cart example) and decreases when they point in opposite directions. The perpendicular component of the acceleration causes the *direction* of the instantaneous velocity to change, which in our particular case of the ball and cart means that the ball does not move in a straight horizontal line the way the cart does. Instead, the ball's instantaneous velocity in any given frame of the film clip points more toward the ground than does its counterpart in the preceding frame. (In short, the ball curves downward.) In summary:

> In two-dimensional motion, the component of the acceleration parallel to the instantaneous velocity changes the speed; the component of the acceleration perpendicular to the instantaneous velocity changes the direction of the instantaneous velocity but not its magnitude.

These ideas are illustrated in **Figure 10.12**.

Figure 10.12 How the parallel and perpendicular components of acceleration affect velocity.

Acceleration parallel to velocity changes *speed:*

Acceleration perpendicular to velocity changes *direction of motion:*

If you wonder how it can be that the perpendicular component changes *only* the direction of the velocity and does not affect its magnitude, examine **Figure 10.13**. An object initially moving in the positive x direction is given an acceleration in the positive y direction. Because of this acceleration, over a small but finite time interval Δt the object's initial velocity $\vec{v}_i$ gains a small component $\Delta\vec{v}$ in the y direction. The final velocity $\vec{v}_f = \vec{v}_i + \Delta\vec{v}$ therefore no longer points along the x axis—as we concluded before, $\vec{a}_y$, being perpendicular to $\vec{v}_i$, changes the direction of $\vec{v}_i$. Why then doesn't it also change the magnitude? The Pythagorean theorem tells us that the magnitude of $\vec{v}_f$ must be greater than that of $\vec{v}_i$, a result that appears to contradict what I just said about a perpendicular acceleration not affecting the magnitude of a horizontal velocity. The resolution of this contradiction lies in realizing that, as the direction of $\vec{v}$ changes, so does the angle between $\vec{v}$ and $\vec{a}_y$: The acceleration, because it is no longer exactly perpendicular to the velocity, now has a small component parallel to the velocity, and it is this component of the acceleration that causes the change in the magnitude of $\vec{v}$. We must therefore restrict our analysis to an infinitesimally small time interval. With this restriction, we can ignore the change in the magnitude of the velocity caused by $\Delta\vec{v}$: $v_i \approx v_f$.

✋ **10.2** In Figure 10.10, the ball's instantaneous velocity $\vec{v}$ does not point in the same direction as the displacement $\Delta\vec{r}$ (it points *above* the final position of the ball). Why?

10.3 Decomposition of forces

Now that you know how to decompose vectors into components, let us see how this technique works with forces. Consider, for example, putting a brick on a horizontal plank and then slowly tilting the plank, as illustrated in **Figure 10.14**. Initially, the brick remains at rest, but when the angle of incline θ exceeds some maximum value θ_{max}, the brick suddenly slides downward. The angle of incline at which an object on an inclined surface begins to slide depends on the materials out of which the surface and the object are made and on their smoothness. It is also strongly affected by the presence of dirt or lubricants.

CONCEPTS

Figure 10.14 The forces exerted on a brick as you raise one end of the plank on which it rests.

(*a*) brick at rest

$\vec{a} = \vec{0}$

$\sum \vec{F}_b = \vec{0}$ Contact force balances gravitational force.

(*b*) brick still at rest

$\vec{a} = \vec{0}$

Angle of incline $< \theta_{max}$

$\sum \vec{F}_b = \vec{0}$ Forces unchanged.

(*c*) brick slides

$\vec{a}$

Angle of incline $> \theta_{max}$

Since brick slides, sum of forces must be nonzero.

$\sum \vec{F}_b$

Because gravitational force is unchanged . . .

. . . contact force must have changed.

When the plank of Figure 10.14 is horizontal, the forces exerted on the brick are a downward gravitational force exerted by Earth and an upward contact force of equal magnitude exerted by the plank, as illustrated in the free-body diagram in Figure 10.14*a*. As long as the brick stays at rest, raising one end of the plank doesn't change the free-body diagram: The force of gravity on the brick does not depend on the inclination of the plank, and because the brick is still at rest we know that the force exerted by the plank must still be upward and equal in magnitude to the force of gravity, as shown in Figure 10.14*b*. When the angle of incline exceeds θ_{max} the situation changes, however. At that point, the contact force provided by the plank is no longer able to balance the downward force of gravity, and the brick accelerates down the incline. Although it is not immediately clear how to draw the free-body diagram, we know that the vector sum of the forces exerted on the brick must point in the same direction as the brick's acceleration (Figure 10.14*c*).

Because the brick is constrained to move along the surface of the plank, its acceleration must always be parallel to the plank, as shown in Figure 10.14*c*. For this reason, it makes sense to analyze the forces in terms of components parallel and perpendicular to the plank, by pointing the *x* axis along the surface that constrains the motion, as shown in **Figure 10.15**. The force components perpendicular to the surface are called **normal components;** those parallel to the surface are called **tangential components.** Because the brick's acceleration must be parallel to the plank, the normal component vectors $\vec{F}^c_{pby}$ and $\vec{F}^G_{Eby}$ must always be equal in magnitude—whether the brick is at rest or sliding. (If these two forces were not of equal magnitude, the brick would accelerate in the direction perpendicular to the plank, and we know this doesn't happen.)

Figure 10.15 Free-body diagrams for a brick on a plank at different angles of inclination.

Angle of incline steepens →

$\vec{a} = \vec{0}$

$\theta < \theta_{max}$

$\vec{a} = \vec{0}$

$\theta < \theta_{max}$

$\vec{a}$

$\theta > \theta_{max}$

Brick stationary:

Components of contact and gravitational forces along incline balance each other . . .

. . . and increase in magnitude as incline gets steeper.

Brick sliding:

Component of contact force along incline no longer balances component of gravitational force . . .

. . . and is *weaker* than just before sliding.

The tangential component vectors $\vec{F}^c_{\text{pb}x}$ and $\vec{F}^G_{\text{Eb}x}$, on the other hand, are equal in magnitude only when the brick is not accelerating down the incline. Note in Figure 10.15 that as the angle of incline is increased, the magnitude of the tangential component vector $\vec{F}^G_{\text{Eb}x}$ of the force of gravity increases. To prevent the brick from sliding down, the magnitude of the tangential component vector $\vec{F}^c_{\text{pb}x}$ of the contact force exerted by the plank on the brick must therefore also increase. When the angle of incline exceeds θ_{max}, the plank is no longer able to provide the sideways support necessary to hold the brick in place. The tangential component vectors of the forces no longer add up to zero, and the vector sum of the forces exerted on the brick is directed down the plank, as shown in Figure 10.14c.

✋ **10.3** A suitcase being loaded into an airplane moves at constant velocity on an inclined conveyor belt. Draw a free-body diagram for the suitcase as it moves up along with the belt. Show the normal and tangential components of the forces exerted on the suitcase.

Let us now return to a question raised in Section 10.2: What set of axes should you choose in a given problem? The example of the brick sliding down the inclined plank suggests an answer:

> **If possible, choose a coordinate system such that one of the axes lies along the direction of the acceleration of the object under consideration.**

This choice of coordinate system allows you to break the problem neatly into two parts because only force components along the direction of acceleration can contribute to the motion.

When the acceleration of the object being considered is zero, choose your axes to coincide with the directions of as many forces as possible because no decomposition is necessary for any force that lies along an axis.

Example 10.2 Pulling a friend on a swing

Using a rope, you pull a friend sitting on a swing (**Figure 10.16**). (a) As you increase the angle θ, does the magnitude of the force $\vec{F}^c_{\text{rp}}$ required to hold your friend in place increase or decrease? (b) Is the magnitude of that force larger than, equal to, or smaller than the magnitude of the gravitational force $\vec{F}^G_{\text{Ep}}$ exerted by Earth on your friend? (Consider the situation for both small and large values of θ.) (c) Is the magnitude of the force $\vec{F}^c_{\text{sp}}$ exerted by the swing on your friend larger than, equal to, or smaller than F^G_{Ep}?

Figure 10.16 Example 10.2.

suspension point

① **GETTING STARTED** I begin by drawing a free-body diagram of your friend (**Figure 10.17**). Three forces are exerted on him: $\vec{F}^G_{\text{Ep}}$, the force of gravity directed vertically downward, the horizontal force $\vec{F}^c_{\text{rp}}$ exerted by the rope, and a force $\vec{F}^c_{\text{sp}}$ exerted by the swing seat. This latter force $\vec{F}^c_{\text{sp}}$ is exerted by the suspension point via the chains of the swing and is thus directed along the chains. I therefore choose a horizontal x axis and a vertical y axis, so that two of the three forces lie along axes. Because your friend's acceleration is zero, the vector sum of the forces must be zero.

Figure 10.17

② **DEVISE PLAN** Because your friend is at rest, the vectors along the two axes must add up to zero. The best way to see how the magnitude of the force $\vec{F}^c_{\text{rp}}$ exerted by the rope must change as θ is increased is to draw free-body diagrams showing different values of θ. To answer parts b and c, I can compare the various forces in my free-body diagrams.

③ **EXECUTE PLAN** (a) I begin by decomposing $\vec{F}^c_{\text{sp}}$ into x and y components (**Figure 10.18a**). Because the forces must add to zero along both axes, I conclude from my diagram that $\vec{F}^c_{\text{sp}y}$ must be equal in magnitude to $\vec{F}^G_{\text{Ep}}$, the downward force of gravity. Likewise, $\vec{F}^c_{\text{sp}x}$ must be equal in magnitude to $\vec{F}^c_{\text{rp}}$, the horizontal force the rope exerts on your friend. Next, I draw a second free-body diagram for a larger angle θ (**Figure 10.18b**). As θ increases, $\vec{F}^c_{\text{sp}y}$ must remain equal in magnitude to $\vec{F}^G_{\text{Ep}}$ (otherwise your friend would accelerate vertically). As Figure 10.18b shows, increasing θ while keeping $\vec{F}^c_{\text{sp}y}$ constant requires the magnitude of $\vec{F}^c_{\text{sp}x}$ to increase. Because your friend is at rest, the forces in the horizontal direction must add up to zero and so $F^c_{\text{rp}} = |F^c_{\text{sp}x}|$. So if the magnitude of $\vec{F}^c_{\text{sp}x}$ increases, the magnitude of $\vec{F}^c_{\text{rp}}$ must increase, too. ✔

Figure 10.18

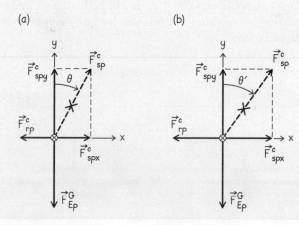

(a)   (b)

(b) From Figure 10.18 I see that $\tan\theta = |F^c_{spx}|/|F^c_{spy}|$. For $\theta < 45°$, $\tan\theta < 1$, and so $|F^c_{spx}| < |F^c_{spy}|$. Because $|F^c_{spy}| = F^G_{Ep}$ and $|F^c_{spx}| = F^c_{rp}$, I discover that for $\theta < 45°$, $F^c_{rp} < F^G_{Ep}$. When $\theta > 45°$, $\tan\theta > 1$, and so $|F^c_{spx}| > |F^c_{spy}|$ and $F^c_{rp} > F^G_{Ep}$. ✔

(c) $|\vec{F}^c_{spy}| = F^G_{Ep}$ and $F^c_{sp} = \sqrt{(F^c_{spx})^2 + (F^c_{spy})^2}$. Therefore, F^c_{sp} must always be larger than F^G_{Ep} when $\theta \neq 0$. ✔

❹ EVALUATE RESULT I know from experience that you have to pull harder to move a swing farther from its equilibrium position, and so my answer to part *a* makes sense. With regard to part *b*, when the swing is at rest at 45°, the forces $\vec{F}^c_{rp}$ and $\vec{F}^G_{Ep}$ on your friend make the same angle with the force $\vec{F}^c_{sp}$, and so $\vec{F}^c_{rp}$ and $\vec{F}^G_{Ep}$ should be equal in magnitude. The force of gravity is independent of the angle, but the force exerted by the rope increases with increasing angle, and so it makes sense that for angles larger than 45°, $\vec{F}^c_{rp}$ is larger than $\vec{F}^G_{Ep}$. In part *c*, because the vertical component of the force $\vec{F}^c_{sp}$ exerted by the seat on your friend always has to be equal to the force of gravity, adding a horizontal component makes $\vec{F}^c_{sp}$ larger than $\vec{F}^G_{Ep}$, as I found.

✋ **10.4** You decide to move a heavy file cabinet by sliding it across the floor. You push against the cabinet, but it doesn't budge. Draw a free-body diagram for it.

10.4 Friction

The force that opposes your push on the file cabinet in Checkpoint 10.4—the tangential component of the contact force exerted by the floor on the cabinet—has to do with friction. If the floor were very slick or if the cabinet had casters, there would be little friction and your push would easily move the cabinet. Instead, you have to lean against it with all your strength until, with a jerk, it suddenly begins to slide. Once you get the cabinet moving, you must keep pushing to keep it in motion. If you stop pushing, friction stops the motion.

✋ **10.5** (a) Suppose you push the file cabinet just enough to keep it moving at constant speed. Draw a free-body diagram for the cabinet while it slides at constant speed. (b) Suddenly you stop pushing. Draw a free-body diagram for the file cabinet at this instant.

Don't skip Checkpoint 10.5! It will be harder to understand the rest of this section if you haven't thought about these situations.

Even though the normal and tangential components of the contact force exerted by the floor on the cabinet belong to the same interaction, they behave differently and are usually treated as two separate forces: the normal component being called the **normal force** and the tangential component being called the **force of friction**.

To understand the difference between normal and frictional forces, consider a brick on a horizontal wooden plank supported at both ends (**Figure 10.19a**). Because the brick is at rest, the normal force $\vec{F}^c_{pb\perp}$ exerted by the plank on it is equal in magnitude to the gravitational force exerted on it. Now imagine using your hand to push down on the brick with a force $\vec{F}^c_{hb}$. Your downward push increases the total downward force exerted on the brick, and, like a spring under compression, the plank bends until the normal force it exerts on the brick balances the combined downward forces exerted by your hand and by Earth on the brick (Figure 10.19b). As you push down harder, the plank bends more, and the normal force continues to increase (Figure 10.19c) until you exceed the plank's capacity to provide support and it snaps, at which point the normal force suddenly disappears (Figure 10.19d). So, normal forces take on whatever value is required to prevent whatever is pushing down on a surface from moving through that surface— up to the breaking point of the supporting material.

Next imagine that instead of pushing down on the brick of Figure 10.19a, you gently push it to the right, as in **Figure 10.20**. As long as you don't push hard, the brick remains at rest. This tells you that the horizontal forces exerted on the brick add to zero, and so the plank must be exerting on the brick a horizontal frictional force that is equal in magnitude to your push but in the opposite direction. This horizontal force is caused by microscopic bonds between the surfaces in contact. Whenever two objects are placed in contact, such bonds form at the extremities of microscopic bumps on the surfaces of the objects. When you try to slide the surfaces past each other, these tiny bonds prevent sideways motion. As you push the brick to the right, the bumps resist bending and, like microscopic springs, each bump exerts a force to the left. The net effect of all these microscopic forces is to hold the brick in place. As you increase the force of your push, the bumps resist bending more and the tangential component of the contact force grows. This friction exerted by surfaces that are not moving relative to each other is called **static friction.**

Figure 10.19 A demonstration of the normal force.

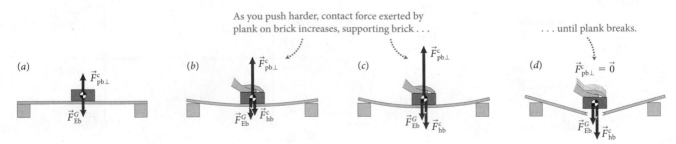

As you push harder, contact force exerted by plank on brick increases, supporting brick . . .

. . . until plank breaks.

Figure 10.20 The microscopic basis for forces of static and kinetic friction (b = brick, p = plank, h = hand).

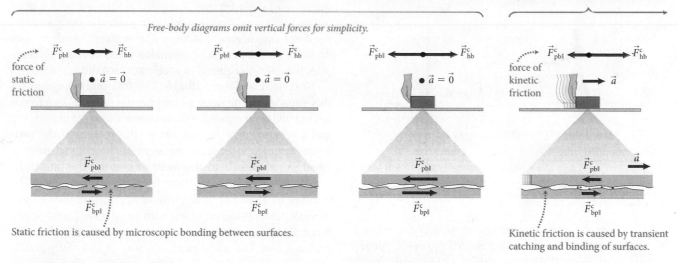

As you push harder, force of static friction exerted by plank on brick increases, keeping brick stationary . . .

. . . until push exceeds maximum force of static friction, and brick accelerates.

Free-body diagrams omit vertical forces for simplicity.

force of static friction

$\vec{F}^c_{pb\parallel}$ $\vec{F}^c_{hb}$ $\vec{a} = \vec{0}$

$\vec{F}^c_{pb\parallel}$

$\vec{F}^c_{bp\parallel}$

Static friction is caused by microscopic bonding between surfaces.

force of kinetic friction

$\vec{F}^c_{pb\parallel}$ $\vec{F}^c_{hb}$ $\vec{a}$

$\vec{F}^c_{pb\parallel}$ $\vec{a}$

$\vec{F}^c_{bp\parallel}$

Kinetic friction is caused by transient catching and binding of surfaces.

The tiny bonds cannot withstand large forces, however, and as you continue to increase your sideways push on the brick, the bonds get ripped apart, the tangential force they provide can no longer resist the push, and the brick starts to slide. The surface of the brick is no longer at rest relative to the surface on which the brick is resting—the two surfaces are said to *slip.*

Once the brick slips, bumps on the surfaces plow into each other, continually forming and breaking microscopic bonds, and microscopic pieces chip off from the surface. This constant bumping, making and breaking of bonds, and chipping cause what is called **kinetic friction.** Even though kinetic friction causes slipping surfaces to wear and to heat up, it is not always undesirable: Kinetic friction makes it possible to slow down the moving wheels of a car or bicycle, to use an eraser, and to warm up your hands by rubbing them, just to name a few examples.

So, just as the normal force takes on whatever value is necessary to prevent motion on a surface, the force of static friction takes on whatever value is necessary to prevent two surfaces from slipping past each other. The main differences between normal forces and forces of static friction are: (1) The maximum value of the force of static friction is generally much smaller than the maximum value of the normal force (it is relatively easy to push the brick across the plank but nearly impossible to push it through the plank), and (2) once the maximum value of the normal force is reached, the normal force disappears, but once the maximum value of the force of static friction is reached, there still is a smaller but nonzero force of kinetic friction.

To distinguish more easily among the various components of the contact force exerted by surface 1 on surface 2, we shall when necessary replace the superscript c by n for the normal force ($\vec{F}^c_{12\perp}$ becomes $\vec{F}^n_{12}$), by s for the force of static friction, and by k for the force of kinetic friction ($\vec{F}^c_{12\parallel}$ becomes $\vec{F}^s_{12}$ or $\vec{F}^k_{12}$).

✋ **10.6** Which type of friction—static or kinetic—plays a role in (a) holding a pencil, (b) chalk making marks on a chalkboard (c) skiing downhill, (d) polishing a metal surface, and (e) walking down an incline?

10.5 Work and friction

Like the normal force, the force of static friction is an elastic force: It causes no irreversible changes. The deformations that take place undo themselves when the force that caused them is removed. If you stop pushing on the file cabinet of Checkpoint 10.4 before it starts moving, for example, you will not scratch the floor. Kinetic friction, however, does cause damage, mainly because of the chipping mentioned earlier. Push the cabinet a short distance, no matter how carefully, and you will cause some damage, both to the bottom surface of the cabinet and to the floor surface. At best the damage is microscopic, but if you were to push the cabinet around the floor all day long, your landlady would probably not renew your lease. The heating and wear caused by kinetic friction turn coherent energy into incoherent energy. To sum up:

The force of kinetic friction is not an elastic force and so causes energy dissipation. The force of static friction is an elastic force and so causes no energy dissipation.

In Section 9.4 I cautioned against choosing a system for which friction occurs at the boundary because you don't know how much of the dissipated energy ends up on each side of the boundary. Now you see that this caveat does not apply to static friction because static friction causes no energy dissipation.

This brings us to the question of whether or not the force of static friction can do work on a system. After all,

Figure 10.21 Two equivalent situations in which an object is accelerated by static friction.

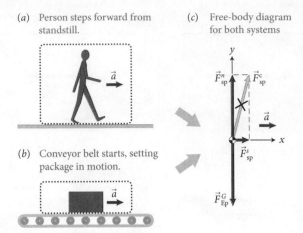

(a) Person steps forward from standstill.

(b) Conveyor belt starts, setting package in motion.

(c) Free-body diagram for both systems

static friction does not involve any motion of the two surfaces relative to each other, and work requires a nonzero force displacement. To answer this question, consider the two situations shown in **Figure 10.21**: A person starts to walk and a package is set in motion by a conveyor belt. In both cases the system (the person in Figure 10.21a and the package in Figure 10.21b) gains kinetic energy. Where does that energy come from, and what is the role of static friction in each case?

Let us first look at Figure 10.21a. To begin walking, the person leans slightly forward and raises one foot, with her other foot pressing on the floor downward and backward. The floor surface then supplies an upward contact force $\vec{F}_{sp}^{c}$ that is tilted forward, as shown in Figure 10.21c. The force $\vec{F}_{ps}^{c}$ of the person pressing down on the surface and the force $\vec{F}_{sp}^{c}$ of the surface pushing up form an interaction pair. Because she is not accelerating in the vertical direction, the forces in that direction must add to zero, and so the normal component of the contact force exerted on the person—the normal force $\vec{F}_{sp}^{c}$—is equal in magnitude to the force of gravity exerted on her. The tangential component $\vec{F}_{sp}^{s}$ is what propels her forward. As long as the foot doesn't slip, this tangential component is due to static friction; the forward acceleration is then equal to the force of static friction divided by the person's inertia.

To determine whether or not the force of static friction exerted by the floor surface on the person does work on the person, we need to look at the force displacement. Because the force of static friction is applied at the foot, which does not move in any direction while it is on the floor surface, the force displacement is zero. The surface therefore does no work on the person. That makes sense because *she* supplies the energy required to accelerate, not the surface.

Next, look at Figure 10.21b. The free-body diagram for this situation is the same as that for the person. Two forces are exerted on the package: a downward force of gravity $\vec{F}_{Ep}^{G}$ and a contact force $\vec{F}_{sp}^{c}$ exerted by the surface of the conveyor belt. The normal component of the contact force is equal in magnitude to the force of gravity; the tangential component (the force of static friction) is what causes the package to accelerate. The point of application of the force of static friction moves along with the package, and so the force of static friction does work on the package. This, too, makes sense: The package has no way of internally generating any kinetic energy; it is the conveyor that must do this. So, like any other elastic contact force, the force of static friction *can* do work on a system, and it is perfectly all right to choose a system in which *static* friction occurs at the boundary. It's only kinetic friction that causes problems because this type of friction dissipates energy, generating thermal energy that is distributed on both sides of the surface.

Figure 10.21 also dispels the often-heard myth that friction always *opposes* motion. In both cases shown in the figure, friction *causes* the motion. Without the forward pointing force of friction, neither the person nor the package would accelerate. Friction opposes the motion of two surfaces *relative to each other,* not motion per se. In Figure 10.21a, for instance, the person's rear foot would slip backward if there were no forward-pointing force of friction. The force of static friction prevents this slipping motion, and in doing so it pushes her forward.

✋ **10.7** Draw energy diagrams for the person and the package in Figure 10.21.

Self-quiz

1. In the diagrams in **Figure 10.22**, the velocity of an object is given along with the vector representing a force exerted on the object. For each case, determine whether the object's speed increases, decreases, or remains constant. Also determine whether the object's direction changes in the clockwise direction, changes in the counterclockwise direction, or doesn't change.

Figure 10.22

2. Draw the sum $\vec{A} + \vec{B}$ and the difference $\vec{A} - \vec{B}$ of each vector pair in **Figure 10.23**.

Figure 10.23

3. Each diagram in **Figure 10.24** indicates the momentum of an object before and after a force is exerted on it. For each case determine the direction of the force.

Figure 10.24

4. While driving to school, you place your coffee cup on the dashboard. Which type of force of friction allows the cup to stay put on the dashboard when the car speeds up? Does this force do any work on the cup?

Answers

1. (a) $\vec{F}$ has component vectors parallel and perpendicular to $\vec{v}$. Because $\vec{F}_\parallel$ is in the same direction as $\vec{v}$, the speed increases. $\vec{F}_\perp$ tilts $\vec{v}$ clockwise from its current position. (b) Because the direction of $\vec{F}_\parallel$ is opposite the direction of $\vec{v}$, the speed decreases. $\vec{F}_\perp$ tilts $\vec{v}$ counterclockwise from its current position. (c) Because $\vec{F}_\parallel = 0$, the speed remains the same; $\vec{F}_\perp$ tilts $\vec{v}$ clockwise. (d) $\vec{F}_\parallel$ decreases the speed. $\vec{F}_\perp = 0$ and so the direction of $\vec{v}$ does not change.

2. The vector sum is equal to the diagonal of a parallelogram drawn using the two vectors placed tail to tail. The vector difference points from the tip of the second vector to the tip of the first vector (**Figure 10.25**).

Figure 10.25

3. In each case the force is parallel to $\Delta\vec{p} = \vec{p}_f - \vec{p}_i$ (**Figure 10.26**).

Figure 10.26

4. Because no sliding occurs, the force of friction must be static. Because the force displacement and the force point in the same direction when the car speeds up, this force does positive work on the cup.

Figure 10.27 Rectangular and polar coordinates.

(a) Rectangular coordinates

(b) Polar coordinates

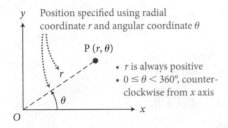

(c) Relationship between the two

10.6 Vector algebra

In a rectangular coordinate system, the position of a point P is specified by the rectangular coordinates x and y (**Figure 10.27a**). Alternatively, we can specify a point using **polar coordinates** (Figure 10.27b). The *radial* coordinate r gives the distance from the origin to the point and is always positive. The *angular* coordinate θ specifies the angle between r and the x axis and is measured counterclockwise from the positive x axis ($0 \leq \theta < 360°$). Any arbitrary point P is specified entirely by either (x, y) or (r, θ).

As can be seen from Figure 10.27c, the radial coordinate r is the hypotenuse of a right triangle with sides x and y, so

$$r = +\sqrt{x^2 + y^2}. \tag{10.1}$$

The plus sign in front of the square root indicates that r is never negative. Trigonometry tells us that $\tan \theta = y/x$, so

$$\theta = \tan^{-1}\left(\frac{y}{x}\right), \tag{10.2}$$

where the signs of x and y determine in which quadrant θ lies. Equations 10.1 and 10.2 allow us to determine polar coordinates from rectangular ones. Using trigonometry, we can also express rectangular coordinates in terms of polar coordinates:

$$x = r \cos \theta$$
$$y = r \sin \theta. \tag{10.3}$$

Exercise 10.3 Polar point

If each major grid unit in Figure 10.27 corresponds to 1 m, specify the location of point P in polar coordinates.

SOLUTION I begin by reading off the rectangular coordinates: $x = +3.6$ m, $y = +2.4$ m. Then I can use Eqs. 10.1 and 10.2 to convert to polar coordinates:

$$r = +\sqrt{x^2 + y^2} = \sqrt{(3.6 \text{ m})^2 + (2.4 \text{ m})^2} = 4.3 \text{ m}$$

and

$$\theta = \tan^{-1}\left(\frac{y}{x}\right) = \tan^{-1}\left(\frac{2.4 \text{ m}}{3.6 \text{ m}}\right) = 34°.$$

So, in polar coordinates point P is at $(r, \theta) = (4.3 \text{ m}, 34°)$. ✔

In rectangular coordinates, the position vector of a point P is

$$\vec{r} \equiv x\,\hat{\imath} + y\,\hat{\jmath}, \tag{10.4}$$

where $\hat{\imath}$ and $\hat{\jmath}$ represent unit vectors along the x and y axes, respectively. The component vectors of $\vec{r}$ are $x\,\hat{\imath}$ and $y\,\hat{\jmath}$. More generally, the decomposition of an arbitrary vector $\vec{A}$ can be written as follows (**Figure 10.28**):

$$\vec{A} = \vec{A}_x + \vec{A}_y = A_x\hat{\imath} + A_y\hat{\jmath}, \tag{10.5}$$

where $\vec{A}_x$ and $\vec{A}_y$ are *component vectors* of $\vec{A}$; A_x and A_y are the *x and y components* of $\vec{A}$. Keep in mind that the x and y components, A_x and A_y, are signed numbers—these symbols do *not* represent the magnitudes of the component

Figure 10.28 Decomposition of a general vector $\vec{A}$ into component vectors.

unit vectors along x and y axes

vectors $\vec{A}_x$ and $\vec{A}_y$. Whenever you see a subscript x or y (and later also z) on a symbol that does not have an arrow over it, the quantity represented by that symbol is a component of a vector and carries an algebraic sign.

Using the Pythagorean theorem, we can write the magnitude of $\vec{A}$ as

$$A \equiv |\vec{A}| = +\sqrt{A_x^2 + A_y^2}, \tag{10.6}$$

where the plus sign in front of the square root indicates that only the positive square root applies because magnitude is always a positive quantity. The angle of $\vec{A}$ with respect to the x axis is specified by

$$\tan \theta = \frac{A_y}{A_x}, \tag{10.7}$$

where the signs of A_x and A_y determine in which quadrant θ lies.

The decomposition of vectors is particularly useful when adding or subtracting them. As **Figure 10.29** shows, the x and y components of the vector sum $\vec{R}$ of two vectors $\vec{A}$ and $\vec{B}$ are equal to the sum of the corresponding components of $\vec{A}$ and $\vec{B}$:

$$\vec{R} = (A_x + B_x)\hat{\imath} + (A_y + B_y)\hat{\jmath} \tag{10.8}$$

$$R_x = A_x + B_x$$
$$R_y = A_y + B_y. \tag{10.9}$$

Figure 10.29 Adding vectors by components.

Sum of components of $\vec{A}$ and $\vec{B}$ equals component of $\vec{R}$.

$R_y = A_y + B_y$

$R_x = A_x + B_x$

Example 10.4 Speeding ball

A ball is thrown at an angle of 30° to the horizontal at a speed of 30 m/s. Write the ball's velocity in terms of rectangular unit vectors.

❶ **GETTING STARTED** I begin by making a sketch showing the velocity vector $\vec{v}$ and its decomposition in a rectangular coordinate system (**Figure 10.30**). I position the x axis along the horizontal in the direction of motion and the y axis along the vertical. I label the x and y components of the ball's velocity v_x and v_y, respectively.

❷ **DEVISE PLAN** Equation 10.5 tells me that the velocity vector can be written as $\vec{v} = v_x\hat{\imath} + v_y\hat{\jmath}$. To determine the x and y components, I apply trigonometry to the triangle made up by v, v_x, and v_y.

❸ **EXECUTE PLAN** From my sketch I see that $\cos \theta = v_x/v$ and $\sin \theta = v_y/v$, where $v = 30$ m/s and $\theta = 30°$. Therefore $v_x = v \cos \theta$ and $v_y = v \sin \theta$. Substituting the values given for v and θ, I calculate the rectangular components:

$$v_x = (30 \text{ m/s})(\cos 30°) = (30 \text{ m/s})(0.87) = +26 \text{ m/s}$$

$$v_y = (30 \text{ m/s})(\sin 30°) = (30 \text{ m/s})(0.50) = +15 \text{ m/s}.$$

The velocity in terms of unit vectors is thus

$$\vec{v} = v_x\hat{\imath} + v_y\hat{\jmath} = (+26 \text{ m/s})\hat{\imath} + (+15 \text{ m/s})\hat{\jmath}. \checkmark$$

❹ **EVALUATE RESULT** The x and y components are both positive, as I expect because I chose the direction of the axis in the direction that the ball is moving, and the magnitude of v_x is larger than that of v_y, as it should be for a launch angle that is smaller than 45°. I can quickly check my math by using Eq. 10.6 to calculate the magnitude of the velocity: $v = \sqrt{v_x^2 + v_y^2} = \sqrt{(26 \text{ m/s})^2 + (15 \text{ m/s})^2} = 30$ m/s, which is the speed at which the ball is launched.

Figure 10.30 Example 10.4

$v = 30$ m/s

30°

QUANTITATIVE TOOLS

Figure 10.31 Ball launched vertically up from
a cart moving at constant velocity in the horizontal direction.

Video frames / **Cartoons showing ball's position and motion**

Vertical component of velocity changes . . .

. . . but horizontal component is constant and is same as that of cart . . .

. . . so ball stays above cart.

10.8 You navigate a ship from a pier to a buoy 1500 m northeast of the pier. There you sail to a point 300 m south and 700 m east of the buoy. What is your distance from the pier at that point?

10.7 Projectile motion in two dimensions

We can now generalize the description of motion in a plane, starting with the position vector of an object:

$$\vec{r} = x\hat{i} + y\hat{j}. \tag{10.10}$$

As in one dimension, the object's instantaneous velocity is

$$\vec{v} \equiv \frac{d\vec{r}}{dt} \equiv \lim_{\Delta t \to 0} \frac{\Delta \vec{r}}{\Delta t}. \tag{10.11}$$

Substituting Eq. 10.10 into Eq. 10.11, we obtain

$$\vec{v} = \lim_{\Delta t \to 0} \frac{\Delta x}{\Delta t}\hat{i} + \lim_{\Delta t \to 0} \frac{\Delta y}{\Delta t}\hat{j} = v_x\hat{i} + v_y\hat{j}, \tag{10.12}$$

$$v_x = \frac{dx}{dt} \quad \text{and} \quad v_y = \frac{dy}{dt}. \tag{10.13}$$

Likewise, the components of the instantaneous acceleration are

$$a_x = \frac{dv_x}{dt} = \frac{d^2x}{dt^2} \quad \text{and} \quad a_y = \frac{dv_y}{dt} = \frac{d^2y}{dt^2}. \tag{10.14}$$

Knowing how to decompose vectors into components allows us to separate motion in a plane into two one-dimensional problems. Consider the motion of a ball launched straight up from a cart moving at constant velocity (**Figure 10.31**). Like the ball dropped from the moving cart in Figure 10.1, the launched ball remains vertically above the cart throughout its trajectory and so falls back into the cart. In the reference frame of the cart, the ball's motion is identical to the one-dimensional projectile motion we studied in Section 3.3. In the Earth reference frame, though, the ball's instantaneous velocity has a component in the horizontal direction in addition to the component in the vertical direction. The resulting two-dimensional projectile motion in the Earth reference frame is the curved trajectory shown in **Figure 10.32**.

How do we obtain the ball's position at some arbitrary instant $t_f = t_i + \Delta t$? Let us begin by writing the initial condition for the ball's motion in the Earth reference frame at instant t_i. Because the ball's acceleration is always vertically downward, we choose a coordinate system that has a horizontal x axis and a vertical y axis. In the Earth reference frame, the ball's initial velocity is thus

$$\vec{v}_i = v_{x,i}\hat{i} + v_{y,i}\hat{j}. \tag{10.15}$$

As viewed from the Earth reference frame, the ball's initial horizontal velocity is equal to the cart's constant velocity. The presence of the horizontal velocity in Eq. 10.15 tells us that, as viewed from the Earth reference frame,

QUANTITATIVE TOOLS

the ball is launched not straight up but at an angle θ relative to the x axis given by

$$\tan \theta = \frac{v_{y,i}}{v_{x,i}}. \tag{10.16}$$

The ball's velocity in the horizontal direction is constant; in the vertical direction, the ball has a constant downward acceleration of magnitude $a_y = -g$. The x component of the ball's instantaneous velocity is not changing. We can obtain the y component at instant t_f from Eq. 3.4:

$$v_{x,f} = v_{x,i} \quad \text{(constant velocity)} \tag{10.17}$$

$$v_{y,f} = v_{y,i} - g\Delta t \quad \text{(constant acceleration)}. \tag{10.18}$$

We can now use the results we derived for one-dimensional projectile motion to determine the position of the ball at any instant. The ball's horizontal position at instant t_f is given by Eq. 2.19, $x_f = x_i + v_{x,i}\Delta t$. For the vertical position we use Eq. 3.8, $x_f = x_i + v_{x,i}\Delta t + \frac{1}{2}a_x(\Delta t)^2$, replacing x by y and then setting $a_y = -g$:

$$x_f = x_i + v_{x,i}\Delta t \quad \text{(constant velocity)} \tag{10.19}$$

$$y_f = y_i + v_{y,i}\Delta t - \frac{1}{2}g(\Delta t)^2 \quad \text{(constant acceleration)}. \tag{10.20}$$

These two equations completely determine the trajectory of a projectile launched with initial velocity $\vec{v}_i$ from point (x_i, y_i).

Equations 10.19 and 10.20 give us x_f and y_f as functions of Δt because $x \propto \Delta t$ and $y \propto (\Delta t)^2$. By eliminating Δt from these equations, we obtain a function $y(x)$ that depends quadratically on x and describes a parabola. Hence the trajectory of a projectile whose initial velocity is not vertical is a parabola.

Figure 10.32 Trajectory of the ball in Figure 10.31 as seen from the Earth reference frame.

Earth reference frame

Example 10.5 Position of highest point

The ball of Figure 10.32 is launched from the origin of an xy coordinate system. Write expressions giving, at the top of its trajectory, the ball's rectangular coordinates in terms of its initial speed v_i and the acceleration due to gravity g.

❶ **GETTING STARTED** Because the ball is launched from the origin, $x_i = 0$ and $y_i = 0$. As the ball moves upward, the vertical component of its velocity, v_y, is positive. After crossing its highest position, the ball moves downward, and so now v_y is negative. As the ball passes through its highest position, therefore, v_y reverses sign, so at that position $v_y = 0$.

❷ **DEVISE PLAN** Taking the highest position as my final position and then substituting $v_{y,f} = 0$ into Eq. 10.18, I can determine the time interval Δt_{top} it takes the ball to travel to this position. Once I know Δt_{top}, I can use Eqs. 10.19 and 10.20 to obtain the ball's coordinates at the top.

❸ **EXECUTE PLAN** Substituting $v_{y,f} = 0$ into Eq. 10.18, I get

$$0 = v_{y,i} - g\Delta t_{top}.$$

Solving for Δt_{top} then yields

$$\Delta t_{top} = \frac{v_{y,i}}{g}. \tag{1}$$

Using $x_i = 0, y_i = 0$ in Eqs. 10.19 and 10.20, I then calculate the location of the highest position:

$$x_{top} = 0 + v_{x,i}\left(\frac{v_{y,i}}{g}\right) = \frac{v_{x,i}v_{y,i}}{g}$$

and

$$y_{top} = 0 + v_{y,i}\left(\frac{v_{y,i}}{g}\right) - \frac{1}{2}g\left(\frac{v_{y,i}}{g}\right)^2$$

$$= \frac{v_{y,i}^2}{g} - \frac{1}{2}\frac{v_{y,i}^2}{g} = \frac{1}{2}\frac{v_{y,i}^2}{g}. \checkmark$$

❹ **EVALUATE RESULT** Because the ball moves at constant velocity in the horizontal direction, the x coordinate of the highest position is the horizontal velocity component $v_{x,i}$ multiplied by the time interval it takes to reach the top (given by Eq. 1). The y coordinate of the highest position does not depend on $v_{x,i}$ as I expect because the vertical and horizontal motions are independent of each other.

QUANTITATIVE TOOLS

Example 10.6 Range of a projectile

How far from the launch position is the position at which the ball of Figure 10.32 is once again back in the cart? (This distance is called the *horizontal range* of the projectile.)

① GETTING STARTED As we saw in Example 3.6, the time interval taken by a projectile to return to its launch position from the top of the trajectory is equal to the time interval Δt_{top} it takes to travel from the launch position to the top. I can therefore use the Δt_{top} expression I found in Example 10.5 to solve this problem.

② DEVISE PLAN If the time interval it takes the ball to travel from its launch position to the top is Δt_{top}, then the time interval the ball is in the air is $2\Delta t_{\text{top}}$. Because the ball travels at constant velocity in the horizontal direction, I can use Eq. 10.19 to obtain the ball's range.

③ EXECUTE PLAN From Example 10.5, I have $\Delta t_{\text{top}} = v_{y,i}/g$, and so the time interval spent in the air is $\Delta t_{\text{flight}} = 2v_{y,i}/g$. Substituting this value into Eq. 10.19 yields

$$x_f = 0 + v_{x,i}\left(\frac{2v_{y,i}}{g}\right) = \frac{2v_{x,i}v_{y,i}}{g}. ✔$$

④ EVALUATE RESULT Because the trajectory is an inverted parabola, the top of the parabola lies midway between the two locations where the parabola intercepts the horizontal axis. So the location at which the parabola returns to the horizontal axis lies a horizontal distance twice as far from the origin as the horizontal distance at the top. In Example 10.5 I found that $x_{\text{top}} = v_{x,i}v_{y,i}/g$. The answer I get for the horizontal range is indeed twice this value.

10.9 Suppose a projectile's initial velocity is specified by the initial speed v_i and launch angle θ instead of by its rectangular components as in Eq. 10.15. (*a*) Using Eqs. 10.3, write expressions for the projectile's maximum height and horizontal range in terms of v_i and θ. (*b*) What angle θ gives the greatest value of y_{max}? (*c*) Of x_{max}?

10.8 Collisions and momentum in two dimensions

As we saw in Chapter 5, collisions in one dimension are entirely described by two equations: Eq. 4.17, $\Delta\vec{p} = \vec{0}$, which states that the momentum of the isolated system of colliding objects does not change, and Eq. 5.18, $e \equiv v_{12f}/v_{12i}$, which defines the coefficient of restitution. The same two equations also apply to collisions in two dimensions, but because momentum is a vector, Eq. 4.17 now yields two separate equations: one for the momentum in the x direction and the other for the momentum in the y direction. Consider, for example, a collision in an isolated system of two objects of inertia m_1 and m_2. For this system, Eq. 4.17 yields

$$\Delta p_x = \Delta p_{1x} + \Delta p_{2x} = m_1(v_{1x,f} - v_{1x,i}) + m_2(v_{2x,f} - v_{2x,i}) = 0 \quad (10.21)$$

$$\Delta p_y = \Delta p_{1y} + \Delta p_{2y} = m_1(v_{1y,f} - v_{1y,i}) + m_2(v_{2y,f} - v_{2y,i}) = 0. \quad (10.22)$$

If we know the initial velocities of the colliding objects, we have values for $v_{1x,i}$, $v_{1y,i}$, $v_{2x,i}$, and $v_{2y,i}$, but these two equations still contain four unknown quantities: $v_{1x,f}$, $v_{1y,f}$, $v_{2x,f}$, and $v_{2y,f}$. To obtain values for these four unknown quantities, we need four equations. Even if we know the coefficient of restitution of the colliding objects, we have only three equations (Eqs. 10.21, 10.22, and 5.18) and so, unlike collisions in one dimension, we cannot determine the outcome of the collision without some additional information about the final velocities.

Example 10.7 Pucks colliding

Pucks 1 and 2 slide on ice and collide. The inertia of puck 2 is twice that of puck 1. Puck 1 initially moves at 1.8 m/s; puck 2 initially moves at 0.20 m/s in a direction that makes an angle of 45° with the direction of puck 1. After the collision, puck 1 moves at 0.80 m/s in a direction that makes an angle of 60° with its original direction. What are the speed and direction of puck 2 after the collision?

① GETTING STARTED Because it takes place on a surface, the collision is two-dimensional. I begin by organizing the given information in a sketch (**Figure 10.33**). I let puck 1 move along the x axis before the collision. Then I add puck 2, which initially moves at an angle of 45° to the x axis. I draw puck 1 after the collision moving upward and to the right along a line that makes an angle of 60° with the x axis. I don't know anything about the motion of puck 2 after the collision, and so I arbitrarily draw it moving to the right and upward. I label the pucks and indicate the speeds I know. I need to determine the final speed v_{2f} of puck 2 and the angle θ between its direction of motion after the collision and the x axis.

Figure 10.33

❷ DEVISE PLAN Equations 10.21 and 10.22 give the relationship between the initial and final velocities of the two pucks. I know the x and y components of both initial velocities and, after decomposing $\vec{v}_{1f}$, the x and y components of the final velocity of puck 1. Thus I can use Eqs. 10.21 and 10.22 to obtain values for the two components of $\vec{v}_{2f}$. Using these component values, I can calculate v_{2f} and θ.

❸ EXECUTE PLAN The two unknown components are $v_{2x,f}$ and $v_{2y,f}$. Solving Eq. 10.21, for $v_{2x,f}$, I get

$$v_{2x,f} = -\frac{m_1}{m_2}(v_{1x,f} - v_{1x,i}) + v_{2x,i}$$

$$= -\tfrac{1}{2}[(0.80 \text{ m/s}) \cos 60° - (1.8 \text{ m/s})]$$

$$+ (0.20 \text{ m/s}) \cos 45°$$

$$= 0.84 \text{ m/s}.$$

Solving Eq. 10.22 for $v_{2y,f}$, I get

$$v_{2y,f} = -\frac{m_1}{m_2}(v_{1y,f} - v_{1y,i}) + v_{2y,i} = -\frac{m_1}{m_2}v_{1y,f} + v_{2y,i}$$

$$= -\tfrac{1}{2}(0.80 \text{ m/s}) \sin 60° + (0.20 \text{ m/s}) \sin 45°$$

$$= -0.21 \text{ m/s}.$$

Using these values, I obtain the final speed of puck 2 and its direction of motion:

$$v_{2f} = \sqrt{v_{2x,f}^2 + v_{2y,f}^2} = \sqrt{(0.84 \text{ m/s})^2 + (-0.21 \text{ m/s})^2}$$

$$= 0.87 \text{ m/s} ✔$$

$$\tan \theta = \frac{v_{2y,f}}{v_{2x,f}} = \frac{-0.21 \text{ m/s}}{0.84 \text{ m/s}} = -0.24$$

or $\quad \theta = -14°. ✔$

❹ EVALUATE RESULT My positive result for $v_{2x,f}$ and negative result for $v_{2y,f}$ tell me that after the collision, puck 2 moves in the positive x direction and the negative y direction. Both of these directions make sense: I can see from my sketch that the x component of the velocity of puck 1 decreases in the collision. The corresponding decrease in the x component of its momentum must be made up by an increase in the x component of the momentum of puck 2. Given that puck 2 initially moves in the positive x direction, it must continue to do so after the collision. In the y direction, I note that because $v_{1y,i}$ is zero, the y component of the momentum of puck 1 increases in the positive y direction by an amount $m_1 v_{1y,f} = m_1[(0.80 \text{ m/s}) \sin 60°] = m_1(0.69 \text{ m/s})$. Therefore the y component of the momentum of puck 2 must undergo a change of equal amount in the negative y direction. Because the initial y component of the momentum of puck 2 is smaller than this value, $m_2 v_{2y,i} = 2m_1 v_{2y,i} = 2m_1[(0.20 \text{ m/s}) \sin 45°] = m_1(0.28 \text{ m/s})$, puck 2 must reverse its direction of motion in the y direction, yielding a negative value for $v_{2y,f}$, in agreement with what I found.

 10.10 Is the collision in Example 10.7 elastic?

10.9 Work as the product of two vectors

In Section 9.5, I showed that the work done by a constant force on a rigid object is equal to the product of the force and the force displacement:

$$W = F_x \Delta x_F \quad \text{(constant nondissipative force, one dimension).} \tag{10.23}$$

Work is a scalar, but force and displacement are vectors. What form does the right side of Eq. 10.23 take if the displacement and the force do not point along the same line? Consider the block sliding down an incline shown in

Figure 10.34 Forces exerted on a block sliding down an incline with negligible friction.

(a)   Block slides with negligible friction.

Orient *x* coordinate in direction of motion.

(b)

Force component along incline causes acceleration.

(c)

Use trigonometry to find magnitude of force component along incline:

$$F^G_{\text{Eb}x} = F^G_{\text{Eb}} \sin \theta = +mg \sin \theta$$

Figure 10.34a. The friction between the block and the surface of the incline is negligible. The (nondissipative) force of gravity exerted on the block does not line up with the block's displacement along the incline. In order to calculate the work done on the block, we evaluate the block's change in kinetic energy ΔK while it slides down the incline. Because there are no changes in the internal energy of the block, the work done on it is equal to ΔK.

To calculate ΔK, we must first determine the block's acceleration. Let us choose a coordinate system that has the x axis parallel to the incline and the y axis perpendicular to it, as shown in Figure 10.34a. The block is subject to two forces: a normal force of magnitude F^n_{sb} exerted by the incline surface and a downward force of gravity of magnitude F^G_{Eb}, which is shown decomposed into components $F^G_{\text{Eb}x}$ and $F^G_{\text{Eb}y}$ in the free-body diagram in Figure 10.34b. (There is no tangential component of the contact force because there is no friction.) The x component of $\vec{F}^G_{\text{Eb}}$ is what causes the block to accelerate downward. Using trigonometry, we see from Figure 10.34c that

$$F^G_{\text{Eb}x} = F^G_{\text{Eb}} \sin \theta = +mg \sin \theta, \tag{10.24}$$

where we have substituted mg for the magnitude of the force of gravity exerted on the block (Eq. 8.17) and where the plus sign indicates that this component points in the positive x direction. This equation tells us that the magnitude of the downward acceleration of the block is

$$a_x = \frac{\sum F_x}{m} = \frac{F^G_{\text{Eb}x}}{m} = \frac{+mg \sin \theta}{m} = +g \sin \theta. \tag{10.25}$$

This is exactly what we found to be the acceleration of a cart rolling down an incline in Section 3.7 (Eq. 3.20). (We now see that the factor $\sin \theta$ in Eq. 3.20 comes from the decomposition of the force of gravity into components parallel and perpendicular to the incline.)

Suppose the block begins at rest on the incline and drops a vertical distance h, as illustrated in **Figure 10.35a.** If we let the origin coincide with the block's initial position, the block's initial condition is $x_i = 0$, $v_{x,i} = 0$, and its acceleration is given by Eq. 10.25. In order for the block to drop a vertical distance h, its displacement along the incline must be

$$\Delta x = +\frac{h}{\sin \theta}. \tag{10.26}$$

The time the block takes to cover this distance is obtained from Eq. 3.7:

$$\Delta x = v_{x,i}\Delta t + \tfrac{1}{2}a_x(\Delta t)^2 = 0 + \tfrac{1}{2}g \sin \theta (\Delta t)^2, \tag{10.27}$$

Figure 10.35 These blocks gain the same amount of kinetic energy because they descend (without friction) through the same vertical distance h.

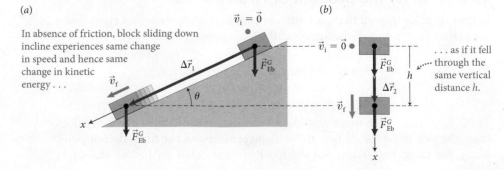

(a)

In absence of friction, block sliding down incline experiences same change in speed and hence same change in kinetic energy . . .

(b)

. . . as if it fell through the same vertical distance h.

and so, from Eqs. 10.26 and 10.27, we obtain

$$(\Delta t)^2 = \frac{2h}{g \sin^2 \theta}. \qquad (10.28)$$

The block's final kinetic energy is then

$$\tfrac{1}{2} m v_{x,f}^2 = \tfrac{1}{2} m (v_{x,i} + a_x \Delta t)^2 = \tfrac{1}{2} m (0 + g \sin \theta \, \Delta t)^2$$

$$= \tfrac{1}{2} m g^2 \sin^2 \theta (\Delta t)^2, \qquad (10.29)$$

where the substitution for $v_{x,f}$ comes from Eq. 3.4 and that for a_x from Eq. 10.25. Substituting Eq. 10.28 into Eq. 10.29, we obtain

$$\tfrac{1}{2} m v_{x,f}^2 = \tfrac{1}{2} m g^2 \sin^2 \theta \left(\frac{2h}{g \sin^2 \theta} \right) = mgh. \qquad (10.30)$$

So, because the block's initial kinetic energy is zero, the change in kinetic energy, which is equal to the work done on the block, is

$$W = \Delta K = K_f - K_i = \tfrac{1}{2} m v_{x,f}^2 - 0 = mgh. \qquad (10.31)$$

This is the same result we found in Section 7.9 for the change in kinetic energy of a freely falling object! So the work done on the freely falling block in Figure 10.35*b* when it drops a vertical distance h is the same as the work done on the sliding block in Figure 10.35*a* when it drops over the same vertical distance.

Note that we could have obtained the same result for the work done on the block along the incline by calculating the work done on it by *the component of the force of gravity along the incline*:

$$W = F^G_{Eb\,x} \Delta x = (+mg \sin \theta)\left(+\frac{h}{\sin \theta} \right) = mgh. \qquad (10.32)$$

This means that neither the normal force nor the y component of the force of gravity—both of which are perpendicular to the displacement of the block— does any work on the block. This makes sense because it is the x component of the force of gravity that causes the displacement of the block and that does all the work on it. The forces in the y direction cause no displacement and thus do no work on it.

These results can be stated more compactly by defining a **scalar product** of two vectors. If the angle between two vectors $\vec{A}$ and $\vec{B}$ is ϕ, the scalar product is

$$\vec{A} \cdot \vec{B} \equiv AB \cos \phi. \qquad (10.33)$$

The right side of Eq. 10.33 shows that the scalar product of vectors $\vec{A}$ and $\vec{B}$ is a scalar and is equal to the product of the magnitude of vector $\vec{A}$ ($|\vec{A}| \equiv A$) and the component of $\vec{B}$ along $\vec{A}$ ($B \cos \phi$). Note that the scalar product is commutative, so that the result is independent of the order of multiplication:

$$\vec{A} \cdot \vec{B} = \vec{B} \cdot \vec{A} = AB \cos \phi = BA \cos \phi, \qquad (10.34)$$

which is shown graphically in **Figure 10.36**. Also, as the name suggests, the scalar product of two vectors is a number (a scalar), not a vector.

Figure 10.36 The scalar product of two vectors.

Scalar product of $\vec{A}$ and $\vec{B}$:
$\vec{A} \cdot \vec{B} = \vec{B} \cdot \vec{A} = AB \cos \phi = BA \cos \phi$

$A \cos \phi$ (component of $\vec{A}$ along $\vec{B}$)

$B \cos \phi$ (component of $\vec{B}$ along $\vec{A}$)

Using the definition of scalar product, we can write **work as a scalar product:**

$$W = \vec{F} \cdot \Delta \vec{r}_F \quad \text{(constant nondissipative force)}. \tag{10.35}$$

In one dimension, when the force and the force displacement both point along the same line, Eq. 10.35 reduces to our old expression for work, $W = F_x \Delta x_F$ (Eq. 9.8). Note that if the force and the displacement are in opposite directions, $\phi = 180°$, and so $\cos \phi = -1$ and the work is negative.

Because $\cos 90° = 0$, the work done by a force perpendicular to $\Delta \vec{r}_F$ is zero. So for a block sliding down an incline, the normal force does no work and the work done by the force of gravity on the block is

$$W = \vec{F}_{Eb}^G \cdot \Delta \vec{r}_F = (mg)\left(\frac{h}{\sin \theta}\right) \cos \phi, \tag{10.36}$$

where θ is the angle of the incline and ϕ the angle between $\vec{F}_{Eb}^G$ and $\Delta \vec{r}_F$. Because $\phi = \frac{\pi}{2} - \theta$ and $\cos(\frac{\pi}{2} - \theta) = \sin \theta$, we see as before, that the work done by the force of gravity on the block is $W = mgh$.

Figure 10.37 shows how we can generalize this result to determine the work done by the gravitational force on an object moving across a surface of any shape. If we approximate the surface by, say, four inclined surfaces, we can apply Eq. 10.36 to each one. The total work done on a block sliding on the surface in Figure 10.37 as it descends from the top to the bottom is

$$W = mgh_1 + mgh_2 + mgh_3 + mgh_4 = mgh. \tag{10.37}$$

To obtain a better approximation we can divide the surface into more, smaller inclined surfaces, but each time we see that the total work done on the block is equal to mgh.

This result also makes sense from an energy perspective. Consider, for example a ball sliding down the surface of Figure 10.37, and let's assume that there is no friction between the ball and the surface. **Figure 10.38** shows two energy diagrams for this situation. For the closed Earth-ball system (Figure 10.38a)

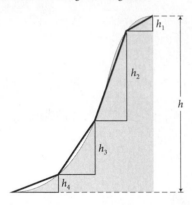

Figure 10.37 An arbitrary incline can be broken into small straight line segments.

Figure 10.38 Two views of the energy changes that occur when a ball slides down an arbitrary incline with negligible friction.

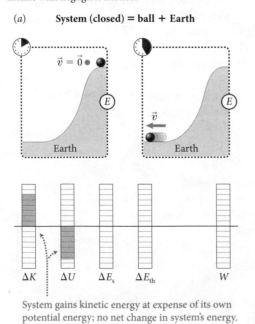

(a)   **System (closed) = ball + Earth**

$\Delta K \quad \Delta U \quad \Delta E_s \quad \Delta E_{th} \quad\quad\quad W$

System gains kinetic energy at expense of its own potential energy; no net change in system's energy.

(b)   **System (open) = ball**

$\Delta K \quad \Delta U \quad \Delta E_s \quad \Delta E_{th} \quad\quad\quad W$

System gains amount of kinetic energy equal to work done on it by gravitational force.

the change in the ball's kinetic energy ΔK_b and the change in the potential energy of the system add up to zero:

$$\Delta K_b + \Delta U^G = 0. \tag{10.38}$$

From Eq. 7.19, we know that the change in the gravitational potential energy is given by $\Delta U^G = -mgh$, and so

$$\Delta K_b = mgh. \tag{10.39}$$

Next let's consider just the ball by itself as our system (Figure 10.38b). There is no change in the ball's internal energy, so the change in the ball's kinetic energy is due to work done on it by the force of gravity: $\Delta K_b = W$. The change in the ball's kinetic energy does not depend on the system chosen, so we see from Eq. 10.39 that the work done on the ball is

$$W = mgh, \tag{10.40}$$

in agreement with Eqs. 10.36 and 10.37. In the process of deriving Eqs. 10.36 and 10.37, however, we derived an expression for the work done by a force that does not point in the same direction as the force displacement (Eq. 10.35).

Let us end by generalizing the result in Eq. 10.35 to a nondissipative force $\vec{F}(\vec{r})$ that is not constant. For such a force we follow the same procedure as in Section 9.7: we divide the force displacement $\Delta \vec{r}_F$ into many small force displacements $\delta \vec{r}_F$, such that the force is approximately constant over each small displacement, and then apply Eq. 10.35 to each small displacement (**Figure 10.39**):

$$W_n \approx \vec{F}(\vec{r}_n) \cdot \delta \vec{r}_{Fn}, \tag{10.41}$$

where $\vec{F}(\vec{r}_n)$ is the force at position $\vec{r}_n$ (at the beginning of each interval, as shown in Figure 10.39). The work done on the system over the entire force displacement $\Delta \vec{r}_F$ is then equal to the sum of the work done over all of the small displacements:

$$W \approx \sum_n W_n = \sum_n \vec{F}(\vec{r}_n) \cdot \delta \vec{r}_{Fn}. \tag{10.42}$$

To get a better approximation, we can divide the force displacement $\Delta \vec{r}_F$ into a larger number of smaller displacements $\delta \vec{r}_{Fn}$, so that the variation of the force over each displacement becomes even smaller. An exact result is obtained if we let $\delta \vec{r}_{Fn}$ approach zero (and the number of small displacements approaches infinity):

$$W = \lim_{\delta r_{Fn} \to 0} \sum_n \vec{F}(\vec{r}_n) \cdot \delta \vec{r}_{Fn}, \tag{10.43}$$

which is the definition of the line integral (Appendix B) of the force:

$$W = \int_{\vec{r}_i}^{\vec{r}_f} \vec{F}(\vec{r}) \cdot d\vec{r} \quad \text{(variable nondissipative force)}, \tag{10.44}$$

where the line integral should be evaluated over the path traced out by the point of application of the force.

For dissipative forces, we can follow the same procedure of dividing up the displacement to our approach of Section 9.7. Equation 9.27 then replaces Eq. 10.35, yielding for the change in thermal energy caused by the dissipative force:

$$\Delta E_{th} = -\int_{\vec{r}_i}^{\vec{r}_f} \vec{F}(\vec{r}_{cm}) \cdot d\vec{r}_{cm} \quad \text{(variable dissipative force)}. \tag{10.45}$$

Note that, in contrast to Eq. 10.44, this expression contains the position of the center of mass of the system rather than the point of application of the force.

Figure 10.39 To evaluate the work done on a system by a variable force, we divide the force displacement into small pieces.

10.11 When is W in Eq. 10.40 positive, and when is it negative? Is your answer consistent with the definition of positive and negative work given in Section 9.2?

10.10 Coefficients of friction

To describe the motion of objects along surfaces, we need a quantitative expression for the force of friction. Like the normal force, the force of static friction can take on a range of values, depending on the situation.

Suppose you are still struggling with the file cabinet of Checkpoint 10.4. As you increase the strength of your push on the cabinet, the force of static friction opposing your push grows. If you change the direction of your push, the force of friction changes direction as well, always opposing your force. The force of static friction has a maximum value, however, evidenced by the fact that if you push hard enough, the cabinet starts sliding. So the question is: What is the *maximum* force of static friction in a given situation?

The answer to this question depends on many variables, but we can establish a number of basic facts. For example—this you know from experience—the maximum force of static friction depends on the force with which the surfaces press against each other. An empty file cabinet slides more easily than a full one, for instance, and the double brick in **Figure 10.40** requires twice as large a force to begin sliding as the single brick does. The reason for this dependence on load is shown in Figure 10.40. If you put a brick down on a large flat plate, the *contact area* between the brick and the plate is given by the surface area of the face of the brick that is touching the plate. At the microscopic level, however, surfaces are never completely flat, so the surfaces of the brick and the plate touch only at the tops of protrusions over a combined *effective contact area* that is much smaller than the contact area (typically only about 1/10,000 of it). When the load increases, protrusions on the surfaces flatten, and the effective contact area increases, strengthening the bond between the surfaces.

Measurements show that the angle $\theta_{\max}$ at which objects begin to slide down an incline (in other words, the angle at which the force of static friction reaches its maximum value) does not depend on the contact area. As illustrated in **Figure 10.41**, two identical bricks begin sliding at the same incline angle regardless of the contact area between the brick and the incline surface. I know it is counterintuitive that the contact area does not determine when the bricks begin to slide, but to understand what is going on, let's go to the microscopic level again. When the brick is oriented so that its largest face is in contact with the inclined surface, the force exerted by the brick on the inclined surface is spread out over a large number of contact points, with the effective contact area having a certain value. When the brick is on its side, there are fewer contact points, but each point now carries a greater share of the load and so flattens out more. This flattening increases the contact area available at each point, with the result that the effective contact area has the same value as when the brick was in the other orientation. Thus the effective contact area doesn't depend on the orientation of the brick—it depends only on the force with which the brick presses against the surface. These observations establish the following important point:

> **The maximum force of static friction exerted by a surface on an object is proportional to the force with which the object presses on the surface and does not depend on the contact area.**

To obtain an expression for the force with which an object presses on an inclined surface, consider **Figure 10.42**. The normal force $\vec{F}_{sb}^{n}$ exerted by the surface

Figure 10.40 On a rough surface, a single brick slides more easily than a double brick. The harder two surfaces press against each other, the larger the effective contact area, and consequently the stronger the bond between the surfaces.

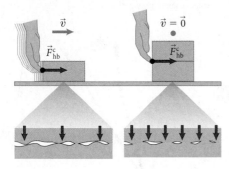

Figure 10.41 Regardless of its orientation, a brick starts sliding at the same angle of incline.

Bricks just starting to slide

$\theta_{\max}$

on the block and the normal force $\vec{F}^n_{bs}$ with which the surface of the block presses against the inclined surface (not shown in Figure 10.42) are an interaction pair and therefore equal in magnitude. As we have just determined, the maximum magnitude of the force of static friction is proportional to F^c_{bs} and therefore must also be proportional to F^n_{sb}, $(F^s_{sb})_{max} = \mu_s F^n_{sb}$. For any two surfaces 1 and 2, we can therefore write

$$(F^s_{12})_{max} = \mu_s F^n_{12}. \tag{10.46}$$

The maximum magnitude of the force of static friction between two surfaces is proportional to the magnitude of the normal force exerted by the surfaces on each other. The unitless proportionality constant μ_s is called the **coefficient of static friction.** Its value depends on the two materials in contact and the condition of their surfaces. Values for a few representative materials are given in Table 10.1.

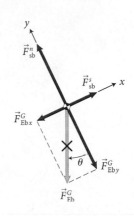

10.12 (a) A brick slides more easily on ice than on wood. For which combination (brick on ice or brick on wood) is μ_s larger? (b) For rubber on dry asphalt, μ_s is about 1. Ignoring any limits due to the runner's skill and condition, what maximum acceleration without slipping can a runner achieve using rubber soles on a dry, horizontal asphalt surface? [Hint: See Figure 10.21.]

The coefficient of static friction expressed in terms of the angle of incline can readily be determined experimentally by raising the incline of Figure 10.42 to the maximum angle at which the block remains at rest. At that angle θ_{max}, the force of static friction $\vec{F}^s_{sb}$ reaches the maximum value given by Eq. 10.46, and because the block remains at rest, the forces along the x axis must add to zero:

$$\sum F_x = F^G_{Ebx} + (F^s_{sb})_{max} = 0 \tag{10.47}$$

and so

$$(F^s_{sb})_{max} = -F^G_{Ebx}. \tag{10.48}$$

Table 10.1 Coefficients of friction

Material 1	Material 2	μ_s	μ_k
aluminum	aluminum	1.1–1.4	1.4
aluminum	steel	0.6	0.5
glass	glass	0.9–1.0	0.4
glass	nickel	0.8	0.6
ice	ice	0.1	0.03
rubber	aluminum	0.5	—
rubber	concrete	1.0–4.0	0.8
rubber	rubber	0.84	—
steel	steel	0.8	0.4
steel	brass	0.5	0.4
steel	copper	0.5	0.4
steel	lead	0.95	0.95
wood	wood	0.25–0.5	0.2

The values given are for clean, dry, smooth surfaces.

Figure 10.42 Free-body diagram for a block at rest on an inclined surface.

Because the block has no acceleration in the y direction, we also have

$$\Sigma F_y = F_{sb}^n + F_{Eby}^G = 0, \tag{10.49}$$

and so

$$F_{sb}^n = -F_{Eby}^G. \tag{10.50}$$

Substituting Eqs. 10.48 and 10.50 into 10.46, we get

$$-F_{Ebx}^G = \mu_s(-F_{Eby}^G) \tag{10.51}$$

$$\mu_s = \frac{F_{Ebx}^G}{F_{Eby}^G}. \tag{10.52}$$

Looking at Figure 10.42, we see that F_{Ebx}^G/F_{Eby}^G is the tangent of θ and so

$$\mu_s = \tan \theta_{max}. \tag{10.53}$$

10.13 (*a*) To what angle θ_{max} does a coefficient of static friction of 1 correspond? (*b*) Put, in turn, a coin, a paper clip, a CD case, and a comb on the cover of this book and tilt the book to obtain the angle at which each object begins to slide. In each case, how close do you get to the angle calculated in part *a*? What do you conclude from these observations about the coefficients of static friction for these combinations of surfaces?

Equation 10.46 gives only the *maximum* value of the force of static friction. All we know in any situation in which this force is present but has not reached its maximum value is that the magnitude of the force of static friction exerted by surface 1 on surface 2 must obey the condition

$$F_{12}^s \leq \mu_s F_{12}^n, \tag{10.54}$$

where F_{12}^n is the magnitude of the normal force exerted by surface 1 on surface 2. How, then, can you determine the magnitude of the frictional force exerted on an object in a given situation? Inequality 10.54 is not of much help, especially because the normal force can also take on almost any value! The key is to use what you know about the object's motion: If you know its acceleration and inertia, you can use the equation of motion, $\vec{a} = \Sigma \vec{F}/m$, to determine the vector sum of the forces exerted on the object. If you know what other forces are exerted on it, you can extract the values of the normal and frictional forces from this sum. The general procedure for dealing with situations involving frictional forces at surfaces is explained in the Procedure box "Working with frictional forces."

Procedure: Working with frictional forces

1. Draw a free-body diagram for the object of interest. Choose your x axis parallel to the surface and the y axis perpendicular to it, then decompose your forces along these axes. Indicate the acceleration of the object.
2. The equation of motion in the y direction allows you to determine the sum of the y components of the forces in that direction:

$$\Sigma F_y = ma_y.$$

Unless the object is accelerating in the normal direction, $a_y = 0$. Substitute the y components of the forces from your free-body diagram. The resulting equation allows you to determine the normal force.

3. The equation of motion in the x direction is

$$\Sigma F_x = ma_x.$$

If the object is not accelerating along the surface, $a_x = 0$. Substitute the x components of the forces from your free-body diagram. The resulting equation allows you to determine the frictional force.

4. If the object is not slipping, the normal force and the force of static friction should obey Inequality 10.54.

Example 10.8 Pulling a friend up a hill

A hiker is helping a friend up a hill that makes an angle of 30° with level ground. The hiker, who is farther up the hill, is pulling on a cable attached to his friend. The cable is parallel to the hill so that it also makes an angle of 30° with the horizontal. If the coefficient of static friction between the soles of the hiker's boots and the surface of the hill is 0.80 and his inertia is 65 kg, what is the maximum magnitude of the force he can exert on the cable without slipping?

❶ GETTING STARTED I begin by making a sketch and drawing the free-body diagram for the hiker (**Figure 10.43**). I chose an x axis that points up the hill and the y axis perpendicular to it. The forces exerted on the hiker are a force $\vec{F}_{ch}^c$ exerted by the cable and directed down the hill (this force forms an interaction pair with the force the hiker exerts on the cable), the force of gravity $\vec{F}_{Eh}^G$, and the contact force exerted by the surface of the hill on the hiker. This last force has two components: the normal force $\vec{F}_{sh}^n$ and the force of static friction $\vec{F}_{sh}^s$. The force of static friction is directed up the hill. If the hiker is not to slip, his acceleration must be zero, and so the forces in the normal (y) and tangential (x) directions must add up to zero.

Figure 10.43

❷ DEVISE PLAN As suggested in the Procedure box on page 250, I'll write the equation of motion along the two axes, setting the acceleration in each direction to zero. Then I use Inequality 10.54 to determine the maximum force that the hiker can exert without slipping.

❸ EXECUTE PLAN Because the magnitude of the force of gravity exerted on the hiker is mg, I have in the y direction

$$\sum F_y = F_{Ehy}^G + F_{sh}^n = -mg\cos\theta + F_{sh}^n = ma_y = 0$$

$$F_{sh}^n = mg\cos\theta, \tag{1}$$

where the minus sign in $-mg\cos\theta$ indicates that F_{Ehy}^G is in the negative y direction. Likewise, I have in the x direction

$$\sum F_x = F_{Ehx}^G + F_{sh}^s - F_{ch}^c$$

$$= -mg\sin\theta + F_{sh}^s - F_{ch}^c = ma_x = 0$$

$$F_{sh}^s = mg\sin\theta + F_{ch}^c. \tag{2}$$

If the hiker is not to slip, the force of static friction must not exceed its maximum value. Substituting Eqs. 1 and 2 into Inequality 10.54, I get

$$mg\sin\theta + F_{ch}^c \leq \mu_s(mg\cos\theta)$$

$$F_{ch}^c \leq mg(\mu_s\cos\theta - \sin\theta).$$

The problem asks me about the magnitude F_{hc}^c of the force exerted *by* the hiker *on* the cable, which is the same as the magnitude F_{ch}^c of the force exerted *by* the cable *on* the hiker, so

$$F_{hc}^c \leq mg(\mu_s\cos\theta - \sin\theta).$$

Substituting the values given, I obtain

$$F_{hc}^c \leq (65\text{ kg})(9.8\text{ m/s}^2)(0.80\cos 30° - \sin 30°)$$

$$= 1.2 \times 10^2\text{ N. } ✔$$

❹ EVALUATE RESULT A force of 1.2×10^2 N corresponds to the gravitational force exerted by Earth on an object that has an inertia of only 12 kg, and so the hiker cannot pull very hard before slipping. I know from experience, however, that unless I can lock a foot behind some solid object, it is impossible to pull hard on an inclined surface, and thus the answer I obtained makes sense.

Example 10.9 Object accelerating on a conveyor belt

While designing a conveyor belt system for a new airport, you determine that, on an incline of 20°, the magnitude of the maximum acceleration a rubber belt can give a typical suitcase before the suitcase begins slipping is 4.0 m/s². What is the coefficient of static friction for a typical suitcase on rubber?

❶ GETTING STARTED: I begin by making a sketch and drawing a free-body diagram for the suitcase, choosing the x axis along the conveyor belt in the direction of acceleration and the y axis upward and perpendicular to it (**Figure 10.44**). I also draw the upward acceleration of the suitcase along the incline.

❷ DEVISE PLAN As in Example 10.8, I write out the equation of motion along both axes. The x component of the acceleration is $a_x = +a$, where the magnitude of the acceleration is

Figure 10.44

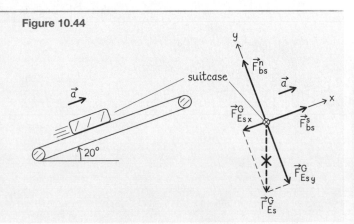

$a = 4.0 \text{ m/s}^2$. I can then use Inequality 10.54 to determine the coefficient of static friction.

❸ **EXECUTE PLAN** The equations of motion in the x and y directions are

$$\sum F_x = F^G_{Esx} + F^s_{bs} = -mg \sin \theta + F^s_{bs} = ma_x \qquad (1)$$

$$\sum F_y = F^G_{Esy} + F^n_{bs} = -mg \cos \theta + F^n_{bs} = ma_y = 0, \qquad (2)$$

with m the inertia of the suitcase. If a_x represents the maximum acceleration at which the suitcase does not slip, the force of static friction must be maximum. Substituting Eq. 10.46 for $(F^s_{bs})_{max}$ into Eq. 1, I get

$$-mg \sin \theta + \mu_s F^n_{bs} = m(+a).$$

Solving this equation for μ_s and substituting $F^n_{bs} = mg \cos \theta$ from Eq. 2, I obtain

$$\mu_s = \frac{ma + mg \sin \theta}{mg \cos \theta} = \frac{a + g \sin \theta}{g \cos \theta}$$

$$= \frac{(4.0 \text{ m/s}^2) + (9.8 \text{ m/s}^2) \sin 20°}{(9.8 \text{ m/s}^2)(\cos 20°)} = 0.80. ✔$$

❹ **EVALUATE RESULT** From Table 10.1, I see that the value I obtained for the coefficient for static friction is close to the coefficient for rubber against rubber and therefore reasonable. I also note that the inertia m of the suitcase, which is not given, drops out of the final result.

Once surfaces slip relative to each other, the force of kinetic friction, like its static counterpart, is proportional to the normal force: It takes a greater force to keep a heavily loaded file cabinet moving than it does to keep an empty one moving. Experiments also show that objects sliding to a stop on a horizontal surface under the influence of kinetic friction undergo a constant acceleration; in other words, the force of kinetic friction between two slipping surfaces is constant and independent of the relative velocity of the two surfaces. In analogy to Eq. 10.46, we can say

$$F^k_{12} = \mu_k F^n_{12}, \qquad (10.55)$$

where μ_k is called the **coefficient of kinetic friction.** The kinetic coefficient μ_k is always smaller than μ_s (or else an object would never slip because it would "stop slipping the instant it starts slipping"). For most surface combinations, the value of μ_k is somewhere between 25% and 100% of the corresponding value of μ_s (Table 10.1).

Note that, unlike the force of static friction, which can take on any value below the maximum limit dictated by μ_s, the force of kinetic friction is constant and therefore always equal to the value given in Eq. 10.55.

✋ **10.14** Imagine putting a single and a double brick on a flat board, as in Figure 10.40, and then slowly raising one end of the board. (*a*) Does the single brick begin to slide before, after, or at the same time as the double brick? (*b*) Once the bricks start sliding, is the acceleration of the double brick larger than, equal to, or smaller than that of the single brick?

Chapter Glossary

SI units of physical quantities are given in parentheses.

Coefficient of friction μ_s, μ_k (unitless): A scalar equal to the ratio of the force of friction to the normal force. The maximum force of static friction exerted by surface 1 on surface 2 is given by

$$(F_{12}^s)_{max} = \mu_s F_{12}^n, \tag{10.46}$$

where μ_s is the *coefficient of static friction* and F_{12}^n is the normal force exerted by surface 1 on surface 2. The force of kinetic friction is given by

$$F_{12}^k = \mu_k F_{12}^n, \tag{10.55}$$

where μ_k is the *coefficient of kinetic friction.*

Component vector Any vector $\vec{A}$ can be decomposed into component vectors $\vec{A}_x$ and $\vec{A}_y$, along some conveniently chosen axes, such that $\vec{A} = \vec{A}_x + \vec{A}_y$.

Frictional force The tangential component of the contact force exerted by a surface on an object. When the two surfaces in contact are not moving relative to each other, the tangential component is called the *force of static friction*; when they are moving, it is called the *force of kinetic friction.*

Normal component The component of a vector perpendicular to a surface.

Normal force The normal component of the contact force exerted by a surface on an object.

Polar coordinate system A coordinate system in which the two coordinates that locate a point are its distance from the origin and the angle between its position vector and the x axis.

Rectangular coordinate system A coordinate system in which two coordinates that locate a point are its perpendicular distances from each of two perpendicular axes. Convenient choices of coordinate systems: For an object that is accelerating, choose one of the axes along the direction of the acceleration; for an object in translational equilibrium, choose your axes such that the largest possible number of forces lie along one of the axes.

Scalar product The product of two vectors yielding a scalar quantity. For two vectors $\vec{A}$ and $\vec{B}$ that make an angle ϕ, the scalar product is defined as

$$\vec{A} \cdot \vec{B} \equiv AB \cos \phi. \tag{10.33}$$

Tangential component The component of a vector parallel to a surface.

Work as scalar product W (J) The work done on an object by a constant nondissipative force $\vec{F}$ exerted on that object during a displacement $\Delta \vec{r}_F$ of the point of application of $\vec{F}$ is equal to the scalar product of $\vec{F}$ and $\Delta \vec{r}_F$:

$$W = \vec{F} \cdot \Delta \vec{r}_F \quad \text{(constant nondissipative force).} \tag{10.35}$$

For a force that is not constant, the work done on a system is

$$W = \int_{\vec{r}_i}^{\vec{r}_f} \vec{F}(\vec{r}) \cdot d\vec{r} \quad \text{(variable nondissipative force).} \tag{10.44}$$

11 Motion in a Circle

CONCEPTS

11.1 Circular motion at constant speed
11.2 Forces and circular motion
11.3 Rotational inertia

QUANTITATIVE TOOLS

11.4 Rotational kinematics
11.5 Angular momentum
11.6 Rotational inertia of extended objects

The motion we have been dealing with so far in this text is called **translational motion** (**Figure 11.1a**). This type of motion involves no change in an object's orientation; in other words, all the particles in the object move along identical parallel trajectories. During **rotational motion,** which we begin to study in this chapter, the orientation of the object changes, and the particles in an object follow different circular paths centered on a straight line called the *axis of rotation* (Figure 11.1b). Generally, the motion of rigid objects is a combination of these two types of motion (Figure 11.1c), but as we shall see in Chapter 12 this combined motion can be broken down into translational and rotational parts that can be analyzed separately. Because we already know how to describe translational motion, knowing how to describe rotational motion will complete our description of the motion of rigid objects.

As Figure 11.1b shows, each particle in a rotating object traces out a circular path, moving in what we call *circular*

motion. We therefore begin our analysis of rotational motion by describing circular motion. Circular motion occurs all around us. A speck of dust stuck to a spinning CD, a stone being whirled around on a string, a person on a Ferris wheel—all travel along the perimeter of a circle, repeating their motion over and over. Circular motion takes place in a plane, and so in principle we have already developed all the tools required to describe it. To describe circular and rotational motion we shall follow an approach that is analogous to the one we followed for the description of translational motion. Exploiting this analogy, we can then use the same results and insights gained in earlier chapters to introduce a third conservation law.

11.1 Circular motion at constant speed

Figure 11.2 shows two examples of circular motion: a block dragged along a circle by a rotating turntable and a puck constrained by a string to move in a circle. The block and puck are said to *revolve* around the vertical axis through the center of each circular path. Note that the axis about which they revolve is external to the block and puck and perpendicular to the plane of rotation. This is the definition of *revolve*—to move in circular motion around an *external* center. Objects that turn about an *internal* axis, such as the turntable in Figure 11.2a, are said to *rotate*. These two types of motion are closely related because a rotating object can be considered as a system of an enormous number of particles, each revolving around the axis of rotation.

Figure 11.1 Translational and rotational motion of a rigid object.

(*a*) Translational motion

All points on object follow identical trajectories.

(*b*) Rotational motion

All points on object trace circles centered on axis of rotation.

axis of rotation

(*c*) Combined translation and rotation

Different points on object follow different trajectories.

Figure 11.2 Examples of circular motion.

(*a*) Block revolves on rotating turntable

Block *revolves* because axis is external to it.

axis of rotation

Turntable *rotates* because axis is internal to it.

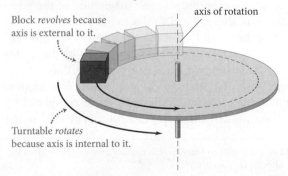

(*b*) Tethered puck revolves on air table

Figure 11.3 Average and instantaneous velocity for an object in circular motion.

Average velocity points in same direction as displacement $\Delta \vec{r}$.

As time interval approaches zero, average velocity approaches instantaneous velocity, which is tangent to circular trajectory.

Figure 11.3 shows an overhead view of a puck moving counterclockwise along the arc of a circle. The puck's average velocity points in the same direction as the puck's displacement $\Delta \vec{r}$, which points from the puck's initial position to its final position. As we consider the motion for increasingly smaller time intervals, the angle between the position vectors $\vec{r}_i$ and $\vec{r}_f$ measured from the center of the circular trajectory approaches zero and $\Delta \vec{r}$ becomes tangent to the circular trajectory. This is true all along the trajectory, and so we can say:

> The instantaneous velocity $\vec{v}$ of an object in circular motion is always perpendicular to the object's position $\vec{r}$ measured from the center of the circular trajectory.

In the first part of this chapter, we study only objects in **circular motion at constant speed;** that is to say, the magnitude of their instantaneous velocity doesn't change.

Because the motion lies entirely in a plane, we can use Cartesian coordinates to describe the puck's position and velocity at any instant. In **Figure 11.4a**, for example, the puck's position is specified by (x_1, y_1) at instant t_1 and by (x_2, y_2) at instant t_2. However, because the magnitude of the position vector $\vec{r}$ is always equal to the radius of the circle, we can also give the magnitude r and the direction of this vector to specify the puck's position, as indicated by the angles θ_1 and θ_2 in Figure 11.4b. To specify the direction, we define the puck's **rotational coordinate,** which is a unitless number that increases by 2π for each circle completed by the revolving puck.* The rotational coordinate is denoted

Figure 11.4 The position of an object in circular motion can be given in Cartesian or polar coordinates.

(a) Cartesian (x, y) coordinates

(b) Polar (r, θ) coordinates

*The adjective *rotational* is used for both rotation and revolution.

Figure 11.5 The rotational coordinate specifies the location of an object on a circle.

(a) Relationship between rotational coordinate and polar angle

(b) Symbol used in this text to specify rotational coordinate system

ϑ increases: counterclockwise   clockwise

by the Greek letter ϑ (script theta); for example, $\vartheta = \pi$ refers to the position of the puck half a revolution after starting from the origin. The rotational coordinate is related to *polar angle* θ as shown in **Figure 11.5a**. Unlike the rotational coordinate, however, the polar angle is not a unitless number but rather expressed in units of revolutions, degrees, or radians.

To measure ϑ we need to choose a direction of increasing ϑ and a zero, just as we need to specify a direction of increasing x and an origin to measure position along an axis. We shall indicate our choice of rotational coordinate system, which will generally be dictated by the motion under consideration, by drawing a curved arrow around the axis of rotation, as shown in Figure 11.5b.

Exercise 11.1 Rotational coordinates

Determine the rotational coordinate of the following objects for the indicated choices of rotational coordinate system. (a) The tip of the hour hand of a clock at 4:30 p.m., when zero is at noon on the same day and ϑ increases in the clockwise direction. (b) A faucet after being turned 3/4 of a turn in a clockwise direction, starting from zero and with ϑ increasing in the counterclockwise direction. (c) The object in Figure 11.4 if $\theta = 78.3°$, when zero is at $\theta = 0°$ and ϑ increases in the counterclockwise direction.

SOLUTION (a) The angle between noon and 4:30 p.m. is 135°, which is $(135°)/(360°) = 0.375$ of one revolution. Because the rotation takes place in the positive direction and because ϑ increases by 2π for each revolution, $\vartheta = (2\pi)(+0.375) = +2.36$. Note that there are no units because ϑ is a unitless quantity. ✔

(b) $\vartheta = (2\pi)(-3/4) = -\frac{3}{2}\pi$. ✔

(c) $\vartheta = (2\pi)(+78.3°)/(360°) = +1.37$. ✔

Figure 11.6 Two pucks in circular motion at constant speed can have different speeds even though their rotational velocity (the rate at which ϑ changes) is the same.

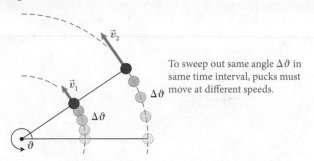

To sweep out same angle $\Delta\vartheta$ in same time interval, pucks must move at different speeds.

Figure 11.7 Instantaneous and rotational velocities for points on a rotating disk.

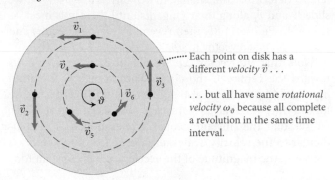

Each point on disk has a different *velocity* $\vec{v}$ . . .

. . . but all have same *rotational velocity* ω_ϑ because all complete a revolution in the same time interval.

We shall represent the rate at which an object's rotational coordinate changes by ω_ϑ (Greek omega). The subscript ϑ indicates that the sign of this quantity depends on our choice of direction for increasing ϑ, just as the sign of v_x (the rate at which an object's x coordinate changes) depends on our choice of x axis. Indeed, just as v_x is the component of a velocity vector $\vec{v}$, ω_ϑ is a component of a *rotational velocity vector* $\vec{\omega}$, which we shall discuss in Chapter 12. For convenience we shall refer to ω_ϑ as the **rotational velocity**, although strictly speaking it is the ϑ component of $\vec{\omega}$.

The magnitude of the rotational velocity is the **rotational speed**, which we denote by ω just as v denotes speed: $\omega = |\vec{\omega}| = |\omega_\vartheta|$. The time interval it takes an object in circular motion at constant speed to complete one revolution is called the **period** and is denoted by the letter T.

For example, if the puck in Figure 11.4 completes three revolutions in the negative ϑ direction in 2.0 s, its average rotational velocity for those three revolutions ($\Delta\vartheta = -3(2\pi) = -6\pi$) is $\omega_{\vartheta,av} = \Delta\vartheta/\Delta t = (-6\pi)/(2.0 \text{ s}) = -9.4 \text{ s}^{-1}$; its average rotational speed is 9.4 s^{-1}; and its period is $T = (2.0 \text{ s})/3 = 0.67$ s. Note that the units of rotational velocity and rotational speed are s^{-1} (*inverse second*).

The rotational coordinate of an object in circular motion at constant speed increases linearly with time. If it takes a puck in circular motion at constant speed 1.0 s to go from $\vartheta = 0$ to $\vartheta = +0.80$, then it also takes the puck 1.0 s to go from $\vartheta = +0.80$ to $\vartheta = +1.6$, and the object's rotational velocity is constant at $\omega_\vartheta = (+1.6 - 0.80)/(1.0 \text{ s}) = +0.80 \text{ s}^{-1}$.

What is the relationship between an object's speed and its rotational velocity? **Figure 11.6** shows two pucks in circular motion. The rotational coordinate of both pucks changes by the same amount $\Delta\vartheta$ during a time interval Δt, and so both have the same rotational velocity. Their speeds, however, are not the same because the puck that moves along the larger circle travels a greater distance along its trajectory than does the puck that moves along the smaller circle.

The advantage of using rotational velocity to describe rotational motion over using the ordinary velocity $\vec{v}$ becomes clear when we look at the rotating disk in **Figure 11.7**. As the velocity vectors $\vec{v}$ show, each point on the disk has a different velocity $\vec{v}$, with points farther from the axis of revolution having a greater speed than points closer to the axis. Yet all points on the disk execute the same number of revolutions per unit time, and so they all have the same rotational velocity ω_ϑ.

The velocity of an object in circular motion constantly changes direction. As **Figure 11.8a** shows, even though the initial and final *speeds* of the object are the same (indicated by the equal magnitudes of the velocity vectors), the vectors $\vec{v}_i$ and $\vec{v}_f$ point in different directions. The object therefore undergoes a change in velocity $\Delta\vec{v}$, which, by our definition of acceleration, means that the object accelerates.

Objects in circular motion have a nonzero acceleration even if they are moving at constant speed.

Because $\vec{r}$ and $\vec{v}$ are always perpendicular, when $\vec{r}$ rotates through an angle θ, $\vec{v}$ rotates through the same angle,

Figure 11.8 Average and instantaneous acceleration of an object in circular motion.

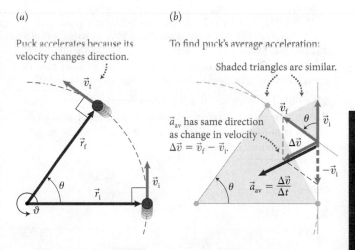

(a)

Puck accelerates because its velocity changes direction.

(b)

To find puck's average acceleration:

Shaded triangles are similar.

$\vec{a}_{av}$ has same direction as change in velocity $\Delta\vec{v} = \vec{v}_f - \vec{v}_i$.

$\vec{a}_{av} = \dfrac{\Delta\vec{v}}{\Delta t}$

(c)

As time interval approaches zero, average acceleration approaches instantaneous acceleration.

Instantaneous acceleration is perpendicular to $\vec{v}$.

CONCEPTS

which means the shaded triangles in Figure 11.8b are similar. To determine the change in velocity $\Delta\vec{v} = \vec{v}_f - \vec{v}_i$, we slide $\vec{v}_i$ and $\vec{v}_f$ along their tangents until their tails meet, as shown in Figure 11.8b, then reverse $\vec{v}_i$ (dashed vector) and add the reversed vector to $\vec{v}_f$.

Note that the vector $\Delta\vec{v}$ we obtain in this way points toward the center of the circle. The average acceleration $\vec{a}_{av} \equiv \Delta\vec{v}/\Delta t$ therefore also points toward the center. As we let the time interval Δt approach zero, as in Figure 11.8c, we see that the (instantaneous) acceleration $\vec{a}$ is perpendicular to the velocity $\vec{v}$. Because the speed of the object is constant, the magnitude of the acceleration is constant too.

> **An object executing circular motion at constant speed has an acceleration of constant magnitude that is directed toward the center of its circular path.**

This acceleration is called the **centripetal acceleration** (*centripetal* is Latin for "center-seeking").

In Chapter 10 we saw that the component of the acceleration parallel to an object's instantaneous velocity causes the speed of the object to change, and the perpendicular component causes the direction of the instantaneous velocity to change. For circular motion at constant speed, there is only a perpendicular component of acceleration (the *centripetal acceleration* we just described), and so only the direction of the velocity changes. Nothing pushes or pulls the object in the direction of motion, and so its speed doesn't change.

Exercise 11.2 Accelerations

Determine the direction of the average acceleration in each of the following situations: (*a*) A car goes over the top of a hill at constant speed. (*b*) A runner slows down after crossing a finish line on level ground. (*c*) A cyclist makes a left turn while coasting at constant speed on a horizontal road. (*d*) A roller-coaster car is pulled up a straight incline at constant speed.

SOLUTION For each situation I make a before-and-after sketch showing the initial and final velocities (**Figure 11.9**). The acceleration is nonzero if the direction of the velocity or the magnitude of the velocity changes.

Figure 11.9

The average acceleration points in the same direction as the change in velocity $\Delta\vec{v}$. To determine the direction of this vector, I draw the vectors $\vec{v}_i$ and $\vec{v}_f$ with their tails together. The change in velocity then points from the tip of $\vec{v}_i$ to the tip of $\vec{v}_f$, as shown in **Figure 11.10**. For each situation, the direction of the average acceleration is given by the direction of $\Delta\vec{v}$. ✔

Figure 11.10

To describe circular motion it is convenient to choose a coordinate system that rotates around with the object under consideration, as illustrated in **Figure 11.11**. The *radial axis*, denoted by the letter r, points in the direction of the radius of the circular trajectory, away from the axis of rotation. The *tangential axis*, denoted by the letter t, points in the direction of increasing ϑ, tangent to the trajectory. Because the tangent to a circle is perpendicular to the radius drawn to the point of contact of the tangent, the r and t axes are always perpendicular to each other. Often we'll need a third axis, denoted by the letter z, to describe the direction of forces exerted on the object. This axis is chosen perpendicular to the plane of motion (and therefore perpendicular to both the r and t axes).

With this choice of coordinate system, the velocity of an object executing circular motion at constant speed is always directed along the t axis and the acceleration of the object is always directed inward along the r axis.

✋ **11.1** Suppose the object in Figure 11.8 is in *accelerated* circular motion, so that $|\vec{v}_f| > |\vec{v}_i|$. In which direction does the object's average acceleration point?

Figure 11.11 Rotating coordinate system used to describe circular motion.

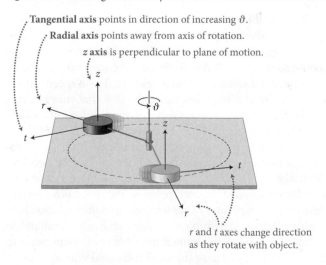

Tangential axis points in direction of increasing ϑ.

Radial axis points away from axis of rotation.

z axis is perpendicular to plane of motion.

r and t axes change direction as they rotate with object.

11.2 Forces and circular motion

The centripetal acceleration of an object in circular motion at constant speed tells us that the vector sum of the forces exerted on the object must be directed toward the center of the circle, continuously adjusting the object's direction. Without this inward-pointing vector sum of forces, the object would move in a straight line.

> An object that executes circular motion at constant speed is subject to a force (or vector sum of forces) of constant magnitude directed toward the center of the circular trajectory.

But wait! Aren't you pushed *outward* when a car makes a sharp turn? Say you are in a car that takes a right turn as illustrated in **Figure 11.12**. Even though the center of the arc describing the car's trajectory is on the right, there is no denying that your left shoulder is pressed against the left door! Don't forget, however, that because the direction of the car's velocity is changing, it has a nonzero acceleration, and so the reference frame of the car is noninertial.

In Chapter 6 we discussed how things are different in noninertial reference frames. Riding in a car that is traveling on a straight road when it makes an emergency stop, you feel as if you are being pushed forward. There is no force pushing you forward, however. Instead, the "push" you think you feel is nothing more than your body obeying the law of inertia and continuing at its original velocity. As your body tries to continue, it collides with the seat belt because the belt, being part of the car, begins to slow down. You exert a forward force on the belt, but it exerts a rearward force on you. Likewise, when a car initially traveling straight ahead makes a sharp right turn, your body has a tendency to continue in a straight line. As the car begins to curve rightward, the force exerted by the left door on you forces your body into the turn. So even though you feel you are being pushed outward, an inward contact force $\vec{F}_{cp}^{c}$ is exerted by the car on you, as illustrated in Figure 11.12. The feeling of being pushed outward

(leftward) arises only from the noninertial nature of the car's reference frame; in reality, your body simply tends to continue moving in a straight line. The moral is:

> **Avoid analyzing forces from a rotating frame of reference because such a frame is accelerating and therefore noninertial.**

The force required to make an object go around a curve can be a push, a pull, or a combination of the two. For example, the puck in Figure 11.2b is pulled inward by the string; in Figure 11.12, the person is pushed inward by the car.

The magnitude of the force required to make an object move in circular motion at constant speed depends on the speed of the object and the radius of the trajectory. To see how this force depends on speed, refer to Figure 11.8b. By mentally increasing the magnitude of the vectors $\vec{v}_i$ and $\vec{v}_f$ (which is equivalent to increasing the speed of the revolving object), you see how the vectors $\Delta\vec{v}$ and $\vec{a}$ also get longer. Because $\sum \vec{F} = m\vec{a}$, an object traveling at higher speed requires a larger inward force.

To see how the inward force depends on radius, look at **Figure 11.13**, which shows two pucks moving at the same speed along circles of different radii. During a given time interval, the rotational coordinate ϑ of the puck moving along the larger circle changes less than that of the puck moving along the smaller circle. Consequently the puck on the larger circle has a smaller change in velocity and a smaller centripetal acceleration. Because force is directly proportional to acceleration, we can say that the larger the radius, the smaller the force required to make the object go

Figure 11.13 Change in velocity for pucks moving along circles of different radius.

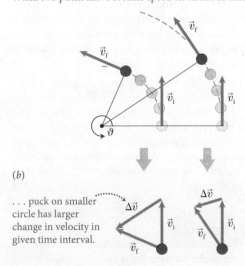

(a)

When two pucks move at same speed on circles of different radius . . .

(b)

. . . puck on smaller circle has larger change in velocity in given time interval.

Figure 11.12 As you round a curve in a car, are you pushed inward or outward?

path of person in absence of forces

$\vec{F}_{cp}^{c}$ .... Car exerts force on person that points toward center of circular trajectory.

Car's centripetal acceleration means car's reference frame is not inertial.

Figure 11.14 The smaller the radius, the sharper the curve and the larger the force required to make the object follow the curve.

in a circle (**Figure 11.14**). As the radius approaches infinity, the object goes in a straight line and no force is required to change the direction of its velocity.

The inward force required to make an object move in circular motion increases with increasing speed and decreases with increasing radius.

Example 11.3 Cube on turntable

A cube lies on a turntable initially rotating at constant speed. The rotational speed of the turntable is slowly increased, and at some instant the cube slides off the turntable. Explain why this happens.

❶ **GETTING STARTED** I'm not given much information, so I begin by making a sketch of the situation (**Figure 11.15a**). As the turntable rotates, the cube executes a circular motion. My task is to explain why the cube does not remain on the turntable as the turntable rotates faster.

Figure 11.15

❷ **DEVISE PLAN** Because the cube executes circular motion, it has a centripetal acceleration, and so the vector sum of the forces exerted on it must point toward the center of the turntable. I therefore need to make a free-body diagram that reflects this combination of forces and determine how the forces change as the rotational speed of the turntable increases.

❸ **EXECUTE PLAN** To draw my free-body diagram, I must answer the question What are the forces exerted on the cube? First there is $\vec{F}^G_{Ec}$, the gravitational force exerted by Earth. This force is directed vertically downward and so cannot contribute to a force directed toward the turntable's center. The only other force exerted on the cube is $\vec{F}^c_{sc}$, the contact force exerted by the surface of the turntable. The normal component $\vec{F}^n_{sc}$ of this force must be equal in magnitude to $\vec{F}^G_{Ec}$ because the cube does not accelerate in the vertical direction. The horizontal component, which is the force of static friction $\vec{F}^s_{sc}$, is what forces the cube toward the center of its circular path. I therefore draw the free-body diagram shown in Figure 11.15b. Because the vertical component of the acceleration is zero, the forces in that

direction add to zero. Thus the vector sum of the forces exerted on the cube equals the force of static friction.

As the rotational speed increases, the magnitude of the centripetal acceleration of the cube also increases. This means that the magnitude of the force of static friction must get larger. At some instant, this force reaches its maximum value and so can no longer increase even though the rotational speed continues to increase. Consequently, the vector sum of the forces exerted on the cube is no longer large enough to give it the centripetal acceleration required for its circular trajectory. When this happens, the distance between the cube and the axis of rotation increases until the cube slides off the edge. ✔

❹ **EVALUATE RESULT** What makes the cube slide off the turntable is its tendency to continue in a straight line (that is, on a trajectory tangent to its circular trajectory). Up to a certain speed the force of static friction is large enough to overcome this tendency and keep the cube moving in a circle. Once the force of static friction reaches its maximum value, the cube begins to slide.

It is all too easy to think that there must be an *outward* force pushing the cube off the turntable as the rotational velocity increases in Example 11.3. As in a car rounding a corner, this thought arises because, without realizing it, you tend to view the situation from the rotating frame of the turntable. Because this is an easy mistake to make in situations involving rotation, you must always make sure you choose an inertial frame of reference.

If you can't imagine the cube moving off the turntable without being *pushed* off, try the following: Put some object—an eraser or your keys will do—on top and near the edge of a book as in **Figure 11.16a** and then gently,

Figure 11.16 The eraser in (b) falls off the book because of inertia, not because of a force "pushing" it off the book.

without touching the object, push the book along the surface of a table. The object moves along because it is being pushed forward by the force of static friction exerted by the book on it. If you give the book a hard shove, however, the object lags behind and falls off the rear edge of the book. Did it get pushed off? Someone moving along with the book might claim it did—just as someone in an accelerating car feels "pushed backward"—but such a person is not in an inertial reference frame. From the point of view of someone in the Earth reference frame, the book got yanked from under the object. The force of static friction exerted by the book on the object is not large enough to give the object the same acceleration as the book, and so the object falls off the rear edge without anything physically pushing it off. If you mark its starting position, you will notice that the object always ends up in front of its starting position, as shown in Figure 11.16b. This observation tells you that, even though it falls off the rear edge of the book, the object must have been pushed in the *forward* direction. It falls off the book not because it has been pushed off, but because the forward push exerted by the book on the object is not

large enough for the object to keep up with the accelerating book.

The same is true for the cube on the turntable: It falls off the edge not because it is pushed off but because the force of static friction between turntable and cube is not large enough to force the cube to go around in a circle.

11.2 Suppose I have two cubes on a turntable at equal distances from the axis of rotation. The inertia of cube 1 is twice that of cube 2. Do both cubes begin sliding at the same instant if I slowly increase the rotational velocity?

Figure 11.17 shows free-body diagrams for three objects moving in circular motion at constant speed. In each case the vector sum of the forces exerted on the object points toward the center of the circular trajectory.

11.3 (a) Does a bicycle always have to lean into a curve as illustrated in Figure 11.17a? (b) The rope holding the bucket in Figure 11.17b makes a small angle with the horizontal. Is it possible to swing the bucket around so that the rope is exactly horizontal?

Figure 11.17 Free-body diagrams for three objects in circular motion at constant speed.

11.3 Rotational inertia

Having established the principles of circular motion at constant speed, let us now examine *changes* in rotational velocity. Imagine two identical pucks A and B on a horizontal air table (**Figure 11.18**). Puck B is initially at rest and fastened to a vertical post in the middle of the table by a short string that constrains the puck's motion to a circle of radius r_B. Suppose we give puck A a shove so that it strikes stationary puck B at speed v, as illustrated in Figure 11.18a. The two pucks collide elastically, and so immediately after the collision puck A is at rest and puck B has speed v. Puck B then begins to move around the post in circular motion at constant speed v. If the change in its rotational coordinate during a time interval Δt is $\Delta\vartheta_B$, then its rotational velocity after the collision is $\omega_{B\vartheta} = \Delta\vartheta_B/\Delta t$.

Now suppose we shove puck A at the same initial speed v toward a third identical puck C initially at rest and attached to a string of length $r_C > r_B$, as in Figure 11.18b. As before, puck A comes to rest after the collision and puck C moves away with speed v. Because both pucks B and C have the same speed v after the collision, they travel the same arc length in the same time interval Δt. However, their *rotational* speeds are different because the radii of their trajectories are different. The magnitude of the change $\Delta\vartheta_C$ in the rotational coordinate of C during the time interval Δt is smaller than that of B, and C's rotational speed, $\omega_C = |\Delta\vartheta_C/\Delta t|$, is therefore smaller than that of B.

If puck C is to attain the same final rotational velocity as B, it needs to be struck by a considerably faster moving puck A. Put differently, it is more difficult to change the rotational velocity of C than it is to change that of B. Note that C and B have the same inertia. If it weren't for the presence of the strings of different lengths, we would not be able to distinguish them: Once hit by A, both C and B would move off in a straight line with the same speed v. Apparently an object's tendency to resist a change in rotational velocity, its **rotational inertia,** is not given by simply the object's inertia—the object's tendency to resist a change in velocity as we defined it in Chapter 4. (The inertia surely plays a role: If I

increase the inertia of puck B, its rotational speed after the collision is lower and so is its change in rotational velocity.) That the longer string on C causes C's rotational velocity to change less than B's suggests that an object's rotational inertia depends on its location relative to the axis of rotation. The greater the distance between the bulk of an object's material and the axis of rotation, the larger its rotational inertia. You can easily verify this using a hammer (**Figure 11.19**). If you hold the hammer near its head, it is easily rotated. If you hold the hammer at the handle, as you would normally, it is more difficult to rotate.

There are many examples of the effect of rotational inertia. Skaters reduce their rotational inertia, and therefore spin more easily, by holding their arms close to their bodies; you run faster with your legs bent than with them extended. Conversely, when trying to keep your balance on a beam, you spread out your arms. This action moves more of your inertia away from the rotation axis and so increases your rotational inertia, which in turn increases your resistance to rotating off the beam. Tightrope walkers use a long pole for the same reason: The pole puts more inertia farther from the rotation axis and so increases the walkers' rotational inertia and gives them more time to adjust their balance.

One final important point: Unlike inertia, which has a single value, rotational inertia depends on the location of the rotation axis. An object can have a small rotational inertia about one axis and a large rotational inertia about another axis—just think of the hammer in Figure 11.19. Therefore the value of rotational inertia cannot be determined unless you specify the axis of rotation.

✋ **11.4** About which axis is the rotational inertia of a pencil (*a*) largest and (*b*) smallest: (1) a lengthwise axis through the core of the pencil; (2) an axis perpendicular to the pencil's length and passing through its midpoint; (3) an axis perpendicular to the pencil's length and passing through its tip?

Figure 11.19 The rotational inertia of a hammer—its resistance to rotational motion—depends on the location of the axis of rotation.

Most of hammer's mass is in head.

Axis of rotation far from center of mass:
Hammer is hard to rotate (has high rotational inertia).

Axis of rotation at center of mass:
Hammer is easy to rotate (has low rotational inertia).

Figure 11.18 When a moving puck strikes a stationary puck attached to a string, the rotational velocity of the puck on the string depends on string length.

(*a*)   (*b*)

Moving at speed v, puck A strikes identical, stationary pucks B and C. After collision, puck A is at rest.

Collision causes pucks B and C to move at same speed v but at *different* rotational speeds $\omega = |\Delta\vartheta/\Delta t|$.

Self-quiz

1. Which of the following is in translational equilibrium? (*a*) An object whose center of mass is undergoing circular motion at constant speed. (*b*) A wheel spinning about an axis through its center of mass.

2. **Figure 11.20** shows the velocities $\vec{v}_i$ and $\vec{v}_f$ of a point on the rim of an object at two instants t_i and t_f for four different motions. For each case, determine the change in velocity $\Delta\vec{v}$ and the direction of the average acceleration during the time interval between t_i and t_f.

Figure 11.20

(*a*)

(*b*)

(*c*)

(*d*)

3. Why doesn't the acceleration in question 2 point toward the center of the circle in all cases?

4. Describe the interaction responsible for providing a centripetal acceleration for (*a*) a car rounding a level curve, (*b*) a car rounding a banked curve, (*c*) a coin rotating along with a turntable, (*d*) a ball swung through a horizontal circle by a string that sweeps out a cone, (*e*) the Moon orbiting Earth, (*f*) clothes spinning in a dryer, (*g*) a marble rolling along the inside of a horizontal hoop, and (*h*) a ball on a string rolling in a horizontal circle.

5. A ball attached to a string (the far end of which is fixed) rolls in a horizontal circle. Under which conditions is the string more likely to break: (*a*) when the speed of the ball is increased for a given radius or (*b*) when the length of the string is increased for a given speed?

Answers

1. (*a*) An object undergoing circular motion at constant speed is accelerated because the direction of its center-of-mass velocity changes continuously. If it is accelerated, the vector sum of the forces exerted on the object is not zero, and the object cannot be in translational equilibrium. (*b*) If the center of mass of a spinning wheel is fixed, $a_{cm} = 0$ and so the object is in translational equilibrium.

2. For each case, $\Delta\vec{v} = \vec{v}_f - \vec{v}_i$ and the average acceleration is parallel to $\Delta\vec{v}$ (**Figure 11.21**).

Figure 11.21

(a)

(b)

(c)

(d)

3. Notice that as the object travels around the circle in parts *b* and *c*, its speed changes. To change the speed, there must be a tangential component to the acceleration as well as a centripetal component. The tangential component requires that the acceleration not point directly toward the center.

4. (*a*) Force of static friction exerted by road on car, (*b*) horizontal component of contact force exerted by road on car, (*c*) force of static friction exerted by turntable on coin, (*d*) horizontal component of tensile force exerted by string on ball, (*e*) gravitational force exerted by Earth on the Moon, (*f*) centripetal component of contact force exerted by drum of dryer on clothes, (*g*) contact force exerted by hoop on marble, and (*h*) tensile force exerted by string on ball.

5. In case *a*, for a given radius, a greater speed means the ball travels through a larger angle during a specific time interval. If the angle is larger, the magnitude of $\Delta\vec{v}$ is larger. A larger magnitude of $\Delta\vec{v}$ requires that the acceleration and force also be larger. The force providing the acceleration is due to the tension in the string. Therefore, the greater speed requires more tension and the string is more likely to break. In case *b*, for a given speed, a larger radius means that the ball travels through a smaller angle in a specific time interval. If the angle is smaller, the magnitude of $\Delta\vec{v}$ is smaller. A smaller $\Delta\vec{v}$ requires a smaller acceleration and a smaller force. Therefore, a large radius requires a smaller tension in the string and the string is less likely to break.

Figure 11.22 Relationships between rotational coordinate ϑ, radius r, and arc length s.

(a)

Rotational coordinate ϑ is defined in terms of radius r and arc length s.

$$\vartheta \equiv \frac{s}{r}$$

Rotational coordinate indicates that s is measured from x axis and increases counterclockwise.

(b)

Relationship of $\Delta\vartheta$ to difference in arc lengths $\Delta s = s_f - s_i$.

11.4 Rotational kinematics

The **rotational coordinate** of an object moving along a circle of radius r is defined as the length of the arc s over which the object has moved divided by the radius:

$$\vartheta \equiv \frac{s}{r}. \tag{11.1}$$

The sign and magnitude of s (and therefore the sign and magnitude of ϑ) depend on our choice of rotational coordinate system. With the choice of rotational coordinate system shown in **Figure 11.22a**, s is measured along the perimeter of the circle, beginning at the positive x axis and ending at the location of the object, and the counterclockwise direction is taken to be positive. Because the rotational coordinate ϑ is a ratio of two lengths, it is a unitless quantity. In contrast, the polar angle θ swept out by the revolving object can be expressed in *radians* (rad), *degrees* (°), or *revolutions* (rev). The relationship between these units is

$$2\pi \text{ rad} = 360° = 1 \text{ rev}. \tag{11.2}$$

Note that, unlike the units for length, time, and inertia, no physical standard is required to specify the units for polar angle.

Rotational coordinate and polar angle are directly related to each other. After one revolution, the arc length s traveled by the object is equal to the circumference of the circle, and so $s = 2\pi r$. Substituting this value for s in Eq. 11.1 yields $\vartheta = 2\pi$ after one revolution. Knowing from Eq. 11.2 that $2\pi \text{ rad} = 1 \text{ rev}$, we see that the rotational coordinate corresponds to the *number of radians in the polar angle*: $\vartheta = \theta/(1 \text{ rad})$.* In other words, given the polar angle θ of the object's position, we can obtain its rotational coordinate by expressing the polar angle in radians and dividing by 1 rad.

The change in the rotational coordinate of an object, the object's final rotational coordinate minus its initial rotational coordinate, is

$$\Delta\vartheta \equiv \vartheta_f - \vartheta_i. \tag{11.3}$$

This quantity is positive for a rotation in the direction of increasing ϑ and negative for a rotation in the direction of decreasing ϑ. Combining this expression with Eq. 11.1 allows us to express $\Delta\vartheta$ as a difference in arc lengths:

$$\Delta\vartheta = \vartheta_f - \vartheta_i = \frac{s_f}{r} - \frac{s_i}{r} = \frac{\Delta s}{r}, \tag{11.4}$$

where Δs is defined as the length of the arc between the final and initial locations of the object, as shown in Figure 11.22b.

11.5 Starting from a position with rotational coordinate zero, an object moves in the positive ϑ direction at a constant speed of 3.0 m/s along the perimeter of a circle of radius 2.0 m. (*a*) What is the object's rotational coordinate after 1.5 s? (*b*) How long does it take the object to complete one revolution? (*c*) What is its rotational coordinate 1.0 s after passing a point on the circle whose polar angle is 90°?

---

*The reason for this division by 1 rad is to cancel out the units of radian. The rotational coordinate ϑ is unitless, but the polar angle θ has units of radians. So for an object that has rotated to an angle of 6.1 rad, the rotational coordinate is $(6.1 \text{ rad})/(1 \text{ rad}) = 6.1$; for an object that has rotated to an angle of 265°, the rotational coordinate is $(265°)(2\pi \text{ rad}/360°)/(1 \text{ rad}) = 4.63$.

In analogy to the definition of average velocity, we can define *average rotational velocity* $\omega_{\vartheta,av}$ as being equal to the change in the rotational coordinate divided by the time interval during which this change takes place:

$$\omega_{\vartheta,av} \equiv \frac{\Delta\vartheta}{\Delta t}. \tag{11.5}$$

The SI unit of average rotational velocity is s^{-1} (inverse second). The subscript ϑ is there to remind us that the average rotational velocity is a signed quantity that can be positive or negative, depending on the choice of positive direction of rotation for ϑ.

The **rotational velocity** ω_{ϑ} is obtained by letting the time interval during which the change in the rotational coordinate is measured approach zero:

$$\omega_{\vartheta} \equiv \lim_{\Delta t \to 0} \frac{\Delta\vartheta}{\Delta t} = \frac{d\vartheta}{dt}. \tag{11.6}$$

The instantaneous rotational velocity is equal to the time derivative of the rotational coordinate just as the instantaneous velocity is equal to the time derivative of position. The **rotational speed** is the absolute value of the rotational velocity:

$$\omega = |\omega_{\vartheta}|. \tag{11.7}$$

The relationship between instantaneous rotational velocity and instantaneous velocity can be obtained by substituting Eq. 11.4 into Eq. 11.5:

$$\omega_{\vartheta} = \frac{d\vartheta}{dt} = \frac{1}{r}\frac{ds}{dt}. \tag{11.8}$$

Because the rate at which the arc length s is swept out is the tangential component of the velocity of the object, $v_t = ds/dt$, we have

$$\omega_{\vartheta} = \frac{v_t}{r} \tag{11.9}$$

or

$$v_t = r\omega_{\vartheta}. \tag{11.10}$$

Both the tangential component of the velocity v_t and the rotational velocity ω_{ϑ} are signed quantities that are positive for motion in the direction of increasing ϑ and negative in the direction of decreasing ϑ. We can also express Eq. 11.10 in terms of speeds:

$$v = r\omega. \tag{11.11}$$

In words, the speed of an object in circular motion equals its rotational speed multiplied by the radius of the circular path. As we concluded when we analyzed Figure 11.6, the speed increases with increasing radius.

We can also define a **rotational acceleration** α_{ϑ} (Greek letter alpha):

$$\alpha_{\vartheta} \equiv \lim_{\Delta t \to 0} \frac{\Delta\omega_{\vartheta}}{\Delta t} = \frac{d\omega_{\vartheta}}{dt} = \frac{d^2\vartheta}{dt^2}. \tag{11.12}$$

The rotational acceleration has SI units s^{-2} (inverse seconds squared). It is a measure of the rate at which the rotational velocity increases.

For *circular motion at constant speed*, the rotational speed $\omega = v/r$ is constant, and so the rotational acceleration is zero. How can rotational acceleration be zero if, as we saw in Section 11.1, circular motion at constant speed requires a nonzero centripetal acceleration? The answer is that rotational acceleration measures the change in the magnitude of the velocity $\vec{v}$ with which an object travels around a circle, while centripetal acceleration measures the change in the *direction* of $\vec{v}$. Even if the object's speed v is constant, meaning its rotational acceleration is zero, the changing direction of $\vec{v}$ means there is a nonzero centripetal acceleration.

To obtain the magnitude of the centripetal acceleration, remember that if the position vector of a revolving object sweeps out an angle θ, the velocity vector $\vec{v}$ sweeps out the same angle, as illustrated in **Figure 11.23**. This means that the two shaded triangles in Figure 11.23 are similar and so

$$\frac{|\Delta \vec{r}|}{r} = \frac{|\Delta \vec{v}|}{v} \tag{11.13}$$

or, rearranging terms and dividing left and right by the time interval Δt during which the change in velocity direction took place,

$$\frac{|\Delta \vec{v}|}{\Delta t} = \frac{v}{r} \frac{|\Delta \vec{r}|}{\Delta t}. \tag{11.14}$$

In the limit for $\Delta t \rightarrow 0$, the term $|\Delta \vec{v}|/\Delta t$ approaches the magnitude of the (centripetal) acceleration, which we shall denote by a_c, and the term $|\Delta \vec{r}|/\Delta t$ approaches the speed v, and so the magnitude of the **centripetal acceleration** is

$$a_c = \frac{v^2}{r} \quad \text{(circular motion).} \tag{11.15}$$

This is the acceleration required to keep an object moving at speed v along the perimeter of a circle of radius r. As we saw in Section 11.1, the centripetal acceleration of an object executing a circular motion at constant speed is directed radially inward.

Although we derived Eq. 11.15 for circular motion at constant speed, *any* object constrained to move along a circle or part of a circle of radius r is subject to a radially inward acceleration of the magnitude given by Eq. 11.15. Because we defined the radial axis to be directed outward from the rotation axis (Figure 11.11), we can write

$$a_r = -\frac{v^2}{r} \quad \text{(any motion along arc of radius } r\text{).} \tag{11.16}$$

When the object's speed is not constant, we have, in addition to this radial component of the acceleration, a component parallel to the velocity (see Checkpoint 11.1). This component is called the **tangential acceleration** because it is always tangent to the trajectory:

$$a_t = \frac{dv}{dt}. \tag{11.17}$$

The tangential component is positive when the speed increases and negative when it decreases.

Figure 11.24 summarizes a number of important facts about circular motion. Figure 11.24a illustrates circular motion at constant speed and Figure 11.24b accelerated circular motion. Note that the velocity is always tangential to the

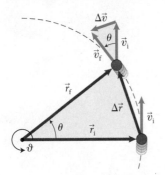

Figure 11.23 Change in the direction of the position $\vec{r}$ and the velocity $\vec{v}$ for an object moving in a circle at constant speed.

trajectory: that is, the radial component of the velocity is always zero. This is true for any type of circular motion, be it at constant speed or accelerated:

$$v_r = 0 \quad \text{(any type of circular motion)}. \tag{11.18}$$

When the circular motion is at constant speed, the radial component of the acceleration is nonzero (Eq. 11.16) and the tangential acceleration is zero:

$$a_t = 0 \quad \text{(circular motion at constant speed)}. \tag{11.19}$$

In that case, the **period** T (the time interval it takes the object to complete one revolution) is

$$T = \frac{2\pi r}{v} = \frac{2\pi}{\omega} \quad \text{(circular motion at constant speed),} \tag{11.20}$$

where we have used Eq. 11.11 relating the speed v to the rotational speed ω.

If the object speeds up or slows down, both components of the acceleration are nonzero. The acceleration no longer points to the center of the circle, as shown in Figure 11.24c, and the magnitude of the acceleration is

$$a = \sqrt{a_r^2 + a_t^2}. \tag{11.21}$$

When the tangential acceleration is nonzero, the rotational acceleration is nonzero too. To relate these two quantities, we substitute Eq. 11.10 for v_t:

$$a_t = \frac{dv_t}{dt} = r\frac{d\omega_\vartheta}{dt}. \tag{11.22}$$

Noting that $d\omega_\vartheta/dt$ is the rotational acceleration α_ϑ (Eq. 11.12), we can write Eq. 11.22 in the form

$$a_t = r\alpha_\vartheta. \tag{11.23}$$

Thus tangential acceleration is related to rotational acceleration in the same way that velocity and rotational velocity are related (Eq. 11.10) and, similarly, arc length and rotational coordinate (Eq. 11.1). For all three we can write (Table 11.1):

translational motion quantity $= r \times$ rotational motion quantity.

If a_t is constant (and so the rotational acceleration is constant too), then the arc length traveled and the tangential velocity are given by the kinematics equations for motion at constant acceleration (Eqs. 3.8 and 3.4):

$$s_f = s_i + v_{t,i}\Delta t + \tfrac{1}{2}a_t(\Delta t)^2 \tag{11.24}$$

$$v_{t,f} = v_{t,i} + a_t\Delta t. \tag{11.25}$$

Dividing both sides of each of these equations by r and substituting the expressions from Table 11.1, we obtain the equivalent kinematics equations for rotational motion:

$$\vartheta_f = \vartheta_i + \omega_{\vartheta,i}\Delta t + \tfrac{1}{2}\alpha_\vartheta(\Delta t)^2 \quad \text{(constant rotational acceleration)} \tag{11.26}$$

$$\omega_{\vartheta,f} = \omega_{\vartheta,i} + \alpha_\vartheta\Delta t \quad \text{(constant rotational acceleration).} \tag{11.27}$$

Table 11.2 gives an overview of the correspondence between translational and rotational kinematic quantities and equations.

Figure 11.24 Circular motion and acceleration.

(a) Circular motion at constant speed

Speed is constant.

(b) Circular motion at increasing speed

Constant tangential acceleration . . .

. . . causes speed to increase.

Radial acceleration also increases.

(c) Acceleration during circular motion

Table 11.1

$s = r\vartheta$	(11.1)
$v_t = r\omega_\vartheta$	(11.10)
$a_t = r\alpha_\vartheta$	(11.23)

Table 11.2 Translational and rotational kinematics

Translational motion (constant acceleration)		Rotational motion (constant rotational acceleration)	
coordinate	x	rotational coordinate	ϑ
x component of displacement	$\Delta x = x_f - x_i$	change in rotational coordinate	$\Delta\vartheta = \vartheta_f - \vartheta_i$
x component of velocity	$v_x = \dfrac{dx}{dt}$	rotational velocity	$\omega_\vartheta = \dfrac{d\vartheta}{dt}$
x component of acceleration	$a_x = \dfrac{dv_x}{dt} = \dfrac{d^2x}{dt^2}$	rotational acceleration	$\alpha_\vartheta = \dfrac{d\omega_\vartheta}{dt} = \dfrac{d^2\vartheta}{dt^2}$
kinematics relationships (constant a_x):	$v_{x,f} = v_{x,i} + a_x\Delta t$	rotational kinematics relationships (constant α_ϑ):	$\omega_{\vartheta,f} = \omega_{\vartheta,i} + \alpha_\vartheta\Delta t$
	$x_f = x_i + v_{x,i}\Delta t + \tfrac{1}{2}a_x(\Delta t)^2$		$\vartheta_f = \vartheta_i + \omega_{\vartheta,i}\Delta t + \tfrac{1}{2}\alpha_\vartheta(\Delta t)^2$
		radial acceleration	$a_r = -\dfrac{v^2}{r} = -r\omega^2$
		tangential acceleration	$a_t = 0$

Example 11.4 Leaning into a curve

A woman is rollerblading to work and, running late, rounds a corner at full speed, sharply leaning into the curve (**Figure 11.25**). If, during the turn, she goes along the arc of a circle of radius 4.5 m at a constant speed of 5.0 m/s, what angle θ must her body make with the vertical in order to round the curve without falling?

Figure 11.25 Example 11.4.

Figure 11.26

❶ GETTING STARTED As she rounds the circular arc at constant speed, the woman executes circular motion at constant speed. She must therefore undergo a centripetal acceleration as a result of the forces exerted on her. To help me determine the forces exerted on her, I draw a free-body diagram (**Figure 11.26**). The forces exerted on the rollerblader are the gravitational force $\vec{F}^G_{Ep}$ and a contact force $\vec{F}^c_{sp}$ exerted by the surface of the road. Now I see why she must lean into the turn: When she stands straight, the contact force is directed straight up, but as she leans, this force develops a component that pushes her toward the center

of the circular arc and provides the necessary centripetal acceleration. I indicate the direction of this centripetal acceleration in my drawing and choose a set of axes—the x axis in the direction of the centripetal acceleration and the y axis upward. (Note that the resulting free-body diagram is similar to that for the bicyclist in Figure 11.17a.) I must determine the angle θ that $\vec{F}^c_{sp}$ makes with the vertical.

❷ DEVISE PLAN From my free-body diagram, I can draw two conclusions. First, the forces in the y direction must add to zero: $\Sigma F_y = 0$. Second, the x component of the contact force provides the centripetal acceleration given by Eq. 11.15. This gives me two equations from which I should be able to determine θ.

❸ EXECUTE PLAN Substituting the centripetal acceleration from Eq. 11.15 into the equation of motion in the x direction, I get

$$\Sigma F_x = ma_x = m(+a_c) = +m\frac{v^2}{r}, \quad (1)$$

where m is the inertia of the rollerblader. (The rollerblader's inertia is not given, but I hope it will drop out and I won't need it.) From my diagram, I see that

$$\Sigma F_x = F^c_{spx} = F^c_{sp}\sin\theta. \quad (2)$$

In the y direction I have $F_{spy}^c = F_{sp}^c \cos \theta$ and $F_{Epy}^G = -mg$. The equation of motion in the y direction then yields

$$\sum F_y = F_{spy}^c + F_{Epy}^G = F_{sp}^c \cos \theta - mg = 0.$$

Solving this equation for F_{sr}^c and substituting the result into Eq. 2, I get

$$\sum F_x = F_{sp}^c \sin \theta = \left(\frac{mg}{\cos \theta}\right) \sin \theta = mg \tan \theta.$$

Substituting this result into Eq. 1 then yields

$$mg \tan \theta = m \frac{v^2}{r}$$

$$\tan \theta = \frac{v^2}{gr} = \frac{(5.0 \text{ m/s})^2}{(9.8 \text{ m/s}^2)(4.5 \text{ m})} = 0.57.$$

This gives an angle $\theta = \tan^{-1}(0.57) = 0.52$ rad, or about 30°. ✔

❹ **EVALUATE RESULT** The angle of the skater in Figure 11.25 is about 30°, and so my answer appears to be reasonable.

✋ **11.6** Estimate the maximum speed with which you could take the curve in Example 11.4. [Hint: What is the maximum coefficient of static friction?]

11.5 Angular momentum

Let us now return to the experiment discussed in Section 11.3: A stationary puck C fastened to a string of length r is struck by an identical puck A initially moving at speed v. For simplicity we'll ignore the pucks' extent and treat them as particles. After the elastic collision, the puck C moves in circular motion at constant speed v. Calling this puck's inertia m, we can say that its kinetic energy is

$$K = \tfrac{1}{2}mv^2. \tag{11.28}$$

Substituting the expression given by Eq. 11.10 for v, we can rewrite this kinetic energy in the form

$$K = \tfrac{1}{2}mv^2 = \tfrac{1}{2}m(r\omega)^2 = \tfrac{1}{2}(mr^2)\omega^2 \tag{11.29}$$

or, defining the term in parentheses as the **rotational inertia** I of puck C about the axis of rotation

$$I \equiv mr^2 \quad \text{(particle)}, \tag{11.30}$$

we get
$$K_{\text{rot}} = \tfrac{1}{2}I\omega^2. \tag{11.31}$$

The rotational inertia of an object about an axis opposes a change in rotational motion about that axis just as inertia opposes a change in translational motion. The SI unit of rotational inertia is $\text{kg} \cdot \text{m}^2$. Because the SI unit of ω is s^{-1}, we get, from Eq. 11.31 SI units of $\text{kg} \cdot \text{m}^2/\text{s}^2$ for the kinetic energy, which is the joule.

Note the remarkable similarity between Eqs. 11.31 and 11.28—inertia m and speed v of Eq. 11.28 are replaced by their rotational equivalents, rotational inertia I and rotational speed ω. The main advantage of writing the kinetic energy in the form of Eq. 11.31 will become clear when we deal with rotating extended objects in Section 11.6: The rotational velocity is the same in all parts of a rotating object, whereas the speed depends on the distance to the axis of rotation (recall Figure 11.7). Because the kinetic energy in Eq. 11.31 is due to rotational motion, it is called the **rotational kinetic energy** of the object.

✋ **11.7** Suppose that in Figure 11.18 $r_C = 2r_B$. (a) What is the ratio of the rotational velocity of B to that of C? (b) What is the ratio of the rotational inertia of B to that of C?

The answers to this checkpoint might surprise you. That the rotational inertia of B is only one-fourth that of C means that B has only one-*fourth* the tendency to resist a change in its rotational motion. So why, when the same force is exerted, is B's rotational velocity only *twice* as large as C's rather than four times as much?

The reason the rotational velocity of B is not as great as you might expect is that the rotational velocity an object acquires depends on how far from the rotation axis it is struck. Increasing the string's length in Figure 11.18 not only increases the puck's rotational inertia but also increases the effectiveness of the blow from the incoming puck. Doubling r for puck C quadruples C's rotational inertia because of the factor r^2 in Eq. 11.30 but also increases puck A's ability to set C in rotational motion. As a result, B's rotational velocity is only twice that of C rather than four times as much.

Figure 11.27 shows two collisions between a bar that is free to rotate about its right end and a puck. In Figure 11.27*a* the puck strikes the end of the rod; in Figure 11.27*b* the rod is struck closer to the axis. Although the rotational inertia of the rod is fixed and although the puck has the same initial momentum, the rod rotates more slowly when struck closer to the rotation axis. (In the extreme case that it is hit right on the axis, the rod doesn't move at all.) So the incoming puck's ability to set other objects in rotational motion depends not only on its momentum but also on how far from the axis it strikes the other object.

Returning to the collision of Section 11.3, we have seen that substituting ω for v and I for m in the expression $\frac{1}{2}mv^2$ yields the final kinetic energy of the struck puck (C in our case), which is equal to the initial kinetic energy of the incoming puck (A):

$$\tfrac{1}{2}mv^2 \to \tfrac{1}{2}I\omega^2 = \tfrac{1}{2}(mr^2)\left(\frac{v}{r}\right)^2 = \tfrac{1}{2}mv^2. \tag{11.32}$$

This relationship tells us that the elastic collision causes all the (translational) kinetic energy initially in puck A to be converted to the rotational kinetic energy of puck C. The sum of the kinetic energy of puck A and the rotational kinetic energy of puck C (that is to say, the kinetic energy of the two-puck system) remains constant, as it should.

What happens if we make the same $m \to I$, $v \to \omega$ substitution in mv, the magnitude of the momentum of puck A? Let's try it:

$$mv \to I\omega = (mr^2)\left(\frac{v}{r}\right) = rmv. \tag{11.33}$$

The result is different this time: The quantity $I\omega$ is not equal to the magnitude mv of the momentum of the incoming puck A. Instead $I\omega$ is equal to the product of mv and the distance r from A to the axis of rotation at the instant of impact. This "rotational momentum" $I\omega$ thus represents precisely what we called the "ability to set in rotational motion" a moment ago: The greater the distance r

Figure 11.27 A rod free to rotate about one end is struck by an incoming puck at different distances from its axis of rotation.

(*a*) Puck strikes rod far from rotation axis

(*b*) Puck strikes rod closer to rotation axis

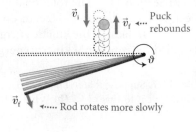

between the location of impact and the axis of rotation, the larger rmv and the easier it is for puck A to make puck C rotate.

The quantity $I\omega$ plays a fundamental role in physics. The larger the value of $I\omega$ for a moving object, the more easily the object can set another object in rotational motion. Because of the analogy to momentum, which measures an object's capacity to set other objects in motion along a straight line, this quantity is called the **angular momentum** and is denoted by the letter L:

$$L_\vartheta \equiv I\omega_\vartheta. \qquad (11.34)$$

The SI units of angular momentum are $kg \cdot m^2/s$. As before, the subscript ϑ means that the angular momentum, like the rotational velocity, is a signed quantity that can be positive or negative, depending on the choice of the positive direction of rotation for ϑ. Substituting Eqs. 11.10 and 11.30 into Eq. 11.34, we get

$$L_\vartheta \equiv I\omega_\vartheta = (mr^2)\left(\frac{v_t}{r}\right) = rmv_t. \qquad (11.35)$$

An object does not need to rotate or revolve in order to possess a nonzero angular momentum. For example, even though it moves in a straight line, the incoming puck A in Figure 11.18 has a nonzero angular momentum—it has the ability to set another puck in rotational motion. You can use Eqs. 11.34 and 11.35 to calculate the angular momentum of objects in circular motion, but what is the angular momentum of an object that moves along a straight line? The first thing to note is that it doesn't make sense to talk about the angular momentum of an object unless we specify an axis of rotation. Figure 11.28 shows how to determine the angular momentum for a particle moving along a straight line. For a given axis of rotation (real or imagined), the value of r in Eq. 11.35 is given by the perpendicular distance $r_\perp$ between the axis of rotation and the straight line defined by the momentum of the object (the radius of the circle for which this line, called the *line of action* of the momentum, is a tangent; see Figure 11.28), while the value of v_t is the speed of the object. The distance $r_\perp$ is called the **lever arm distance**, or simply **lever arm**, of the momentum relative to the axis of rotation. The magnitude of the angular momentum of a particle that moves along a straight line is thus

$$L = r_\perp mv \quad \text{(particle)}. \qquad (11.36)$$

The sign of the angular momentum is determined by the choice of the positive direction of rotation for ϑ. For example, the rotational coordinate of the particle in Figure 11.28 is increasing as it moves along its straight trajectory, and so the angular momentum of the particle is positive.

Figure 11.28 Relative to an axis of rotation, a particle of inertia m moving along a straight line has an angular momentum of magnitude $r_\perp mv$, where $r_\perp$ is the lever arm distance and v is the speed of the object.

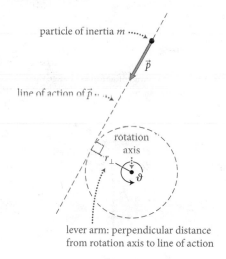

lever arm: perpendicular distance from rotation axis to line of action

Exercise 11.5 Angular momenta

Determine the angular momenta of objects A and B in **Figure 11.29** relative to (*a*) axis 1 and (*b*) axis 2. The inertia of the objects are $m_A = 2.0$ kg and $m_B = 0.50$ kg, and their speeds are $v_A = 0.60$ m/s and $v_B = 1.0$ m/s. The tall side of the rectangle is 2.0 m long and object B travels along the diagonal, which makes an angle of 30° with the long side of the rectangle.

SOLUTION (*a*) Object A: The lever arm distance relative to axis 1 is the long side of the rectangle: $r_\perp = 2.0$ m. The angular momentum is therefore

$$L_{A\vartheta} = +(2.0\text{ m})(2.0\text{ kg})(0.60\text{ m/s}) = +2.4\text{ kg} \cdot m^2/s.$$

The plus sign indicates that the rotational coordinate of A relative to axis 1 increases. ✔

Object B: B's line of motion is the diagonal of the rectangle and so goes through axis 1. Therefore $r_\perp = 0$ and thus $L_{B\vartheta} = 0.$ ✔

Figure 11.29 Exercise 11.5.

Figure 11.30

(b) Object A: The lever arm distance relative to axis 2 is the long side of the rectangle: $r_\perp = 2.0$ m. The angular momentum is therefore $L_{A\vartheta} = -(2.0\text{ m})(2.0\text{ kg})(0.60\text{ m/s}) = -2.4$ kg·m²/s. The minus sign indicates that the rotational coordinate of A relative to axis 2 decreases. ✔

Object B: To determine $r_\perp$ relative to axis 2, I draw a straight line perpendicular to B's line of motion (**Figure 11.30**). Using trigonometry, I see that $\sin 30° = r_\perp /(2.0\text{ m})$, or $r_\perp = (0.5)(2.0\text{ m}) = 1.0$ m, and so $L_{B\vartheta} = +(1.0\text{ m})(0.50\text{ kg})(1.0\text{ m/s}) = +0.50$ kg·m²/s. The plus sign indicates that the rotational coordinate of B relative to axis 2 increases. ✔

Going back to the experiment we discussed in Section 11.3, if we substitute the values of m, $r_\perp$, and v for puck A in Figure 11.18 just before impact, we obtain a value for the angular momentum of puck A just before the impact that is the same as that of puck B after the impact:

$$L_{A\vartheta,i} = L_{B\vartheta,f} = +r_B mv. \qquad (11.37)$$

Because puck A comes to rest after the impact, the change in its angular momentum is $\Delta L_{A\vartheta} = L_{A\vartheta,f} - L_{A\vartheta,i} = 0 - r_B mv = -r_B mv$. The change in the angular momentum of puck B is $\Delta L_{B\vartheta} = L_{B\vartheta,f} - L_{B\vartheta,i} = +r_B mv - 0 = +r_B mv$. As you can readily verify, angular momentum is an extensive quantity (see Section 4.4), and so we can define the angular momentum of the system comprising both pucks as $L_\vartheta = L_{A\vartheta} + L_{B\vartheta}$. Because the change in the angular momentum of one puck is compensated for by the change in the angular momentum of the other puck, the angular momentum of the system does not change in the impact: $\Delta L_\vartheta = 0$.

This observation suggests that angular momentum, like momentum, is a conserved quantity. Indeed, if it weren't for friction, objects in circular motion would tend to continue their circular motion, just as objects in translational motion tend to continue to move along a straight line (see Section 4.1). The more we reduce friction, the longer a spinning wheel keeps turning. In the absence of friction, it would keep turning forever and its angular momentum would be constant. Consider, for example, the particle in circular motion shown in **Figure 11.31**. The particle is subject to a force $\vec{F}$ that has both a radial and a tangential component. The radial component keeps the particle moving in circular motion. The tangential component, which is tangent to the circular trajectory and points in the direction opposite the direction of motion, causes the particle to slow down. In the absence of any tangential forces, however, the angular momentum remains constant.

Strictly speaking, the fact that the angular momentum of the colliding pucks in Figure 11.18 remains constant is a consequence of conservation of momentum—the change in the momentum of B is compensated for by a change in the momentum of A. It turns out, however, that conservation of angular momentum is just as fundamental as conservation of momentum and conservation of energy. We can generalize this new conservation law to situations where it cannot be deduced from other conservation principles, which tells us that **conservation of angular momentum** is a fundamental law of physics:

> **Angular momentum can be transferred from one object to another, but it cannot be created or destroyed.**

This means that whenever the angular momentum of an object changes, there must be a compensating change of the opposite sign in the environment.

The angular momentum of an object or system on which no tangential forces are exerted is therefore constant:

$$\Delta L_\vartheta = 0 \quad \text{(no tangential forces).} \qquad (11.38)$$

Figure 11.31 Tangential forces change the angular momentum.

Tangential component changes speed and angular momentum.

Radial component causes centripetal acceleration.

Exercise 11.6 Spinning faster

Divers increase their spin by tucking in their arms and legs (**Figure 11.32**). Suppose the outstretched body of a diver rotates at 1.2 revolutions per second before he pulls his arms and knees

Figure 11.32 Exercise 11.6.

into his chest, reducing his rotational inertia from 9.4 kg · m² to 3.1 kg · m². What is his rotational velocity after he tucks in his arms and legs?

SOLUTION Once the diver is off the board, the only force exerted on his is the gravitational force exerted by Earth. This force does not affect the angular momentum of the diver (dropped objects do not spontaneously start to rotate), and so his angular momentum must remain constant. If his angular momentum before he tucks is $L_{\vartheta,i}$ and that after is $L_{\vartheta,f}$, then

$$L_{\vartheta,f} = L_{\vartheta,i}$$

and so, from Eq. 11.34, $I_f\omega_{\vartheta,f} = I_i\omega_{\vartheta,i}$

$$\omega_{\vartheta,f} = \frac{I_i}{I_f}\omega_{\vartheta,i}$$

$$= \frac{9.4\ \text{kg} \cdot \text{m}^2}{3.1\ \text{kg} \cdot \text{m}^2}(1.2\ \text{s}^{-1}) = 3.6\ \text{s}^{-1}. ✔$$

 11.8 Does the rotational kinetic energy of the diver in Exercise 11.6 change as he pulls her arms in? Explain.

Example 11.7 Dumbbell collision

In **Figure 11.33**, two identical pucks B and C, each of inertia m, are connected by a rod of negligible inertia and length ℓ that is free to rotate about a fixed axis through its center. A third identical puck A, initially moving at speed v_i, strikes the combination as shown. After the elastic collision, what are the rotational velocity of the dumbbell and the velocity of puck A?

Figure 11.33 Example 11.7

① GETTING STARTED I begin with a two-part sketch (**Figure 11.34**), choosing an x axis in the direction of A's initial motion and choosing counterclockwise as the positive direction of rotation (this is the direction in which I expect the dumbbell to rotate after the collision. Because A hits B head-on and because the inertia of the dumbbell is twice that of A, I expect A

to bounce back and move in the negative x direction after the collision, as my after-collision sketch shows.

Figure 11.34

initial   final

② DEVISE PLAN In elastic collisions the kinetic energy of the system remains constant (see Section 5.5). In this collision I need to consider the kinetic energy of puck A and the rotational kinetic energy of the dumbbell. Because there are two unknowns—A's final velocity and the dumbbell's final rotational velocity—I need an additional law to determine both. To this end I apply conservation of angular momentum (Eq. 11.38) to the system comprising puck A and the dumbbell.

(Continued)

❸ **EXECUTE PLAN** The initial kinetic energy of the system is that of puck A, $\frac{1}{2}mv_i^2$. The final kinetic energy is the sum of the (translational) final kinetic energy of A and the rotational kinetic energy of the dumbbell, $K_f = \frac{1}{2}mv_f^2 + \frac{1}{2}I\omega_f^2$, where I is the rotational inertia of the dumbbell. Ignoring the negligible inertia of the rod, I can say that each puck in the dumbbell contributes a rotational inertia $m(\ell/2)^2$ given by Eq. 11.30, so that the rotational inertia of the dumbbell is

$$I = 2m(\ell/2)^2 = \tfrac{1}{2}m\ell^2. \tag{1}$$

Because the collision is elastic, the final kinetic energy must equal the initial kinetic energy, and so

$$\tfrac{1}{2}mv_i^2 = \tfrac{1}{2}mv_f^2 + \tfrac{1}{2}I\omega_f^2 = \tfrac{1}{2}mv_f^2 + \tfrac{1}{2}(\tfrac{1}{2}m\ell^2)\omega_f^2,$$

where I have substituted for I the expression I obtained in Eq. 1. Dividing both sides by $\frac{1}{2}m$ gives $v_i^2 = v_f^2 + \frac{1}{2}\ell^2\omega_f^2$. Because puck A moves along the x axis, $v_i^2 = v_{x,i}^2$ and $v_f^2 = v_{x,f}^2$. Because $\omega_f^2 = \omega_{\vartheta,f}^2$ I get

$$v_{x,i}^2 = v_{x,f}^2 + \tfrac{1}{2}\ell^2\omega_{\vartheta,f}^2. \tag{2}$$

Next I turn to conservation of angular momentum. The change in A's angular momentum is, from Eq. 11.36,

$$\Delta L_{A\vartheta} = L_{A\vartheta,f} - L_{A\vartheta,i} = (\ell/2)mv_{x,f} - (\ell/2)mv_{x,i}$$

$$= (\ell/2)m(v_{x,f} - v_{x,i}).$$

The initial angular momentum of the dumbbell $L_{d\vartheta,i}$ about the rotation axis is zero; its final angular momentum about this axis is, from Eq. 11.34, $L_{d\vartheta,f} = I\omega_{\vartheta,f}$. The change in the dumbbell's angular momentum is thus

$$\Delta L_{d\vartheta} = I\omega_{\vartheta,f} - 0 = \tfrac{1}{2}m\ell^2\omega_{\vartheta,f}.$$

Because the system is isolated, its angular momentum doesn't change (Eq. 11.38), and so

$$\Delta L_{\vartheta} = \Delta L_{A\vartheta} + \Delta L_{d\vartheta}$$

$$= (\ell/2)m(v_{x,f} - v_{x,i}) + \tfrac{1}{2}m\ell^2\omega_{\vartheta,f} = 0$$

or $\qquad\qquad v_{x,i} = v_{x,f} + \ell\omega_{\vartheta,f}. \tag{3}$

Solving Eq. 3 for $v_{x,f}$, substituting the result into Eq. 2, and using the quadratic equation to solve for the rotational velocity of the dumbbell, I get

$$\omega_{\vartheta,f} = \frac{4v_{x,i}}{3\ell} = +\frac{4v_i}{3\ell}. \checkmark$$

Substituting this result back into Eq. 3, I obtain for the final velocity of puck A $v_{x,f} = -\frac{1}{3}v_{x,i} = -\frac{1}{3}v_i$. ✔

❹ **EVALUATE RESULT** The final rotational velocity is positive, indicating that the dumbbell in Figure 11.34 rotates counterclockwise, in agreement with my drawing. The x component of the final velocity of puck A is negative, indicating that it bounces back, as I expected.

Figure 11.35 Procedure for determining the rotational inertia of an extended object.

(a) To determine rotational inertia of an extended object . . .

(b) . . . divide object into small segments of inertia δm and add up their rotational inertias.

✋ **11.9** (a) Follow the line of reasoning used in working from Eq. 11.28 to Eq. 11.31 to verify that the rotational inertia of the dumbbell in Example 11.7 is indeed $\frac{1}{2}m\ell^2$. (b) Does the momentum of the system remain constant in the collision of Figure 11.33?

11.6 Rotational inertia of extended objects

We can apply the concept of rotational inertia to extended rigid objects. Consider, for example, the rotating object in **Figure 11.35**. If you imagine breaking down the object into many small segments of equal inertia δm, each segment has a different velocity $\vec{v}$, but all move in circles about the axis at the same rotational speed ω.

The rotational kinetic energy of the rotating object is the sum of the kinetic energies of the segments:

$$K_{rot} = \tfrac{1}{2}\delta m_1 v_1^2 + \tfrac{1}{2}\delta m_2 v_2^2 + \cdots = \sum_n (\tfrac{1}{2}\delta m_n v_n^2). \tag{11.39}$$

Because each segment has a different velocity, it is difficult to evaluate this expression. Substituting Eq. 11.11, however, we obtain

$$K_{rot} = \sum_n \left[\tfrac{1}{2}\delta m_n(\omega r_n)^2\right] = \tfrac{1}{2}\left[\sum_n \delta m_n r_n^2\right]\omega^2, \tag{11.40}$$

where r_n measures the distance from segment n to the rotation axis. Because

$\delta m_n r_n^2$ is the rotational inertia I_n of segment n (Eq. 11.30), we can write this expression in the form

$$K_{\text{rot}} = \tfrac{1}{2}\left[\sum_n I_n\right]\omega^2 = \tfrac{1}{2}I\omega^2, \tag{11.41}$$

where I is the rotational inertia of the entire object. So, once we know the object's rotational inertia, it is straightforward to calculate its rotational kinetic energy.

Equations 11.40 and 11.41 show that the rotational inertia of an extended object can be obtained by dividing the object into small segments and computing the sum of the contributions of the small segment:

$$I = \sum_n \delta m_n r_n^2. \tag{11.42}$$

To evaluate this sum for the extended object, we take the limit of this expression as $\delta m_n \to 0$. In this limit, the sum becomes an integral:

$$I = \lim_{\delta m_n \to 0} \sum_n \delta m_n r_n^2 \equiv \int r^2 dm \quad \text{(extended object).} \tag{11.43}$$

This integral is difficult to evaluate for an arbitrarily shaped object. As the next few examples will show, however, the integral is relatively easy to calculate for objects that exhibit some symmetry and are *uniform* (that is to say, the inertia is uniformly distributed over the volume of the object). **Table 11.3** lists the results of additional calculations.

Table 11.3 Rotational inertia of uniform objects of inertia M about axes through their center of mass

Rotation axes oriented so that object could roll on surface: For these axes, rotational inertia has the form cMR^2, where $c = I/MR^2$ is called the *shape factor*. The farther the object's material from the rotation axis, the larger the shape factor and hence the rotational inertia.

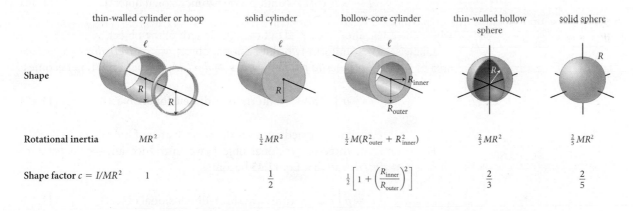

	thin-walled cylinder or hoop	solid cylinder	hollow-core cylinder	thin-walled hollow sphere	solid sphere
Rotational inertia	MR^2	$\tfrac{1}{2}MR^2$	$\tfrac{1}{2}M(R_{\text{outer}}^2 + R_{\text{inner}}^2)$	$\tfrac{2}{3}MR^2$	$\tfrac{2}{5}MR^2$
Shape factor $c = I/MR^2$	1	$\tfrac{1}{2}$	$\tfrac{1}{2}\left[1 + \left(\dfrac{R_{\text{inner}}}{R_{\text{outer}}}\right)^2\right]$	$\tfrac{2}{3}$	$\tfrac{2}{5}$

Other axis orientations

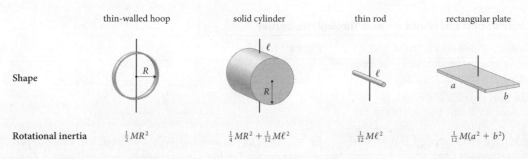

	thin-walled hoop	solid cylinder	thin rod	rectangular plate
Rotational inertia	$\tfrac{1}{2}MR^2$	$\tfrac{1}{4}MR^2 + \tfrac{1}{12}M\ell^2$	$\tfrac{1}{12}M\ell^2$	$\tfrac{1}{12}M(a^2 + b^2)$

Example 11.8 Rotational inertia of a hoop about an axis through its center

Calculate the rotational inertia of a hoop of inertia m and radius R about an axis perpendicular to the plane of the hoop and passing through its center.

① GETTING STARTED I begin by drawing the hoop and a coordinate system (**Figure 11.36**). Because the axis goes through the center of the hoop, I let the origin be at that location. The axis of rotation is perpendicular to the plane of the drawing and passes through the origin.

Figure 11.36

② DEVISE PLAN Equation 11.43 gives the rotational inertia of an object as the sum of the contributions from many small segments. If I divide the hoop into infinitesimally small segments each of inertia dm, I see that each segment lies the same distance $r = R$ from the rotation axis (one such segment is shown in Figure 11.36). This means I can pull the constant $r^2 = R^2$ out of the integral in Eq. 11.43, making it easy to calculate.

③ EXECUTE PLAN Substituting $r = R$ in Eq. 11.43, I obtain

$$I = \int r^2\, dm = R^2 \int dm = mR^2. \checkmark$$

④ EVALUATE RESULT This result makes sense because all the material contained in the hoop lies at the same distance R from the rotation axis. Therefore the rotational inertia of the hoop is the same as that of a particle of inertia m located a distance R from the rotation axis, which I know from Eq. 11.30: $I = mR^2$.

For objects in which not all the material is the same distance from the rotation axis, we need to express dm in terms of either Cartesian or polar coordinates in order to evaluate the integral in Eq. 11.43. For uniform one-dimensional objects, we place the object along a positive x axis and introduce a new quantity: *inertia per unit length* $\lambda \equiv dm/dx$. Each small segment dm of the object can then be written as the product of λ and an infinitesimal length dx: $dm = \lambda\, dx$. Equation 11.43 thus becomes, after substituting x for r,

$$I = \lambda \int x^2 dx \quad \text{(uniform one-dimensional object)}, \tag{11.44}$$

where the integration is carried out over the length of the object.

Likewise, for a uniform two-dimensional object, we convert dm to a surface area by defining an *inertia per unit area* $\sigma \equiv dm/dA$, so that Eq. 11.43 becomes

$$I = \sigma \int r^2 dA \quad \text{(uniform two-dimensional object)}, \tag{11.45}$$

where the integration is carried out over the surface area of the object.

For a uniform three-dimensional object, we introduce an *inertia per unit volume* $\rho \equiv dm/dV$, so that Eq. 11.43 becomes

$$I = \rho \int r^2 dV \quad \text{(uniform three-dimensional object)}, \tag{11.46}$$

where the integration is carried out over the volume of the object.

Example 11.9 Rotational inertia of a rod about an axis through its center

Calculate the rotational inertia of a uniform solid rod of inertia m and length ℓ about an axis perpendicular to the long axis of the rod and passing through its center.

① GETTING STARTED I begin with a sketch of the rod. For this one-dimensional object, I choose an x axis that lies along the rod's long axis, and because the rotation being analyzed is about a rotation axis located through the rod's center, I choose this point for the origin of my x axis (**Figure 11.37**).

Figure 11.37

② DEVISE PLAN Because the rod is a uniform one-dimensional object, I can use Eq. 11.44 to calculate its rotational inertia. First

I determine the inertia per unit length λ. Then I carry out the integration from one end of the rod ($x = -\ell/2$) to the other ($x = +\ell/2$).

❸ **EXECUTE PLAN** The inertia per unit length is $\lambda = m/\ell$. Substituting this expression and the integration boundaries into Eq. 11.44, I get

$$I = \lambda \int x^2 dx = \frac{m}{\ell} \int_{-\ell/2}^{+\ell/2} x^2 dx = \frac{m}{\ell}\left[\frac{x^3}{3}\right]_{-\ell/2}^{+\ell/2} = \frac{1}{12}m\ell^2. \checkmark$$

❹ **EVALUATE RESULT** If I approximate each half of the rod as a particle located a distance $\ell/4$ from the origin I chose in Figure 11.37, the rotational inertia of the rod would be, from Eq. 11.30, $2(\frac{1}{2}m)(\frac{1}{4}\ell)^2 = \frac{1}{16}m\ell^2$. This is not too far from the value I obtained, so my answer appears to be reasonable.

✋ **11.10** Calculate the rotational inertia of the rod in Example 11.9 about an axis perpendicular to the long axis of the rod and passing through one end.

Example 11.10 Rotational inertia of hollow-core cylinder

Calculate the rotational inertia of a uniform hollow-core cylinder of inner radius R_{inner}, outer radius R_{outer}, length ℓ, and inertia m about an axis parallel to the cylinder's length and passing through its center, as in **Figure 11.38**.

Figure 11.38 Example 11.10.

Figure 11.39

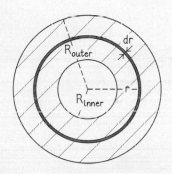

❶ **GETTING STARTED** As in Example 11.9, I will divide this cylinder into segments and integrate the contributions of all the segments over the volume of the cylinder. There are many ways to divide the cylinder into small segments dm, but I can simplify the integration by exploiting the cylindrical symmetry. Starting at the inner face of the wall, at R_{inner}, and moving toward the outer face, at R_{outer}, I divide the wall into a series of many thin-walled cylindrical shells, each of thickness dr and length ℓ and all concentric with the original cylinder, as shown in my top-down sketch of the cylinder (**Figure 11.39**). Because each shell is infinitely thin, all the material in each shell is the same distance r from the axis of rotation, which simplifies the calculation.

❷ **DEVISE PLAN** The hollow-core cylinder is a uniform, three-dimensional object, so I should use Eq. 11.46. First, I must determine the inertia per unit volume, m/V, for it. Next, I must express the infinitesimal volume dV of each shell in terms of r and dr. Finally, I should carry out the integration for values of r from R_{inner} to R_{outer}.

❸ **EXECUTE PLAN** Each thin-walled shell has an inertia $dm = \rho\, dV$, where ρ is inertia per unit volume and dV is the

volume of the shell. To determine $\rho = m/V$ for the cylinder, I divide its inertia m by its volume V. The volume of the solid part of the cylinder plus the empty space that forms its core is $\pi R_{outer}^2 \ell$ and that of the core is $\pi R_{inner}^2 \ell$. So the volume of the cylinder is $V = \pi(R_{outer}^2 - R_{inner}^2)\ell$, and $\rho = m/\pi(R_{outer}^2 - R_{inner}^2)\ell$.

Each shell has an outer surface area of $2\pi r\ell$ and thickness dr, and so its volume is $dV = 2\pi r\ell\, dr$. The rotational inertia of the entire cylinder is thus

$$I = \rho\int r^2 dV = \rho\int_{R_{inner}}^{R_{outer}} r^2(2\pi r\ell)dr = 2\pi\rho\ell\int_{R_{inner}}^{R_{outer}} r^3 dr.$$

Working out the integral, I get

$$I = 2\pi\rho\ell\left[\frac{r^4}{4}\right]_{R_{inner}}^{R_{outer}} = \frac{\pi\rho\ell(R_{outer}^4 - R_{inner}^4)}{2}$$

$$= \frac{\pi\ell(R_{outer}^4 - R_{inner}^4)}{2}\frac{m}{\pi\ell(R_{outer}^2 - R_{inner}^2)}.$$

Factoring $R_{outer}^4 - R_{inner}^4 = (R_{outer}^2 + R_{inner}^2)(R_{outer}^2 - R_{inner}^2)$, I get for the rotational inertia of the hollow-core cylinder

$$I_{hollow\text{-}core\ cylinder} = \tfrac{1}{2}m(R_{outer}^2 + R_{inner}^2). \checkmark$$

❹ **EVALUATE RESULT** In the limit $R_{inner} = R_{outer}$, the cylinder becomes a thin-walled cylindrical shell of radius R_{outer}, and my result becomes $I = mR_{outer}^2$, as I expect for an object that has all its material a distance R from the axis of rotation.

The result from Example 11.10 allows us to determine the rotational inertia of a solid cylinder by setting R_{inner} equal to zero and R_{outer} equal to the radius R of the cylinder. About the long axis of the cylinder, we have

$$I_{\text{solid cylinder}} = \tfrac{1}{2}mR^2. \tag{11.47}$$

11.11 Note in Example 11.10 that the rotational inertia of a thick cylindrical shell is $\frac{1}{2}m(R^2_{\text{outer}} + R^2_{\text{inner}})$ while that of a solid cylinder is $\frac{1}{2}mR^2_{\text{outer}}$. Does the fact that the factor $R^2_{\text{outer}} + R^2_{\text{inner}}$ is larger than the factor R^2_{outer} mean that you can increase the rotational inertia of a solid cylinder by drilling a hole through it?

Figure 11.40 The parallel-axis theorem relates the rotational inertia about an axis through the center of mass to the rotational inertia about other parallel axes.

(a)

(b)

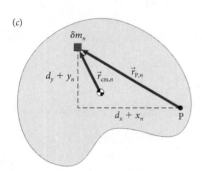

(c)

Because rotational inertia depends on the location of the rotation axis, tables such as Table 11.3 may seem to be of limited utility. However, there is a simple relationship between the rotational inertia of an object about an axis through its center of mass and its rotational inertia about any axis parallel to the center-of-mass axis. Consider the object shown in **Figure 11.40**. Let us derive an expression relating the rotational inertia of the object about an axis through its center of mass to the rotational inertia about a parallel axis through an arbitrary point P.

According to Eq. 11.42, the rotational inertia of the object about an axis through its center of mass is

$$I_{\text{cm}} = \sum_n \delta m_n r^2_{\text{cm},n} = \sum_n \delta m_n (x^2_n + y^2_n), \tag{11.48}$$

where I have used the Pythagorean theorem for the shaded right triangle in Figure 11.40b to substitute for $r^2_{\text{cm},n}$. The rotational inertia about a parallel axis through P a distance d away from the center of mass is

$$I = \sum_n \delta m_n r^2_{\text{P},n} = \sum_n \delta m_n[(d_x + x_n)^2 + (d_y + y_n)^2], \tag{11.49}$$

where now the Pythagorean substituting comes from the right triangle in Figure 11.40c. Working out the right side, I obtain

$$I = \sum_n \delta m_n(d^2_x + 2d_x x_n + x^2_n + d^2_y + 2d_y y_n + y^2_n). \tag{11.50}$$

From the definition of the center of mass (Eq. 6.24), I know that if the center of mass is at the origin, then

$$\sum_n \delta m_n x_n = \sum_n \delta m_n y_n = 0, \tag{11.51}$$

and because d_x and d_y are constant, the terms that contain $2d_x x_n$ and $2d_y y_n$ drop out of Eq. 11.50, leaving me with

$$I = \sum_n \delta m_n[(d^2_x + d^2_y) + (x^2_n + y^2_n)] = \sum_n \delta m_n d^2 + I_{\text{cm}}. \tag{11.52}$$

The factor d^2 can be pulled out of the summation, and so we see that the rotational inertia about the parallel axis is

$$I = I_{\text{cm}} + md^2. \tag{11.53}$$

This relationship is called the **parallel-axis theorem**.

Example 11.11 Rotational inertia of a rod about an axis through one end

Use the parallel-axis theorem to calculate the rotational inertia of a uniform solid rod of inertia m and length ℓ about an axis perpendicular to the length of the rod and passing through one end.

❶ GETTING STARTED I first make a sketch of the rod, showing its center of mass and the location of the rotational axis (**Figure 11.41**). Because I am told to use the parallel-axis theorem, I know I have to work with the rod's center of mass. I know that for a uniform rod, the center of mass coincides with the geometric center, and so I mark that location in my sketch.

Figure 11.41 A solid rod of length ℓ rotating about an axis at one end.

❷ DEVISE PLAN In Example 11.9, I determined that the rotational inertia about an axis through the rod's center is $I = \frac{1}{12}m\ell^2$. For a uniform rod, the center of mass coincides with the geometric center, so I can use Eq. 11.53 to determine the rotational inertia about a parallel axis through one end.

❸ EXECUTE PLAN The distance between the rotation axis and the center of mass is $d = \frac{1}{2}\ell$, and so, with $I_{cm} = \frac{1}{12}m\ell^2$ from Example 11.9, Eq. 11.53 yields

$$I = I_{cm} + md^2 = \tfrac{1}{12}m\ell^2 + m\left(\frac{\ell}{2}\right)^2 = \tfrac{1}{3}m\ell^2. \checkmark$$

❹ EVALUATE RESULT I obtained the same answer in Checkpoint 11.10 by directly working out the integral.

 11.12 About what axis is the rotational inertia of an extended object smallest?

Chapter Glossary

SI units of physical quantities are given in parentheses.

Angular momentum L_ϑ $(\text{kg} \cdot \text{m}^2/\text{s})$ The capacity of an object to make other objects rotate:

$$L_\vartheta \equiv I\omega_\vartheta. \tag{11.34}$$

Centripetal acceleration a_c (m/s^2) The acceleration required to make an object go around a circular trajectory. An object going at speed v through an arc of radius r has a radially inward acceleration of magnitude

$$a_c = \frac{v^2}{r} \quad \text{(circular motion)}. \tag{11.15}$$

Circular motion at constant speed Motion at constant speed along a circular path. Any object in circular motion at constant speed is subject to a force (or vector sum of forces) directed toward the center of the circular path.

Conservation of angular momentum Angular momentum can be transferred from one object to another, but it cannot be created or destroyed.

Lever arm distance $r_\perp$ (m) The perpendicular distance between an axis of rotation and the line of action of a vector.

Parallel-axis theorem The relationship between the rotational inertia of an object about an axis through its center of mass and its rotational inertia about any parallel axis a distance d away:

$$I = I_{cm} + md^2. \tag{11.53}$$

Period T (s) The time interval it takes an object to complete one revolution:

$$T = \frac{2\pi r}{v} = \frac{2\pi}{\omega} \quad \text{(circular motion at constant speed)}. \tag{11.20}$$

Rotational acceleration α_ϑ (s^{-2}) The rate at which an object's rotational velocity changes:

$$\alpha_\vartheta = \frac{d\omega_\vartheta}{dt} = \frac{d^2\vartheta}{dt^2}. \tag{11.12}$$

The rotational acceleration changes the speed of an object moving in a circle of radius r. It is related to the tangential acceleration by

$$a_t = r\alpha_\vartheta. \tag{11.23}$$

Rotational coordinate ϑ (unitless) A scalar that specifies the position of an object on a circle. It is defined as the length of arc s measured from the positive x axis divided by the radius r of the circle:

$$\vartheta \equiv \frac{s}{r}. \tag{11.1}$$

Rotational inertia I $(\text{kg} \cdot \text{m}^2)$ A scalar that is a measure of an object's tendency to resist changes in rotational velocity. For a particle of inertia m, the rotational inertia about an axis a distance r from the particle is

$$I \equiv mr^2 \quad \text{(particle)}. \tag{11.30}$$

For an extended object,

$$I \equiv \int r^2 dm \quad \text{(object)}. \tag{11.43}$$

Rotational kinetic energy K_{rot} (J) The kinetic energy associated with rotational motion. For an object of rotational inertia I with a rotational speed ω:

$$K_{rot} = \tfrac{1}{2}I\omega^2. \tag{11.31}$$

Rotational motion The type of motion for which the particles in an object follow different circular paths centered on a straight line called the *axis of rotation*.

Rotational speed ω (s^{-1}) The magnitude of the rotational velocity, $\omega = |\omega_\vartheta|$.

Rotational velocity ω_ϑ (s^{-1}) The rate at which an object's rotational coordinate changes:

$$\omega_\vartheta = \frac{d\vartheta}{dt}. \tag{11.6}$$

For an object moving along a circle of radius r, the rotational velocity ω_ϑ and the tangential velocity v_t are related by

$$v_t = r\omega_\vartheta. \tag{11.10}$$

Tangential acceleration The component of the acceleration parallel to a circular trajectory; for circular motion at constant speed, $a_t = 0$.

Translational motion The type of motion that involves no change in an object's orientation. For such motion, all the particles in the object move along identical parallel trajectories.

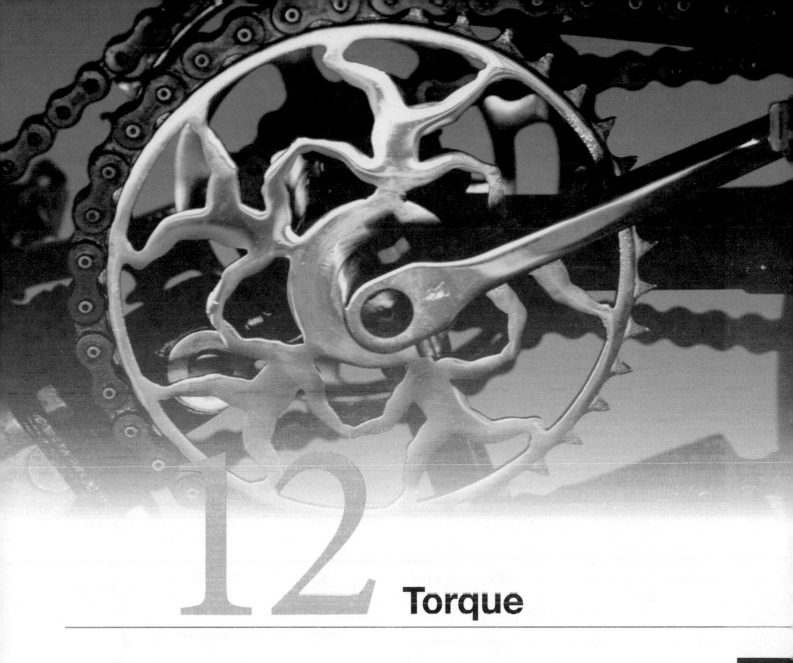

12 Torque

12.1 Torque and angular momentum

12.2 Free rotation

12.3 Extended free-body diagrams

12.4 The vectorial nature of rotation

12.5 Conservation of angular momentum

12.6 Rolling motion

12.7 Torque and energy

12.8 The vector product

CONCEPTS

QUANTITATIVE TOOLS

Having described the basic principles of rotational motion, we now turn our attention to the cause of changes in this motion. Continuing to exploit the analogy between translational and rotational motion, we introduce a rotational analog of force called *torque*. A torque causes an object's angular momentum to change, in the same way that a force causes an object's momentum to change. We also study how to describe rotations that take place about an axis that is not fixed. To complete our description of rotations, we examine rotations in more than one dimension.

12.1 Torque and angular momentum

In the preceding chapter we studied how objects can be made to rotate. As I mentioned in Section 11.5, tangential components of forces cause the angular momentum of an object to change (Figure 11.31). If you exert a force on the edge of a stationary wheel in a direction tangential to the rim, as illustrated in **Figure 12.1a**, the wheel starts to rotate. To twist the cap off a jar, you exert a tangential force at the edge of the cap, as in Figure 12.1b.

When you exert a force on an object to set it in translational motion, only the magnitude and direction of that force play a role: The object accelerates in the direction of the force, and the greater your force, the greater the acceleration. When you exert a force on an object to twist or rotate the object, not only the magnitude and the direction of the force but also the point at which you exert it determine how effective that force is in rotating the object. For example, if you push on a seesaw to lift a child seated on the opposite end, as illustrated in **Figure 12.2**, it is best to push as far as possible from the pivot of the seesaw and to push in a direction perpendicular to the seesaw. If you push very close to the pivot or if you push in a direction not perpendicular to the seesaw, it is more difficult to rotate the seesaw about its pivot. For a force of a given magnitude, the ability to rotate the seesaw is greatest when the force is exerted as indicated in Figure 12.2a.

The reason that the ability of a force to rotate objects depends on the point of application is most easily understood in terms of energy and work. Suppose you raise the child of Figure 12.2 by exerting a force $\vec{F}$ straight down

on the opposite end of the seesaw, as in **Figure 12.3a**. Raising the child a vertical distance Δy means increasing the gravitational potential energy of the Earth-child system by an amount $mg\,\Delta y$, where m is the child's inertia. This increase in potential energy is due to work done by you on the system. As you raise the child a distance Δy, your end of the seesaw goes down an equal amount. The work done by you on the system is equal to the magnitude of the force times the force displacement, or $F\,\Delta y_F$. If the child begins and ends at rest, so that there is no change in kinetic energy, the work done by you on the system must equal the change in potential energy of the Earth-child system: $mg\,\Delta y = F\,\Delta y_F$. So we see that to lift the child by pushing on the opposite end of the seesaw, the magnitude of the force $\vec{F}$ must be equal to the magnitude mg of the force of gravity on the child.

Suppose, however, you had pushed not on the far end of the seesaw but rather halfway between the pivot and the end. As Figure 12.3b shows, that point of the seesaw moves down only half the original force displacement, and so to do the same amount of work, the force you must exert is twice as great as before. The closer to the pivot you push, the greater the force required to raise the child.

We can use the same line of reasoning to understand why the force is most effective when it is oriented perpendicular to the seesaw. If the exerted force points in any

Figure 12.2 Easier and harder ways to rotate a seesaw.

Seesaw is easier to rotate if you push straight down on end of board . . .

(a)

pivot

. . . than if you push closer to pivot . . .

(b)

. . . or at angle to board.

(c)

Figure 12.1 To (a) make a wheel rotate and (b) twist a cap off a jar, you must exert a force tangential to their rims.

(a)

(b)

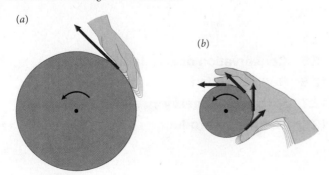

other direction, we can decompose it into components parallel and perpendicular to the seesaw (Figure 12.3c). The component parallel to the seesaw merely pushes the seesaw against the pivot and doesn't contribute to any rotational displacement of the seesaw: In the extreme case that the force is directed entirely along the seesaw, nothing happens. So it is only the component perpendicular to the seesaw, $\vec{F}_\perp$, that causes the seesaw to rotate.

To find out more accurately what determines the turning ability of a force, consider the rod in **Figure 12.4**. The rod is suspended by a pivot attached at a point that is off-center, and the rod is free to rotate about that point. Two objects of unequal inertias m_1 and m_2 are suspended on either end of the rod, keeping the rod in balance so that it is at rest. For simplicity we assume that the inertia of the rod is negligible compared to m_1 and m_2. Before reading on, complete the following checkpoint.

12.1 (a) Draw a free-body diagram for the rod of Figure 12.4. Let the inertia of the rod be negligible compared to m_1 and m_2. (b) Would the free-body diagram change if you slide object 2 to the left? (c) Experiments show that when $m_1 = 2m_2$ the rod is balanced for $r_2 = 2r_1$. How is the ratio r_1/r_2 related to the ratio m_1/m_2? (d) What would happen if you remove object 1 from the rod? (e) What would happen if you double the inertia of object 1? (f) What would happen if you carefully place a penny on top of object 1? Let the inertia of the two objects be significantly larger than that of the penny. (g) Is there a difference between what would happen in parts e and f?

Figure 12.3 The reason you can rotate the seesaw most easily by pushing downward on the end of the board.

(a) Pushing downward on board's end minimizes force you must exert on child + seesaw system because . . .

(b) . . . work done on system is proportional to force displacement Δy_F, which increases with distance from pivot.

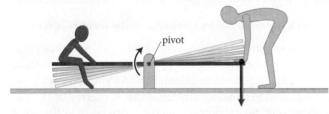

(c) Only the component of $\vec{F}$ perpendicular to board does work on seesaw.

The forces exerted by the two objects in Figure 12.4 each have the ability to rotate the rod—object 1 tends to rotate the rod in a counterclockwise direction, object 2 in a clockwise direction. This ability of a force to rotate an object about an axis is called the **torque** about that axis. Torque is the rotational analog of force: Forces cause (translational) acceleration; torques cause rotational acceleration about an axis. The rod in Figure 12.4 is balanced because the torques caused by the two forces—their ability to rotate the rod—are equal in magnitude, but the rotations they tend to cause are in opposite directions, and so they sum to zero.

Note that the magnitudes of the two forces that cause these equal torques in opposite directions are not themselves equal: $F_1 = m_1 g$ and $F_2 = m_2 g$, with $m_2 \neq m_1$. From experiment we know, however, that the rod is balanced when $r_1 F_1 = r_2 F_2$. This suggests that the torque caused by each force is $r_\perp F$, the product of the magnitude of that force and the lever arm distance of the force relative to the axis of rotation (the perpendicular distance between the line of action of the force and the pivot; see Section 11.5). The line of action of the upward force exerted by the pivot on the rod (see Checkpoint 12.1) goes through the axis of rotation. Consequently, the corresponding lever arm distance is zero, and so this force does not cause any torque about the pivot.

In Figure 12.4, the forces exerted on the rod are perpendicular to it. **Figure 12.5** shows two equivalent ways to determine the torque caused by a force that is not perpendicular to the radial line from the pivot to the point of application of the force. One way is to decompose the force into components parallel and perpendicular to this axis (Figure 12.5a). Only the perpendicular component causes the lever to rotate; the parallel component simply pulls on the pivot. The torque caused by $\vec{F}$ is thus $rF_\perp = r(F \sin \theta)$, where r is the length of the vector pointing from the axis of rotation to the point of application of the force. Note that we can also write this torque as $(r \sin \theta)F$, which is precisely $r_\perp F$, as we surmised. Figure 12.5b shows how to determine $r_\perp$: It is the perpendicular distance between the line of

Figure 12.4 Unequal weights balance a rod that is suspended off-center.

(a)

(b)

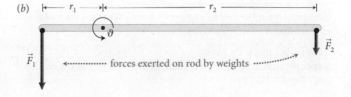

Figure 12.5 Two ways to determine the torque caused by a force exerted on a lever at an angle θ.

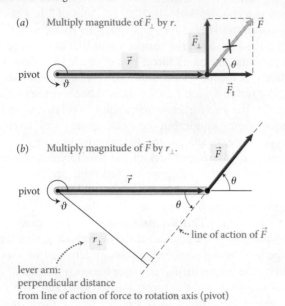

(a) Multiply magnitude of $\vec{F}_\perp$ by r.

pivot

(b) Multiply magnitude of $\vec{F}$ by $r_\perp$.

pivot

line of action of $\vec{F}$

lever arm:
perpendicular distance
from line of action of force to rotation axis (pivot)

action of the force and the axis of rotation. So, the torque caused by a force exerted on an object is the product of the magnitude of the force and its lever arm distance. It can be written equivalently as $rF_\perp$ and as $r_\perp F$.

Like other rotational quantities, torque carries a sign that depends on the choice of direction for increasing ϑ. In Figure 12.4, for example, the torque caused by $\vec{F}_1$ about the pivot tends to rotate the rod in the direction of increasing ϑ and so is positive; the torque caused by $\vec{F}_2$ is negative. The sum of the two torques about the pivot is then $r_1 F_1 + (-r_2 F_2)$. As we've seen, the two torques are equal in magnitude when the rod is balanced, and so the sum of the torques is zero. When the sum of the torques is not zero, the rod's rotational acceleration is nonzero, and so its rotational velocity and angular momentum change.

In the situations depicted in Figures 12.4 and 12.5 we used the pivot to calculate the lever arm distances. This is a natural choice because that is the point about which the object under consideration is free to rotate. However, torques also play a role for stationary objects that are suspended or supported at several different points and that are not free to rotate—for example, a plank or bridge supported at either end. To determine what reference point to use in such cases, complete the following exercise.

Exercise 12.1 Reference point

Consider again the rod in Figure 12.4. Calculate the sum of the torques about the left end of the rod.

SOLUTION I begin by making a sketch of the rod and the three forces exerted on it, showing their points of application on the rod (**Figure 12.6**).

Figure 12.6

reference point

The lever arm distances must now be determined relative to the left end of the rod. The lever arm distance of force $\vec{F}_1$ to this point is zero, and so the torque caused by that force about the left end of the rod is zero. If I choose counterclockwise as the positive direction of rotation, $\vec{F}_2$ causes a negative torque about the left end of the rod; the force $\vec{F}_{pr}^c$ exerted by the pivot causes a positive torque about the left end of the rod. The lever arm distance of $\vec{F}_2$ about the left end of the rod is $r_1 + r_2$; that of $\vec{F}_{pr}^c$ is r_1. Because the rod is at rest, the magnitude of the force exerted by the pivot is equal to the sum of the forces $\vec{F}_1$ and $\vec{F}_2$. Taking into account the signs of the torques, we find that the sum of the torques about the left end of the rod is $r_1(F_1 + F_2) - (r_1 + r_2)F_2 = r_1 F_1 - r_2 F_2$. This is the same result we obtained for the torques about the pivot, and so the sum of the torques about the left end is zero. ✔

Exercise 12.1 shows that the sum of the torques about the left end of the rod is zero, just like the sum of the torques about the pivot. You can repeat the calculation for the torques about the right end of the rod or any other point, and each time you will find that the sum of the torques is zero. The reason is that the rod is not rotating about any point, and so the sum of the torques must be zero about any point. In general we can say:

For a stationary object, the sum of the torques is zero.

For a stationary object we can choose any reference point we like to calculate torques. It pays to choose a reference point that simplifies the calculation. As you have seen, we do not need to consider any force that is exerted at the reference point. So, by putting the reference point at the point of application of a force, we can eliminate that force from the calculation.

12.2 In the situation depicted in Figure 12.2a, you must continue to exert a force on the seesaw to keep the child off the ground. The force you exert causes a torque on the seesaw, and yet the seesaw's rotational acceleration is zero. How can this be if torques cause objects to accelerate rotationally?

Example 12.2 Torques on lever

Three forces are exerted on the lever of **Figure 12.7**. Forces $\vec{F}_1$ and $\vec{F}_3$ are equal in magnitude, and the magnitude of $\vec{F}_2$ is half as great. Force $\vec{F}_1$ is horizontal, $\vec{F}_2$ and $\vec{F}_3$ are vertical, and the lever makes an angle of $45°$ with the horizontal. Do these forces cause the lever to rotate about the pivot? If so, in which direction?

CONCEPTS

Figure 12.7 Example 12.2.

Figure 12.8

❹ **EVALUATE RESULT** Looking at Figure 12.7, I see that the two larger forces ($\vec{F}_1$ and $\vec{F}_3$) cause counterclockwise torques about the pivot, and only the smaller force $\vec{F}_2$ causes a clockwise torque. Thus it makes sense that the lever rotates in the counterclockwise direction.

✋ **12.3** (*a*) Without changing the magnitude of any of the forces in Example 12.2, how must you adjust the direction of $\vec{F}_3$ to prevent the lever from rotating? (*b*) If, instead of adjusting the direction of $\vec{F}_3$, you adjust the magnitude of $\vec{F}_2$, by what factor must you change it?

12.2 Free rotation

So far we have considered only rotations about a *fixed axis,* one that constrains the object to rotate about that axis and prevents it from moving away from the axis. Examples of such physical axes are axles, pivots, fulcrums, joints, and hinges. Objects don't need a physical axis to rotate, however. Put a pencil on your desk and flick one end with your finger. The pencil will move away from your hand while executing a rotating motion. A Frisbee flies through the air spinning about its center—without a physical axis through it. The rotation of objects that are not constrained by a physical axis or by other external constraints is called **free rotation.** About what point or axis do freely rotating objects like the pencil and the Frisbee rotate? Can an object be made to rotate about any point if nothing constrains it to rotate about some particular point?

Figure 12.9 shows the motion of a wrench after being launched as shown at the bottom of the figure. Hold the wrench by the end of the handle and sharply flip your wrist clockwise while launching the wrench upward. As the wrench moves upward, it executes a free rotation. The strobe photograph in Figure 12.9 allows us to analyze this motion. As you can see, the trajectory of the end of the handle is neither linear nor circular. Note, however, that the motion of the white dot on the wrench is remarkably simple: The dot moves straight up. What point does this white dot correspond to?

In Section 8.12, I showed that when external forces are exerted on the particles in a many-particle system, the system's center of mass moves as though all the particles in the system were concentrated at the center of mass and all external forces were exerted at that point. This statement is a direct result of conservation of momentum and of the definition of center of mass. The wrench, which consists of many atoms, is a many-particle system, and as it moves upward, Earth exerts a downward gravitational force on each atom in the wrench. The result we obtained in Section 8.12 thus states that the center of mass of the wrench should move upward as if it were a particle moving under the influence of gravity. Indeed, if you closely examine the spacing of the dots in Figure 12.9, you can see that the spacing decreases. This tells you that the dot slows down

❶ **GETTING STARTED** I begin by arbitrarily choosing counterclockwise as the direction of increasing ϑ. With that choice of ϑ, $\vec{F}_1$ and $\vec{F}_3$ cause positive torques about the pivot, while $\vec{F}_2$ causes a negative torque. To answer the question, I need to determine the magnitude and sign of the sum of these three torques about the pivot.

❷ **DEVISE PLAN** The forces are not perpendicular to the long axis of the lever, and so I need to follow one of the two procedures shown in Figure 12.5 to determine the torques about the pivot. I arbitrarily choose to determine the lever arm distances. To determine these distances relative to the pivot, I make a sketch showing the forces and the perpendicular distance from the pivot to the line of action of each force (**Figure 12.8**). I can then get the magnitude of each torque by multiplying each force magnitude by the corresponding lever arm distance. Knowing the sign and magnitude of each torque, I can determine the combined effect of the three torques.

❸ **EXECUTE PLAN** I know that $F_1 = 2F_2$. My sketch tells me that $r_{1\perp} = (\ell/3)\sin 45°$ and $r_{2\perp} = (2\ell/3)\cos 45°$, and so $r_{1\perp} = \frac{1}{2}r_{2\perp}$ because $\sin 45° = \cos 45°$. Therefore the torques caused by these two forces about the pivot are equal in magnitude: $r_{1\perp}F_1 = (\frac{1}{2}r_{2\perp})(2F_2) = r_{2\perp}F_2$. Because the two torques carry opposite signs, their sum is thus zero and their effects cancel. This means that the torque caused by $\vec{F}_3$ determines whether or not the lever rotates and, if so, in which direction. Because this torque is nonzero and counterclockwise, the lever rotates in a counterclockwise direction. ✔

CONCEPTS

Figure 12.9 Motion of a wrench that is launched upward so that it rotates.

strobe photo of wrench
tossed upward while
spinning

motion in Earth
reference frame

motion in reference
frame of center of mass

········· trajectory of center of mass

········· trajectory of dot on handle

**hand puts wrench
in motion**

········· white dot marks center of mass

as it moves upward. Quantitative analysis of the motion of the dot shows that the magnitude of the dot's downward acceleration is exactly g—that is, equal to that of an object launched without rotation.

So, the white dot on the wrench is the center of mass of the wrench, and other points on the wrench rotate around it. The center of mass is in translational motion at constant acceleration and thus cannot be rotating. This is true in general:

Objects that are made to rotate without external constraints always rotate about the center of mass.

This statement shows how remarkably powerful the concept of center of mass is. It allows us to break down the complex motion of the freely rotating wrench into two separate parts: the translational motion of the center of mass and a rotational motion of the wrench about the center of mass. This separation greatly simplifies the analysis of the motion because we can treat each part separately with the tools we have already developed.

✋ **12.4** As the wrench in Figure 12.9 moves upward, the upward translational motion of its center of mass slows down. Does the rotation about the center of mass also slow down? Which way does the wrench rotate when it falls back down after reaching its highest position?

12.3 Extended free-body diagrams

In Chapter 9 we developed a procedure for making free-body diagrams. These diagrams help us determine the *vector sum of the forces exerted on* an object, which, in turn, determines the motion of the object's center of mass. Free-body diagrams, however, do not provide any insight into the rotation of an object. For instance, if you push against the right end of a pencil that lies on a table, the pencil moves and rotates counterclockwise; pushing on the left end makes it rotate clockwise. If you push at the center of the pencil, you can even make it move without rotation. The free-body diagram for the pencil, however, is the same regardless of where you push.

To account for the rotation of an object, we must determine what torques are caused by the forces exerted on that object, and so we must know the lever arm distance of each force—information that is not contained in the free-body diagram because all forces are drawn with their tail at the center of the object. We must therefore develop a new kind of diagram that shows not only the forces exerted on an object but also the location of the point of application of each force relative to some chosen reference point. Such a diagram is called an **extended free-body diagram.** The procedure for making these diagrams is described in the Procedure box on page 7.

Drawing an extended free-body diagram and choosing a reference point help you determine the lever arm distances to that point so you can calculate the magnitude and direction of the torques about that point.

Procedure: Extended free-body diagrams

1. Begin by making a standard free-body diagram for the object of interest (the *system*) to determine what forces are exerted on it. Determine the direction of the acceleration of the center of mass of the object, and draw an arrow to represent this acceleration.

2. Draw a cross section of the object in the plane of rotation (that is, a plane perpendicular to the rotation axis) or, if the object is stationary, in the plane in which the forces of interest lie.

3. Choose a reference point. If the object is rotating about a hinge, pivot, or axle, choose that point. If the object is rotating freely, choose the center of mass. If the object is stationary, you can choose any reference point. Because forces exerted at the reference point cause no torque, it is most convenient to choose the point where the largest number of forces is exerted or where an unknown force is exerted. Mark the location of your reference point and choose a positive direction

of rotation. Indicate the reference point in your diagram by the symbol ⊙.

4. Draw vectors to represent the forces that are exerted on the object and that lie in the plane of the drawing. Place the tail of each force vector at the point where the force is exerted on the object. Place the tail of the gravitational force exerted by Earth on the object at the object's center of mass.* Label each force.

5. Indicate the object's rotational acceleration in the diagram (for example, if the object accelerates in the positive ϑ direction, write $\alpha_\vartheta > 0$ near the rotation axis). If the rotational acceleration is zero, write $\alpha_\vartheta = 0$.

---

*Is the gravitational force really exerted at the center of mass? Suppose the gravitational force exerted by Earth were exerted at some other point. The force would then cause a permanent torque about the center of mass, and any object dropped from rest would begin spinning, which is not true.

Exercise 12.3 Holding a ball

You hold a ball in the palm of your hand, as shown in **Figure 12.10**. The bones in your forearm act like a horizontal lever pivoted at the elbow. The bones are held up by the biceps muscle, which makes an angle of about 15° with the vertical. Draw an extended free-body diagram for your forearm.

Figure 12.10 Exercise 12.3.

SOLUTION I begin by making a standard free-body diagram for the forearm, which is in contact with the upper-arm bone (the *humerus*), the biceps muscle, and the ball, all of which exert contact forces on it. In addition, there is the gravitational force $\vec{F}^G_{Ef}$ to show in my diagram. I know the direction of $\vec{F}^c_{bf}$ (down), $\vec{F}^c_{mf}$ (up and to the left), and $\vec{F}^G_{Ef}$ (down) but not the direction of $\vec{F}^c_{hf}$.

How do I come up with a reasonable direction for $\vec{F}^c_{hf}$ in my diagram? I know that the forearm is at rest, which means its linear acceleration is zero, and so the vector sum of the forces exerted on the forearm must be zero. This means that the component of $\vec{F}^c_{hf}$ parallel to the forearm must be equal in magnitude to the parallel component of $\vec{F}^c_{mf}$ but pointing in the opposite direction. Because I cannot determine off-hand what the perpendicular component of $\vec{F}^c_{hf}$ is, I draw a force vector pointing down at some arbitrary angle and adjust its length so that the two parallel components are equal in length. Finally I adjust all the perpendicular components so that their

sum is zero. This gives me the free-body diagram shown in **Figure 12.11a**. Because the arm is at rest, I write $\vec{a}_{cm} = \vec{0}$ next to the diagram. The zero acceleration tells me that the vector sum of the forces exerted on the arm is zero.

Figure 12.11

(a) Free-body diagram   (b) Extended free-body diagram

Next I turn to the extended free-body diagram. I represent the forearm as a horizontal rod, with the pivot on the left, as shown in Figure 12.11b. Because the forearm is at rest, I can choose any point as the reference point. Because I know the least about $\vec{F}^c_{hf}$, however, it makes sense to choose my reference point at the pivot where that force is exerted. I choose the positive direction of rotation to be counterclockwise and write $\alpha_\vartheta = 0$ next to it because the forearm is not rotating.

Finally I draw the same forces as in the free-body diagram, placing their tails at their points of application. The result is shown in Figure 12.11b. The perpendicular component of $\vec{F}^c_{mf}$ causes a positive torque, $\vec{F}^G_{Ef}$ and $\vec{F}^c_{bf}$ cause negative torques, and $\vec{F}^c_{hf}$ causes no torque because its lever arm distance is zero. ✔

You will work out a quantitative solution to this problem in Checkpoint 12.8.

CONCEPTS

✋ **12.5** (*a*) If the biceps muscle in Figure 12.10 were attached farther out toward the wrist, would the torque generated by the muscle about the pivot get greater, get smaller, or stay the same? (*b*) As the hand is raised above the level of the elbow, so that the forearm makes an angle of 15° with the horizontal, does the arm's capacity to lift objects increase, decrease, or stay the same?

As you may have noticed, the information in the extended free-body diagram overlaps with that in the free-body diagram. Is it then necessary to draw both? I strongly recommend doing so until you have gained some practice. The standard free-body diagram helps you find the vector sum of the forces exerted on the object, which determines the object's translational motion. In the extended free-body diagram, it is more cumbersome to decompose vectors and add components, and so it is easier to make errors. The extended free-body diagram, however, is necessary to determine the torques caused by the forces that are exerted on the object. The next exercise helps clarify the purpose of each diagram.

Exercise 12.4 Pushing a large crate

You are moving a large crate mounted on swivel wheels, exerting an off-center force $\vec{F}^c_{pc}$ as shown in **Figure 12.12**. Draw an extended free-body diagram for the crate. You can ignore any friction in the wheels.

Figure 12.12 Exercise 12.4.

$\vec{F}^c_{pc}$

SOLUTION The forces exerted on the crate are a downward force of gravity, an upward contact force exerted by the floor, and your horizontal push. I therefore draw the free-body diagram shown in **Figure 12.13a**.

Figure 12.13

(a) Side view

(b) View from above

The free-body diagram shows that the vector sum of the forces exerted on the crate is nonzero. From this information I conclude that the push causes the center of mass of the crate to accelerate in the direction of the push. I therefore draw an arrow next to the free-body diagram to indicate the direction of this center-of-mass acceleration.

The crate is not constrained to rotate about a fixed axis. The floor and the wheels it is resting on, however, do constrain it to rotate in the horizontal plane. In addition to accelerating the center of mass of the crate, the off-center push therefore causes the crate to rotate about a vertical axis through the center of mass. Because the rotation is in the horizontal plane, I draw an outline of the crate as seen from above for the extended free-body diagram.

The crate is not constrained to rotate about any fixed axis in the plane I have drawn, so the center of mass is the reference point I must use. I assume the crate to be uniform, so its center of mass is at the center. I mark the reference point in my diagram and choose counterclockwise as the direction of positive rotation.

The only force that lies in this plane is $\vec{F}^c_{pc}$, so the extended free-body diagram contains just one force (Figure 12.11*b*). The lever arm distance of $\vec{F}^c_{pc}$ is the distance between its line of action and the center of mass of the crate. From the diagram, I thus conclude that $\vec{F}^c_{pc}$ causes a counterclockwise torque. This torque causes the crate to rotate counterclockwise, and I write $a_\vartheta > 0$ next to the diagram to indicate that the rotational acceleration of the crate is positive. ✔

✋ **12.6** Suppose the force $\vec{F}^c_{pc}$ in Exercise 12.4 gives the center of mass of the crate an acceleration $\vec{a}_{cm}$. Would this acceleration be greater, smaller, or the same if the force were exerted exactly at the center of the crate?

12.4 The vectorial nature of rotation

So far we've treated all rotational quantities as if they were scalars. There are two reasons a scalar treatment of rotational quantities cannot be complete, however: Rotations have direction, and the rotation axis has a definite orientation in space. For rotations that lie in a single plane, an algebraic sign is sufficient to indicate the direction of rotation in the same way that an algebraic sign indicates direction in one-dimensional translational motion, as shown in **Figure 12.14**.

For rotations in three dimensions, the algebraic sign alone is not sufficient to determine the direction of rotation. Consider, for example, the two spinning disks in **Figure 12.15**. If you view them from the angle shown in Figure 12.15*a*, you could claim that the disk A spins counterclockwise and disk B clockwise. Seen from below, as in Figure 12.15*b*, however, disk A spins clockwise and the rotation of disk B, now seen sideways, is neither clockwise nor counterclockwise. So, in three dimensions the terms *clockwise* and *counterclockwise* are insufficient to specify the direction of a rotation, just as *positive* and *negative* are not enough to specify a displacement vector in more than one dimension.

Can a rotation be characterized by a vector? The vectors $\vec{r}$, $\vec{v}$, and $\vec{a}$ of an object in circular motion at constant

Figure 12.14 For both translation in one dimension and rotation in a plane, the two possible directions of motion can be distinguished by their algebraic sign.

(*a*) Translational motion in one dimension

(*b*) Rotational motion in a plane

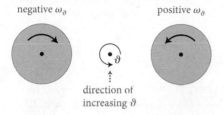

Figure 12.16 Right-hand rule and directions associated with rotations.

(*a*) Vectors $\vec{r}$, $\vec{v}$, and $\vec{a}$ cannot be associated with a direction of rotation

(*b*) The right-hand rule connects direction of rotation about an axis with a direction along the rotation axis

Right-hand rule: Curl fingers of right hand in direction of rotation; thumb will point in direction of vector representing rotation.

speed all lie in the plane of the trajectory, as shown in **Figure 12.16a**. Their directions change every instant, and because all directions in the plane are equivalent, it makes no sense to associate a vector in this plane with the rotation. How would we agree on which direction to pick? The direction of the rotation axis, a direction in which the vectors $\vec{r}$, $\vec{v}$, and $\vec{a}$ never point, is the only direction associated with the rotation that remains fixed. We can specify the orientation of the rotation axis by a vector. Given that vector, you know the orientation of the plane in which the rotation takes place.

If we use a vector to specify the orientation of the rotation axis in space, we can use the two possible directions along this axis to represent the two possible directions of rotation about the axis. The convention for associating a vector along the rotation axis with the direction of rotation is illustrated in Figure 12.16*b* and is called the **right-hand rule:**

When you curl the fingers of your right hand along the direction of rotation, your thumb points in the direction of the vector that specifies the direction of rotation.

Figure 12.15 For rotations in three dimensions, it is no longer possible to specify the direction of rotation unambiguously by algebraic sign or by the terms *clockwise* and *counterclockwise*.

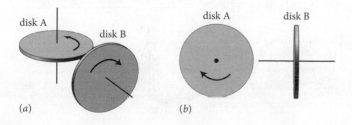

Armed with this rule, you can now specify the direction of any rotation and the orientation of the axis about which that rotation takes place with a vector and avoid the ambiguity of terms like *clockwise* and *counterclockwise*. For example, for the two disks in Figure 12.15*a* the right-hand rule yields the directions given by the two blue vectors in **Figure 12.17**. The advantage of the vectors is that we

Figure 12.17 The right-hand rule applied to the spinning disks of Figure 12.15.

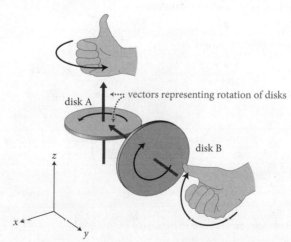

can specify them by giving their x, y, and z components. The vector representing the rotation of disk A points in the positive z direction, and so it has the form $(0, 0, +A)$. The vector representing the rotation of disk B has the form $(0, -B, 0)$, where A and B are positive numbers.

Note that the vector associated with a rotation always lies along the axis of that rotation. If you invert the direction of rotation, the vector points in the opposite direction along the axis. For example, if disk A in Figure 12.17 were rotating in the opposite direction from the one illustrated, you'd have to curl your fingers in the opposite direction, and so your thumb would point in the negative z direction, opposite the direction shown.

Regardless of your observation angle, the right-hand rule always yields the same direction for a given rotation. Suppose, for example, that you are tightening bolts into a plate as in **Figure 12.18**. When you tighten a bolt, it is natural to consider the bolt's rotation as being clockwise because you usually look at the head of the bolt when tightening it. Now imagine tightening a bolt on the backside of the plate by reaching around it. From where you stand, you must turn in a *counterclockwise* direction to tighten that bolt! The statement "to tighten a bolt, you must rotate it in a clockwise direction" holds only when you are facing the head of the bolt. As Figure 12.18 shows, however, when you align your right-hand thumb in the direction you want the bolt to move, your fingers curl in the correct direction, regardless of where you stand relative to the plate.

The right-hand rule can be used to determine not only the direction of a vector representing a rotation but also the other way around. Given a vector, we can use the right-hand rule to determine the corresponding rotation (**Figure 12.19**). Either one uniquely determines the other.

What kind of a vector is the vector we have just introduced? All the vector quantities we have encountered up to now are derived from the displacement vector—an arrow that points from an object's initial position to its final position. As we've seen, displacement vectors obey a commutation principle: The sum of several displacements is

Figure 12.18 The right-hand rule tells you how to tighten a bolt regardless of your position relative to the bolt.

Whether a bolt turns counterclockwise or clockwise depends on which end you look at.

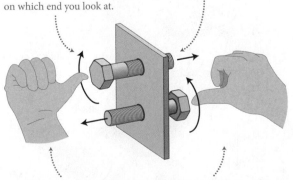

But if you point thumb of right hand in direction bolt should move, curled fingers *always* show which way to turn it.

Figure 12.19 The right-hand rule used two ways.

Given rotating object . . .   . . . curl right-hand fingers in direction of rotation . . .   . . . thumb specifies unique direction in space.

Given direction in space . . .   . . . point right-hand thumb in that direction . . .   . . . curled fingers specify unique rotation.

independent of the sequence in which the displacements are added. Displacement vectors commute in two and in three dimensions. Do rotational displacements commute? Rotations in a plane do, as you can easily verify by adding two angles. The result is independent of the order in which the two angles are added: $15° + 23° = 23° + 15° = 38°$. As **Figure 12.20** illustrates, however, rotations in three dimensions do not commute: If you give a beach ball two successive rotations over 90° angles about perpendicular axes, the final orientation of the ball depends on the sequence of the rotations. So, rotational displacements cannot be vectors because in three dimensions $\vartheta_1 + \vartheta_2 \neq \vartheta_2 + \vartheta_1$.

Figure 12.20 Rotational displacements are not commutative: The order in which you perform them matters.

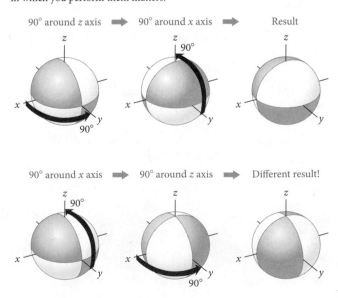

90° around z axis ➡ 90° around x axis ➡ Result

90° around x axis ➡ 90° around z axis ➡ Different result!

Figure 12.21 Successive rotations over very small angles are commutative. The dashed lines show the initial positions of the ball's seams.

For successive rotations over very small angles, order doesn't matter.

If, instead of rotating the ball twice over 90° angles, you rotate it over two small angles θ_1 and θ_2, the difference in the ball's final orientation is much smaller. As **Figure 12.21** shows, for two successive rotations over 6° angles, the difference is no longer noticeable. Why small angles commute can be understood by looking at **Figure 12.22**, which shows a close-up of the displacement of the seams on the ball in Figure 12.21. Each rotational displacement $\Delta\vartheta$ corresponds to a displacement over an arc of length $\Delta s = r\,\Delta\vartheta$, where r is the radius of the ball. For very small rotational displacements $d\vartheta_1$ and $d\vartheta_2$, the corresponding arcs ds_1 and ds_2 are approximately straight lines on a nearly flat surface.

The smaller the angles θ_1 and θ_2, the more the arcs behave like vectors in two dimensions and so commute.

So, infinitesimally small rotational displacements do commute: $d\vartheta_1 + d\vartheta_2 = d\vartheta_2 + d\vartheta_1$. This means that rotational velocity—the rate at which the rotational displacement changes, $\omega = d\vartheta/dt$—obeys the commutation law: $\omega_1 + \omega_2 = \omega_2 + \omega_1$. We can therefore introduce a *rotational velocity vector* $\vec{\omega}$ whose direction is given by the right-hand rule and whose magnitude is ω. The rotational velocity vector is the basic vector describing rotational motion, much as displacement is the basic vector for translational motion. **Figure 12.23** shows two spinning tops with their rotational velocity vectors. Each vector determines the orientation of the top's axis of rotation, the direction in which the top rotates around this axis, and the rotational speed. The arrow representing the rotational velocity of top A is longer than the arrow of top B, indicating that A spins faster than B. We shall examine the vector nature of other rotational quantities in Section 12.8.

Vectors associated with a direction of rotation are called **axial vectors;** vectors derived from the displacement vector are called **polar vectors.** Axial vectors play an important role in physics, not only in rotation but also in electricity and magnetism.

12.7 Suppose the rotation of top A in Figure 12.23 slows down without a change in the direction of its axis of rotation. (*a*) In which direction does the vector $\Delta\vec{\omega}$ point? (*b*) Can the top's rotational acceleration be represented by a vector? If so, in which direction does this vector point?

Figure 12.22 Detail of the balls of Figure 12.21 in their final orientation. Because the displacements along the arcs corresponding to each rotation are nearly straight lines, the rotations commute.

Figure 12.23 Representing rotational velocity vectors.

Rotational velocity vector:

- *Direction* indicates rotation direction (via right-hand rule).
- *Length* indicates speed of rotation.

top A   top B

Self-quiz

1. A rope supports one end of a beam as shown in **Figure 12.24**. Draw the lever arm distance for the torque caused by the rope about the pivot.

2. Draw a free-body diagram and an extended free-body diagram for (*a*) a door hanging on two hinges and (*b*) a bridge supported from each end, with a car positioned at one-quarter of the bridge's length from one support.

3. Which diagram in **Figure 12.25**—1, 2, or 3—shows the alarm clock on the left after it has been rotated in the directions indicated by (*a*) 90° about the *x* axis and then 90° about the *y* axis and (*b*) 90° about the *y* axis and then 90° about the *x* axis? Does the order of the rotation change your answer?

Figure 12.24

pivot

Figure 12.25

1   2   3

4. Give the direction of the rotational velocity vector associated with each spinning object shown in **Figure 12.26**.

Figure 12.26

(*a*)   (*b*)   (*c*)   (*d*)

Answers

1. The lever arm distance $r_\perp$ is the perpendicular distance between the pivot and the line of action of the force exerted by the rope on the beam, as shown in **Figure 12.27**.

2. See **Figure 12.28**. (*a*) The door interacts with three objects: Earth, the top hinge, and the bottom hinge. Without the top hinge, the force of gravity would tend to rotate the door about an axis perpendicular to the door through the bottom hinge. The force exerted by the top hinge must balance the clockwise torque caused by the force of gravity about the axis through the bottom hinge. The horizontal components of the forces exerted by the hinges must cancel each other. (*b*) The bridge interacts with four objects: Earth, the right support, the left support, and the car. The upward forces from the supports must balance the downward gravitational forces of the car and the bridge. Because these forces must also counteract the counterclockwise torque caused by the car, the force exerted by the support closer to the car must be greater than the force exerted by the other support.

Figure 12.27

pivot

Figure 12.28

(*a*)   (*b*)

3. (*a*) 3; (*b*) 2. The order of rotation does make a difference.

4. Wrapping the fingers of your right hand in the direction of spin gives rotational velocity vectors that point (*a*) to the right, (*b*) up, (*c*) out of the page, and (*d*) into the page.

12.5 Conservation of angular momentum

In Section 11.5 we saw that angular momentum is a conserved quantity and that the angular momentum of a system rotating in a plane on which no tangential forces are exerted remains constant. Let us now examine how tangential forces are related to the concept of torque introduced in the first part of this chapter and derive mathematical expressions that relate the various rotational quantities and torque.

Consider the situation shown in **Figure 12.29**. A force $\vec{F}$ is exerted on a particle of inertia m that is constrained to move along a circular trajectory of radius r about a pivot. Because $\vec{F}$ has a component that is tangential to the circular trajectory, the particle speeds up. In the language we developed in the first part of this chapter, the particle's rotational acceleration is nonzero because $\vec{F}$ causes a torque on the particle about the pivot. The magnitude of this torque, which we denote by the Greek letter τ (*tau*), is given by

$$\tau \equiv rF\sin\theta = r_\perp F = rF_\perp, \tag{12.1}$$

where θ is the angle between the radius vector $\vec{r}$ and $\vec{F}$ and where $F_\perp$ is the magnitude of the tangential component of the force: $F_\perp = |F_t|$. Because torque is the product of a force and a distance, it has SI units of newton-meters (N · m). Work, being the product of displacement and force, has the same units. Torque and work represent two very different and unrelated quantities, however. Work corresponds to the transfer of energy by a force; torque is the ability of a force to change the rotational motion of an object. To avoid confusion, we shall always use joules for work and newton-meters for torque.

Let us now relate this torque to the particle's tangential acceleration a_t (which is perpendicular to the radius vector $\vec{r}$). This acceleration is given by

$$F_t = ma_t. \tag{12.2}$$

Combining Eqs. 12.1 and 12.2, we obtain

$$\tau_\vartheta = r(ma_t), \tag{12.3}$$

where the subscript ϑ means that τ_ϑ is a signed quantity. Although strictly speaking τ_ϑ is the component of a torque *vector,* we shall refer to it simply as torque. The algebraic sign of the torque is determined by the sign of the rotational acceleration it causes. The torque caused by the force $\vec{F}$ in Figure 12.29, for example, is positive because it causes the particle to accelerate in the positive ϑ direction ($a_t > 0$).

As we saw in Chapter 11, the tangential acceleration is related to the rotational acceleration by $a_t = r\alpha_\vartheta$, so we can write

$$\tau_\vartheta = rm(r\alpha_\vartheta) = mr^2\alpha_\vartheta. \tag{12.4}$$

The quantity mr^2 is the rotational inertia of the particle, so Eq. 12.4 becomes

$$\tau_\vartheta = I\alpha_\vartheta. \tag{12.5}$$

Equation 12.5 shows how the torque caused by a force exerted on a particle relates to the particle's rotational acceleration. Notice the remarkable parallel between Eqs. 12.2 and 12.5: Instead of "force equals inertia times acceleration," we have "torque equals rotational inertia times rotational acceleration." Torque is to rotation what force is to translation, and therefore Eq. 12.5 is sometimes called the *rotational equation of motion*.

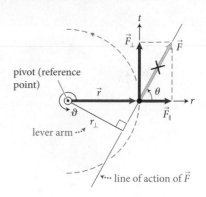

Figure 12.29 A force $\vec{F}$ is exerted on a particle that is constrained to move in a circle.

Figure 12.30 A rigid object constrained to rotate about an axis.

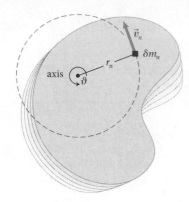

To find a similar expression for extended objects, consider the rotating extended object illustrated in **Figure 12.30**. Imagine breaking down the object into small particles of inertia δm_n, with each particle located a distance r_n from the axis and having velocity $\vec{v}_n$. Let each particle be subject to a torque $\tau_{n\vartheta}$ about the axis; this torque is caused by forces exerted by surrounding particles and by external forces. For each particle we can write an expression analogous to Eq. 12.4:

$$\tau_{n\vartheta} = \delta m_n\, r_n^2\, \alpha_{n\vartheta}. \tag{12.6}$$

The sum of the torques on all particles is then

$$\sum_n \tau_{n\vartheta} = \sum_n (\delta m_n r_n^2 \alpha_{n\vartheta}) = \left(\sum_n \delta m_n r_n^2\right)\alpha_\vartheta, \tag{12.7}$$

where we have used the fact that all particles in a rigid rotating object must have the same rotational acceleration α_ϑ. The sum on the right side is the rotational inertia I of the extended object (Eq. 11.42), and so Eq. 12.7 becomes

$$\sum_n \tau_{n\vartheta} = I\alpha_\vartheta. \tag{12.8}$$

Figure 12.31 The internal torques caused by two interacting particles within a rotating rigid object have the same lever arm distance, so they cancel.

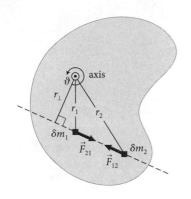

The sum on the left side contains torques caused by external forces (*external torques* for short) and internal torques. To find the contribution from internal torques, consider two interacting particles within the extended object, as illustrated in **Figure 12.31**. Because particles 1 and 2 interact with each other, they exert forces on each other that are equal in magnitude: $F_{12} = F_{21}$. As Figure 12.31 shows, the lever arm distance for the two forces is the same ($r_\perp$), and so the torque caused by $\vec{F}_{12}$ is equal in magnitude to the torque caused by $\vec{F}_{21}$ but opposite in direction. Their sum is therefore zero:

$$\tau_{21\vartheta} + \tau_{12\vartheta} = r_\perp F_{21} - r_\perp F_{12} = r_\perp(F_{21} - F_{12}) = 0. \tag{12.9}$$

Because this cancellation holds for all pairs of interacting particles within the object, all internal torques drop out of the sum on the left side of Eq. 12.8. Only torques caused by external forces remain. The expression we obtain for an extended object is therefore identical to that for a particle:

$$\sum \tau_{\text{ext}\,\vartheta} = I\alpha_\vartheta. \tag{12.10}$$

Another useful expression can be obtained by recognizing that the particle's rotational velocity and rotational acceleration are related by

$$\alpha_\vartheta = \frac{d\omega_\vartheta}{dt}. \tag{12.11}$$

Substituting this expression into Eq. 12.10 and recalling that angular momentum $L_\vartheta = I\omega_\vartheta$ (Eq. 11.34), we get

$$\sum \tau_{\text{ext}\,\vartheta} = I\frac{d\omega_\vartheta}{dt} = \frac{d}{dt}(I\omega_\vartheta) = \frac{dL_\vartheta}{dt}, \tag{12.12}$$

where we have used the fact that the rotational inertia I of a rigid object is constant. So torque is the time rate of change of angular momentum, much as force is the time rate of change of momentum. Equation 12.12 shows that if the sum of the torques caused by external forces exerted on an object is zero, the object's angular momentum does not change:

$$\sum \tau_{\text{ext}\,\vartheta} = \frac{dL_\vartheta}{dt} = 0 \quad \Rightarrow \quad \Delta L_\vartheta = 0. \tag{12.13}$$

Whenever the sum of the torques caused by the forces exerted on an object is zero—in other words, whenever its angular momentum is constant—the object is said to be in **rotational equilibrium.** In Chapter 8 we learned that an object is in *translational equilibrium* when its momentum is constant and that this condition is met when the vector sum of the external forces exerted on the object is zero. Now we can expand that notion to include angular momentum, which remains constant when the sum of the torques caused by external forces exerted on it is zero. An object that is in both translational and rotational equilibrium is said to be in **mechanical equilibrium:**

$$\sum \tau_{\text{ext}\,\vartheta} = 0 \quad \text{and} \quad \sum \vec{F}_{\text{ext}} = \vec{0} \quad \Leftrightarrow \quad \text{mechanical equilibrium.} \tag{12.14}$$

For a system that is not in rotational equilibrium, we have

$$\Delta L_\vartheta = J_\vartheta, \tag{12.15}$$

where J_ϑ represents the transfer of angular momentum from the environment to the system. The quantity J_ϑ is called the **rotational impulse** delivered to the system. Like angular momentum it has SI units of $\text{kg} \cdot \text{m}^2/\text{s}$. In analogy to the momentum law (Eq. 4.18) and the energy law (Eq. 9.1), which embody conservation of momentum and energy, respectively, Eq. 12.15 embodies conservation of angular momentum and is called the **angular momentum law.**

To calculate the rotational impulse, we can use Eq. 12.12. For a system that is subject to constant torques, the time rate of change of the angular momentum is constant, so over a time interval Δt,

$$\sum \tau_{\text{ext}\,\vartheta} = \frac{\Delta L_\vartheta}{\Delta t}$$

$$\Delta L_\vartheta = \left(\sum \tau_{\text{ext}\,\vartheta}\right)\Delta t. \tag{12.16}$$

Comparing Eqs. 12.15 and 12.16, we see that the rotational impulse is

$$J_\vartheta = \left(\sum \tau_{\text{ext}\,\vartheta}\right)\Delta t \quad \text{(constant torques).} \tag{12.17}$$

Equation 12.17, called the **rotational impulse equation,** allows us to calculate the change in angular momentum for a system subject to constant external torques. **Figure 12.32** illustrates how conservation of angular momentum gives rise to the angular momentum law and how to treat isolated and nonisolated systems. Notice that the structure of this figure is identical to that of Figure 9.16, which illustrates the same principles for momentum and energy.

🤚 **12.8** Use the conditions of mechanical equilibrium to express $\vec{F}_{\text{hf}y}^c$ in Figure 12.11*b* in terms of $\vec{F}_{\text{Ef}}^G$ and $\vec{F}_{\text{bf}}^c$. Let the distance between the ball and the pivot be ℓ and the distance from the point where the biceps muscle is attached to the pivot be $\ell/5$.

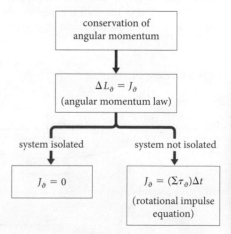

Figure 12.32 Angular momentum change for isolated and nonisolated systems.

Example 12.5 Flywheel

A motor exerts a constant force of 120 N tangential to the rim of a 20-kg cylindrical flywheel of radius 0.50 m. The flywheel is free to rotate about an axis through its center and runs perpendicular to its face. If the flywheel is initially at rest and the motor is turned on for 2.0 s, how much work does the motor do on the flywheel?

❶ GETTING STARTED I begin by making a sketch of the situation to organize the information (**Figure 12.33**). The force exerted by the motor causes the flywheel to start spinning, which means the wheel's rotational kinetic energy changes. This is the only energy change in the system, and I know from the energy law (Eq. 9.1) that $\Delta E = W$. Therefore $\Delta K_{rot} = W$, and so to calculate the work done by the motor, I need to determine this change in rotational kinetic energy. Because the flywheel is at rest initially, I know that $\Delta K_{rot} = K_{rot,f}$.

Figure 12.33

$F = 120$ N
$R = 0.50$ m
$m = 20$ kg
$\Delta t = 2.0$ s

❷ DEVISE PLAN To obtain $K_{rot,f}$, I can use Eq. 11.31, $K_{rot} = \frac{1}{2}I\omega^2$. The rotational inertia I of the flywheel (which is a solid cylinder) is $\frac{1}{2}mR^2$ (see Table 11.3). Because I'm interested in $K_{rot,f}$, I need the final value for ω, the wheel's rotational speed. How can I connect ω_f to anything I know in this problem? The relationship between ω and angular momentum is $L_\vartheta \equiv I\omega_\vartheta$ (Eq. 11.34), and I know from Eq. 12.16 that $\Delta L_\vartheta = \tau_\vartheta \Delta t$. I know Δt, but do I know anything about τ in terms of the information given—a force, an inertia, and a wheel radius? Yes, Eq. 12.1:

$\tau = rF_\perp$. Thus my plan is to express ω_f in terms of R and F and then use that expression for ω_f in $K_{rot} = \frac{1}{2}I\omega^2$ to calculate $K_{rot,f} = W$.

❸ EXECUTE PLAN The magnitude of the torque caused by the motor is $\tau = RF$, where R is the radius of the wheel and F is the magnitude of the force exerted by the motor. Equation 12.16 then gives

$$\Delta L_\vartheta = \left(\sum \tau_{ext\,\vartheta}\right)\Delta t = +RF\Delta t.$$

Because the initial angular momentum is zero, I know that $\Delta L_\vartheta = I\omega_{\vartheta,f} = +I\omega_f$, and so I have

$$\Delta L_\vartheta = RF\Delta t = I\omega_f$$

$$\omega_f = \frac{RF\Delta t}{I}.$$

The final rotational kinetic energy is thus

$$K_{rot,f} = \frac{1}{2}I\omega_f^2 = \frac{1}{2}I\left(\frac{RF\Delta t}{I}\right)^2$$

$$= \frac{(RF\Delta t)^2}{2I} = \frac{(RF\Delta t)^2}{mR^2} = \frac{(F\Delta t)^2}{m},$$

and the work done on the flywheel is

$$W = K_{rot,f} = \frac{[(120\text{ N})(2.0\text{ s})]^2}{20\text{ kg}} = 2880\text{ J} = 2.9\text{ kJ}. ✔$$

❹ EVALUATE RESULT Delivering 2.9 kJ in 2.0 s corresponds to a power of $(2.9\text{ kJ})/(2.0\text{ s}) = 1.4$ kW, which is not an unreasonable amount for a large motor.

Example 12.6 Spinning up a compact disc

When you load a compact disc into a drive, a spinning conical shaft rises up into the opening in the center of the disc, and the disc begins to spin (**Figure 12.34**). Suppose the disc's rotational inertia is I_d, that of the shaft is I_s, and the shaft's initial rotational speed is ω_i. Does the rotational kinetic energy of the disc-shaft system remain constant in this process? Assume for simplicity that no external forces cause torques on the shaft.*

❶ GETTING STARTED I am given rotational inertias for a disc and a shaft, plus the initial rotational speed of the shaft, and my task is to determine whether or not the system's rotational kinetic energy changes when these two units interact: $\Delta K_{rot} \overset{?}{=} 0$. The disc is initially at rest, but as the shaft comes in contact with it, the two exert on each other forces that cause torques. The shaft speeds up the rotation of the disc, and the disc slows down the rotation of the shaft. The disc has no rotational velocity before the shaft touches it, and so initially all the system's rotational kinetic energy is in the shaft. After they reach a common rotational speed ω_f, both have rotational kinetic energy. I need to calculate the initial and final rotational kinetic energies of the shaft-disc system to answer the question.

Figure 12.34 Example 12.6.

*In reality, the shaft is connected to a motor that keeps it rotating at the correct rotational speed, and thus there is a force that causes a torque on the shaft.

❷ **DEVISE PLAN** The rotational kinetic energy of a rotating object is given by Eq. 11.31, $K = \frac{1}{2}I\omega^2$. I know the initial rotational speed of the shaft and its rotational inertia, so I can use this equation to calculate the initial rotational kinetic energy of the shaft-disc system. I do not know the final rotational speed of the system, but I do know that because there are no external torques on the system, Eq. 12.13 tells me that the angular momentum must remain constant: $\Delta L_\vartheta = 0$. Expressing ΔL_ϑ as the difference between the final and initial values gives me an expression containing ω_f and ω_i, which means I can probably get an expression for ω_f/ω_i that I can then use to compare the ratio $K_{rot,f}/K_{rot,i}$ and thereby determine whether or not $\Delta K_{rot} = 0$. Because the problem is stated in symbols rather than numerical values, my comparison will be between two algebraic expressions.

❸ **EXECUTE PLAN** Because the torques that the disc and shaft cause on each other are internal and because there are no external torques, I have for the system's angular momentum

$$\Delta L_\vartheta = (I_s + I_d)\omega_{\vartheta,f} - I_s\,\omega_{\vartheta,i} = 0. \tag{1}$$

If I let the initial direction of rotation of the shaft be positive, $\omega_{\vartheta,i} = +\omega_i$ and so $\omega_{\vartheta,f}$ is also positive. Rearranging terms

in Eq. 1, I find that the ratio of the final and initial rotational speeds is

$$\frac{\omega_f}{\omega_i} = \frac{I_s}{I_s + I_d}.$$

The system's initial rotational kinetic energy is $K_i = \frac{1}{2}I_s\,\omega_i^2$, its final rotational kinetic energy is $K_f = \frac{1}{2}(I_s + I_d)\omega_f^2$, and the ratio of the two is

$$\frac{K_f}{K_i} = \frac{\frac{1}{2}(I_s + I_d)}{\frac{1}{2}I_s}\frac{\omega_f^2}{\omega_i^2} = \frac{I_s}{I_s + I_d} < 1,$$

so $K_f < K_i$, or $\Delta K \neq 0$. The rotational kinetic energy of the system is not constant. ✔

❹ **EVALUATE RESULT** The spinning up of the disc is like an inelastic "rotational collision": The disc initially at rest comes in contact with the spinning shaft, and the two reach a common rotational speed. While the disc is spinning up, some of the system's initial rotational kinetic energy is converted to thermal energy because of friction between disc and shaft, and so it makes sense that the system's rotational kinetic energy decreases.

✋ **12.9** Consider the situation in Example 12.6. (*a*) Is the vector sum of the forces exerted by the shaft on the compact disc nonzero while the disc is spinning up? (*b*) Is the disc isolated?

12.6 Rolling motion

The rotations we have considered so far fall into two classes: rotations about a fixed axis and free rotations. Forces exerted on objects that are constrained to rotate about a fixed axis cause rotational motion only because the axis prevents any translational motion. Forces exerted on freely rotating objects cause both translational motion of the center of mass and rotation about that point. These two motions are *independent* of each other. When you throw a Frisbee, for example, its translational speed v_{cm} is independent of its rotational speed ω (**Figure 12.35**). The Frisbee can have any combination of spin and translational speed: You can throw it so that it spins fast and moves away from you slowly, spins slowly and moves away from you fast, and so on.

The rolling motion of a wheel or ball represents an intermediate case between fixed and free rotations because rolling puts a constraint on the relationship between the translational and rotational motions. Furthermore, a rolling wheel or ball always rotates about its geometric center. We shall restrict our discussion to symmetric objects for which the center of mass is at the geometric center.

Figure 12.35 The translational and rotational motions of a thrown Frisbee are independent of each other.

Motion of flying, spinning disk . . .

. . . combines translation of center of mass with rotation around center of mass. In a free rotation, these two motions are *independent* of each other.

Earth reference frame

disk reference frame

Figure 12.36 When an object rolls without slipping, its translational and rotational motions are coupled.

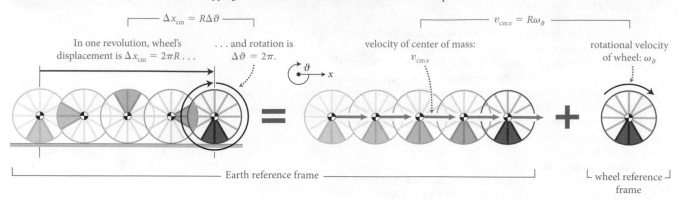

Consider the wheel of radius R rolling along a straight line on a flat surface in **Figure 12.36**. To describe this rolling motion we need to choose both a direction of rotation and a direction of the x axis. Usually it is advisable to choose these directions such that a positive change in ϑ corresponds to a positive change in x, as shown in Figure 12.36. If the wheel does not slip, its center advances a distance equal to its circumference, $2\pi R$, during each full revolution. Because the wheel's rotational displacement in one full revolution is 2π, the center-of-mass displacement Δx_{cm} caused by the rolling is related to the rotational displacement $\Delta\vartheta$ by

$$\Delta x_{cm} = R\Delta\vartheta. \tag{12.18}$$

Note that this expression is valid for any displacement; for example, for a quarter revolution $\Delta\vartheta = 2\pi/4 = \pi/2$ and $\Delta x_{cm} = 2\pi R/4 = (\pi/2)R = R\Delta\vartheta$. Dividing the left and right sides by the time interval Δt it takes to advance this distance and taking the limit of both sides for $\Delta t \to 0$ yield

$$v_{cmx} = R\omega_\vartheta \quad \text{(rolling motion without slipping).} \tag{12.19}$$

This equation expresses the **condition for rolling motion without slipping.** By coupling the translational and rotational speeds, this condition puts a constraint on the motion of any object that rolls without slipping. Unlike a Frisbee, whose (translational) speed is independent of its rotational speed, the speed of a moving car that is not skidding is proportional to the rotational speed of its wheels.

Equation 12.19 resembles Eq. 11.10 relating the translational and rotational speeds of an object in circular motion:

$$v_t = r\omega_\vartheta. \tag{12.20}$$

These two equations mean very different things, however. Equation 12.19 describes the translational motion of the wheel in the Earth reference frame, whereas Eq. 12.20 gives the tangential speed of any point on the rotating wheel in a reference frame moving along with the center of mass of the wheel. The velocity of a point on the wheel in the Earth reference frame is obtained by adding these two velocities, as shown in **Figure 12.37**. A point on the rim moves with a continuously

Figure 12.37 The trajectory of a point on the rim of a rolling wheel. Such a trajectory is called a *cycloid*.

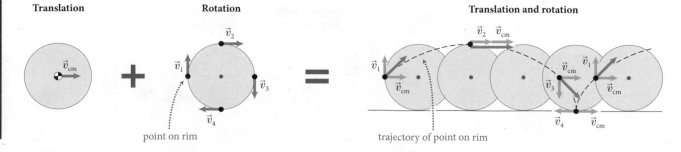

changing velocity along a trajectory resembling that of the handle of the wrench in Figure 12.9. Note in particular that whenever a point on the rim is in contact with the surface over which the wheel is rolling, that point has zero instantaneous velocity (on the rim $r = R$ and $v_t = r\omega_\vartheta$ points in the direction opposite the direction of $v_{cm} = R\omega$). This zero instantaneous velocity of the rim point in contact with the surface is a direct consequence of the requirement that the object rolls without slipping: The relative velocity of the two surfaces in contact must be zero for there to be no slipping. **Figure 12.38** shows that points on the rim move in a direction perpendicular to the surface just before and just after reaching the bottom.

Let us next turn to the dynamics of rolling motion. Suppose a round object of inertia m and radius R is released from rest on a ramp as shown in **Figure 12.39a**. Why does the object roll down instead of sliding down as would a block of wood? The reason is that the force of static friction, which forces the instantaneous point of contact to be motionless, causes a torque about the center of the object. To understand the motion of the object, we must find the vector sum of the forces exerted on it and the sum of the torques caused by these forces. Figure 12.39b shows a free-body diagram for the object, which is subject to two forces: the force of gravity and a contact force exerted by the ramp, which has a normal component $\vec{F}^n_{ro}$ in the y direction and a tangential component $\vec{F}^s_{ro}$ in the x direction due to static friction. As we have done with other problems involving ramps, we chose the x axis to be along the ramp. For the object to accelerate down the ramp, the vector sum of the forces must point in the positive x direction, so $\sum F_y = F^G_{Eoy} + F^n_{ro} = 0$ and $\sum F_x = F^G_{Eox} - F^s_{ro} > 0$. The vector sum of the forces and the center-of-mass acceleration are related by

$$\sum F_x = F^G_{Eox} - F^s_{ro} = mg \sin\theta - F^s_{ro} = ma_{cm\,x}. \qquad (12.21)$$

This equation contains two unknowns: the magnitude of the force of static friction F^s_{ro} and $a_{cm\,x}$. All we know about F^s_{ro} is that it must be less than or equal to its maximum value $(F^s_{ro})_{max}$, but this fact doesn't help us solve Eq. 12.21. Let us therefore turn to the extended free-body diagram shown in Figure 12.39c, which shows the object with the forces exerted on it at their points of application. Because the object rotates about its center of mass, we determine the sum of the torques about the center of mass. Neither $\vec{F}^G_{Eo}$ nor $\vec{F}^n_{ro}$ causes a torque because their lines of action go through the center of mass, and so the lever arm distances for these forces are zero. Only $\vec{F}^s_{ro}$ causes a torque; its lever arm distance is the radius R of the object. Equation 12.10 then yields

$$\sum \tau_{ext\,\vartheta} = +F^s_{ro}R = I\alpha_\vartheta, \qquad (12.22)$$

where I is the object's rotational inertia and α_ϑ is its rotational acceleration. Although this yields another equation, we have now added a third unknown: α_ϑ.

Figure 12.38 The point of contact of a wheel rolling without slipping has zero instantaneous velocity.

motion of wheel

trajectory ····▸
of point on
rim

$\vec{v}$

Point on rim moves straight down just before touching road . . .

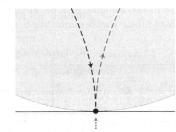

. . . has zero velocity the instant it touches road . . .

. . . and moves straight up just after touching road.

Figure 12.39 A round object rolls down a ramp.

(a) Object rolls down ramp

(b) Free-body diagram

(c) Extended free-body diagram

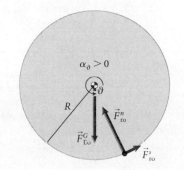

Because the object is rolling without slipping, its rotational and translational motions are coupled, and so its rotational and center-of-mass accelerations must be related. Differentiating both sides of Eq. 12.19, $v_{cmx} = R\omega_\vartheta$, with respect to time yields

$$a_{cmx} = R\alpha_\vartheta. \tag{12.23}$$

Substituting α_ϑ from Eq. 12.23 into Eq. 12.22 and solving for F_{ro}^s, we find

$$F_{ro}^s = \frac{I}{R^2} a_{cmx}. \tag{12.24}$$

Substituting this result for F_{ro}^s into Eq. 12.21 and solving for a_{cmx}, we obtain

$$a_{cmx} = +\frac{g\sin\theta}{1 + \dfrac{I}{mR^2}} = +\frac{g\sin\theta}{1 + c}, \tag{12.25}$$

where $c \equiv I/mR^2$ is the *shape factor* of the object ($0 < c \leq 1$; see Table 11.3). The numerator in Eq. 12.25 is the acceleration of an object sliding down a ramp with negligible friction (see Eq. 3.20). The denominator shows by what factor this acceleration is reduced for rolling motion. Because c is independent of m and R, Eq. 12.25 shows that the acceleration of the object does not depend on the values of m and R. Only the shape of the object matters because it affects the shape factor c. For all objects of a given shape, the time interval to roll down a ramp is thus the same. A large cylinder takes the same time interval as a small one, but a thin cylindrical shell takes longer than a solid cylinder because the shape factor of the shell is greater.

We can now also find an expression for the magnitude of the force of static friction $\vec{F}_{ro}^s$. Substituting a_{cmx} from Eq. 12.25 into Eq. 12.24 and eliminating the rotational inertia using $c \equiv I/mR^2$, which gives $I = cmR^2$, we obtain

$$F_{ro}^s = \frac{I}{R^2} a_{cmx} = \frac{cmR^2}{R^2}\frac{g\sin\theta}{1+c} = \frac{mg\sin\theta}{c^{-1}+1}. \tag{12.26}$$

Note that the force of static friction plays a dual role. It decreases the center-of-mass speed and acceleration of the rolling object by reducing the magnitude of the vector sum of the forces exerted on it: $\sum F_x = F_{Eox}^G - F_{ro}^s$. It also causes the torque that gives the object a rotational acceleration. In the absence of static friction, there would be no torque and objects would never roll—they would only slide.

Wheels certainly make it easier to push objects, but as Eq. 12.26 shows, they do not eliminate friction. In fact, the force of static friction to which wheels are subject slows them down, and as we have seen, the force of static friction can be *greater* than the force of kinetic friction. The next examples help clarify this paradox.

12.10 (*a*) A cylindrical shell and a solid cylinder, made of the same material and having the same inertia m and radius R, roll down a ramp. Is the force of static friction exerted on the shell greater than, smaller than, or equal to that on the solid cylinder? Explain. (*b*) For $\mu_s = 1$, what is the maximum angle of incline θ on which these objects can roll without slipping?

Example 12.7 Bicycle friction

As you accelerate from rest on a bicycle, how does the magnitude of the force of friction exerted by the road surface on the rear wheel compare with the magnitude of the force of friction exerted by the road surface on the front wheel? Ignore air resistance, assume both wheels have the same inertia m_w and the same radius R, and let m_{comb} be the combined inertia of you and your bicycle (including both wheels).

❶ GETTING STARTED I begin by making a sketch of my bicycle (Figure 12.40a). As I push on the pedals, the chain causes a torque on the rear wheel that makes the wheel rotate so that it exerts a rearward force on the road. Consequently the road surface exerts on the rear wheel a contact force in the opposite direction, and the tangential component of this force—the force of static friction—is what makes the bicycle go forward. This force, which I label $\vec{F}^s_{sr}$, is one of the forces I need for my comparison. (Note the subscripts here: r stands for "rear," not "road"; this is the frictional force exerted by the (road) surface on the rear wheel.)

The front wheel, because it is not connected to the chain, is merely pushed along with the rest of the bicycle. To make this wheel rotate in the right direction, the road surface must exert on it a rearward-pointing force of static friction $\vec{F}^s_{sf}$ (subscript f for "front" here). The torque caused by this frictional force is what makes the front wheel rotate, and this is the second force in my comparison.

Armed with this information, I make a free-body diagram for the bicycle (Figure 12.40b), showing the two frictional forces, the upward component of the contact force $\vec{F}^n_{sb}$ exerted by the road surface, and the downward force of gravity $\vec{F}^G_{Eb}$. Because the bicycle accelerates forward, I draw the vector arrow for $\vec{F}^s_{sr}$ longer than the vector arrow for $\vec{F}^s_{sf}$. Finally, I show the direction in which the bicycle's center of mass accelerates and choose a set of axes, letting the x axis point in the direction of motion. I also choose clockwise as the direction of increasing ϑ because that is the direction in which the wheels rotate.

Figure 12.40

❷ DEVISE PLAN The equation of motion in the form given by Eq. 8.45, $\vec{a}_{cm} = \Sigma\vec{F}_{ext}/m$, relates the vector sum of the forces shown in my free-body diagram to the acceleration $\vec{a}_{cm}$ of the bicycle's center of mass. Thus this equation gives me an expression that contains the two forces I'm after and seems a good place to begin. This expression contains the translational

acceleration, however, whereas the variables in this problem are rotational, so I will probably need Eq. 12.23 relating α_ϑ and a_{cmx}. Focusing on the front wheel first, I can use the rotational equation of motion, Eq. 12.5, $\tau_\vartheta = I\alpha_\vartheta$, to relate the torque caused by $\vec{F}^s_{sf}$ to α_ϑ for this wheel and then use Table 11.3 to express everything in terms of the given variables m_w and R. Once I have my expression for the magnitude F^s_{sf}, I can work with Eq. 8.45 to obtain an expression for F^s_{sr} in terms of F^s_{sf} and make my comparison.

❸ EXECUTE PLAN The vector sum of the forces in the x direction is, from Eq. 8.45

$$\Sigma F_x = F^s_{sr} - F^s_{sf} = m_{comb}\, a_{cmx}, \tag{1}$$

so I have an expression that contains both of the forces I'm after.

According to Eq. 12.23, the rotational acceleration of the rear wheel is $\alpha_\vartheta = a_{cmx}/R$, and the rotational acceleration of the front wheel must be the same as that of the rear wheel. To give the front wheel rotational acceleration α_ϑ, the force $\vec{F}^s_{sf}$ must cause a torque $\tau_\vartheta = I\alpha_\vartheta$ on the wheel, where I is the wheel's rotational inertia. If I treat the wheel as a thin hoop of inertia m_w, I have, from Table 11.3, $I = m_w R^2$, which means the torque on the front wheel is $\tau_\vartheta = m_w R^2\alpha_\vartheta$. The lever arm distance for this torque is equal to the radius R of the wheel, and so for this wheel $\tau_\vartheta = F^s_{sf}R = m_w R^2\alpha_\vartheta$. I know that for both wheels $\alpha_\vartheta = a_{cmx}/R$, however, so I can write

$$F^s_{sf}R = (m_w R^2)\left(\frac{a_{cmx}}{R}\right).$$

Dividing both sides by R yields one of the two forces I must compare:

$$F^s_{sf} = m_w a_{cmx}. \tag{2}$$

This is the magnitude of the force of static friction required to make the front wheel roll when the bicycle has acceleration a_{cmx}. The smaller the inertia of the wheel, the smaller this force magnitude.

Turning to the other force I need for my comparison—the force exerted on the rear wheel—I begin by eliminating a_{cmx} from Eq. 1 using Eq. 2 to get

$$F^s_{sr} - F^s_{sf} = \frac{m_{comb}}{m_w}F^s_{sf}$$

or $\qquad F^s_{sr} = F^s_{sf}\left(1 + \frac{m_{comb}}{m_w}\right) = F^s_{sf}\left(\frac{m_{comb} + m_w}{m_w}\right).$

The magnitude of the force of static friction exerted on the rear wheel is greater than that exerted on the front wheel by the factor $(m_{comb} + m_w)/m_w$. ✔

❹ EVALUATE RESULT Because $m_{comb} \gg m_w$, the magnitude of the force of static friction exerted on the front wheel is much smaller than that on the rear wheel, as I expect.

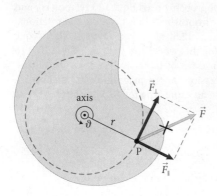

Figure 12.41 A rigid object subject to a constant torque caused by a force $\vec{F}$ exerted on it undergoes a rotational displacement $\Delta\vartheta$.

🖐 **12.11** (*a*) In Example 12.7, does the force of static friction exerted on the rear wheel cause a torque on the wheel? If so, in which direction? If not, why not? (*b*) In what direction is the sum of the torques on the rear wheel? What does this tell you about the relative magnitudes of the individual torques on the wheel?

12.7 Torque and energy

Torques cause objects to accelerate rotationally and thus cause a change in their rotational kinetic energy. To calculate this energy change, consider the object shown in **Figure 12.41**. A force $\vec{F}$ is exerted at point P on the object, a distance r from the axis of rotation. Let this force be such that the magnitude of its component perpendicular to r remains constant as the object rotates. This component thus causes a constant torque $\tau_\vartheta = +rF_\perp$ about the axis. Equation 12.10 relates the sum of the torques to the rotational acceleration. By applying the chain rule (Appendix B), we can write this equation in the form

$$\sum \tau_{\text{ext }\vartheta} = I\alpha_\vartheta = I\frac{d\omega_\vartheta}{dt} = I\frac{d\omega_\vartheta}{d\vartheta}\frac{d\vartheta}{dt} = I\frac{d\omega_\vartheta}{d\vartheta}\omega_\vartheta, \quad (12.27)$$

so

$$\left(\sum \tau_{\text{ext }\vartheta}\right)d\vartheta = I\omega_\vartheta\, d\omega_\vartheta. \quad (12.28)$$

Integrating the left side of this equation yields

$$\int_{\vartheta_i}^{\vartheta_f}\left(\sum\tau_{\text{ext }\vartheta}\right)d\vartheta = \left(\sum\tau_{\text{ext }\vartheta}\right)\int_{\vartheta_i}^{\vartheta_f}d\vartheta = \left(\sum\tau_{\text{ext }\vartheta}\right)\Delta\vartheta. \quad (12.29)$$

Integrating the right side after pulling the (constant) rotational inertia I out of the integral gives

$$\int_{\omega_{\vartheta,i}}^{\omega_{\vartheta,f}} I\omega_\vartheta\, d\omega_\vartheta = I\int_{\omega_{\vartheta,i}}^{\omega_{\vartheta,f}}\omega_\vartheta\, d\omega_\vartheta = I\left[\tfrac{1}{2}\omega_\vartheta^2\right]_{\omega_{\vartheta,i}}^{\omega_{\vartheta,f}}$$

$$= \tfrac{1}{2}I\omega_{\vartheta,f}^2 - \tfrac{1}{2}I\omega_{\vartheta,i}^2 = K_{\text{rot,f}} - K_{\text{rot,i}}. \quad (12.30)$$

Equations 12.28–12.30 thus show that the change in the rotational kinetic energy, $\Delta K_{\text{rot}} \equiv K_{\text{rot,f}} - K_{\text{rot,i}}$, is

$$\Delta K_{\text{rot}} = \left(\sum\tau_{\text{ext }\vartheta}\right)\Delta\vartheta \quad \text{(constant torques, rigid object).} \quad (12.31)$$

This equation states that the change in an object's rotational kinetic energy is equal to the product of the sum of the torques on the object and the object's rotational displacement. Note the analogy to Eq. 9.14, which relates the change in an object's center-of-mass kinetic energy to the product of the vector sum of the forces exerted on it and the object's displacement:

$$\Delta K_{\text{cm}} = \left(\sum F_{\text{ext}}\right)\Delta x_{\text{cm}} \quad \text{(constant forces, one dimension).} \quad (12.32)$$

The kinetic energy of an object or system that is in both translational and rotational motion is equal to the sum of its center-of-mass and rotational kinetic energies:

$$K = K_{\text{cm}} + K_{\text{rot}} = \tfrac{1}{2}mv_{\text{cm}}^2 + \tfrac{1}{2}I\omega^2, \quad (12.33)$$

and the change in this kinetic energy is given by the sum of the changes in Eqs. 12.31 and 12.32:

$$\Delta K = \Delta K_{\text{cm}} + \Delta K_{\text{rot}}. \quad (12.34)$$

Example 12.8 Rolling down a ramp

A solid cylindrical object of inertia m, rotational inertia I, and radius R rolls down a ramp that makes an angle θ with the horizontal. By how much does the cylinder's energy increase if it is released from rest and its center of mass drops a vertical distance h?

❶ **GETTING STARTED** I am given information about an object in the shape of a solid cylinder—inertia, rotational inertia, radius, and initial speed—and my task is to find out how much the object's energy has increased once it has rolled down a ramp such that its center of mass has traveled a vertical distance h. The object accelerates down the incline under the influence of the force of gravity. I therefore begin by making a sketch of the situation and drawing both free-body and extended free-body diagrams (**Figure 12.42**). The object is subject to a gravitational force exerted by Earth and a contact force exerted by the ramp. If I choose my axes as shown in my sketch, the contact force exerted by the ramp has a normal component $\vec{F}_{ro}^{n}$ in the y direction and a tangential component $\vec{F}_{ro}^{s}$ in the negative x direction due to static friction.

❷ **DEVISE PLAN** As the object rolls, both its translational and rotational kinetic energies increase. Because the shape of the object does not change and because static friction is nondissipative, the object's internal energy does not change. I can use Eq. 12.32 for the change in translational kinetic energy and Eq. 12.31 for the change in rotational kinetic energy. To express the two factors on the right in Eq. 12.32 in terms of my given variables, I use the geometry of the situation to express both factors in terms of $\sin \theta$.

❸ **EXECUTE PLAN** The change in translational kinetic energy is given by Eq. 12.32, $\Delta K_{cm} = (\sum F_{ext\,x}) \Delta x_{cm}$, and the vector sum of the forces exerted on the object in the x direction is

$$\sum F_{ext\,x} = mg \sin \theta - F_{ro}^{s}$$

or, using Eq. 12.26,

$$\sum F_{ext\,x} = +mg \sin \theta \left(1 - \frac{1}{1 + c^{-1}} \right),$$

where c is the object's shape factor. Because the displacement of the object's center of mass along the plane is $\Delta x_{cm} = h/\sin \theta$, the change in its translational kinetic energy is

$$\Delta K_{cm} = (\sum F_{ext\,x}) \Delta x_{cm} = mgh \left(1 - \frac{1}{1 + c^{-1}} \right).$$

Next, I use Eq. 12.31 to calculate the change in the object's rotational kinetic energy. From my extended free-body diagram I see that only the force of static friction causes a (positive) torque, so $\sum \tau_{ext\,\vartheta} = +F_{ro}^{s} R$. I can find the object's rotational displacement $\Delta \vartheta$ from Eq. 12.18:

$$\Delta \vartheta = \frac{\Delta x_{cm}}{R} = \left(\frac{h}{\sin \theta} \right) \left(\frac{1}{R} \right) = +\frac{h}{R \sin \theta},$$

so, from Eq. 12.31,

$$\Delta K_{rot} = (F_{ro}^{s} R) \left(\frac{h}{R \sin \theta} \right) = \left(\frac{mg \sin \theta}{1 + c^{-1}} \right) \left(\frac{h}{\sin \theta} \right) = \frac{mgh}{1 + c^{-1}},$$

where I have again used Eq. 12.26 to substitute for F_{ro}^{s}. Adding the two changes in kinetic energy, I obtain

$$\Delta E = \Delta K_{cm} + \Delta K_{rot} = mgh \left(1 - \frac{1}{1 + c^{-1}} \right)$$

$$+ mgh \left(\frac{1}{1 + c^{-1}} \right) = mgh. ✔$$

❹ **EVALUATE RESULT** My result indicates that the object's energy changes by the same amount it would change if it were simply in free fall! In other words, the only work done on the object is the work done by the gravitational force: $\vec{F}_{Eo}^{G} \cdot \Delta \vec{r} = mgh$ (see Section 10.9). This implies that the work done by all other forces on the object is zero. The normal force does no work on the object because it is perpendicular to the displacement of the object, but what is the work done by the force of static friction on the object? The object's displacement, $h/\sin \theta$, lies along the line of action of the force of static friction, and so it is tempting to write $-F_{ro}^{s} (h/\sin \theta)$ for the work done by the force of static friction on the object. However, the point of application for $\vec{F}_{ro}^{s}$ has zero velocity. At each instant, a different point on the object's surface touches the ramp, but the instantaneous velocity of that point is zero. The force displacement for $\vec{F}_{ro}^{s}$ is thus zero, so the work done by this force on the object is zero as well.

Figure 12.42

Figure 12.43 For a rotation about a fixed axis, the rotational velocity, rotational acceleration, and torque vectors all point along the rotation axis.

Right-hand rule gives direction of rotational vectors.

$\vec{\omega}$

$\vec{\tau}$

$\vec{\alpha}$ points in same direction as $\vec{\omega}$ because $\vec{\omega}$ is increasing in magnitude.

$\vec{\alpha}$

O

$\vec{r}$

$\vec{F}$

P

θ

Example 12.8 shows that *the force of static friction does no work on a rolling object!* The only thing it does is take away some of the translational kinetic energy and generate an equal amount of rotational kinetic energy. It takes away translational kinetic energy by reducing the magnitude of the vector sum of the forces and converts it to rotational kinetic energy by causing a torque.

12.12 In Figure 12.41, does the force exerted on the rigid object do work on the object?

12.8 The vector product

To complete our treatment of rotation, we must examine the vectorial nature of the rotational components. As we saw in the first part of this chapter, an object's rotational velocity can be described by a vector $\vec{\omega}$. Angular momentum, which is the product of a scalar and $\vec{\omega}$, $\vec{L} = I\vec{\omega}$, is therefore also a vector and points in the same direction as $\vec{\omega}$. Because the rotational acceleration $\vec{\alpha}$ is the time derivative of $\vec{\omega}$, it must be a vector, too. Torque, which is the product of a scalar and $\vec{\alpha}$, $\vec{\tau} = I\vec{\alpha}$, therefore points in the same direction as $\vec{\alpha}$.

Consider the object in **Figure 12.43**. A force $\vec{F}$ exerted at point P increases the object's rotational velocity about the rotation axis at O. As the rotational velocity increases, the length of the vector representing $\vec{\omega}$ increases. Because the rotation takes place in a plane, the direction of $\vec{\omega}$ remains along the axis of rotation. The direction of $\vec{\alpha}$ is related to the direction of the vector representing the change in rotational velocity $\Delta\vec{\omega}$. Because the direction of $\vec{\omega}$ remains along the axis of rotation, $\Delta\vec{\omega}$, $\vec{\alpha}$, and $\vec{\tau}$ also lie along the rotation axis.

The magnitude of the torque is $rF \sin \theta$, where θ is the angle between $\vec{r}$ and $\vec{F}$. In Section 10.9, I showed that work on a system can be written as a scalar product of two vectors. To account for the vectorial nature of torque, we must introduce a new kind of product of two vectors: one that generates a new vector. Specifically, this product of the vectors $\vec{r}$ and $\vec{F}$ must generate a vector whose magnitude is $rF \sin \theta$ and whose direction is as indicated in **Figure 12.44**. Such a product is called the **vector product.** The vector product of two vectors $\vec{A}$ and $\vec{B}$, written $\vec{A} \times \vec{B}$, is a vector whose magnitude is

$$|\vec{A} \times \vec{B}| \equiv AB \sin \theta, \qquad (12.35)$$

where θ is the angle between $\vec{A}$ and $\vec{B}$ when they are placed tail to tail (and $\theta \leq 180°$). The direction of the vector $\vec{A} \times \vec{B}$ is determined as illustrated in Figure 12.44a: Place vectors $\vec{A}$ and $\vec{B}$ with their tails together and apply the right-hand rule to the direction of rotation obtained by rotating $\vec{A}$ into $\vec{B}$ through the

Figure 12.44 The vector product of two vectors.

(*a*) Vector product $\vec{A} \times \vec{B}$

$\vec{A} \times \vec{B}$

smallest angle between $\vec{A}$ and $\vec{B}$ ($\theta \leq 180°$)

$\vec{A}$

θ

$\vec{B}$

(*b*) Finding the direction of a vector product

Align fingers of right hand with first vector in product ($\vec{A}$) . . .

. . . and curl fingers toward second vector ($\vec{B}$).

$\vec{A} \times \vec{B}$

$\vec{A}$

$\vec{B}$

Thumb points in direction of vector product.

(*c*) Magnitude of a vector product

Magnitude of $\vec{A} \times \vec{B}$ equals area of rectangle: $|\vec{A} \times \vec{B}| = AB \sin \theta$.

$\vec{A}$

A

θ

$B \sin \theta$

$\vec{B}$

Triangles are equal, so rectangle has same area as dotted parallelogram.

smallest angle. When you point the fingers of your right hand along the direction of the first vector in the product and curl them toward the direction of the second vector, your thumb points in the direction of the vector product (Figure 12.44b).

Figure 12.44c shows a geometric interpretation of the magnitude of the vector product. The area of the shaded rectangle is equal to $AB \sin \theta$, and because the two triangles are identical, the area of the parallelogram defined by the vectors $\vec{A}$ and $\vec{B}$ is equal to the area of the shaded rectangle. Therefore:

The magnitude of the vector product of two vectors is equal to the area of the parallelogram defined by them.

The magnitude of the vector product is greatest when the two vectors are perpendicular to each other and $\sin \theta = \sin 90° = 1$. When the two vectors are parallel, the parallelogram is reduced to a straight line and the vector product is zero. In particular, the vector product of a vector with itself is zero:

$$\vec{A} \times \vec{A} = \vec{0}. \tag{12.36}$$

Another interesting property of the vector product is that the multiplication sequence is important. The vector product $\vec{B} \times \vec{A}$ is equal in magnitude to $\vec{A} \times \vec{B}$ but points in the opposite direction, as shown in **Figure 12.45**:

$$\vec{B} \times \vec{A} = -(\vec{A} \times \vec{B}). \tag{12.37}$$

Using the definition of vector product, we can write the torque about the origin caused by a force $\vec{F}$ as

$$\vec{\tau} = \vec{r} \times \vec{F}. \tag{12.38}$$

You can easily verify that this product has the correct magnitude and direction.

Because torque is the time derivative of angular momentum (Eq. 12.12) and force is the time derivative of momentum (Eq. 8.4), we can write Eq. 12.38 as

$$\frac{d\vec{L}}{dt} = \vec{r} \times \frac{d\vec{p}}{dt}. \tag{12.39}$$

To see what this expression means, we use the product rule (Appendix B) to find the time derivative of the vector product $\vec{r} \times \vec{p}$:

$$\frac{d}{dt}(\vec{r} \times \vec{p}) = \frac{d\vec{r}}{dt} \times \vec{p} + \vec{r} \times \frac{d\vec{p}}{dt}. \tag{12.40}$$

The first term on the right side vanishes because the vector product of a vector and itself is zero:

$$\frac{d\vec{r}}{dt} \times \vec{p} = \vec{v} \times (m\vec{v}) = m(\vec{v} \times \vec{v}) = 0. \tag{12.41}$$

Therefore the right side of Eq. 12.39 is equal to the time derivative of the vector product $\vec{r} \times \vec{p}$:

$$\frac{d\vec{L}}{dt} = \frac{d}{dt}(\vec{r} \times \vec{p}). \tag{12.42}$$

The angular momentum vector can therefore be written as

$$\vec{L} = \vec{r} \times \vec{p}. \tag{12.43}$$

Figure 12.45

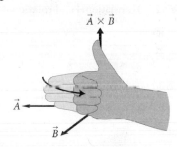

Vector products $\vec{A} \times \vec{B}$ and $\vec{B} \times \vec{A}$ point in opposite directions

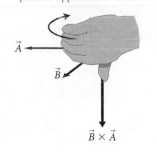

QUANTITATIVE TOOLS

Figure 12.46 The angular momentum of an isolated particle about an arbitrary point (called origin O here) is constant because $r \sin \theta = r_\perp$ is the same regardless of the position of the particle.

Like the rotational velocity vector, $\vec{L}$ is perpendicular to the plane defined by $\vec{r}$ and $\vec{p}$, a direction in which nothing moves—there is certainly no momentum in this direction.

Because it applies to any type of motion and not just rotational motion, the expression $\vec{L} = \vec{r} \times \vec{p}$ is much more general than $\vec{L} = I\vec{\omega}$. Consider, for example, the motion of the isolated particle in **Figure 12.46**. Because the particle is isolated, its trajectory is a straight line and its momentum is constant. From Eq. 12.35 we see that the magnitude of the particle's angular momentum with respect to the origin O is

$$L = r\,mv \sin \theta = r_\perp mv, \tag{12.44}$$

where θ is the angle between $\vec{r}$ and $\vec{p}$ and $r_\perp$ is the lever arm distance of $\vec{p}$ relative to O. This is the same result we obtained in Chapter 11 (Eq. 11.36). The right side of Eq. 12.44 is indeed constant. Even though $\vec{r}$ changes in direction and magnitude, the lever arm distance $r_\perp$ remains constant. Consequently the product $\vec{r} \times \vec{p}$, perpendicular to the plane defined by O and the particle's trajectory, is unchanged in direction and magnitude.

Table 12.1 Translational and rotational dynamics

	Translation	Rotation	Relationship
Momentum	$\vec{p} \equiv m\vec{v}$	$\vec{L} \equiv I\vec{\omega}$	$\vec{L} = \vec{r} \times \vec{p}$
Momentum change	$\Delta \vec{p} = \sum \vec{F}_{ext} \Delta t$	$\Delta \vec{L} = \sum \vec{\tau}_{ext} \Delta t$	
Force	$\sum \vec{F}_{ext} \equiv \dfrac{d\vec{p}}{dt} = m\vec{a}_{cm}$	$\sum \vec{\tau}_{ext} = \dfrac{d\vec{L}}{dt} = I\vec{\alpha}$	$\vec{\tau} = \vec{r} \times \vec{F}$
Kinetic energy	$K_{cm} = \frac{1}{2}mv^2$	$K_{rot} = \frac{1}{2}I\omega^2$	
Kinetic energy change	$\Delta K_{cm} = (\sum \vec{F}_{ext}) \cdot \Delta \vec{r}_{cm}$	$\Delta K_{rot} = (\sum \tau_{ext\,\vartheta}) \Delta \vartheta$	

Table 12.2 Corresponding translational and rotational quantities

position	$\vec{r}$	$\leftrightarrow$	ϑ
velocity	$\vec{v}$	$\leftrightarrow$	$\vec{\omega}$
acceleration	$\vec{a}$	$\leftrightarrow$	$\vec{\alpha}$
inertia	m	$\leftrightarrow$	I

Table 12.1 summarizes the results obtained in this chapter and the remarkable parallels between the equations that describe the dynamics of translational and rotational motion. The two sets of equations are mathematically identical given the correspondences in **Table 12.2**. The only new mathematical tool we have introduced in this chapter is the vector product. Apart from this product, which is required to account for the vectorial nature of rotation, the mathematical framework for the two types of motion is identical. Finally, note that—unlike their translational counterparts—rotational inertia, angular momentum, and torque depend on the choice of origin and axis. You should therefore always specify your choice of axis when dealing with these quantities and—most important—consistently use the same axis for the different quantities throughout your calculations.

✋ **12.13** Consider a particle moving at constant speed along a circular trajectory centered on the origin. Write the relationship of the particle's velocity $\vec{v}$, rotational velocity $\vec{\omega}$, and position vector $\vec{r}$ in the form of a vector product.

Chapter Glossary

SI units of physical quantities are given in parentheses.

Angular momentum law The law that accounts for the change in the angular momentum of a system or object. Because angular momentum is conserved, the angular momentum of a system can change only if there is a transfer of angular momentum between the environment and the system:

$$\Delta L_\vartheta = J_\vartheta. \tag{12.15}$$

Axial vector A vector associated with a direction of rotation. The vector points along the rotation axis, with its direction given by the right-hand rule.

Condition for rolling motion without slipping The translational and rotational motions of a round object of radius R that rolls along a surface without slipping are coupled. The center-of-mass velocity and the rotational velocity of a rolling object are related by

$$v_{\text{cm}\,x} = R\omega_\vartheta. \tag{12.19}$$

Rolling motion occurs because of the force of static friction between the rolling object and the surface on which it moves. This force of static friction does no work on the object.

Extended free-body diagram A sketch showing a single object with all the forces exerted on it at their points of application. See the Procedure box on page 7.

Free rotation A rotation that is not constrained by a physical axis or by other external constraints. Freely rotating objects rotate about their center of mass. Their translational and rotational motions are independent of each other—the first determined by the vector sum of the forces exerted on the object and the second by the sum of the torques caused by the forces exerted on it.

Mechanical equilibrium Any object that is simultaneously in translational equilibrium and in rotational equilibrium is in mechanical equilibrium.

Polar vector A vector associated with a displacement or derived from it.

Right-hand rule The rule that relates the direction of a vector to a direction of rotation: When you curl the fingers of your right hand along the direction of rotation, your outstretched thumb points in the direction of the vector that specifies the direction of rotation.

Rotational equilibrium Any object or system whose angular momentum is not changing is in rotational equilibrium. This state requires the sum of the torques on the object to be zero:

$$\sum \vec{\tau}_{\text{ext}} = \vec{0} \Rightarrow \Delta \vec{L} = \vec{0} \quad \text{(rotational equilibrium).} \tag{12.13}$$

Rotational impulse J_ϑ $(\text{kg} \cdot \text{m}^2/\text{s})$ The amount of angular momentum transferred from the environment to a system.

Rotational impulse equation The equation that allows us to calculate the change in a system's angular momentum caused by torques on the system during a time interval Δt. For constant torques;

$$J_\vartheta = \left(\sum \tau_{\text{ext}\,\vartheta} \right) \Delta t \quad \text{(constant torques).} \tag{12.17}$$

Torque $\vec{\tau}\,(\text{N} \cdot \text{m})$ An axial vector that describes the tendency of a force to give an object a rotational acceleration. The torque caused by a force $\vec{F}$ exerted on an object about a point O is

$$\vec{\tau} = \vec{r} \times \vec{F}, \tag{12.38}$$

where $\vec{r}$ is the vector pointing from O to the point of application of $\vec{F}$. The direction of the torque is given by the right-hand rule; the torque magnitude is

$$\tau \equiv rF \sin \theta = r_\perp F = rF_\perp. \tag{12.1}$$

Vector product The product of two vectors that forms a new vector. The vector product of vectors $\vec{A}$ and $\vec{B}$ that make an angle θ is written as $\vec{A} \times \vec{B}$. This product is another vector whose magnitude is equal to the area $AB \sin \theta$ of the parallelogram defined by $\vec{A}$ and $\vec{B}$ and whose direction can be obtained by applying the right-hand rule to the direction of rotation obtained by rotating $\vec{A}$ into $\vec{B}$ through the smallest angle.

13 Gravity

CONCEPTS

13.1 Universal gravity
13.2 Gravity and angular momentum
13.3 Weight
13.4 Principle of equivalence

QUANTITATIVE TOOLS

13.5 Gravitational constant
13.6 Gravitational potential energy
13.7 Celestial mechanics
13.8 Gravitational force exerted by a sphere

The motion of celestial bodies has fascinated humankind since antiquity. What keeps Earth's Moon, the planets, and other heavenly objects moving along their orbits? Motivated largely by aesthetics, Greek philosophers proposed that celestial bodies move in circles because they believed that circular motion was the most "natural" and the most perfect form of motion. As we have seen, however, objects travel in a straight line when they are not subject to any external forces. In the early 17th century, the German astronomer Johannes Kepler suggested that the Sun was somehow driving the planets around their orbits.

If the laws of physics are truly universal, then phenomena on a cosmic scale should follow the same laws that govern objects around us. In this chapter we see that we can indeed apply our notions of mechanics to describe the motion of celestial bodies.

13.1 Universal gravity

Careful analysis of the motion of the Moon and the planets shows that the Moon revolves around Earth and that Earth and the other planets revolve around the Sun at roughly constant speed in nearly circular orbits.* In other words, to a good approximation they move in circular motion at constant speed. These bodies generally rotate about an axis through their centers in addition to revolving around the Sun, but in this chapter we are concerned with their *orbital* motion—that is, rotational quantities associated with the revolving motion of objects.

As we saw in Chapter 11, any object that is in circular motion at constant speed has a centripetal acceleration. As illustrated in **Figure 13.1**, in the reference frame of the Sun,

Figure 13.1 Both Earth and the Moon have nearly circular orbits and thus have a centripetal acceleration.

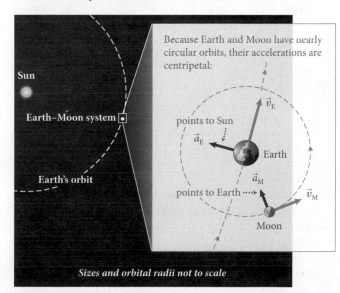

Earth has an acceleration that points toward the Sun; in the reference frame of Earth, the Moon has an acceleration that points toward Earth.

To get some feel for the quantities involved in celestial mechanics, do the following checkpoint before proceeding.

13.1 The orbital period of the Moon around Earth is 27.32 days; that of Earth around the Sun is 365.26 days. (*a*) Which has the greater rotational speed: Earth or the Moon? Are the rotational speeds of Earth and the Moon around the Sun great or small relative to the rotational speeds you encounter in daily life? (*b*) The radius of the Moon's orbit around Earth is $R_M = 3.84 \times 10^8$ m; that of Earth's orbit around the Sun is $R_E = 1.50 \times 10^{11}$ m. Which has the greater speed? (*c*) Calculate the centripetal acceleration of Earth in the reference frame of the Sun and the centripetal acceleration of the Moon in the reference frame of Earth. (*d*) How do these accelerations compare with the acceleration due to gravity near Earth's surface?

As we saw in Chapter 11, some force is required to supply a centripetal acceleration. All examples we have considered so far involve contact forces. Neither the Moon nor Earth is in contact with anything, however, and so the force that holds them in orbit must be a field force. In the late 17th century, Isaac Newton made the bold proposal that the force that holds celestial bodies in orbit is a gravitational force—the same force that causes objects near Earth's surface to fall (**Figure 13.2**). Every piece of matter in the universe—feather or planet—attracts every other piece of matter. In other words, a gravitational attraction between Earth and the Moon is responsible for the centripetal acceleration of the Moon, just as a gravitational attraction between a terrestrial object and Earth is responsible for the free fall of that object. The reason the Moon does not fall to Earth like a freely falling ball is that the Moon has just the right speed to keep moving in a circle around Earth.

Figure 13.2 The invisible tether that holds the Moon in orbit is, in reality, the same kind of gravitational interaction that causes a ball to fall near Earth's surface. The Moon's orbit is not to scale.

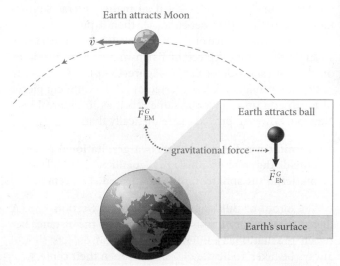

Figure 13.3 Light that strikes a surface area a^2 located a distance r from the source strikes a surface of area $2a \times 2a = 4a^2$ at a distance $2r$ and a surface of area $3a \times 3a = 9a^2$ at a distance $3r$. The intensity—the amount of light per unit area—decreases with distance r as $1/r^2$.

Figure 13.4 (a) A solid sphere exerts a gravitational force as if all of the sphere's matter were concentrated at the center of the sphere. (b) Because the magnitude of the gravitational force between two objects depends on the distance between them, the gravitational forces exerted by the various "chunks" of Earth's interior represented by δm have different magnitudes.

(a) Gravitational interaction between Earth and ball near Earth's surface

Ball interacts with Earth as though all of Earth's inertia m_E is concentrated at Earth's center.

(b) Reason gravitation acts as though from Earth's center

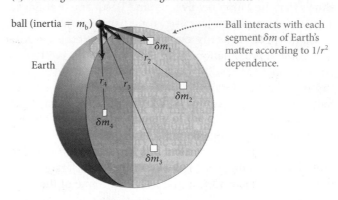

Ball interacts with each segment δm of Earth's matter according to $1/r^2$ dependence.

Newton furthermore postulated that the effect of gravity weakens with distance, much as the effect of a magnet weakens with distance. If gravity spreads out uniformly from an object, as the rays from a light source do, then the effect of gravity should fall off as $1/r^2$—the inverse of the square of the distance (**Figure 13.3**). The radius of the Moon's orbit is 60 times the radius of Earth, so the gravitational force exerted by Earth on the Moon should be smaller by a factor of $(\frac{1}{60})^2$ than the gravitational force exerted by Earth on an object near the ground. An object at the same distance from Earth as the Moon should therefore experience an acceleration due to gravity of magnitude $\frac{1}{3600}g = (9.8 \text{ m/s}^2)/3600 = 0.00272 \text{ m/s}^2$. This value is in excellent agreement with the Moon's centripetal acceleration (see Checkpoint 13.1), confirming the $1/r^2$ dependence of the gravitational force.

There is one catch in this reasoning: The dilution of the gravitational force by a factor of $1/r^2$ assumes that the object near Earth's surface is one Earth radius away from the point of attraction. In other words, a ball falling near the surface of Earth interacts with Earth as if all the matter were concentrated at its center—6378 km below the surface—as illustrated in **Figure 13.4a**. Yet if all matter interacts gravitationally with a $1/r^2$ dependence, then a piece of Earth-matter near the surface of Earth attracts the ball much more strongly than does a piece of Earth-matter deep inside or on the opposite side of Earth (Figure 13.4b). It is certainly not obvious that the forces exerted by all the different pieces of Earth add up to give the same result as in Figure 13.4a. Newton, however, proved mathematically that:

A uniform solid sphere exerts a gravitational force outside the sphere with a $1/r^2$ dependence as if all the matter in the sphere were concentrated at its center.

The proof of this statement is given in Section 13.8. A direct consequence of this statement is that the distance between gravitationally interacting spherical objects should always be taken to be the distance between their centers.

13.2 If the force of gravity decreases with the inverse square of the distance, why were we allowed, in all our earlier work on the gravitational force, to say that an object sitting on the ground, an object sitting in a tree 10 m above the ground, and an object flying at an altitude of 10 km all experience the same 9.8-m/s² acceleration due to gravity?

Further evidence of the $1/r^2$ dependence of the gravitational force is provided by the observed relationship between the radii R and the periods T of the planetary orbits. As it orbits the Sun, each planet has centripetal acceleration $a_c = v^2/R$, where $v = 2\pi R/T$ is the planet's linear speed and R is the radius of its orbit. So $a_c = 4\pi^2 R/T^2$ or $a_c \propto R/T^2$.* If this centripetal acceleration is provided by a gravitational attraction exerted by the Sun on the planet, the magnitude of the force (and hence the centripetal acceleration) should fall off as $1/R^2$. So, the $1/r^2$ dependence of the gravitational force requires that $a_c \propto 1/R^2$. Combining this

---

*The symbol $\propto$ means "is proportional to." That is, $a_c \propto R/T^2$ means that there is some number k such that $a_c = kR/T^2$.

Figure 13.5 The planetary period T versus the radius R of the orbit. The data are plotted on a logarithmic grid to accommodate the large range of values. To convince yourself of the $T^2 \propto R^3$ dependence, compare the values of T at $R = 1$ Earth radius and $R = 100$ Earth radii.

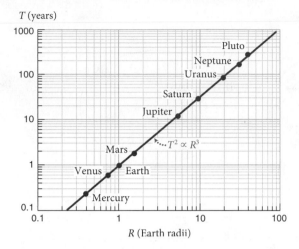

result with $a_c \propto R/T^2$, we get $1/R^2 \propto R/T^2$, or $T^2 \propto R^3$. In words:

The square of the period of a planetary orbit is proportional to the cube of the orbit's radius.

Kepler had established this fact from astronomical data in 1619, providing support for the $1/r^2$ dependence of the gravitational force proposed later by Newton. The excellent agreement with astronomical observations is shown in **Figure 13.5**.

13.3 Suppose the universe were two dimensional rather than three dimensional. (a) Following the line of reasoning illustrated in Figure 13.3, describe how the strength of the gravitational force would depend on distance in this flat universe. (b) How would the periods of the planetary orbits be related to their radii in this universe?

What determines the strength of the gravitational attraction? To answer this question, consider two identical lumps of clay, each of inertia m. If we let the lumps fall freely, each is subject to a single downward force of gravity and undergoes an acceleration g. To give each lump this acceleration, Earth must exert a force mg on it. Now imagine combining the two lumps. The double lump has twice the inertia, which means it is twice as hard to accelerate as either single lump. Yet, like any other object near Earth's surface, the double lump undergoes an acceleration g. From this observation, we conclude that Earth pulls twice as hard on the double lump as it does on either single lump. Apparently the gravitational pull on an object is proportional to the quantity of material in it, a quantity called the **mass** of the object. The double lump has twice the mass of either single lump.

The gravitational pull exerted by Earth on an object is proportional to the object's mass.

The acceleration of a freely falling object near Earth's surface does not depend on the type of material: In the absence of air resistance, all objects, regardless of their composition, configuration, or any other property of the object, have the same acceleration in free fall. This observation suggests that the inertia of an object and the force of gravity exerted on it are proportional to each other. Given that the force of gravity is proportional to the object's mass, we can consider mass and inertia to be equal and let the SI unit of mass be the kilogram (kg). As we shall see in the next chapter, this equality between mass and inertia breaks down for motion at very high speeds. In everyday situations, however, we can say:

The mass of an object is equal to the object's inertia.

For the description of everyday situations, therefore, we can denote both by the same symbol m and express each in units of kilograms. Unless we need to refer explicitly to an object's resistance to a change in velocity or account for effects that occur at very high speeds, we henceforth shall call both simply the *mass* of the object.

The equality of inertia and mass may seem obvious, but consider the two experiments shown in **Figure 13.6**. The collision experiment in Figure 13.6*a* allows us to determine the ratio of the objects' inertias. Now suppose we suspend the same two objects, from a beam that is supported at its center of mass. We arrange the objects' suspension points so that the beam is balanced as shown in Figure 13.6*b*. Experimentally we discover that for *any* two objects, the ratio m_1/m_2 determined in the first experiment is exactly equal to the ratio r_2/r_1 determined in the second experiment. As we saw in Chapter 12, when the beam is balanced, the torques on the beam add up to zero, so $r_1 F^G_{E1} = r_2 F^G_{E2}$, which means that

$$\frac{F^G_{E1}}{F^G_{E2}} = \frac{r_2}{r_1}.$$

Figure 13.6 Establishing the equivalence between inertia and mass.

(*a*) Collision between objects gives ratio of inertias

$$\frac{m_1}{m_2} = \frac{|\Delta v_{2x}|}{|\Delta v_{1x}|}$$

(*b*) Beam in equilibrium gives ratio of gravitational forces

$$\frac{\vec{F}^G_{E1}}{\vec{F}^G_{E2}} = \frac{r_2}{r_1}$$

Figure 13.7 Tracing an ellipse. The greater the separation of the foci, the more eccentric (elongated) the ellipse ($0 < e < 1$). In the special case where the two foci coincide ($e = 0$), the ellipse becomes a circle of radius a.

(a) Drawing an ellipse with two pins and a string

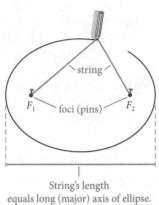

String's length equals long (major) axis of ellipse.

(b) Eccentricity of ellipse

Eccentricity e is ratio of distance between foci to long (major) axis of ellipse.

When foci coincide, $e = 0$ and ellipse is a circle.

(c) Axes of ellipse

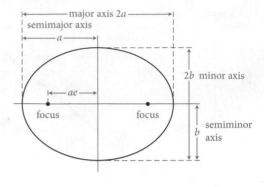

Combining this with the experimental observation that

$$\frac{m_1}{m_2} = \frac{r_2}{r_1},$$

we see that

$$\frac{F^G_{E1}}{F^G_{E2}} = \frac{m_1}{m_2}.$$

In words, for any two objects, the ratio of the gravitational forces they experience is equal to the ratio of their inertias. If you think about it, there is no reason to expect this result. The two experiments are completely different: The collision measures the objects' tendencies to resist a change in velocity—their *inertias*—and involves no gravity; the balancing experiment measures the gravitational pull on the objects—their *mass* — and involves no motion. This equivalence is therefore truly remarkable.

Because the gravitational force exerted by Earth on an object is proportional to that object's mass, we can expect the gravitational force exerted by Earth on the Moon to be proportional to the Moon's mass: $F^G_{EM} \propto m_M$. The attraction between Earth and the Moon is mutual, and so symmetry requires the force of gravity exerted by the Moon on Earth to be proportional to the mass of Earth: $F^G_{ME} \propto m_E$. In addition, we know that $F^G_{EM} = F^G_{ME}$, and so the force of gravity must be proportional to the product $m_M m_E$.

Combining this conclusion with the $1/r^2$ dependence, we can now write for the gravitational attraction between any two material objects of masses m_1 and m_2 separated by a distance r:

$$F^G_{12} \propto \frac{m_1 m_2}{r^2}.$$

This is Newton's **law of gravity.** It applies to all the mass in the universe: Every piece of matter attracts every other piece of matter in the universe according to this law.

The $1/r^2$ dependence also explains the shape of the planetary orbits. Using conservation of energy and angular momentum, we can show that the orbit of a body moving under the influence of gravity must be an ellipse (**Figure 13.7**), a circle, a parabola, or a hyperbola. A comet, for example, moves in an elliptical orbit with the Sun at one focus of the ellipse. The planets also move in elliptical orbits with the Sun at one focus. As you can see from the data in **Table 13.1**, however, the planetary orbits are close to circular, even for dwarf planet Pluto, whose orbit has the greatest eccentricity of all. Even though the effect of the eccentricity on the shape of the orbit is minimal, its effect on the speed is considerable. The Sun is appreciably off-center for Pluto's orbit, and so the distance to the Sun and the speed vary as the planet moves between the closest point to the Sun, the *perihelion*, and the farthest point, the *aphelion* (**Figure 13.8**).

Figure 13.8 In spite of having the greatest eccentricity in Table 13.1, Pluto's orbit (dashed line) is remarkably close to a circle (solid line). Because the Sun is off-center, Pluto's speed varies appreciably along the orbit.

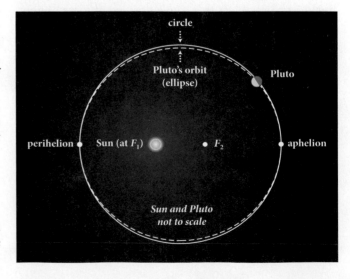

Table 13.1 Solar system data (in SI units and relative to Earth)

| | Mass | | Equatorial radius | | Orbit[†] | | | | |
	(kg)	(m_E)	(m)	(R_E)	semimajor axis (m)	(a_E)	eccentricity	period (s)	(years)
Sun	2.0×10^{30}	3.3×10^5	7×10^8	110	–	–	–	–	–
Mercury	3.30×10^{23}	0.06	2.440×10^6	0.38	5.79×10^{10}	0.39	0.206	7.60×10^6	0.24
Venus	4.87×10^{24}	0.81	6.052×10^6	0.95	1.082×10^{11}	0.72	0.007	1.94×10^7	0.62
Earth	5.97×10^{24}	1	6.378×10^6	1	1.496×10^{11}	1	0.017	3.16×10^7	1
Mars	6.42×10^{23}	0.11	3.396×10^6	0.53	2.279×10^{11}	1.52	0.09	5.94×10^7	1.88
Jupiter	1.90×10^{27}	318	7.149×10^7	11.2	7.783×10^{11}	5.20	0.05	3.74×10^8	11.86
Saturn	5.68×10^{26}	95.2	6.027×10^7	9.45	1.427×10^{12}	9.54	0.05	9.29×10^8	29.45
Uranus	8.68×10^{25}	14.5	2.556×10^7	4.01	2.871×10^{12}	19.2	0.05	2.65×10^9	84.02
Neptune	1.02×10^{26}	17.1	2.476×10^7	3.88	4.498×10^{12}	30.1	0.01	5.20×10^9	164.8
Pluto	1.31×10^{22}	0.002	1.151×10^6	0.18	5.906×10^{12}	39.5	0.25	7.82×10^9	247.9
Moon	7.3×10^{22}	0.012	1.737×10^6	0.27	3.84×10^8	0.0026	0.055	2.36×10^6	0.075

[†]The elliptical orbits of the planets and the Moon are specified by their *semimajor axis a* (half the major axis) and eccentricity *e*; see Figure 13.7. With the exception of Mercury and Pluto, the eccentricity is small and so the orbits are close to being circular.

13.4 Suppose the force of gravity between two objects 1 and 2 of masses m_1 and m_2 were proportional to the sum $m_1 + m_2$ rather than to the product $m_1 m_2$. (a) Would this dependence be consistent with the following two requirements: (i) The force exerted by 1 on 2 is equal in magnitude to the force exerted by 2 on 1. (ii) The force of gravity exerted by Earth on two identical objects is equal to the sum of the forces exerted on the individual objects. (b) Can you think of any other combination of m_1 and m_2 that satisfies requirements (i) and (ii)? (c) Suppose you are given a lump of matter of mass M. How should you divide this lump into two parts to maximize the force of gravity between the two parts?

Example 13.1 Comparing gravitational pulls

Compare the gravitational force exerted by Earth on you with (a) that exerted by a person standing 1 m away from you and (b) that exerted by Earth on Pluto.

❶ **GETTING STARTED** Although I don't know yet how to calculate a numerical value for the gravitational force, I know that the gravitational force between two objects with masses m_1 and m_2 separated by a distance r is proportional to the factor $m_1 m_2 / r^2$. To compare gravitational forces, I should therefore compare these factors for each given situation.

❷ **DEVISE PLAN** My mass is about 70 kg, and I can get the masses of Earth and Pluto from Table 13.1. When I stand on the surface of Earth, the distance between me and the center of the planet is its radius, which is given in Table 13.1. To do part b, I need to know the distance between Pluto and Earth, which is not given in the table. Planetary orbits are very nearly circular, however, so I can consider the semimajor axis a to be the radius of each (nearly) circular orbit. Table 13.1 shows that the "radius" of Pluto's orbit is about 40 times greater than that of Earth's orbit, and so I make only a small error by taking the Sun-Pluto distance as a measure of the (average) Earth-Pluto distance. Armed with this information, I'll calculate the factor

$m_1 m_2 / r^2$ first for Earth and me, then for the two situations described in the two parts of this problem.

❸ **EXECUTE PLAN** When I stand on the surface of Earth, $r = R_E$, and so the factor $m_1 m_2 / r^2$ is

$$\frac{m_1 m_E}{R_E^2} = \frac{(70 \text{ kg})(5.97 \times 10^{24} \text{ kg})}{(6.38 \times 10^6 \text{ m})^2} = 1.0 \times 10^{13} \text{ kg}^2/\text{m}^2.$$

(a) For two 70-kg people separated by 1 m, I get

$$\frac{m_1 m_2}{r_{12}^2} = \frac{(70 \text{ kg})^2}{(1 \text{ m})^2} = 4.9 \times 10^3 \text{ kg}^2/\text{m}^2.$$

Thus the gravitational force exerted by a person standing 1 m from me is $(4.9 \times 10^3 \text{ kg}^2/\text{m}^2)/(1.0 \times 10^{13} \text{ kg}^2/\text{m}^2) = 4.9 \times 10^{-10}$ times the gravitational force exerted by Earth on me. ✔

(b) For Earth and Pluto, I have

$$\frac{m_E m_P}{r_{EP}^2} = \frac{(5.97 \times 10^{24} \text{ kg})(1.36 \times 10^{22} \text{ kg})}{(5.9 \times 10^{12} \text{ m})^2}$$

$$= 2.3 \times 10^{21} \text{ kg}^2/\text{m}^2.$$

This is $(2.3 \times 10^{21} \text{ kg}^2/\text{m}^2)/(1.0 \times 10^{13} \text{ kg}^2/\text{m}^2) = 2.3 \times 10^8$ times greater than the attraction between Earth and me. ✔

❹ **EVALUATE RESULT** That the gravitational force exerted by another person on me is more than a billion times smaller than that exerted by Earth on me makes sense: Only the gravitational attraction between Earth and objects on Earth is noticeable. That the gravitational force exerted by Earth on Pluto is 200,000,000 times greater than that exerted by Earth on me, even though Pluto is 1,000,000 times farther from Earth's center than I am, is amazing. Of course, Pluto's mass is about 10^{20} times greater than mine, and that factor more than makes up for the large difference between the Earth-me distance and the Earth-Pluto distance.

CONCEPTS

✋ **13.5** In part *a* of Example 13.1, what would the distance between the other person and you have to be for the gravitational force between the two of you to match the gravitational force exerted by Earth on you? Is it possible to verify your prediction?

13.2 Gravity and angular momentum

The force of gravity is a **central force**—a force whose line of action always lies along the straight line that connects the two interacting objects. A planet orbiting the Sun, for example, is subject to a force that is always directed toward the Sun. The fact that the force is central has an important consequence for angular momentum.

For example, consider an isolated system of two gravitationally interacting stars of masses m_1 and m_2 (**Figure 13.9**).

Figure 13.9 Gravitation is a central force, as illustrated by two stars orbiting their common center of mass.

(a) **Two stars follow elliptical orbits around common center of mass**

star 1   center of mass   star 2

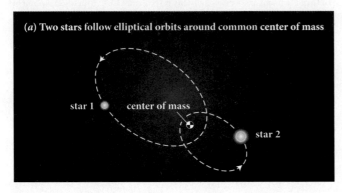

(b) Gravitational forces stars exert on each other point along straight line connecting star centers. (Stars are shown at two instants in orbit.)

$\vec{F}_{21}^G$ star 1 $\vec{v}_2$ star 2 $\vec{v}_1$ $\vec{F}_{12}^G$

$\vec{v}_1$ star 1 $\vec{F}_{21}^G$ $\vec{F}_{12}^G$ star 2 $\vec{v}_2$

(c) Ratio r_1/r_2 of distances between each star and center of mass remains constant.

star 1 $\vec{r}_1$ $\vec{r}_2$ star 2

star 1 $\vec{r}$ $\vec{r}_2$ star 2

We choose a coordinate system such that the origin is at the center of mass of the system. Because the system is isolated, the center of mass remains fixed at the origin. This means that the ratio r_1/r_2 of the objects' distances from the center of mass must remain the same regardless of the objects' motion (when $\vec{r}_{cm} = \vec{0}$, $m_1\vec{r}_1 + m_2\vec{r}_2 = \vec{0}$ and so $r_1/r_2 = m_2/m_1$; see Section 6.6). Note how the ratio r_1/r_2 in Figure 13.9 remains constant and how the orbits of the two stars have the same shape (scaled by the factor r_1/r_2.)

Because the center of mass always lies on the line of action of the gravitational forces, the torques caused by each of these forces about the center of mass are zero and therefore the angular momentum of each star about the center of mass doesn't change. So, not only is the angular momentum of the two-star system constant, but the angular momentum of each star about the center of mass is constant, too.

> **In an isolated system of two objects interacting through a central force, each object has a constant angular momentum about the center of mass.**

Often we consider situations in which one of the two interacting objects is much more massive than the other, as shown in **Figure 13.10**. In that case, the center of mass lies nearly at the center of the more massive object. This permits us to view the situation from the position of the more massive object, which we can consider fixed at the origin. In Figure 13.10*a*, for example, the Earth moves in a nearly circular orbit about the Sun. Because the Sun is so much more massive than Earth, the center of the Sun is very close to the center of mass of the Sun-Earth system. We therefore can ignore the small difference and consider the two centers to coincide. If we consider the orbit to be circular, the center of mass also coincides with the center of the orbit. Figure 13.10*b* shows a comet moving along an elliptical orbit under the influence of a gravitational force exerted by the Sun. The center of mass again lies at the center of the Sun, which is at one of the foci of the ellipse (not at the center of the ellipse).

✋ **13.6** (*a*) If we ignore the influence of other celestial objects, the Earth-Sun system is isolated, and so it must rotate about the system's center of mass. Using the data in Table 13.1, determine how far from the center of the Sun the center of mass of the system is and what fraction of the Sun's radius this distance is. (*b*) As it passes the point shown in Figure 13.10*b*, does the comet speed up, slow down, or travel at constant speed? If the trajectory shown is part of an ellipse, where is the comet's velocity greatest? Where is it smallest?

Because the force is central and because the center of mass is at the Sun in Figure 13.10, the angular momentum

Figure 13.10 Whether an orbit is circular or elliptical, the gravitational force on the orbiting body points toward the Sun. If the orbit is elliptical, the Sun is at one focus, not at the center of the ellipse.

(a) Orbits of Earth and hypothetical comet (not to scale)

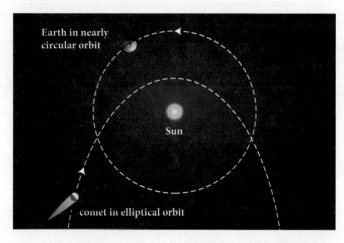

(b) Force exerted by Sun on Earth and comet points toward Sun

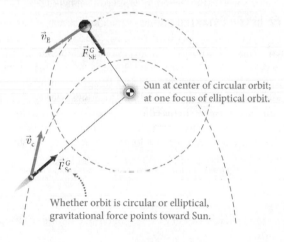

Sun at center of circular orbit; at one focus of elliptical orbit.

Whether orbit is circular or elliptical, gravitational force points toward Sun.

Figure 13.11 The position vectors of an object moving (a) with constant momentum along a straight line and (b) with constant angular momentum along an arbitrary path sweep out equal areas in equal time intervals.

(a) Object moving with constant momentum along straight line

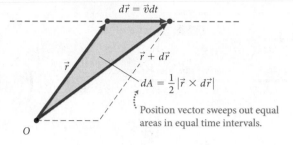

$d\vec{r} = \vec{v}dt$

$\vec{r} + d\vec{r}$

$dA = \frac{1}{2}|\vec{r} \times d\vec{r}|$

Position vector sweeps out equal areas in equal time intervals.

(b) Object moving with constant angular momentum along curve

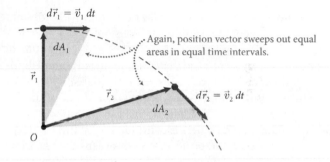

$d\vec{r}_1 = \vec{v}_1\, dt$

dA_1

Again, position vector sweeps out equal areas in equal time intervals.

$\vec{r}_1$

$\vec{r}_2$

dA_2

$d\vec{r}_2 = \vec{v}_2\, dt$

area of the dashed parallelogram in Figure 13.11a—twice the area dA of the shaded triangle. Because the particle's displacement can be written as $d\vec{r} = \vec{v}\, dt$, we have $dA = \frac{1}{2}|\vec{r} \times \vec{v}|\, dt = \frac{1}{2}L/m\, dt$. The rate at which the area A is swept out by the position vector is thus $dA/dt = \frac{1}{2}L/m$. In words:

The angular momentum of a particle about an origin is proportional to the rate at which area is swept out by the particle's position vector.

So, when the angular momentum of a particle is constant, the rate dA/dt is also constant. Figure 13.11b shows the motion of an object along a curved trajectory. In two equal time intervals dt, the position vector sweeps out areas dA_1 and dA_2. If the angular momentum of the object about O is constant, then $dA_1 = dA_2$. The motion caused by a central force directed to the origin is such that the radius vector from the origin sweeps out equal areas in equal time intervals *regardless of the shape of the trajectory*. In the early 17th century, before Newton formulated the law of gravity and long before the concept of angular momentum was introduced, Johannes Kepler had already deduced from astronomical observations that the straight line from the Sun to each planet sweeps out equal areas in equal time intervals. (See the box "Kepler's laws of planetary motion.")

of each of the orbiting objects about the Sun is constant. The meaning of this statement for a circular orbit is simple: If the angular momentum is constant, then the object's speed must be constant (that is, we are dealing with circular motion at constant speed).

To understand the meaning for any other type of orbit, we must first introduce a geometric interpretation of angular momentum. Consider first the particle moving along a straight line illustrated in **Figure 13.11a**. As we saw in Section 12.8 the angular momentum of any moving particle about the origin can be written as $\vec{L} = \vec{r} \times \vec{p}$, where $\vec{r}$ is the position of the particle (Eq. 12.43). In a time interval dt, the position vector $\vec{r}$ sweeps out the area of the shaded triangle in Figure 13.11a. As we saw in Section 12.8, the magnitude of the vector product of two vectors is equal to the area of the parallelogram defined by them. So $|\vec{r} \times d\vec{r}|$ is the

Figure 13.12 Three forms of motion with constant angular momentum.

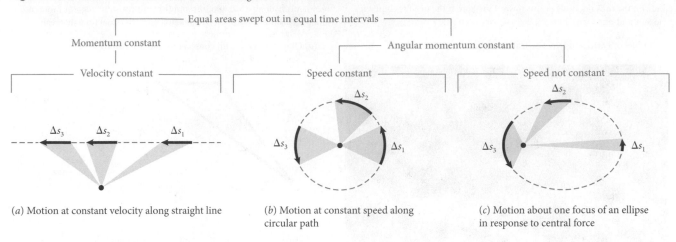

(a) Motion at constant velocity along straight line

(b) Motion at constant speed along circular path

(c) Motion about one focus of an ellipse in response to central force

Figure 13.12 shows three types of motion with constant angular momentum: motion at constant speed along a straight line (no force; constant velocity), circular motion at constant speed (central force; constant speed), and elliptical motion (central force; constant rate of area swept). For the third it is not immediately obvious that the angular momentum is constant: Neither the velocity direction nor the speed of the moving object is constant. For all three types of motion, however, the position vector sweeps out the same area in equal time intervals. To do so an object in elliptical motion (Figure 13.12c) must move fastest when it is closest to the object it is orbiting and slowest when it is the farthest away, in agreement with the answer to Checkpoint 13.6, part b.

Example 13.2 Pluto

Of all the objects in Table 13.1, Pluto has the orbit with the greatest eccentricity. (a) What is the ratio of the orbit's semiminor axis b to its semimajor axis a? (b) What is the ratio of Pluto's speed at perihelion to its speed at aphelion?

❶ **GETTING STARTED** I begin by making a sketch of Pluto's orbit, using the Sun as one focus (**Figure 13.13**). From Figure 13.8 I know that the orbit is very nearly circular but the Sun is off-center, making the orbit slightly elliptical. I mark the perihelion (shortest Sun-orbit distance) and aphelion (longest Sun-orbit distance) and show velocity vectors at those locations because I am asked about speeds there. In the ellipse as I have oriented it, with the line defining the foci horizontal, the semiminor axis b extends from the center of the major axis to point P at the top of the ellipse.

Kepler's laws of planetary motion

The German mathematician and astrologer Johannes Kepler devoted much of his life to analyzing celestial motion data collected by Tycho Brahe. Kepler discovered three laws of planetary motion.

Kepler's first law describes the shape of the planetary orbits:

> **All planets move in elliptical orbits with the Sun at one focus.**

Although the deviation from circular orbits is small, this statement was a radical departure from the accepted wisdom, dating back to Plato, that the planets, being heavenly bodies, were perfect and therefore could move in only perfect circles or combinations of circles.

Kepler's second law reveals that, even if planets are not in circular motion at constant speed, their motions obey the following requirement:

> **The straight line from any planet to the Sun sweeps out equal areas in equal time intervals.**

Kepler's third law relates the planetary orbits to one another:

> **The squares of the periods of the planets are proportional to the cubes of the semimajor axes of their orbits around the Sun.**

Kepler discovered this third law by painstakingly examining, over a period of many years, countless combinations of planetary data.

In keeping with Aristotelian notions, Kepler believed that a force was necessary to drive the planets along their orbits, not to keep them in orbit. Consequently, Kepler was unable to provide a correct explanation for these three laws. It was not until Newton that the single unifying reason for these laws was established. As we've seen, Kepler's three laws follow directly from the law of gravity: The first and third laws are a consequence of the $1/r^2$ dependence, and the second law reflects the central nature of the gravitational force.

Figure 13.13

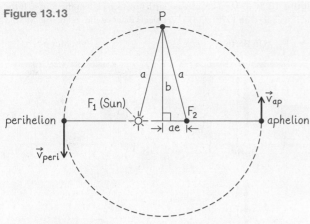

The ratio of the semimajor and semiminor axes can be obtained from either right triangle in Figure 13.13. Because the sum of the distances from any point on an ellipse to the two foci is $2a$ (see Figure 13.7), I know that $\overline{F_1 P} = \overline{F_2 P} = a$.

❷ **DEVISE PLAN** For part a, I can use the Pythagorean theorem and the values in Table 13.1 to calculate the ratio b/a. For part b I know that the planet's angular momentum about the Sun must be constant because the force exerted by the Sun on Pluto is a central force. I can therefore calculate the angular momentum at perihelion and at aphelion and set the two equal to obtain the ratio $v_{\text{peri}}/v_{\text{ap}}$.

❸ **EXECUTE PLAN** (a) Applying the Pythagorean theorem to the right triangle containing F_2 gives $b = \sqrt{a^2 - (ac)^2} = a\sqrt{1 - e^2}$. Using the value of e from Table 13.1, I get $b/a = \sqrt{1 - (0.25)^2} = 0.97$. ✔

(b) At perihelion, the Sun-Pluto distance is $(a - ac)$, and the angular momentum is $L_{\text{peri}} = m(a - ae)v_{\text{peri}} = ma(1 - e)v_{\text{peri}}$ (Eq. 11.36); at aphelion, $L_{\text{ap}} = ma(1 + e)v_{\text{ap}}$. Because $L_{\text{peri}} = L_{\text{ap}}$, I get

$$ma(1 - e)v_{\text{peri}} = ma(1 + e)v_{\text{ap}},$$

so

$$\frac{v_{\text{peri}}}{v_{\text{ap}}} = \frac{1 + e}{1 - e} = \frac{1 + 0.25}{1 - 0.25} = 1.7. ✔$$

❹ **EVALUATE RESULT** The semiminor and semimajor axes are equal to within 3%, which agrees with what is shown in Figure 13.8. That v_{peri} is greater than v_{ap} agrees with my answer to Checkpoint 13.6, part b.

Conservation of angular momentum is also responsible for the flat, disk shape of most galaxies (like the one seen from the side in the opening picture of this chapter) and of our solar system. **Figure 13.14** illustrates the gravitational contraction of a slowly rotating cloud of interstellar gas and dust. Because the cloud's rotational inertia decreases as it contracts, its rate of rotation must increase, just as a skater spins faster with her arms pulled in. In the plane perpendicular to the rotation axis, part of the gravitational force directed toward the center of the cloud goes into providing the centripetal acceleration. Regions near this plane therefore undergo less contraction than do regions along the axis. This differential contraction results in the characteristic disk shape of many galaxies.

Figure 13.14 (a) Gravitational contraction of a slowly rotating cloud of interstellar gas and dust. (b) Conservation of angular momentum requires the rotational velocity to increase as the cloud contracts and its rotational inertia decreases. (c) Contraction is less efficient in the plane perpendicular to the rotation axis because part of the gravitational interaction goes into supplying the centripetal acceleration.

13.3 Weight

The law of gravity states that the force of gravity depends on location. **Figure 13.15** shows astronauts orbiting Earth at an altitude of about 400 km. Are they floating "weightlessly" inside their spacecraft because the force of gravity at their location has been reduced to a negligible value? The calculation is easy and worth doing, as the next checkpoint shows.

13.7 The space shuttle typically orbits Earth at an altitude of about 300 km. (a) By what factor is the shuttle's distance to the center of Earth increased over that of an object on the ground? (b) The gravitational force exerted by Earth on an object in the orbiting shuttle is how much smaller than the gravitational force exerted by Earth on the same object when it is sitting on the ground? (c) What is the acceleration due to gravity at an altitude of about 300 km? (d) While in orbit, the shuttle's engines are off. Why doesn't the shuttle fall to Earth?

After answering this checkpoint, you may be wondering in what sense objects inside the space shuttle are "weightless." To resolve this issue, we must define what we mean by *weight*.

Figure 13.15 Astronauts Shane Kimbrough and Sandra Magnus float "weightlessly" in Space Shuttle Endeavour during mission STS-126.

Figure 13.16 Two methods for weighing a brick.

(a) Spring scale

Compression measures force exerted by brick on spring.

(b) Balance

Downward pull of brick on rod counterbalances pull of known-mass object.

Figure 13.17 Using a balance at Earth's surface and on the Moon. If the rod is balanced on Earth, the same objects balance the rod on the Moon.

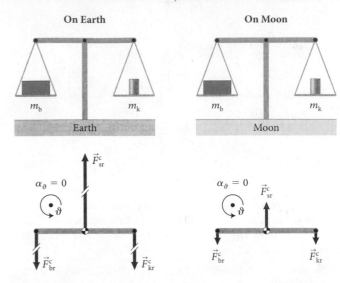

On Earth | On Moon

Figure 13.16 illustrates two types of devices used for weighing objects. When a load is put on a **spring scale,** the load either compresses or stretches a spring inside the scale (Figure 13.16a). The change in the spring's length is proportional to the force exerted on it by the load: $F^c_{ls\,x} = k(x - x_0)$ (Eq. 8.18). The deformation of the spring therefore provides a measure of the downward force exerted on it by the load. When you stand on a bathroom scale, for example, the downward force exerted by your body on the scale compresses a spring inside it, which, in turn, rotates a dial, and you read your weight off the dial. The rotation of the dial is proportional to the force exerted by your body on the scale. (The scale was calibrated at the factory by putting objects of known mass on it.)

13.8 A 1.0-kg brick is placed on a spring scale. (a) What is the magnitude of the force exerted by Earth on the brick? (b) What is the magnitude of the force exerted by the brick on the scale? (c) How many steps are required to answer part b? (d) Does the spring scale measure the pull of gravity on the brick?

Another type of weighing device, the **balance,** illustrated in Figure 13.16b, works as follows. A brick whose mass m_b is to be determined is suspended from one end of a rod pivoted about its center, and objects of known masses are suspended from the other end until the rod is in mechanical equilibrium. In mechanical equilibrium, the downward forces exerted by the loads on the two ends of the rod are equal, and so m_b must be equal to the sum m_k of the known masses.

Don't both devices measure the same thing? You may be surprised to learn that the answer to this question is *no.* To see why, suppose we repeat the experiments illustrated in Figure 13.16 on the surface of the Moon. The gravitational force exerted by the Moon on an object sitting on the lunar surface is about six times smaller than the gravitational force exerted by Earth on the same object sitting on Earth's

surface. If you were carrying a heavy load on the Moon, you would discover that the force needed to support it is less than on Earth; on the Moon the load feels a lot lighter. As the extended free-body diagrams in **Figure 13.17** show, however, the smaller gravitational pull of the Moon does not affect the mechanical equilibrium of the balance: The downward pull diminishes on *both* sides, and so the rod remains in mechanical equilibrium. With the balance, we still obtain $m_b = m_k$, just as we do on Earth.

The reading of the spring scale on the Moon, however, is not the same as it is on Earth. Because of the weaker pull of gravity on the Moon, the deformation of the spring is smaller, as shown in **Figure 13.18**. Spring scale readings on the Moon are about six times smaller than on Earth. So the spring scale tells us that the load weighs less on the Moon than on Earth, while the balance tells us that it weighs the same. This difference arises because:

A spring scale measures the downward force exerted on it by its load, but a balance compares gravitational forces and measures mass.

The result obtained with a spring scale depends on the strength of the gravitational pull on the load; the result obtained with a balance does not depend on the strength of the gravitational pull.*

13.9 A 1.0-kg brick is placed on a spring scale inside the space shuttle orbiting Earth at 300 km altitude. (a) What is the magnitude of the force exerted by Earth on the brick? (b) What is the magnitude of the force exerted by the brick on the spring scale? (Hint: See the astronauts in Figure 13.15.) (c) Does the spring scale measure the pull of gravity on the brick? (d) Why is your answer different from your answer to Checkpoint 13.8, part d?

---

*Many modern weighing devices are called "balances" even though in reality they operate like spring scales. Typically, these devices employ a pivoted rod, but instead of comparing gravitational forces, one end of the rod is connected to a spring or other mechanism for generating a calibrated force.

Figure 13.18 Free-body diagrams for a brick on a spring scale on the surface of Earth and the Moon. Because of the smaller gravitational attraction by the Moon, the spring's compression on the Moon is less than it is on Earth.

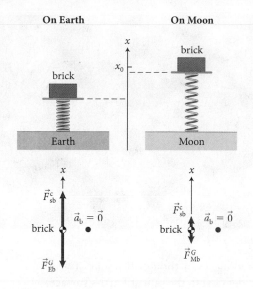

The answers to this checkpoint show that the reading of a spring scale depends not only on the gravitational pull on its load but also on the acceleration of the scale. To see this point more clearly, consider the situation shown in **Figure 13.19a**. Two bricks of identical mass m are placed on two identical spring scales, one on solid ground and the other in an elevator that is accelerating downward. Figure 13.19b shows the free-body diagrams for both bricks.

Figure 13.19 A spring scale holding a brick gives a different reading when it is stationary and when it is in an elevator accelerating downward. Because of the acceleration of the elevator, $\Delta x_{\text{elev}} < \Delta x_{\text{stat}}$.

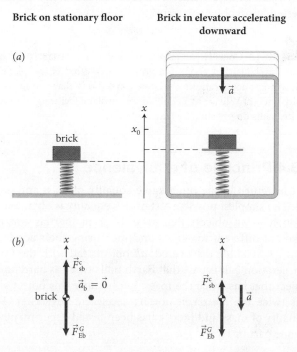

Because the brick in the elevator has a downward acceleration, we know that the vector sum of the forces exerted on it has to be nonzero and directed downward. The downward force of gravity has not changed, however. Consequently, the upward force exerted by the scale on the brick must be *smaller* than the magnitude of the downward force of gravity acting on it. Because the force exerted by the scale on the brick and the force exerted by the brick on the scale form an interaction pair, we conclude that the force exerted by the brick on the scale in the elevator is smaller than that exerted by the identical brick on the stationary spring scale. The spring scale in the elevator therefore gives a lower reading than the stationary scale.

If you are surprised that the result of weighing an object with a spring scale depends on acceleration, try the following experiment. Put an object in the palm of your hand with your arm stretched out in front of you, then rapidly move your hand downward. While you accelerate your hand downward, you can feel that the object presses less on your hand than it does when you hold your hand still. In other words, while your hand accelerates downward, the object in it feels lighter—it feels as though it "weighs" less.*

13.10 (*a*) An object is placed on a spring scale in an elevator moving upward at a constant speed. Is the reading of the scale greater than, smaller than, or the same as the reading obtained in a stationary elevator? (*b*) How does the reading of a scale in an elevator that has upward acceleration $a = 0.5g$ compare with the reading obtained in a stationary elevator? (*c*) What if the elevator has downward acceleration $a = g$?

As this checkpoint shows, objects in an elevator that is in free fall produce a zero spring scale reading. No force is necessary to support them: They, too, fall freely along with the elevator. Inside a freely falling elevator, a spring scale under your feet—falling away underneath you, together with the elevator and everything inside it—reads zero. If you were to hold a briefcase in the freely falling elevator, you would discover that the briefcase does not need to be supported by your hand because the force of gravity gives it the same downward acceleration g as you. The briefcase feels weightless—you could even let go and the briefcase would continue to hover next to you.

Any object in free fall—that is, any object subject to only a force of gravity—experiences weightlessness.

---

*You can also try this by accelerating your hand upward, in which case the object feels heavier. The effect, however, is less pronounced because it is more difficult to accelerate your arm upward. In the downward direction, gravity and your muscles work together to provide the acceleration; in the upward direction, your muscles have to not only accelerate your arm but also counteract the effect of gravity.

Figure 13.20 As a spacecraft orbits Earth a distance h above the ground, it falls a distance Δh. Because the craft moves so fast in a direction tangential to the (curved) ground, the ground "falls away" at the same rate, and the distance between the craft and the ground remains constant.

Height h of orbit remains constant because of distance Δh spacecraft falls.

Figure 13.21 If an airplane briefly follows a parabolic path such that it has a downward acceleration g, the airplane and the people inside it are in free fall. In this picture, astronaut candidates aboard a KC-135 Stratotanker briefly experience weightlessness as they and the plane are in a short free fall.

If this appears odd, consider once again the astronauts in orbit in Figure 13.15. The only force exerted on them is the force of gravity, and so they *are* in free fall! This free fall is precisely what makes them weightless. Because of their large speed and the curvature of Earth, however, they do not come closer to the ground. As they fall, the ground below them recedes at the same speed as they fall (**Figure 13.20**).

13.11 (*a*) How far does the space shuttle in Figure 13.20, 300 km above Earth, fall in 1.0 s? (*b*) If the radius of Earth is 6400 km, what is the shuttle's speed?

You don't need to be an astronaut to experience weightlessness. When you jump off a chair, you are momentarily weightless; during your short free fall, an object in the palm of your hand hovers weightlessly above your hand. A plane flying across a large parabolic arc may be in a controlled free fall for short time intervals. As shown in **Figure 13.21**, people inside such an airplane float weightlessly, just as astronauts in orbit do.

13.12 Planes can be put (safely) into free fall for periods up to 40 s. (*a*) If the plane shown in Figure 13.21 was flying horizontally before being put into free fall, how much altitude does it lose in those 40 s? (*b*) What is the plane's final vertical speed of descent? (*c*) At the instant shown, is the vertical component of the plane's velocity directed upward, directed downward, or zero?

The discussion in this section shows that our notion of *weight* corresponds most closely to the reading of a spring scale: The perceived "heaviness" of an object depends, as does the reading on the scale, not only on the pull of gravity on the object but also on its acceleration. The "weightless" astronauts in the space shuttle would indeed register a zero scale reading, even though the pull of gravity on them is almost identical to the pull at Earth's surface.

Because spring scale readings depend on acceleration, however, weight is often defined as the force of gravity exerted *on* an object. Spring scale readings are then called *apparent* or *effective weight*. With this definition, the astronauts in Figure 13.15 and the people in Figure 13.21 are not weightless because the force of gravity on them (their "weight") is the same as it is on Earth's surface, and so they must be called *apparently weightless*. To avoid all these difficulties and the conflict between our intuitive notion of weight (spring scale reading) and the common definition of weight (force of gravity), we therefore avoid using the word *weight* in this book. Instead we shall use the more precise "force of gravity" to refer to the downward pull of gravity on an object and "scale reading" to refer to the force exerted by an object on a spring scale.

13.13 Consider an airplane flying at a constant speed of 900 km/h, 10 km above the ground. (*a*) What is the plane's downward acceleration? (*b*) Draw a free-body diagram for the airplane. (*c*) Why don't people in the airplane feel weightless as astronauts do traveling 290 km higher up?

13.4 Principle of equivalence

Let us return to the remarkable equality of mass and inertia. The simplest possible test of this equality is obtained by dropping two objects that have different inertias and are made of different materials and measuring their accelerations. As Galileo discovered, *all* objects fall with the same acceleration g. It is true that Earth pulls twice as hard on an object that has twice the mass, but because this object also has twice the inertia, it doesn't accelerate any faster. The equality of mass and inertia has been tested experimentally to one part in 10^{12}.

The equality of mass and inertia may seem obvious because we are so accustomed to the fact that heavier objects not only take more effort to support against gravity but also take more effort to be set in motion. Intuitively, both properties simply go by the amount of matter in the object. Yet this equality suggests a much deeper connection between gravity and acceleration.

In Section 13.3 we encountered another manifestation of this equivalence between gravity and inertia: The reading on a spring scale depends not only on the gravitational pull on the load but also on the acceleration of the scale. We can change the reading of the scale—our notion of weight—simply by accelerating the scale. This raises an interesting question: Can we design an experiment that distinguishes between gravity and an accelerated reference frame?

Consider a brick placed on a spring scale inside a container at rest on the surface of Earth, as illustrated in **Figure 13.22a**. Because of the gravitational attraction exerted by Earth on the brick, the brick compresses the spring to a scale reading x_E. To an observer in the Earth

Figure 13.22 If you observe a brick compressing a spring scale in an enclosed container, you cannot tell whether the compression is due to a gravitational interaction or to acceleration of the container.

(a)
Container at rest on Earth

(b)
Container accelerating in space, far from star or planet

(c)

Earth reference frame: Brick at rest: downward force of gravity balanced by upward spring force.

(d)

Earth reference frame: Brick accelerated by upward spring force.

(e)

Accelerated reference frame: Brick at rest; spring compressed as though something "pulls brick down."

reference frame the brick is at rest, and so the upward force exerted by the scale is equal in magnitude to the downward force exerted by Earth (see Figure 13.22c). Now picture the same arrangement in space, far away from any planet or star, where the influence of gravity is negligible and so we can say that $g = 0$. Suppose the container is towed by a spaceship; if the spaceship fires its rockets, the container accelerates, as illustrated in Figure 13.22b. Objects inside the container no longer float weightlessly, but being dragged along by the container, they rest against the bottom of the container. If the brick is placed on the scale, the scale registers a reading proportional to the force exerted by the spring on the brick. This force is required to give the brick the same acceleration $\vec{a}$ as the container. From the point of view of an observer in the Earth reference frame, the brick has an upward acceleration $\vec{a}$ (see Figure 13.22d).

If the rockets are fired such that $a = g$, could you, from inside the container, tell the difference between being accelerated in space and being on Earth? To you, the scale and the scale reading appear just as they do on Earth. An object released from your hand falls with an acceleration g, just as it does on Earth. From inside the container, with both of your feet solidly on the floor, everything looks and feels just as it does on Earth—all objects appear to be attracted to the container floor.

Having observed all this, you draw the free-body diagram shown in Figure 13.22e: From your point of view, the brick is at rest, and so the vector sum of the forces exerted on it must be zero. So, in addition to an upward force exerted by the compressed spring on the brick, you draw a downward force, equal in magnitude to that of the upward force. To you, it appears as if this force is due to a downward attraction experienced by all objects inside the container. Without peeking outside, you cannot determine whether this attraction is present because underneath the container there is a planet or because the container is accelerating upward in space.

Notice that the fictitious attractive force experienced by objects inside the container is no less mysterious than the force of gravity. Both forces have the same effect: Objects are pulled toward the bottom of the container according to their mass or inertia (the distinction has now disappeared). Although the gravitational force is more familiar, and although Newton's law of gravity describes its behavior, we really have no idea how gravity "works." The conclusion is thus:

> **One cannot distinguish locally between the effects of a constant gravitational acceleration of magnitude g and the effects of an acceleration of the reference frame of magnitude $a = g$.**

This statement, called the **principle of equivalence**, is the starting point for the theory of general relativity developed by Albert Einstein in the early 1900s. The word *locally* is necessary because on a large scale, the $1/r^2$ dependence of the gravitational force becomes apparent: For a very tall

A Boeing 747-8 flight simulator.

container in Figure 13.22, the gravitational acceleration at the top of the container would be smaller than at the bottom; for a very wide container, it would become noticeable that objects are falling not parallel to one another but toward a single point—the attracting object's center. In the theory of general relativity, the effects of gravity are explained in an entirely geometric way. Gravity and acceleration are one.

On a practical note, our inability to distinguish between gravity and acceleration is exploited in aircraft flight simulators and motion simulators in the amusement industry. These devices are programmed to tilt in concert with a film simulating a ride in a vehicle, airplane, or spaceship. The effect is a startlingly realistic sensation of motion. The principle of operation is shown in **Figure 13.23**. Suppose you are in a closed container, with a ball suspended from the ceiling.

If the container rolls at constant speed along a track, as in Figure 13.23a, you cannot *feel* the motion and the string hangs vertically, although sounds from the wheels and little bumps in the track might give away that the container is in motion. The law of inertia (see Section 6.2) tells us, however, that you cannot determine the difference between moving at constant speed and sitting at rest. So, with the container on a stationary base, as in Figure 13.23b, if the container shakes a bit to simulate bumps and you hear the same sounds and see a movie of a landscape that flows by at constant speed, the illusion of moving at constant speed is complete.

Now suppose the container speeds up, as in Figure 13.23c. The chair presses against your back to accelerate you along with the container, and as a result you feel pushed backward against the chair. As Figure 13.23d shows, the same effect can be obtained by tilting a stationary container backward (together with appropriate sounds and visual clues). In both cases, also, the ball suspended from the ceiling tilts toward you, and objects don't fall straight to the floor. From inside the container, you cannot tell whether these things happen because the container accelerates or because gravity is in a different direction.

To simulate slowing down (see Figure 13.23e), the container needs to be tilted forward (see Figure 13.23f). The result is that you feel pushed forward, as in a sharply braking car, and the ball tilts away from you. Again you cannot tell whether the container is slowing down or gravity is pulling in a different direction.

13.14 How should the simulator in Figure 13.23 be tilted to simulate a right turn?

Figure 13.23 The principle of equivalence states that an observer inside a closed container cannot distinguish between motion at constant speed and rest, between speeding up and tilting backward, or between slowing down and tilting forward.

Vehicle: Effects caused by acceleration

(*a*) Constant velocity

(*c*) Forward acceleration (speeding up)

(*e*) Rearward acceleration (slowing down)

Simulator: Identical effects caused by tilting

(*b*) No tilt

(*d*) Backward tilt

(*f*) Forward tilt

Figure 13.24 A light pulse traverses an accelerating container.

(a)   **Earth reference frame**

light pulse

Elevator floor accelerates upward toward light pulse.

(b)   **Reference frame of elevator**

Pulse behaves as though falling in response to gravity.

The simulator example may give you the impression that the principle of equivalence has more to do with our senses than with the properties of the universe. This is not so, however. Because anything that moves along a straight line in an inertial reference frame must move along a curved path in an accelerated reference frame, the principle of equivalence tells us that *anything* that moves near an object that has mass must move along a curved path. **Figure 13.24** shows that a light pulse that travels along a straight line in the Earth reference frame but then enters an accelerating elevator must move along a curved path as

viewed from inside the elevator. This effect is purely kinematic, and so given the equivalence between gravity and acceleration, the bending should also occur if the elevator, instead of accelerating upward, were placed on top of an object with a large mass.

13.15 Light travels at approximately 3.0×10^8 m/s. (a) How long does it take for a light pulse to cross an elevator 2.0 m wide? (b) How great an acceleration is necessary to make the pulse deviate from a straight-line path by 1.0 mm? Is it likely that this effect can be observed? (c) If light is bent by the gravitational pull of an object, light should "fall" when traveling parallel to the surface of Earth. How far does a beam of light travel in 0.0010 s, and how much does it fall over that distance? Is it likely that this effect can be observed?

Although the calculations in this checkpoint show that detection of the gravitational bending of light is difficult, the effect was observed within a few years of its prediction in 1915. Because of the large mass of the Sun, a ray that passes close to the Sun should undergo a deflection. Although it is normally impossible for us earthlings to see any stars close to the Sun, the light from the Sun is blocked by the Moon during a solar eclipse (**Figure 13.25**). By comparing a picture of stars near the Sun taken during an eclipse with a picture of the same stars taken when the Sun is far away from them (in other words, at night), it is possible to observe the bending of light caused by the Sun's gravitational attraction. The measured values of such deflections are in excellent agreement with the theoretical values.

13.16 (a) What would the scale reading be if the container in Figure 13.22b were traveling at constant speed instead of accelerating? (b) Describe the path of the light pulse in the reference frame of the elevator in Figure 13.24b if the elevator were traveling at constant speed.

Figure 13.25 When the Sun passes close to our line of sight to a star, the Sun's gravity bends the star's light, slightly shifting the star's apparent location in the sky. This effect is visible only during a solar eclipse, when the Moon blocks the Sun's glare. Diagram not to scale.

Sun's gravity bends light . . .   . . . by 1.75 arc-seconds (shown exaggerated).

apparent direction to star

deflected ray from star

Earth

Moon

Sun

actual direction to star

Deflection is visible only during solar eclipse, when Moon blocks Sun's glare.

light rays from star

Self-quiz

1. Determine the ratio of Earth's gravitational force exerted on a 1.0-kg object at the following positions to that at sea level: (*i*) the top of Mt. Everest, altitude 8848 m, (*ii*) a shuttle orbiting at 200 km; (*iii*) the orbit of the Moon. Is the 1.0-kg object weightless in any of these circumstances?

2. The orbital period of Jupiter around the Sun is 11.86 times that of Earth. What is the ratio of their distances to the Sun?

3. If the speed of a planet in its orbit around the Sun changes, how can the planet's angular momentum be constant?

4. A brick of unknown mass is placed on a spring scale. When in equilibrium, the scale reads 13.2 N. Which of the following statements is/are true? (*i*) Earth always exerts a gravitational force of 13.2 N on the brick. (*ii*) The normal force the scale exerts on the brick is 13.2 N. (*iii*) The brick has an inertia of 1.32 kg.

5. Draw a free-body diagram of an individual experiencing weightlessness in an elevator. What must the elevator's acceleration be for this to occur?

6. If you were to travel in a vertical circle, at what point in the circle would you be most likely to experience weightlessness?

Answers

1. The gravitational force is proportional to the inverse square of the distance between Earth and the object. For each case, we have $F_{pos}/F_{sea\ level} = r^2_{sea\ level}/r^2_{pos}$, where $r_{sea\ level} = 6.378 \times 10^6$ m (Earth's radius) and r_{pos} is the distance between the position in question and Earth's center. (*i*) The distance to Earth's center is the sum of Earth's radius and the altitude of Mt. Everest: $r_{pos} = (6.378 \times 10^6$ m$) + (8848$ m$) = 6.387 \times 10^6$ m; $F_{pos}/F_{sea\ level} = 0.997$. (*ii*) $r_{pos} = (6.378 \times 10^6$ m$) + (200{,}000$ m$) = 6.578 \times 10^6$ m; $F_{pos}/F_{sea\ level} = 0.940$. (*iii*) The distance to Earth's center is the radius of the Moon's orbit. Given that the Moon's orbit is nearly circular, I use the value of the semimajor axis in Table 13.1: $r_{pos} = 3.84 \times 10^8$ m; $F_{pos}/F_{sea\ level} = 0.000276$. The object is never weightless because, in each case, it experiences a gravitational force and, in all but the last case, the magnitude of this force is very close to the magnitude at sea level on Earth.

2. The period squared is proportional to the cube of the orbital radius. Therefore, the square of the ratio of the periods ($11.86^2 = 141$) is equal to the cube of the ratio of the orbital radii. The ratio of the radii is then $141^{1/3} = 5.2$. Check this value against the data in Table 13.1.

3. If the angular momentum is constant but the speed changes, the rotational inertia must change. When a planet's speed increases, either its inertia must decrease or it must move nearer the object it orbits to keep the angular momentum constant. Conversely, when a planet's speed decreases, either its inertia must increase or it must move away from the object it orbits.

4. Only statement (*ii*) is true. The scale reading may change from location to location, and the inertia of the brick is 1.32 kg only when the gravitational acceleration at the specific location is 10 m/s².

5. If a person experiences weightlessness, the only force acting on her or him is the gravitational force. Contact with the elevator floor is not necessary. If the person is in free fall, the elevator must also be in free fall. The free-body diagram consists of just one force vector, $\vec{F}^G_{Ep}$ downward.

6. To experience weightlessness, the only force acting on you is the gravitational force exerted by Earth, which points downward. This downward force provides the centripetal acceleration needed for traveling in a circle. The only position from which the center of the circle is downward is the top of the circle.

13.5 Gravitational constant

As we saw in Section 13.1, Newton's **law of gravity** states that the gravitational force exerted by a object of mass m_1 on a object of mass m_2 is an attractive, central force that is proportional to the product of the masses and inversely proportional to the square of the distance between them. If the positions of the two objects are given by the vectors $\vec{r}_1$ and $\vec{r}_2$, then the distance between them is $r_{12} = |\vec{r}_2 - \vec{r}_1|$, as shown in **Figure 13.26**. We can thus write the magnitude of the gravitational force as

$$F^G_{12} = G \frac{m_1 m_2}{r^2_{12}}, \qquad (13.1)$$

where the proportionality constant G is called the **gravitational constant.** The force is attractive and directed along the straight line joining the objects.

What is the relationship between Eq. 13.1 and the magnitude mg of the gravitational force near Earth's surface? To answer this question, let object 1 in Eq. 13.1 be Earth with mass m_E and let object 2 be an arbitrary object of mass m_o near Earth's surface:

$$F^G_{Eo} = G \frac{m_E m_o}{r^2_{Eo}}. \qquad (13.2)$$

For an object a distance h above the ground, the distance between the object and Earth's center is $r_{Eo} = R_E + h$, where R_E is the radius of Earth. Near the ground, $h \ll R_E$, $r_{Eo} \approx R_E$, and Eq. 13.2 becomes

$$F^G_{Eo} = \frac{G m_E m_o}{r^2_{Eo}} \approx G \frac{m_E m_o}{R^2_E} = m_o \left(\frac{G m_E}{R^2_E} \right) \quad \text{(near Earth's surface).} \quad (13.3)$$

The term in parentheses represents the acceleration of the object due to the force F^G_{Eo}. Knowing from our study of the gravitational force that $F^G_{Eo} = m_o g$, we see that

$$g = \frac{G m_E}{R^2_E} \quad \text{(near Earth's surface).} \qquad (13.4)$$

Because G, m_E, and R_E are all constant, the law of gravity does indeed give a constant acceleration near the surface of Earth.

✋ **13.17** For an object released from a height $h \approx R_E$ above the ground, does the acceleration due to gravity decrease, increase, or stay the same as the object falls to Earth?

Working in about 1677, Newton knew the radius of Earth but not its mass, and so he could get only a rough value of G by estimating m_E (as you did in Checkpoint 1.16). The magnitude of G was determined experimentally by Henry Cavendish in 1798. The basic principle of Cavendish's measurement is shown in **Figure 13.27**. Two small lead spheres connected by a light rod are suspended from a long thin fiber. When two large lead spheres are placed near the small spheres, the gravitational attraction between the large and small spheres causes the rod to rotate, thus twisting the fiber. Equilibrium is reached when the torque caused by the gravitational forces is equal in magnitude to the opposing torque caused by the twisted fiber. By calibrating the degree to which known forces twist the fiber, Cavendish was able to measure the gravitational force between the lead spheres. Knowing this force, he then found the value of G by measuring the separation and inertias of the spheres. The value determined with modern instruments is

$$G = 6.6738 \times 10^{-11} \text{ N} \cdot \text{m}^2/\text{kg}^2. \qquad (13.5)$$

Figure 13.26 The distance between two objects whose positions are given by the vectors $\vec{r}_1$ and $\vec{r}_2$ is equal to the magnitude of the vector $\vec{r}_2 - \vec{r}_1$.

Distance between objects is magnitude of this vector.

Figure 13.27 Schematic representation of Cavendish's experimental setup to determine the gravitational constant. The entire setup is enclosed in a box to shield it from air currents.

Magnitude of gravitational forces between spheres can be deduced from torsion in fiber.

Because G is exceedingly small, the force exerted by two 1-kg objects that are 1 m apart is a mere 6.7×10^{-11} N. For comparison, the force of gravity exerted by Earth on a hair is around 10^{-3} N—15 million times stronger! This comparison shows how exceedingly small the gravitational force is. Only when at least one of the two interacting objects has a very large mass (10^{11} kg at the minimum) does the gravitational force become sizeable.

Example 13.3 Weighing Earth

Cavendish is said to have "weighed Earth" because his determination of G provided the first value for the planet's mass m_E. Given that the radius of Earth is about 6400 km and given the value of G in Eq. 13.5, determine m_E.

❶ **GETTING STARTED** I am given Earth's radius and G and must use these values to determine Earth's mass. An expression containing G and the acceleration due to gravity g seems a good place to begin.

❷ **DEVISE PLAN** Equation 13.4 gives the acceleration due to gravity near Earth's surface, g, in terms of G, R_E, and m_E. Knowing the values of g, G, and R_E, I can determine m_E.

❸ **EXECUTE PLAN** From Eq. 13.4, I obtain $m_E = gR_E^2/G$,

so $m_E = \dfrac{(9.8 \text{ m/s}^2)(6.4 \times 10^6 \text{ m})^2}{(6.6738 \times 10^{-11} \text{ N} \cdot \text{m}^2/\text{kg}^2)} = 6.0 \times 10^{24}$ kg. ✔

❹ **EVALUATE RESULT** Table 13.1 gives 5.97×10^{24} kg, which agrees with my answer to within less than 1%. Instead of looking up the value, I can also estimate Earth's mass to check my answer. Remember that we carried out that estimate in Checkpoint 1.16 and obtained 5×10^{24} kg, which is within 20% of my answer.

13.6 Gravitational potential energy

In Section 7.9 we determined the potential energy associated with the force of gravity near Earth's surface. Let us now obtain general expressions for the gravitational potential energy from the law of gravity. To do so, we consider two objects 1 and 2 of masses m_1 and m_2. Suppose the mass of object 1 is much greater than the mass of object 2, $m_1 \gg m_2$, so that if we place object 1 at the origin, we can consider it being fixed there. Now let object 2 move along the x axis from x_i to x_f under the influence of the gravitational attraction between the two (**Figure 13.28**). What is the work done by the gravitational force exerted by object 1 on object 2?

If we choose the x axis pointing to the right as indicated in Figure 13.28, the x component of the force exerted by object 1 on object 2 when object 2 is at some arbitrary position x is

Figure 13.28 An object of mass m_2 moves toward an object of mass $m_1 \gg m_2$ held fixed at the origin.

$$F_{12x}^G = -G\frac{m_1 m_2}{x^2}. \tag{13.6}$$

The x component of the force is negative because the force points in the negative x direction. The gravitational force varies with distance, and so to evaluate the work done by object 1 on object 2, we must evaluate the integral (see Eq. 9.22):

$$W = \int_{x_i}^{x_f} F_x(x)dx. \tag{13.7}$$

Substituting Eq. 13.6 into Eq. 13.7, we obtain

$$W = -Gm_1 m_2 \int_{x_i}^{x_f}\left(\frac{1}{x^2}\right)dx = Gm_1 m_2\left[\frac{1}{x}\right]_{x_i}^{x_f} = Gm_1 m_2\left(\frac{1}{x_f} - \frac{1}{x_i}\right). \tag{13.8}$$

This is the work done by the gravitational force exerted by object 1 on the system consisting of object 2 only (**Figure 13.29a**). Because the force and the displacement point in the same direction, we know that the work must be positive. Indeed, the right side of Eq. 13.8 is positive because $x_f < x_i$.

As object 2 moves from x_i to x_f, it accelerates, and so its kinetic energy increases. Because no other energy associated with it changes, the increase in the kinetic energy must be equal to the work done on it by object 1, $\Delta K = W$, as illustrated in the energy diagram in Figure 13.29a.

If, instead of object 2 by itself, we now consider the (closed) system of the two interacting objects as a whole, then the increase in the kinetic energy of object 2 is due not to the work done by the external gravitational force exerted by object 1 on it but to a decrease in the gravitational potential energy of the system (Figure 13.29b and compare with Figure 9.18). This gravitational potential energy is a measure of the configuration of the system. The change in the gravitational potential energy of the system is thus $\Delta U^G = -\Delta K$. Because the change in kinetic energy does not depend on the choice of system, we see that the change in potential energy of the two-object system is the negative of W in Eq. 13.8:

$$\Delta U^G = Gm_1m_2\left(\frac{1}{x_i} - \frac{1}{x_f}\right). \qquad (13.9)$$

It is customary to choose the gravitational potential energy of a system to be zero at infinite separation ($x = \infty$), which is the separation distance at which the gravitational force is zero: $U^G(\infty) = 0$. So, if we let object 2 move in from $x = \infty$ to an arbitrary position x under the influence of the gravitational acceleration due to object 1, Eq. 13.9 yields

$$\Delta U^G = U^G(x) - U^G(\infty) = U^G(x) - 0 = Gm_1m_2\left(0 - \frac{1}{x}\right), \quad (13.10)$$

so the **gravitational potential energy** is

$$U^G(x) = -G\frac{m_1m_2}{x}, \qquad (13.11)$$

which is zero at infinite x. As object 2 moves in from infinitely far away, its kinetic energy increases, and so the potential energy of the two-object system decreases. Therefore setting $U^G(\infty) = 0$ at $x = \infty$ causes the potential energy to be negative for all values of $x < \infty$.

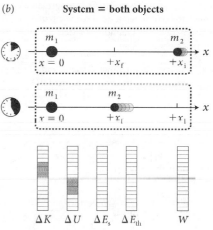

Figure 13.29 Energy diagrams for the situation shown in Figure 13.28.

(a) **System = object 2**

(b) **System = both objects**

Example 13.4 Gravitational potential energy near Earth's surface

The distance between Earth's surface and an object of mass m is changed by an amount Δx. Show that when $x \approx R_E$ and $\Delta x \ll R_E$, where R_E is the radius of Earth, the general expression for gravitational potential energy, Eq. 13.9, reduces to the expression $\Delta U^G = mg\Delta x$ (Eq. 7.19).

❶ **GETTING STARTED** I begin by choosing an x axis that is perpendicular to Earth's surface and has the origin $x = 0$ at Earth's center. I then mark off a distance $x = R_E$ on this axis (**Figure 13.30a**). Because I'm told that $x \approx R_E$ and $\Delta x \ll R_E$, I let the initial position x_i be right at Earth's surface, $x = R_E$, and the final position x_f be just to the right of x_i.

To get some feel for the situation, I also graph the gravitational potential energy of Earth from Eq. 13.11, marking the object's initial and final positions (Figure 13.30b). Basically, the problem requires me to show that when x_i and x_f lie sufficiently close to each other, ΔU^G is linearly proportional to Δx. Graphically this is already clear from my graph: If I blow up the region around $x_i = R_E$, the $U^G(x)$ curve is linear.

❷ **DEVISE PLAN** If I substitute $x_i = R_E$ and $x_f = R_E + \Delta x$ into Eq. 13.9, I can obtain an expression showing how ΔU^G depends on Δx. I can then approximate the resulting expression for $\Delta x \ll R_E$.

Figure 13.30

(a)

(b) $U(x)$

❸ **EXECUTE PLAN** After I substitute the masses of Earth and the object, $x_i = R_E$, and $x_f = R_E + \Delta x$, Eq. 13.9 becomes

$$\Delta U^G = Gm_E m \left(\frac{1}{R_E} - \frac{1}{R_E + \Delta x} \right). \qquad (1)$$

I know that $\Delta x \ll R_E$ in this problem, so I can write the second term in the parentheses as

$$\frac{1}{R_E + \Delta x} = \frac{1}{R_E} \left(\frac{1}{1 + \Delta x/R_E} \right) \approx \frac{1}{R_E} \left(1 - \frac{\Delta x}{R_E} \right) \qquad (2)$$

because, for any small number $\epsilon \ll 1$, $1/(1 + \epsilon) \approx 1 - \epsilon$ (see Appendix B). Substituting Eq. 2 into Eq. 1, I obtain

$$\Delta U^G = Gm_E m \left[\frac{1}{R_E} - \frac{1}{R_E} \left(1 - \frac{\Delta x}{R_E} \right) \right]$$

$$= Gm_E m \frac{\Delta x}{R_E^2} = m \frac{Gm_E}{R_E^2} \Delta x.$$

When I substitute, from Eq. 13.4, $g = Gm_E/R_E^2$, this expression becomes $\Delta U^G = mg\Delta x.$ ✔

❹ **EVALUATE RESULT** This result confirms the conclusion I drew from my sketch: $U^G(x)$ is curved, but for sufficiently small displacements Δx, the curve can be approximated by a straight line. Near Earth's surface the slope of this line is mg.

Figure 13.31 To calculate the work done by object 1 on object 2 while object 2 moves along the dashed path from P to Q, we approximate the path by (a) one radial and one circular displacement or (b) a number of successive such displacements.

(a) Trajectory approximated by one radial segment PR and one circular segment RQ

Along circular segment RQ, force perpendicular to displacement, so no work done on object 2.

Along radial segment PR, force not perpendicular to displacement, so work done on object 2.

(b) Trajectory approximated by multiple radial and circular segments

Along circular segments, no work done on object 2.

Radial segments add up to length of PR.

Because the force of gravity is a central force, we can easily generalize Eq. 13.11 to more than one dimension. Suppose object 2 moves from P to Q in **Figure 13.31a** along part of an elliptical orbit. Let us first approximate the displacement of object 2 by two successive displacements: one along the radial direction from P to R and one along a circular arc from R to Q. The work done by the force of gravity on object 2 over the radial displacement is given by Eq. 13.8. Along the circular arc RQ, the magnitude of the force of gravity is constant but always oriented perpendicular to the displacement. Because the work in more than one dimension is given by the scalar product of the force and the force displacement (Eq. 10.35), the work done by the force of gravity on object 2 along the circular arc is zero:

$$W_{R \to Q} = \int_R^Q \vec{F}_{12}^G \cdot d\vec{r} = 0. \qquad (13.12)$$

So the work done by object 1 on object 2 as it moves from P to Q along the path PRQ is equal to the work done along the radial displacement only.

A better approximation of the actual path of object 2 can be obtained by breaking down the motion into small segments and approximating each segment by the sum of radial and circular displacements, as shown in Figure 13.31b. Again, the work done on object 2 along each circular displacement is zero. Furthermore, all the radial displacements simply add up to the same radial displacement as in Figure 13.31a. So only the change in radial distance matters and the gravitational work done by object 1 on object 2 while object 2 moves from P to Q is

$$W_{P \to Q} = Gm_1 m_2 \left(\frac{1}{r_Q} - \frac{1}{r_P} \right), \qquad (13.13)$$

where r_P and r_Q are the magnitudes of the position vectors of object 2 at P and Q, respectively. Following the same line of reasoning that led from Eq. 13.8 to Eq. 13.11, we can write for the gravitational potential energy of the system

$$U^G(\vec{r}) = -G \frac{m_1 m_2}{r} \quad \text{(zero at infinite } r\text{)}, \qquad (13.14)$$

where r is the distance between the two objects.

Note that the result we obtained in Eq. 13.13 holds for *any* path that leads from P to Q. Any arbitrary path can be broken down into small radial and circular segments, and as Figure 13.31b shows, the work done by the gravitational force depends only on the position of the endpoints relative to m_1, not on the path taken. Consider for example paths 1 and 2 from P to Q in **Figure 13.32a**. The work done is the same along both paths:

$$W_{P \to Q, \text{ path 1}} = W_{P \to Q, \text{ path 2}}. \tag{13.15}$$

This path independence is characteristic of nondissipative interactions (see Section 7.8).

We also know that the work done along a path moving in one direction is the negative of the work done along that path moving in the opposite direction. This can readily be seen in Figure 13.31b: Reversing the direction of travel inverts the sign of the displacement (and therefore the sign of the work) along all radial components. So if we let object 2 move from Q to P along path 2 in Figure 13.32a, the work done on it is

$$W_{Q \to P, \text{ path 2}} = -W_{P \to Q, \text{ path 2}}. \tag{13.16}$$

A consequence of Eq. 13.15 and 13.16 is that if an object moves from P to Q along path 1 and then back to P along path 2, as shown in Figure 13.32b, then the work done by the gravitational force on the object is zero:

$$W = W_{P \to Q, \text{ path 1}} + W_{Q \to P, \text{ path 2}} = W_{P \to Q, \text{ path 2}} + (-W_{P \to Q, \text{ path 2}}) = 0. \tag{13.17}$$

A path like the one shown in Figure 13.32b, in which any object following the path returns to its original position, is called a **closed path.** Because the gravitational potential energy depends only on the position of the endpoints and the endpoints are the same, the change in the potential energy of the two-object system is zero. Consequently the work done by the gravitational force exerted by one object on the other as it moves along a closed path is zero, as Eq. 13.17 shows.

✋ **13.18** Near Earth's surface, when $\Delta U^G = mg\Delta x$, it is customary to let the gravitational potential energy be zero at Earth's surface, instead of at infinite separation as we did in Eq. 13.10. Does this choice of zero yield greater or smaller values for the gravitational potential energy? By what amount?

13.7 Celestial mechanics

Now that we have derived an expression for the gravitational potential energy, we can write an expression for the energy of a system of two celestial objects. Consider a system consisting of two objects of which one has a much greater mass than the other ($M \gg m$), so that we can consider the center of mass of the two-object system to be fixed at the center of the larger object (see Section 13.2). Examples of such a system are a planet orbiting a star, a moon orbiting a planet, and a satellite orbiting Earth (**Figure 13.33**). For convenience we'll refer to the object with the greater mass M as the *star* and the object with the smaller mass m as the *satellite*, but the results apply to any pair of celestial objects with $M \gg m$. We shall consider the system to be closed and isolated so that neither its energy nor its angular momentum can change:

$$\Delta E = 0 \quad \text{and} \quad \Delta \vec{L} = \vec{0}. \tag{13.18}$$

The energy of the system consists of the gravitational potential energy and the kinetic energy. Because only the satellite is in motion, we have

$$E = K + U^G = \tfrac{1}{2}mv^2 - \frac{GMm}{r}, \tag{13.19}$$

where v is the speed of the satellite and r is the distance between the satellite and the star.

Figure 13.32 The gravitational work done on object 2 depends only on the endpoints.

(*a*)

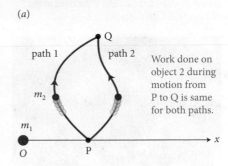

Work done on object 2 during motion from P to Q is same for both paths.

(*b*)

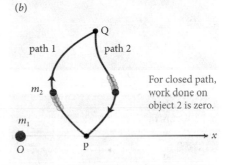

For closed path, work done on object 2 is zero.

Figure 13.33 When one object orbits another that has much greater mass, we can consider the center of mass of the system to be fixed at the center of the larger object.

(a)

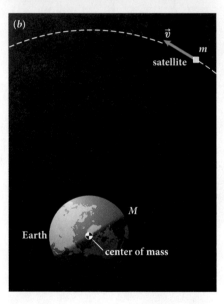

(b)

Because the force of gravity is central, the angular momentum of each object is constant. For the satellite we have

$$L = r_\perp mv. \tag{13.20}$$

Equations 13.18–13.20 allow us to determine the shape of the satellite's orbit given the values of $\vec{r}$ and $\vec{v}$ at any given instant.

13.19 (a) If an object of mass m is released from rest a distance r from a star of mass $M \gg m$ and radius R_s, is the mechanical energy of the star-object system E_{mech} positive, negative, or zero? (b) Describe the motion of the object, and determine the maximum and minimum values of its kinetic energy during its motion. (c) Does the motion you described in part b satisfy conservation of angular momentum about the center of the star? (d) Suppose the object is now launched with nonzero velocity in a direction perpendicular to the straight line joining it and the center of the star. Is E_{mech} positive, negative, or zero?

As this checkpoint shows, the mechanical energy E_{mech} of a star-satellite system can be negative because U^G is always negative when we let the gravitational potential energy be zero at infinite separation. To understand the consequences of the energy being negative, look at **Figure 13.34**, which shows the gravitational potential energy U^G as a function of the distance r between satellite and star. As we saw in Section 13.6, U^G has a $1/r$ dependence and approaches zero as r goes to infinity. If the energy E of the system is negative, then there is a value $r = r_{max}$ for which $U^G = E_{mech}$—all of the mechanical energy is in the form of potential energy, and thus the satellite's kinetic energy is zero. Any separation distance r greater than r_{max} would yield a negative kinetic energy because $U^G > E_{mech}$ for $r > r_{max}$. Because the kinetic energy cannot be negative, the satellite's motion for negative values of E_{mech} is restricted to values of $r < r_{max}$ for which $U^G < E_{mech}$. The maximum separation distance r_{max} occurs when $U^G = E_{mech}$:

$$-\frac{GMm}{r_{max}} = E_{mech} \tag{13.21}$$

$$r_{max} = \frac{GMm}{-E_{mech}}. \tag{13.22}$$

In words, we say that for negative E_{mech}, the satellite is *bound* to the star: It cannot escape to infinity because it does not have enough kinetic energy. When the mechanical energy E_{mech} is positive, the gravitational potential energy is *always* smaller than E_{mech}, and so even at infinite separation, where the gravitational potential energy is maximum, there still is a positive amount of kinetic energy. Therefore there is no limit on the separation distance r for $E_{mech} > 0$; in this case, we say the satellite is *unbound* because it has enough energy to "escape" to infinity.

13.20 (a) If our satellite of mass m were to reach the position r_{max} given by Eq. 13.22, what would its angular momentum be? (b) What would its trajectory have to be to satisfy conservation of angular momentum? (c) If its angular momentum is nonzero, can the satellite ever reach r_{max}?

To determine the shape of the satellite's orbit, we must solve Eqs. 13.18–13.20. The solution of these simultaneous equations yields orbits that correspond to the *conic sections* illustrated in **Figure 13.35**, with the star at the focus of the section. The sections shown in the figure fall into two categories: *ellipses* (including the

Figure 13.34 When the mechanical energy E_{mech} of a system is negative, the separation distance r between two objects in the system is limited to the region where $U^G < E_{mech}$.

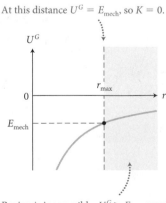

At this distance $U^G = E_{mech}$, so $K = 0$.

Region is inaccessible: $U^G > E_{mech}$ would require $K < 0$.

Conic sections

Second-degree equations in two variables of the form

$$Ax^2 + Bxy + Cy^2 + Dx + Ey + F = 0$$

are called **conic sections** because the curves they represent can be obtained by intersecting a plane and a circular cone (Figure 13.35). These curves can also be written in the form

$$\frac{x^2}{a^2} + \frac{y^2}{a^2(1 - e^2)} = 1, \tag{1}$$

where a is the semimajor axis (see Figure 13.7) of the section and e is the eccentricity.

Ellipse: For $0 \leq e < 1$, we obtain an ellipse with a semimajor axis a and a semiminor axis b with

$b^2 = a^2(1 - e^2)$, where e is the eccentricity of the ellipse. For each point on the ellipse, the sum of the distances to the two foci at $(\pm ae, 0)$ is equal to $2a$. A special type of ellipse is obtained for $e = 0$: The two foci coincide, and the ellipse becomes a **circle** of radius a.

Hyperbola: When $e > 1$, the term that contains y^2 becomes negative, and Eq. 1 yields the two branches of a hyperbola with foci at $(\pm ae, 0)$ and oblique asymptotes $y = \pm(b/a)x$, with $b^2 = a^2(e^2 - 1)$. For each point on the hyperbola, the difference of the distances to the foci is equal to $2a$.

The limiting case between an ellipse and a hyperbola, which occurs when $e = 1$, yields a **parabola** of the form $y^2 = 4px$. The parabola can be thought of as an elongated ellipse with one focus at $(p, 0)$ and the other at $(\infty, 0)$.

Figure 13.35 Conic sections.

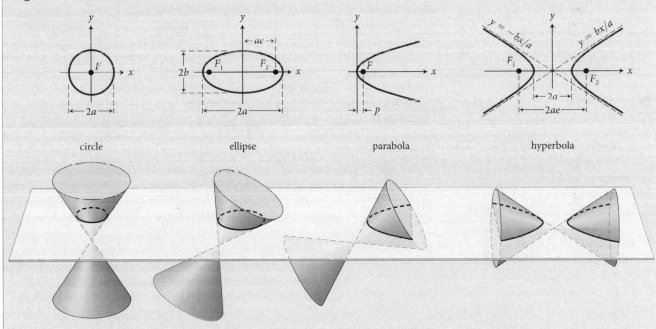

circle, which is a special type of ellipse) and *hyperbolas*. The limiting section between these two categories is the *parabola*. Ellipses are bound and therefore correspond to negative mechanical energy; hyperbolas are unbound and thus correspond to positive mechanical energy. The limiting case between bound and unbound motion occurs for $E_{mech} = 0$, when the satellite has just enough kinetic energy to approach infinity (with zero kinetic energy). The corresponding orbit is the parabola. Summarizing, we have

$$E_{mech} < 0: \quad \text{elliptical orbit}$$

$$E_{mech} = 0: \quad \text{parabolic orbit}$$

$$E_{mech} > 0: \quad \text{hyperbolic orbit}$$

Example 13.5 Rocket science

A satellite of mass m_{sat} is in an elliptical orbit around a star of mass $m_{star} \gg m_{sat}$. If the mechanical energy of the star-satellite system is E_{mech} and the magnitude of the angular momentum of the satellite about the star is L, what are the semimajor axis a and the eccentricity e of the satellite's orbit?

❶ **GETTING STARTED** I begin by making a drawing of the system (**Figure 13.36**), placing the star at one focus (F) of the ellipse. I also mark the positions of smallest (P) and and greatest (Q) separation between star and satellite, because at those locations the position vector $\vec{r}$ from star to satellite is perpendicular to the satellite's velocity $\vec{v}$, and therefore it is relatively easy to calculate the angular momentum.

Figure 13.36

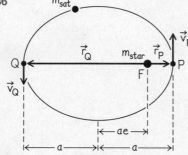

❷ **DEVISE PLAN** From my diagram I see that the major axis of the ellipse is equal to the sum of the distances FP and FQ: $2a = r_P + r_Q$. I also see that the distance FP is equal to $a - ae = a(1 - e)$, and so $a(1 - e) = r_P$. If I know r_P and r_Q, I can determine a and e. I know that the satellite's angular momentum at P must be the same as its angular momentum at Q. I also know that the mechanical energy of the system must be the same at these two locations. Thus I have two equations, $L_P = L_Q = L$ and $E_P = E_Q = E_{mech}$, from which I can determine r_P and r_Q.

❸ **EXECUTE PLAN** The magnitude of the satellite's angular momentum at P is the same as that at Q, so $L = m_{sat}r_P v_P = m_{sat}r_Q v_Q$. Using this expression, I can write for the satellite's kinetic energy at P:

$$K_P = \tfrac{1}{2}m_{sat}v_P^2 = \frac{m_{sat}^2 v_P^2 r_P^2}{2m_{sat}r_P^2} = \frac{L^2}{2m_{sat}r_P^2}.$$

The energy of the system at P is then

$$E_{mech} = K_P + U_P^G = \frac{L^2}{2m_{sat}r_P^2} - \frac{Gm_{sat}m_{star}}{r_P}. \qquad (1)$$

After writing corresponding expressions for position Q and setting the system energy at P equal to that at Q, I get

$$\frac{L^2}{2m_{sat}r_P^2} - \frac{Gm_{sat}m_{star}}{r_P} = \frac{L^2}{2m_{sat}r_Q^2} - \frac{Gm_{sat}m_{star}}{r_Q}.$$

I now put both terms containing L on the left and combine them over their common denominator, put both terms containing G on the right and combine them over their common denominator, and work through the algebra to get

$$\frac{L^2}{2m_{sat}}(r_P + r_Q) = Gm_{sat}m_{star}r_P r_Q.$$

Substituting $r_P + r_Q = 2a$, $r_P = a(1 - e)$, and $r_Q = 2a - r_P = a(1 + e)$, I obtain, after some algebra,

$$L^2 = Gm_{sat}^2 m_{star}a(1 - e^2). \qquad (2)$$

Substituting this expression for L^2 into Eq. 1 and solving for a give

$$a = -\frac{Gm_{sat}m_{star}}{2E_{mech}}. \checkmark$$

Substituting this result for a into Eq. 2 and solving for e, I finally obtain

$$e = \sqrt{1 + \frac{2E_{mech}L^2}{G^2 m_{sat}^3 m_{star}^2}}. \checkmark$$

❹ **EVALUATE RESULT** The orbit being elliptical means that E_{mech} is negative, and so a is positive and e is smaller than 1, as they should be for an ellipse. When $E_{mech} = 0$, the orbit should turn into a parabola and the satellite can go to infinity. Indeed, as I let E_{mech} approach zero, a approaches infinity and $e = 1$, and the ellipse turns into a parabola (see the box "Conic sections" on page 331).

13.21 Consider a planet of mass m moving at constant speed v in a circular orbit of radius R under the influence of the gravitational attraction of a star of mass M. (a) What is the planet's kinetic energy, in terms of m, M, G, and R? (b) What is the energy of the star-planet system? (c) Using the expression for the eccentricity obtained in Example 13.5, obtain an expression for E_{mech} for the circular orbit. (d) Compare your answers to parts b and c.

The results obtained in Example 13.5 show that the length $2a$ of the major axis of the ellipse depends on only the mechanical energy E_{mech} of the system. Because E_{mech} is negative, the greater E_{mech}, the closer it is to zero and the greater a.

Figure 13.37 shows five orbits with the same fixed energy E_{mech} but different values of L. The energy $E_{mech} = U^G + K$ is fixed because the satellite is launched

Figure 13.37 Orbits of a satellite of mass m launched in different directions with fixed speed and a fixed distance from an object of mass M. Because the mechanical energy E_{mech} of the system is always the same, the length $2a$ of the orbit's major axis (dashed line) is constant. As the angle between $\vec{v}_i$ and $\vec{r}_i$ is decreased, the angular momentum decreases and the eccentricity of the orbit increases.

For whole series:

Initial speed is same, so K is same.

Initial distance is same, so U^G is same.

Therefore, $E_{mech} = K + U^G$ is same, so major axis length is same.

However, as angle between $\vec{v}_i$ and $\vec{r}_i$ decreases, L decreases, so eccentricity increases. ⟶

at a fixed initial speed (so K is fixed) from a point P that is a fixed distance r_i from the center of the larger object of mass M (so U^G is fixed). Because E_{mech} is fixed, the length $2a$ of the major axis is the same for all orbits. As the direction of $\vec{v}_i$ is changed (without changing the speed v_i and therefore E_{mech} and $2a$), the magnitude of the angular momentum changes, affecting the eccentricity of the orbit, which depends on both L and E_{mech}. For a fixed mechanical energy E_{mech} (that is to say, for a fixed value of the major axis), e increases as L decreases. So, as the angle between $\vec{v}_i$ and $\vec{r}_i$ gets smaller, the ellipse becomes more elongated. In all cases, the object of mass M is at one of the foci of the ellipse.

Figure 13.38 shows the orbits of an object launched multiple times from a fixed location that is a distance r_i from Earth's center. All launches are in the same direction, perpendicular to the straight line connecting the object to Earth's center, but the launch speed is increased for each successive launch. Because the initial gravitational potential energy U^G is always the same, the value of the mechanical energy E_{mech} is determined by the initial kinetic energy: $E_{mech} = U^G + K$.

If the object is released from rest, $K = 0$ and so $E_{mech} = U^G$. As you saw in Checkpoint 13.19, the object falls in a straight line toward the surface of Earth. When the object is given a small initial speed, however, the orbit is an ellipse

Figure 13.38 Orbits of an object launched at different speeds from a fixed location that is a fixed distance r_i from Earth's center.

with Earth's center at the focus farther from the launch point. For small v_i, the orbit intersects Earth and the object crashes. As v_i is increased, the ellipse becomes rounder and longer, and for sufficiently great v_i, the object makes it around the planet.

As we continue to increase v_i, we reach a point when v_i has just the right magnitude to make v_i^2/r_i equal to the centripetal acceleration caused by Earth's gravitational force, and the object goes in a circular orbit. For greater v_i, the orbit is again elliptical, but Earth's center now coincides with the nearer focus of the ellipse.

As we continue to increase v_i, we reach a point where the mechanical energy E_{mech} of the Earth-object system is no longer negative and the orbit is unbound. This happens when

$$E_{mech} = \tfrac{1}{2}mv_{esc}^2 - \frac{Gmm_E}{r_i} = 0, \tag{13.23}$$

where v_{esc} is the object's *escape speed*, m is the mass of the launched object, m_E is Earth's mass, and r_i is the distance from the launch point to Earth's center. An object launched at the escape speed and moving without any further propulsion travels out to infinity along a parabolic path. At launch speeds greater than v_{esc} the orbit corresponds to one branch of a hyperbola.

13.22 (*a*) Determine an expression for the escape speed at Earth's surface. (*b*) What is the value of this escape speed? (*c*) Does it matter in which direction an object is fired at the escape speed?

13.8 Gravitational force exerted by a sphere

Central to Newton's law of gravity is the statement that a solid sphere exerts a gravitational force on an object outside the sphere as if all its mass were concentrated at the center of the sphere. To prove this statement, we'll calculate the force exerted on a particle of mass m by a thin spherical shell of mass M and radius R; the distance between the particle and the center of the shell is r. Once we have a result for the shell, we can obtain the result for a solid sphere by treating the solid sphere as a large number of concentric spherical shells, like the layers of an onion.

Consider first a vertical ring-shaped piece of the shell—the portion contained between the angles θ and $\theta + d\theta$ in **Figure 13.39a**. The force exerted by a small segment of the ring near P is $\vec{F}_{Pp}^G$; the force by a small segment near Q is $\vec{F}_{Qp}^G$. Only the components of these forces along the x axis contribute to the vector sum of the forces exerted on the particle. The same cancellation occurs for every pair of diametrically opposite small segments that make up the entire ring. To calculate the vector sum of the forces exerted on the particle, we therefore need to consider only the x components. The x component of the force exerted by a small segment of the ring of mass dm near P on the particle is

$$dF_{Ppx}^G = -G\frac{m\,dm}{s^2}\cos\alpha, \tag{13.24}$$

where α is the angle between the force and the straight line from the particle to the center of the shell and s is the distance from the particle to P. The x components of the forces exerted by all segments of the ring have the same magnitude. The vector sum of the forces exerted by the whole ring is thus equal to the sum of the contributions from all segments of the ring:

$$dF_{rpx}^G = -G\frac{m\,dM}{s^2}\cos\alpha, \tag{13.25}$$

Figure 13.39 To calculate the gravitational force exerted by a spherical shell of mass M on an object of mass m, the shell is divided into vertical rings.

(*a*)

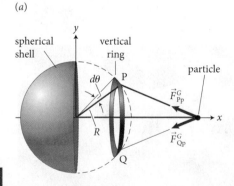

(*b*) Geometry of red triangle in part *a*.

where dM is the mass of the entire ring (the sum of the masses of all segments). The width of the ring being equal to the arc length $R\,d\theta$, the area of the ring is (length) $\times$ (width) $= (2\pi R \sin \theta)(R\,d\theta) = 2\pi R^2 \sin \theta\, d\theta$. If the mass M of the entire shell is uniformly distributed over the shell, then the mass per unit area is $M/(4\pi R^2)$, so

$$dM = 2\pi R^2 \sin \theta\, d\theta \frac{M}{4\pi R^2} = \frac{M}{2} \sin \theta\, d\theta \qquad (13.26)$$

or, combining Eqs. 13.25 and 13.26,

$$dF^G_{\mathrm{rp}x} = -\frac{GMm}{2} \frac{\cos \alpha \sin \theta\, d\theta}{s^2}. \qquad (13.27)$$

Equation 13.27 gives the force exerted by one vertical ring of our spherical shell on the particle. Now we must integrate this result over the entire shell. Before we can carry out this integration, we must reduce the variables α, s, and θ, which are all related, to one variable. From Figure 13.39b we see that

$$\cos \alpha = \frac{r - R \cos \theta}{s}, \qquad (13.28)$$

and from the law of cosines (see Appendix B), we have

$$s^2 - R^2 + r^2 - 2rR \cos \theta. \qquad (13.29)$$

Differentiating the left side of this equation with respect to s yields $2s$. For the right side we get

$$\frac{d}{ds}(R^2 + r^2 - 2rR \cos \theta) = \frac{d}{d\theta}(R^2 + r^2 - 2rR \cos \theta)\frac{d\theta}{ds}$$

$$= 2rR \sin \theta \frac{d\theta}{ds}. \qquad (13.30)$$

Equating the derivatives on the two sides, we get

$$2s = 2rR \sin \theta \frac{d\theta}{ds} \qquad (13.31)$$

$$\sin \theta\, d\theta = \frac{s\,ds}{rR}. \qquad (13.32)$$

Substituting Eq. 13.32 and $R \cos \theta$ from Eq. 13.29 into Eq. 13.28 and then into Eq. 13.27 yields

$$dF^G_{\mathrm{rp}x} = -\frac{GMm}{4r^2R}\frac{(r^2 + s^2 - R^2)ds}{s^2} = -\frac{GMm}{4r^2R}\left(\frac{r^2 - R^2}{s^2} + 1\right)ds. \qquad (13.33)$$

To obtain the force exerted by the entire shell, we must integrate this expression from $s = r - R$ (at $\theta = 0$) to $s = r + R$ (at $\theta = \pi$):

$$F^G_{\mathrm{sp}x} = \int_{r-R}^{r+R} dF^G_{\mathrm{rp}x} = -\frac{GMm}{4r^2R}\int_{r-R}^{r+R}\left(\frac{r^2 - R^2}{s^2} + 1\right)ds. \qquad (13.34)$$

Working out the integral (see Checkpoint 13.23), we get

$$\int_{r-R}^{r+R}\left(\frac{r^2 - R^2}{s^2} + 1\right)ds = 4R \tag{13.35}$$

so

$$F_{\text{sp}x}^G = -G\frac{Mm}{r^2} \quad \text{(shell)}, \tag{13.36}$$

where the minus sign indicates that the force points toward the center of the shell. So we see that the shell exerts a force as if its entire mass M were concentrated at the center.

We can now easily extend this result to a solid sphere by considering many concentric shells. For each shell, we obtain an expression of the form given by Eq. 13.36; adding all terms (one for each shell) then yields

$$F_{\text{sp}}^G = G\frac{mM_{\text{sphere}}}{r^2} \quad \text{(sphere)} \tag{13.37}$$

for the magnitude of the gravitational force exerted by a solid sphere of mass M_{sphere} on a particle of mass m placed a distance r from the sphere's center. Equation 13.37 shows that the solid sphere exerts a force as if its entire mass M were concentrated at the center.

✋ **13.23** (*a*) Work out the integral in Eq. 13.35. (*b*) Show that Eq. 13.33 still holds if the particle of mass m is inside the shell. (*c*) What are integration limits with this particle inside the shell? What is the value of the integral in Eq. 13.35 for these limits?

Chapter Glossary

SI units of physical quantities are given in parentheses.

Balance A device that uses a pivoted rod to compare the gravitational force exerted on an object of unknown mass with that exerted on objects of known mass.

Central force A force whose line of action always lies along the straight line connecting the two interacting objects.

Closed path A path in which any object that follows the path returns to its original position.

Conic sections Mathematical curves that are obtained by intersecting a plane and a circular cone. The shape of the orbit of two gravitationally interacting objects is a conic section.

Gravitational constant A fundamental constant that determines the strength of the gravitational interaction:

$$G = 6.6738 \times 10^{-11}\,\text{N} \cdot \text{m}^2/\text{kg}^2. \tag{13.5}$$

See also *law of gravity*.

Gravitational potential energy U^G (J) The potential energy associated with a system of interacting objects. If the gravitational potential energy of a system of two objects with masses m_1 and m_2 is chosen to be zero at infinite separation, it is

$$U^G(\vec{r}) = -G\frac{m_1 m_2}{r} \tag{13.14}$$

when the separation of the objects is r.

Kepler's laws Laws that describe celestial orbits deduced from measurements of the motions of the planets. Kepler's laws are a direct consequence of the law of gravity.

Law of gravity The law that describes the gravitational attraction between all objects that have mass. An object of mass m_1 exerts on an object of mass m_2 a distance r away an attractive central force of magnitude

$$F_{12}^G = G\frac{m_1 m_2}{r_{12}^2}, \tag{13.1}$$

where G is the gravitational constant.

Mass m (kg) A scalar property of every piece of matter that determines the strength of its gravitational interaction with other pieces of matter. Except at very high speeds, the mass of an object is equal to the object's inertia.

Principle of equivalence A basic principle of the theory of general relativity that states that one cannot distinguish locally between the effects of a constant gravitational acceleration of magnitude g and an acceleration of the reference frame of magnitude $a = g$.

Spring scale A device that measures the downward force exerted on it by a load, by determining the deformation of a calibrated spring.

14

Special Relativity

14.1 Time measurements

14.2 *Simultaneous* is a relative term

14.3 Space-time

14.4 Matter and energy

14.5 Time dilation

14.6 Length contraction

14.7 Conservation of momentum

14.8 Conservation of energy

CONCEPTS

QUANTITATIVE TOOLS

Time is the basic fabric of life because living means *changing* and change—a concept central to all we have discussed up to now—cannot exist without time. Time is so basic that we take for granted that we all agree on what it is. If, for instance, you and I arrange to meet here tomorrow at three o'clock and we make sure our watches agree now, we expect to see each other here tomorrow when our watches read three o'clock.

As we see in this chapter, however, our commonsense experience of time fails to explain certain experimental observations. In 1905 Albert Einstein realized these shortcomings and revised the basic notions of space and time with his *theory of special relativity*. The basic principles of this theory are the principle of relativity, which we discussed in Chapter 6, and the experimental fact that the measured value of the speed of light is independent of the motion of the source relative to the observer making the measurement. The revised notions of space and time require us to adjust our understanding of inertia, momentum, and energy. However, the conservation principles—the unifying principles of this text and the most fundamental laws of physics—continue to hold, as required by the principle of relativity.

14.1 Time measurements

Since the advent of clocks, the measurement of time has been so straightforward that it hardly requires much thought. Just as spatial coordinates determine *where* something happens, time tells us *when* it happens. Let's define an **event** as something that happens at a specific location at a specific instant. Take, for example, your act of reading this sentence. If you and I agree on a coordinate grid (for example, longitude, latitude, and altitude) and a time zone, you can specify the location and time of this event in such a way that it is uniquely and precisely defined. You are reading this sentence, say, in Helena, Montana (46.595°N, 112.030°W, alt. 1138 m), at 9:33 p.m. today.

Let's concentrate for now on the time part of describing events. By referring to the watch on your wrist, you can measure the instant at which any event near you occurs. There are two reasons you can count on this procedure to work. First, it is possible to construct a device—a clock—that measures equal, calibrated time intervals (say, seconds). Clocks serve as a "ruler" for time, just as an ordinary ruler helps us measure space. Second, we can *synchronize* clocks; that is, we can make sure two clocks run at the same rate and their readings agree.

Keeping time helps us sort out the sequence of events and establish a possible causal relationship between events (see Section 1.4). If you are at the location of two successive events, it's straightforward to determine which event happened first and what the time interval between them is. How, though, can you determine the sequence for two events that occur at different locations?

We need to be able to detect some sort of signal (such as sound or light) to observe an event, and all such signals

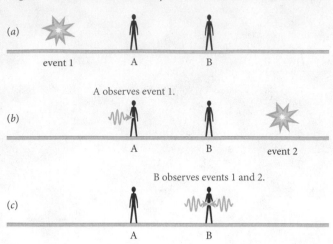

Figure 14.1 Two observers with synchronized clocks observe two events.

(a) event 1   A   B

A observes event 1.

(b)   A   B   event 2

B observes events 1 and 2.

(c)   A   B

travel at some finite speed. Of all signals known, light travels the fastest and therefore is the most convenient for timing events.

Figure 14.1 shows two events—the emission of light signals at two locations—and their observation by two observers using synchronized clocks. The light signals are of short duration, like a flash, so that we can consider each emission to take place at a definite instant. The signals travel at the speed of light (3.00×10^8 m/s in vacuum or air) and carry the message that the event has occurred. Observer A is closer to event 1 than to event 2; observer B is closer to event 2 than to event 1. In Figure 14.1a, event 1 occurs but the signal has not yet reached either observer. In Figure 14.1b, the signal from event 1 reaches observer A and event 2 occurs. Note that the signal from event 1 has not yet reached observer B and that the signal from event 2 has reached neither observer. A little later, the signals from both events reach observer B (Figure 14.1c) but the signal from event 2 has not yet reached observer A.

✋ **14.1** In Figure 14.1, based on the time of arrival of the light signals, which event is observed first according to (a) observer A and (b) observer B?

As this checkpoint shows, if you go by the instants at which the signals reach the two observers, the observers do not agree on the sequence of the two events. Observer A sees the events as occurring at two different instants, but observer B sees them as occurring at the same instant. The instant of *observation*, however, is not the instant at which the light signals *are emitted*. For events that occur around you in daily life, the difference between the instant each event happens and the instant you observe it is negligible because light travels so fast. Light emitted by the Sun, however, takes about 8 minutes to reach us. Thus, if a solar flare occurs at the surface of the Sun, that event takes place 8 minutes before we observe it. Light emitted by the Andromeda Galaxy takes 2 million years to reach Earth. If you look at the Andromeda Galaxy on a dark, moonless

Figure 14.2 One way to measure the time interval between two events is to travel from one event to the other, using a single clock to record the instant at which each occurs.

(a)

event 1

(b)

(c)

event 2

night, you see the light it emitted 2 million years ago. A lot could have happened to that galaxy in those 2 million years—for all you know, the entire galaxy might not be there anymore!

Even though we do not deal with these astronomical distances here in our discussion of time measurements, we still need to take into account the *signal delay* between event and observation. This signal delay is the time interval it takes for the signal to travel from the location of the event to the location of the observer. For nearby events, the signal delay is negligible. For events separated by an appreciable distance, we can avoid signal-delay complications in several ways. One straightforward, if not always practical, way is shown in **Figure 14.2**: An observer travels from the location of event 1 to the location of event 2 and records the two events on the same clock. In the observer's reference frame, the two events take place *at the same location* (the origin if you imagine axes attached to the observer) but at different instants. To avoid the complications of a noninertial reference frame (see Chapter 6), the observer should travel at constant velocity. The time interval obtained this way is called the **proper time interval:**[*]

> The time interval between any two events that occur at the same position in a particular reference frame is called the proper time interval between the two events.

Not all pairs of events are separated by a proper time interval: If an observer does not have enough time to travel from the first event to the second event to observe both events at his location, there is no proper time interval for those events.

---

[*] From the French *propre* meaning *own,* as in one's "own time."

Example 14.1 Proper time interval

You are flying in a plane, and a friend is on the ground. Which of you measures the proper time interval between (a) the beginning and end of a brief in-flight video program and (b) two successive signals from a warning light on a tall building along your flight path?

❶ GETTING STARTED The problem involves two observers (my friend and I) and two pairs of related events. My friend is in the Earth reference frame (E); I am in the reference frame of the plane (P). To simplify the discussion, I denote the beginning and end of the movie as events 1 and 2, respectively, and the two successive flashes of the warning light as events 3 and 4.

❷ DEVISE PLAN To see who measures the proper time interval, I should make a sketch for each pair of events, showing the positions of the E and P reference frames. If either observer sees either pair of events as occurring at the same location, that observer measures the proper time interval.

❸ EXECUTE PLAN (a) **Figure 14.3** shows that the beginning (event 1) and end (event 2) of the video program take place at the same location in reference frame P. Because that is my reference frame, I measure the proper time interval between these events. Figure 14.3 also shows that to my friend, standing at one location in the Earth reference frame, the two events happen at different locations (event 1 high and to his left, event 2 high and to his right). Thus he cannot measure the proper time interval. ✔

Figure 14.3

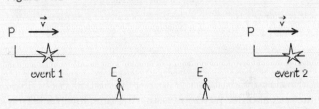

(b) **Figure 14.4** shows that the two flashes take place at the same place in reference frame E. Because this is my friend's reference frame, he measures the proper time interval between the two flashes. As for me, I see the first flash as coming from right below the plane but the second flash as coming from behind the plane. Two different locations from my point of view mean that I cannot measure the proper time interval between the flashes. ✔

Figure 14.4

❹ EVALUATE RESULT The video "happens" in the plane, so the plane is the reference frame in which to measure the proper time interval—the screen on which the video is projected is at rest in the plane. Likewise, the warning light is at rest in the Earth reference frame. My answers make sense.

Figure 14.5 Synchronized clocks can be used to measure the time interval between events that occur in different locations. (*a*) Each observer records the instant at which a nearby event occurs. (*b*) To synchronize their clocks, the two observers record the instant at which a single event occurs.

(*a*)

(*b*)

Because measuring a proper time interval is not always practical, another way to measure the time interval between events that occur in two locations is to place observers with identical clocks near each event, so that each observer can record the nearby event according to his clock (**Figure 14.5a**). Once the events are over, the two observers can communicate their clock readings and determine which event occurred first.

To synchronize the clocks, the observers can use the procedure illustrated in Figure 14.5*b*. An event sends out light signals to both observers, and each observer records the instant at which the signal reaches his clock. They then measure the distance from each clock to the location of the event and correct for the signal delay. If the clocks are synchronized, the observers obtain the same instant for the event after they subtract the signal delay from their recorded clock reading. If they don't obtain the same instant, they can use this procedure to adjust their clocks.

Because we don't always know where events are going to occur, it makes sense to construct a reference frame that has identical clocks arranged in a grid at regular fixed spacings, as shown in **Figure 14.6**. We can synchronize the clocks by sending a signal from the clock at the origin (the *reference clock*) to all the other clocks and correcting each

Figure 14.6 The scaffold of time: a reference frame made up of a grid of synchronized clocks. An event can occur anywhere in the grid, and the instant at which the event occurs is the instant shown on the clock nearest the event.

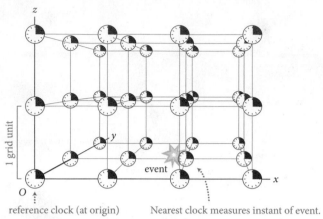

clock's reading for the signal delay. We can then define the instant in that reference frame at which any event occurs as the reading on the clock whose position coincides with that event. From now on, when we say "measuring the instant at which an event occurs in a given reference frame," we shall understand this to mean that we are using this procedure and that *an observer* in this reference frame is the observer stationed at the clock nearest the event.

Now that we have established a procedure for determining the instant at which an event occurs in a certain reference frame, we can determine the order of events in that reference frame. Two events that occur at different positions in the reference frame are **simultaneous** when the readings of the two clocks at the two locations of the events are identical. When the events are not simultaneous, the clock readings at the locations of the events allow us to determine the sequence of the events.

Exercise 14.2 Synchronizing clocks

Suppose you want to synchronize the network of clocks in Figure 14.6 by emitting a single light pulse at the origin. This signal triggers each clock to start running from some initial setting. If it takes the signal 1 s to travel along one grid unit and if the reference clock is set initially to 12 o'clock, what should the initial settings be for each clock (*a*) along the *x* axis and (*b*) along the diagonal in the *y* = 0 plane?

SOLUTION (*a*) Along the *x* axis, the signal arrives at the first clock to the right of the reference clock 1 s after the emission, when the reference clock reads 12:00:01, and so I set the first clock to 12:00:01. The next clock along the *x* axis starts running when the signal triggers it at 12:00:02, and so I set each clock on the *x* axis 1 s ahead of the clock immediately to its left. ✔

(*b*) The light must travel $\sqrt{2}$ grid units to reach the first clock along the diagonal. We must therefore set that clock ahead of the reference clock by $\sqrt{2}$ s = 1.414 s. The next clock along the diagonal is set ahead by $2\sqrt{2}$ s, and so on. ✔

Figure 14.7 A detector located midway between two light sources can detect whether signals are emitted (*a*) simultaneously or (*b*) not simultaneously.

(a)

(b)

event 1   event 2   event 1

— source   simultaneity detector   event 2

simultaneous!   NOT simultaneous!

🖐 **14.2** Suppose an observer is standing at the origin in Figure 14.6 and all the clocks are synchronized. (*a*) Which of the following is true? The observer sees that (*i*) all the clocks read the same time, (*ii*) nearby clocks display later times than more distant clocks, (*iii*) nearby clocks display earlier times than more distant clocks. (*b*) Does the observer see all the clocks running at the same rate?

14.2 *Simultaneous* is a relative term

Suppose we determine that two events—for example, the emission of light signals by two sources—are simultaneous in a certain reference frame. Are these events also simultaneous in another reference frame that is in motion relative to the first? To help answer this question, we use a *simultaneity detector*: a device that emits a blue light when it receives two signals at the same instant.

When we position the detector midway between the positions where the two events take place, as illustrated in Figure 14.7, the time interval it takes to travel to the detector is the same for both signals. This means that, if the two signals reach the detector at the same instant and the blue light comes on, the events were simultaneous in the reference frame of the detector (Figure 14.7*a*). If the events occur at different instants, the two signals do not arrive at the detector at the same instant and the blue light does not come on (Figure 14.7*b*). The blue light thus tells us whether or not the two emission events were simultaneous *in the reference frame of the detector*. One advantage of this device is that we do not need to be in the reference frame of the detector to determine whether the two events are simultaneous in its reference frame. As long as the simultaneity detector is placed midway between the two events, the blue light tells

us whether the events are simultaneous in the detector's reference frame.

Up to now we have discussed only measurements made by an observer (or detector) at rest with respect to the sources of the signals. What happens to the transmission of signals when the source and observer are moving relative to each other? To find out, let's start by reviewing the relativity of speeds for everyday objects that move much more slowly than light.

Example 14.3 Fast ball

Consider a spring-loaded device that ejects a ball at some unknown everyday speed v_b. To measure this speed, you measure the time interval it takes the ball to pass through a stationary tube of known length ℓ (**Figure 14.8**). Now suppose the tube is moving at speed v_t toward the ejection device. What speed do you obtain by dividing the length ℓ of the tube by the time interval Δt it takes the ball to pass through the tube? Express your answer in terms of v_b and v_t.

Figure 14.8 Example 14.3.

$\vec{v}_b$

$\vec{v}_t = \vec{0}$

tube

t

$t + \Delta t$

ℓ

① GETTING STARTED I begin by drawing the ball at the instant it enters and the instant it exits the moving tube (**Figure 14.9**). I choose my positive x axis to be in the direction of the ball's motion and use d to denote the distance the tube moves while the ball passes through. The distance the ball travels as it passes through the tube is thus $\ell - d$.

Figure 14.9

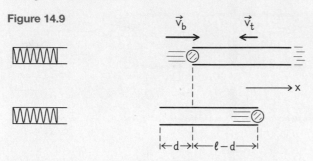

② DEVISE PLAN From my sketch I see that during the time interval Δt, two things happen: The tube advances a distance d, and the ball travels a distance $\ell - d$. Because speed equals distance traveled divided by the time interval needed to travel this distance, I can relate these two distances to the speeds v_b and v_t. This gives me two equations, from which I can solve for the two unknowns d and Δt. I also note that dividing ℓ by Δt gives me the speed v_{Mb}, which is the speed of the ball measured by an observer M moving along with the tube.

③ EXECUTE PLAN Because the tube advances a distance d in the time interval Δt, I have $v_t = d/\Delta t$. Likewise, for the ball: $v_b = (\ell - d)/\Delta t = \ell/\Delta t - d/\Delta t$. The first term equals the speed v_{Mb} I am asked to determine. The second term is the speed of the tube v_t, and so $v_b = v_{Mb} - v_t$. Rearranging terms, I get $v_{Mb} = v_b + v_t$. The speed of the tube is added to that of the ball. ✔

④ EVALUATE RESULT Using the subscript cancellation rule (Eq. 6.14), I can write $\vec{v}_{Mb} = \vec{v}_{ME} + \vec{v}_{Eb}$. With my choice of positive x axis to the right in Figure 14.9, I get $v_{Mbx} = v_{MEx} + v_{Ebx}$. Because $\vec{v}_{ME}$ is the velocity of Earth relative to an observer moving with the tube, I have $v_{MEx} = v_t$. Likewise $\vec{v}_{Eb}$ is the velocity of the ball relative to Earth, and so $v_{Ebx} = v_b$. Therefore, $v_{Mbx} = v_{MEx} + v_{Ebx} = v_t + v_b$, which confirms the result I obtained.

✋ 14.3 In Example 14.3 what is the time interval Δt it takes the ball to pass through the moving tube if $v_b = v_t = v$? Express your answer in terms of ℓ and v.

Example 14.3 reaffirms what we learned in Chapter 6: The speed of an everyday object relative to an observer depends on the motion of both the object and the observer. Relative to an observer moving along with the tube in Figure 14.9, the ball moves not at speed v_b but at speed $v_b + v_t$. Measurements of the **speed of light in vacuum**, denoted by c_0, however, show something very different:*

The measured value of the speed of light propagating in vacuum is c_0, independent of the motion of the source relative to the observer making the measurement.

---

*The subscript zero on c_0 is there to remind us that this is the value obtained in vacuum. The zero indicates the absence of any medium through which the light propagates.

This counterintuitive result was first suspected after an experiment done by A.A. Michelson and E.W. Morley in 1887. Many experiments since then have provided extensive confirmation of the Michelson-Morley results. To help you grasp the full meaning of this remarkable result, imagine that we shine a beam of light from a source into a device that is at rest relative to the source and that measures the speed of light in vacuum (**Figure 14.10a**; such an apparatus exists). The result is a value of 299,792,458 m/s (see Section 1.3), which we shall round off to 3.00×10^8 m/s. If we now move the measuring device toward the source at speed v_d and measure the speed of light, we obtain not $c_0 + v_d$ but again c_0 (Figure 14.10b)! This baffling result is like discovering that the speed of the ball with respect to the tube in Figure 14.8 is the same regardless of the motion of the tube relative to Earth.

Experiments show that it makes no difference whether we move the source, move the measuring device, or move both. In all cases, the device measures the speed of light in vacuum to be c_0 (Figure 14.10c and d). This result holds even when the source or detector moves at a substantial fraction of c_0: If a source moves toward you at a speed of $0.2c_0$, you still measure the light traveling toward you at c_0, not $c_0 + 0.2c_0 = 1.2c_0$. After more than 100 years of repeated experiments, we can most certainly rule out an error in measurement.

Any quantity whose value does not depend on the choice of reference frame is called an **invariant.** Because the speed of light is the same in all inertial reference frames, it is an invariant. Invariants play an important role in physics because we want to develop theories and laws that are the same in different reference frames. To construct these theories and laws, we first need to establish which physical quantities are invariants. The invariance of these quantities tells us something fundamental about the underlying laws of the universe.

Measuring the speed of light involves nothing more complicated than measuring the distance traveled by light

Figure 14.10 The measured value of the speed of light in vacuum does not depend on the speeds of the source and the measuring device.

in a certain time interval and dividing that distance by the time interval. The unsettling conclusion from Figure 14.10 is that measured values of distances and time intervals must somehow depend on the motions of the source and the reference frame. This conclusion forces us to reexamine what we mean by *distances* and *time intervals,* two of the most basic quantities we introduced back in Chapter 2.

Let us start with the experimental fact that the speed of light in vacuum is always exactly c_0 and examine the consequences this result has on the experiment of Figure 14.7a. Suppose the entire setup—the two light sources and the simultaneity detector midway between them—now moves at a very high speed v past an observer at rest on the ground, as in **Figure 14.11**. (By *very high* I mean a speed large enough for the detector to move an appreciable distance in the time interval it takes the light signals to reach the detector.) Suppose further that the observer sees the two emission events occur at the same instant; that is, he is midway between the two sources at the instant they emit a light signal, and so the two signals reach him at the same instant (middle panel in Figure 14.11a). In other words, *the events are simultaneous in the observer's reference frame.*

As you can see from Figure 14.11a, however, the simultaneity detector moves to the right as the signals travel toward it, and so it receives signal 2 before it receives signal 1. Therefore the blue light does not go on. In the reference frame of the detector, the two signals were *not* emitted simultaneously! Meanwhile, the observer is confused: In his reference frame, the two signals *were* emitted simultaneously, and so why didn't the blue detector light come on?

14.4 Suppose the observer in Figure 14.11a, at rest relative to the ground and standing midway between the two sources when they emit signals, is joined by another observer who moves along with the simultaneity detector. (*a*) Based on what the detector tells them, do the observers agree that the light signals do not reach the detector at the same instant? (*b*) How does each observer explain why the signals don't reach the detector at the same instant?

Suppose the sources in Figure 14.11 emit the signals in such a way that the fast-moving detector receives them at the same instant and the blue light turns on. To the observer at rest on the ground, source 1 must have emitted its light signal before source 2 emitted its signal because signal 1 has to catch up with the detector moving away from it (Figure 14.11b). In his reference frame, the two events are *not* simultaneous, and so he is once again confused by what

Figure 14.11 If the sources and the simultaneity detector move together at high speed relative to an observer, then (*a*) events that are simultaneous to the observer will not be so to the detector. (*b*) To make the signals strike the simultaneity detector at the same instant, the source behind the detector must emit its signal before the source in front of the detector.

(*a*) Events are simultaneous to observer

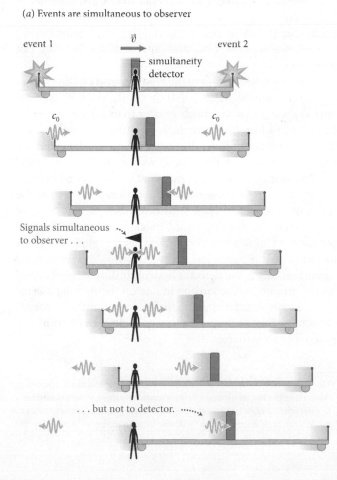

(*b*) Events are simultaneous to simultaneity detector

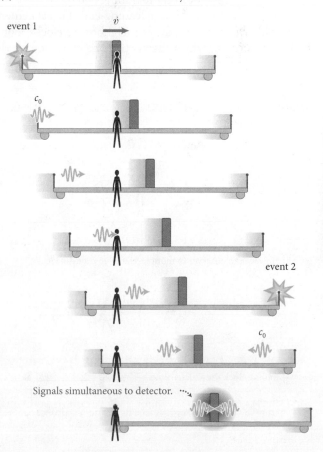

the detector is "saying": Blue light on means the events were simultaneous. The blue light tells us that the detector sees exactly the situation depicted in Figure 14.7a, and so in the reference frame of the detector the emission events are simultaneous. From these experiments we infer that:

Events that are simultaneous in one reference frame need not be simultaneous in another reference frame that is moving relative to the first.

What does this relativity of simultaneity imply for the grid of synchronized clocks of Figure 14.6? To answer this question, consider a pair of synchronized clocks at rest relative to observer A midway between the two clocks in **Figure 14.12**. The clocks are mounted on opposite ends of a rod that is one grid unit long. Because the clocks are synchronized, they strike 3 o'clock at the same instant according to observer A. Now consider the situation from the point of view of observer B, who is moving to the left at constant speed relative to A.

From B's perspective, the two-clock unit moves to the right, just like the simultaneity detector in Figure 14.11. Suppose events 1 and 2 in Figure 14.11 are our two clocks striking 3 o'clock. As Figure 14.11b shows, these two events occur at the same instant in the reference frame of the detector. Relative to observer B, however, the left clock strikes 3 o'clock (event 1) before the right clock does (event 2). So, in Figure 14.12b, too, the left clock strikes 3 o'clock *before* the right clock in the reference frame of observer B. In other words, the clock on the trailing end of the grid unit runs ahead of the clock on the leading end. This statement must hold true for any pair of neighboring clocks along the line of motion, which means that the clocks on a grid

Figure 14.12 Two synchronized clocks are unsynchronized in the reference frame of an observer moving relative to the clocks.

(a) Observer at rest relative to clocks sees clocks as synchronized.

(b) However, to observer in motion relative to frame of clocks . . .

. . . clocks are *not* synchronized; trailing clock shows later time.

Figure 14.13 Desynchronization of time in a moving reference frame.

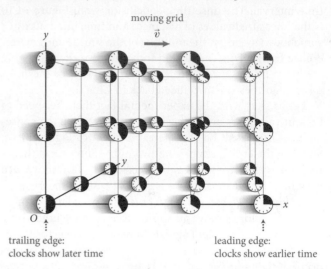

trailing edge: clocks show later time

leading edge: clocks show earlier time

moving relative to an observer desynchronize as shown in **Figure 14.13**. If you were to move along with the grid, all clocks would strike, say, 3 o'clock at the same instant. If the grid moves relative to you, however, the clocks at the trailing end of the grid strike 3 o'clock before those at the leading end.

What is one instant in one reference frame is a multitude of different instants in a reference frame that is moving relative to the first reference frame. As we saw in analyzing Figures 14.11 and 14.12, events that are simultaneous in one reference frame are not simultaneous in a reference frame that is moving relative to the first one.* Simultaneity is a relative concept, and time intervals are therefore not invariants.

The reason this notion of the relative nature of simultaneity defies common sense is that these effects are observable only at speeds that are much greater than everyday speeds. In Figure 14.11a, for example, in the time interval it takes the light to travel half the distance between the two sources, the simultaneity detector travels one-fourth of that distance. In other words, the detector moves at half the speed of light, or 1.5×10^8 m/s, close to a million times faster than the speed of an airplane! Had it instead moved at the speed of an airplane, the displacement between the top and bottom pictures in Figure 14.11 would have been negligible, and so, for all practical purposes, the signals would have arrived simultaneously at the detector both according to an observer on the ground and according to one on the moving assembly. It is only when observers (or detectors) move at speeds close to c_0 relative to each other that deviations from our everyday experience cannot be ignored.

---

* The only events we consider here are ones that occur at different positions along the line of motion of two reference frames in motion relative to each other. Events occurring along an axis perpendicular to the line of motion can be simultaneous in both reference frames.

✋ **14.5** Suppose the setup in Figure 14.11 is 10 m long. (*a*) How long does it take a light signal to travel from source to detector? (*b*) If the setup moves at 20 m/s, how far does it travel in the time interval you calculated in part *a*? (*c*) By how much does the displacement of the detector shorten (or lengthen) the travel time of the light signals? (*d*) Do you expect the time interval you calculated in part *c* to be measurable? (*e*) Repeat parts *b–d* for a detector moving at 1.0×10^8 m/s.

14.3 Space-time

The fact that simultaneity is relative rather than absolute makes us rethink the whole concept of time. If simultaneity depends on the motion of observers relative to each other, shouldn't the rate at which a clock is observed to tick depend on the motion of the observer relative to the clock? The answer is yes, and here is the easiest way to see that. Consider the device shown in **Figure 14.14**, called a *light clock*. At the bottom is a source that emits a very short light signal; at the top is a mirror that reflects the signal back down. At the instant the reflected signal reaches the bottom, the source is triggered to emit a new light signal. The up-and-down motion of the signals determines the period of this clock. If the mirror is a distance h away from the source, it takes each light signal a time interval h/c_0 to travel from the source up to the mirror and the same time interval to travel back down to the source. The period of this clock is thus $2h/c_0$. Just as the ticking of a mechanical clock defines the unit of time for the clock, this period defines the unit of time for the light clock.

Consider this clock from the perspective of two observers, one at rest relative to the clock (observer A, Figure 14.14*a*) and one moving to the left at very high speed v relative to the clock (observer B, Figure 14.14*b*). To observer A the clock signals move straight up and down. To observer B, however, the signals move along a longer diagonal path. Because the signals travel at exactly c_0 according to both observers, observer B sees the signals take longer to travel from source to mirror and from mirror to source.

✋ **14.6** (*a*) In Figure 14.14, is the period of the clock according to observer B greater than, equal to, or less than the period according to A? (*b*) Does the period of the clock according to B increase, decrease, or stay the same if we increase v?

Because the distance the signal travels from source to mirror and back to source is greater according to B than according to A, it takes longer for the clock to complete a cycle according to observer B. Therefore, the clock period is longer for B than it is for A. Observer B sees the clock as running more slowly than observer A. The greater the speed at which the clock moves relative to B, the more slowly she observes it ticking off its units of time. This

Figure 14.14 Because the speed of light in vacuum is always c_0, the light signal in a light clock takes longer to reach the mirror according to an observer moving relative to the clock than to an observer at rest relative to the clock.

(*a*) Light clock as seen by observer A at rest relative to clock

(*b*) Light clock as seen by observer B moving left relative to clock

effect is called **time dilation** because the units of time appear stretched out (dilated):

When a clock is in motion relative to an observer, that observer sees the time units of the clock as being longer than the time units of an identical clock at rest relative to her. Consequently, she measures the clock in motion as running slow relative to the clock at rest.

Figure 14.15 Each observer sees the other observer's clock run more slowly.

(a) **Reference frame of observer A**

Relative to A, clock 2 moving and therefore running slow

(b) **Reference frame of observer B**

Relative to B, clock 1 moving and therefore running slow

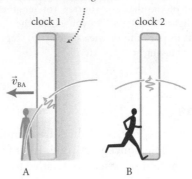

14.7 On your desk in front of you are two watches, one mechanical and one electronic. For each minute on the electronic watch, the mechanical watch advances by only 59 s. (a) Is the mechanical watch fast or slow relative to the electronic one? (b) Using the mechanical watch as the standard, is the electronic one fast or slow?

Ordinarily, if your watch runs slow relative to some clock, that clock runs fast relative to your watch, as you just saw in Checkpoint 14.7. Things are different when dealing with time dilation. Consider, for example, two identical clocks: clock 1, which is at rest relative to observer A, and clock 2, which is traveling along with observer B. To observer A, clock 2 is in motion and therefore running slow compared to clock 1 (**Figure 14.15a**). To observer B, however, clock 2 is at rest and clock 1 is moving (Figure 14.15b). From B's perspective, it is now the signal in clock 1 that takes longer to reach its mirror. So to B, clock 1 appears to run slowly relative to clock 2. The effect of time dilation is thus symmetrical, as required by the principle of relativity: Each observer sees the other observer's clock run more slowly.

Note that in Figure 14.14b the light signal leaves the source when the clock is at one position and returns to the source when the clock is at a different position. This means that the time interval between these events measured in B's reference frame is not the proper time interval. Observer A measures the proper time interval because the emission and return take place at the same position relative to A. This means that the proper time interval between the two events is the shortest, and we can say:

An observer who measures the proper time interval between two events (that is, an observer for whom the events occur at the same location) obtains the shortest time interval between those two events.

Example 14.4 My nap was shorter

You are flying in a plane, and a friend is on the ground. Who measures a shorter duration of (a) a nap you take and (b) a nap your friend takes?

❶ GETTING STARTED Like Example 14.1, this problem involves two observers (my friend and I) and two pairs of events (the beginning and end of each person's nap). My friend is in the Earth reference frame (E); I am in the reference frame of the plane (P). To simplify the discussion, I denote the beginning and end of my nap as events 1 and 2, respectively, and the beginning and end of my friend's nap as events 3 and 4, respectively.

❷ DEVISE PLAN The proper time interval between two events is the shortest time interval between them. Therefore this problem boils down to determining who measures the proper time interval for each nap. I should therefore make a sketch for each pair of events.

❸ EXECUTE PLAN (a) **Figure 14.16** shows the beginning (event 1) and end (event 2) of my nap on the plane. To me, the two events take place at the same location, which means that the time interval I measure is the proper time interval. To my friend, the two events take place at different locations (I fall asleep far to his left and wake up directly overhead), so the interval he measures is not the proper one. Thus I measure the shorter duration for my nap. ✔

Figure 14.16

(*b*) **Figure 14.17** shows the beginning (event 3) and end (event 4) of my friend's nap on the ground. To my friend, the two events take place at the same location, which means that the time interval he measures is the proper time interval. To me, the two events take place at different locations (my friend falls asleep in front and below the plane and he wakes up directly underneath), so the interval I measure is not the proper one. Thus my friend measures the shorter duration for his nap. ✔

Figure 14.17

event 3   event 4

❹ **EVALUATE RESULT** Each nap happens in the reference frame of the napper, and so it makes sense that each person measures the proper time interval of her or his nap.

You may ask yourself if this slowing down of moving clocks is just a peculiarity of the type of clock we have constructed. Who measures time with light clocks anyway? Suppose you have two identical mechanical clocks adjusted so that their periods are the same as those of a pair of identical light clocks. Now suppose you pair each mechanical clock with one of the light clocks and set one pair in motion. The stationary pair remains synchronized. Likewise, the moving pair must remain synchronized for this reason: If the motion of the clocks caused them to become unsynchronized, an observer moving along with them would note the difference in ticking rates and from this difference be able to determine his state of motion, which would violate the principle of relativity (see Section 6.3). Indeed, no one has ever observed a pair of initially synchronized clocks becoming unsynchronized because the pair's state of motion changes. So, we know that (1) moving light clocks run more slowly and (2) mechanical clocks behave just as light clocks do. We therefore conclude that moving mechanical clocks—or any other clock, for that matter, including your biological clock—must exhibit the same time-dilation effects as a light clock. It is time itself that dilates!

Even though time dilation is extremely small at everyday speeds, it has been measured by comparing two atomic clocks (which are not light clocks), one at rest on the surface of Earth and the other aboard an aircraft (see the box "Desynchronized twins").

Direct evidence that the time interval between two events depends on the motion of the observer is provided

Desynchronized twins

Suppose one member of a set of twins embarks on a space trip, flying away from Earth at a speed of $0.98c_0$. Ten years after her departure, she turns around and returns to Earth, again traveling at speed $0.98c_0$. To observers on Earth monitoring the trip, clocks on the space ship run five times more slowly than clocks on Earth. Likewise, the twin's heart—a clock—beats five times more slowly. Consequently, by the time she returns to Earth, she has aged not 20 years but 4 years (20 years/5)! When she meets her twin brother again, who has remained Earthbound this whole time interval, he's 16 years older than she is. According to him, she's been gone 20 years, but to her, the trip lasted only 4 years.

This scenario is disturbing because it defies our commonsense notion of time. The experiment has been carried out with a pair of identical ("twin") atomic clocks, one flown Eastward twice around the world while the other sat at the airport. Upon its return, the flown clock was behind the airport clock, and the time difference matched what theory predicts.

This desynchronization of twins (or twin clocks) is sometimes called the *twin paradox* because viewing the situation from the perspective of the traveling twin appears to yield a contradiction: To her it is her brother on Earth who is moving at $0.98c_0$, and so *he* should be the one aging more slowly! The paradox is that, as explained earlier, she does not see him as being 16 years younger—both agree that she is the younger one once the trip is over. In other words, even though she sees Earth/brother moving at $0.98c_0$ and so should see Earth clocks running *slow*, these Earth clocks measure a *longer* duration for her trip than her own clocks. How can this be?

The key to resolving this paradox is to remember that the brother remains in an inertial reference frame during the entire trip, but the sister doesn't. The spaceship has to turn around to return to Earth, and this change in direction means acceleration. During this acceleration, a marble initially at rest on the floor of the spaceship does not remain at rest, and thus there is a time interval during the trip when she is in a noninertial reference frame. In contrast, a marble initially at rest on Earth's surface is not affected by the spaceship's acceleration: in other words, the Earth remains an inertial reference frame all the while the traveling twin is away. Thus the physical situation is different in the two reference frames: the Earth reference frame always inertial, the reference frame of the spaceship not always inertial. The theory of special relativity shows that during the time interval in which she is accelerating, the sister would see Earth clocks speed *up*, so that when she gets back to Earth, she is not at all surprised to see that her brother has aged much more than she has.

by cosmic-ray muons, fast-moving elementary particles created when highly energetic protons from deep space collide with atoms some 10 km up in Earth's atmosphere. Laboratory experiments show that muons at rest have a *half-life* of 1.5×10^{-6} s. That is, if you have 100 muons at some instant $t = 0$, half of them will decay into some other type of particle during one half-life. Thus you will have only 50 muons left at $t = 1.5$ μs, 25 left at $t = 3.0$ μs, and so on.

Traveling at a speed nearly equal to c_0, a muon travels 450 m in 1.5×10^{-6} s, and so the number of muons should decrease by a factor of 2 each 450 m they travel through the atmosphere. Experiments done at the top of Mt. Washington at an altitude of 1900 m showed that 568 muons strike a certain detector per hour. At sea level the muons have traveled an additional 1900 m, or about four times 450 m, and so the count should be diminished by a factor of $(\frac{1}{2})^4$, yielding approximately 35 muons per hour. When the same detector is placed at sea level, however, not 35 but 412 muons per hour are detected—more than ten times as many as expected. How can this be?

Because of the time dilation that occurs at the speed they travel, the muons' half-life of 1.5×10^{-6} s is stretched to 1.4×10^{-5} s in our reference frame at rest on the ground. So, in the Earth reference frame the muons exist long enough for a substantial fraction of them to reach the ground before disintegrating.

14.8 Could you lengthen your life by traveling at high speed?

Motion is a relationship between time and distance. Thus, now that we understand how relative motion changes our ideas about time measurements, a logical next question to investigate might be whether motion changes the measurement of *distance*. In other words, is there a length change analogous to time dilation? An intriguing thought

experiment shows us that the answer is yes. Picture yourself traveling along with some muons as they move from the summit of Mt. Washington to sea level. They are at rest relative to you, and so there is no time dilation in your reference frame: According to your clock, the muons have a (proper) half-life of 1.5×10^{-6} s. If you are traveling with the muons (at rest in their reference frame), you see the ground rushing toward you at a speed of nearly c_0. Thus it should still take 4 half-lives for the surface of the sea to travel the 1900 m toward you, and as a result you should again see about 35 muons by the time sea level reaches you. You see 412, though, just as before. Because you "know" that the muon half-life is 1.5×10^{-6} s, you are forced to conclude that the height of Mt. Washington has somehow shrunk!

Another way to see that length measurements are affected by motion is to imagine measuring the length of a *moving* car. One way would be to record the positions of the front and back of the car on the pavement and then measure the distance between those marks. You need to make sure that you record the two positions simultaneously, however, because the car is moving relative to you. If you record the back position at one instant and the front position some time later, you won't get a correct result. Remember, however, that simultaneity is a relative concept, and therefore we can expect length measurements also to depend on the motion of an observer relative to the object whose length the observer is measuring.

To see how length measurements are affected by motion, consider again a grid unit with a pair of clocks. The unit is at rest and the clocks are synchronized in the reference frame of observer A (**Figure 14.18a**). Suppose a second observer B speeds up leftward when the clocks read 3 o'clock in A's reference frame. Because the clocks are synchronized, both of them read 3 o'clock in A's reference frame when observer B begins speeding up. From observer B's perspective, observer A and the clocks speed up to the right (Figure 14.18b). Because observer B is moving relative to the grid unit, the clocks are desynchronized, with the clock on the trailing

Figure 14.18 Length contraction of an accelerating grid.

(a) **Reference frame of observer A**

Observer A sees clocks synchronized.

$\vec{v}_{AB,i}$

····· At 3:00, A sees B begin accelerating.

A   B

$\vec{v}_{AB,f}$

B   A

(b) **Reference frame of observer B**

Grid moves relative to B, so clocks not synchronized. Trailing clock shows later time.

$\vec{v}_{BA,i}$ $\vec{v}_{BA,i}$

B

Trailing clock starts accelerating when it strikes 3:00.

$\vec{v}_{BA,f}$ $\vec{v}_{BA,i}$

····· Leading clock starts accelerating when it strikes 3:00.

B

Because trailing clock accelerates first, B sees grid unit shortened.

end being ahead of the clock on the leading end (see Figure 14.13). In observer B's reference frame, therefore, the clock on the trailing end strikes 3 o'clock and begins speeding up *before* the clock on the leading end does. Consequently B sees the distance between the clocks (and the length of the rod between them) decrease. Whenever the unit speeds up in B's reference frame, B sees the length of the rod decrease. The faster the unit moves, the shorter the rod appears to B.

When the unit slows down relative to observer B, the opposite happens: The clock on the trailing end begins slowing down *before* the clock on the leading end begins slowing down, and so B sees the rod become longer again. When the unit is at rest relative to B, she measures the rod to have its **proper length:**

> **The length of an object measured by an observer at rest relative to the object is called the object's proper length.**

An observer measuring the length of an object moving relative to the observer always measures a value that is shorter than the object's proper length.

✋ **14.9** Suppose observer B in Figure 14.18 carries a unit of two synchronized clocks that is identical to the unit that is at rest relative to A. Observer B begins speeding up when the clocks in her reference frame read 3 o'clock. What happens to the length of B's unit according to observer A?

As this checkpoint shows, the shortening of the rod's length, like time dilation, is symmetrical, in agreement with the principle of relativity. Each observer sees the other observer's grid move at the same relative speed and therefore shortened by the same amount.

Note that the shortening occurs only in the direction of motion. To see why, consider our clock grid unit aligned as in Figure 14.19. With the unit at rest, pegs are placed above and below it so that it fits snugly between them (Figure 14.19*a*). If the unit were to get shorter when it is in motion, it would fit more easily between the pegs (Figure 14.19*b*). Now imagine observing the same situation while traveling along with the unit. The unit is now at rest from your point of view and so does not shorten. The pegs, however, are in motion relative to you, and so the distance between them becomes smaller and the clocks hit the pegs. However, whether or not the clocks hit the pegs cannot depend on the reference frame of the observer, and so there cannot be any shortening in a direction perpendicular to the direction of motion.

When we discussed time dilation and considered the moving light clock in Figure 14.14*b*, we tacitly assumed its height to be fixed. Now we see that this assumption was justified.

The shortening of objects in the direction of motion is called **length contraction:**

> **When an object moves relative to an observer, the observer measures the length of the object in the direction of its motion to be shorter than the proper length of the object.**

Length contraction is a direct consequence of the relativity of simultaneity. Returning to the cosmic-ray muons, we can now see why they reach Earth's surface. To them, Earth's atmosphere flies by at nearly the speed of light. Length contraction reduces the thickness of the atmosphere so much that the atmosphere passes by the muons before they decay. To us on the ground, time dilation lengthens the half-life of the muons, and so they can cross the proper length of the atmosphere. To them, length contraction decreases the distance to the ground, and so they reach the ground during their proper lifetime.

Figure 14.19 Length contraction cannot occur in a direction perpendicular to the direction of motion.

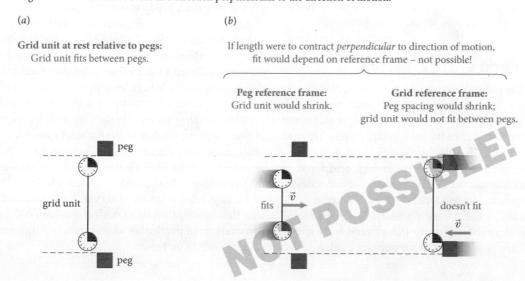

(*a*)

Grid unit at rest relative to pegs:
Grid unit fits between pegs.

(*b*)

If length were to contract *perpendicular* to direction of motion, fit would depend on reference frame – not possible!

Peg reference frame:
Grid unit would shrink.

Grid reference frame:
Peg spacing would shrink; grid unit would not fit between pegs.

peg

grid unit

peg

fits $\vec{v}$

doesn't fit $\vec{v}$

NOT POSSIBLE!

Common sense and special relativity

That observers who are in motion relative to each other assign different values to the length of an object and to the time interval between two events clashes with common sense. Even though experiments confirm the predictions of special relativity, it is hard to believe that, say, the length of a rod and the time interval between your lunch and dinner do not have fixed, absolute values. This difficulty arises from the fact that in everyday circumstances we can get away with treating lengths and time intervals as invariants.

How "real" then is length contraction or the slowing down of clocks? It is just as real as the pitch of an approaching car horn sounding higher than that of a stationary or receding car. (This phenomenon is called the *Doppler effect*; see Section 17.7.) Riding along in a car with a stuck car horn, you measure the same pitch a roadside observer would measure when the car is at rest. Yet there is no denying that the pitch is perceived to change when car and observer are in motion relative to each other. These observations don't mean that the horn changes when it moves relative to an observer. What changes is the pitch *perceived by the observer*.

The same statements can be made about a moving rod. Any observer measuring the rod's length when the rod is at rest relative to him obtains the same value as you would (the proper length). Just as the pitch of a moving car horn is perceived to be changing, so is the measured length of a moving rod. The rod itself doesn't change—the *measurement of its length* yields a different value. In that sense relativistic effects are every bit as real as the changing pitch of a horn. For example, few muons would make it across what we measure to be 10 km of atmosphere if that length did not appear to be shortened to less than 1 km to them.

Time and space are connected. If we consider time and space to constitute a four-dimensional *space-time* entity, we see that, depending on the reference frame, the time dimension stretches (dilates) and one of the three spatial dimensions contracts. As we shall see in Section 14.5, a quantity called the *space-time interval* remains unaffected by this distortion of space-time geometry. At everyday speeds, these distortions are so small that they are not perceived. For motions at very high speeds, such as that of cosmic-ray muons, however, the consequences of these effects can be significant (see the box "Common sense and special relativity").

✋ **14.10** Consider a long pole moving through a tunnel, with the direction of motion being along the long axis of the pole. An observer on the ground determines that the moving pole has the same length as the tunnel. Does an observer moving along with the pole agree that the pole fits exactly in the tunnel?

14.4 Matter and energy

We developed the entire framework of mechanics from our everyday notions of space and time. In Chapters 2 and 3, we introduced the definitions of displacement, velocity, and acceleration. Then we introduced inertia, which depends on a ratio of changes in velocity (see Section 4.5). Many other quantities, such as momentum, energy, and force, in turn depend on inertia. So all the physics we have developed so far hinges on our concepts of space and time.

As we just saw in the preceding sections, however, everyday notions of space and time fail at very high speed. Additionally, there is plenty of experimental evidence that our notion of energy fails at very high speeds. For example, experiments show that quadrupling the kinetic energy of an electron initially moving at $0.8c_0$ by doing work on it increases its speed by just 20% rather than doubling it as we would expect from the expression $K = \frac{1}{2}mv^2$.

Figure 14.20a shows the energy diagram for accelerating an electron from rest to $0.8c_0$. (The diagram is simplified by lumping all internal energy into one bar.) Because electrons have no known internal structure, $\Delta E_{int} = 0$, and so only their kinetic energy can change by doing work on them. The change in kinetic energy must thus be equal to the work done on the electron.

Now suppose we do additional work on the electron after it has attained a speed of $0.8c_0$. If the additional work is three times the amount of work done in accelerating the electron from rest to $0.8c_0$, our expression for kinetic energy, $K = \frac{1}{2}mv^2$, predicts a new speed that is twice the original speed: $v_f = 1.6c_0$. Experiments show, however, that the speed increases by just 20% and the value we obtain for ΔK using the expression $K = \frac{1}{2}mv^2$ is very much smaller than expected (Figure 14.20b). We must therefore conclude that our expression for kinetic energy is not valid at high speeds.

This experiment shows that it is more difficult to accelerate an electron when it is moving at $0.8c_0$ than when it is at rest. Now remember that an object's inertia is a measure of its resistance to acceleration (Section 4.2). We have so far assumed that an object's inertia is constant—an intrinsic property that is independent of the object's physical state or motion relative to an observer. Experimental data show that this assumption does not hold as an object's speed approaches c_0. In particular, as its kinetic energy increases, the object's inertia increases.

CONCEPTS

Figure 14.20 Simplified energy diagrams for accelerating an electron.

(a) Electron accelerated from 0 to $0.8c_0$

measured work
done on electron

$\Delta K \qquad \Delta E_{\text{int}} \qquad W$

zero because electron has
no internal structure

(b) Doing three times as much work increases electron's
speed by just 20%

kinetic energy
change $\Delta K = W$

additional work
done on electron

ΔK calculated
using $K = \frac{1}{2}mv^2$ ····▸

$\Delta K \qquad \Delta E_{\text{int}} \qquad W$

14.11 Do two observers, one moving at very high speed relative to the other, agree on the inertia of an object? Why or why not?

As Checkpoint 14.11 shows, inertia depends on the reference frame and therefore is not an invariant. In Chapter 13 we introduced mass—the property that determines the gravitational interaction of objects. The way in which objects interact gravitationally cannot depend on the motion of an observer relative to the interacting objects, which means that, in contrast to inertia, mass must be an invariant. That is to say, all observers should agree on the value of the mass of an object, regardless of their motion relative to the object. That mass is an invariant and inertia is not implies that there *is* a difference between mass and inertia, contrary to what we established in Chapter 13. As we shall see in Section 14.7, the difference between the two becomes apparent only at very high speeds.

Let us now turn to the nonkinetic part of energy: internal energy. Remember that the internal energy of an object or system is a quantitative measure of the state of that object or system. Because the state of an object cannot depend on the motion of the observer relative to the object, internal energy also must be an invariant.

So, we see that kinetic energy and inertia are not invariants, but internal energy and mass are. We also found that inertia depends on kinetic energy. Experiments show a similar connection between mass and internal energy. The primary example is provided by nuclear reactions, such as those taking place in the Sun. One of these reactions is the fusion of a proton and a deuteron D (the nucleus of a hydrogen isotope consisting of one neutron and one proton) to form a helium-3 nucleus (two protons and one neutron), while 8.80×10^{-13} J is released as radiation energy:

$$p + D \rightarrow {}^3\text{He} + \text{radiation}.$$

Figure 14.21 shows a simplified energy diagram for this reaction. Given that this is a nuclear reaction, nuclear energy (a form of internal energy) must be converted to radiation energy. Because the radiation energy leaves the system, the internal energy decreases.

Measurements show that the sum of the mass of the proton and the mass of the deuteron ($m_p + m_D = 5.01621 \times 10^{-27}$ kg) is greater than the mass of the helium-3 nucleus (5.00641×10^{-27} kg). In other words, the mass of the system decreases as its internal energy decreases.

Figure 14.21 Simplified energy diagram for the fusion of a proton and a deuteron. During the reaction, nuclear energy is emitted in the form of radiation. Experiments show that the amount of energy released is 8.80×10^{-13} J.

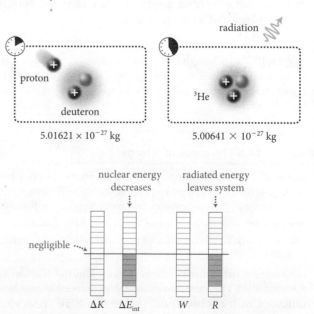

radiation

proton

deuteron

^{3}He

5.01621×10^{-27} kg

5.00641×10^{-27} kg

nuclear energy
decreases

radiated energy
leaves system

negligible ····▸

$\Delta K \qquad \Delta E_{\text{int}} \qquad W \qquad R$

Figure 14.22 An ionized deuterium molecule and a helium ion contain the same elementary particles, yet have different masses. (Nuclei not to scale.)

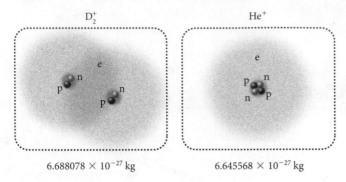

D_2^+

He^+

6.688078×10^{-27} kg

6.645568×10^{-27} kg

Another example of the connection between mass and internal energy is provided by comparing the masses of an ionized deuterium molecule and an ionized helium atom (**Figure 14.22**). Both consist of two protons, two neutrons, and an electron, but the two particles have different configurations. Accurate measurements show that this different in configuration—which means a difference in internal energy—results in a small mass difference.

These observations indicate a relationship between mass and internal energy that is parallel to the one between inertia and kinetic energy:

Increasing the internal energy of a system increases the mass of the system.

Mass is a property we associate with particles or objects that have physical substance—made of what we call "matter." Internal energy is a quantitative measure of the object's state. Now we see that the two are proportional to each other and that whenever a system's state changes, both its internal energy and its mass change.

✋ **14.12** In each of the following situations, does the mass of the system increase, decrease, or stay the same? (*a*) A spring is compressed (system: spring). (*b*) A cup of coffee cools down (system: coffee).

Exercise 14.5 The mass of energy

(*a*) In the nuclear reaction illustrated in Figure 14.21, what amount of mass is "lost"? (*b*) What is the ratio of energy decrease to mass loss as a result of the reaction? (*c*) Show that the units of your answer to part *b* are equivalent to m^2/s^2.

SOLUTION (*a*) The mass decreases by $(5.00641 \times 10^{-27}$ kg$) - (5.01621 \times 10^{-27}$ kg$) = -9.80 \times 10^{-30}$ kg. ✔

(*b*) The text states that the energy released in the reaction is 8.80×10^{-13} J. Therefore the ratio of energy decrease to mass loss is $(8.80 \times 10^{-13}$ J$)/(9.80 \times 10^{-30}$ kg$) = 8.98 \times 10^{16}$ J/kg. ✔

(*c*) J/kg $= (\text{kg} \cdot m^2/s^2)/\text{kg} = m^2/s^2$. ✔

Example 14.6 Spring mass

A spring of spring constant $k = 0.16$ N/m is compressed to half its 50-mm relaxed length. Using the result of Exercise 14.5, determine the change in the spring's mass.

❶ **GETTING STARTED** I begin by drawing a simplified energy diagram for the compressed spring (**Figure 14.23**). The work done on the spring during the compression increases the spring's potential energy and therefore the spring's internal energy. I need to determine the increase in mass corresponding to this energy increase.

Figure 14.23

❷ **DEVISE PLAN** To calculate the increase in the spring's potential energy, I can use Eq. 9.23, $\Delta U_{spring} = \frac{1}{2}k(x - x_0)^2$. In part *b* of Exercise 14.5, I determined the ratio of energy change to mass change. I can use this ratio to convert the spring's energy change to a mass change.

❸ **EXECUTE PLAN** The spring has been compressed by an amount $x - x_0 = 50$ mm $- 25$ mm $= 2.5 \times 10^{-2}$ m. From Eq. 9.23, I get $\Delta U_{spring} = \frac{1}{2}(0.16$ N/m$)(2.5 \times 10^{-2}$ m$)^2 = 5.0 \times 10^{-5}$ J. In Exercise 14.5*b*, I found that the ratio of energy change to mass change is 8.98×10^{16} J/kg, so the change in the spring's mass is $(5.0 \times 10^{-5}$ J$)/(8.98 \times 10^{16}$ J/kg$) = 5.6 \times 10^{-22}$ kg. ✔

❹ **EVALUATE RESULT** The change in the spring's mass is much too small to be measured. That is reassuring because in my experience I've never been able to observe any change in mass when compressing springs.

Exercise 14.5 and Example 14.6 show that the ratio of mass change to energy change is very small; that is, a tiny amount of mass corresponds to an enormous amount of energy. **Table 14.1** lists the fractional changes in mass for a number of changes in state (corresponding to changes in energy). As a rule of thumb, nuclear reactions release an amount of energy corresponding to about 10^{-3} of the mass; chemical reactions release an amount of energy corresponding to about 10^{-9} of the mass. As you can see from the table, other processes cause even smaller fractional changes in mass. For example, no one has been able to

Table 14.1 Changes in energy and fractional mass changes due to changes in state

System before	System after	Energy change (J)	Fractional change in system's mass
1-kg book and Earth	1-kg book and Earth separated by an additional 1 m	10	2×10^{-41}
cup of tea	cup of tea heated by 10 °C	4000	5×10^{-13}
1 mole of H_2 molecules	2 moles of H atoms	5×10^5	3×10^{-9}
p + D	^{3}He	9×10^{-13}	2×10^{-3}

observe the change in mass that occurs when we heat a cup of tea because this change is on the order of 10^{-13} kg, much too small to measure.

In Chapter 13 we established that mass and inertia are equivalent at everyday speeds. Consequently increasing the internal energy of an object at rest must increase not only the object's mass but also its inertia. So, whereas mass depends on internal energy only, inertia depends on both internal energy and kinetic energy:

Increasing the energy $E = K + E_{int}$ of a system increases its inertia. The increase in inertia is the same whether the added energy goes into kinetic energy K, internal energy E_{int}, or a combination of the two.

Table 14.2 summarizes the correspondence between matter and energy. The mass and internal energy of a system are invariants—that is, independent of the motion of observer and system relative to each other. Inertia and

energy are not invariants. In addition, energy is a conserved quantity. In the second part of this chapter, we'll use the conservation principles to derive quantitative expressions for the relationships between mass and internal energy and between inertia and energy.

Table 14.2 Matter and energy

Quantity	Invariant?	Conserved?	Related to
E_{int}	yes	no	mass
E	no	yes	inertia

14.13 Do the inertia and mass of the system increase, decrease, or remain the same when (*a*) an elementary particle is accelerated (system: particle) and (*b*) an elementary particle slams into a metal target (system: particle and target)?

Self-quiz

1. Imagine you are at the origin of Figure 14.6, where, as in Exercise 14.2, a light pulse takes 1 s to travel one grid unit. When your clock reads 12:00:05, what do you observe as the reading on the clocks at positions $(3, 0)$ and $(0, 2)$?

2. Which of the following statements are true when we compare a moving light clock and one at rest in the Earth reference frame? (*i*) The signal in the moving clock travels a greater distance during one cycle. (*ii*) The signal in the moving clock takes more time to complete one cycle. (*iii*) The cycle on the moving clock is longer. (*iv*) Time on the moving clock runs more slowly. (*v*) The moving clock completes an hour first.

3. Standing near the finish line at a race track, you measure the time interval between two cars as they cross the finish line. Is the time interval between these events as measured by the driver in the second car the same as, greater than, or less than the time interval you measure?

4. A particle of mass m is moving at speed v toward an identical particle that is at rest in the Earth reference frame. Is the inertia of the particles in their zero-momentum reference frame greater than, equal to, or less than m?

5. An observer on the ground observes a car moving past a gate and notes that the car is longer than the gate. For an observer in the car, which of the following are possibilities? (*i*) The gate is longer than the car. (*ii*) The gate is the same length as the car. (*iii*) The gate is shorter than the car.

Answers

1. Because it takes 1 s for light to travel one grid unit, it takes 3 s for the clock at $(3, 0)$ to be seen by you. Its time is thus 3 s earlier than that of the origin clock, or 12:00:02. The light from the clock at $(0, 2)$ takes 2 s to reach you, and so that clock reads 12:00:03.

2. All but (*v*) are true. Because the signal in the moving clock travels an equal vertical distance but a greater horizontal distance, the overall distance is greater. At constant speed, a greater distance requires a longer time interval. This longer time interval makes the duration of the clock's cycle longer, and the clock runs slow. If the clock runs slow, the hour passes less quickly.

3. Because you measure both events at the same position, you obtain the proper time interval between them. The driver in the second car moves relative to you, and so, according to the argument used in the solution to Example 14.4, measures a longer time interval.

4. In the zero-momentum reference frame both particles are moving, and therefore each particle has an inertia that is greater than the mass m.

5. Because moving objects contract in the direction of motion, the gate gets shorter to the observer in the car. Because the gate is shorter than the car in the Earth reference frame, it is also shorter in the car's reference frame. Thus only (*iii*) is possible.

14.5 Time dilation

Let us determine how the period of a light clock depends on the motion of the clock relative to the observer. The time interval between the instant a light signal is emitted at the bottom of a light clock and the instant the signal returns to the bottom is the period of that clock. In the reference frame of observer A in **Figure 14.24a**, the clock of height h is at rest, and so the period measured by observer A is $T_A = 2h/c_0$. In the reference frame of observer B, the clock is in motion and the signal follows the inverted-V path shown in Figure 14.24b. Because this path is longer than $2h$, the period T_B measured by observer B is longer than T_A.

During one round trip of its light signal, the clock moves a distance vT_B to the right in B's reference frame. From the right triangle in Figure 14.24b, we see that the distance d traveled by the signal during that time interval must satisfy

$$\left(\frac{d}{2}\right)^2 = h^2 + \left(v\frac{T_B}{2}\right)^2. \tag{14.1}$$

Because the signal travels at speed c_0, we have $d = c_0 T_B$. Substituting this relationship into Eq. 14.1 and multiplying the result by 4 to remove any fractions, we get

$$(c_0 T_B)^2 = 4h^2 + (vT_B)^2 \tag{14.2}$$

or

$$(c_0^2 - v^2)T_B^2 = 4h^2. \tag{14.3}$$

Dividing both sides of this equation by c_0^2 gives

$$\frac{c_0^2 - v^2}{c_0^2} T_B^2 = \frac{4h^2}{c_0^2} = T_A^2, \tag{14.4}$$

where we have used $T_A = 2h/c_0$. Rearranging terms, we get

$$T_B = \sqrt{\frac{c_0^2}{c_0^2 - v^2}}\, T_A = \frac{1}{\sqrt{1 - v^2/c_0^2}}\, T_A. \tag{14.5}$$

Because the factor in front of T_A is greater than 1 for $0 < v < c_0$, we see that $T_B > T_A$, as expected.

Figure 14.24 The period of a light clock moving relative to an observer is determined by the time interval it takes the light signal to travel the two diagonal distances $d/2$.

(*a*) **Reference frame of observer A:** clock at rest relative to observer

(*b*) **Reference frame of observer B:** clock moving relative to observer

Figure 14.25 As the speed v at which any object travels approaches c_0, the Lorentz factor γ approaches infinity. Up to a speed of about $0.1c_0$, γ is very close to 1.

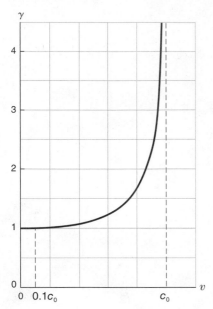

Table 14.3 Gamma factor

v/c_0	γ
0	1
0.1	1.005
0.5	1.15
0.9	2.3
0.98	5.0
0.99	7.1
0.999	22.4
0.9999	70.71
0.99999	223.61
0.999999	707.107

The factor on the right side of Eq. 14.5 is often represented by the Greek letter gamma, γ, and called the **Lorentz factor:**

$$\gamma \equiv \frac{1}{\sqrt{1 - v^2/c_0^2}}. \tag{14.6}$$

This factor is a measure of how pronounced relativistic deviations are from our everyday notions of time and space. At ordinary speeds, $v \ll c_0$, and so $\gamma \approx 1$; at high speeds, γ approaches infinity, as shown in **Figure 14.25**.

Table 14.3 lists values of γ for some values of v/c_0. Note that γ remains very close to 1 even up to very high speeds. For example, an object traveling at $0.1c_0$ could circle Earth in about 1 s, and yet the deviation of γ from 1 is less than 1%, meaning that the effects of time dilation are very small. As a rule of thumb, we can say that for speeds less than $0.1c_0$ the deviation of γ from 1 is negligible. We'll refer to speeds less than $0.1c_0$ as *nonrelativistic speeds* and speeds greater than $0.1c_0$ as *relativistic speeds*.

Conversely, we can obtain the ratio v^2/c_0^2 from γ by first squaring Eq. 14.6:

$$\gamma^2 = \frac{1}{1 - v^2/c_0^2} \tag{14.7}$$

and then inverting this equation:

$$\frac{1}{\gamma^2} = 1 - \frac{v^2}{c_0^2}, \tag{14.8}$$

so

$$\frac{v^2}{c_0^2} = 1 - \frac{1}{\gamma^2}. \tag{14.9}$$

For nonrelativistic speeds, we can approximate γ as*

$$\gamma = \frac{1}{\sqrt{1 - v^2/c_0^2}} \approx 1 + \tfrac{1}{2}\frac{v^2}{c_0^2} \quad (v/c_0 \ll 1), \tag{14.10}$$

so

$$\gamma - 1 \approx \tfrac{1}{2}\frac{v^2}{c_0^2} \quad \text{(within two significant digits when } v < 0.1c_0.) \tag{14.11}$$

As you will see shortly, this equation is useful for calculating γ when $v < 0.1c_0$.

14.14 Taking each motion to be relative to the Earth reference frame, calculate γ for (*a*) a car moving at 30 m/s, (*b*) an airplane moving at 250 m/s, (*c*) a spacecraft moving at 10,000 m/s, and (*d*) an electron moving at $0.60c_0$.

Using the factor γ, we can simplify Eq. 14.5 to

$$T_B = \gamma T_A. \tag{14.12}$$

---

*From the binomial expansion $\left[\sqrt{1 + \epsilon}\,\right]^{-1} = 1 - \tfrac{1}{2}\epsilon + \tfrac{3}{8}\epsilon^2 + \cdots$ (see Appendix B). For small ϵ, we can ignore terms of order ϵ^2 and higher.

This equation provides an exact quantitative expression for time dilation. In words, the period T_B measured by an observer in motion relative to the clock is lengthened by a factor γ relative to the period T_A measured by an observer at rest relative to the clock. Note that T_B is not a proper time interval between the emission of successive light signals because these events occur at different positions in the reference frame of the observer. Only an observer at rest relative to the clock can measure the proper time interval between the emission of successive light signals. To this observer, the clock is at rest, and so the light signal travels a distance $2h$ between successive emission events. The proper time interval between the emission of successive signals in the clock is thus $2h/c_0$.

Time dilation does not occur in light clocks only. As we pointed out in Section 14.3, the principle of relativity tells us that any clock should exhibit the same effects. Time dilation affects the measurement of the time interval between any two events and therefore time itself. Generalizing Eq. 14.12, we can say that the time intervals between two events as measured by two observers in motion relative to each other are related by

$$\Delta t_v = \gamma \Delta t_{proper}, \tag{14.13}$$

where Δt_{proper} is the time interval measured by an observer for whom both events occur at the same position, Δt_v is the time interval between the same two events measured by a second observer moving at speed v relative to the first observer, and γ is the factor given by Eq. 14.6.

Note that Eq. 14.13 involves two observers measuring the time interval Δt between two events. When applying this equation, you must therefore always begin by identifying the two events and the two observers. Next you should determine which observer measures the proper time interval and what speed v to use in Eq. 14.13. As an example, consider **Figure 14.26**. In Figure 14.26a two events occur at the same position relative to observer A, and so A measures the proper time interval Δt_{proper}. Observer B moves at speed v_{AB} relative to A, and so she measures a time interval $\Delta t_v = \gamma \Delta t_{proper}$, where the v in γ is equal to v_{AB}. In Figure 14.26b two events occur at the same position relative to B, and so B measures the proper time interval Δt_{proper}. Observer A moves at speed $v_{BA} = v_{AB}$ relative to B and so he measures a time interval $\Delta t_v = \gamma \Delta t_{proper}$, where the v in γ is equal to v_{AB}.

Figure 14.26 Proper time measurements.

(a) Events occur at same position in A's reference frame

(b) Events occur at same position in B's reference frame

A measures Δt_{proper} between events.

B measures Δt_v between events, with $v = v_{AB}$.

A measures Δt_v between events, with $v = v_{AB}$.

B measures Δt_{proper} between events.

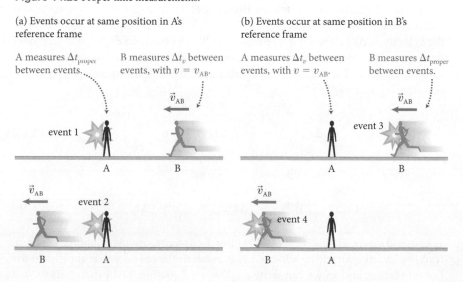

Example 14.7 Flight delay

You are on an airplane flying at a steady 250 m/s at cruising altitude. At noon the pilot announces that you are passing over the center of London and exactly 6.0 h later, according to your watch, comes on the address system to say that you are passing over Abu-Dhabi. (*a*) Do observers on the ground measure a longer, equal, or shorter time interval between these two events? (*b*) Is the difference between the time interval measured on the ground and that measured by your watch detectable?

❶ GETTING STARTED This problem involves two reference frames (the Earth reference frame and the reference frame of the plane) and two events (plane passing over London and plane passing over Abu-Dhabi). I denote the plane passing over the city as event 1 and the plane passing over Abu-Dhabi as event 2. The time interval between these events is 6.0 h in the reference frame of the plane.

❷ DEVISE PLAN The proper time interval is the shortest time interval between the events, and so this problem boils down to determining who measures the proper time interval. Once I have determined that, I can use Eq. 14.13 to determine the time interval measured by the ground observers and determine the difference between the two intervals.

❸ EXECUTE PLAN (*a*) Relative to the plane, events 1 and 2 occur at the same position. Therefore the 3.0-h time interval I measure is the proper time interval in the plane reference

frame. The ground observers move at 250 m/s relative to my reference frame, and so, according to Eq. 14.13, they measure a longer time interval. ✔

(*b*) To determine the difference, I subtract the proper time interval from both sides of Eq. 14.13:

$$\Delta t_v - \Delta t_{\text{proper}} = \gamma \Delta t_{\text{proper}} - \Delta t_{\text{proper}} = (\gamma - 1)\Delta t_{\text{proper}}.$$

From Eq. 14.11 I have

$$\gamma - 1 \approx \frac{1}{2}\frac{v^2}{c_0^2} = \frac{(250 \text{ m/s})^2}{2(3.00 \times 10^8 \text{ m/s})^2} = 3.47 \times 10^{-13}.$$

The difference in the time intervals is thus $(3.47 \times 10^{-13})(6.0 \text{ h})$ $(3600 \text{ s}/1 \text{ h}) = 7.5 \times 10^{-9}$ s, which is orders of magnitude smaller than can be detected with ordinary clocks. ✔

❹ EVALUATE RESULT That the difference in time intervals is too small to be easily measured is reassuring in two ways. First, from experience I know that my watch doesn't stop telling the correct time while flying (other than time zone adjustments). Second, the speed of the airplane is just a small fraction of the speed of light $(250 \text{ m/s})/(3.00 \times 10^8 \text{ m/s}) \approx 10^{-6}$, and so, for all practical purposes, $\gamma = 1$.

Figure 14.27 Observer B can determine the proper time interval between any pair of events by measuring the time interval between them and the distance separating them.

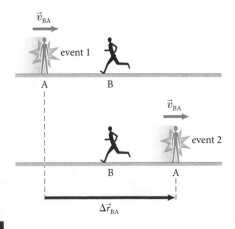

Reference frame of observer B

Let's examine Figure 14.26*a* from observer B's point of view and see if there is any way that B can determine the proper time interval between the two events without the need to refer to observer A's reference frame. In B's reference frame, the events occur at two locations (**Figure 14.27**). Let's choose the *x* axis such that we can denote A's displacement in B's reference frame by Δx. Relative to B, A moves at velocity $\vec{v}_{\text{BA}}$. If B measures a time interval Δt between the two events, then the *x* component of A's displacement is

$$\Delta x = v_{\text{BA}x}\Delta t = v_{\text{BA}x}\gamma\Delta t_{\text{proper}}, \tag{14.14}$$

where we have used Eq. 14.13 to convert Δt to the proper time interval between the events. Equation 14.14 relates the proper time interval to measurements taken entirely in B's reference frame (Δx and Δt), but the equation also contains the velocity of A's reference frame relative to B. To obtain an expression that does not contain this velocity requires a bit of algebraic manipulation on the expression $(c_0\Delta t_{\text{proper}})^2$. We begin by multiplying and dividing this quantity by γ^2, substituting Eq. 14.8 for $1/\gamma^2$:

$$(c_0\Delta t_{\text{proper}})^2 = \gamma^2(c_0\Delta t_{\text{proper}})^2\left(1 - \frac{v^2}{c_0^2}\right). \tag{14.15}$$

Multiplying out the term in parentheses, we get

$$(c_0\Delta t_{\text{proper}})^2 = c_0^2\gamma^2(\Delta t_{\text{proper}})^2 - v^2\gamma^2(\Delta t_{\text{proper}})^2. \tag{14.16}$$

Because $\Delta t = \gamma\Delta t_{\text{proper}}$ (Eq. 14.13), the first term on the right is equal to $(c_0\Delta t)^2$. The magnitude of velocity $\vec{v}_{\text{BA}}$ is equal to the speed v that appears in the Lorentz factor, and so we can write $v_{\text{BA}x}^2 = v^2$. Equation 14.14 then tells us that the second term on the right in Eq. 14.16 is equal to $(\Delta x)^2$, and so we can rewrite this equation as

$$(c_0 \Delta t_{\text{proper}})^2 = (c_0 \Delta t)^2 - (\Delta x)^2. \tag{14.17}$$

Note that the right side of this expression contains only measurements made in B's reference frame: the time interval Δt and the spatial separation Δx of the events. The quantity $c_0 \Delta t$ represents the distance traveled by a light signal in the time interval between the events. The quantity

$$s^2 \equiv (c_0 \Delta t)^2 - (\Delta x)^2 \tag{14.18}$$

is called the **space-time interval** between two events. Because both terms on the right in Eq. 14.18 have units m^2, we see that s^2 represents a distance squared.

Depending on how $c_0 \Delta t$ compares to Δx, we can distinguish between different types of event pairs. When the distance $c_0 \Delta t$ traveled by a light signal in the time interval between the events is greater than the distance between the events, $(c_0 \Delta t)^2 > (\Delta x)^2$, and Eq. 14.18 tells us that $s^2 > 0$. For such a pair of events, there is an inertial reference frame for which the two events occur at the same position ($\Delta x = 0$) and the events are separated in time only. For this reason the space-time interval of a pair of events for which $s^2 > 0$ is said to be *timelike*. A clock in the reference frame in which the two events occur at the same position measures the proper time interval Δt_{proper} between the events and uniquely determines their sequence in time. Because the speed of light c_0 and the proper time interval Δt_{proper} between two events have definite values, any observer who measures the distance and time interval between the two events must obtain the same space-time interval $s^2 = (c_0 \Delta t_{\text{proper}})^2$ between them. In other words, the space-time interval is an invariant, even though neither Δx nor Δt is an invariant.

In a reference frame where the two events do not occur at the same position, $\Delta x > 0$. When $s^2 > 0$, Eq. 14.17 tells us that, for any reference frame in which $\Delta x > 0$, the time interval Δt between the events is greater than Δt_{proper}, as we concluded earlier. When Δt_{proper} is positive, Δt must be positive in all reference frames, and so a sequence of events that has a timelike space-time interval is the same in all inertial reference frames.

When the distance $c_0 \Delta t$ traveled by a light signal in the time interval between the events is less than the distance Δx between them, Eq. 14.18 tells us that $s^2 < 0$. For such a pair of events, there is no inertial reference frame for which the two events occur at the same position and therefore the events have no proper time interval. There is, however, a reference frame for which the events are simultaneous ($\Delta t = 0$) and separated in space only: $(\Delta x)^2 = -s^2$. The space-time interval for a pair of events for which $s^2 < 0$ is therefore said to be *spacelike*. In any other reference frame, the events are not simultaneous, and we cannot uniquely determine their sequence. Depending on the reference frame, Δt can be positive, zero, or negative, and so either event may precede the other.

When two events are exactly separated by the distance that light travels in the time interval between them, $s^2 = 0$ and the space-time interval is said to be *lightlike*. When you look at a source of light (your desk lamp or a star, say), the emission of the light and your observation of that light are separated by a lightlike space-time interval.

Because the space-time interval s^2 is an invariant, it is timelike, spacelike, or lightlike regardless of the reference frame. How does the nature of the space-time interval affect the principle of causality we discussed in Chapter 1? To distinguish cause and effect, it is necessary to determine the sequence of events. For a pair of events that have a timelike space-time interval ($s^2 > 0$), there is a reference frame in which we can study both events at the same position, and so we can determine their sequence with certainty and establish their causal relationship. For a pair of events that has a spacelike space-time interval ($s^2 < 0$), we cannot ascertain the time order of events and therefore cannot determine any causal relationship. For two events to be causally related, they must be able to interact physically. When $s^2 < 0$, the events occur in such rapid succession that a light signal cannot travel from one event to the other in the time interval between them. Because no information can travel faster than the speed of light, such events cannot interact and so cannot be causally related. Only events that have a timelike space-time interval can be causally related, and for such events the time sequence can be uniquely determined.

14.15 An elementary particle is observed to disintegrate after traveling 120 m in 5.0×10^{-7} s from the location where it was created. How long does the particle exist before disintegrating according to an observer at rest relative to the particle?

14.6 Length contraction

In Section 14.3 we saw that the length of an object measured by an observer moving relative to the object is shortened. Remember also that time dilation and length contraction are two manifestations of the same effect. To work out the amount of shortening, we now turn the clocks from Figure 14.24 on their side as in **Figure 14.28**, which shows the clock from the perspective of an observer A at rest relative to the clock and from the perspective of an observer B in motion relative to the clock.

We denote the proper length of the clocks by ℓ_{proper}. Our goal is to see what shortened length ℓ_v observer B obtains. According to A, the period of the clock is

$$T_{\text{A}} = \frac{2\ell_{\text{proper}}}{c_0}. \tag{14.19}$$

The period of the clock measured by B is given by Eq. 14.12: $T_{\text{B}} = \gamma T_{\text{A}}$. This period is the sum of two time intervals: the time interval Δt_{right} during which the light signal travels to the right from source to mirror and the time interval

Figure 14.28 By calculating the distance traveled by the light pulse in the reference frame of the observer moving relative to the clock, we can work out by how much the length of the clock is shortened.

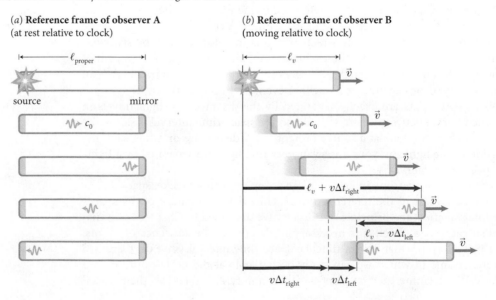

(*a*) **Reference frame of observer A**
(at rest relative to clock)

(*b*) **Reference frame of observer B**
(moving relative to clock)

Δt_{left} during which the signal travels from mirror to source. During Δt_{right}, the clock moves a distance $v\Delta t_{\text{right}}$ as measured by B. The distance traveled by the signal during that time interval is thus $d_{\text{right}} = \ell_v + v\Delta t_{\text{right}}$. Because the signal travels at speed c_0 independent of the motion of the source or the motion of the observer, the distance traveled by the signal in the time interval Δt_{right} must be $d_{\text{right}} = c_0\Delta t_{\text{right}}$. Equating the two expressions for d_{right}, we have

$$c_0\Delta t_{\text{right}} = \ell_v + v\Delta t_{\text{right}}. \tag{14.20}$$

Solving for Δt_{right} yields

$$\Delta t_{\text{right}} = \frac{\ell_v}{c_0 - v}. \tag{14.21}$$

While the signal in the clock returns from the mirror to the source, the clock moves an additional distance $v\Delta t_{\text{left}}$.* The signal therefore travels a distance $d_{\text{left}} = \ell_v - v\Delta t_{\text{left}}$ again as measured by observer B. Because the signal travels at speed c_0 independent of the motion of the source or observer, the distance traveled by the signal in the time interval Δt_{left} must be $d_{\text{left}} = c_0\Delta t_{\text{left}}$. Equating the two expressions for d_{left}, we have

$$c_0\Delta t_{\text{left}} = \ell_v - v\Delta t_{\text{left}}. \tag{14.22}$$

Solving for Δt_{left} yields

$$\Delta t_{\text{left}} = \frac{\ell_v}{c_0 + v}. \tag{14.23}$$

Combining this result with Eq. 14.21, we get for the sum of the two time intervals

$$T_{\text{B}} = \Delta t_{\text{right}} + \Delta t_{\text{left}}$$

$$= \ell_v\left(\frac{1}{c_0 - v} + \frac{1}{c_0 + v}\right). \tag{14.24}$$

Combining terms, we obtain

$$T_{\text{B}} = \frac{2\ell_v c_0}{c_0^2 - v^2}. \tag{14.25}$$

Dividing the numerator and denominator on the right by c_0^2, we get

$$T_{\text{B}} = \frac{2\ell_v}{c_0}\left(\frac{1}{1 - v^2/c_0^2}\right) = \frac{2\ell_v}{c_0}\gamma^2, \tag{14.26}$$

where we have substituted γ^2 from Eq. 14.7. Substituting this expression for T_{B} and Eq. 14.19 for T_{A} into Eq. 14.12, we get

$$\frac{2\ell_v}{c_0}\gamma^2 = \gamma\frac{2\ell_{\text{proper}}}{c_0} \tag{14.27}$$

or

$$\ell_v = \frac{\ell_{\text{proper}}}{\gamma}. \tag{14.28}$$

---

*The subscript *left* refers to the motion of the light, not the motion of the clock.

Figure 14.29 Length measurements.

(a) Object is at rest in A's reference frame

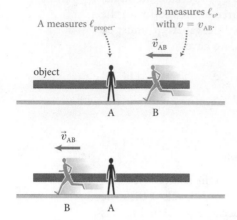

(b) Object moves with observer B

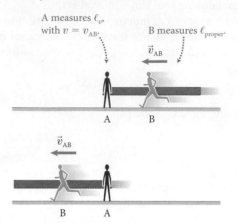

Because $\gamma > 1$, the measured length ℓ_v of the clock moving relative to us (or any other object moving relative to us) is shorter than its proper length ℓ_{proper}.

Note that Eq. 14.28 involves two observers measuring the length of an object: observer A at rest relative to the object and observer B in motion relative to it. When applying this equation, you must therefore always begin by identifying (1) the observers and (2) the observer's reference frame, if any, in which the object is at rest. The observer in this reference frame measures the object's proper length. As an example, consider the two observers in **Figure 14.29**. In Figure 14.29*a* the object is at rest in A's reference frame, and so A measures the proper length ℓ_{proper}. Observer B moves at speed v_{AB} relative to A, and so he measures a length $\ell_v = \ell_{\text{proper}}/\gamma$, where the v in γ is equal to v_{AB}. In Figure 14.29*b* the object is at rest relative to B, and so B measures the proper length ℓ_{proper}. Observer A moves at speed $v_{\text{BA}} = v_{\text{AB}}$ relative to B, and so she measures a length $\ell_v = \ell_{\text{proper}}/\gamma$, where the v in γ is equal to v_{AB}.

The Procedure box "Time and length measurements at very high speeds" summarizes how to treat time intervals and distances when dealing with motion at very high speeds.

Procedure: Time and length measurements at very high speeds

At very high speeds, measurements of lengths and time intervals depend on the reference frame. Problems involving objects or observers moving at very high speeds therefore require extra care when we consider lengths and time intervals.

1. Identify each observer or reference frame with a letter and determine in which reference frame each numerical quantity given in the problem statement is measured.
2. If the problem involves any time intervals, identify the events that define that time interval. Determine in which observer's reference frame, if any, the two events occur at the same position. This observer measures the proper time interval between the events (Figure 14.26).
3. Identify any distances or lengths mentioned in the problem. Determine for which observer, if any, the object defining that distance or length remains at rest. This observer measures the proper length (Figure 14.29).
4. Use Eqs. 14.13 and 14.28 to determine the time intervals and lengths in reference frames other than the ones in which the intervals and lengths are given.

Example 14.8 Electron dash

An electron moving at $0.80c_0$ relative to the Earth reference frame travels the 100-m length of a building. What is the length of the building according to an observer moving along with the electron?

❶ GETTING STARTED This problem involves two reference frames: the reference frame of the building (which is the Earth reference frame) and the reference frame of the electron. Although the problem doesn't mention this explicitly, the 100-m length of the building is likely to be the length measured in Earth's reference frame, and so it is the building's proper length. I summarize this information in a table:

	Electron reference frame	Earth reference frame
$v_{electron}$	0	$0.8c_0$
$\ell_{building}$	?	100 m

❷ DEVISE PLAN Equation 14.28 relates the building length measured by the observer in the electron's reference frame to the proper length. I know the building's proper length (100 m) and the speed of the observer relative to the reference frame in which the proper length is measured ($0.80c_0$). I can calculate γ from Eq. 14.6 and then use Eq. 14.28 to obtain the length of the building in the electron's reference frame.

❸ EXECUTE PLAN $\gamma = 1/\sqrt{1 - v^2/c_0^2} = 1/\sqrt{1 - (0.80)^2} = 1.67$, and so $\ell_v = \ell_{building} = (100 \text{ m})/1.67 = 60 \text{ m}.$ ✔

❹ EVALUATE RESULT From our length contraction discussion in Section 14.3, I know that an observer measuring the length of an object that is moving relative to her measures a length shorter than the proper length. In this example, the observer is in the electron's reference frame, and the building being measured is moving relative to that reference frame. Therefore I expect the measured length to be shorter than the proper length.

Example 14.9 Cosmic ray longevity

A proton strikes an air molecule in Earth's atmosphere, creating a muon 6.0 km above the ground. The muon travels toward Earth at nearly c_0 and decays just before reaching the ground. An observer traveling along with the muon determines that it lives for 2.2×10^{-6} s. According to this observer, what is the distance between the ground and the muon at the instant the muon is created?

❶ GETTING STARTED The problem mentions two reference frames: the Earth reference frame and the reference frame of the muon. The altitude is measured in the Earth reference frame, whereas the muon's lifetime is measured in the reference frame of the muon. The muon's lifetime is the time interval between its creation at an altitude of 6.0 km (event 1) and its decay at the ground (event 2). The speed of the muon in the Earth reference frame is (nearly) c_0. I summarize this information in tabular form:

	Earth reference frame	Muon reference frame
Δt		2.2×10^{-6} s (proper time interval)
h_{atm}	6.0 km (proper length)	?
v_{muon}	c_0	

❷ DEVISE PLAN The 6.0-km distance traveled by the muon in the Earth reference frame is the proper length of the atmosphere. To calculate the (contracted) distance traveled by the muon in the muon reference frame, I can use Eq. 14.28, but I first need to determine γ for the motion of the muon. I can determine the time interval between events 1 and 2 in the Earth reference frame by dividing the distance traveled in the Earth reference frame (6.0 km) by the muon speed, which I take to be c_0. This time interval is the lifetime of the muon in the Earth reference frame. Because I know the muon lifetime in the reference frame of the muon (2.2×10^{-6} s), which is the proper time interval, I can use Eq. 14.13 to determine γ.

❸ EXECUTE PLAN The distance traveled in the Earth reference frame is 6.0×10^3 m, and so in this reference frame the time interval between events 1 and 2 is $\Delta t_v = (6.0 \times 10^3 \text{ m})/(3.00 \times 10^8 \text{ m/s}) = 2.0 \times 10^{-5}$ s. In the muon reference frame, the muon is at rest and exists for the proper time interval $\Delta t_{proper} = 2.2 \times 10^{-6}$ s. I can obtain γ from Eq. 14.13:

$$\gamma = \frac{\Delta t_v}{\Delta t_{proper}} = \frac{2.0 \times 10^{-5} \text{ s}}{2.2 \times 10^{-6} \text{ s}} = 9.1.$$

Using this value for γ, I determine the distance ℓ_v traveled by the muon in its reference frame from Eq. 14.28:

$$\ell_v = \frac{\ell_{proper}}{\gamma} = \frac{6.0 \times 10^3 \text{ m}}{9.1} = 6.6 \times 10^2 \text{ m}.$$ ✔

❹ EVALUATE RESULT The muon lifetime in the Earth reference frame is longer than the muon's proper lifetime, as it should be. Because the muon lives longer in the Earth reference frame, it can travel a greater distance (6.0 km instead of 660 m). I can also check my result by considering the situation from the muon's reference frame. In that reference frame, the atmosphere flies by at nearly the speed of light for a time interval corresponding to the muon's proper lifetime, and so $\ell_v = c_0\Delta t_{proper} = (3.00 \times 10^8 \text{ m/s})(2.2 \times 10^{-6} \text{ s}) = 6.6 \times 10^2$ m, which is the result I got.

Figure 14.30 A muon created at the top of the atmosphere is able to reach the ground before decaying—but observers in the Earth reference frame and the muon reference frame would explain this result differently.

(*a*) **Earth reference frame**

Muon reaches ground because its clock runs slow.

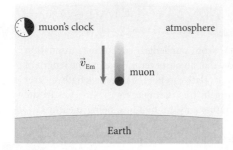

(*b*) **Muon reference frame**

Muon reaches ground because atmosphere moves relative to it and hence is contracted.

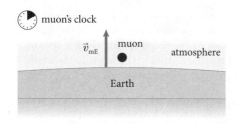

Table 14.4 Muon math

Reference frame	ℓ (km)	Δt (s)
Earth	6.0	2.0×10^{-5}
muon	0.66	2.2×10^{-6}

Figure 14.30 is a graphical representation of Example 14.9. To the observer in the Earth reference frame, the length of the muon's path is equal to the thickness (proper length) of the atmosphere, but the particle's lifetime is lengthened by time dilation (Figure 14.30*a*). Figure 14.30*b* shows the same decay viewed by the observer attached to the muon. To this observer, the muon is at rest and decays in the proper time interval, but the moving atmosphere is contracted. What appears as time dilation of the muon's lifetime to one observer appears as length contraction of the atmosphere to the other (**Table 14.4**). Time dilation and length contraction are thus two manifestations of the same effect.

In Chapter 6 we derived the Galilean transformation equations (Eqs. 6.4 and 6.5) to relate the coordinates of an event e in any two inertial reference frames A and B moving at constant velocity relative to each other. At very high speeds, these equations have to be replaced with equations that take into account the effects of time dilation and length contraction. For two reference frames A and B that have origins that coincide at $t_A = t_B = 0$ and that are moving at constant velocity in the x direction relative to each other, the new equations, called the **Lorentz transformation equations,** are (see Appendix E):

$$t_{Be} = \gamma\left(t_{Ae} - \frac{v_{ABx}}{c_0^2}x_{Ae}\right) \tag{14.29}$$

$$x_{Be} = \gamma(x_{Ae} - v_{ABx}t_{Ae}) \tag{14.30}$$

$$y_{Be} = y_{Ae} \tag{14.31}$$

$$z_{Be} = z_{Ae}. \tag{14.32}$$

At nonrelativistic speeds, these equations reduce to the Galilean transformation equations.

From the Lorentz transformation equations, we obtain that the x component of the velocity of an object o in reference frame A, v_{Aox}, is related to that in reference frame B, v_{Box}, by the expression (see Appendix E)

$$v_{Box} = \frac{v_{Aox} - v_{ABx}}{1 - \frac{v_{ABx}}{c_0^2}v_{Aox}}. \tag{14.33}$$

For nonrelativistic speeds, the denominator is approximately equal to 1 and we obtain the usual addition of velocities: $v_{Box} = v_{Aox} - v_{ABx}$ (see Eq. 6.9).

14.16 A car travels 1.0 km down a straight road at 100 km/h. How much shorter is the road in the car's reference frame?

14.7 Conservation of momentum

In Chapter 4 we introduced inertia to account for velocity changes in collisions and took the momentum of a particle to be the product of its inertia and its velocity. This approach led us to conservation of momentum, one of the fundamental principles that we have used throughout this text. In Section 14.4 we found that inertia depends on energy and therefore on speed. Because conservation principles are fundamental and because they embody an appealing simplicity, we would like to preserve them in light of the modifications required by special relativity. To this end, we begin again by taking the momentum of a particle as the product of its inertia and its velocity but this time allowing the inertia to depend on velocity:

$$\vec{p} \equiv m_v\vec{v}. \tag{14.34}$$

The subscript v on the inertia symbol m_v is there to remind us that inertia is no longer an invariant. We now examine what modifications are needed to our concept of inertia to preserve conservation of momentum.

To obtain an expression for m_v, let us look at an elastic collision between two identical particles and require the system to be isolated so that the momentum of the two particles remains constant. The particles are projected at each other at speed u (**Figure 14.31**). Their velocities are equal in magnitude but opposite in direction, both before and after the collision. The position of the center of mass of this system is at the location where the particles collide and it remains at rest. In other words, Figure 14.31 represents the collision viewed from the zero-momentum reference frame. We begin our analysis of this collision by choosing our axes as shown in **Figure 14.32a**.

In the zero-momentum reference frame, the speeds of the particles are the same before and after the collision, and so we gain no information on how inertia depends on speed. Let us therefore consider the same collision from the point of view of an observer A moving parallel to the x axis of Figure 14.32 with a velocity equal to the component of the velocity of particle 1 along the x axis. To this observer, particle 1 moves up and down parallel to the y axis (Figure 14.32b). For convenience, let's denote the event when particle 1 leaves observer A as the *throw* and its return to observer A as the *catch*.

To an observer B moving along the x axis with a velocity equal to the component of the velocity of particle 2 along the x axis, the collision looks exactly the same except that particles 1 and 2 are interchanged (Figure 14.32c).

14.17 In Figure 14.32, is the time interval between the throw and the catch of particle 1 in reference frame A greater than, equal to, or less than the time interval between the throw and the catch of particle 2 in reference frame B?

Note that in all three reference frames only the y components of $\vec{v}_1$ and $\vec{v}_2$ change. Because the observers' motion is always in the x direction, there is no length contraction in the y direction, and so to both observers the particles travel the same distance d in the y direction between throw and catch.

In reference frame A, the y component of the velocities of the two particles have the same magnitudes, but the x components are different. Therefore particles 1 and 2 move at different speeds v_1 and v_2, respectively, and so even though we began by declaring the two particles to be identical, the inertia m_{v1} of particle 1

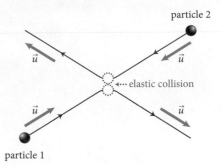

Figure 14.31 Collision between two identical particles as seen in the zero-momentum reference frame.

particle 2

elastic collision

particle 1

Figure 14.32 Analysis of the trajectories in Figure 14.31 from three reference frames, showing our choice of axes.

(a) **Zero-momentum reference frame**

(b) **Observer A's reference frame**

(c) **Observer B's reference frame**

measured in reference frame A must be different from the inertia m_{v2} of particle 2 measured in this frame. We can obtain the ratio of these inertias by requiring the momentum of the two-particle system to remain constant. To this end, let us evaluate the velocity changes caused by the collision in reference frame A. Let the time intervals between the throw and catch of particles 1 and 2 in reference frame A be Δt_{A1} and Δt_{A2}, respectively. The changes in the y component of the velocities in reference frame A are thus

$$\Delta v_{A1y} = -\frac{d}{\Delta t_{A1}} \quad \text{and} \quad \Delta v_{A2y} = \frac{d}{\Delta t_{A2}}. \tag{14.35}$$

The time interval Δt_{A1} measured by observer A between the throw and catch of particle 1 in reference frame A is the proper time interval between these two events because they occur at the same position according to observer A: $\Delta t_{A1} = \Delta t_{proper}$. The time interval Δt_{A2} observer A measures between the throw and catch of particle 2, however, is not a proper time interval because for observer A these two events occur at different positions (Figure 14.32b).

Relative to observer B, the throw and catch of particle 2 occur at the same position (Figure 14.32c), and so the time interval measured by B is the proper time interval. Because of symmetry, the collision seen by observer A is identical to that seen by observer B, and so the proper time interval measured by A between the throw and catch of particle 1 is equal to the proper time interval measured by B between the throw and catch of particle 2, as you saw in Checkpoint 14.17:

$$\Delta t_{A1} = \Delta t_{B2} = \Delta t_{proper}. \tag{14.36}$$

Equation 14.13, $\Delta t_v = \gamma \Delta t_{proper}$, tells us that if observer B measures the proper time interval between the throw and catch of particle 2, observer A moving relative to B obtains that the time interval between those events is $\gamma \Delta t_{proper}$, where γ depends on the relative velocity of A and B. Therefore

$$\Delta t_{A2} = \gamma \Delta t_{proper}, \tag{14.37}$$

where v in $\gamma = 1/\sqrt{1 - v^2/c^2}$ is the speed of B relative to A: $v = |\vec{v}_{A2x}|$. Substituting Eq. 14.36 into Eq. 14.37 yields $\Delta t_{A2} = \gamma \Delta t_{A1}$, and so Eq. 14.35 becomes

$$\Delta v_{A1y} = -\frac{d}{\Delta t_{A1}} \quad \text{and} \quad \Delta v_{A2y} = \frac{d}{\gamma \Delta t_{A1}}. \tag{14.38}$$

Because the two-particle system is isolated, the sum of the particles' momentum changes in reference frame A must add to zero:

$$\Delta p_{A1y} + \Delta p_{A2y} = m_{v1} \Delta v_{A1y} + m_{v2} \Delta v_{A2y}$$

$$= -m_{v1} \frac{d}{\Delta t_{A1}} + m_{v2} \frac{d}{\gamma \Delta t_{A1}} = 0, \tag{14.39}$$

which means that in reference frame A,

$$m_{v2} = \gamma m_{v1}. \tag{14.40}$$

According to observer A, the inertia of particle 2 is greater than the inertia of particle 1.

14.18 (a) According to observer A in Figure 14.32, which particle is moving faster? (b) Does A conclude that the inertia of a particle increases or decreases with speed? (c) Answer these two questions for observer B.

Equation 14.40 gives us the relationship between the inertias of two particles moving relative to each other and relative to us. To determine the relationship between the inertia of a particle moving relative to us and that of an identical particle at rest relative to us, consider the limit in which the y components of the velocities are very small. In that case, particle 1 in Figure 14.32b is virtually at rest in reference frame A, $v_{A1} \approx 0$, and particle 2 moves horizontally along with observer B at speed $v_{A2} \approx |\vec{v}_{A2x}| = v$. When the particle is at rest relative to us, its inertia and mass are equivalent and so $m_v \approx m$, where m is the mass of the particle. If we denote the inertia of the moving particle by m_v, Eq. 14.40 shows us how a particle's **inertia** m_v, which depends on speed, is related to its mass m, which is an invariant:

$$m_v = \gamma m. \qquad (14.41)$$

The first thing to note is that for speeds up to about $0.1c_0$, $\gamma \approx 1$, and so mass and inertia are virtually indistinguishable, in agreement with what we established in Chapter 13. As the speed approaches c_0, however, m_v increases to infinity. Because inertia is a measure of an object's resistance to being accelerated, m_v approaching infinity means it becomes more and more difficult to speed up the particle as its speed approaches c_0. We therefore must conclude that no object or particle that has mass can be accelerated to speed c_0.

Exercise 14.10 Sluggish electron

By what factor does the inertia of an electron increase (a) as the electron is accelerated to $\frac{1}{3}c_0$ and (b) as its speed is increased by another 20%? (c) Does the mass of the electron change as it is accelerated?

SOLUTION From Eq. 14.41, I know that the factor by which the inertia increases is $m_v/m = \gamma$. (a) At $\frac{1}{3}c_0$, $\gamma = 1/\sqrt{1 - (\frac{1}{3})^2} = 1.06$. The inertia increases by 6%. ✔

(b) Increasing the speed by another 20% means adding

$$\tfrac{1}{5}\left(\tfrac{1}{3}c_0\right) = \tfrac{1}{15}c_0$$

to the speed $\frac{1}{3}c_0$, giving

$$v = \tfrac{1}{3}c_0 + \tfrac{1}{15}c_0 = \tfrac{2}{5}c_0$$

$$\gamma = \frac{1}{\sqrt{1 - (\frac{2}{5})^2}} = 1.09.$$

The inertia of the electron increases by another 3%. ✔

(c) No. Mass is an invariant. Thus the mass of an object is independent of the motion of either the observer or the object. ✔

14.19 To what fraction of c_0 must an electron at rest in the Earth reference frame be accelerated in order for its inertia to increase by a factor of 1000?

Now that we have an expression for the inertia of a moving particle (Eq. 14.41), we can obtain an expression for the particle's momentum in terms of its mass and velocity. Substituting Eq. 14.41 into Eq. 14.34 gives

$$\vec{p} = \gamma m\vec{v}. \qquad (14.42)$$

Unlike the expression for momentum you learned in Chapter 4, $\vec{p} = m\vec{v}$, Eq. 14.42 does not show the momentum increasing linearly with increasing velocity. At ordinary speeds, Eq. 14.42 reduces to the familiar form $\vec{p} = m\vec{v}$. As the speed approaches c_0, the momentum increases rapidly to infinity (**Figure 14.33**). Experiments such as the one described in the next example have conclusively shown that Eq. 14.42 correctly accounts for the momentum of a particle at all speeds up to c_0.

Figure 14.33 As the speed of a particle approaches c_0, the magnitude of its momentum approaches infinity. Up to a speed of about $0.1c_0$, the magnitude of the momentum is very close to mv.

QUANTITATIVE TOOLS

Example 14.11 Fast collision

A fast-moving electron collides head-on with a proton moving at $0.60c_0$ as measured in the Earth reference frame. What is the electron's initial speed if the two particles combine to form a system that after the collision is at rest in the Earth reference frame? The mass of the proton is 1836 times that of the electron.

❶ **GETTING STARTED** I begin by making a sketch showing the electron-proton system before and after the collision (**Figure 14.34**). I choose the positive x axis to be in the initial direction of motion of the electron. I can consider the electron-proton system to be isolated, and so the initial momentum of the system must be equal to the final momentum (which is zero).

Figure 14.34

initial   final

$v_{ex,i} = ?$ $v_{px,i} = -0.60c_0$

❷ **DEVISE PLAN** I can use Eq. 14.42 to calculate the initial momentum of each particle and then set the sum of these momenta equal to zero. The resulting expression contains four quantities: the unknown initial velocity component $v_{ex,i}$ of the electron, the initial velocity component $v_{px,i}$ of the proton ($-0.60c_0$), the mass m_p of the proton, and the mass m_e of the electron. Because I am given that $m_p/m_e = 1836$, I can solve for the unknown initial velocity of the electron.

❸ **EXECUTE PLAN** The initial momentum of the system must be zero, so

$$p_{px,i} + p_{ex,i} = \gamma_{p,i}\, m_p v_{px,i} + \gamma_{e,i}\, m_e v_{ex,i} = 0, \qquad (1)$$

where I have added subscripts to the Lorentz factors to keep the factor for the proton separate from the factor for the electron. Dividing the two terms containing γ in Eq. 1 by m_e, and using Eq. 14.6 to write out the Lorentz factors, I can rewrite Eq. 1 as

$$\frac{m_p}{m_e}\, \frac{v_{px,i}}{\sqrt{1 - v_{px,i}^2/c_0^2}} = -\frac{v_{ex,i}}{\sqrt{1 - v_{ex,i}^2/c_0^2}}.$$

When I square both sides and then substitute the values for the mass ratio and the speed of the proton, I get

$$(1836)^2\, \frac{(-0.60c_0)^2}{1 - (-0.60)^2} = \frac{v_{ex,i}^2}{1 - (v_{ex,i}/c_0)^2},$$

which I can solve for $v_{ex,i}$:

$$v_{ex,i} = (1 + 5.3 \times 10^{-7})^{-1/2} c_0 = 0.99999974\, c_0. ✔$$

I show eight significant digits because the 1 in the above expression is exact (infinite number of significant digits) and so the sum $1 + 5.3 \times 10^{-7}$ is known to the eighth decimal place (1.00000053).

❹ **EVALUATE RESULT** I note that this speed is close to c_0 (but not greater than or equal to it). The fact that the electron needs to travel at such a high speed is not surprising because the proton's mass is nearly 2000 times that of the electron.

✋ **14.20** In Example 14.11, (a) is the collision elastic, inelastic, or totally inelastic (see Section 5.1)? (b) How fast would the electron have to move if the expression for momentum were $\vec{p} = m\vec{v}$ instead of Eq. 14.42?

14.8 Conservation of energy

Now we turn our attention to energy. Suppose we accelerate a particle from rest to a speed approaching c_0.* To determine the increase in its kinetic energy, let us calculate the work done on the particle. From Chapter 9, we know that the work done on the particle is given by Eq. 9.22:

$$W = \int_{x_i}^{x_f} F(x)\,dx = \int_{x_i}^{x_f} \frac{dp}{dt}\,dx, \qquad (14.43)$$

where we have substituted the definition of force (Eq. 8.4). Substituting $p = \gamma mv$ and noting that the mass m is constant, we can write the integrand in Eq. 14.43 as

$$\frac{dp}{dt}\,dx = \frac{d}{dt}(\gamma mv)\,dx = m\frac{d(\gamma v)}{dt}\,dx. \qquad (14.44)$$

---

*From here on, speeds are assumed to be relative to the Earth reference frame unless stated otherwise.

Note that because γ is a function of v, it varies with time and cannot be pulled out of the differentiation. Using $dx = v\,dt$ and canceling the dt factors, we get

$$\frac{dp}{dt}dx = m\frac{d(\gamma v)}{dt}dx = m\frac{d(\gamma v)}{dt}v\,dt = mv\,d(\gamma v), \qquad (14.45)$$

and so the work done on the particle is

$$W = m\int_i^f v\,d(\gamma v) = m\int_i^f (v^2\,d\gamma + v\gamma\,dv), \qquad (14.46)$$

where we have used the chain rule $d(\gamma v) = \gamma\,dv + v\,d\gamma$ (Appendix B).

The relationship between v^2 and γ is given by Eq. 14.9: $v^2/c_0^2 = 1 - 1/\gamma^2$. Differentiating both sides of Eq. 14.9 with respect to time yields

$$\frac{2v}{c_0^2}\frac{dv}{dt} = 0 - \frac{-2}{\gamma^3}\frac{d\gamma}{dt}, \qquad (14.47)$$

and then multiplying both sides by $\frac{1}{2}c_0^2\gamma\,dt$ yields

$$\gamma v\,dv = \frac{c_0^2}{\gamma^2}d\gamma. \qquad (14.48)$$

From Eq. 14.8, $1/\gamma^2 = 1 - v^2/c_0^2$, we can say

$$\frac{1}{\gamma^2} = \frac{c_0^2 - v^2}{c_0^2} \quad \text{and} \quad \frac{c_0^2}{\gamma^2} = c_0^2 - v^2, \qquad (14.49)$$

and so c_0^2/γ^2 in Eq. 14.48 can be replaced by $c_0^2 - v^2$, yielding $\gamma v\,dv = (c_0^2 - v^2)d\gamma$. Substituting this result into Eq. 14.46 and noting that $\gamma - 1$ when $v = 0$ at the lower integration boundary, we get

$$W = m\int_1^\gamma [v^2\,d\gamma + (c_0^2 - v^2)d\gamma] = mc_0^2\int_1^\gamma d\gamma = (\gamma - 1)mc_0^2. \quad (14.50)$$

All of this work done on the particle goes toward increasing its kinetic energy, and so the particle's final **kinetic energy** is

$$K = (\gamma - 1)mc_0^2 = \gamma mc_0^2 - mc_0^2 = m_v c_0^2 - mc_0^2, \qquad (14.51)$$

where we have used the expression for the inertia, $m_v = \gamma m$, from Eq. 14.41.

This expression for the kinetic energy of a particle looks completely different from the expression we have used so far, $K = \frac{1}{2}mv^2$ (see Section 5.2). In particular, as the speed approaches c_0, the particle's kinetic energy becomes infinitely great (**Figure 14.35**). Therefore it would take an infinite amount of energy to accelerate a particle to speed c_0, so c_0 is the limiting speed at which any object can travel relative to another other object.

✋ **14.21** Use Eq. 14.11, $\gamma - 1 \approx 0.5(v^2/c_0^2)$, to show that Eq. 14.51 reduces to the familiar $K = \frac{1}{2}mv^2$ at ordinary speeds ($v \ll c_0$).

Each term on the right of Eq. 14.51 represents a quantity of energy, so Eq. 14.51 gives us the kinetic energy of a particle as the difference between two amounts of energy. In Chapter 5 we defined the energy of a system as the sum of that

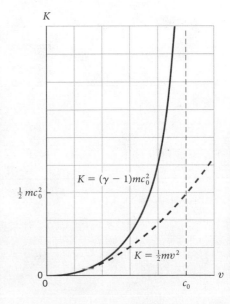

Figure 14.35 As the speed of a particle approaches c_0, its kinetic energy approaches infinity. Up to speeds of about $0.25c_0$, the kinetic energy is very close to $\frac{1}{2}mv^2$.

K

$K = (\gamma - 1)mc_0^2$

$\frac{1}{2}mc_0^2$

$K = \frac{1}{2}mv^2$

system's kinetic and internal energies, $E \equiv K + E_{int}$ (Eq. 5.21), and so we see that the kinetic energy of a system is obtained by subtracting the internal energy from the system's energy:

$$K = E - E_{int}. \tag{14.52}$$

In the right side of Eq. 14.51, note that the first term in the difference is proportional to inertia m_v and the second is proportional to mass m. In Section 14.4 we established that there is a relationship between inertia and energy and a relationship between mass and internal energy. Comparing Eqs. 14.51 and 14.52 thus suggests that the energy is given by

$$E = m_v c_0^2 \tag{14.53}$$

and the **internal energy** is given by

$$E_{int} = m c_0^2. \tag{14.54}$$

The assignment made in Eqs. 14.53 and 14.54 may look like a leap of faith, but in Section 14.4 we found that in a nuclear reaction between a proton and a deuteron, both the internal energy and the mass of the system decrease. Equation 14.54 tells us that the changes in internal energy and mass should be related as

$$\Delta E_{int} = E_{int,f} - E_{int,i}$$
$$= m_f c_0^2 - m_i c_0^2 = \Delta m c_0^2, \tag{14.55}$$

or $\Delta E_{int}/\Delta m = c_0^2$. The experimental data show that the ratio $\Delta E_{int}/\Delta m = c_0^2$ is $8.98 \times 10^{16} \text{ m}^2/\text{s}^2$ (see Example 14.5), which is precisely c_0^2, confirming Eq. 14.54. The term E_{int} in Eq. 14.54 thus represents the energy that corresponds to *all* of the mass of the particle.

All forms of internal energy we have discussed so far require an arbitrary choice of reference point (see, for example, Eq. 7.21), and so we usually considered only differences in internal energy. Equation 14.54, however, provides us with a measure of internal energy that does not depend on any choice of reference point. What is more, we can calculate E_{int} from the mass m, which is a quantity we can determine experimentally.

For example, a proton, as mentioned in Chapter 7, is made up of quarks held together by the strong nuclear interaction. If we add up the values of the masses of these quarks (which are determined from a combination of theory and experiment and known only approximately), we discover that their sum is just 1% of the mass of the proton. The remaining 99% of the mass of the proton must therefore come from the nuclear potential energy that binds the quarks together. Because protons (and neutrons, which also consist of three quarks) are the basic building blocks of all matter, it follows that most of what we consider matter really *is* energy! Even though we have no mathematical expression for nuclear potential energy, we can determine its value from the masses of the proton and the quarks, and the relationship $E_{int} = m c_0^2$.

14.22 (*a*) Draw a simplified energy diagram for the totally inelastic collision between two identical objects moving at speed v toward each other. After the collision, the two objects form a compound object that is at rest. (*b*) Which of the following quantities are constant in the collision: kinetic energy, mass, energy?

Example 14.12 Alpha emission

A uranium nucleus ^{238}U at rest decays to a thorium nucleus ^{234}Th by emitting an alpha particle (which is a helium nucleus ^{4}He):

$$^{238}\text{U} \rightarrow {}^{234}\text{Th} + {}^4\text{He}.$$

The mass of the uranium atom is $m_U = 395.292599 \times 10^{-27}$ kg, the mass of the thorium atom is $m_{Th} = 388.638509 \times 10^{-27}$ kg, and the mass of the helium atom is $m_{He} = 6.646478 \times 10^{-27}$ kg. What is the combined kinetic energy of the fragments?

❶ GETTING STARTED I begin by drawing a simplified energy diagram for the alpha emission (**Figure 14.36**), choosing the

Figure 14.36

uranium nucleus and the fragments as my (closed) system. Because the system is closed, the change in kinetic energy is the negative of the change in internal energy: $\Delta K = -\Delta E_{int}$.

❷ DEVISE PLAN Because the initial kinetic energy is zero, the final kinetic energy of the fragments is equal to $-\Delta E_{int}$. To determine this change in internal energy, I can calculate the change in the mass of the system and then use Eq. 14.55.

❸ EXECUTE PLAN

$$\Delta m = (m_{Th} + m_{He}) - m_U = -7.61 \times 10^{-30} \text{ kg}.$$

Substituting this value into Eq. 14.55 yields

$$\Delta E_{int} = \Delta m c_0^2 = (-7.61 \times 10^{-30} \text{ kg})(3.00 \times 10^8 \text{ m/s})^2$$

$$= -6.85 \times 10^{-13} \text{ J},$$

so the final kinetic energy of the fragments is 6.85×10^{-13} J. ✔

❹ EVALUATE RESULT The answer I obtain is a tiny amount of energy, contrary to my expectations for nuclear energy! However, this is the energy liberated by the nucleus of a single atom. One atom is about 10^{-10} m in diameter, which means a cube of matter 1 mm on a side contains about $[(10^{-3} \text{ m})/(10^{-10} \text{ m})]^3 = 10^{21}$ atoms. If each atom liberates an amount of energy equal to the answer I got, my cube yields $(10^{21})(6.85 \times 10^{-13} \text{ J}) = 7 \times 10^8$ J of energy, which is a very large amount and more in line with what I'd expect.

14.23 An atom in the filament of a light bulb emits energy in the form of light. (*a*) Draw a simplified energy diagram representing this emission. (*b*) Does the mass of the atom increase, decrease, or stay the same? (*c*) Does the inertia of the atom increase, decrease, or stay the same? Assume the atom remains at rest in the Earth reference frame.

We can obtain a useful relationship from our expressions for momentum, $\vec{p} = \gamma m \vec{v}$ (Eq. 14.42), and energy, $E = m_v c_0^2$ (Eq. 14.53), by evaluating the quantity $E^2 - (c_0 p)^2$. Substituting γm for m_v in Eq. 14.53, we have

$$E^2 - (c_0 p)^2 = \gamma^2 m^2 c_0^4 - c_0^2 \gamma^2 m^2 v^2 = \gamma^2 m^2 c_0^2 (c_0^2 - v^2). \quad (14.56)$$

From Eq. 14.49, we see that $c_0^2 - v^2 = c_0^2/\gamma^2$, and so

$$E^2 - (c_0 p)^2 = (m c_0^2)^2. \quad (14.57)$$

The right side of this expression is an invariant, and so its value does not depend on the reference frame. The left side, however, contains the energy E and the momentum magnitude p of the system under consideration, both of which depend on the reference frame! Again, we have constructed an invariant from two quantities that are not invariants themselves. Equation 14.57 tells us that if we measure the energy and the magnitude of the momentum of a system in a certain reference frame and then compute the quantity $E^2 - (c_0 p)^2$, we obtain the same value as the corresponding combination in any other reference frame. In each case, the result is equal to $(m c_0^2)^2$, and so the quantity $E^2 - (c_0 p)^2$ is an invariant.

Energy and momentum are conserved quantities when evaluated with respect to each reference frame, and so for a system that is both isolated and closed, the energy and momentum laws tell us that $E_i = E_f$ and $\vec{p}_i = \vec{p}_f$. We have used these equations extensively to determine E_f and p_f given E_i and p_i. Equation 14.57 relates values of E and p to values of m. Because values of m are known from separate measurements, Eq. 14.57 allows us to eliminate momentum from the problem. The next example and checkpoint illustrate the usefulness of Eq. 14.57.

Example 14.13 Proton collision

Two protons, each of mass $m_p = 1.67 \times 10^{-27}$ kg, collide to produce a particle that has a mass 300 times the mass of each proton. What is the minimum kinetic energy that one of the protons must have in order to create this particle if the other proton is initially at rest?

❶ **GETTING STARTED** I begin by organizing the information in a sketch (**Figure 14.37**). I denote the incoming proton by 1 and the proton initially at rest by 2. The two protons form an isolated, closed system, and so the energy law requires $E_{1i} + E_{2i} = E_f$ and the momentum law requires $\vec{p}_{1i} = \vec{p}_f$ (because $\vec{p}_{2i} = 0$).

Figure 14.37

❷ **DEVISE PLAN** The initial kinetic energy K_{1i} of proton 1 is given by Eq. 14.52, with the internal energy E_{1int} given by Eq. 14.54. I must therefore determine the initial energy E_{1i} of proton 1. I can use Eq. 14.57 to relate the energy E of each particle to its momentum p and then combine this with the energy and momentum law to solve for the initial energy of proton 1.

❸ **EXECUTE PLAN** Applying Eq. 14.57 to proton 1, proton 2, and the final particle, I get

$$E_{1i}^2 - (c_0 p_{1i})^2 = (m_p c_0^2)^2 \qquad (1)$$

$$E_{2i}^2 = (m_p c_0^2)^2 \qquad (2)$$

$$E_f^2 - (c_0 p_f)^2 = (300 m_p c_0^2)^2. \qquad (3)$$

Substituting $E_{1i} + E_{2i} = E_f$ and $p_{1i} = p_f$ into Eq. 3 yields

$$(E_{1i} + E_{2i})^2 - (c_0 p_{1i})^2 = (300 m_p c_0^2)^2.$$

Working out the left side, I get

$$E_{1i}^2 + 2E_{1i}E_{2i} + E_{2i}^2 - (c_0 p_{1i})^2 = E_{1i}^2 - (c_0 p_{1i})^2 + E_{2i}^2 + 2E_{1i}E_{2i}$$

$$= (300 m_p c_0^2)^2,$$

so, after substituting from Eqs. 1 and 2, I have

$$(m_p c_0^2)^2 + (m_p c_0^2)^2 + 2E_{1i}(m_p c_0^2) = (300 m_p c_0^2)^2.$$

Solving for E_{1i} gives

$$E_{1i} = \frac{(300 m_p c_0^2)^2 - 2(m_p c_0^2)^2}{2(m_p c_0^2)} = \tfrac{1}{2}(300^2 - 2)m_p c_0^2. \qquad (4)$$

From Eqs. 14.52 and 14.54, I have $K_{1i} = E_{1i} - m_p c_0^2$, so

$$K_{1i} = \left[\tfrac{1}{2}(300^2 - 2)m_p c_0^2\right] - m_p c_0^2 = \tfrac{1}{2}(300^2 - 4)m_p c_0^2$$

$$= \tfrac{1}{2}(300^2 - 4)(1.67 \times 10^{-27}\text{ kg})(3.00 \times 10^8\text{ m/s})^2$$

$$= 6.76 \times 10^{-6}\text{ J.} ✔$$

❹ **EVALUATE RESULT** My answer is large for a particle that has a mass on the order of 10^{-27} kg. Comparing my result in Eq. 4 with Eq. 14.51, however, I see that $\gamma - 1 = (300^2 - 4)/2$, or $\gamma = 4.5 \times 10^4$, and so the proton has to be accelerated to very close to the speed of light. It is therefore not unreasonable that the energy of the proton is on the order of microjoules.

14.24 In Example 14.13, what is the minimum kinetic energy of each proton if they have the same initial speed and collide head-on?

Chapter Glossary

SI units of physical quantities are given in parentheses.

Event A physical occurrence that takes place at a specific location at a specific instant.

Inertia m_v (kg) A scalar that is a quantitative measure of an object's tendency to resist any change in its velocity. Inertia is related to the object's mass m:

$$m_v = \gamma m. \tag{14.41}$$

At nonrelativistic speeds, the inertia of an object is virtually indistinguishable from the object's mass: $m_v \approx m$.

Internal energy E_{int} (J) Any energy not associated with the motion of an object or system. Internal energy is a quantitative measure of the state of the object or system. The internal energy of an object is an invariant and is related to the mass m of the object by

$$E_{int} = mc_0^2. \tag{14.54}$$

Invariant A quantity whose value does not depend on the choice of reference frame.

Kinetic energy K (J) The energy associated with the motion of an object. The kinetic energy of a particle moving at speed v is

$$K = (\gamma - 1)mc_0^2. \tag{14.51}$$

At nonrelativistic speeds, this expression simplifies to $K = \frac{1}{2}mv^2$.

Length contraction When an object moves at speed v relative to an observer, the observer measures the length ℓ_v of the object in the direction of its motion to be shorter than the proper length ℓ_{proper} of the object:

$$\ell_v = \frac{\ell_{proper}}{\gamma}. \tag{14.28}$$

Lorentz factor γ (unitless) A scalar factor that appears frequently in special relativity:

$$\gamma \equiv \frac{1}{\sqrt{1 - v^2/c_0^2}}. \tag{14.6}$$

This factor is a measure of how pronounced relativistic deviations are from our everyday notions of time and space. At nonrelativistic speeds, $\gamma \approx 1$; at relativistic speeds, $\gamma > 1$ and γ approaches infinity as v approaches c_0.

Lorentz transformation equations The relationships between the coordinates of an event e in two reference frames A and B that are coinciding at $t_A = t_B = 0$ and that are moving at constant velocity $\vec{v}_{AB}$ in the x direction relative to each other:

$$t_{Be} = \gamma\left(t_{Ae} - \frac{v_{ABx}}{c_0^2}x_{Ae}\right) \tag{14.29}$$

$$x_{Be} = \gamma(x_{Ae} - v_{ABx}t_{Ae}) \tag{14.30}$$

$$y_{Be} = y_{Ae} \tag{14.31}$$

$$z_{Be} = z_{Ae}. \tag{14.32}$$

Proper length ℓ_{proper} (m) The length of an object measured by an observer at rest relative to the object.

Proper time interval Δt_{proper} (s) The time interval between two events that occur at the same position (and can therefore be measured by a single clock at rest). An observer measuring the proper time interval between two events records the shortest time interval between those events.

Simultaneity Events are *simultaneous* when they are observed to occur at the same instant in a reference frame made up of a grid of synchronized clocks. Events that are simultaneous in one reference frame need not be simultaneous in a different reference frame.

Space-time interval s^2 (m^2) An invariant given by

$$s^2 \equiv (c_0\Delta t)^2 - (\Delta x)^2. \tag{14.18}$$

For events that have a proper time interval, the space-time interval is equal to the square of the distance traveled by light in the proper time interval.

Speed of light The speed at which light travels. The value of this speed is independent of the motion of the source or observer and is the limiting speed at which any object can travel relative to any other object. In vacuum the speed of light is $c_0 = 299,792,458$ m/s.

Time dilation The effect that causes a clock moving relative to an observer to be measured as running more slowly than an identical clock at rest with respect to that observer. If Δt_{proper} is the proper time interval between two events measured by an observer for whom both events occur at the same position, then the time interval between those events measured by an observer moving at speed v relative to the first observer is

$$\Delta t_v = \gamma\Delta t_{proper}. \tag{14.13}$$

15 Periodic Motion

CONCEPTS

15.1 Periodic motion and energy

15.2 Simple harmonic motion

15.3 Fourier's theorem

15.4 Restoring forces in simple harmonic motion

QUANTITATIVE TOOLS

15.5 Energy of a simple harmonic oscillator

15.6 Simple harmonic motion and springs

15.7 Restoring torques

15.8 Damped oscillations

ny motion that repeats itself at regular time intervals is called **periodic motion.** The motion of, say,
the Moon revolving around Earth or Earth revolving around the Sun is one type of familiar periodic motion,
as is the rotation of the hands of a clock. In this chapter,
we are interested in a particular type of periodic motion—
namely, back-and-forth periodic motion. Such motion,
called either **vibration** or **oscillation** (the two words mean
the same thing), is common at all scales in the universe.
A rocking chair, a swing, the pendulum of a grandfather
clock, the strings on a guitar, the wings of a mosquito all
oscillate. At the atomic level, atoms oscillate inside solids.
At the cosmic level, the entire universe may oscillate in an
ever-repeating cycle of expansion and contraction. The
physical natures of these periodic motions are very different from one another, and yet they are all closely related
and their mathematical descriptions are always of the same
form, differing only in the quantities involved.

In this chapter, we first develop a model for the simplest
type of oscillation, called *simple harmonic motion,* and relate it to a periodic motion we are already familiar with:
rotational motion. Then we show that any oscillation can
be described in terms of simple harmonic motions. After
presenting a number of examples, we discuss the effects of
energy dissipation during oscillations.

15.1 Periodic motion and energy

Figure 15.1 shows the periodic motion of a spring-cart
system. The system, initially at rest, is compressed and then
released from rest. After being released, the cart oscillates
back and forth along the low-friction track, alternately
compressing and stretching the spring.

> 👆 **15.1** (*a*) List the forces exerted on the spring-cart system
> of Figure 15.1 right after it is released, and draw a free-body dia-
> gram for each object in the system. (*b*) Which of these forces do
> work on the system as it oscillates? (*c*) As the hand pushes on
> the cart and compresses the spring, is the work done by the cart
> on the spring positive, negative, or zero? (*d*) How does the work
> done by the cart on the spring compare with the work done by
> the spring on the cart?

To understand why the motion of the cart in Figure 15.1
is periodic and why the cart doesn't simply return to its initial position and remain there, let us look at the mechanical energy in the cart-spring system. As the spring is compressed by the hand, elastic potential energy is stored in the
system. Just before the cart is released, the system is at rest,
so the mechanical energy of the system consists entirely of
potential energy (**Figure 15.2a**). After the cart is released,
the spring-cart system is closed—none of the forces exerted
on it does any work on it—and so the energy of the system
must remain constant.

In order to analyze the system's energy changes in more
detail, we choose an *x* axis that points in the initial direction of motion of the cart and that has its origin at the

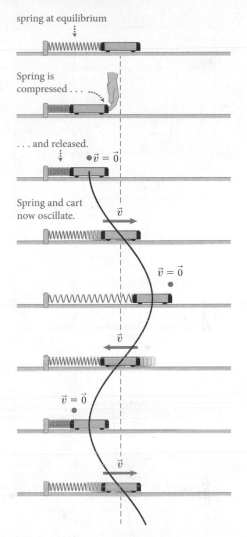

Figure 15.1 Compressing and releasing the spring cause the cart to
oscillate back and forth on the track.

center of the cart's equilibrium position. As the expanding
spring speeds up the cart in the positive *x* direction, the
kinetic energy increases and the potential energy decreases
(Figure 15.2*b*). When the cart reaches the equilibrium position at *x* = 0, the potential energy is zero (Figure 15.2*c*).
The cart, however, does not stop at this position because its
kinetic energy is not zero. The cart therefore overshoots the
equilibrium position and begins stretching the spring. As
the spring stretches, it exerts on the cart a restoring force
that slows the cart down and converts kinetic energy back
to elastic potential energy (Figure 15.2*d*). This continues
until the kinetic energy falls to zero, at which point the cart
reverses its direction of travel (Figure 15.2*e*). The potential
energy is converted back to kinetic energy (Figure 15.2*f*),
and the cart again returns to the equilibrium position, this
time traveling leftward (Figure 15.2*g*). The potential energy is zero again, but with the cart's kinetic energy being
nonzero, it overshoots the equilibrium position once again.
Provided no energy is dissipated, the system returns to its
initial state (compare Figure 15.2*a* and 15.2*i*). A new cycle
begins, and the cart repeats its back-and-forth motion.

Figure 15.2 Periodic motion is the result of a continuous exchange between kinetic and potential energy.

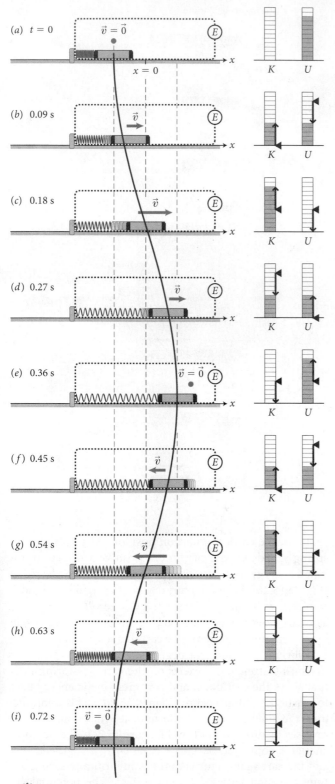

The time interval it takes to complete a full cycle of the motion is the *period T* (see Section 11.1). For the motion shown in Figure 15.2 the period is equal to the time elapsed between (*a*) and (*i*): $T = 0.72$ s. The inverse of the period, called the **frequency** of the motion, $f = 1/T$, gives the number of cycles completed per second. In Figure 15.2, $f = 1/(0.72 \text{ s}) = 1.4 \text{ s}^{-1}$ and so the cart completes 1.4 cycles each second.

The magnitude of the cart's maximum displacement from the equilibrium position is called the **amplitude** *A* of the periodic motion. The amplitude is related to the mechanical energy of the system. In Figure 15.2, for example, the greater the initial compression of the spring, the greater the amplitude and the greater the initial potential energy.

In practice, periodic motion in mechanical systems does not continue indefinitely because some energy is always dissipated (friction in the cart's bearings, air resistance, heating of the spring). This dying out of periodic motion due to dissipation of energy is called *damping*. Initially, we shall ignore damping and, with this simplification, we find that:

Periodic motion is characterized by a continuous conversion between potential and kinetic energy in a closed system.

All systems that exhibit this behavior have one common feature: a restoring interaction that tends to return the system to equilibrium. Some examples are illustrated in **Figure 15.3**. Each of these systems executes periodic motion when disturbed from its equilibrium position, and in each case the amplitude of the motion is a measure of the mechanical energy of the system.

15.3 For each system in Figure 15.3, identify (*a*) the restoring force and (*b*) the type of potential energy associated with the motion.

15.2 (*a*) In Figure 15.2*e*, the cart's displacement from the equilibrium position is maximum. Is the *x* component of the cart's acceleration at that instant positive, negative, or zero? (*b*) At which instant(s) in Figure 15.2 is the magnitude of the cart's acceleration greatest? At which instant(s) is it smallest? (Use the blue position curve to answer these questions.)

Figure 15.3 Examples of oscillating systems.

Figure 15.4 The oscillation of an object suspended from a spring is isochronous: The period T does not depend on the amplitude of the oscillation.

15.2 Simple harmonic motion

Measuring the period of any oscillating system reveals a surprising fact: When the amplitude of the motion is not too great, the period is independent of the amplitude. For example, an object suspended from a spring has a fixed period of oscillation regardless of its amplitude (**Figure 15.4**). The period of a pendulum, too, is independent of the amplitude of its swing, which is why pendulums are used to regulate the movement of mechanical clocks. Likewise, when you pluck a guitar string, the pitch of the sound, which is determined by the string's period of oscillation, is the same regardless of how far back you pull the string.

A system that exhibits equal periods for all amplitudes is called *isochronous*. Provided their amplitudes are not too great, all the systems shown in Figure 15.3 are isochronous. Individual systems have different periods that are determined by the properties of the system, but any given system has a period that is essentially independent of amplitude.

The graph of displacement versus time for an isochronous oscillating system is shown in **Figure 15.5**. The $x(t)$ curves for an isochronous oscillation are all sine functions. For this reason they are referred to as *sinusoidal curves*. Any

periodic motion that yields a sinusoidal $x(t)$ curve is called **simple harmonic motion**, and a system that executes such motion is called a *simple harmonic oscillator*. For small amplitudes, all the systems shown in Figure 15.3 yield this type of $x(t)$ curve, and so all are examples of simple harmonic motion. The motion is called harmonic because in musical instruments harmonic motion is responsible for the sound emitted by the instruments.

The fact that simple harmonic motion is isochronous allows us to draw some important conclusions. Consider, for example, the two isochronous $x(t)$ curves in Figure 15.5, one with twice the amplitude of the other. These could be the curves of two identical pendulums or any other of the systems shown in Figure 15.3, with one oscillating object moving twice as far out as the other. In one period, object 1 always covers twice the distance that object 2 covers. Because the periods are the same, the velocity of object 1 must always be twice as great as that of object 2 at the same instant in the periodic motion. Neither motion has constant velocity or constant acceleration—the velocities and accelerations change constantly. However, in order for the velocity of object 1 always to be twice that of object 2, the acceleration of object 1 must, at each instant, be twice as great as the acceleration of object 1.

Figure 15.5 Positions-versus-time graphs for two isochronous objects.

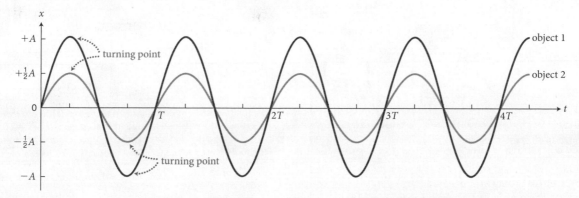

As you saw in Checkpoint 15.2, the acceleration is greatest when the displacement from the equilibrium position is greatest (that is, at the *turning points*, which are the positions where the object turns around). This tells us that the acceleration of object 1 at its turning point $x_1 = A$ is twice as great as that of object 2 at its turning point $x_2 = \frac{1}{2}A$. Given that the two objects are identical, we conclude that the acceleration of an isochronous object is proportional to the displacement from the equilibrium position. Because the acceleration of an object is proportional to the vector sum of the forces exerted on it, this tells us that the restoring force exerted on the oscillating object is also proportional to the displacement from the equilibrium position. We already know that springs exert linear restoring forces (Hooke's law, Section 8.9). The observation that all systems in Figure 15.3 are isochronous tells us, then, that the restoring forces in all these systems must also be linearly proportional to the displacement from the equilibrium position.

A object executing simple harmonic motion is subject to a linear restoring force that tends to return the object to its equilibrium position and is linearly proportional to the object's displacement from its equilibrium position.

✋ **15.4** Suppose the spring in Figure 15.1 is compressed twice as much. (*a*) By how much does the mechanical energy of the spring-cart system increase? (*b*) What is the relationship between the amplitude of the oscillation and the mechanical energy in the oscillating system?

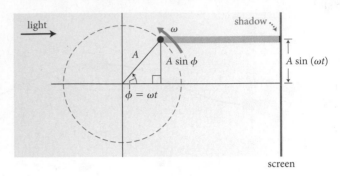

Figure 15.6 If we project the shadow of a ball moving in a circle at constant speed onto a screen perpendicular to the plane of the motion, the shadow moves up and down in simple harmonic motion.

Simple harmonic motion is closely related to a periodic motion we have already studied: circular motion at constant speed. To see how the two are related, imagine projecting the shadow of a small sphere in circular motion at constant speed onto a screen perpendicular to the plane of the motion (**Figures 15.6** and **15.7**). While the sphere sweeps out a circular trajectory, its shadow oscillates up and down on the screen. The position of the shadow at any instant is given by the vertical component of the sphere's position vector at that instant. If the sphere begins on the horizontal axis and moves with a constant rotational speed ω, the angle ϕ between the sphere's position vector and the horizontal axis grows steadily with time: $\phi = \omega t$. The position of the sphere's shadow on the screen is then described by $A \sin(\omega t)$, where A is the radius of the sphere's trajectory. Because it is described by a sinusoidal function, the projection of circular motion at constant speed is simple harmonic motion.

Figure 15.7 Correspondence between circular motion at constant speed and simple harmonic motion for (*a*) an object suspended from a spring and (*b*) a pendulum.

Figure 15.8 Fourier analysis of a periodic function into sinusoidal functions. The period of each function is indicated by the shading. (*a*) Original periodic function. (*b*) Set of harmonics used to describe the function in (*a*). (*c*) Successive sum of harmonics showing an increasingly improving match to the original periodic function.

(*a*) Original curve

Harmonics:
$$h_n(t) = \sin(2\pi f_n t) \qquad f_n = n/T$$

(*b*) Harmonics

(*c*) Sum of harmonics

The correspondence between circular motion at constant speed and simple harmonic motion can be demonstrated experimentally by projecting the shadows of an object in simple harmonic motion and an object in circular motion at constant speed on a screen, as in Figure 15.7. If the rotational speed is adjusted so that its period equals that of the oscillation, the shadows of the two objects move synchronously.

15.5 What are (*a*) the direction of the velocity of the shadow on the screen in Figure 15.6 and (*b*) the direction of the shadow's acceleration?

15.3 Fourier's theorem

Simple harmonic motion is important because, as Figure 15.3 suggests, it is very common. Another reason it is important is that, according to a rule known as **Fourier's theorem,*** any periodic function can be written as a sum of sinusoidal functions of frequency $f_n = n/T$, where $n \geq 1$ is an integer and T is the period of the function. This means that *any* periodic motion can be treated as a superposition of simple

harmonic motions. So, if we understand simple harmonic motion, we can deal with any other type of periodic motion by breaking it down into its simple harmonic components. Because any motion that is nonrepetitive can be thought of as periodic motion that has an infinitely long period, Fourier's theorem has broad implications: The time-dependent motion of *any* system can be expressed in terms of sinusoidal functions.

Consider, for example, the periodic motion represented by the nonsinusoidal curve in **Figure 15.8a**. Although very different from simple harmonic motion, this motion can be expressed as the sum of a few simple harmonic components, shown in the sinusoidal curves of Figure 15.8*b*. The first component has the same frequency $f_1 = 1/T$ as the original periodic function; this frequency, the lowest in the sum, is called the **fundamental frequency** or **first harmonic.** All other components, called **higher harmonics,** are at integer multiples of the fundamental frequency: $f_n = nf_1 = n/T.$[†] When these higher harmonics are added to the first harmonic, the shape of the resulting periodic function is not sinusoidal, but the period remains the same (Figure 15.8*c*).

---

*After the French mathematician Jean-Baptiste Joseph Fourier (1768–1830).

[†]In general, an infinite sum of sines and cosines is required to break down arbitrary periodic functions. Only periodic functions for which $f(t) = -f(-t)$ (that is, they are odd in t, such as the one shown in Figure 15.8) can be analyzed with only sines (which are also odd in t).

Figure 15.9 (*a*) Periodic function and (*b*) amplitudes of the harmonic functions in the Fourier series of the function shown in part *a*. (*c*) Spectrum of the periodic function, obtained by plotting the squares of the amplitudes.

Figure 15.10 Spectrum analyzer display on a stereo component.

By adjusting the amplitude of each harmonic, we can make the sum of harmonics fit the original periodic function.

The breaking down of a function into harmonic components is called *Fourier analysis,* and the resulting sum of sinusoidal functions is called a *Fourier series.* **Figure 15.9** shows one way of graphically representing the Fourier series: The amplitudes A_n of all the harmonics are plotted against the frequencies of the harmonics. As you saw in Checkpoint 15.4, the energy of a simple harmonic oscillator is proportional to the square of the amplitude. For this reason, it is customary to plot A_n^2 as a function of frequency, as shown in Figure 15.9*c*; such a plot is called the **spectrum** of the periodic function.

The spectrum shows the contribution of each harmonic to the original periodic function. A similar type of visual display of frequency content is found on some stereophonic components. Displays such as the one shown in **Figure 15.10** provide a visual representation of the frequency content of the sound being played.

Figure 15.11 shows some important relationships between a periodic function and its spectrum. The period T of the function determines the frequency of the first harmonic. In other words, the duration of the slowest component of the function determines the lowest frequency in the spectrum. Conversely, the duration $T_{\min}$ of the fastest component in the function determines the highest frequency in the spectrum.

Fourier analysis has many applications, ranging from electronic signal processing to chemical analysis and voice recognition. The ear functions as a Fourier analyzer because the inner ear breaks down the oscillations produced by sound into simple harmonic components, each producing a nerve impulse proportional to the amplitude of that component.

The inverse of Fourier analysis—the creation of periodic functions by adding sinusoidal functions together—is called *Fourier synthesis.* A musician's electronic synthesizer, for example, produces a sum of harmonics that add up to produce different periodic functions. When the amplitudes of the different harmonics are adjusted so that they match the frequency content of real instruments, the synthesizer simulates the sounds of many musical instruments.

15.6 (*a*) What does the spectrum of a single sinusoidal function of period T look like? (*b*) As T is increased, what change occurs in the spectrum?

Figure 15.11 Relationship between a periodic function and its spectrum.

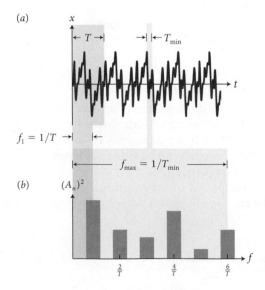

15.4 Restoring forces in simple harmonic motion

Periodic motion takes place about a position of translational or rotational equilibrium (see Section 12.5) and requires a restoring force that tends to return the object to the equilibrium position. Consider, for example, an object moving along an x axis and subject to the vector sum of forces whose x component is shown graphically in **Figure 15.12**. The object is in translational equilibrium at each position where the vector sum is zero: at x_1, x_2, and all values of $x > x_3$. Can the object oscillate about any of these positions? From the graph we see that $\sum F_x$ is positive to the left of x_1, and so the vector sum $\sum \vec{F}$ points toward x_1. To the right of x_1 $\sum F_x$ is negative, and so the vector sum of forces again points toward x_1. The forces exerted on the object tend to return the object to x_1 whenever it moves away from x_1. Around x_1 the vector sum of forces "restores" the translational equilibrium so that the object can oscillate around x_1.

Because the vector sum of the forces always pushes the object back to x_1, this equilibrium position is said to be *stable*. You can visualize this position by imagining a ball at the bottom of a bowl: When the ball is displaced in any direction, a restoring force accelerates it back toward the bottom.

On either side of equilibrium position x_2, the direction of the vector sum of the forces is such that the object accelerates away from the equilibrium position. Such an equilibrium position is called *unstable* because the forces tend to amplify any disturbance from equilibrium. Imagine balancing a ball on top of a hill: The slightest displacement of the ball in any direction is enough to make it accelerate away from the equilibrium position.

Positions for which $x > x_3$ represent a *neutral* equilibrium: Moving the ball in any direction has no effect on its subsequent acceleration.

What all this tells us is that objects tend to oscillate about *stable* equilibrium positions because the forces about such positions tend to restore the equilibrium. A consequence of the restoring forces about stable equilibrium positions is:

In the absence of friction, a small displacement of a system from a position of stable equilibrium causes the system to oscillate.

15.7 (*a*) Are there any equilibrium positions in the force-versus-distance graph in **Figure 15.13**? If so, is the equilibrium stable, unstable, or neutral? (*b*) Compare the magnitude of the restoring force for equal displacements on either side of x_0 in Figure 15.13.

Figure 15.13 shows why so many systems move in simple harmonic motion. As we saw in Section 15.2, simple harmonic motion requires *linear* restoring forces—that is, forces that are linearly proportional to the displacement from the equilibrium position. In Checkpoint 15.7*b* you saw that the restoring force about the stable equilibrium position x_0 in Figure 15.13 is not linear. However, as illustrated by the successive enlargements in Figure 15.13, the curve, which gives the relationship between force and position, becomes indistinguishable from a straight line for small displacements from the equilibrium position x_0 (say, within the shaded region). In other words:

For sufficiently small displacements away from the equilibrium position, restoring forces are always linearly proportional to the displacement. Consequently, for small displacements, objects execute simple harmonic motion about any stable equilibrium position.

Figure 15.12 Whenever the vector sum of the forces exerted on an object is zero, the object is in translational equilibrium. This graph shows stable, unstable, and neutral equilibria.

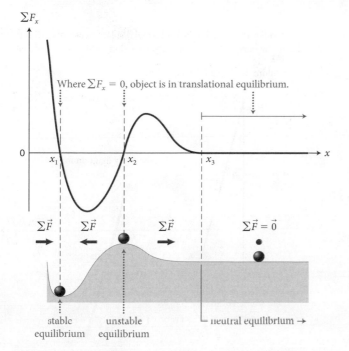

Figure 15.13 For sufficiently small displacements near a stable equilibrium position, the restoring force is linear in the displacement.

Figure 15.14 Cause of the restoring force for a taut string displaced from equilibrium.

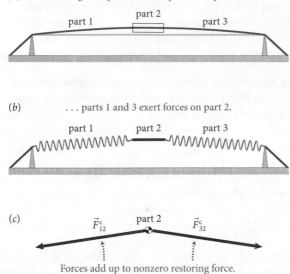

(a) When string is displaced from equilibrium position . . .

part 1   part 2   part 3

(b)   . . . parts 1 and 3 exert forces on part 2.

part 1   part 2   part 3

(c) $\vec{F}^c_{12}$ part 2 $\vec{F}^c_{32}$

Forces add up to nonzero restoring force.

Figure 15.15 Cause of the restoring torque on a beam bent away from its equilibrium shape.

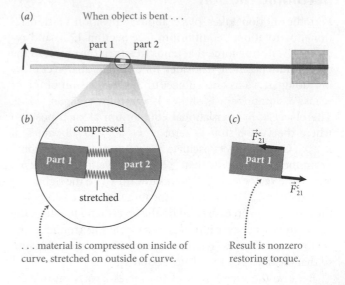

(a)   When object is bent . . .

part 1   part 2

(b)   compressed

part 1   part 2

stretched

. . . material is compressed on inside of curve, stretched on outside of curve.

(c) $\vec{F}^c_{21}$

part 1

$\vec{F}^c_{21}$

Result is nonzero restoring torque.

The restoring forces in the examples in Figure 15.3 fall into two categories: elastic (*b*, *d*) and gravitational (*a*, *c*). We saw in Chapter 8 that, for small displacements from the equilibrium position, the elastic restoring force of a spring is linearly proportional to the displacement. The same is true for other elastic restoring forces. **Figure 15.14**, for example, shows a string displaced from its equilibrium position. Each part of the stretched string is subject to elastic (contact) forces exerted by the parts immediately adjacent to it. Part 2 in the middle of the string in Figure 15.14*b*, for instance, is subject to a force exerted by part 1 and a force exerted by part 3. In the equilibrium position, when the string is straight, the elastic forces exerted by parts 1 and 3 on part 2 add to zero. As the string is displaced, however, the elastic forces exerted by the two neighboring parts no longer line up (Figure 15.14*c*) and their vector sum provides a restoring force that tends to return the string to its equilibrium position. For small displacements, as we just saw, this restoring force is linearly proportional to the displacement from the equilibrium position.

The same line of reasoning applies to the restoring forces that arise when materials are twisted or bent. **Figure 15.15** shows that bending an object compresses the material that lies on the inside of the curve and stretches the material that lies on the outside of the curve. The resulting internal elastic forces cause torques on each part of the object, torques that tend to return the object to its equilibrium shape. For small displacements, the internal elastic forces are linearly proportional to the displacement, and consequently the restoring torque, too, is linearly proportional to the (rotational) displacement.

Let us next examine a pendulum, where the restoring force is due to gravity. **Figure 15.16*a*** shows a pendulum bob of mass *m* suspended from a string of length ℓ. If the bob is much more massive and much smaller than the string that supports the bob, we can ignore the mass of the string and treat the bob as a particle. Such a pendulum is called

a *simple pendulum*. The bob is pulled back over an arc of length *s*. As the free-body diagram in Figure 15.16*b* shows, the bob is subject to two forces: a contact force exerted by the string and a gravitational force. The restoring force is provided by the component of the gravitational force perpendicular to the string, $\vec{F}^G_{Eb\perp}$. From Figure 15.16*b*, we see that the magnitude of $\vec{F}^G_{Eb\perp}$ is equal to $mg\sin\vartheta$ and from Figure 15.16*a* that $\sin\vartheta = x/\ell$, and so the magnitude of the restoring force exerted on the bob is $mg\sin\vartheta = (mg/\ell)x$. Provided the rotational displacement is small, the bob's displacement from its equilibrium position along the circular arc *s* is approximately equal to the bob's horizontal displacement *x*, $s \approx x$. For small angles, therefore, the restoring force is linearly proportional to the bob's displacement .

Figure 15.16 For small angles the horizontal displacement *x* of a pendulum is almost the same as the length of the arc *s* along which it is displaced.

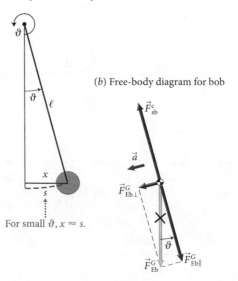

(a) Pendulum displaced from equilibrium

ϑ

ϑ ℓ

x

s

For small ϑ, $x \approx s$.

(b) Free-body diagram for bob

$\vec{F}^c_{sb}$

$\vec{a}$

$\vec{F}^G_{Eb\perp}$

ϑ

$\vec{F}^G_{Eb}$ $\vec{F}^G_{Eb\parallel}$

Example 15.1 Displaced string

Show that for small displacements the restoring force exerted on part 2 of the displaced string in Figure 15.14 is linearly proportional to the displacement of that part from its equilibrium position.

❶ GETTING STARTED Figure 15.14c shows the forces exerted by parts 1 and 3 on part 2 when the string is displaced from its equilibrium position. I'll assume that these forces are much greater than the force of gravity exerted on part 2 so that I can ignore gravity in this problem. The force that pulls the string away from the equilibrium position is not shown, which means the string has been released after being pulled away from the equilibrium position.

I begin by making a free-body diagram and choosing a set of axes (**Figure 15.17**). The x components of the forces $\vec{F}^c_{12}$ and $\vec{F}^c_{32}$ cancel; the sum of the y components is the restoring force. The magnitude of the y components is determined by the angle θ between the x axis and either $\vec{F}^c_{12}$ or $\vec{F}^c_{32}$.

Figure 15.17

I also make a sketch of the displaced string, showing the displacement Δy of part 2 from its equilibrium position. I denote the length of the string in its equilibrium position by ℓ and the length of the displaced string by ℓ'.

❷ DEVISE PLAN The forces $\vec{F}^c_{12}$ and $\vec{F}^c_{32}$ are equal in magnitude and their y components are determined by $\sin \theta$, which is equal to $\Delta y/(\frac{1}{2}\ell')$. If the displacement is small, I can assume that the length of the string doesn't change much from its equilibrium value, so that $\ell \approx \ell'$. Because the forces $\vec{F}^c_{12}$ and $\vec{F}^c_{32}$ are proportional to the tension in the string, I can also consider these forces to be constant. Using this information, I can express the restoring force in terms of the displacement Δy.

❸ EXECUTE PLAN From my sketch I see that the restoring force is $F^c_{12y} + F^c_{32y}$. Because $\vec{F}^c_{12}$ and $\vec{F}^c_{32}$ are equal in magnitude, I can write the sum of the y components as $2F^c_{12y} = 2F^c_{12} \sin \theta$. I also know that $\sin \theta = \Delta y/(\frac{1}{2}\ell') \approx \Delta y/(\frac{1}{2}\ell)$. Combining these two relationships, I obtain for the magnitude of the restoring force: $F_{\text{restoring}} = 2F^c_{12y} \approx (4F^c_{12}/\ell)\Delta y$. For small displacements, the term in parentheses is constant and so the restoring force is, indeed, proportional to the displacement Δy. ✔

❹ EVALUATE RESULT I made two assumptions to derive my answer. The first is that gravity can be ignored. Indeed, taut strings tend to be straight, indicating that gravity (which would make the strings sag) doesn't play an appreciable role. The other

assumption I made was that the length of the string doesn't change much when it is displaced from its equilibrium position. This assumption is also justified because the displacement of a string tends to be several orders of magnitude smaller than the string length.

✋ 15.8 Using a calculator, determine the percent error in the approximation $\sin \theta \approx \theta$ for polar angles of 1°, 5°, 10°, and 20°.

In Section 15.1, I showed how oscillations arise from a continuous conversion between kinetic energy and potential energy. Another way to look at oscillations is to say:

Oscillations arise from an interplay between inertia and a restoring force.

When an object that is subject to a restoring force is displaced from its equilibrium position, the restoring force accelerates it back toward the equilibrium position. Once it gets there, however, it has a nonzero velocity, and its inertia causes it to overshoot the equilibrium position.

This picture of an interplay between inertia and restoring force allows us to make some qualitative predictions about the period of an oscillator. The greater the mass of the oscillating object, the harder it is to accelerate and so the longer the period.* Increasing the restoring force has the opposite effect: The greater the restoring force, the greater the object's acceleration and the shorter the period—a stiff spring causes a much more rapid oscillation than a soft, sloppy one.

The period of an oscillating object increases when its mass is increased and decreases when the magnitude of the restoring force is increased.

This relationship does not hold for pendulums, however, because for a pendulum the restoring force and mass are proportional to each other. Increasing the mass of a pendulum bob makes the pendulum harder to accelerate but increases the magnitude of the gravitational force exerted on the pendulum bob—the restoring force—in proportion (see Figure 15.16b). The two effects cancel, and so:

The period of a pendulum is independent of the mass of the pendulum.

✋ 15.9 (a) What effect, if any, does increasing the length ℓ of a simple pendulum have on its period? (b) A pendulum and an object suspended from a spring are taken to the Moon, where the acceleration due to gravity is smaller than that on Earth. How does the period of the pendulum on the Moon compare with its period on Earth? (c) How does the period of the suspended object on the Moon compare with its period on Earth?

---

*You can demonstrate this as follows: Position a plastic or thin wooden ruler on a table so that about half its length overhangs the edge of the table. While pressing the ruler down on the table, pull the free end down and release, noting the rapid oscillations. Next attach an eraser or other small object on top of the overhanging part of the ruler and repeat the experiment. Because of the increased mass, the period is now much longer.

Self-quiz

1. Is an oscillating object in translational equilibrium?

2. A pendulum bob swings through a circular arc defined by positions A and D in **Figure 15.18**. (*a*) At A, B, and C, what are the possible directions of the velocity of the bob and of the restoring force exerted on it? (*b*) What is the direction of the bob's acceleration at A and C?

3. (*a*) In the cart-spring system shown in **Figure 15.19**, is the cart's speed greater at A or at B? (*b*) At which of these two positions is the restoring force acting on the cart greater? (*c*) At which of these two positions is the cart's acceleration greater?

Figure 15.18

Figure 15.19

equilibrium   A   B x_{max}

Figure 15.20

A

B

4. A T-shaped wooden structure is balanced on a pivot in the two configurations shown in **Figure 15.20**. Which configuration is in stable equilibrium? Which configuration is likely to oscillate?

Answers

1. No. When an object is in translational equilibrium, the sum of the forces exerted on it is zero. An oscillating object is subject to a variable force that accelerates the object back and forth.

2. (*a*) The velocity is always tangent to the bob's trajectory; the restoring force always points along the arc toward the equilibrium position C. At A, the bob reaches its maximum displacement, so its velocity must be zero; the restoring force points along the arc toward C. At B, the velocity can be in either direction along the arc as the bob swings back and forth, but the restoring force always points along the arc towards C. At C, the velocity can be to the right or left, but the restoring force is zero because this is the equilibrium position. (*b*) At A, the acceleration is tangent along the arc toward C. At C, the bob does have a centripetal radial acceleration directed vertically upward, but no tangential acceleration.

3. (*a*) Once released from the stretched position shown, the cart speeds up as it moves left toward the equilibrium position, so its speed is greater at A than at B. (*b*) The restoring force is proportional to the displacement from the equilibrium position, so it is greater at B than at A. (*c*) The acceleration is proportional to the restoring force, so it, too, is greater at B.

4. If the structure in configuration A is tipped slightly to the left as shown in **Figure 15.21**, the gravitational force exerted on the part to the left of the vertical line through the pivot is greater than that exerted on the part to the right of the pivot, and so the torques caused by these forces make it tip farther in the same direction, away from the equilibrium position. Conversely, if it is tipped to the right, it tips farther to the right. This configuration is unstable, and so the structure does not oscillate. If the structure in configuration B is tipped slightly either way, the torques caused by gravitational forces exerted on the parts on either side of the pivot cause it to move in the opposite direction, back toward the equilibrium position. Configuration B is stable, and so the structure oscillates.

Figure 15.21

A

B

15.5 Energy of a simple harmonic oscillator

In Section 15.2, you saw that there is a correspondence between simple harmonic motion and circular motion at constant speed. We begin our quantitative description of simple harmonic motion by exploiting this correspondence.

Figure 15.22 shows a sinusoidally varying, time-dependent function describing some simple harmonic motion represented by a rotating arrow of length A whose tip traces out a circle. The circle is called a **reference circle,** and the arrow is called a **phasor.** The phasor rotates in a counterclockwise direction with a constant rotational speed ω. The vertical component of the phasor varies sinusoidally with time (see Figures 15.6 and 15.7).

Let us first establish a relationship between the rotational speed of the phasor and the frequency f of the corresponding simple harmonic motion. If the phasor completes one revolution in a period T, its rotational speed is

$$\omega \equiv \frac{\Delta \vartheta}{\Delta t} = \frac{2\pi}{T}, \tag{15.1}$$

and the frequency of the corresponding simple harmonic motion is, as noted in Section 15.1,

$$f \equiv \frac{1}{T}. \tag{15.2}$$

The derived SI unit of frequency is the **hertz** (Hz) after the 19th-century German physicist Heinrich Hertz, who produced the first radio waves:

$$1 \text{ Hz} \equiv 1 \text{ s}^{-1}. \tag{15.3}$$

Substituting $1/T$ from Eq. 15.2 into Eq. 15.1, we find

$$\omega = 2\pi f. \tag{15.4}$$

So the rotational speed ω of the phasor is greater than the frequency f of the simple harmonic motion by a factor of 2π. The reason for this factor is that ω measures the change in rotational position per unit time, and in one revolution the rotational position ϑ changes by 2π. Frequency, on the other hand, measures the number of cycles per unit time, and one revolution on the reference circle corresponds to one oscillation cycle (Figure 15.22).

In the context of oscillations, ω is often called the **angular frequency** because it has the same unit (s^{-1} or inverse second) as the frequency f. Keep in mind, however, that the frequency f and the angular frequency ω are not equal (see Eq. 15.4). To facilitate remembering the distinction between the two, we use the SI unit hertz for f and the SI unit s^{-1} for ω.

Figure 15.22 Reference circle and $x(t)$ curve for a simple harmonic oscillator.

Figure 15.23 The phase of a simple harmonic oscillator at any instant is given by the angle between the phasor and the positive horizontal axis measured in the counterclockwise direction.

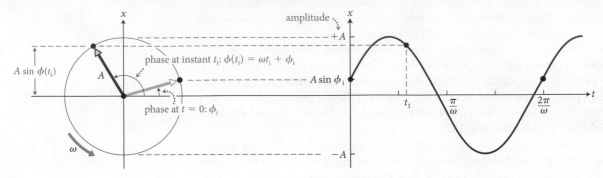

The rotational position of the tip of the phasor relative to the positive horizontal axis is called the **phase** of the motion (**Figure 15.23**). The phase is represented by the symbol $\phi(t)$. For constant angular frequency, the phase increases linearly with time:

$$\phi(t) = \omega t + \phi_i \quad \text{(constant angular frequency)}, \tag{15.5}$$

where the constant ϕ_i is the *initial phase* at $t = 0$. The phase $\phi(t)$ tells us at what point in the cycle the motion is; the initial phase ϕ_i is the phase at $t = 0$. Because rotational position is a unitless number, the phase is unitless too. You determine the phase by expressing the angle between the phasor and the positive horizontal axis in radians and dividing by 1 rad.

The vertical component of A in Figure 15.23 can now be written in the form

$$x(t) = A \sin \phi(t) = A \sin(\omega t + \phi_i) \quad \text{(simple harmonic motion)}, \tag{15.6}$$

where the **amplitude** A of the oscillation is equal to the length of the phasor. Equation 15.6 gives a general expression for the position of a simple harmonic oscillator as a function of time when the equilibrium position is at $x = 0$—a pendulum bob, an object suspended from a spring, a taut string. Because the motion is periodic, $x(t)$ has the same value each time the phase increases by 2π. For a crest (where $x(t) = A$ and the sine function in Eq. 15.6 has the value 1), the phase could be $\frac{\pi}{2}$, or $\frac{\pi}{2}$ plus an integer multiple of 2π; for a trough (where $x(t) = -A$ and the sine function in Eq. 15.6 has the value -1), the phase could be $\frac{3\pi}{2}$, or $\frac{3\pi}{2}$ plus an integer multiple of 2π.

Exercise 15.2 Oscillation phases

Consider the spring-cart system of Figure 15.1 again. The cart is pulled away from its equilibrium position in the positive x direction and then released at $t = 0$. (*a*) What is the initial phase of the cart's oscillation? What is the phase of the cart's oscillation (*b*) half a period later and (*c*) one period later? What are the cart's initial phases in the following two situations? (*d*) The cart is at its equilibrium position when, at $t = 0$, it is given a sharp blow in the negative x direction so that it starts oscillating. (*e*) The cart is first pulled back a distance d in the positive x direction, and then at $t = 0$ it is given a sharp blow, also in the positive x direction, so that it carries out an oscillation of amplitude $A = 2d$.

SOLUTION (*a*) The cart starts at maximum amplitude in the positive x direction, so the phasor is pointing straight up and the initial phase of the cart's oscillation is $\phi_i = (90°)(2\pi \text{ rad}/360°)/(1 \text{ rad}) = \pi/2.$ ✔

(*b*) In one period, the phasor completes a full cycle, so half a period later the phasor has traversed half a cycle (180°). The angle between the phasor and the horizontal axis is thus $90° + 180° = 270°$, and thus $\phi(t) = (270°)(2\pi \text{ rad}/360°)/(1 \text{ rad}) = 3\pi/2.$ ✔

(c) In one period the phasor has completed a full cycle, so the phase is equal to the initial phase $\phi_i + 2\pi = \frac{\pi}{2} + 2\pi = \frac{5\pi}{2}$. ✔

(d) If the cart is in the equilibrium position, the phasor must be parallel to the horizontal axis and so the phasor is at 0° or 180°. When the phasor is at 0°, the cart moves in the positive x direction; when it is at 180°, the cart moves in the negative x direction, so the initial phase is $\phi_i = (180°)(2\pi \text{ rad}/360°)/(1 \text{ rad}) = \pi$. ✔

(e) The displacement of the cart is given by Eq. 15.6. At $t = 0$: $x(0) = A \sin \phi_i$. I am given that $x(0) = +d$ and $A = 2d$, so $+d = 2d \sin \phi_i$, or $\sin \phi_i = \frac{1}{2}$, and so $\phi_i = \pi/6$ or $5\pi/6$. Because the cart moves in the positive x direction at $t = 0$, the initial phase must be $\phi_i = \pi/6$. ✔

By differentiating Eq. 15.6 with respect to time, we can obtain general expressions for the x components of the velocity and acceleration of a harmonic oscillator:

$$v_x \equiv \frac{dx}{dt} = \omega A \cos(\omega t + \phi_i) \qquad \text{(simple harmonic motion)} \qquad (15.7)$$

$$a_x \equiv \frac{d^2x}{dt^2} = -\omega^2 A \sin(\omega t + \phi_i) \quad \text{(simple harmonic motion)}. \qquad (15.8)$$

Equations 15.6–15.8 are the basic kinematic equations for simple harmonic motion. We derived them without considering any particular system—everything followed from the fact that simple harmonic motion corresponds to the projection onto a screen of some object moving in circular motion at constant speed.

✋ **15.10** (a) What are the algebraic signs of x, v_x, and a_x when the phase $\phi(t) = \omega t + \phi_i$ is between 0 and $\frac{\pi}{3}$? (b) Repeat for $\pi < \phi(t) < \frac{3\pi}{2}$.

Substituting Eq. 15.6 into Eq. 15.8, we find that the x component of the acceleration of an object in simple harmonic motion is proportional to the displacement and points in the direction opposite the displacement (that is, toward the equilibrium position):

$$a_x = -\omega^2 x \quad \text{(simple harmonic motion)}. \qquad (15.9)$$

Substituting the definition of the acceleration into Eq. 15.9, we obtain a second-order differential equation in the variable x:

$$\frac{d^2x}{dt^2} = -\omega^2 x \quad \text{(simple harmonic motion)}. \qquad (15.10)$$

This equation is called the **simple harmonic oscillator equation** because any system that satisfies this equation undergoes simple harmonic motion. As we shall see in the next two sections, the symbols may take on different meanings for different types of simple harmonic motion, but the mathematical form is always that given in Eq. 15.10.

Multiplying both sides of Eq. 15.9 by the mass of the oscillating object, we have

$$ma_x = -m\omega^2 x \quad \text{(simple harmonic motion)}. \qquad (15.11)$$

The left side of Eq. 15.11 is equal to the x component of the vector sum of the forces acting on the oscillating object, $ma_x = \Sigma F_x$, and so

$$\Sigma F_x = -m\omega^2 x \quad \text{(simple harmonic motion)}. \qquad (15.12)$$

Because m and ω are positive constants, Eq. 15.12 tells us that an object in simple harmonic motion is subject to a force that always points in a direction opposite the object's displacement x from the equilibrium position and is linearly proportional to x—in other words, a *linear restoring force* as we already concluded in Section 15.4.

Let us next examine the mechanical energy of a simple harmonic oscillator, using kinematic Equations 15.6–15.8. The work done by the forces exerted on the oscillating object when it is moving from the equilibrium position to position x is found by integrating the x component of the position-dependent force exerted on the oscillator (Eq. 9.22):

$$W = \int_{x_0}^{x} \Sigma F_x(x)dx = -\int_{x_0}^{x} m\omega^2 x \, dx, \qquad (15.13)$$

where we have substituted the restoring force given in Eq. 15.12. This work causes the kinetic energy of the oscillating object to change, and so Eq. 15.13 gives us the change in kinetic energy ΔK. Working out the integration thus yields

$$\Delta K = -m\omega^2 \int_{x_0}^{x} x dx = -m\omega^2 \left[\tfrac{1}{2}x^2 \right]_{x_0}^{x} = \tfrac{1}{2}m\omega^2 x_0^2 - \tfrac{1}{2}m\omega^2 x^2. \quad (15.14)$$

Because the interaction that causes the oscillation is reversible, this change in kinetic energy must be provided by some form of potential energy. (In the examples we discussed, the energy was provided by gravitational potential energy or the elastic potential energy of a spring). If we include the object that causes the oscillation in our system, the system must be closed, so $\Delta E = \Delta K + \Delta U = 0$. Therefore the change in potential energy of the (closed) system is $\Delta U = -\Delta K$, or, substituting Eq. 15.14,

$$\Delta U = U(x) - U(x_0) = \tfrac{1}{2}m\omega^2 x^2 - \tfrac{1}{2}m\omega^2 x_0^2. \qquad (15.15)$$

If we let the potential energy at the equilibrium position be zero, $U(x_0) = 0$, then we see that the potential energy of the oscillating system is $U(x) = \tfrac{1}{2}m\omega^2 x^2$, and so the mechanical energy is

$$E = K + U = \tfrac{1}{2}mv^2 + \tfrac{1}{2}m\omega^2 x^2 \qquad (15.16)$$

or, substituting for x from Eq. 15.6 and for v_x from Eq. 15.7,

$$E = \tfrac{1}{2}m\omega^2 A^2 \cos^2(\omega t + \phi_i) + \tfrac{1}{2}m\omega^2 A^2 \sin^2(\omega t + \phi_i)$$

$$= \tfrac{1}{2}m\omega^2 A^2 \quad \text{(simple harmonic motion)}, \qquad (15.17)$$

where we have used the fact that $\cos^2 \phi + \sin^2 \phi = 1$ for all ϕ. Equation 15.17 shows that the mechanical energy of a simple harmonic oscillator is constant and proportional to the square of the amplitude, as we concluded earlier.

15.11 (*a*) Use Eq. 15.15 to determine the maximum potential energy of a simple harmonic oscillator. (*b*) Does your answer to part *a* agree with Eq. 15.17?

15.6 Simple harmonic motion and springs

Whenever an object undergoes reversible deformation as a result of stretching, compressing, bending, or twisting, it exerts an elastic restoring force. Consider, for example, the spring-cart system in **Figure 15.24**. The spring exerts on the oscillating cart a force $F_{scx}^c = -k(x - x_0)$ (Eq. 8.20), where k is the spring constant and $x - x_0$ is the displacement of the cart from its equilibrium position at x_0, where the spring is relaxed.

We can use this information about the restoring force to obtain an equation for the cart's motion in terms of the amplitude, angular frequency, and phase of the motion. If we let the origin be at the equilibrium position, $x_0 = 0$ and so

$$F_{scx}^c = -kx. \tag{15.18}$$

The equation of motion for the cart in the horizontal direction is then

$$\sum F_{cx} = ma_x = -kx, \tag{15.19}$$

where m is the cart's mass, or

$$ma_x = m\frac{d^2x}{dt^2} = -kx \tag{15.20}$$

or

$$\frac{d^2x}{dt^2} = -\frac{k}{m}x. \tag{15.21}$$

The solution to this simple harmonic oscillator equation is a sinusoidal function $x(t)$, and comparison with Eq. 15.10 tells us that $k/m = \omega^2$. Therefore the angular frequency of the oscillation is

$$\omega = +\sqrt{\frac{k}{m}}. \tag{15.22}$$

The plus sign in front of the square root means that we must take the positive square root because ω is always positive.

The motion of the cart is given by Eq. 15.6:

$$x(t) = A\sin\left(\sqrt{\frac{k}{m}}t + \phi_i\right). \tag{15.23}$$

Figure 15.25 shows a number of different sinusoidal functions of the form given by Eq. 15.23 that satisfy Eq. 15.21. All of the functions $x(t)$ shown in Figure 15.25 complete one cycle in a period T, and so they all have the same angular frequency ω, whose value is fixed by properties of the system—the spring constant k and the cart's mass m (Eq. 15.22). However, the peak heights tell you that the curves do not all have the same amplitude A, and the fact that each curve reaches its maximum at a different instant tells you that they have different initial phases ϕ_i. Without information in addition to the values of k and m, we cannot determine the amplitude A and initial phase ϕ_i.

In order to determine A and ϕ_i, we have to know the position and x component of the velocity at some instant. The next examples illustrate how to determine these quantities for some specific situations.

Figure 15.24 Restoring force exerted by spring on cart when cart is displaced from its equilibrium position x_0.

equilibrium

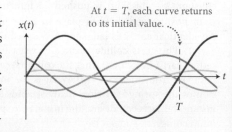

Figure 15.25 Four of the infinite number of solutions that satisfy Eq. 15.21.

At $t = T$, each curve returns to its initial value.

QUANTITATIVE TOOLS

Example 15.3 Cart pulled away and released from rest

A cart of mass $m = 0.50$ kg fastened to a spring of spring constant $k = 14$ N/m is pulled 30 mm away from its equilibrium position and then released with zero initial velocity. What are the cart's position and the x component of velocity 2.0 s after being released?

❶ **GETTING STARTED** I begin by making a sketch of the initial condition and representing the oscillation by a reference circle and a graph of position versus time (**Figure 15.26**). I choose the positive x axis to be in the same direction as the cart's initial displacement, with the origin of the axis at the equilibrium position. Because the cart is released with zero initial velocity, its initial kinetic energy at $x = +30$ mm is $K = 0$, and so each time it returns to that position it again has $K = 0$. This tells me that the cart's initial displacement is also its maximum displacement, and so $A = 30$ mm. Because the cart begins at its maximum positive displacement, I know that the oscillation begins with the phasor straight up, and so the initial phase is $\phi_i = +\pi/2$.

Figure 15.26

❷ **DEVISE PLAN** To determine the position of the cart at $t = 2.0$ s, I can use Eq. 15.6. This equation contains the angular

frequency ω, which I can determine from Eq. 15.22, and the amplitude A and initial phase ϕ_i, which I already determined. To calculate the x component of the cart's velocity, I can use Eq. 15.7.

❸ **EXECUTE PLAN** From Eq. 15.22, I get for the angular frequency of the oscillation:

$$\omega = \sqrt{\frac{k}{m}} = \sqrt{\frac{14 \text{ N/m}}{0.50 \text{ kg}}} = \sqrt{28 \text{ s}^{-2}} = 5.3 \text{ s}^{-1}.$$

Substituting this angular frequency, $t = 2.0$ s, $A = 30$ mm, and $\phi_i = +\pi/2$ into Eq. 15.6, I obtain for the cart's position at $t = 2.0$ s:

$$x(2.0 \text{ s}) = (30 \text{ mm}) \sin\left[(5.3 \text{ s}^{-1})(2.0 \text{ s}) + \frac{\pi}{2}\right] = -12 \text{ mm.} ✔$$

Substituting the same values into Eq. 15.7, I obtain for the x component of the cart's velocity:

$$v_x(2.0 \text{ s}) = (5.3 \text{ s}^{-1})(30 \text{ mm}) \cos\left[(5.3 \text{ s}^{-1})(2.0 \text{ s}) + \frac{\pi}{2}\right]$$

$$= +1.5 \times 10^2 \text{ mm/s.} ✔$$

❹ **EVALUATE RESULT** The magnitude of the value I obtained for x is smaller than the amplitude, as it should be. The phase at $t = 2.0$ s is $\phi(t) = (5.3 \text{ s}^{-1})(2.0 \text{ s}) + \pi/2 = 12$, which corresponds to $12/(2\pi) = 1.9$ cycles, so the phasor is in the fourth quadrant, which confirms that x should be negative. The cart moves a distance of $4A = 0.12$ m in one cycle, which takes $2\pi/\omega = 1.2$ s, and so the cart's average speed is $(0.12 \text{ m})/(1.2 \text{ s}) = 0.10$ m/s, indicating that the magnitude of the velocity component I obtain is reasonable. Because the cart is moving in the positive x direction when the phasor is in the fourth quadrant, the x component of the velocity should be positive, as I found.

✋ **15.12** (a) In Example 15.3 is the initial condition that $v_x = 0$ satisfied by Eq. 15.7? (b) Is it correct to say that the x component of the velocity given by Eq. 15.7 must be positive whenever x is negative so as to make sure that the cart moves back to its equilibrium position?

Example 15.4 Cart struck with spring already compressed

Cart 1 of mass $m = 0.50$ kg fastened to a spring of spring constant $k = 14$ N/m is pushed 15 mm in from its equilibrium position and held in place by a ratchet (**Figure 15.27**). An identical cart 2 is launched at a speed of 0.10 m/s toward cart 1. The carts collide elastically, releasing the ratchet and setting cart 1 in motion. After the collision, cart 2 is immediately removed from the track. (a) What is the maximum compression of the spring? (b) How many seconds elapse between the instant the carts collide and the instant the spring reaches maximum compression?

Figure 15.27 Example 15.4

cart 1

cart 1   cart 2

❶ **GETTING STARTED** If I ignore the effect of the spring during the collision, I can say that the elastic collision interchanges the velocities of the two carts. I make a sketch of the initial condition of cart 1 just before the collision, choosing the positive x axis to the right, the equilibrium position at $x = 0$, and the initial displacement of the cart 15 mm to the left of $x = 0$. I also draw a reference circle and sketch the oscillation resulting from the collision (**Figure 15.28**). With this choice of axis, the x component of the initial velocity of cart 1 is $v_{x,i} = -0.10$ m/s. Because m and k are the same as in Example 15.3, the angular frequency is again $\omega = 5.3$ s^{-1}.

Figure 15.28

In contrast to the situation in Example 15.3, the initial displacement of cart 1 is not equal to the amplitude of the oscillation because the collision increases the cart's displacement from the equilibrium position. In other words, cart 1 moves leftward immediately after the collision. It continues moving in this direction until the elastic restoring force building up in the compressing spring causes the cart to stop. This maximum-compression position gives the amplitude of the oscillation.

❷ **DEVISE PLAN** I can determine the value of the amplitude from the mechanical energy of the cart-spring system, which is the sum of the initial potential energy in the spring and the initial kinetic energy of the cart. The potential energy in the spring is given by Eq. 9.23; because the equilibrium position x_0 is at the origin, this equation reduces to $U_{spring} = \frac{1}{2}kx^2$. The kinetic energy is given by $K = \frac{1}{2}mv^2$. At the position of maximum compression, all of the mechanical energy is stored in the spring, $x = -A$, and so $E_{mech} = U_{spring} = \frac{1}{2}kA^2$.

Once I know A, I can determine the initial phase from Eq. 15.6. I can then use that same equation to solve for t at the position of maximum compression, where $x = -A$.

❸ **EXECUTE PLAN** (a) The initial kinetic and potential energies of the cart-spring system are

$K = \frac{1}{2}(0.50 \text{ kg})(-0.10 \text{ m/s})^2 = 0.0025$ J

$U = \frac{1}{2}kx^2 = \frac{1}{2}(14 \text{ N/m})(-15 \text{ mm})^2 \left(\dfrac{1.0 \text{ m}}{1000 \text{ mm}}\right)^2 = 0.0016$ J

so

$E_{mech} = K + U = (0.0025 \text{ J}) + (0.0016 \text{ J}) = 0.0041$ J.

At the position of maximum compression, all of this energy is stored in the spring, and so $\frac{1}{2}kA^2 = 0.0041$ J, or with the k value given,

$$A = \sqrt{\frac{2(0.0041 \text{ J})}{14 \text{ N/m}}} = 0.024 \text{ m} = 24 \text{ mm}. ✔$$

(b) Substituting the value for A determined in part a and the initial condition $x_i = -15$ mm at $t = 0$ into Eq. 15.6, I obtain

$x(0) = A \sin(0 + \phi_i) = (24 \text{ mm}) \sin \phi_i = -15$ mm

$\sin \phi_i = \dfrac{-15 \text{ mm}}{24 \text{ mm}} = -0.63 \quad$ or $\quad \phi_i = \sin^{-1}(-0.63)$.

Two initial phases satisfy this relationship, $\phi_i = -0.68$ and $\phi_i = -\pi + 0.68 = -2.5$, but only the latter gives a negative x component of the velocity (see Eq. 15.7), as required by the initial condition.

At the first instant of maximum compression, $\sin(\omega t + \phi_i) = -1$, which means $\omega t + \phi_i = -\frac{1}{2}\pi$. Solving for t yields $t = (-\frac{1}{2}\pi - \phi_i)/\omega = [-\frac{1}{2}\pi - (-2.5)]/(5.3 \text{ s}^{-1}) = 0.17$ s. ✔

❹ **EVALUATE RESULT** At 24 mm, the amplitude is greater than the 15-mm initial displacement from the equilibrium position, as I would expect. From the reference circle part of my sketch I see that it takes about one eighth of a cycle to go from the position of impact to the position of maximum compression. From Eq. 15.11 I see that the number of seconds needed to complete one cycle is $T = 2\pi/\omega = 2\pi/(5.3 \text{ s}^{-1}) = 1.2$ s, and so the 0.17-s value I obtained for seconds elapsed between collision and maximum compression is indeed close to one-eighth of a cycle. The assumption that the influence of the spring can be ignored during the collision is justified because the force exerted by the spring is small relative to the force of the impact: At a compression of 15 mm, the magnitude of the force exerted by the spring is $(14 \text{ N/m})(0.015 \text{ m}) = 0.21$ N. The force of impact is given by the time rate of change in the cart's momentum, $\Delta \vec{p}/\Delta t$. The magnitude of the momentum change is $\Delta p = m\Delta v = (0.50 \text{ kg})(0.10 \text{ m/s}) = 0.050$ kg·m/s. If the collision takes place in, say, 20 ms, the magnitude of the force of impact is $(0.050 \text{ kg·m/s})/(0.020 \text{ s}) = 2.5$ N, which is more than 10 times greater than the magnitude of the force exerted by the spring.

✋ **15.13** Suppose cart 2 were not removed from the track of Figure 15.27 immediately after the collision but instead were left stationary at the collision point. (a) At what instant do the two carts collide again? (b) Describe the motion of the two carts after this second collision.

Example 15.5 Vertical oscillations

A block of mass $m = 0.50$ kg is suspended from a spring of spring constant $k = 100$ N/m. (a) How far below the end of the relaxed spring at x_0 is the equilibrium position x_{eq} of the suspended block (**Figure 15.29a**)? (b) Is the frequency f with which the block oscillates about this equilibrium position x_{eq} greater than, smaller than, or equal to that of an identical system that oscillates horizontally about x_0 on a surface for which friction can be ignored (**Figure 15.29b**)?

Figure 15.29 Example 15.5.

(a)

(b)

❶ **GETTING STARTED** I begin by making a free-body diagram for the suspended block, choosing the positive x axis pointing downward. Two forces are exerted on the block: an upward force $\vec{F}^c_{sb}$ exerted by the spring and a downward gravitational force $\vec{F}^G_{Eb}$ exerted by Earth (**Figure 15.30a**). When the suspended block is in translational equilibrium at x_{eq} (which lies below x_0), the vector sum of these forces must be zero. With the block at x_{eq}, the spring is stretched such that the end attached to the block is also at x_{eq}. When the block is below x_{eq}, the spring is stretched farther, causing the magnitude of $\vec{F}^c_{sb}$ to increase, and so now the vector sum of the forces exerted on the block points upward. When the block is above x_{eq} (but below the position x_0 of the end of the spring when it is relaxed), the spring is stretched less than when the block is at x_{eq}, causing the magnitude of $\vec{F}^c_{sb}$ to decrease, and so the vector sum of the forces exerted on the block points downward. The vector sum of $\vec{F}^c_{sb}$ and $\vec{F}^G_{Eb}$ thus serves as a restoring force.

Figure 15.30

(a)

(b)

I also make a free-body diagram for the horizontal arrangement (**Figure 15.30b**), showing only the horizontal forces (the force of gravity and the normal force exerted by the surface cancel out). I let the positive x axis point to the right. In this case, the restoring force is $\vec{F}^c_{sb}$ only.

❷ **DEVISE PLAN** In translational equilibrium, the vector sum of the forces exerted on the suspended block is zero, and so I can determine the magnitude of the force exerted by the spring. I can then use Hooke's law (Eq. 8.20) to determine the distance between the equilibrium position and x_0. To compare the oscillation frequencies of the two systems, I should write the simple harmonic oscillator equation for each system in the form given by Eq. 15.12.

❸ **EXECUTE PLAN** (a) For translational equilibrium, I have

$$\sum F_x = F^c_{sbx} + F^G_{Ebx} = -k(x_{eq} - x_0) + mg = 0,$$

where $x_{eq} - x_0$ is the displacement of the spring's end from its relaxed position. Solving for $x_{eq} - x_0$, I obtain

$$x_{eq} - x_0 = \frac{mg}{k} = \frac{(0.50 \text{ kg})(9.8 \text{ m/s}^2)}{100 \text{ N/m}} = 0.049 \text{ m.} ✔$$

(b) For the horizontal arrangement, I have in the situation depicted in my sketch (Figure 15.30b)

$$\sum F_x = F^c_{sbx} = -k(x - x_0), \tag{1}$$

so if I let the origin of my x axis be at the position of the end of the relaxed spring, $x_0 = 0$, the rightmost factor in Eq. 1 reduces to $-kx$ and thus $\sum F_x = -kx$. Next I turn to the vertical arrangement. In the position illustrated in Figure 15.30a, the x component of the upward force exerted by the spring is

$$F^c_{sbx} = -k(x - x_0) = -k(x - x_{eq}) - k(x_{eq} - x_0). \tag{2}$$

From part a I know that $k(x_{eq} - x_0)$ is equal to mg. The x component of the vector sum of the forces exerted on the block at position x is thus

$$\sum F_x = F^G_{Ebx} + F^c_{sbx} = mg - k(x - x_{eq}) - mg$$

$$= -k(x - x_{eq}).$$

If, as usual, I let the origin be at the equilibrium position, $x_{eq} = 0$, then this result for $\sum F_x$ is identical to Eq. 1. Comparing these results to Eq. 15.12, I see that in both cases $k = m\omega^2$ and so the oscillation frequencies $f = \omega/2\pi$ of the two systems are the same: $f_{vert} = f_{hor}.$ ✔

❹ **EVALUATE RESULT** The two oscillations take place about different equilibrium positions (x_0 for the horizontal case, x_{eq} for the vertical case), but the effect of the combined gravitational and elastic forces in the vertical arrangement is the same as that of just the elastic force in the horizontal arrangement because the force exerted by the spring is linear in the displacement.

👋 **15.14** Convince yourself that the argument presented in the solution to Example 15.5 is also valid for displacements of the block above x_{eq}.

15.7 Restoring torques

Some simple harmonic oscillators involve rotational rather than translational displacements. As an example, consider the disk suspended from a thin fiber shown in **Figure 15.31**. Such a setup is called a *torsional oscillator*. If the disk is rotated in the horizontal plane over an angle ϑ_{max}, the fiber is twisted, and elastic potential energy is stored in the fiber. When the disk is released, it oscillates as energy is converted back and forth between the elastic potential energy in the fiber and the rotational kinetic energy of the disk. Translational oscillations, as in our simple pendulum and block-spring setup, are due to the interplay between a restoring force and inertia; rotational oscillations are due to an interplay between a restoring torque and rotational inertia.

For a quantitative description of the disk's oscillation, we use the rotational form of the equation of motion for the disk, which relates the sum of the torques caused by the forces acting on the disk to its rotational acceleration α_ϑ (Eq. 12.10):

$$\sum \tau_\vartheta = I \alpha_\vartheta, \tag{15.24}$$

where I is the rotational inertia of the disk.

To complete the description, we must relate the torque to the rotational displacement—just as we related force to translational displacement for translational oscillations. In the case of the rotating disk, the torque is caused by the twisted fiber: A clockwise rotation of the fiber causes a counterclockwise torque, and vice versa; greater rotational displacements of the disk cause greater torques. For small rotational displacements, we might expect that the relationship between rotational displacement and torque is linear:

$$\tau_\vartheta = -\kappa(\vartheta - \vartheta_0). \tag{15.25}$$

The minus sign indicates that the direction of the torque is opposite the direction of the rotational displacement: The torque tends to rotate the disk back toward its equilibrium position. This rotational Form of Hooke's law is found to hold for a wide variety of materials. The constant κ (the Greek letter kappa), called the *torsional constant*, depends on the properties of the material being twisted. Just as stiff springs have large spring constants, stiff materials have large torsional constants.

If we let the rotational position at equilibrium be zero, $\vartheta_0 = 0$, we can combine Eqs. 15.24 and 15.25, yielding

$$I\alpha_\vartheta = I\frac{d^2\vartheta}{dt^2} = -\kappa\vartheta \tag{15.26}$$

or

$$\frac{d^2\vartheta}{dt^2} = -\frac{\kappa}{I}\vartheta. \tag{15.27}$$

Figure 15.31 Torsional oscillator.

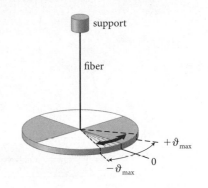

Notice the similarity between this equation and two earlier ones: Eq. 15.10 for a generic harmonic oscillator and Eq. 15.21 for a mass oscillating on a spring. The meaning of the symbols is different, but the mathematical form is identical. The disk therefore executes simple harmonic motion, and the rotational position $\vartheta(t)$ is a sinusoidal function of time.

To find the position as a function of time, we exploit the correspondence between Eqs. 15.21 and 15.27, substituting rotational displacement ϑ for translational displacement x in Eq. 15.23 and rotational inertia I for mass m and the torsional constant κ for the spring constant k in Eq. 15.22:

$$\vartheta = \vartheta_{\max} \sin(\omega t + \phi_i) \tag{15.28}$$

$$\omega = \sqrt{\frac{\kappa}{I}} \quad \text{(torsional oscillator)}, \tag{15.29}$$

where $\vartheta_{\max}$ in Eq. 15.28 is the maximum rotational displacement (the amplitude of the rotational oscillation). Note that the ω in Eq. 15.29 represents the angular frequency of the torsional oscillator, not its rotational speed.

15.15 For the torsional oscillator shown in Figure 15.31, what effect, if any, does a decrease in the radius of the disk have on the oscillation frequency f? Assume the disk's mass is kept the same.

The pendulum is another example of a rotational oscillator. For a pendulum, however, the restoring torque is not caused by an elastic force, and so we cannot use Eq. 15.25. Instead, we must write an expression for the restoring torque due to gravity and relate the magnitude of this torque to the rotational displacement of the pendulum. Consider an object suspended about a rotation axis located a distance ℓ_{cm} from the object's center of mass, as illustrated in **Figure 15.32a**. The restoring torque is provided by the component of the force of gravity perpendicular to ℓ_{cm}: $F^G_{Eo\perp} = -mg \sin \vartheta$ (Figure 15.32b). The lever arm of this force relative to the rotation axis is ℓ_{cm}, and so for a rotational displacement ϑ, the torque caused by the force of gravity about the axis is

$$\tau_\vartheta = -\ell_{cm}(mg \sin \vartheta), \tag{15.30}$$

where m is the object's mass. For small rotational displacements, $\sin \vartheta \approx \vartheta$, and so once again we obtain a restoring torque that is linearly proportional to the rotational displacement:

$$\tau_\vartheta = -(m\ell_{cm} g)\vartheta. \tag{15.31}$$

After $\tau_\vartheta = I\alpha_\vartheta = I\, d^2\vartheta/dt^2$ is substituted for the left side of Eq. 15.31, we get

$$\frac{d^2\vartheta}{dt^2} = -\frac{m\ell_{cm} g}{I}\vartheta, \tag{15.32}$$

and so the angular frequency of oscillation is

$$\omega = \sqrt{\frac{m\ell_{cm} g}{I}} \quad \text{(pendulum)}. \tag{15.33}$$

Figure 15.32 (a) Oscillating pendulum. (b) Extended free-body diagram for the pendulum.

(a)

(b)

Example 15.6 The simple pendulum

Suppose a simple pendulum consisting of a bob of mass m suspended from a string of length ℓ is pulled back and released. What is the period of oscillation of the bob?

❶ GETTING STARTED I begin by making a sketch of the simple pendulum (**Figure 15.33**), indicating the equilibrium position by a vertical dashed line.

Figure 15.33

❷ DEVISE PLAN The period of the pendulum is related to the angular frequency (Eq. 15.1). To calculate the angular frequency, I can use Eq. 15.33 with $\ell_{cm} = \ell$. If I treat the bob as a particle, I can use Eq. 11.30, $I = mr^2$, with $r = \ell$ to calculate the bob's rotational inertia about the point of suspension.

❸ EXECUTE PLAN Substituting the bob's rotational inertia into Eq. 15.33, I get

$$\omega = \sqrt{\frac{m\ell g}{m\ell^2}} = \sqrt{\frac{g}{\ell}},$$

so, from Eq. 15.1, $\omega = 2\pi/T$, I obtain

$$T = \frac{2\pi}{\omega} = 2\pi\sqrt{\frac{\ell}{g}}. \checkmark$$

❹ EVALUATE RESULT My result says that T is independent of the mass m of the bob, in agreement with what is stated in Section 15.4. Increasing g decreases the period as it should: A greater g means a greater restoring force, and so the bob is pulled back to the equilibrium position faster. It also makes sense that increasing ℓ increases the period: As my sketch shows, for greater ℓ the bob has to move a greater distance to return to the equilibrium position.

Example 15.7 Measuring g

The oscillations of a thin rod can be used to determine the value of the acceleration due to gravity. A rod that is 0.800 m long and suspended from one end is observed to complete 100 oscillations in 147 s. What is the value of g at the location of this experiment?

❶ GETTING STARTED I begin by making a sketch of the situation. To simplify the problem, I assume that the rod pivots about the fixed end (**Figure 15.34**).

Figure 15.34

$\ell = 0.800$ m

❷ DEVISE PLAN I calculated the rotational inertia of a thin rod about one end in Example 11.11: $I = \frac{1}{3}m\ell^2$, where m is the rod's mass and ℓ its length. I can use this equation and Eq. 15.33 to solve for g, noting that ℓ_{cm} in Eq. 15.33 is half the length of the rod ($\ell_{cm} = \frac{1}{2}\ell$).

❸ EXECUTE PLAN Substituting the rod's rotational inertia and the center-of-mass distance $\ell_{cm} = \frac{1}{2}\ell$ into Eq. 15.33, I get

$$\omega = \sqrt{\frac{m\frac{1}{2}\ell g}{\frac{1}{3}m\ell^2}} = \sqrt{\frac{3g}{2\ell}}.$$

Solving for g yields $g = \frac{2}{3}\omega^2\ell$. The period of the rod is $(147 \text{ s})/(100) = 1.47$ s, and the angular frequency is $\omega = 2\pi f = 2\pi(1/T) = 2\pi/(1.47 \text{ s}) = 4.27 \text{ s}^{-1}$. Substituting this information into the expression for g yields $g = \frac{2}{3}(4.27 \text{ s}^{-1})^2(0.800 \text{ m}) = 9.74 \text{ m/s}^2$. ✔

❹ EVALUATE RESULT I note that the rod's mass does not appear in my expression for ω. Because ω is proportional to $1/T$, this again confirms what Section 15.4 says about the period of a pendulum being independent of the pendulum's mass because the restoring force is proportional to the pendulum's mass. The value I obtained, 9.74 m/s^2, is reasonably close to the acceleration due to gravity near Earth's surface, giving me confidence in my solution.

15.16 Can you use the experiment described in Example 15.7 to measure the gravitational constant G?

Example 15.8 The simple pendulum as a one-dimensional oscillator

The angular frequency ω of a simple pendulum can be calculated by treating the pendulum as a one-dimensional oscillator. In Section 15.4, we used this approach to analyze the restoring force exerted on a pendulum, considering the effect of the force of gravity on the horizontal displacement of the bob and ignoring the slight difference between the horizontal displacement x and the arc length s along which the bob swings. Show that this treatment yields for ω the same expression I obtained in Example 15.6, $\omega = \sqrt{g/\ell}$.

❶ **GETTING STARTED** I make a sketch of the pendulum, showing the bob displaced a horizontal distance x from its equilibrium position, the distance I must concentrate on in this problem (**Figure 15.35a**). I also draw a free-body diagram for the

Figure 15.35

bob (Figure 15.35b), showing $\vec{F}^{G}_{Eb\parallel}$ and $\vec{F}^{G}_{Eb\perp}$, with the component vectors of $\vec{F}^{G}_{Eb}$ parallel to and perpendicular to the string in its displaced orientation.

❷ **DEVISE PLAN** The component of the gravitational force perpendicular to the string in its displaced orientation, $\vec{F}^{G}_{Eb\perp}$, provides the restoring force. For small displacements, this component is nearly parallel to the x axis, and so I can take $F^{G}_{Eb\perp}$ to be the restoring force in the x direction. This expression will permit me to use the simple harmonic oscillator equation (Eq. 15.10) to obtain an express for ω.

❸ **EXECUTE PLAN** From my free-body diagram, I see that

$$F^{G}_{Eb\perp} = -mg\sin\theta = -mg\frac{x}{\ell},$$

The x component of the force exerted on the bob is equal to $F^{G}_{Eb\perp}\cos\theta$. In the small-angle approximation, $F^{G}_{Eb\perp}\cos\theta \approx F^{G}_{Eb\perp}$. Thus I can write Eq. 15.11 as

$$ma_x \approx -\frac{mg}{\ell}x,$$

or

$$a_x \equiv \frac{d^2x}{dt^2} \approx -\frac{g}{\ell}x.$$

Comparing this result with Eq. 15.10, $d^2x/dt^2 = -\omega^2 x$, tells me that $-\omega^2 x = -(g/\ell)x$, an equality that yields the same angular frequency of oscillation as in Example 15.6: $\omega = \sqrt{g/\ell}$. ✔

❹ **EVALUATE RESULT** Given that my result is the same as that obtained using a different method, I feel confident that it is correct.

Figure 15.36 Damped oscillating systems.

(a) Oscillating block is slowed by friction

(b) Oscillating cart is slowed by air drag on vane

✋ **15.17** Imagine placing a pendulum in an elevator. While the elevator accelerates upward, is the frequency f of the pendulum greater than, smaller than, or equal to the frequency when the elevator is at rest?

15.8 Damped oscillations

Up to this point, we have ignored any dissipation of energy in simple harmonic motion. Mechanical oscillations always involve some friction, however, and so the energy of the oscillation is slowly converted to thermal energy. As this conversion takes place, the oscillating object slows down. The general term for this slowing down because of energy dissipation is *damping,* and the system is said to execute a **damped oscillation.**

Consider, for example, the two systems in **Figure 15.36**. Figure 15.36a shows a block oscillating under the action of a spring. In Figure 15.36b the block is replaced by a cart with a vane on top. As the block oscillates, it rubs against the floor, and its motion is slowed down by friction with the floor. The motion of the cart is hindered by air drag caused by the vane.

The figure also shows the free-body diagrams for the block and the cart. Each object is subject to two forces in the horizontal direction: a restoring force exerted by the spring and a *damping force*—a force due to friction or drag that dissipates the energy of the oscillation. Damping forces can take many forms. For the oscillating block rubbing on the floor, the magnitude of the force of kinetic friction is $F^{k}_{fb} = \mu_k(mg)$, with μ_k the coefficient of kinetic friction. The direction of this force is always opposite the direction of motion (that is, in the direction opposite the direction of the velocity vector).

Drag forces exerted by air or liquids at low speeds tend to be proportional to the velocity of the object: The faster you ride your bicycle, for instance, the greater the drag force exerted on you by the air. So

$$\vec{F}_{ac}^{d} = -b\vec{v} \quad \text{(low speed)}, \tag{15.34}$$

where the coefficient b, called the *damping coefficient*, depends on the shape of the object on which the drag force acts and on the properties of the gas or liquid exerting the force. The SI units of the damping coefficient are kg/s. The minus sign tells you that the direction of the drag force is opposite the direction of the velocity.

For most oscillators, velocity-dependent drag forces are the main cause of energy dissipation. In the presence of drag, the equation of motion for the cart in Figure 15.36 becomes

$$\sum F_x = F_{scx}^{c} + F_{acx}^{d} = -kx - bv_x = ma_x, \tag{15.35}$$

where k is the spring constant and m the mass of the cart. When we write the x components of the velocity and the acceleration as time derivatives of x, Eq. 15.35 can be written in the form

$$m\frac{d^2x}{dt^2} + b\frac{dx}{dt} + kx = 0. \tag{15.36}$$

As long as the damping is not too great, the solution to this differential equation is a sinusoidally varying function whose amplitude decreases with time. The solution, given here without proof, is

$$x(t) = Ae^{-bt/2m}\sin(\omega_d t + \phi_i), \tag{15.37}$$

where the angular frequency ω_d of the damped oscillator is given by

$$\omega_d = \sqrt{\frac{k}{m} - \frac{b^2}{4m^2}} = \sqrt{\omega^2 - \left(\frac{b}{2m}\right)^2}. \tag{15.38}$$

Figure 15.37 shows oscillations for various values of the damping coefficient b. For $b = 0$, there is no damping, which means $\omega_d = \omega$ and $e^{-bt/2m} = 1$. In this case,

Figure 15.37 Damped simple harmonic motion for various values of the damping coefficient b not so great as to prevent oscillations.

Eq. 15.37 is identical to Eq. 15.6, the equation for the position of an undamped simple harmonic oscillator. For light damping (small b), the second term in the square root in Eq. 15.38 is negligible, and the damping does not affect the angular frequency of the oscillation: $\omega_d \approx \omega_0$. As Figure 15.37 shows, however, damping decreases the amplitude of the oscillation with each swing. Mathematically, this is expressed by the exponential (see Appendix B) factor $e^{-bt/2m}$ in Eq. 15.37, which makes the amplitude at any given instant equal to $x_{max} = Ae^{-bt/2m}$, where x_{max} is the time-dependent amplitude of the damped oscillator and A is the (constant) amplitude of the undamped system. In the figure, this decreasing amplitude x_{max} is indicated by the dashed exponential curves, called the *envelope* of the oscillation. The stronger the damping, the faster the amplitude decreases. For very large damping, oscillations cease to occur and the system just returns to the equilibrium position. Such a system is said to be *overdamped*.

The ratio m/b has units of time, and it is customary to call this ratio the **time constant** $\tau \equiv m/b$. (Even though the symbol for the time constant is the same as that for torque, there is no relationship between the two.) With this simplification, the decreasing amplitude can be written as

$$x_{max}(t) = Ae^{-t/2\tau}. \tag{15.39}$$

The mechanical energy of the oscillator, which is proportional to the square of the amplitude (Eq. 15.17), thus decreases as

$$E(t) = \tfrac{1}{2}m\omega^2 x_{max}^2 = (\tfrac{1}{2}m\omega^2 A^2)e^{-t/\tau} = E_0\, e^{-t/\tau}, \tag{15.40}$$

where $E_0 = \tfrac{1}{2}m\omega^2 A_0^2$ is the initial mechanical energy. Equation 15.40 shows that after a time interval equal to the time constant, so that $t = \tau$, the energy has decreased to $e^{-\tau/\tau} = e^{-1} \approx 0.37$ of its initial value; only about one-third of the initial energy remains. During each time interval of duration τ, the energy again decreases by the factor e^{-1}. After two time constants, for instance, only about 10% of the initial energy remains.

Because oscillation periods vary widely, it is often convenient to express the time constant τ in terms of the period T so that we know after how many *cycles* (rather than seconds) the energy has decreased by a certain factor. In terms of cycles, the decay of the oscillation can be characterized by the *quality factor*, defined as

$$Q \equiv \omega\tau = 2\pi\frac{\tau}{T}. \tag{15.41}$$

The quality factor is a unitless ratio similar to the rotational coordinate ϑ—if $Q = 2\pi$, then $\tau = T$, and so the energy decays by a factor of e^{-1} in one cycle. When $Q = 1000(2\pi)$, it takes 1000 cycles for the energy to decay by a factor of e^{-1}. A high Q implies that $\omega_d \approx \omega_0$. For mechanical oscillators with low friction (piano strings, tuning forks), Q can be as large as a few thousand, meaning the oscillator executes thousands of oscillations before its energy decreases by a factor of e^{-1}. A bell with a large Q rings for a longer time interval than one with a small Q.

15.18 A tuning fork that sounds the tone musicians call middle C oscillates at frequency $f = 262$ Hz. If the amplitude of the fork's oscillation decreases by a factor of 3 in 4.0 s, what are (*a*) the time constant of the oscillation and (*b*) the quality factor?

Chapter Glossary

SI units of physical quantities are given in parentheses.

Angular frequency $\omega\,(\text{s}^{-1})$ A positive scalar equal to the rotational speed of a rotating object whose projection produces an oscillation of frequency f, so that

$$\omega = 2\pi f. \tag{15.4}$$

Amplitude $A\,(\text{m})$ A positive scalar equal to the magnitude of the maximum displacement in a periodic motion.

Damped oscillation An oscillation whose amplitude decreases over time due to dissipation of energy.

Fourier's theorem Any periodic function with period T can be written as a sum of sinusoidal functions of frequency $f_n = n/T$, where n is a positive integer.

Frequency $f\,(\text{Hz})$ A positive scalar equal to the number of cycles per second of a periodic motion. The frequency is the inverse of the period:

$$f \equiv 1/T. \tag{15.2}$$

Fundamental frequency $f_1\,(\text{Hz})$ The frequency of the first term ($n = 1$) in the sum of sinusoidal functions of frequency $f_n = n/T$ that add up to describe a periodic function.

Harmonic A term in a sum of sinusoidal functions used to describe periodic functions. The lowest frequency term is called the *first harmonic*. The other terms are called *higher harmonics*.

Hertz (Hz) The derived SI unit of frequency; $1\ \text{Hz} \equiv 1\ \text{s}^{-1}$.

Oscillation Periodic back-and-forth motion. Also called *vibration*.

Periodic motion Any motion that repeats itself at regular time intervals, called the *period T* of the motion.

Phase ϕ (unitless) A scalar that specifies the time-dependent argument of the sine function describing simple harmonic motion:

$$\phi(t) = \omega t + \phi_{\text{i}}. \tag{15.5}$$

The constant ϕ_{i}, the *initial phase*, specifies the phase at $t = 0$.

Phasor A rotating arrow whose component on a vertical axis traces out a simple harmonic motion.

Reference circle A circle traced out by the tip of a phasor.

Simple harmonic motion Motion for which the displacement is a sinusoidally varying function of time given by

$$x(t) = A\sin(\omega t + \phi_{\text{i}}), \tag{15.6}$$

where A is the *amplitude,* ω the *angular frequency*, and ϕ_{i} the *initial phase* of the motion. The period T of a simple harmonic oscillator is independent of the amplitude A.

Simple harmonic oscillator equation An equation satisfied by any system that undergoes simple harmonic motion:

$$\frac{d^2x}{dt^2} = -\omega^2 x, \tag{15.10}$$

where x represents some sort of displacement and ω is the angular frequency of the oscillation. Any such system is called a *simple harmonic oscillator*.

Spectrum A graph that shows the squares of the amplitude A of the simple harmonic components of a periodic function versus frequency f. The spectrum provides a visual display of the frequency content of the function.

Time constant $\tau\,(\text{s})$ A scalar that gives the interval over which the energy of a damped simple harmonic oscillator is reduced by a factor of $1/e$.

Vibration See *oscillation*.

16 Waves in One Dimension

CONCEPTS

16.1 Representing waves graphically

16.2 Wave propagation

16.3 Superposition of waves

16.4 Boundary effects

QUANTITATIVE TOOLS

16.5 Wave functions

16.6 Standing waves

16.7 Wave speed

16.8 Energy transport in waves

16.9 The wave equation

Many phenomena around us involve waves. Throw a stone into a pond and ripples move outward along the surface of the water. Clap your hands and a sound wave travels outward. A large earthquake is detected all over the world because the earthquake causes a wave to propagate through Earth's interior. In general, a **wave** is a *disturbance* propagating (moving) either through a material or through empty space.

The most important feature of waves is that they do not carry matter from one place to another. After a wave has passed through a medium, the medium looks just as it did before it was disturbed. You prove this every time you and a stadium full of other fans work together to create a wave (**Figure 16.1**). Once you've done your small part—stand up, sit down—you are sitting in the same seat; in other words, you haven't moved from one location to another in the stadium. Or throw a rock into a still pond and watch the motion of a floating leaf: The leaf rises and falls as the wave created by the rock passes by but never moves away from its original position. Once the pond is still again, the leaf is just where it was before. A little thought will tell you that the same is true for every molecule of water in the pond. As we shall see, momentum and energy—not matter—are what move along with any wave.

Waves are collective phenomena: A stadium full of fans can create a wave that travels around the stadium; a single person, on the other hand, cannot create such a wave. The person can move up and down or run from one place to another, but neither motion is a wave. A wave can thus never exist at a single position in space: A single water molecule does not make a wave—a water wave requires an extended volume of water.

The examples with which I opened this chapter—water waves, sound waves, seismic waves—are all *mechanical waves,* which are waves that involve the (temporary) displacement of particles. Such waves require a *medium* to propagate along

or through. The propagation is caused by the interaction of the particles in the medium. The medium for water ripples is the water; for the sound of clapping hands, the medium is the air; for seismic waves, it is the material that makes up Earth's interior. Some waves, such as radio waves and light, do not require any medium; they can propagate through empty space as well as through a medium. Even though such *nonmechanical waves* are very different in origin and nature from the mechanical waves we discuss in this chapter and the next, they share many of the properties of mechanical waves. For this reason, when we deal with nonmechanical waves in later chapters, we shall carry over many results derived for mechanical waves.

16.1 Representing waves graphically

Suppose one end of a long, taut string is rapidly displaced up and down once, as shown in **Figure 16.2**. As the end of the string is raised, it pulls up the neighboring part of the string. As that neighboring part begins moving up,

Figure 16.2 Generation of a wave pulse that propagates along a string.

Figure 16.1 Fans at a stadium creating a wave. People get up and raise their arms as soon as the person next to them does so. Because of the small delay between one person and the next, not everyone gets up at the same instant, and the wave travels around the stadium at some finite speed.

it pulls up the next part of the string, which, in turn, pulls up the next part, and so forth. The upward displacement of the end of the string is thus transmitted along the string because neighboring pieces of the string pull on each other. As the end of the string is moved back down, a similar chain of events occurs in the reverse direction. This pulling along of neighboring pieces of string, first up and then down, produces a **wave pulse,** which travels along the string at constant speed without changing shape. It is important that you do not confuse the horizontal motion of the pulse with the vertical-only motion of the string. The medium through which the pulse passes does not move in the horizontal direction. Each particle of the string moves only once up and once down as the pulse passes through it. **Figure 16.3** shows this vertical-only motion for a string of beads.

🖐 **16.1** (*a*) Using the choice of axes shown in Figure 16.3, draw a position-versus-time graph showing how the *x* and *y* components of the position of the large bead change with time. (*b*) Are the *x* and *y* components of the velocity of the large bead positive, zero, or negative while the bead is on the leading edge of the pulse? Repeat for the trailing edge.

Figure 16.3 shows that the wave motion is different from the motion of the particles of the medium through

Figure 16.3 Video frames sequence of a wave pulse propagating along a string of beads.

0

Motion of bead is entirely vertical . . .

0.06 s

0.12 s

. . . while pulse propagates to the right.

0.18 s

0.24 s

0.30 s

0.36 s

which the pulse travels. The beads move in the vertical direction only, with each bead executing the same motion— first up and then down. Each bead moves at a different instant, however: first bead 1, then bead 2, then bead 3, and so on. At the leading edge of the pulse, each bead's motion is upward; at the trailing edge, it is downward. After the pulse has passed, all the beads are back in their initial positions.

An important point to keep in mind therefore is:

The motion of a wave (or of a single wave pulse) is distinct from the motion of the particles in the medium that transmits the wave (or pulse).

To emphasize this point, we shall use the letter *c* to denote the **wave speed** of a wave through a medium (along a string in this case) and *v* to denote the speed of the particles in the medium (the vertical motion of the beads in this case).*

🖐 **16.2** (*a*) Is the wave speed *c* of the pulse in Figure 16.3 constant? (*b*) Determine that speed if the distance between adjacent beads is 5.0 mm.

As this checkpoint shows:

The wave speed *c* of a wave pulse along a string is constant.

The motion of the various parts of the string, however, is not so simple. As the pulse propagates down the string, the displacements of various particles depend on time *and* on position along the string. At any given instant, different particles on the string have different displacements. Figures 16.2 and 16.3 show "snapshots" of a wave pulse along a string. Each snapshot shows the displacements of the particles on the string from their equilibrium positions as a function of position at one instant. For example, **Figure 16.4a** shows a snapshot of a triangular wave pulse traveling along a string. Such a triangular wave pulse is created by moving the end of the string first upward and then more rapidly downward. The snapshot is superimposed on a calibrated grid so that we can read off the displacements of various particles of the string from their equilibrium positions. The vector $\vec{D}$ in Figure 16.4a represents the **displacement** of the particle at $x = 1.0$ m at instant $t = 0.94$ s. In the context of waves, displacement is denoted by the symbol $\vec{D}$, and the initial position is always taken to be the equilibrium position of the particle.

The graphic representation of all the particle displacements at this instant is shown in Figure 16.4b, which gives the *y* components of the displacements of the particles

*We use *c* for the speed of *any* wave, not just light (which is also a wave). The important point is never to confuse the speed of a wave with the speed of the particles being disturbed by the wave.

Figure 16.4 Distinction between the wave function and displacement curves for a triangular wave pulse propagating along a string parallel to the *x* axis.

(*a*) Snapshot of wave at *t* = 0.94 s

(*b*) Wave function at *t* = 0.94 s

(*c*) Displacement curve for particle located at *x* = 0

(*d*) Displacement curve for particle located at *x* = 1.0 m

of the string as a function of position *x* along the string (the left end of the string being at *x* = 0). The function shown in Figure 16.4*b* is called the **wave function.** The wave function represents the shape of the wave at a given instant and changes with time as the wave travels along the string.

16.3 From Figure 16.4*a*, determine the displacement of a point (*a*) 1.0 m, (*b*) 1.5 m, and (*c*) 2.0 m from the end of the string. (*d*) On a snapshot taken a short time interval later, is the displacement at *x* = 1.5 m greater than, equal to, or smaller than that shown in Figure 16.4*a*?

A complementary way of representing the wave pulse of Figure 16.4*a* is to plot the displacement of one particle on the string as a function of time. Figure 16.4*c*, for example, shows the *y* component of the displacement of the end of the string at *x* = 0 as a function of time. The function shown in Figure 16.4*c* is called the **displacement curve.** The graph shows that the end of the string started moving up at *t* = 0, reached a maximum displacement of about +0.50 m at about *t* = 0.50 s, and then quickly moved back down to its initial position, which it reached at about 0.63 s. This is the motion that generated the triangular wave pulse propagating along the string.

The displacement curve for any string through which a wave pulse moves is different for different particles on the string, as you can see by comparing Figure 16.4*c* and *d*. Figure 16.4*d* shows the displacement curve for the particle at *x* = 1.0 m. The displacement remains zero until the leading edge of the pulse has traveled from *x* = 0 to *x* = 1.0 m. This happens at *t* = 0.50 s, and at that instant the leading edge of the pulse begins raising the *x* = 1.0 m particle until it reaches its maximum displacement at *t* = 1.0 s. The much steeper trailing end of the pulse shown in Figure 16.4*a* then quickly returns the particle to its equilibrium position between *t* = 1.0 s and *t* = 1.1 s.

Why is the displacement curve the mirror image of the wave function? Because the wave pulse travels to the right, the leading edge of the pulse is on the right on the wave function graph. The displacement curve, on the other hand, has small values of *t* (earlier instants) on the left and large values of *t* (later instants) on the right. So in Figure 16.4*c* the leading edge of the pulse is on the *left*. (To convince yourself, look at the particle at *x* = 1.0 m in Figure 16.4*a* and visualize the motion of that particle as the pulse travels past it. Sketch the displacement of the particle as a function of time and compare your result with Figure 16.4*d*).

Note that the displacement curves in Figure 16.4*c* and *d* have the same form: The one for *x* = 1.0 m is simply shifted to the right. This tells us that both particles execute the same motion at different instants.

16.4 (*a*) From Figure 16.4*c* and *d*, determine how long it takes the pulse to travel from *x* = 0 to *x* = 1.0 m. (*b*) Using your answer to part *a*, determine the wave speed.

Mechanical waves are divided into two categories, depending on how the medium moves relative to the wave motion. For a wave propagating along a string, the medium movement is perpendicular to the pulse movement. Such waves are called **transverse waves.** In the other type of

Figure 16.5 Longitudinal wave pulse propagating along a spring.

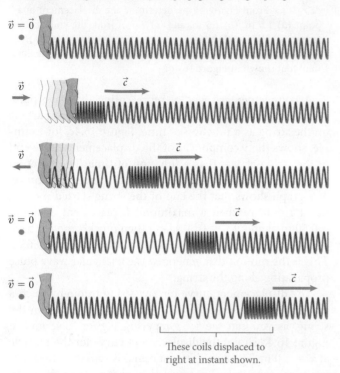

These coils displaced to right at instant shown.

Figure 16.6 Wave function and displacement curve for a longitudinal wave pulse propagating along a spring.

(*a*) Snapshot of wave pulse at instant t_1

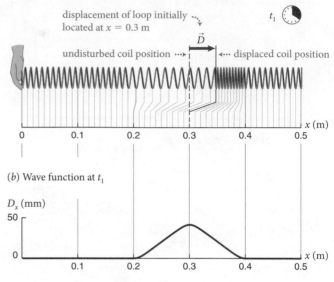

(*b*) Wave function at t_1

(*c*) Displacement curve for coil located at $x = 0$

mechanical wave, the medium movement is parallel to the pulse movement, and waves that behave this way are called **longitudinal waves.** Let's now look at this second type of wave in more detail.

Consider a long coil spring whose end is rapidly displaced back and forth as in **Figure 16.5**. As the left end of the spring is displaced to the right, each coil pushes on the next, displacing the coils one after the other to the right. When the left end is pulled back to its original position, each coil pulls the next one back. The result is again a wave pulse propagating to the right, with each coil temporarily being displaced in the direction of propagation of the wave pulse.

Even though the direction of motion of the individual coils coincides with the direction of propagation of the wave pulse, the motion of the coils and that of the pulse are still distinct. The individual coils move back and forth, but the wave pulse travels at constant speed along the spring.

Longitudinal waves can also be represented using wave functions and displacement curves, but now the wave functions no longer look like a snapshot of the propagating wave. **Figure 16.6***a* shows a snapshot of a pulse propagating along a spring at some instant t_1, overlaid on a calibrated grid. The corresponding wave function is shown in Figure 16.6*b*—the wave function gives the x component of the displacement of each coil as a function of the coil's position. The coils between $x = 0$ and $x = +0.20$ m are undisturbed, and hence the displacement $\vec{D}$ is zero between $x = 0$ and $x = +0.20$ m. The coils between $x = +0.20$ m and $x = +0.40$ m are all displaced rightward. The x component of the displacement is positive because the

displacement is in the positive x direction. To the right of $x = +0.40$ m, the displacement is again zero because the pulse has not yet reached that part of the spring.

Figure 16.6*c* shows the displacement curve for the end of the spring at $x = 0$.

16.5 (*a*) The pulse in Figure 16.6*b* is symmetrical even though Figure 16.6*a* shows that the length of the stretched portion of the spring is 0.15 m and the length of the compressed portion of the spring is only 0.05 m. Explain how the symmetrical curve of Figure 16.6*b* is a correct representation of the asymmetrical situation shown in Figure 16.6*a*. (*b*) Suppose that instead of the end of the spring moving to the right, as illustrated in Figure 16.6, the end is moved to the left. Would this disturbance still cause a wave pulse to travel to the right? If yes, sketch the wave function for this wave pulse at some instant $t > 0$. If no, what happens instead?

16.2 Wave propagation

A wave pulse is not an object—it has no mass—and so the description of wave motion is very different from the description of the motion of objects. To study the propagation of a wave pulse along a string, let us consider a collection of beads connected by short strings. The mass of the strings is negligible relative to that of the beads. **Figure 16.7***a* shows

Figure 16.7 Forces and accelerations that cause a wave pulse to propagate along a string of beads.

(*a*) Wave pulse propagates along string of beads

(*b*) Free-body diagrams for bead 3

(*c*) Velocity and acceleration vectors for bead 3

the first ten of these beads as a pulse travels along the string. The vertical gray lines show that the motion of the beads is entirely vertical.

Let us focus on the third bead along the string. At t_1 the left end of the string has just begun moving up, and only bead 1 is displaced from its initial position. The top free-body diagram in Figure 16.7b shows the two contact forces exerted on bead 3. If the string is held taut, $\vec{F}_{23}^c$ and $\vec{F}_{43}^c$ point in opposite horizontal directions. (This amounts to saying that the force of gravity on the beads is negligible relative to the contact forces exerted by the strings, and because the bead does not accelerate, the vector sum of the forces exerted on it must be zero.)

16.6 Answer these five questions about the situation at t_1 in Figure 16.7, assuming the right end of the string of beads is attached to a wall that is not shown. (a) If $F_{43}^c = 5$ N, what is the magnitude of the force exerted by the wall on the rightmost bead? (b) What is the magnitude of the horizontal component of $\vec{F}_{12}^c$? (c) What is the direction of the force exerted by the hand on the string? (d) How does the magnitude of this force compare with the magnitude F_{43}^c? (e) What are the effects of the horizontal and vertical components of this force?

This checkpoint makes an important point: If the string is held taut, the magnitudes of the horizontal components of all the contact forces between adjacent beads are equal to the tension $\mathcal{T}$ in the string.

At t_2 the leading edge of the pulse has propagated to bead 3. Because of the displacement of bead 2, $\vec{F}_{23}^c$ is no longer horizontal. The displacement of 2 also causes the string between 2 and 3 to stretch, and so the magnitude F_{23}^c increases.

The magnitude of the horizontal component of $\vec{F}_{23}^c$ is still equal to $\mathcal{T}$, but the vector sum of the forces exerted on bead 3 is now nonzero and points vertically upward. Consequently, bead 3 now has a nonzero upward acceleration and so begins moving upward (Figure 16.7c). As it moves upward, it stretches and changes the direction of the string connecting it to bead 4, and so the magnitude and direction of $\vec{F}_{43}^c$ change. These changes in $\vec{F}_{43}^c$ have two effects: $\vec{F}_{43}^c$ begins to slow down bead 3, and the reciprocal force $\vec{F}_{34}^c$ begins to accelerate bead 4 upward.

At some instant between t_3 and t_4, $\vec{F}_{23}^c$ and $\vec{F}_{43}^c$ again become equal in magnitude and opposite in direction (but this time with $\vec{F}_{23}^c$ directed upward and to the left and $\vec{F}_{43}^c$ directed downward and to the right), and so the vector sum of the forces exerted on bead 3 is zero. As the bead continues to move upward, the vector sum of the forces begins to oppose the bead's motion (free-body diagram at t_4). Consequently the bead slows down until it comes to a stop at t_5. At that instant, the bead has reached its maximum displacement, and the vector sum of the forces exerted on it points downward. As the bead moves back down, the vector sum of the forces exerted on it decreases. At t_7 the vector sum points upward again, slowing the downward motion of the

bead until it reaches its initial position again at t_8. Once the pulse has moved beyond bead 3 and the string around it is straight again, the vector sum of $\vec{F}_{23}^c$ and $\vec{F}_{43}^c$ is again zero, and so the bead remains at rest.

16.7 (a) Note that the displacement of bead 4 at t_4 in Figure 16.7a is the same as that of bead 3 at t_3. How do the velocity and acceleration of bead 4 at t_4 compare with those of bead 3 at t_3? (b) You move one end of two different strings, A and B, up and down in the same way. Suppose the resulting pulse travels twice as fast on string A as on string B. How does the velocity of a particle of string A compare with the velocity of a particle of string B that has the same nonzero displacement? (c) Sketch the pulses as they propagate along the two strings and point out any differences between the two. (d) For each string, consider a particle located 0.20 m from the left end. Sketch a displacement-versus-time graph for each particle, and point out any differences between your two graphs.

Be sure not to skip Checkpoint 16.7 because it makes two very important—and somewhat counter-intuitive—points:

When a particle of the string is displaced from its equilibrium position, its velocity $\vec{v}$ and acceleration $\vec{a}$ are determined only by the initial disturbance and are independent of the wave speed c.

All particles of the string execute the same motion as that caused by the initial disturbance, *regardless of wave speed c* (which determines only how quickly they execute this motion after one another). As Checkpoint 16.7 shows, however, the *shape* of the pulse depends on c:

For a given disturbance, high wave speeds yield wave pulses that are stretched out and low wave speeds result in pulses that are more compressed.

Regardless of the pulse shape, however, any particle of the string that reaches a certain displacement has the same velocity and acceleration as any other particle at the instant it reaches that same displacement in the same part of the pulse.

What determines the wave speed? Our analysis of Figure 16.7 shows that the propagation of a wave pulse along a string is due to the forces exerted by each piece on the neighboring pieces. This suggests that wave speed is related to the strength of these forces. Let us therefore investigate what happens if we change the magnitude of the tension in the string.

Suppose that at instant t_3 in Figure 16.7, when bead 3 is on the leading edge of the pulse, this bead has an acceleration $\vec{a}$ when its vertical displacement is $\vec{D}$ (**Figure 16.8a**). This acceleration is caused by the vector sum $\Sigma \vec{F}$ of the forces exerted on the bead. If we now increase the tension in the string (Figure 16.8b), the magnitudes of the horizontal components of the contact forces increase by the same amount. Because the contact forces are now greater, the vector sum of the forces exerted on bead 3 reaches the same value as in Figure 16.8a with a smaller displacement

Figure 16.8 Effects of tension and mass on wave speed. (*a*) The free-body diagrams show the angle between $\vec{F}^c_{23}$ and $\vec{F}^c_{43}$ that is required to cause an acceleration $\vec{a}$ at a displacement $\vec{D}$. (*b*) When the tension is greater, a shallower angle is required to produce the same condition so the wave propagates faster. (*c*) When the mass is greater, a sharper angle is required to produce the same condition so the wave propagates more slowly.

of bead 2. In other words, it takes a shorter time interval for the pulse to propagate from one bead to the next. A greater tension in the string thus causes a higher wave speed.

Increasing the mass of the beads accomplishes the opposite effect: For a given tension, increasing the mass of each bead decreases the beads' accelerations. To give this larger bead 3 the same acceleration $\vec{a}$ that the smaller bead 3 in Figure 16.8*a* has, bead 2 must now be displaced farther. Thus now it takes a longer time interval for the pulse to propagate from one bead to the next (Figure 16.4*c*). Increasing the mass of the beads corresponds to increasing the mass per unit length of a continuous string.

The speed *c* of a wave propagating along a string increases with increasing tension in the string and decreases with increasing mass per unit length along the string.

This result makes sense: A greater tension means a greater restoring force and therefore a greater tendency to pass the displacement along, resulting in a higher wave speed. If the mass is greater, there is a greater resistance to passing the displacement along, and so the wave speed is lower.

16.8 Two strings, A and B, are identical except that the tension in A is greater than that in B. Suppose you move the left end of each string rapidly up and down once. For each string, sketch (*a*) the wave functions at the instant the pulse on A has traveled halfway down the length of the string and (*b*) the displacement curve for a particle midway down the string.

If the end of a string is made to execute a periodic motion, the resulting wave is called a **periodic wave. Figure 16.9** shows a special type of periodic wave, called a **harmonic wave,** obtained by moving the end of the string so that it oscillates harmonically. The result is a sinusoidally shaped wave traveling along the string.

16.9 Plot the displacement of the left end of the string in Figure 16.9 as a function of time. What similarities and differences exist between your graph and the shape of the wave in Figure 16.9?

Note how the shape of the string in Figure 16.9 resembles the curves representing simple harmonic oscillations from Chapter 15. The shape in Figure 16.9, however, represents the displacement of the medium as a function of *position*, whereas the simple harmonic oscillator curves in Chapter 15 represented displacement as a function of *time*. If you focus on one particle of the string as the wave moves through it, however, you would see that its up-and-down motion is a delayed version of the hand's periodic motion. So a number of quantities we have used to describe periodic motion are also useful to describe waves (*amplitude:* maximum displacement of any given particle of the medium from its equilibrium position; *frequency:* number of cycles per second executed by each particle of the medium; *period:* time interval taken to complete one cycle). A periodic wave repeats itself over a distance called the **wavelength,** denoted by the symbol λ (Figure 16.9). Each time the left end of the

CONCEPTS

Figure 16.9 If the end of a string is made to execute a simple harmonic motion, the resulting traveling wave is sinusoidal in shape. During one period of the motion, the wave advances by one wavelength.

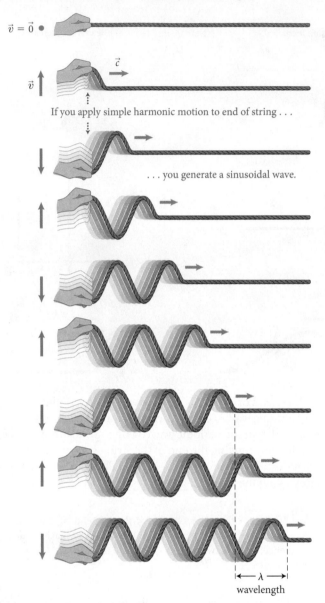

If you apply simple harmonic motion to end of string . . .

. . . you generate a sinusoidal wave.

wavelength

Figure 16.10 The effect on a wave pulse of the speed with which the hand moves up and down. In each case the leading edge of the pulse propagates the same distance during the same time interval, showing that the wave speed c is independent of the velocities $\vec{v}$ of the particles in the string.

(*a*) String moved slowly   (*b*) String moved quickly

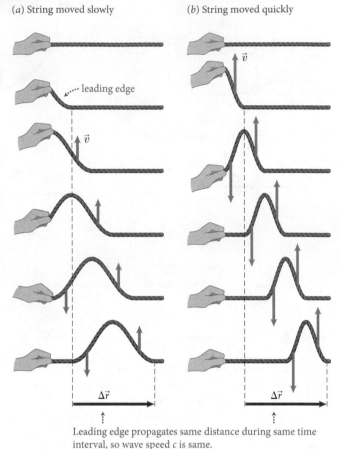

leading edge

Leading edge propagates same distance during same time interval, so wave speed c is same.

string executes a complete oscillation, the wave advances by one wavelength. If the speed at which the wave propagates is c, then the wave advances a distance cT during the period T of the sinusoidal motion. Therefore:

> **The wavelength of a periodic wave is equal to the product of the wave speed and the period of the wave motion.**

Contrary to what you may expect, moving your hand up and down more quickly does not generate a faster-traveling pulse. **Figure 16.10** shows two pulses generated on identical strings held under identical tensions. The end of the string in Figure 16.10*b* is displaced up and down more quickly than that in Figure 16.10*a*. Both pulses have the same

displacement $\Delta\vec{r}$ during a time interval Δt, so the wave speed c is the same for both pulses. To a very good approximation, we determine experimentally that:

> **The speed c of a wave propagating along a string is independent of the velocities $\vec{v}$ of the individual pieces of string. The value of c is determined entirely by the properties of the medium.**

If wave speed depended on the velocity of the particles, the shape of a wave pulse would change as it propagates because some parts of it would propagate more quickly than others. As long as the displacement caused by the wave is not too large, however, the shape of the waves remains unchanged (see Figure 16.3).

✋ **16.10** Consider a harmonic wave traveling along a string. Are the following quantities determined by the source of the wave, by the properties of the string, or by both: (*a*) the period of oscillation of a particle of the string; (*b*) the speed c at which the wave travels along the string; (*c*) the wavelength; (*d*) the maximum speed v of a particle of the string?

CONCEPTS

Figure 16.11 A wave pulse carries kinetic and potential energy. If there is no energy dissipation, the amount of energy in (b) is the same as that in (a).

(a)

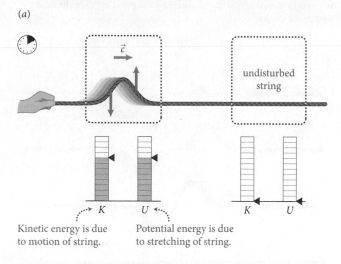

Kinetic energy is due to motion of string.

Potential energy is due to stretching of string.

(b)

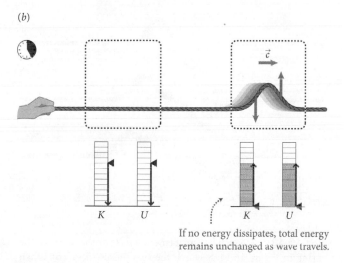

If no energy dissipates, total energy remains unchanged as wave travels.

Figure 16.12 Constructive interference. Two pulses propagating in opposite directions interfere constructively if they displace the string particles in the same direction (here, upward). When the pulses cross, their displacements add algebraically, giving rise to a displacement greater than that caused by either pulse individually. The pulses do not interact with each other: After they separate, their shapes are unaltered.

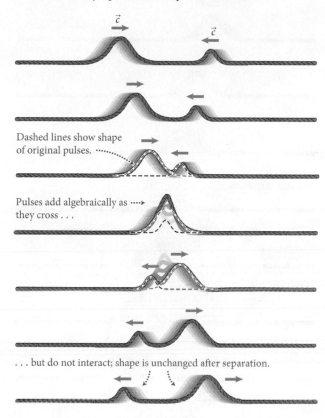

Dashed lines show shape of original pulses.

Pulses add algebraically as they cross . . .

. . . but do not interact; shape is unchanged after separation.

Figure 16.11 illustrates how a propagating wave pulse carries two forms of energy along with it: kinetic energy associated with the motion of individual particles and elastic potential energy associated with the stretching of the string as the pulse is passing through. In Section 16.3 we shall see that a mechanical wave always carries equal amounts of these two forms of energy.

16.11 Does the wave pulse in Figure 16.11 also carry along momentum? Justify your answer.

16.3 Superposition of waves

Waves have a remarkable property: Two waves can pass straight through each other without changing each other's shape. **Figure 16.12** shows a series of snapshots of two pulses propagating toward each other along a string. When the two pulses overlap, the displacements caused by the two waves add algebraically, provided the medium obeys Hooke's law (see Section 8.9) for the combined displacement. This phenomenon is called the **superposition of waves:**

> If two or more waves overlap in a medium that obeys Hooke's law, then the resulting wave function at any instant is the algebraic sum of the individual wave functions.

The resulting wave may have a very complicated shape when the waves overlap, but when they separate again, each wave still has its original shape.

The superposition of waves further distinguishes waves from objects: Two objects cannot occupy the same location in space at the same instant, but two waves *can* occupy the same location at the same instant.

Because the wave functions of two overlapping waves add algebraically, the resultant displacement is greater than that of either wave when the individual displacements have the same sign (Figure 16.12). When they have opposite signs (**Figure 16.13**), the wave with the smaller displacement decreases the displacement caused by the other wave.

When two waves overlap, we say that the waves *interfere* with each other, and the phenomenon is called **interference.** The adding of waves of the same sign, as in Figure 16.12,

Figure 16.13 Destructive interference. Two pulses propagating in opposite directions interfere destructively if they displace the string particles in opposite directions. When the pulses cross, their displacements add algebraically, giving rise to a decreased displacement. After the pulses separate, their shapes are unaltered.

Figure 16.14 Complete destructive interference of two pulses of identical shape propagating in opposite directions while displacing string particles in opposite directions. At the instant the pulses overlap, their displacements add to zero.

Dashed lines show shape of original pulses.

Point where pulses meet never moves up or down.

is called *constructive interference,* and the adding of waves of opposite signs, as in Figure 16.13, is called *destructive interference.* This terminology is somewhat misleading because the waves do not *interact* in any way. As you can see from Figures 16.12 and 16.13, when the two waves separate, their shapes are unchanged. Although there is no destruction or construction, interference of waves does affect the displacement that occurs at specific locations, as the next checkpoint shows.

16.12 (*a*) Is the maximum displacement the same for all particles of the string in Figure 16.12? For all particles of the string in Figure 16.13? (*b*) For each string, sketch a displacement curve for a point near the left end of the string. (*c*) Repeat part *b* for the point of each string at which the pulses meet. (*d*) Reconcile your answer to part *a* with your sketches for parts *b* and *c*.

An extreme form of destructive interference occurs when the two pulses crossing each other are the same size and shape but of opposite algebraic signs, as in **Figure 16.14**. At the instant the two pulses overlap, the displacements cancel and the string is flat. Even though it appears as though both pulses have disappeared, they continue unchanged after the superposition.

16.13 (*a*) Sketch a displacement curve for the point on the string in Figure 16.14 at which the two pulses meet. (*b*) When two wave pulses overlap, how is the velocity of a point in the overlap region related to the velocities of the corresponding points of the individual pulses?

As Checkpoint 16.13 shows, the point at which the two pulses in Figure 16.14 meet never moves. When the two pulses overlap, they cause equal displacements in opposite directions, and so the vector sum of the displacements is zero. A point that remains stationary in a medium through which waves move is called a **node.**

We can deduce a useful fact by examining what happens to the energy in the pulses when they overlap exactly. Because the two pulses are identical, each carries the same amount of energy $E_1 = K_1 + U_1$, and the total energy in the two pulses is thus $2K_1 + 2U_1$ (**Figure 16.15a**). When the string displacements caused by the two pulses cancel each other exactly (the pulses interfere destructively), the string is straight, and so the elastic potential energy is zero. The kinetic energy, however, is not zero. The upward-moving leading edge of pulse 1 adds to the upward-moving trailing edge of pulse 2, and likewise for the downward-moving edges. The result is that the points within the overlapping

CONCEPTS

Figure 16.15 Interference of two pulses traveling in opposite directions. At the instant the pulses overlap, the string displacement is zero everywhere, and so the potential energy is zero; all the energy is kinetic.

(*a*) Two pulses of identical shape traveling in opposite directions and having displacements in opposite directions

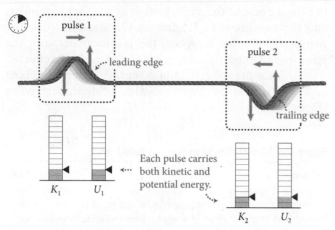

(*b*) At the instant the pulses overlap, the string displacement is zero everywhere, and so the potential energy is zero; all the energy is kinetic

Figure 16.16 Reflection of a pulse at a boundary where the string end is fixed and so cannot move.

pulses move twice as fast as those within the individual pulses before and after the overlap. Because kinetic energy depends on the square of the velocities, the kinetic energy of points in the overlap region is four times as great as that of an individual pulse. The energy during the instant shown in Figure 16.15*b* is thus $4K_1$, which must be equal to the initial energy $2K_1 + 2U_1$ of the two separate pulses. So we determine that $2K_1 + 2U_1 = 4K_1$, which can be true only if $K_1 = U_1$—in other words, if each pulse has an equal amount of kinetic and potential energy. Because these arguments do not depend on the shape of the pulse, it follows that:

> **A wave contains equal amounts of kinetic and potential energy.**

16.4 Boundary effects

When a wave pulse reaches a boundary where the transmitting medium ends, the pulse is *reflected*, which means that its direction of propagation is reversed. After reaching the boundary, a pulse originally traveling to the right starts moving to the left through the medium, and a pulse originally traveling to the left starts moving to the right. Before the pulse reaches the boundary, we refer to it as the *incident pulse*; after reflection, it is the *reflected pulse*. Whether or not a reflected pulse has the same orientation as the incident pulse depends on the properties of the boundary. Consider first a pulse propagating along a string toward the end of the string that has been anchored so that it cannot move (**Figure 16.16**). As the leading edge of the pulse reaches the fixed end, the pulse pulls the end upward. The effect of this upward pull is that the fixed end exerts a downward force on the string.* This downward force exerted on the string produces an *inverted* reflected pulse. If no energy is lost in the reflection, the reflected pulse is identical in shape to the incident pulse.

---

*If you think it is hard to imagine that the fixed end pulls the string downward, imagine pulling yourself up from a chinning bar. When you do so, you exert a downward force on the bar, and the bar exerts an upward force on you. Because the bar is fixed, you end up moving up even though you pull down on the bar.

16.14 The string in Figure 16.16 is perfectly straight at t_4. What has happened to the energy in the incident pulse at that instant?

Notice the similarity between Figures 16.16 and 16.14. If you cover the right half of Figure 16.14 with a piece of paper so that the left edge of the paper goes through the point at which the pulses meet, the two figures are identical. Indeed, as we saw in Checkpoint 16.13, the point at which the pulses meet in Figure 16.14 is a node, precisely like the fixed end of the string in Figure 16.16.

The correspondence between Figure 16.16 and the left side of Figure 16.14 suggests a procedure for determining the shape of a reflected wave pulse: On the incident pulse superpose an identical, but inverted, pulse that approaches from the opposite side of the fixed end and reaches the fixed end at the same instant as the incident pulse. This procedure is best illustrated using an example involving a pulse with an asymmetrical shape (**Figure 16.17**).

Figure 16.17 Reflection of a triangular pulse at a boundary where the string end cannot move.

(a)

incident pulse

$\vec{c}$

imaginary pulse: mirrored across boundary and inverted; traveling opposite to incident pulse

$\vec{c}$

(b)

incident pulse

resulting string shape

reflected pulse

(c)

(d)

reflected pulse

Figure 16.17a shows a triangular wave pulse approaching the fixed end of a string. To construct the reflected pulse we first draw an inverted triangular pulse on the opposite side of the fixed point and moving in the opposite direction. This inverted "reflected pulse" reaches the fixed point at the same instant as the incident pulse, and the two interfere (Figure 16.17b and c). While the two pulses overlap in space, the resulting shape of the pulse is obtained by adding the incident and reflected waves. Once the reflected pulse separates from the fixed end, its shape is the inverse of the incident wave pulse (Figure 16.17d).

Example 16.1 Reflection from a fixed end

Consider a triangular wave pulse approaching the fixed end of a string (**Figure 16.18**). Sketch the shape of the string (a) when a point halfway up the leading edge of the pulse has reached the fixed end and (b) when the peak of the pulse has reached the fixed end.

Figure 16.18 Examples 16.1 and 16.2.

$\vec{c}$

❶ **GETTING STARTED** I begin by sketching the pulse at the two instants given in the problem, pretending that the fixed end is not there and no reflection has occurred (**Figure 16.19**). I use a dashed line for the pulse to indicate that this is not the actual shape of the string at these instants (because reflection *has* occurred), and I draw a vertical line to indicate the (horizontal) position of the fixed end.

Figure 16.19

incident pulse

boundary

location of fixed end

❷ **DEVISE PLAN** Once any part of the pulse reaches the fixed end, reflection begins. To determine the pulse shape during reflection, I must draw a reflected pulse that is both inverted and reversed relative to the incident pulse and then add that reflected pulse to my incident pulses in Figure 16.19.

3 **EXECUTE PLAN** (*a*) At the fixed end, the sum of the displacement of the incident pulse and the displacement of the reflected pulse is zero. In the region where the two pulses do not overlap, the sum of the displacements of the two pulses is equal to the displacement of the trailing edge of the incident pulse. Between this no-overlap region and the fixed end, I add the dashed and dotted lines algebraically to determine the shape of the string. The resulting shape is shown in **Figure 16.20a**. ✔

(*b*) Following the same procedure yields Figure 16.20*b*. ✔

Figure 16.20

4 **EVALUATE RESULT** The pulses I drew terminate at the node at the fixed end, as expected. In Figure 16.20*b* the string shape resembles the reflected pulse more than the incident pulse because most of the incident pulse has traveled past the fixed end.

Next consider reflection from a free end. To maintain the tension in the string at the free end, we connect the end to a light ring that can slide freely along a vertical rod (**Figure 16.21**). When it reaches a height equal to the maximum height of the pulse, however, the free end keeps moving upward, as you can see in Figure 16.21. The reason for this overshooting is that there are no string particles to the right of the free end exerting a downward force. As it overshoots, the free end exerts an upward force on the string to its left, pulling the string above the maximum height of the pulse. After reaching its maximum height, the ring moves back down to the equilibrium level. This up and down motion of the ring creates a left-moving pulse in the string, just as the up and down motion of the hand at the left created the original pulse. This leftward-moving pulse is the reflection of the original pulse. Although the reflected pulse is left–right reversed, it is not inverted.

To construct the reflected pulse, we follow the same procedure we used to construct a pulse reflected from a fixed end, but we do not invert the reflected pulse.

Figure 16.21 Reflection of a wave pulse at a boundary where the string end is free to move vertically.

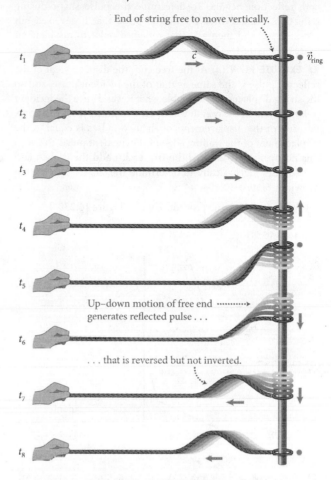

Example 16.2 Reflection from a free end

Let the triangular wave pulse of Figure 16.18 approach the free end of a string. Sketch the shape of the string (*a*) when a point halfway up the leading edge of the incident pulse has reached the fixed end and (*b*) when the peak of the pulse has reached the fixed end.

1 **GETTING STARTED** I begin by sketching the pulse at the two instants given in the problem, ignoring the free end (**Figure 16.22**). I use a dashed line for the pulse to indicate that this is not the actual shape of the string at these instants, and I draw a vertical line to indicate the (horizontal) position of the free end of the string.

Figure 16.22

❷ **DEVISE PLAN** Once any part of the pulse reaches the free end, reflection begins. To determine the pulse shape during reflection, I must draw a reflected pulse that is reversed but not inverted and then add that reflected pulse to my incident pulses in Figure 16.22.

❸ **EXECUTE PLAN** (*a*) At the free end, the displacement of the reflected pulse is the same as that of the incident pulse, and so the string displacement is double what it was before the incident pulse arrived. In the region where the two pulses do not overlap, the sum of the displacements of the two pulses is equal to the displacement of the trailing edge of the incident pulse. Between this no-overlap region and the free end, I add the dashed and dotted lines algebraically to determine the shape of the string shown in **Figure 16.23a**. ✔

(*b*) Following the same procedure yields Figure 16.23*b*. ✔

Figure 16.23

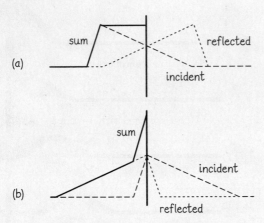

❹ **EVALUATE RESULT** Once the incident pulse arrives at the free end, the displacement of the free end at any given instant is twice that of the incident pulse, and therefore the free end swings far up in Figure 16.23*b*, in agreement with what I expect from Figure 16.21.

✋ **16.15** (*a*) When the free end of the string in Figure 16.21 reaches its maximum displacement at t_5, what is the kinetic energy in the pulse? (*b*) What is the potential energy in the pulse? (*c*) Is the energy in the pulse at this instant the same as the energy at t_1?

A case intermediate between a boundary where the end of the string is fixed and a boundary where it is free to move vertically is when a pulse reaches the boundary between two different mediums. The pulse is partially transmitted to the second medium and partially reflected. **Figure 16.24a** shows a heavy string connected to a lighter string. String 1 has a greater mass per unit length—a quantity

called the **linear mass density** and represented by the symbol μ—than string 2. The wave speed along string 1 is c_1, and that along string 2 is c_2. The tensions in the two strings are equal, but because of the difference in mass density, $c_2 > c_1$. Because string 2 is much less massive than string 1, the end of string 1 behaves somewhat like a free end, and so the reflected pulse is not inverted.

Figure 16.24*b* illustrates a pulse propagating along the same string 1 toward a string 2 that has a greater linear mass density. String 2 restricts the movement of the end of string 1, so now the boundary behaves like a fixed end, reflecting an inverted pulse back along string 1. The tensions in the two strings are again equal, but because of the difference in linear mass density, $c_2 < c_1$ and so the transmitted pulse travels more slowly than the incident pulse.

✋ **16.16** For the strings and pulse in Figure 16.24, what happens in the limit where (*a*) $\mu_2 \to 0$, (*b*) $\mu_2 \to \infty$, and (*c*) $\mu_2 = \mu_1$? (*d*) Why is the transmitted pulse in Figure 16.24*a* wider than the incident pulse?

Figure 16.24 Reflection and transmission of a wave pulse at the boundary between two strings that have different linear mass densities.

(*a*) Pulse propagates into string of smaller mass density: $\mu_1 > \mu_2$, so $c_2 > c_1$

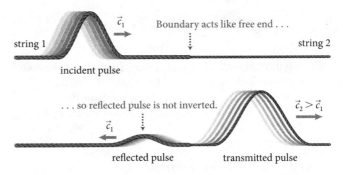

(*b*) Pulse propagates into string of greater mass density: $\mu_1 < \mu_2$, so $c_2 < c_1$

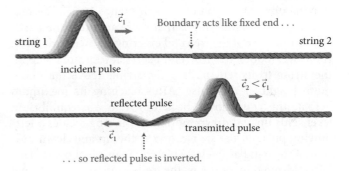

Self-quiz

1. Given the wave function for $t = 0.50$ s shown in **Figure 16.25**, draw the displacement curves of particles at $x = 0$ and $x = 1.0$ m as the wave passes them. If the wave pulse was generated at $x = 0$, what is the speed of the wave?

Figure 16.25

wave function at $t = 0.50$ s

2. Given the displacement curve shown in **Figure 16.26** for a bead at $x = 0$ on a string as a wave with a speed of 2.0 m/s passes, draw the wave function at $t = 2.0$ s.

Figure 16.26

displacement curve at $x = 0$

3. The two pulses shown in **Figure 16.27** are traveling in opposite directions with a speed of 1.0 m/s. Draw the sum of the two pulses at $t = 1.0$ s, $t = 2.0$ s, and $t = 3.0$ s.

Figure 16.27

wave function at $t = 0$

Answers

1. See **Figure 16.28**. The leading edge of the wave travels 0.50 m in 0.50 s, giving a wave speed of 1.0 m/s. In the displacement for the particle at $x = 0$, the leading edge passes $x = 0$ at $t = 0$ and the trailing edge passes $x = 0$ at 0.50 s. In the displacement curve for the particle at $x = 1.0$ m, the leading edge passes $x = 1.0$ m at $t = 1.0$ s and the trailing edge passes $x = 1.0$ m at 1.5 s.

Figure 16.28

displacement curve for $x = 0$ displacement curve for $x = 1.0$ m

2. See **Figure 16.29**. With a wave speed of 2.0 m/s and 1.0 s needed for the whole wave to pass $x = 0$, the length of the wave must be 2.0 m. At $t = 1.0$ s, the leading edge of the wave passes $x = 2.0$ m. At $t = 2.0$ s, the leading edge passes $x = 4.0$ m and the trailing edge passes 2.0 m.

Figure 16.29

wave function at $t = 2.0$ s

3. See **Figure 16.30**. The two pulses start out 1.0 m apart, and each has a width of 2.0 m. With a relative speed of 2.0 m/s, they begin to interfere at $t = 0.5$ s. At $t = 1.0$ s, the pulses overlap by half their width, with the trailing edges sticking out. At $t = 2.0$ s, the pulses also overlap by half their width, but now the leading edges are sticking out. At $t = 3.0$ s, the waves are separated again.

Figure 16.30

16.5 Wave functions

The displacement of the medium caused by a traveling wave is a function of both space and time, and so the mathematical description of a one-dimensional traveling wave requires a function in two variables. Let us begin by examining a traveling wave of constant shape, looking at the pulses first from a reference frame moving along with the wave and then from the Earth reference frame, which is stationary relative to the medium. In the moving reference frame, the wave is stationary and so its description is simple.

Figure 16.31a shows a transverse wave on a string at instant $t = 0$ when the origins of the two reference frames coincide. The wave travels in the positive x direction at speed c without changing its shape. Figure 16.31b shows the situation at some instant t, when the wave and the moving reference frame have traveled a distance ct to the right. As seen from the reference frame moving along with the wave, the wave remains stationary (Figure 16.31c and d). If the curve in the moving reference frame is described by some function $f(x_M)$, then the y component of the displacement $\vec{D}_M$ of any particle of the string as seen from the moving reference frame is given by

$$D_{My} = f(x_M). \tag{16.1}$$

What this tells us is that when we view the situation from the moving reference frame, x_M is the only variable we need to specify to determine the displacement D_{My}. The function $f(x_M)$, which specifies the (constant) shape of the wave as seen from the moving reference frame, is called the *time-independent wave function*.

When we view from the Earth reference frame, the wave has the same shape as in the moving reference frame but it is moving in the positive direction along the x axis. We must therefore specify both x and t in order to determine the displacement $\vec{D}$, and so we write $D_y = f(x, t)$. The function $f(x, t)$, called the *time-dependent wave function*, completely specifies the changing shape of the wave disturbance in the medium as seen from the Earth reference frame. To visualize this function, we need to make a three-dimensional

Figure 16.31 Traveling wave pulses seen from the Earth reference frame and from a reference frame moving along with the pulse at instant $t = 0$ (when the origins of the two reference frames overlap) and at some instant t later.

Figure 16.32 Time-dependent wave function.

(a) Shape of the medium at instants $t = 0$ and $t = t_1$

(b) Displacement of the medium at a fixed position as a function of time

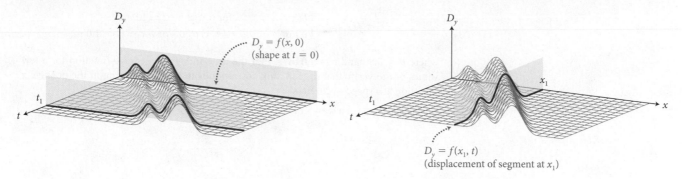

$D_y = f(x, 0)$
(shape at $t = 0$)

$D_y = f(x_1, t)$
(displacement of segment at x_1)

graph of $f(x, t)$ versus the variables x and t (**Figure 16.32a**). The surface shown in the graph gives the value of $D_y = f(x, t)$ for each pair of values of x and t. A vertical cut through the surface along the x axis yields the curve labeled $D_y = f(x, 0)$. This curve gives the shape of the wave disturbance at $t = 0$. A vertical cut through the surface parallel to the x axis intercepting the t axis at t_1 gives $D_y = f(x, t_1)$, the shape of the wave disturbance at t_1. As you can see, the wave has advanced in the positive x direction. Vertical cuts parallel to the t axis give the displacement at a fixed position in the medium as a function of time (Figure 16.32b). The curve $f(x_1, t)$, for example, shows how the displacement at x_1 changes with time.

The surface in Figure 16.32 is completely determined by the constant shape shown in Figure 16.31c and the wave speed c. To see how this is true, imagine sliding the curve in Figure 16.31c diagonally across the xt plane in Figure 16.32a. Because three-dimensional graphs are difficult to draw and to read, we shall use two-dimensional graphs to represent traveling waves that are constant in shape.

Let us now relate the displacement viewed from a moving reference frame to the displacement viewed from the Earth reference frame. At instant t, the y component of the displacement of any point P on the three-dimensional surface of an $f(x, t)$ graph is given by $D_y = f(x, t)$ in the Earth reference frame and by $D_{My} = f(x_M)$ in the moving reference frame (Figure 16.31b). Because the displacement of the string particles does not depend on which reference frame we use, we must have $D_y = D_{My}$. From Figure 16.31b we see that $x_M = x - ct$, so

$$f(x_M) = f(x - ct). \tag{16.2}$$

Substituting these relationships into Eq. 16.1, we discover that the y component of the displacement viewed from the Earth reference frame is given by

$$D_y = f(x - ct). \tag{16.3}$$

This equation describes a wave of constant form $f(x)$ traveling in the positive x direction at speed c. For a wave traveling in the negative x direction at speed c, we have

$$D_y = f(x + ct). \tag{16.4}$$

Any wave traveling along the x axis has either the form $f(x - ct)$ or the form $f(x + ct)$. Provided the quantities x, c, and t appear in the combination $(x - ct)$ or $(x + ct)$ in a function, that function can represent a traveling wave. Thus, the function $\sin[k(x - ct)]$, where k is a constant, represents a harmonic wave that travels in the positive direction along the x axis. The function $\sin[k^2(x^2 - c^2t^2)]$, however, does not represent a traveling harmonic wave.

Exercise 16.3 Traveling waves

(*a*) Consider the time-dependent wave function

$$D_y = f(x, t) = \begin{cases} b(x - ct) & \text{for } 0 < x - ct \leq 1.0 \text{ m} \\ 0 \text{ for} & x - ct \leq 0 \quad \text{or} \quad x - ct > 1.0 \text{ m}, \end{cases}$$

where $b = 0.80$ and $c = 2.0$ m/s. Plot the time-independent wave function for a few values of t to verify that the function corresponds to a wave traveling in the positive x direction at a speed of 2.0 m/s.

(*b*) Let the shape of a wave at $t = 0$ be described by the function

$$f(x, 0) = \frac{a}{x^2 + b}.$$

If the wave travels in the negative x direction at a speed c, what is the mathematical form of the time-dependent wave function $f(x, t)$?

SOLUTION (*a*) Because I need to plot the function versus x, I first add ct to each term in the inequality $0 < x - ct \leq 1.0$ m and get $ct < x \leq (1.0 \text{ m}) + ct$. For $t = 0$, the function is nonzero when $0 < x \leq 1.0$ m; for $t = 1.0$ s when 2.0 m $< x \leq$ 3.0 m; for $t = 2.0$ s when 4.0 m $< x \leq$ 5.0 m; and so on. So, for $t = 0$ I plot the function $(0.80)x$ between $x = 0$ and $x = 1.0$ m; for $t = 1.0$ s I plot the function $0.80(x - 2.0 \text{ m})$ between $x = 2.0$ m and $x = 3.0$ m; and so on (**Figure 16.33**). My graphs show a triangular wave that is constant in shape and displaced in the positive x direction by +2.0 m each second. ✔

Figure 16.33

Region satisfying inequality $0 < x - (2.0 \text{ m/s})t \leq 1.0$ m

(*b*) When viewed from a reference frame traveling along with the wave, the wave function does not depend on time and has the form

$$f(x_M) = \frac{a}{x_M^2 + b}.$$

Equation 16.2 gives me the relationship between the displacement viewed from the Earth reference frame and one moving along with the pulse in the positive x direction. Because the pulse in part b of this exercise moves in the negative direction, I have to invert the sign in front of the speed c, so $f(x + ct) = f(x_M)$ and $x_M = x + ct$. Substituting these relationships into $f(x_M)$, I obtain the time-dependent wave function

$$f(x, t) = \frac{a}{(x + ct)^2 + b}. \checkmark$$

Let us consider a transverse harmonic wave traveling along a string aligned with an x axis. Such a wave can be generated by making the end of the string execute a simple harmonic motion. **Figure 16.34a** shows the shape of the string at an instant at which the left end, at $x = 0$, is in the equilibrium position. For convenience, we choose this instant to be $t = 0$. The time-independent wave function is

$$f(x) = A \sin(kx), \tag{16.5}$$

where A is the amplitude of the wave and k is a constant. The wave repeats itself over a distance λ (the wavelength), so the displacement $f(x)$ is the same at both ends of a wavelength—that is, at x and $x + \lambda$:

$$A \sin(kx) = A \sin(kx + k\lambda), \tag{16.6}$$

Because a sine function repeats itself when its argument is increased by 2π, it follows from Eq. 16.6 that $k\lambda = 2\pi$, so

$$k = \frac{2\pi}{\lambda}. \tag{16.7}$$

The constant k, called the **wave number** of the motion, thus gives the number of wavelengths in a length of 2π m. Because wavelength has units of meters, the wave number k has SI units of m^{-1}.

If the wave travels at speed c in the positive x direction, the time-dependent wave function is obtained by replacing x in Eq. 16.5 by $(x - ct)$:

$$D_y = f(x, t) = A \sin[k(x - ct)]. \tag{16.8}$$

Figure 16.34 Wave function of a harmonic wave (a) at $t = 0$ and (b) after one period. (c) The corresponding displacement curve for $x = 0$.

Figure 16.34*b* shows the wave function after the string end at $x = 0$ has executed one complete cycle (that is, at $t = T$, where T is the period of the motion). During this cycle, the wave has advanced by a distance corresponding to one wavelength. To see what this means, compare the positions of the black dots in Figure 16.34*a* and *b*. Think of these two dots as representing the same point on the traveling wave. In the time interval from $t = 0$ to $t = T$, this point of the wave has moved a distance λ. (Do *not* think of the dots as representing the same particle *of the string* because, remember, the medium does not move horizontally in this wave motion; only the momentum and energy associated with the wave move horizontally.) Because the wave moves at wave speed c, this distance corresponds to

$$\lambda = cT \tag{16.9}$$

or, substituting the frequency $f \equiv 1/T$,

$$\lambda f = c. \tag{16.10}$$

Because the period of the motion is T, we have for $x = 0$ $\sin(kct) = \sin[kc(t + T)]$. This can be true only if $kcT = 2\pi$, or

$$kc = \frac{2\pi}{T} \equiv \omega, \tag{16.11}$$

where ω is the angular frequency as defined in Section 15.5: $\omega = 2\pi f = 2\pi/T$. Using the angular frequency, we can rewrite the time-dependent wave function in Eq. 16.8 in the form:

$$D_y = f(x, t) = A \sin(kx - \omega t). \tag{16.12}$$

Let us now analyze the vertical displacement of the string as the wave passes through. We can use Eq. 16.12 to examine the vertical displacement of any particle of the string as a function of time. For instance, substituting $x = 0$ into Eq. 16.12 and using the trigonometric identity $\sin(-\alpha) = -\sin \alpha$, we obtain

$$D_y = f(0, t) = A \sin(-\omega t) = -A \sin(\omega t). \tag{16.13}$$

The displacement curve for this function $D_y(0, t)$ is shown in Figure 16.34*c*. (If you are having trouble understanding why the displacement curve dips downward initially, think about what is going to happen in Figure 16.34*a* to the string particle located at $x = 0$ just after $t = 0$: It is going to be pulled down below the x axis.)

Next we consider a point a distance d from the end of the string. Substituting $x = d$ into Eq. 16.12 yields

$$D_y = f(d, t) = A \sin(kd - \omega t) = A \sin(-\omega t + kd) \tag{16.14}$$

or, using the trigonometric identity $\sin(-\alpha) = \sin(\alpha - \pi)$,

$$D_y = f(d, t) = A \sin(\omega t - kd - \pi) = A \sin(\omega t + \text{constant}). \tag{16.15}$$

This expression, which gives the y component of the displacement of the string at any arbitrary position $x = d$, shows that all points along the string execute a simple harmonic motion with a period $2\pi/\omega = T$.

Figure 16.35 Any wave can be expressed in terms of sinusoidally varying (harmonic) waves.

(*a*) Snapshot of wave pulse

(*b*) Set of harmonic waves that add up to produce wave pulse

In deriving Eq. 16.8, we assumed that $f = 0$ at $x = 0$ and $t = 0$. To obtain a more general expression that allows for a nonzero initial displacement, we add to the argument of the sine in Eq. 16.12 (the *phase* of the wave, see Section 15.5) an initial phase ϕ_i:

$$D_y = f(x, t) = A \sin(kx - \omega t + \phi_i). \qquad (16.16)$$

The initial phase specifies the initial condition: At $x = 0$ and $t = 0$, Eq. 16.16 becomes $D_y = f(0, 0) = A \sin \phi_i$, and so, for a given amplitude, ϕ_i determines the initial value of the vertical displacement at $x = 0$.

In Section 15.3 we discussed Fourier's theorem, which states that the time dependence of any function can be expressed in terms of sinusoidally varying functions of time. Because of the superposition principle, the same theorem can be applied to waves: Any wave can be expressed in terms of sinusoidally varying waves (harmonic waves). **Figure 16.35a**, for example, shows a wave pulse obtained by adding together the harmonic waves shown in Figure 16.35*b*. At the center, all of the harmonic waves add up to form the pulse; everywhere else, they add up to nearly zero (surprising, but true!). So, if we understand harmonic waves, we can deal with more complicated waves by determining the harmonic waves that add up to give these waves.

 16.17 (*a*) Which of the following functions could represent a traveling wave?

(*i*) $A \cos(kx + \omega t)$ (*ii*) $e^{-k|x - ct|^2}$

(*iii*) $b(x - ct)^2 e^{-x}$ (*iv*) $-(b^2 t - x)^2$

(*b*) Which of the following functions can be made into a traveling wave?

(*i*) $x/(1 + bx^2)$ (*ii*) xe^{-kx} (*iii*) x^2

16.6 Standing waves

When a harmonic wave travels along a string that has a fixed end, the reflected wave interferes with the incident wave. **Figure 16.36** shows the striking pattern that results from this interference. Initially the wave travels to the right, but as the reflected wave begins traveling back at t_3, the two waves traveling in opposite directions create a pulsating *stationary* pattern. Some particles of the string—the nodes (see Section 16.3)—do not move at all, while the sinusoidal loops between the nodes move up and down rather than along the string. The motion has its greatest amplitude at points halfway between the nodes; these points are called **antinodes.** The pulsating stationary pattern caused by harmonic waves of the same amplitude traveling in opposite directions is called a **standing wave.**

Figure 16.36 When a harmonic wave is reflected from the fixed end of a string, the reflected wave interferes with the incident wave, forming a standing wave.

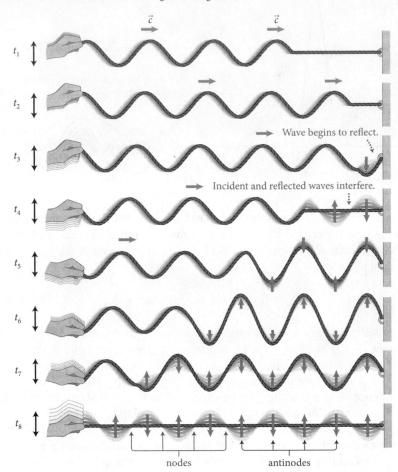

Figure 16.37 illustrates how standing waves come about. Each diagram shows a blue wave propagating to the right and a red wave propagating to the left. The two waves have the same amplitude and wavelength. The speed at which they propagate is determined by the medium and is therefore the same for both waves. The bottom part of each diagram shows the sum of the two waves, obtained by adding, for each value of x, the vertical displacements of the two waves at that value of x. In the diagram labeled $t = 0$, the crests of the red wave have the same x coordinate as the crests of the blue wave, and the same is true for the troughs: Each trough in the red wave aligns with a trough in the blue wave. Waves like this, where comparable points align, are said to be *in phase* (their phases are the same). The two waves reinforce each other—they interfere constructively—and adding them yields a wave that has twice the amplitude. A quarter period later, at $t = \frac{1}{4}T$, one has a crest when the other has a trough and the waves are 180° *out of phase*. The two waves now interfere destructively, and the string is flat at this instant.

16.18 (a) In the standing wave pattern of Figure 16.37, how is the energy distributed between kinetic and potential at $t = 0$, $t = \frac{1}{8}T$, and $t = \frac{1}{4}T$? (b) Is the energy in a length of the string corresponding to one wavelength constant? (c) Does the standing wave transport energy? If so, in which direction? If not, why not?

To see why certain points are nodes, let us denote the y components of the displacements of the red and blue waves by $D_{1y} = f_1(x, t)$ and $D_{2y} = f_2(x, t)$, respectively, and look at what happens at the points $x = \lambda/2$ and $x = \lambda$. At

Figure 16.37 Standing wave created by two counterpropagating waves f_1 and f_2.

waves in phase:
interfere constructively

waves 180° out of phase:
interfere destructively

$t = 0$, we have $D_{1y} = D_{2y} = 0$, and so $D_{1y} + D_{2y} = 0$. Now consider the situation at $t = \frac{1}{8}T$. Wave f_1 has advanced to the right, while wave f_2 has moved an equal distance to the left. At $\lambda/2$, the vertical displacement of the string caused by wave f_1 is now positive, but that caused by wave f_2 is negative and equal in magnitude, so the two add to zero and the string does not move from its equilibrium position. At $x = \lambda$ in the $t = \frac{1}{8}T$ diagram, we see the same thing but with the displacement directions reversed: f_1 displaces the string in the negative y direction, and f_2 displaces it by the same amount in the positive y direction. Because both waves always travel equal distances in opposite directions, the displacements caused by them at the points $x = \lambda/2$ and $x = \lambda$ are *always* equal in magnitude and opposite in sign. Consequently $D_{1y} + D_{2y}$ remains zero at these points for all t.

We can analyze the situation quantitatively by writing the wave traveling to the right as

$$D_{1y} = f_1(x, t) = A \sin(kx - \omega t) \tag{16.17}$$

and the wave traveling to the left as

$$D_{2y} = f_2(x, t) = A \sin(kx + \omega t). \tag{16.18}$$

The combined wave then is

$$D_y = f_1(x, t) + f_2(x, t) = A[\sin(kx - \omega t) + \sin(kx + \omega t)]. \tag{16.19}$$

Using the trigonometric identities $\sin \alpha + \sin \beta = 2 \sin\frac{1}{2}(\alpha + \beta) \cos\frac{1}{2}(\alpha - \beta)$ and $\cos \alpha = \cos(-\alpha)$ (see Appendix B), we can write Eq. 16.19 as

$$D_y = f_1(x, t) + f_2(x, t) = 2A \sin kx \cos \omega t = [2A \sin kx]\cos \omega t. \tag{16.20}$$

This is *not* a traveling wave because it is not a function of $x - ct$ or of $x + ct$ (see the text immediately following Eq. 16.4). Instead this function describes a standing wave on a string, one in which the string displacement oscillates harmonically as $\cos \omega t$ with an amplitude that varies along x as $2A \sin kx$ (**Figure 16.38**).

Figure 16.38 A standing wave is a stationary harmonic wave with an amplitude that varies like a sine. The spacing between adjacent nodes is equal to $\lambda/2$.

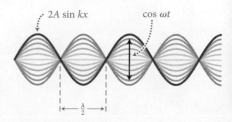

2A sin kx   cos ωt

For a standing wave of the form given in Eq. 16.20 the displacement is *always* zero at the locations where $\sin kx$ is zero. These points are the nodes; they occur when kx is a whole-number multiple of π. Using the fact that $k = 2\pi/\lambda$ (Eq. 16.7), we obtain

$$\frac{2\pi}{\lambda}x = n\pi \qquad n = 0, \pm 1, \pm 2, \ldots, \tag{16.21}$$

and so nodes occur at

$$x = 0, \pm\frac{\lambda}{2}, \pm\lambda, \pm\frac{3\lambda}{2}, \ldots. \tag{16.22}$$

The displacement has its maximum value at the points where $\sin kx = \pm 1$. These antinodes occur when kx is an odd whole-number multiple of $\pi/2$:

$$\frac{2\pi}{\lambda}x = \frac{n\pi}{2} \qquad n = \pm 1, \pm 3, \pm 5, \ldots, \tag{16.23}$$

and so antinodes occur at

$$x = \pm\frac{\lambda}{4}, \pm\frac{3\lambda}{4}, \pm\frac{5\lambda}{4}, \ldots. \tag{16.24}$$

Note that, as shown in Figure 16.38, adjacent nodes are separated by a distance $\lambda/2$. Adjacent antinodes are also spaced by a distance $\lambda/2$ and lie midway between the nodes.

16.19 (*a*) Do two counterpropagating waves that have the same wavelength but different amplitudes cause standing waves? (*b*) Do two counterpropagating waves that have the same amplitude but different wavelengths cause standing waves?

16.7 Wave speed

To determine a quantitative expression for the wave speed c, consider the situation shown in **Figure 16.39**. The end of a taut horizontal string is moved vertically upward at a constant velocity $\vec{v}$. The displacement of the end causes a triangular wave pulse to propagate along the string. The bend on the leading edge travels in the horizontal direction with wave speed c. Just as with the string of beads in Section 16.2, all segments of the string execute the same motion as the end of the string: Each segment begins at rest and then, as the pulse reaches it, moves vertically upward at speed v.

Let us consider the motion of the string during a small time interval Δt beginning at some instant t. At the beginning of the interval, the end of the string has been raised a distance vt and the bend has traveled a distance ct (Figure 16.39b). The slanted segment of the string moves vertically up at constant speed v; at the instant represented in Figure 16.39b, segment A moves up while the rest of the string remains horizontal. A short time interval Δt later, segment A has moved farther up and is still moving at v, so the momentum of segment A has not changed.

Let us choose the x axis in the direction of the wave and the y axis in the upward direction. During the time interval Δt, the bend has advanced by a distance $\Delta x = c\Delta t$, and so an additional length $c\Delta t$ of string (segment B) now also moves vertically upward with speed v. The mass of this segment is $\mu(c\Delta t)$,

Figure 16.39 Procedure for obtaining a quantitative expression for the wave speed c.

(a) Triangular wave pulse generated by lifting end of string at constant velocity

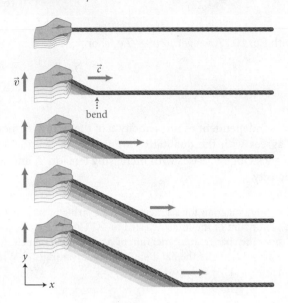

(b) In time interval Δt, bend advances distance $c\Delta t$

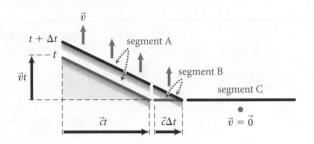

(c) Free-body diagram for segment B

where μ is the mass per unit length, or **linear mass density,** of the string. For a uniform string of length ℓ and mass m, the linear mass density is

$$\mu \equiv \frac{m}{\ell} \quad \text{(uniform linear object).} \tag{16.25}$$

The SI units of linear mass density are kg/m. The change in the momentum of segment B is equal to the mass of B times its change in velocity $\Delta \vec{v}_B = \vec{v} - 0 = \vec{v}$. The mass of B is equal to the linear mass density of the string times the equilibrium length of B, $m_B = \mu(c\Delta t)$, and so $\Delta \vec{p}_B = m_B \Delta \vec{v}_B = \mu(c\Delta t)\vec{v}$. This change in momentum occurs during the time interval Δt, and so the rate of change is

$$\frac{\Delta \vec{p}_B}{\Delta t} = \frac{\mu(c\Delta t)\vec{v}}{\Delta t} = \mu c\vec{v}. \tag{16.26}$$

The rate of change in momentum of segment B of the string is by definition equal to the vector sum of the forces exerted on it:

$$\sum \vec{F}_B = \frac{\Delta \vec{p}_B}{\Delta t} = \mu c\vec{v}. \tag{6.27}$$

Figure 16.39c shows the free-body diagram for segment B. Segment A exerts on B a force slanting upward along the direction of segment A; segment C exerts on B a force in the horizontal direction. The x components of these two forces must balance because segment B is not accelerating in the horizontal direction. We also know that the x components of these two forces are equal in magnitude to the tension $\mathcal{T}$ in the string. The vector sum of the forces exerted on B is thus equal to the vertical component of the force exerted by A on B. Finally, we note that the shaded triangles in Figure 16.39b and c are similar, so

$$\frac{F^c_{ABy}}{F^c_{ABx}} = \frac{F^c_{ABy}}{\mathcal{T}} = \frac{vt}{ct} = \frac{v}{c}, \tag{16.28}$$

and thus the vector sum of the forces acting on segment B of the string is

$$\sum F_y = F^c_{ABy} = \frac{Tv}{c}. \tag{16.29}$$

Combining this result with Eq. 16.27, we get $\mu c v = Tv/c$, or

$$c = \sqrt{\frac{T}{\mu}}. \tag{16.30}$$

Note that the wave speed is independent of the velocity v of the string segments. The result in Eq. 16.30 agrees with the qualitative arguments in Section 16.2: The speed of a pulse along a string increases with increasing tension T and with decreasing linear mass density.

✋ **16.20** (a) Draw a free-body diagram for segment A of the string at instant t in Figure 16.39. What is the vector sum of the forces exerted on A? (b) What does your answer to part a tell you about the change in momentum of A? Does your conclusion about A's momentum make sense? (c) Does the hand do work on the string? (d) What happens to the energy of the string as the end moves upward?

Example 16.4 Measuring mass

You use a hammer to give a sharp horizontal blow to a 10-kg lead brick suspended from the ceiling by a wire that is 5.0 m long. It takes 70 ms for the pulse generated by the sudden displacement of the brick to reach the ceiling. What is the mass of the wire?

❶ **GETTING STARTED** I begin by making a sketch of the situation (**Figure 16.40a**). Because I know the pulse travels 5.0 m in 70 ms, I can determine the wave speed along the wire: $c = (5.0 \text{ m})/(0.070 \text{ s}) = 71 \text{ m/s}$. This wave speed depends on

Figure 16.40

(a)

5.0 m ↑70 ms

10 kg

(b)

the linear mass density of the wire and the tension in the wire. The latter is determined by the force exerted by the brick on the wire. Because the force exerted by the brick on the wire and the force exerted by the wire on the brick are equal in magnitude, I draw a free-body diagram for the brick (Figure 16.40b) to help me determine that magnitude.

❷ **DEVISE PLAN** To determine the mass of the wire, I can use Eq. 16.25. To use this equation, I must know the length of the wire, which is given, and the linear mass density μ, which I can calculate from Eq. 16.30. To obtain μ from Eq. 16.30, I need to know c (which I already calculated) and the tension T in the wire. This tension is equal to F^c_{bw}, which in turn is equal to F^c_{wb}. From my free-body diagram, I see that $F^c_{wb} = F^G_{Eb}$, and so I know F^c_{bw} and therefore T.

❸ **EXECUTE PLAN** The tension is equal to the downward force of gravity exerted on the brick: $T = F^G_{Eb} = (10 \text{ kg})(9.8 \text{ m/s}^2) = 98 \text{ N}$. Substituting the values for T and c into Eq. 16.30, I calculate the linear mass density of the wire $\mu = T/c^2 = (98 \text{ N})/(71 \text{ m/s})^2 = 0.019 \text{ kg/m}$. The mass of the wire is thus $m = (0.019 \text{ kg/m})(5.0 \text{ m}) = 9.5 \times 10^{-2} \text{ kg}$. ✔

❹ **EVALUATE RESULT** The value I obtain—about 0.1 kg—is not unreasonable for a 5.0-m-long wire that can support a lead brick.

16.8 Energy transport in waves

Imagine moving the end of a very long, taut string up and down so that a harmonic wave begins traveling along the string at the wave speed c given in Eq. 16.30. Energy moves along with the wave, and so, as you shake the string end, you must supply energy to the string. At what rate must you supply this energy? To answer this question, let us first consider the energy involved in generating a simple triangular wave as shown in **Figure 16.41**.

As it raises the end of the string, the hand does work on the string. The work done by the hand on the string during a time interval Δt is equal to the scalar product of the force $\vec{F}^c_{hA}$ exerted by the hand on segment A of the string and the force displacement. From Figure 16.41a and b, we see that

$$W = F^c_{hAy}(v\Delta t), \tag{16.31}$$

where F^c_{hAy} is the y component of $\vec{F}^c_{hA}$ and $v\Delta t$ is the y component of the force displacement. If we ignore the force of gravity on segment A of the string, the force exerted by the hand on A is transmitted undiminished to B, and so $\vec{F}^c_{hA}$ is equal in magnitude to the force $\vec{F}^c_{AB}$ exerted by A on B. Using Eq. 16.29, we then have

$$F^c_{hAy} = \mathcal{T}\frac{v}{c}. \tag{16.32}$$

Substituting this result and $\mathcal{T} = \mu c^2$ from Eq. 16.30 into Eq. 16.31, we discover that the work done by the hand on the string during the time interval Δt is

$$W = \left(\mathcal{T}\frac{v}{c}\right)v\Delta t = \mu c\, v^2\Delta t. \tag{16.33}$$

The energy law, $\Delta E = W$ (Eq. 9.1), tells us that the work done by the hand on the string changes the energy of the string. The average rate at which the hand supplies energy to the string (the *average power*) is equal to the change in the energy of the string divided by the time interval over which the energy changes (Eq. 9.29), and so $P_{av} \equiv \Delta E/\Delta t = \mu c v^2$.

As the hand does work on the string, the kinetic energy and the potential energy of the string change: The kinetic energy changes because more of the string is set in motion, and the potential energy changes because the raising stretches the string, storing elastic potential energy. Let us first calculate the change in kinetic energy. After a time interval Δt, segment A has a velocity v, and so its kinetic energy is $\frac{1}{2}m_A v^2$, where m_A is the mass of A. The original length of segment A is $c\Delta t$ (Figure 16.41a), and so $m_A = \mu c\Delta t$. The change in kinetic energy is thus

$$\Delta K = \tfrac{1}{2}(\mu c\Delta t)v^2 - 0 = \tfrac{1}{2}\mu c v^2\Delta t, \tag{16.34}$$

which, Eq. 16.33 tells us, is exactly half the energy supplied to the string!

The other half must be potential energy associated with the stretching of segment A (the rest of the string is undisturbed). Let the length of A at the instant shown in Figure 16.41a be ℓ_A. The change in the length of the string is then $\Delta \ell = \ell_A - c\Delta t$. If $\Delta \ell$ is small, we can treat the string as a spring of spring constant k_s, and so Eq. 9.23 tells us the change in potential energy stored in the stretched string is

$$\Delta U = \tfrac{1}{2}k_s\Delta\ell^2 = \tfrac{1}{2}(k_s\Delta\ell)\Delta\ell = \tfrac{1}{2}F^c_{hA}\Delta\ell, \tag{16.35}$$

where we have used Hooke's law, Eq. 8.18, to substitute $F^c_{hA} = k_s\Delta\ell$. Because segment A is not accelerating, we see from the free-body diagram for segment A (Figure 16.41b) that $\vec{F}^c_{hA} = -\vec{F}^c_{BA}$. Because the force exerted by segment B on segment A and the force exerted by segment A on segment B form an interaction pair, we have $\vec{F}^c_{hA} = \vec{F}^c_{AB}$. Comparing the similar shaded triangles in Figure 16.41a and the free-body diagram for segment B (Figure 16.41c), we see that

$$\frac{F^c_{AB}}{F^c_{ABx}} = \frac{F^c_{hA}}{\mathcal{T}} = \frac{\ell_A}{c\Delta t} \tag{16.36}$$

Figure 16.41 Procedure for determining the energy involved in generating a simple triangular wave.

(a) Triangular wave pulse generated by lifting end of string at constant velocity

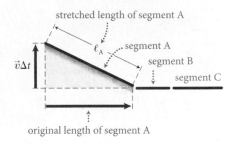

stretched length of segment A

original length of segment A

(b) Free-body diagram for segment A

(c) Free-body diagram for segment B

or $F_{hA}^c = T\ell_A/(c\Delta t)$, and so Eq. 16.35 becomes

$$\Delta U_A = \tfrac{1}{2}\frac{T\ell_A}{c\Delta t}\Delta\ell = \tfrac{1}{2}(\mu c^2)\frac{\ell_A}{c\Delta t}\Delta\ell = \tfrac{1}{2}\frac{\mu c}{\Delta t}\ell_A\Delta\ell, \qquad (16.37)$$

where we have used Eq. 16.30 to eliminate T. As long as the vertical displacement of the end of the string is small, $\ell_A \approx c\Delta t$, and so

$$\ell_A\Delta\ell = \ell_A(\ell_A - c\Delta t) = \ell_A^2 - \ell_A(c\Delta t) \approx \ell_A^2 - (c\Delta t)^2 \qquad (16.38)$$

or, when we apply the Pythagorean theorem to the shaded triangle in Figure 16.41a, $\ell_A\Delta\ell = (v\Delta t)^2$, and therefore

$$\Delta U = \tfrac{1}{2}\frac{\mu c}{\Delta t}(v\Delta t)^2 = \tfrac{1}{2}\mu c v^2 \Delta t. \qquad (16.39)$$

So, in the limit of small displacement, the change in elastic potential energy is indeed equal to the change in kinetic energy, and the triangular pulse contains equal amounts of kinetic and potential energy.

Let us next consider the energy carried in a harmonic wave described by $y(x, t) = A\sin(kx - \omega t)$. We begin by calculating the amount of energy E_λ stored in a length of string corresponding to one wavelength of the harmonic wave. Because during each period T the wave advances by one wavelength, E_λ is the amount of energy that must be supplied in one period. The average power is then

$$P_{av} \equiv \frac{\Delta E}{\Delta t} = \frac{E_\lambda}{T}. \qquad (16.40)$$

To calculate E_λ, we first divide the string into very small segments, each of length dx. If the linear mass density of the string is μ, the mass of each segment is $dm = \mu\,dx$. Each segment carries out a simple harmonic motion, and the energy associated with this simple harmonic motion is $\tfrac{1}{2}(dm)\omega^2 A^2$ (Eq. 15.17). At any given instant, part of this energy is in the form of kinetic energy associated with the motion of the segment and part is in the form of potential energy associated with its deformation. The sum of the two, however, always equals $\tfrac{1}{2}(dm)\omega^2 A^2$. All the segments in a length of string one wavelength long add up to a mass of $\sum dm = m$, and from the definition of linear mass density, we have $m = \mu\lambda$. In a length of string one wavelength long, therefore, the combined energy contributed by all the segments of length dx is

$$E_\lambda = \tfrac{1}{2}(\mu\lambda)\omega^2 A^2. \qquad (16.41)$$

The average power that must be supplied is thus

$$P_{av} = \tfrac{1}{2}\mu\lambda A^2\omega^2/T = \tfrac{1}{2}\mu A^2\omega^2 c, \qquad (16.42)$$

where we have used the fact that $\lambda/T = c$ (Eq. 16.9). This result makes sense: It takes more effort to generate a wave of greater (angular) frequency or amplitude (in each case you must shake the end with a greater velocity). Furthermore, as we would expect, a string of greater linear mass density requires more energy. Finally, if the wave speed increases, the energy is carried away more quickly, and so the rate at which it needs to be supplied increases.

Example 16.5 Delivering energy

A wire with linear mass density $\mu = 0.0500$ kg/m is held taut with a tension of 100 N. At what rate must energy be supplied to the wire to generate a traveling harmonic wave that has a frequency of 500 Hz and an amplitude of 5.00 mm?

❶ **GETTING STARTED** The rate at which energy must be supplied to the wire is the power. Because none of the quantities given varies with time, the (instantaneous) power is equal to the average power, which is given by Eq. 16.42.

❷ **DEVISE PLAN** To calculate the average power, I need to know μ and A, both of which are given, as well as ω and c. The angular frequency ω is related to the frequency f by Eq. 15.4, $\omega = 2\pi f$, and I can obtain the wave speed c from Eq. 16.30.

❸ **EXECUTE PLAN** From Eq. 16.30 I obtain $c = \sqrt{T/\mu} = \sqrt{(100 \text{ N})/(0.0500 \text{ kg/m})} = 44.7$ m/s. Equation 15.4 yields $\omega = 2\pi f = 2\pi(500 \text{ Hz}) = 3.14 \times 10^3 \text{ s}^{-1}$. Substituting these values into Eq. 16.42 gives

$$P_{av} = \tfrac{1}{2}(0.0500 \text{ kg/m})(0.00500 \text{ m})^2(3.14 \times 10^3 \text{ s}^{-1})^2(44.7 \text{ m/s})$$

$$= 275 \text{ W}. ✔$$

❹ **EVALUATE RESULT** The answer I obtain is a fairly large power—comparable to the power delivered by a 250-W light bulb or by a person exercising. The wave travels very fast, though, and the frequency is high, so the answer is not unreasonable.

🖐 **16.21** Suppose that instead of shaking the end of a very long, taut string, you shake a point in the center of the string, keeping the amplitude and the frequency the same. Is the rate at which you must supply energy smaller than, equal to, or greater than if you shake the end?

16.9 The wave equation

In Chapter 15 I argued that simple harmonic oscillations are common because linear restoring forces are common. Linear restoring forces give rise to the equation of motion for a simple harmonic oscillator, which in turn gives rise to sinusoidally oscillating solutions. Waves are equally common because whenever a medium is disturbed it tends to oscillate sinusoidally and the oscillation couples to neighboring regions of the medium. As we shall show in this section, systems of coupled simple harmonic oscillators give rise to an equation called the wave equation, whose solutions are traveling waves. Here we derive this equation for the special case of a transverse wave traveling along a string; we shall encounter the same equation again when discussing electromagnetic waves.

Figure 16.42a shows a piece of a string that has been displaced from equilibrium by a passing wave. Let us focus on segment B between the positions x_i and $x_f = x_i + \Delta x$ and write the equation of motion for that segment. The segment is subject to two forces, one from each of the two adjacent pieces of string (we again ignore the force of gravity because it is much smaller than the tension). Figure 16.42b shows the free-body diagram for segment B. As we saw in Section 16.2, the x components of the forces are equal in magnitude to the tension T in the string and add to zero. The vector sum of the forces exerted on B is thus equal to the sum of the y components:

$$\sum F_{By} = F^c_{ABy} + F^c_{CBy} = T \tan \theta_f - T \tan \theta_i, \quad (16.43)$$

where θ_i and θ_f are the directions of the tangents to the string at x_i and x_f. For small displacements, these angles are small, and so we can use the small-angle approximation $\tan \theta \approx \theta$ and rewrite Eq. 16.43 as

$$\sum F_{By} \approx T(\theta_f - \theta_i) = T\Delta\theta. \quad (16.44)$$

The equation of motion for segment B is

$$\sum F_{By} = m_B a_{By} = (\mu\Delta x)a_{By}, \qu(16.45)$$

where m_B is the mass of segment B, a_{By} is the y component of its acceleration,

Figure 16.42 Segment of a string transmitting a wave pulse.

(a) String transmitting wave pulse

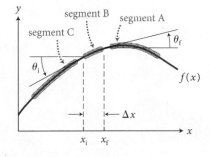

(b) Free-body diagram for segment B

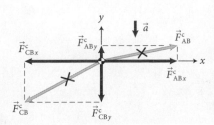

and μ is its linear mass density. Substituting $\mathcal{T}\Delta\theta$ from Eq. 16.44 into the left side of Eq. 16.45 and rearranging terms yields

$$\frac{\Delta\theta}{\Delta x} = \frac{\mu}{\mathcal{T}} a_{By}. \tag{16.46}$$

In the limit $\Delta x \to 0$, the left side of this expression yields the derivative of the angle θ with respect to x. The angle θ is determined by the function f that describes the shape of the string in Figure 16.42a—the derivative of f with respect to x is equal to the slope, $\tan \theta$. A complication is that the shape of the string changes with time and so is a function of both x and t. We therefore have to use the *partial derivative* of $f(x, t)$ with respect to x, which means that we hold t constant while taking the derivative with respect to x (see Appendix B). The partial derivative of $f(x, t)$ with respect to x is written $\partial f/\partial x$, so we have

$$\tan \theta = \frac{\partial f}{\partial x}. \tag{16.47}$$

For small θ we can write $\tan \theta \approx \theta$, and so, in the limit $\Delta x \to 0$, the left side of Eq. 16.46 becomes the second partial derivative of $f(x, t)$ with respect to x:

$$\lim_{\Delta x \to 0} \frac{\Delta\theta}{\Delta x} \equiv \frac{\partial\theta}{\partial x} \approx \frac{\partial}{\partial x}\left(\frac{\partial f}{\partial x}\right) \equiv \frac{\partial^2 f}{\partial x^2}. \tag{16.48}$$

Next we consider the right side of Eq. 16.46. The acceleration a_{By} is given by the second derivative with respect to time of the vertical position $y = f(x, t)$ of segment B. So the first partial derivative with respect to time $\partial f/\partial t$ gives the y component of the velocity of segment B, and the second partial derivative gives the y component of the acceleration:

$$a_{By} = \frac{\partial^2 f}{\partial t^2}. \tag{16.49}$$

Substituting Eqs. 16.48 and 16.49 into Eq. 16.46, we get

$$\frac{\partial^2 f}{\partial x^2} = \frac{\mu}{\mathcal{T}}\frac{\partial^2 f}{\partial t^2}, \tag{16.50}$$

and substituting Eq. 16.30, $c = \sqrt{\mathcal{T}/\mu}$, yields

$$\frac{\partial^2 f}{\partial x^2} = \frac{1}{c^2}\frac{\partial^2 f}{\partial t^2}. \tag{16.51}$$

This is the one-dimensional **wave equation.** Any function of the form $f(x - ct)$ or $f(x + ct)$ is a solution to this equation (the proof of this is left as a homework exercise). All waves, mechanical and nonmechanical, result from equations of this form (but only for a taut string do we get Eq. 16.50 with $c = \sqrt{\mathcal{T}/\mu}$).

It is helpful to keep in mind what the terms in the wave equation tell us about the wave. The second partial derivative of f with respect to x on the left is related to the curvature of the string carrying the wave—the greater $\partial^2 f/\partial x^2$, the sharper the curvature of the string. The right side is the acceleration of particles of the string divided by the square of the wave speed. Thus the wave equation tells us that the curvature of the wave increases as the medium acceleration increases and decreases as the wave speed increases.

For a fixed wave speed, the greater the acceleration of the particles in the medium, the greater the curvature. A downward curvature (concave down or $\partial^2 f/\partial x^2 < 0$) corresponds to a downward acceleration ($\partial^2 f/\partial t^2 < 0$). An upward curvature (concave up or $\partial^2 f/\partial x^2 > 0$) corresponds to an upward acceleration

$(\partial^2 f/\partial t^2 > 0)$. This is shown graphically in **Figure 16.43**. In Figure 16.43a, the curvature of the string is greatest (and downward) at the top. As we have seen, the acceleration is also greatest (and downward) at that point (compare with Figure 16.7c). At point Q, the curvature is upward; indeed, as the pulse travels to the right, point Q has to accelerate in the upward direction. At point R, the curvature and acceleration are both zero. Another illustration of the acceleration-curvature relationship at fixed wave speed is seen by comparing Figure 16.43a and b: If we move the end of the string up and down more quickly, the acceleration at point P increases and the pulse becomes narrower, giving a greater curvature at P.

The inverse relationship between curvature and wave speed is seen by comparing Figure 16.43a and c. With P (as well as all other points) having the same acceleration in the two drawings, the greater wave speed in part c stretches the string horizontally, decreasing the curvature.

Exercise 16.6 Sinusoidal solution to the wave equation

Show that a sinusoidal traveling wave of the form $f(x, t) = A \sin(kx - \omega t)$ satisfies the wave equation for any value of k and ω.

SOLUTION The first partial derivative of $f(x, t)$ with respect to x is

$$\frac{\partial f}{\partial x} = kA \cos(kx - \omega t),$$

and so the second partial derivative with respect to x is

$$\frac{\partial^2 f}{\partial x^2} = -k^2 A \sin(kx - \omega t). \tag{1}$$

The first partial derivative of $f(x, t)$ with respect to t is

$$\frac{\partial f}{\partial t} = -\omega A \cos(kx - \omega t).$$

Differentiating again gives

$$\frac{\partial^2 f}{\partial t^2} = -\omega^2 A \sin(kx - \omega t).$$

Multiplying both sides of this equation by $1/c^2$ and using $k = \omega/c$ (Eq. 16.11), I obtain

$$\frac{1}{c^2}\frac{\partial^2 f}{\partial t^2} = -\frac{\omega^2}{c^2}A \sin(kx - \omega t) = -k^2 A \sin(kx - \omega t). \tag{2}$$

Because the right sides of Eqs. 1 and 2 are equal, the left sides must also be equal, so

$$\frac{\partial^2 f}{\partial x^2} = \frac{1}{c^2}\frac{\partial^2 f}{\partial t^2},$$

which is Eq. 16.51, and so the wave equation is satisfied. ✔

🖐 **16.22** If any time-dependent sinusoidal harmonic function, $f(x, t) = A \sin(kx - \omega t)$, satisfies the wave equation, what determines the values of the wave number k and the angular frequency ω for, say, a wave on a string?

Figure 16.43 Relationships among curvature, acceleration, and wave speed.

One-dimensional wave equation

curvature   acceleration

$$\frac{\partial^2 f}{\partial x^2} = \frac{1}{c^2} \frac{\partial^2 f}{\partial t^2}$$

(a)

negative curvature: downward acceleration

zero curvature: no acceleration

positive curvature: upward acceleration

(b)

strong curvature: great acceleration

(c)

small curvature: small acceleration

Chapter Glossary

SI units of physical quantities are given in parentheses.

Antinode A point in space crossed by two or more waves simultaneously, where the amplitude of the displacement is greatest.

Displacement (of particle in wave) $\vec{D}$(m) A vector that points from the equilibrium position to the actual position of a particle in a medium disturbed by a wave.

Displacement curve A curve that shows how the displacement of a specific particle in a medium disturbed by a wave varies as a function of time.

Harmonic wave A periodic wave whose displacement can be represented by a sinusoidally varying function of space and time:

$$f(x, t) = A \sin[k(x - ct) + \phi_i], \qquad (16.16)$$

where k is the wave number, c the wave speed, and ϕ_i the initial phase.

Interference When two or more waves are simultaneously present at a certain point, they interfere with each other. If the displacements are in the same direction, the interference is said to be *constructive*; if they are in opposite directions, the interference is said to be *destructive*.

Linear mass density μ (kg/m) A scalar that represents the amount of mass per unit length of uniform strings and other uniform one-dimensional objects:

$$\mu \equiv \frac{m}{\ell}. \qquad (16.25)$$

Longitudinal waves Waves for which the displacement is parallel to the direction of propagation.

Node A point in space that is crossed by two or more waves simultaneously, where the displacement remains zero.

Periodic wave A wave for which the displacement of particles in the medium at any fixed position is a periodic function of time.

Standing wave A pulsating stationary pattern caused by two counterpropagating waves of identical amplitude A and wavelength λ. The pattern is characterized by a series of *nodes* separated by $\lambda/2$.

Superposition of waves In a medium that obeys Hooke's law, the resultant displacement of two or more overlapping waves is the algebraic sum of the displacements of the individual waves. Consequently two waves can pass through each other without changing shape.

Transverse waves Waves for which the displacement is perpendicular to the direction of propagation.

Wave A disturbance that propagates through a material or through space. Waves involve transfer of energy without transfer of matter. *Mechanical waves* require a medium in order to be transmitted and are due to the coupling of the particles that make up the medium.

Wave equation The equation that is satisfied by any function that represents a wave traveling at wave speed c:

$$\frac{\partial^2 f}{\partial x^2} = \frac{1}{c^2}\frac{\partial^2 f}{\partial t^2}. \qquad (16.51)$$

All such functions are of the form $f(x - ct)$ or $f(x + ct)$.

Wave function A function that describes the displacement caused by a wave. The *time-dependent wave function* is a function in two variables (x and t) that gives the displacement as a function of space and time. The *time-independent wave function* is a function in one variable (x) that gives the displacement as a function of space at one specific instant.

Wave number k (m^{-1}) A scalar that represents the number of wavelengths that fit in a length of 2π m:

$$k = \frac{2\pi}{\lambda} = \frac{\omega}{c}. \qquad (16.7, 16.11)$$

Wave pulse A single isolated propagating disturbance.

Wave speed c (m/s) The speed at which a wave propagates. For mechanical waves, this speed, denoted by the letter c, is determined by the properties of the medium. The wave speed is distinct from the velocity of the particles in the medium.

Wavelength λ (m) A scalar that gives the minimum distance over which a periodic wave repeats itself.

$$\lambda = cT. \qquad (16.9)$$

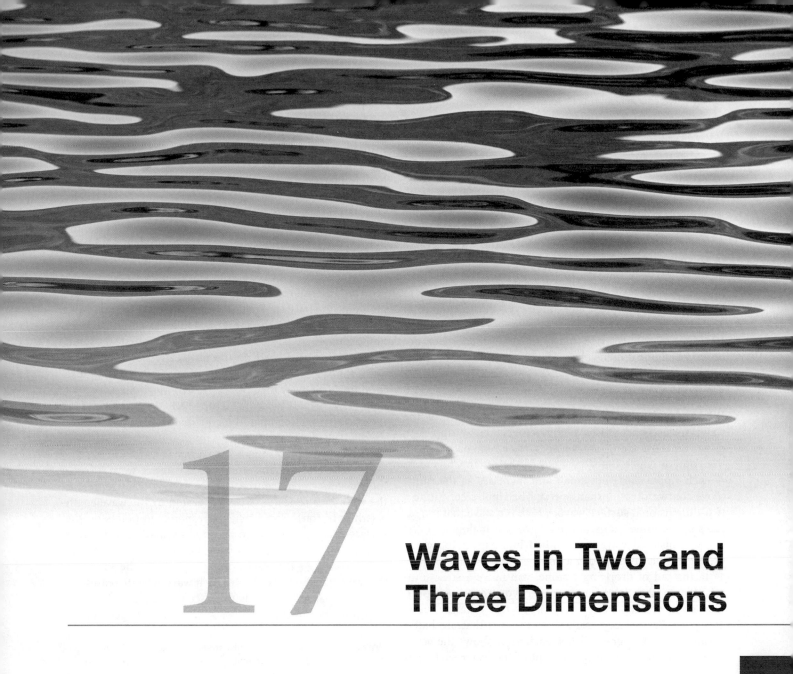

17

Waves in Two and Three Dimensions

17.1 Wavefronts

17.2 Sound

17.3 Interference

17.4 Diffraction

17.5 Intensity

17.6 Beats

17.7 Doppler effect

17.8 Shock waves

CONCEPTS

QUANTITATIVE TOOLS

Now that we have treated waves in one dimension, we can extend our description to waves that propagate in more than one dimension—for example, waves on a water surface, which propagate in two dimensions, and sound waves, which propagate in three dimensions. The basic mechanism for these waves is the same as that for one-dimensional waves: When particles in a medium are coupled together, a disturbance caused at one point in a medium propagates to the surrounding points. Because the basic mechanism is the same, most of what we know about waves in one dimension carries over to the waves treated in this chapter. However, there are important differences between waves in one dimension and waves in more than one dimension. For example, waves propagating in more than one dimension lose amplitude even in the absence of energy dissipation, and wave interference in more than one dimension gives rise to a number of phenomena not observed in one dimension.

17.1 Wavefronts

When you drop a stone in water, the stone disturbs the water surface and causes a number of circular ripples to travel outward along the water surface, emanating from the point at which the stone entered the water. The radius of each ripple starts out small and increases as the ripple moves outward at constant speed. The ripples constitute a two-dimensional **surface wave,** which is a wave that propagates in two dimensions. Surface waves are analogous to the one-dimensional waves we studied in Chapter 16, where propagation is always along a line.

If, instead of dropping a stone, you move a stick sinusoidally up and down in the water, you generate a periodic surface wave. **Figure 17.1** shows two cutaway views of a periodic surface wave at two instants that are half a period apart. The graph below each view shows the vertical component of the displacement of the water surface as

a function of the radial distance r to the source—in other words, the *wave function* of the wave. Because the wave is circular, the wave function is the same in all radial directions. Note the similarity between the shape of the curves in these graphs and the shape of the wave in Figure 16.9 for a periodic wave on a string. Because the surface wave has circular symmetry, all points that are equidistant from the source have the same phase of oscillation. For example, at instant t_i all points that are a distance λ from the source have reached their maximum displacement above the equilibrium surface, forming a circular crest. Half a period later, the same points have reached their maximum displacement below the surface, forming a circular trough.

When the source of the wave can be localized to a single point in space—a small stone dropped in a pond, the stick in Figure 17.1—the source is said to be a **point source.** Point sources are treated as if they have no physical extent. The actual source need not be physically small, however. Stars, for example, are much larger than Earth, yet because they are so far away they can be treated as a point source of light (a wave). Likewise, in Figure 17.1, if the diameter of the stick is small compared to the diameter of the ripples, we can consider the stick to be a point source.

The blue region of **Figure 17.2** shows a top view of the circular crests and troughs of a periodic surface wave spreading out from a point source. We can schematically represent the wave by a series of circles separated by the wavelength λ (white region). Each circle corresponds to points on the surface that have the same phase of oscillation. Curves or surfaces on which all points have the same phase constitute a **wavefront.** As the wave travels away from the source at the wave speed c, the radius of each wavefront increases.

This expansion of circular surface waves causes the wave energy to be spread out over a larger and larger region.

Figure 17.2 Top view of the circular crests and troughs formed in a periodic surface wave. We represent the wave schematically as a series of wavefronts.

Figure 17.1 Cutaway views of a wave on the surface of a liquid and the corresponding vertical displacement of the surface as a function of distance r from the oscillating wave source, which is located at $r = 0$.

(*a*) Wave at instant t_i

(*b*) Half a period later $\left(t_i + \frac{1}{2}T\right)$

circular crest

D_z $\vec{c}$ r
1λ 2λ 3λ

circular trough

D_z $\vec{c}$ r
1λ 2λ 3λ

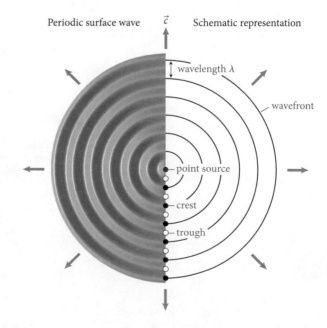

Periodic surface wave $\vec{c}$ Schematic representation

wavelength λ

wavefront

point source

crest

trough

Figure 17.3 A surface wave moving at speed c. Because surface waves expand in two dimensions, the wave energy is distributed over a larger and larger circumference.

(a) t_1

As circular ripple expands . . .

$\vec{c}$

. . . energy per unit circumference must decrease.

(b) t_2

$\vec{c}$

$\leftarrow R_1 \rightarrow$ $\leftarrow R_2 \rightarrow$

Consider, for example, the spreading ripples in **Figure 17.3**. At instant t_1 the ripples cross a circle of radius R_1 centered on the wave source; at instant t_2 they are about to cross a circle of radius R_2. If there is no loss of wave energy as the wave moves from R_1 to R_2—that is, if there is no dissipation of energy—the amount of energy that crosses the circle of radius R_2 must be the same as the amount that crosses the circle of radius R_1. Because the circumference increases, there is less energy per unit length along the circumference at t_2 than there is at t_1.

17.1 Let $t_2 = 2t_1$ in Figure 17.3. (*a*) How does R_1 compare with R_2? (*b*) If the energy in the wave is E and there is no dissipation of energy, what is the energy per unit length along the circumference at R_1? At R_2? (*c*) How does the energy per unit length along a wavefront vary with radial distance r?

As Checkpoint 17.1 shows, the expansion of circular wavefronts causes the energy per unit length along a wavefront to decrease as $1/r$. Because the energy in the wave is proportional to the square of the wave amplitude (Eq. 16.41, $E_\lambda = \frac{1}{2}\mu\lambda\omega^2 A^2$), it follows that the amplitude is proportional to $1/\sqrt{r}$. (You can see this amplitude decrease in the cutaway view in **Figure 17.4**.) Keep in mind that

Figure 17.4 Cutaway view of a periodic surface wave. Because the energy in a given wavefront is spread out over an increasingly large circumference as the wavefront moves away from the source, the amplitude decreases as the wavefront moves away from the source.

Amplitude decreases with distance from source.

Figure 17.5 The wavefronts from a point source emitting waves in three dimensions are uniformly expanding, concentric spheres.

$\vec{c}$ concentric wavefronts

this amplitude decrease has nothing to do with energy dissipation: It is due entirely to the spreading out of the wave, which causes the energy to be distributed over a larger circumference.

Some waves—sound waves and light waves are two examples—spread out in three dimensions. If the source is a point source and the spreading is uniform in all three dimensions, the wavefronts are spherical (**Figure 17.5**). The resulting waves are called **spherical waves.** As a three-dimensional wave propagates, each wavefront expands outward at the wave speed c, and the energy carried by the wavefront is spread out over a larger and larger spherical area. When a wavefront reaches a distance r from the source, the energy in the wavefront is spread out over a surface area of $A = 4\pi r^2$, and so the energy per unit area carried by the wavefront is proportional to $1/r^2$ (**Figure 17.6**). The amplitude of a spherical wave is therefore proportional to $1/r$ (Eq. 16.41 again).

Figure 17.6 The inverse-square relationship between energy and radius for a wave expanding uniformly in three dimensions without dissipation. All the energy that crosses area A_1 also crosses A_2 and A_3. Because the area of a sphere is proportional to r^2 ($A_{\text{sphere}} = 4\pi r^2$), the energy per unit of surface area decreases as $1/r^2$.

For spherical wavefronts, area $A = 4\pi r^2$ . . .

A_3

A_2

A_1

r_1

r_2

r_3

. . . so energy per unit area decreases as $1/r^2$ (inverse-square relationship).

Because it is difficult to represent wavefronts in three dimensions, we usually represent spherical wavefronts by a series of circles, just as we do for two-dimensional waves. Keep in mind, however, that there is an important difference between waves in two and in three dimensions:

The amplitude of waves in two dimensions decreases with distance r from the source as $1/\sqrt{r}$; in three dimensions it decreases as $1/r$. This decrease is due purely to the spreading out of the wavefronts and involves no loss of energy.

Example 17.1 Ripple amplitude

The amplitude of a surface wave for which $\lambda = 0.050$ m is 5.0 mm at a distance of 1.0 m from a point source. What is the amplitude of the wave (a) 10 m from the source and (b) 100 m from the source? During a time interval equal to 100 periods, by what percentage does the amplitude of a wavefront decrease (c) after the wavefront passes a position 1.0 m from the source and (d) after it passes a position 100 m from the source?

❶ **GETTING STARTED** I am given that the amplitude $A = 5.0$ mm at $r = 1.0$ m. As the wave spreads out, its amplitude diminishes, and I need to calculate the amplitude at $r = 10$ m and $r = 100$ m. In addition I need to determine by how much the wave attenuates as it propagates over a 100-period time interval past these two positions.

❷ **DEVISE PLAN** Because the wave is a two-dimensional surface wave, the amplitude is proportional to $1/\sqrt{r}$. I know the amplitude $A_{1.0\,\text{m}}$ at $r = 1.0$ m, so I can use this dependence to determine the amplitude at other distances from the source. For parts a and b, I need to determine $A_{10\,\text{m}}$ and $A_{100\,\text{m}}$ at $r = 10$ m and $r = 100$ m. In 100 periods, the wavefront travels a distance equal to 100 wavelengths, which is $100 \times (0.050\text{ m}) = 5.0$ m, so for parts c and d, I also need to determine the amplitudes 5 m beyond those positions.

❸ **EXECUTE PLAN** (a) The ratio of the amplitudes at 1.0 m and 10 m is $\sqrt{(1.0\text{ m})}/\sqrt{(10\text{ m})} = \sqrt{(1.0/10)} = 0.32$, and so the amplitude at 10 m is $0.32 \times (5.0\text{ mm}) = 1.6$ mm. ✔

(b) At 100 m, $\sqrt{(1.0\text{ m})}/\sqrt{(100\text{ m})} = 0.10$, and so the amplitude is $0.10 \times (5.0\text{ mm}) = 0.50$ mm. ✔

(c) 100 periods after passing the 1.0-m position, the wavefront is 6.0 m from the source and the amplitude decreases by a factor of $\sqrt{(1.0\text{ m})}/\sqrt{(6.0\text{ m})} = 0.41$. This means $A_{6.0\,\text{m}}$ is 41% of $A_{1.0\,\text{m}}$: $A_{6.0\,\text{m}} = 0.41(5.0\text{ mm}) = 2.0$ mm, a decrease of about 60%. ✔

(d) Then 100 periods after passing the 100-m position, the wavefront is 105 m from the source and the amplitude decreases by a factor of $\sqrt{(100\text{ m})}/\sqrt{(105\text{ m})} = \sqrt{(1/1.05)} = 0.98$. This means that $A_{105\,\text{m}}$ is 98% of $A_{100\,\text{m}}$: $A_{105\,\text{m}} = 0.98(0.50\text{ mm}) = 0.49$ mm, a decrease of 2%—a mere 0.02% each period. ✔

❹ **EVALUATE RESULT** The amplitudes at 10 m and 100 m are both smaller than the amplitude at 1.0 m, which is what I expect. That the amplitude decrease over 100 wavelengths is less farther away from the source agrees with what I expect from the $1/\sqrt{r}$ dependence.

Figure 17.7 Far from the source, wavefronts are nearly flat, so amplitude changes little with additional distance from the source.

Close to source: wavefronts spherical, $\vec{c}$ vectors diverge quickly . . .

Far from source: wavefronts nearly planar, $\vec{c}$ vectors nearly parallel . . .

. . . so amplitude decreases quickly with distance from source.

. . . so amplitude changes little with distance from source.

As this example demonstrates, the decrease in amplitude is most pronounced close to the source; far from the source, the decrease is hardly noticeable. **Figure 17.7** illustrates the same point in a different way: Far from the source, the wavefronts are nearly flat rather than curved, and as a wavefront straightens, a fixed length of it diverges less. Far from a point source, a spherical wavefront essentially becomes a two-dimensional flat wavefront called a **planar wavefront.** Likewise, far from a point source, a circular surface wavefront essentially becomes a one-dimensional straight wavefront.

✋ **17.2** Notice that in the views of the surface wave in Figure 17.1 the amplitude does not decrease with increasing radial distance r. How could such waves be generated?

17.2 Sound

The human ear can detect longitudinal waves at frequencies in the range from about 20 Hz to 20 kHz. Such waves, which propagate through any kind of material—solid, liquid, or gas—constitute what we call **sound.** Sound propagates through any medium that can exert elastic restoring forces. If you find it hard to think of a gas as being able to exert an elastic force, squeeze an empty plastic bottle first with a tightly sealed cap and then without it. Without the cap, squeezing the bottle simply pushes some air out of the bottle. With the cap, the bottle exerts an elastic force because of the air in it. It is this elastic force that is responsible for transmitting sound waves.

Figure 17.8 shows a simple wave pulse propagating through a long, air-filled tube. One end of the tube is fitted with a piston. Starting at t_2, the piston is rapidly moved back and forth, first pushing the molecules in the layer of air adjoining the piston closer together and then letting them expand again. These molecules, in turn, push and pull on the molecules in a neighboring layer, and so on, creating a disturbance that propagates through the air in the tube. The disturbance consists of a *compression* (region where the molecules are crowded together) and a *rarefaction*

Figure 17.8 A piston generates a longitudinal sound pulse that propagates along an air-filled tube. The disturbance consists of a compression and a rarefaction. The wave function is similar to the one for a longitudinal wave in a spring (see Figure 16.6).

(*a*) Longitudinal wave pulse created by in-and-out movement of piston

(*b*) Wave function of pulse at instant t_6

(region where they are spaced far apart). The resulting wave is called a *compressional wave*. The wave speed c at which the disturbance travels through the tube depends on the density and the elastic properties of the medium. For dry air at a temperature of 20 °C, the speed of sound waves is 343 m/s.

Exercise 17.2 Wavelength of audible sound

Given that the speed of sound waves in dry air is 343 m/s, determine the wavelengths at the lower and upper ends of the audible frequency range (20 Hz–20 kHz).

SOLUTION The wavelength is equal to the distance traveled in one period. At 20 Hz, the period is $1/(20 \text{ Hz}) = 1/(20 \text{ s}^{-1}) = 0.050$ s, so the wavelength is $(343 \text{ m/s})(0.050 \text{ s}) = 17$ m. ✔ The period of a wave of 20 kHz is $1/(20{,}000 \text{ Hz}) = 5 \times 10^{-5}$ s, so the wavelength is $(343 \text{ m/s})(5.0 \times 10^{-5} \text{ s}) = 17$ mm. ✔

Figure 17.9 A simple mechanical model for longitudinal waves.

(*a*) Identical beads coupled by springs

(*b*) Snapshot of longitudinal wave propagating along chain

(*c*) Corresponding wave function

The wave pulse in Figure 17.8 is longitudinal—the air molecules are displaced in the same direction as that in which the wave propagates. In bulk gases and liquids that have no internal friction, there can be no transverse waves because such gases and liquids do not exert elastic forces in the transverse direction. Notice the similarity between the wave pulse shown in Figure 17.8 and the longitudinal wave pulse propagating through a coil spring shown in Figure 16.5.

Figure 17.9a shows a chain of identical beads coupled together by springs, which can serve as a simple mechanical model for studying longitudinal waves. A snapshot of a harmonic longitudinal wave propagating through the chain is shown in Figure 17.9b. The leftmost bead is made to oscillate back and forth harmonically. Because each bead executes, in turn, the same longitudinal oscillation, a compressional wave propagates along the chain. Although the beads move in the same direction as the wave, there is no permanent displacement of beads in that direction. What are transported along the chain, however, are energy (as kinetic energy of the beads and elastic potential energy of the springs) and momentum.

✋ **17.3** Does the wave speed along the chain shown in Figure 17.9 increase or decrease when (*a*) the spring constant of the springs is increased and (*b*) the mass of the beads is increased?

From Section 16.1, you know that a snapshot of a transverse wave gives us the wave function directly. Things are not so simple with longitudinal waves, however. Because with these waves the displacement of the medium is along the axis of wave propagation, it is cumbersome to interpret any wave snapshots. The wave function shown in Figure 17.9c, however, provides an alternative representation of the wave and reveals its harmonic nature, which is not immediately obvious in Figure 17.9b. This graph is obtained by plotting the displacement of each bead from

CONCEPTS

The perception of sound

The human ear is capable of detecting longitudinal waves transmitted through a gas, liquid, or solid medium in what is called the *audible frequency range*. This range, which varies with age and also from person to person, extends from about 20 Hz to 20 kHz. The sensitivity of the ear varies greatly over this range, however, peaking at about 3 kHz. Waves outside this range cause no auditory nerve signals in humans, although large-amplitude waves of very low frequency, called *subsonic waves* (such as earthquakes), can be felt. Some animals, such as bats, can detect longitudinal waves of frequencies up to 120 kHz, called *ultrasonic waves* because they are above the audible frequency range for humans.

The perception of sound is a complicated and subjective matter. The mechanical part of this process, which is determined by the physiology of the ear, is well understood. A sound wave that reaches the ear propagates through a complex system of solid and liquid parts of the outer and middle ear to the inner ear, where the wave causes *hair cells* to oscillate. These oscillations cause the auditory nerve to send signals to the brain.

The neurological processing of these signals by the brain is not yet fully understood. The properties of sound are typically described using terms such as *loudness, pitch,* and *timbre* or *tonal quality*. These terms are subjective, however, and so there is no simple correlation between them and the parameters used to describe waves in physics (amplitude, frequency, harmonic content).

Loudness: The perception of loudness is connected to sound wave energy and therefore amplitude. Because the ear is capable of detecting waves over a large range of wave energies—from the very faint sound of a pin drop to the loud roar of an airliner taking off—the response is highly nonlinear (discussed in Section 17.5). The correlation between loudness and energy is complicated by the fact that the perception of loudness also depends on frequency: A 1-kHz wave sounds louder than a 200-Hz wave of equal energy (see Figure 17.26).

Pitch: The sensation of pitch is related to the physical property of frequency. The correlation is nonlinear; if the frequencies of two sound waves differ by a factor of 2, their pitches are said to be an *octave* apart. Sounds at 256 Hz and 512 Hz are one octave apart, but so are sounds at 3 kHz and 6 kHz. The perceived pitch also depends on the amplitude of the sound wave. Above 3 kHz, pitch increases with increasing sound wave amplitude; below 2 kHz, pitch decreases with increasing amplitude.

Timbre: We can readily distinguish two musical instruments even when they emit tones of identical pitch because they produce different mixtures of harmonics. The pitch is typically related to the lowest, or fundamental, frequency in the series of harmonics, and two instruments playing the same pitch usually produce the same fundamental. They differ, however, in the content of the higher harmonics, which is what determines the timbre of the instrument. Even though the ear and the brain constitute a remarkable Fourier analyzer in the sense that they can distinguish sounds of different harmonic contents, we cannot characterize timbre with a precise statement about measurable parameters. (An alternative term you might run across for timbre is *tonal quality*.)

its equilibrium position versus the bead's equilibrium position. To create Figure 17.9c, the displacement vector of each bead in Figure 17.9b is rotated 90° counterclockwise and its tail placed on the x axis at the *equilibrium* position of the bead given in Figure 17.9a.

✋ **17.4** (*a*) Plot the velocity of the beads along the chain in Figure 17.9b as a function of their equilibrium position x. (*b*) Plot the linear density (number of beads per unit length) as a function of x.

As Checkpoint 17.4 suggests, we can also represent the wave in Figure 17.9 by plotting the linear density versus position. Comparing the linear density curve of Figure S17.4b with the $D_x(x)$ curve of Figure S17.4a gives us some important information:

The compressions and rarefactions in longitudinal waves occur at the locations where the medium displacement is zero.

(You can get this same information by comparing Figure 17.9b and c.)

The propagation of sound through a medium is very similar to that of a compressional wave through the chain in Figure 17.9. Disturbed molecules in a solid, liquid, or gas are subject to intermolecular forces that tend to return the molecules to their equilibrium positions. For small displacements, the restoring force is proportional to the displacement. It is this restoring force that is responsible for the propagation of the disturbance caused by the piston in Figure 17.8.

When not confined to a tube, a compressional wave traveling through air spreads out in three dimensions because, unlike beads along a string, air molecules interact with the surrounding molecules in all three directions. Consequently, sound waves tend to form spherical wavefronts. **Figure 17.10** shows a sound wave generated by an oscillating tuning fork. A series of spherical shells of compression and rarefaction travel outward from the fork. Each molecule in the air executes a sinusoidal back-and-forth movement

Figure 17.10 The periodic wave emitted by a tuning fork causes a series of outward-traveling spherical wavefronts. The dot represents an air molecule that oscillates about its equilibrium position as the wavefronts pass by.

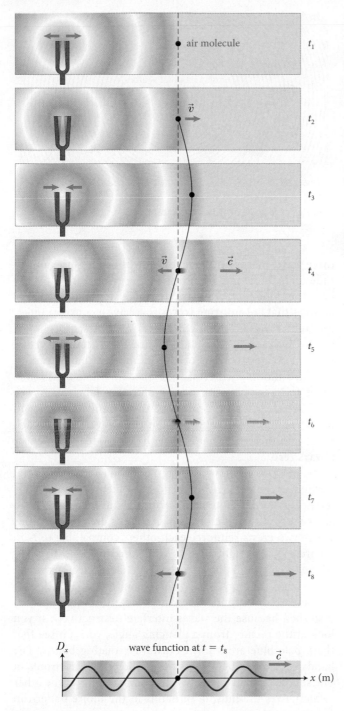

Figure 17.11 Image of the spherical compressional wavefronts produced by sound waves emanating from a telephone. This image was obtained using laser illumination. Reprinted with the permission of Alcatel-Lucent USA, Inc.

with the high speed at which sound waves travel make it impossible to directly see the compressional wavefronts that accompany sound. Only under special laser illumination is it possible to observe these wavefronts (**Figure 17.11**).

Notice how the wavefronts shown in Figures 17.10 and 17.11 resemble the circular wavefronts of a surface wave, such as the one represented in Figure 17.2. The compressions correspond to crests, and the rarefactions correspond to troughs. When we draw circles to represent the spherical wavefronts of sound waves, which are longitudinal waves, the circles represent not crests and troughs but rather compressions and rarefactions.

17.5 Even though the sound of a loudspeaker carries in all directions, the loudness in front of the speaker is considerably greater than the loudness behind it. What is the shape of the wavefronts produced by a loudspeaker?

17.3 Interference

The superposition of overlapping waves in two and three dimensions leads to a number of interesting phenomena. Consider first the situation illustrated in **Figure 17.12** on the next page, where two identical circular wave pulses traveling on a liquid surface cross as they expand. At t_2 the two crests meet at a point midway between the two sources, giving rise to constructive interference. At this point the displacement of the liquid surface is twice as great as that due to the individual pulses. As the pulses continue to expand, this point of overlap splits into two points, one moving upward and the other moving downward. At t_3 the crest of each pulse meets the trough of the other pulse, leading to destructive interference. Because the height of

as successive shells travels by; the sine curve in the figure shows the motion of one molecule.

The displacements of air molecules disturbed by a sound wave are very small. At a distance of a few hundred meters, for example, the deafening roar of an airliner taking off causes displacements of only 10^{-6} m—about one-hundredth of the width of a hair. These small displacements coupled

Figure 17.12 Interference of two identical sets of circular wave pulses expanding on a liquid surface.

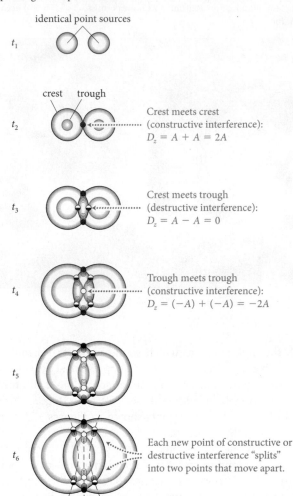

identical point sources

t_1

crest trough

t_2

Crest meets crest (constructive interference):
$D_z = A + A = 2A$

t_3

Crest meets trough (destructive interference):
$D_z = A - A = 0$

t_4

Trough meets trough (constructive interference):
$D_z = (-A) + (-A) = -2A$

t_5

t_6

Each new point of constructive or destructive interference "splits" into two points that move apart.

Figure 17.13 Moiré pattern formed by the overlapping wavefronts of two closely spaced, coherent wave sources (located at the centers of the two concentric sets of circles). The center of each band in the pattern corresponds to a nodal line.

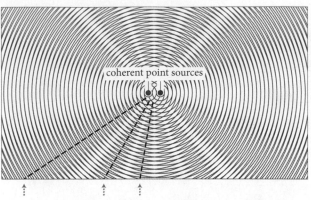

coherent point sources

nodal lines (lines along which waves interfere destructively)

the crest is equal to the depth of the trough, the vector sum of the medium displacement is zero.* Each of these points splits into two points that move vertically away from each other. At t_4 the two troughs meet and reinforce each other, giving rise to constructive interference again. At this point the depression of the medium is doubled. Note that, as shown at t_6, the points of constructive interference move along a straight line perpendicular to the line that connects the two sources, while the points of destructive interference move along curved paths.

Let us now apply these ideas to the overlapping of periodic surface waves. When periodic circular waves from two nearby sources cross each other, the crests and troughs overlap in many places, giving rise to a complex interference pattern. **Figure 17.13** shows the circular wavefronts for two sources separated by a distance equal to

three wavelengths and emitting waves of the same amplitude and frequency. In addition, the two sources always have the same phase and are therefore said to be *in phase.* Sources that are emitting waves that have a constant phase difference are said to be **coherent.** The pattern produced by the overlapping circles in Figure 17.13, called a *moiré pattern,* creates the illusion of a number of bands radiating out from the center of the figure (*moiré* is the French word for the wavy finish seen in some fabrics). As we shall see shortly, the centers of these bands correspond to **nodal lines**—lines where the two waves cancel each other and the vector sum of the medium displacement is always zero.

Figure 17.14a shows a magnified view of the central portion of Figure 17.13 overlaid on a picture of the interference pattern. White areas in the picture correspond to areas where the medium displacement is greatest—regions where two crests reinforce each other (comparable to t_2 in Figure 17.12). Bright blue areas also correspond to areas where the medium displacement is greatest—regions where two troughs reinforce each other (t_4 in Figure 17.12). Pale blue areas correspond to regions where the surface is undisturbed because the waves interfere destructively. If you look at the picture from a glancing angle, you can see that these pale blue areas form outward radiating bands. The bands coincide with the positions where the wavefronts of one source fall halfway between the wavefronts of the other (which gives the illusion of bands in the moiré pattern in Figure 17.13).

Figure 17.14b shows a detail of the interference pattern. In addition to the solid dark blue arcs that indicate wavefronts marking the crests of the waves generated by each source, bright blue arcs indicate the locations of the troughs halfway between each pair of neighboring crests. Figure 17.14c shows the same region half a period later. All wavefronts have advanced by half a wavelength, and the nodes (•) and

---

*The waves do not cancel exactly close to the sources because the amplitudes of the two waves differ due to the $1/\sqrt{r}$ factor in the wave amplitude. Far from the sources, however, this difference is negligible.

Figure 17.14 Details of the interference pattern in the central region of Figure 17.13. White and blue regions represent, respectively, areas of maximum positive and maximum negative medium displacement. The intermediate regions of zero displacement line up to form the gray nodal bands seen in Figure 17.13.

(*a*)

(*b*)

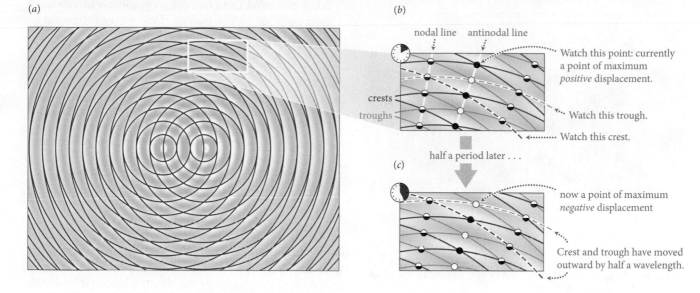

(*c*)

antinodes (• and ○) have moved along with the wavefronts. See, for example, the node at the intersection of the dashed dark blue crest from the left source and the dashed bright blue trough from the right source—in Figure 17.14*b* it is the second node from the top; in Figure 17.14*c* it is the uppermost. In addition, all white and bright blue areas are interchanged, as are all filled and unfilled circles (see, for example, the highlighted filled and open circles in Figure 17.14*b* and *c*). Where two crests initially reinforced each other, two troughs now meet. (Of course, the nodal lines stay in place, by definition.)

17.6 (*a*) What is the medium displacement at a point halfway between a filled circle and a neighboring open circle in Figure 17.14*b*? (*b*) Sketch the variation of this displacement as a function of time. (*c*) What is the medium displacement at all points between two neighboring half-filled circles? (*d*) Sketch the variation of this displacement as a function of time at the midpoint between two neighboring half-filled circles.

The half-filled circles line up to form a path, and as Checkpoint 17.6 demonstrates,* *all* points along this path remain undisturbed and are therefore nodes. The line that connects the half-filled circles is thus a nodal line, and the pale blue bands that appear in Figure 17.13 are thus centered on nodal lines. The filled and open circles line up to form what are called **antinodal lines.** Points on these antinodal lines have the greatest amplitude of oscillation; in other words, these points are antinodes.

---

*I cannot overstress the importance of doing Checkpoint 17.6. By completing this checkpoint, you will be teaching yourself the key feature of interference of waves in more than one dimension.

17.7 Is a point halfway between a filled and a neighboring open circle in Figure 17.14*b* a node?

The interference pattern formed by overlapping waves in two dimensions can readily be observed for waves generated on a water surface (**Figure 17.15**). The nodal lines are clearly visible in the picture. All waves in more than one dimension—sound waves, light waves, x-ray waves, radio waves—set up interference patterns that contain nodal and antinodal lines. For example, two loudspeakers that are some distance apart and that emit sound waves of the same frequency set up an interference pattern that is not very different from the ones for circular water waves. By adjusting

Figure 17.15 Photograph of the interference pattern caused by overlapping circular waves on a water surface.

nodal lines

Figure 17.16 Less can be more. (*a*) When both sources generate waves, point Q lies on a nodal line and thus never experiences displacement of the medium (because the waves from the two sources interfere destructively there). If these were sound waves, there would be silence at Q. (*b*) However, when only one source generates waves, Q experiences their full effect.

(*a*) Both sources generate waves

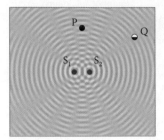

(*b*) Only S_2 generates waves

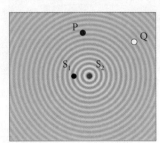

your position in front of the speakers, you can find regions where the destructive interference occurs, causing the loudness of the sound to be low.

The existence of nodal regions has a number of consequences. Consider, for example, the interference pattern shown in **Figure 17.16*a***. Two coherent sources S_1 and S_2 emit circular waves. The waves cause the medium displacement at point P to vary, but at point Q, located on a nodal line, the medium displacement *remains zero*. If you were standing at that location, you could not tell whether the sources were emitting waves or not! Each source separately, however, does emit waves in the direction of Q. Figure 17.16*b* shows that, with S_1 is turned off, the wavefronts from S_2 that reach Q are not interfered with. In other words, if you were standing at Q, you would hear sound when S_1 is turned off but not when both sources are on. So, *removing* a source *increases* the amplitude of the wave at Q! Conversely, adding a second source (in other words, returning to the situation in Figure 17.16*a*)

decreases (or even eliminates) the wave amplitude in certain regions. So:

> When the waves from two coherent sources interfere, the amplitude of the sum of these waves in certain directions is less than that of a single source.

17.8 (*a*) If the amplitude of the wave generated by each source in Figure 17.16 is *A* at points P and Q, what is the overall amplitude at P in Figure 17.16*a*? In Figure 17.16*b*? (*b*) Given that the wave energy that passes Q in Figure 17.16*b* becomes zero when S_1 is turned on, do you expect the energy that passes P to increase or decrease? (*c*) Use your answer to part *a* to determine by what factor the amount of energy that passes P changes, and reconcile your answer with your answer to part *b*.

Just what a given interference pattern looks like is determined by the wavelength and the spacing between the two sources. The greater the source separation relative to the wavelength, the greater the number of nodal lines. We determine the number of nodal lines in a pattern by imagining a straight line running through the centers of the two sources and then counting the number of nodal lines on either side of this line:

> If two coherent sources located a distance *d* apart emit identical waves of wavelength **λ**, then the number of nodal lines on either side of a straight line running through the centers of the sources is the greatest integer smaller than or equal to $2(d/\lambda)$.

You can study the appearance of nodal lines as the separation between the sources is varied in **Figure 17.17**.

17.9 By how many wavelengths are the sources in Figure 17.16*a* separated?

Figure 17.17 The effect of changing the separation between two point sources.

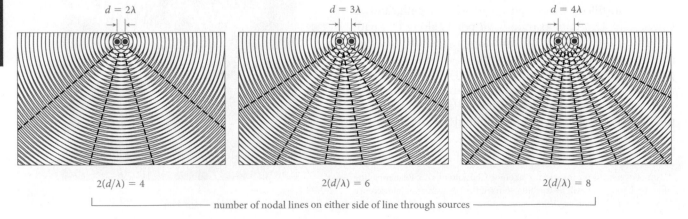

$d = 2\lambda$ $d = 3\lambda$ $d = 4\lambda$

$2(d/\lambda) = 4$ $2(d/\lambda) = 6$ $2(d/\lambda) = 8$

number of nodal lines on either side of line through sources

Example 17.3 Nodes

For the situation shown in Figure 17.16*a*, how many nodes are there along the line segment S_1S_2 that connects the centers of the two sources?

❶ GETTING STARTED The sources are coherent and so send identical waves in opposite directions along S_1S_2. This means there is a standing wave (see Section 16.6) along that segment. From Figure 17.16*b* I can tell that exactly three wavelengths fit between S_1 and S_2.

❷ DEVISE PLAN The two sources are in phase, so I can determine the number of nodes by plotting the amplitudes of the waves due to each source along S_1S_2 at two instants and then adding those amplitudes. The nodes occur wherever the amplitude of the combined wave remains zero.

❸ EXECUTE PLAN Figure 17.18*a* shows, for the instant at which the medium displacement at both sources is maximum, the medium displacement caused by S_1 and S_2 and the sum of the two. Figure 17.18*b* shows the displacements one-quarter cycle later. Comparing the two graphs, I see that six positions along line segment S_1S_2 (denoted by the black dots in the bottom graphs) remain stationary, indicating six nodes. ✔

Figure 17.18

displacement of medium at sources is:

resultant standing wave:

❹ EVALUATE RESULT Because the sources are separated by a distance equal to three wavelengths and because there is one node for each half-wavelength (see Section 16.6), my answer makes sense.

Example 17.3 shows us why there are twice as many nodes and therefore twice as many nodal lines as there are wavelengths between the sources. Each node corresponds to a nodal line, and so you now see why there is a connection between the number of nodal lines and the source spacing.

✋ **17.10** Along the leftward and rightward extensions of the straight line joining S_1 and S_2 in Figure 17.16, why are there no nodes to the left of S_1 and to the right of S_2?

Figure 17.19 on the next page shows what happens when additional coherent sources are added between the two sources of Figure 17.14. Let us focus our attention on the two points P and Q. When just two sources are present (Figure 17.19*a*), P is on a nodal line and Q is on an antinodal line. The path length diagram in Figure 17.19*a* shows the waves arriving at P and Q. The distance from source 1 to P is 7λ; the distance from source 2 to P is $9\frac{1}{2}\lambda$. Consequently the two waves *always* arrive at P out of phase—they cause medium displacements in opposite directions and so always cancel. The distance from source 1 to Q is 8λ; the distance from source 2 is 9λ. So the two waves arrive in phase at Q and always reinforce each other.

Figure 17.19*b* shows how the addition of a single source halfway between the two original sources redistributes the flow of wave energy and concentrates the waves in fewer triangular areas. The phase of the wave arriving from the additional source is approximately halfway between that from sources 1 and 2. In other words, source 3 is about $8\frac{1}{4}\lambda$ from P and $8\frac{1}{2}\lambda$ from Q. Because the waves from 1 and 2 cancel each other at P, the wave from 3 arrives undisturbed at P, so P is no longer on a nodal line. At Q, the additional wave from 3 arrives out of phase with those from 1 and 2, so the additional source diminishes the wave amplitude at Q.

If two additional sources are added, almost all the wave energy becomes concentrated in a narrow cone perpendicular to the straight line that connects the sources (Figure 17.19*c*). The phases of the waves are such that, even though there are five sources instead of two, the amplitude of the waves arriving at Q is *smaller* than before and that of the waves arriving at P is very small.

With ten coherent sources, all the waves are concentrated in a cone along the direction perpendicular to the straight line that joins the sources (Figure 17.19*d*). Outside of this cone, the waves—all arriving at any given point, including P and Q, with a different phase—cancel each other. **Figure 17.20** on page 445 shows what happens when 100 coherent sources are placed close together, now forming a row 10λ wide: A *beam* of nearly straight wavefronts emanates in a direction perpendicular to the row of sources. There are hardly any waves outside the beam because the waves from all the different sources tend to cancel each other. Summarizing:

When many coherent point sources are placed close together along a straight line, the waves nearly cancel out in all directions except the direction perpendicular to the axis of the sources.

✋ **17.11** How does the wave amplitude along the beam of wavefronts in Figure 17.20 change with distance from the row of sources?

Figure 17.19 When additional coherent sources are added between the two sources spaced by three wavelengths, the interference pattern changes: The greater the number of sources, the more the waves are concentrated along the axis perpendicular to the sources. The displacement curves show the displacements at P and Q for each source and the sum of these displacements (bold curve).

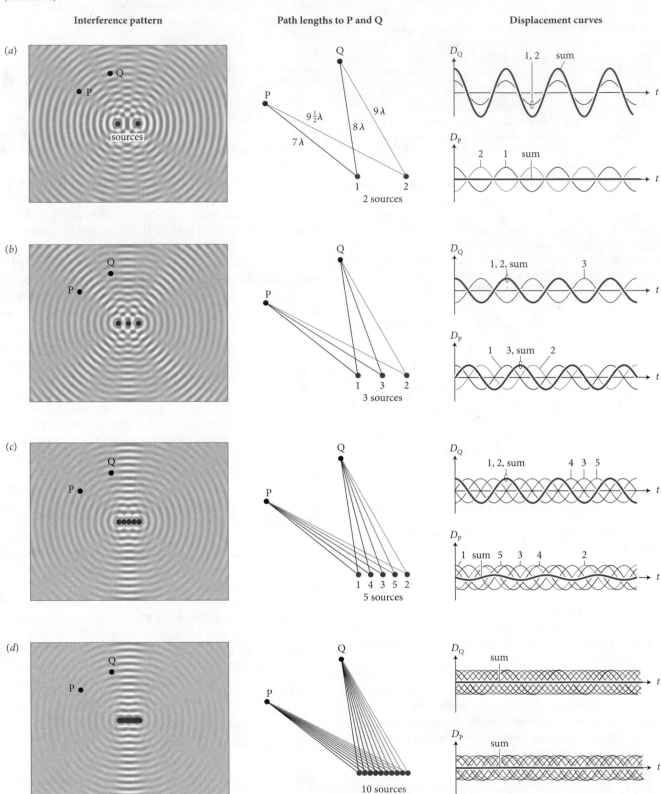

Figure 17.20 A 10λ-wide row of 100 coherent sources produces nearly planar wavefronts. The flow of energy is entirely along a beam perpendicular to the row of sources.

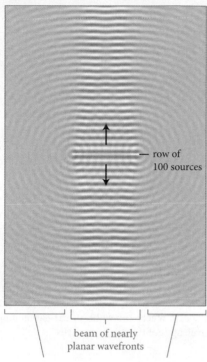

— row of 100 sources

beam of nearly planar wavefronts

Outside of beam, wave energy is negligible.

Figure 17.21 According to Huygens' principle, any wavefront can be regarded as a collection of closely spaced, coherent point sources. Advancing wavefronts can then be constructed by drawing circular wavelets centered at points along an earlier wavefront.

old wavefront

point sources

wavelets of radius $c\Delta t$

new wavefront

17.4 Diffraction

The nearly straight wavefronts that emanate from continuous rows of coherent sources suggest that *any* wavefront may be regarded as having originated from a collection of many closely spaced, coherent point sources emitting waves in all directions. The waves cancel in all directions except the direction perpendicular to the wavefront. This picture of wavefronts consisting of closely spaced, coherent point sources is called **Huygens' principle** after the 17th-century Dutch physicist Christiaan Huygens.

Figure 17.21 illustrates how Huygens' principle can be used to construct a future wavefront given the wavefront at a certain instant. We begin by dividing the original wavefront into a series of closely spaced point sources. All those point sources emit in phase because they are all on the same wavefront. After a short time interval Δt, each source has emitted a small circular wavefront, called a *wavelet*, of radius $c\Delta t$. Wavelets of neighboring sources overlap in such a way that they interfere destructively with each other except in the forward direction. All these forward-moving wavelets combine to form the wavefront we aim to construct, labeled "new wavefront" in Figure 17.21.*

---

*For a *single* row of coherent point sources, wavefronts emanate in *two* directions along a line perpendicular to the straight line connecting the sources (Figure 17.20). When additional rows of coherent point sources are added in front of or behind this row and these sources are given the proper phases, propagation in one of the two directions is suppressed by interference.

Huygens' principle also helps explain how waves spread around corners. If you stand near an open window, you hear sounds from the street even if you are not standing directly in front of the window. Likewise, if you stand behind a tree, you can hear sounds coming from in front of the tree because the sound waves spread around the tree.

Figure 17.22 on the next page shows nearly planar wavefronts incident on gaps of various size. If the gap is much larger than the wavelength, the gap lets through a *beam* of wavefronts with very little spreading. As the gap gets narrower, the waves beyond the gap spread out more and more, so that what gets through the gap no longer constitutes a beam. When the gap width is smaller than the wavelength, the wavefronts beyond the gap spread out in all directions—in essence, the gap now acts like a single point source. This spreading, called **diffraction,** is another characteristic feature that distinguishes waves from objects: Waves spread out when going through a narrow opening, but objects do not. If you throw a handful of buckshot through an opening, for instance, the "beam" of buckshot doesn't spread out after passing the opening.

The reason waves diffract is directly related to the observation that many coherent point sources in a row give rise to waves in just one direction because the waves emitted by each source cancel in all but the forward direction (Figure 17.20). Here we see the opposite occurring: As the number of point sources is reduced (the gap is narrowed in our example), the cancellation of waves along directions away from the straight line perpendicular to the line of sources becomes less complete and spreading occurs. As the width of the gap becomes comparable to the wavelength, the gap acts like a point source, leading to spreading of the wave in all directions.

Figure 17.22 When a planar wavefront passes through a gap, some spreading, called diffraction, occurs. The smaller the gap, the greater the amount of spreading. When the width d of the gap is smaller than the wavelength λ, the gap acts like a point source.

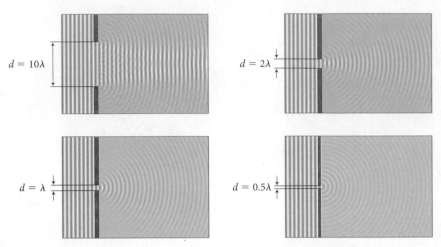

Obstacles or apertures whose width is smaller than the wavelength of an incident wave give rise to considerable spreading of that wave.

The amount of spreading depends strongly on the wavelength. For a given aperture, low-frequency sounds diffract more strongly than higher-frequency ones. If a band marches by below your window and you are not standing directly in the window opening, you hear the low-frequency drone of drums and tubas more than the high-frequency sounds of cymbals and piccolos. Move near the window and the sound of the band turns from dull to sharp as the high-frequency sounds emitted by it now also reach your ears.

A direct consequence of wave diffraction is that it is impossible to create a beam of waves that is narrower than the wavelength of the waves. This means that diffraction limits the ability of waves to locate objects. For example, it is impossible for a person to locate small objects by detecting reflected sound waves because, with their relatively long wavelengths (0.02 m to 20 m), these waves diffract around most objects. We therefore locate objects using visible light, whose wavelength is in the range of 4×10^{-7} m to 7×10^{-7} m (less than one-hundredth the width of a human hair). Only objects and apertures that are smaller than the wavelength of visible light diffract light.

Bats can detect ultrasonic waves of frequencies up to 120 kHz. The wavelength of these waves is about 3 mm. By emitting such waves and detecting their reflections, bats can locate small insects. Ultrasonic waves are also used for diagnostic purposes in medicine. Because of their short wavelength, it is possible to emit a narrow beam of ultrasonic waves. The beam is rapidly scanned across a sample to create an image from the reflections of the beam that occur inside the sample (**Figure 17.23**).

17.12 Suppose the barriers in Figure 17.22 were held at an angle to the incident wavefronts. Sketch the transmitted wavefronts for the case where the width of the gap is much smaller than the wavelength of the incident waves.

Figure 17.23 Ultrasound image of a three-month-old fetus in utero. The 2-MHz waves (1 megahertz = 1 MHz = 10^6 Hz) used to obtain this picture have a wavelength of 0.7 mm.

Self-quiz

1. A circular wave travels such that a crest occurs at radius r_1 at instant t_1. The same crest has a radius $r_2 = 2r_1$ at $t_2 = 2t_1$. (a) What is the wave speed? (b) Where is the crest at $t_3 = 3t_1$? (c) What is the ratio (energy per unit length at t_3)/(energy per unit length at t_1)?

2. A spherical wave travels such that a crest occurs at radius r_1 at instant t_1. The same crest has a radius $r_2 = 2r_1$ at $t_2 = 2t_1$. (a) What is the wave speed? (b) Where is the crest at $t_3 = 3t_1$? (c) What is the ratio (energy per unit area at t_3)/(energy per unit area at t_1)?

3. Two circular wavefronts interfere as shown in **Figure 17.24**. (a) Draw the antinodal lines. (b) Is the medium displacement along these lines constant?

Figure 17.24

4. Two coherent sources are placed two wavelengths apart. Point P lies on a nodal line in the interference pattern of the two sources, and point Q lies on an antinodal line. (a) If one source is turned off, does the energy arriving at P increase, decrease, or remain the same? (b) If one source is turned off, does the energy arriving at Q increase, decrease, or remain the same? (c) Do your answers depend on which source is turned off?

5. Because sound waves diffract around an open doorway, you can hear sounds coming from outside the doorway. You cannot, however, see objects outside the doorway unless you are directly in line with them. What does this observation imply about the wavelength of light?

Answers

1. (a) The speed is the distance traveled divided by the time interval over which the motion occurs: r_1/t_1. (b) At $3t_1$ the crest is at $3r_1$. (c) The energy per unit length at r_1 is proportional to $1/r_1$. That at r_3 is proportional to $1/r_3 = 1/3r_1$. The ratio of the energies per unit length at the two instants is thus $1/3$.

2. (a) The speed is r_1/t_1. (b) The crest is at $3r_1$. The answers to parts a and b to this and the preceding question have to do with only the speed of the waves, not their dimensionality. (c) The energy per unit area at r_1 is proportional to $1/r_1^2$. That at r_3 is proportional to $1/r_3^2 = 1/(3r_1)^2$. The ratio of the energies per unit area at the two instants is $1/9$.

3. (a) See **Figure 17.25**. (b) No. The medium displacement at any point on an antinodal line varies as a function of time.

Figure 17.25

4. (a) Being on a nodal line, P initially receives no energy. After one source is turned off, it receives energy from the other source, and so the energy P receives increases. (b) Being on an antinodal line, Q receives four times the energy of a single source because the amplitude at Q is twice that of a single source. When one source is turned off, Q receives only the energy from a single source, and so the energy received at Q decreases. (c) It does not matter which source is turned off. The interference pattern exists only when both sources are on, and each point receives the energy from only a single source when the second source is turned off.

5. Because light does not diffract as it travels through the doorway, this observation implies that the wavelength of the light must be smaller than the width of the doorway. Given that visible light has wavelengths between 4×10^{-7} m and 7×10^{-7} m and most doorways are about 1 m wide and 2 m tall, this is indeed the case.

17.5 Intensity

As we saw in Section 17.1, the propagation of waves in more than one dimension causes the wave energy to be diluted over a larger and larger region. For waves in three dimensions, we define the **intensity** I as the energy delivered by the wave per unit time per unit area normal to the direction of propagation. Because the energy delivered per unit time is the definition of power, we can say

$$I \equiv \frac{P}{A}, \qquad (17.1)$$

where P is the power delivered by the wave over an area A. For three-dimensional waves, the SI unit of intensity is thus W/m^2.

Consider a point source sending out waves uniformly in all directions. If there is no dissipation of energy, all the energy generated by the source must cross an imaginary sphere centered on the source. If the power delivered by the source is P_s, the intensity is

$$I = \frac{P_s}{A_{sphere}} = \frac{P_s}{4\pi r^2} \quad \text{(uniformly radiating point source)}, \qquad (17.2)$$

and so we see that the intensity of a wave in three dimensions is proportional to $1/r^2$, as we concluded in Section 17.1.

For a two-dimensional surface wave, the intensity is defined as the energy incident per unit time per unit *length* normal to the direction of propagation. For a surface wave that delivers a power P over a length L,

$$I_{surf} \equiv \frac{P}{L}. \qquad (17.3)$$

Consequently the SI unit of the intensity of a surface wave is W/m because we must replace the area of a sphere in Eq. 17.2 by the circumference of a circle: $I = P_s/(2\pi r)$. The intensity of two-dimensional waves is thus proportional to $1/r$.

Example 17.4 Sound wave energy

The minimum intensity audible to the human ear is called the *threshold of hearing*. For a 1.0-kHz sound wave, this threshold is approximately 10^{-12} W/m^2. The maximum tolerable intensity, called the *threshold of pain*, is about 1.0 W/m^2 for a 1.0-kHz sound wave. (*a*) For a 1.0-kHz sound wave, estimate the amount of energy delivered to the ear in 1.0 s at the threshold of hearing and at the threshold of pain. (*b*) If the sound is produced by a loudspeaker 1.0 m away from the ear, what is, in each case, the power emitted by the loudspeaker?

❶ **GETTING STARTED** I am given two intensities, which give the power per unit area, and asked in part *a* to calculate the energy arriving at the ear in 1.0 s for each intensity. Because energy per unit time is power, part *a* reduces to identifying the area over which the energy is delivered. For part *b*, I am given a loudspeaker-to-ear distance, and I need to calculate the power for each loudspeaker at that distance.

❷ **DEVISE PLAN** For part *a*, to estimate the energy delivered to the ear in 1.0 s, I have to estimate the surface area of the ear. I can then use Eq. 17.1 to calculate the power delivered to the ear. To obtain the energy delivered, I multiply the power by the time interval. For part *b*, I assume that the loudspeaker is a point source that radiates sound uniformly in all directions. With this assumption, I can use the given intensities and source-to-ear distance in Eq. 17.2 to calculate the power emitted by the speaker.

❸ **EXECUTE PLAN** (*a*) The surface area of the outer ear is approximately $(0.030 \text{ m})^2 \approx 9.0 \times 10^{-4} \text{ m}^2$, so the power delivered to the ear at the threshold of hearing is about

$$P = IA = (10^{-12} \text{ W/m}^2)(9.0 \times 10^{-4} \text{ m}^2) = 9.0 \times 10^{-16} \text{ W}$$

$$= 9.0 \times 10^{-16} \text{ J/s}.$$

In 1.0 s, a mere 9.0×10^{-16} J—about a millionth of a billionth of a joule—gets delivered to the ear when a sound source emits at an intensity equal to the threshold of hearing. ✔
At the threshold of pain, the power delivered to the ear is

$$(1.0 \text{ W/m}^2)(9.0 \times 10^{-4} \text{ m}^2) = 9.0 \times 10^{-4} \text{ W},$$

and so 0.90 mJ is delivered to the ear in 1.0 s. ✔

(*b*) For the power emitted by the loudspeaker at the two thresholds, Eq. 17.2 gives

threshold of hearing:

$$P_s = I(4\pi r^2) = (10^{-12} \text{ W/m}^2)[4\pi(1.0 \text{ m})^2]$$

$$= 1.3 \times 10^{-11} \text{ W} ✔$$

threshold of pain:

$$P_s = (1.0 \text{ W/m}^2)[4\pi(1.0 \text{ m})^2] = 13 \text{ W}. ✔$$

❹ **EVALUATE RESULT** The energies delivered at the threshold of hearing are very small, and I have no good way of evaluating those. I do know that the ear can detect sounds made by the tiniest of movements—the rustle of a leaf, for example—and these movements cannot transmit much energy, so at least I know that the values I obtained are not unreasonably large. I know that headphones and loudspeakers can easily emit power levels at the threshold of pain. The fact that headphones can be powered with tiny batteries tells me that the 0.9-mW answer I obtained in part *a* is not unreasonable. Most stereo systems are rated at tens to hundreds of watts, so the 13 W in part *b* is also in the right range.

As Example 17.4 illustrates, the human ear is capable of handling sound waves over a tremendous range of intensities—intensities that differ by as much as a factor of 10^{12}. To deal conveniently with such an enormous intensity range, it is common to use a logarithmic scale for intensity. For example, if the intensity *I* increases by a factor of 10^{12}, as it does when going from the threshold of hearing to the threshold of pain, the common logarithm (see Appendix B), log *I*, increases by only 12. The intensity of a sound wave can then be expressed as part of a ratio that also includes the intensity I_{th} at the threshold of hearing:

$$\log\left(\frac{I}{I_{th}}\right). \tag{17.4}$$

Because the reference level ($I_{th} = 10^{-12} \text{ W/m}^2$) is chosen arbitrarily, the quantity $\log(I/I_{th})$, even though it is unitless, is given an artificial unit. This unit is the *bel* (B), in honor of the American scientist Alexander Bell (1847–1922). It is customary to express intensity levels of sound in **decibels** (dB), one-tenth of a bel: 1 dB = 0.1 B. The **intensity level** β of a sound, measured in decibels, is thus defined as

$$\beta \equiv (10 \text{ dB}) \log\left(\frac{I}{I_{th}}\right). \tag{17.5}$$

QUANTITATIVE TOOLS

Figure 17.26 Average auditory response of the human ear. The ear is sensitive to longitudinal waves in air ranging in frequency from 20 Hz to 20 kHz. The sensitivity is greatest at 3 kHz, where the threshold of hearing is lowest. The curves give the intensity levels required to produce harmonic tones of the same perceived loudness.

Table 17.1 Approximate intensity levels

Source	distance (m)	β (dB)	Description
Jet engine	50	140	pain
Pneumatic hammer	10	110	
Shout	1.5	100	very loud
Car horn	10	90	
Hair dryer	0.2	80	loud
Automobile interior		70	
Conversation	1	60	moderate
Office background		50	
Library background		40	
Suburban bedroom		30	quiet
Whisper	1	20	
Normal breathing	5	10	barely audible

At the threshold of hearing, where the intensity is $I = 10^{-12}$ W/m², we have $\log(I/I_{\text{th}}) = \log(1) = 0$, and so the intensity level $\beta = (10 \text{ dB})(0) = 0$ dB. At the threshold of pain, where the intensity is $I = 1$ W/m², we have $\log[(1 \text{ W/m}^2)/(10^{-12} \text{ W/m}^2)] = 12$, and so the intensity level is $\beta = (10 \text{ dB})(12) = 120$ dB.

As **Figure 17.26** illustrates, the thresholds for hearing and pain vary with frequency. The five curves between the two threshold curves give the intensity required to produce harmonic sounds that a listener perceives as all being equally loud. For example, a sinusoidal 200-Hz tone of intensity 10^{-8} W/m² and a sinusoidal 1-kHz tone of intensity 10^{-10} W/m² are perceived to have the same loudness by the average listener. The right vertical scale gives the corresponding intensity level in decibels. **Table 17.1** gives the intensity levels in decibels of a number of common sound sources.

Exercise 17.5 Doubling the intensity

A clarinet can produce about 70 dB of sound. By how much does the intensity level increase if a second clarinet is played at the same time?

SOLUTION If the intensity of the sound produced by one clarinet is I_c, the intensity level of one clarinet is

$$\beta_1 = (10 \text{ dB}) \log\left(\frac{I_c}{I_{\text{th}}}\right) = 70 \text{ dB}.$$

The second clarinet doubles the intensity, so the intensity level becomes

$$\beta_2 = (10 \text{ dB}) \log\left(\frac{2I_c}{I_{\text{th}}}\right) = (10 \text{ dB})\left[\log 2 + \log\left(\frac{I_c}{I_{\text{th}}}\right)\right]$$

$$= (10 \text{ dB})\log 2 + \beta_1,$$

where I have used the logarithmic relationship $\log AB = \log A + \log B$. Because $\log 2 \approx 0.3$, the intensity level increases to $\beta_2 \approx (10 \text{ dB})(0.3) + 70 \text{ dB} = 73$ dB. So, even though the intensity doubles, the intensity *level* increases by only 3 dB. ✔

17.13 In Exercise 17.5, how many clarinets must play at the same time in order to increase the intensity level from 70 dB to 80 dB?

Figure 17.27 When two sources emit waves of equal amplitude but slightly different frequencies, the waves superpose to produce a wave that has a pulsating amplitude (dashed line). We call this phenomenon *beating*.

(*a*) Displacement curves for two waves of equal amplitude but slightly different frequencies

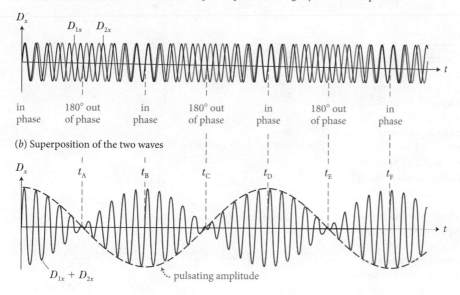

(*b*) Superposition of the two waves

17.6 Beats

In the first part of this chapter, the only type of interference we considered was interference between sources that emit waves of the same frequency. Let us now consider two sources that emit waves of equal amplitude but slightly different frequencies f_1 and f_2. Let the medium displacements caused by the individual waves at some fixed location be given by

$$D_{1x} = A \sin(2\pi f_1 t) \qquad (17.6)$$

$$D_{2x} = A \sin(2\pi f_2 t). \qquad (17.7)$$

These displacements are plotted in **Figure 17.27a**. Note that because the frequencies are different, the phase relationship between the two sources is not constant. At $t = 0$, the displacements are in phase, but over time they get out of phase, with the phase of one wave getting ahead of the other. At some instants the two waves are in phase (0, t_B, t_D, . . .), and at these instants their crests coincide, giving rise to oscillations of double amplitude. At other instants, however, the waves are 180° out of phase (t_A, t_C, . . .), and at these instants the crests and troughs of the two waves cancel each other.

The medium displacement that results from the superposition of the two waves is shown in Figure 17.27b. The resultant wave is an oscillation that changes amplitude with time. At instants 0, t_B, t_D, and t_F the amplitude is maximal; at instants t_A, t_C, and t_E the amplitude is zero. This phenomenon, called **beating,** can be heard clearly with two tuning forks that oscillate at slightly different frequencies. Each maximum in the amplitude (at 0, t_B, t_D, . . .) corresponds to what sounds like a *beat*. When both tuning forks simultaneously produce sound, you hear a tone whose intensity periodically fades in and out.

This phenomenon is similar to the moiré pattern in **Figure 17.28**, produced by two striped bands that have slightly different line spacings. At some places the lines of the two bands overlap, producing bright regions (labeled P, Q, R, S), while at others the lines fall precisely in between one another, producing dark regions.

Figure 17.28 Moiré pattern showing beating between two patterns with slightly different line spacings.

17.14 The lines in band A in Figure 17.28 are more closely spaced than those in band B. (*a*) How many more lines does band A have between points P and S? (*b*) Describe what happens to the pattern if band B is displaced downward by one-half the spacing between its lines.

Example 17.6 Lapping rounds

You and a friend are running laps around a race track. You begin together, and both of you run at constant speed, but you run faster than she does. Because the time interval T_y you take to complete one lap is smaller than the time interval T_f your friend takes to complete one lap, you finish the first lap ahead of her. Each lap you get farther ahead, until eventually you overtake your friend after she has run n laps (**Figure 17.29**). What is the frequency $f_{overtake}$ at which you overtake her? Express your answer in two ways: first in terms of T_y and T_f and then in terms of the frequencies f_y and f_f at which each of you completes one lap.

❶ **GETTING STARTED** Regardless of how many laps my friend has run, when I overtake her I have completed exactly one lap more than she has. So, if she has completed n laps, I have completed $(n + 1)$ laps. At that instant, the process starts over, and I overtake her again when I have completed another $(n + 1)$ laps. Note that n need not be a whole number of laps; for example, if I first overtake my friend after 8.2 laps (she having completed 7.2 laps) and we both keep running at constant speed, the next overtaking occurs when I have completed 16.4 laps.

❷ **DEVISE PLAN** The frequency at which I overtake my friend is the reciprocal of the time interval it takes me to overtake her. I know that she completes n laps, each of duration T_f, at the same instant I complete $(n + 1)$ laps, each lap of duration T_y. From this information I can determine n and the instant at which I first overtake her. The frequency at which I overtake her is the reciprocal of the period between that instant and the beginning of the race.

❸ **EXECUTE PLAN** At the instant I first overtake my friend, I have run for a time interval $(n + 1)T_y$ and she has run for a

time interval nT_f. Because we started at the same instant, I have $nT_f = (n + 1)T_y$, giving me

$$n = \frac{T_y}{T_f - T_y}.$$

The instant at which the first overtake occurs is

$$t_{overtake} = nT_f = \frac{T_y T_f}{T_f - T_y},$$

and so the overtaking frequency is

$$f_{overtake} = \frac{1}{t_{overtake}} = \frac{T_f - T_y}{T_y T_f}. \checkmark$$

To express $f_{overtake}$ in terms of f_y and f_f, I use $f_y = 1/T_y$ and $f_f = 1/T_f$ and write

$$f_{overtake} = \frac{T_f - T_y}{T_y T_f} = \frac{1}{T_y} - \frac{1}{T_f} = f_y - f_f. \checkmark$$

❹ **EVALUATE RESULT** Because $f_y > f_f$, the overtaking frequency is positive, as I expect. My result shows that if both of us run laps at the same frequency, $f_y = f_f$, the overtaking frequency is zero. That makes sense because, running at the same rate, we never overtake each other. Another limiting case is when my friend remains at rest. In that case f_f is zero and so the overtaking frequency is equal to the frequency at which I complete laps. My answer makes sense in the limiting cases, which gives me confidence it is correct.

Figure 17.29 Example 17.6.

On each lap, you pull farther ahead...

...eventually, you "lap" your friend (complete one more lap).

0 lap counter

you
friend

0

1

1

2

2

n + 1

n

track

Suppose that in Example 17.6 your friend had run faster than you. In that case we could apply the same reasoning, but the indices y and f would now have been switched and the end result would have been $f_{overtake} = f_f - f_y$. (Because $f_y < f_f$, the overtaking frequency is again positive.) The general result, in case we do not know which frequency is greater, is thus $f_{overtake} = |f_f - f_y|$.

We can apply the reasoning I used in solving this example to the beating of two waves: The phases of the two waves catch up each time the wave of higher frequency has completed one more full oscillation than the other wave. If the wave frequencies are f_1 and f_2, then the frequency at which the beats occur, called the **beat frequency,** must, in analogy to the result from Example 17.6, be

$$f_{beat} \equiv |f_1 - f_2|. \tag{17.8}$$

We can reach the same conclusion by adding the expressions for the displacements of the two waves given by Eqs. 17.6 and 17.7:

$$D_x = D_{1x} + D_{2x} = A(\sin 2\pi f_1 t + \sin 2\pi f_2 t). \tag{17.9}$$

The sum of two sine functions can be written using the identity

$$\sin \alpha + \sin \beta = 2 \cos\tfrac{1}{2}(\alpha - \beta) \sin\tfrac{1}{2}(\alpha + \beta), \tag{17.10}$$

so

$$D_x = 2A \cos\tfrac{1}{2}[2\pi(f_1 - f_2)t] \sin\tfrac{1}{2}[2\pi(f_1 + f_2)t]. \tag{17.11}$$

Because $\cos \theta = \cos(-\theta)$, we can replace the term $(f_1 - f_2)$ in Eq. 17.11 by $(f_2 - f_1)$ when $f_1 < f_2$. If we write $\Delta f = |f_1 - f_2|$ for the absolute value of the difference in frequency and $f_{av} = \tfrac{1}{2}(f_1 + f_2)$ for the average frequency, we can rewrite Eq. 17.11 in the form

$$D_x = 2A \cos\left[2\pi\left(\tfrac{1}{2}\Delta f\right)t\right] \sin(2\pi f_{av}t). \tag{17.12}$$

This expression tells us that the resulting wave has a frequency that is the average of the two original frequencies and an amplitude that varies with time. The factor $2A \cos\left[2\pi(\tfrac{1}{2}\Delta f)t\right]$ corresponds to the dashed curve in Figure 17.27b. It represents the slow variation in the amplitude of the combined wave.

The frequency of the amplitude variation is $\tfrac{1}{2}\Delta f = \tfrac{1}{2}|f_1 - f_2|$. However, *two* beats occur in each cycle of this amplitude variation. In Figure 17.27, one cycle in the amplitude variation lasts from $t = 0$ to $t = t_D$ (look at the dashed curve in Figure 17.27b and notice how it returns to its starting value at t_D). During this period *two* beats occur, one at t_A and the other at t_C. The beat frequency is therefore *twice* the amplitude variation frequency $\tfrac{1}{2}|f_1 - f_2|$, and so we see that the beat frequency is indeed equal to the absolute value of the difference in the frequencies of the two waves: $f_{beat} = |f_1 - f_2|$.

Exercise 17.7 Tuning a piano

Your middle-C tuning fork oscillates at 261.6 Hz. When you play the middle-C key on your piano together with the tuning fork, you hear 15 beats in 10 s. What are the possible frequencies emitted by this key?

SOLUTION The beat frequency—the number of beats per second—is equal to the difference between the two frequencies (Eq. 17.8). I am given the frequency of the tuning fork, $f_t = 261.6$ Hz, and the beat frequency, $f_B = (15 \text{ beats})/(10 \text{ s}) = 1.5$ Hz. I do not know, however, whether the frequency f_p of the struck middle-C piano key is higher or lower than that of the tuning fork.

If it is higher, I have $f_B = f_p - f_t$.

If it is lower, then $f_B = f_t - f_p$.

So

$$f_p = f_t \pm f_B = 261.6 \text{ Hz} \pm 1.5 \text{ Hz}$$

and the possible frequencies emitted by the out-of-tune middle-C key are 260.1 Hz and 263.1 Hz. ✔

17.15 Do two sound waves of slightly different frequencies and *different* amplitudes cause beats?

17.7 Doppler effect

When an observer and a source of waves move relative to each other, the observed wave frequency is not the same as the frequency emitted by the source. When observer and source move toward each other, the observed frequency is higher than the emitted frequency; when they move away from each other, the observed frequency is lower than the emitted frequency. This phenomenon is called the **Doppler effect.**

Let us determine how the observed frequency deviates from the actual frequency of the source, depending on the speeds of source and observer relative to the medium through which the waves propagate. In **Figure 17.30a**, a loudspeaker that is stationary relative to a medium emits a sound wave that is detected by a microphone that is also stationary relative to the medium. The period of the wave is T, and so one wavefront of a given phase (a crest, for example) leaves the loudspeaker each period T. Once the first wavefront reaches the microphone, it thereafter receives one wavefront each period T, and so the frequency received

Figure 17.30 The Doppler effect demonstrated by a speaker and a microphone. Notice that motion of the speaker toward the microphone and motion of the microphone toward the speaker both cause the frequency received by the microphone to increase—but not by the same amount. The two situations are not symmetrical because motion of the speaker shortens the wavelength of the propagating sound, whereas motion of the microphone does not.

(a) Speaker and microphone are stationary relative to medium

(b) Speaker moves toward microphone

(c) Microphone moves toward speaker

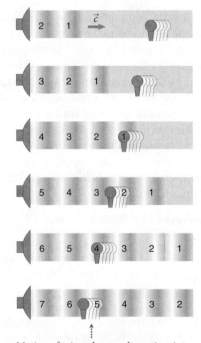

Motion of speaker reduces spacing between wavefronts . . .

Motion of microphone reduces time interval between arrival of successive wavefronts . . .

$D_x(t)$ graphs for waves received by microphone

Frequency received by microphone is same as frequency emitted by speaker.

. . . so microphone observes higher frequency.

. . . so microphone observes higher frequency (but not as high as in part b).

by the microphone is identical to the frequency emitted by the loudspeaker. The graph at the bottom of Figure 17.30a shows the longitudinal medium displacement caused by the sound wave at the location of the microphone as a function of time.

Figure 17.30b shows what happens when the loudspeaker emits the same sound wave while moving at constant velocity toward the microphone. Because of the motion of the loudspeaker, each wavefront is emitted closer to the previous wavefront than if the loudspeaker were stationary. Because the speed of the wavefronts, which is determined by the properties of the medium (air in this case), does not depend on the motion of the loudspeaker, the more closely spaced wavefronts generated by the moving loudspeaker reach the microphone at shorter time intervals than those of the stationary loudspeaker. For example, between $t = 5T$ and $t = 7T$ only two cycles between wavefronts 1 and 3 pass the microphone when the source is stationary (Figure 17.30a), but four wave cycles between wavefronts 1 and 5 pass the microphone when the source is moving (Figure 17.30b). So the frequency detected by the microphone for the moving source is (4 cycles)/(7T − 5T) = (4 cycles)/(2T), or two cycles per period instead of one cycle per period; in other words, the frequency heard by the microphone is twice the frequency emitted by the moving loudspeaker.

To obtain a general expression for the frequency received from a source S moving at speed v_s, let us evaluate the spacing between wavefronts. **Figure 17.31** shows the motion of the source during one period. (For now we consider the case when the source moves more slowly than the wave, $v_s < c$; in the next section we consider what happens when $v_s > c$.) The labeled wavefront was emitted when the source was at $x = 0$. During the time interval T, the source has moved from $x = 0$ to $x_1 = +v_s T$, at which point it emits the next wavefront. The first wavefront meanwhile has moved from $x = 0$ out to a radius $x_2 = cT$. To an observer somewhere to the right of Figure 17.31, the distance between the two wavefronts is decreased: $\Delta x = x_2 - x_1 = cT - v_s T = (c - v_s)T$. The period T_o of the wave that reaches this observer is equal to the time interval between the

Figure 17.31 Doppler effect for a source moving toward an observer. The observer is off to the right and not shown.

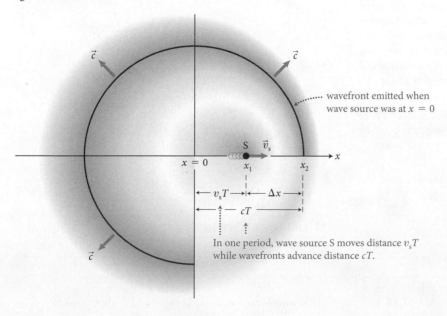

wavefront emitted when
wave source was at $x = 0$

In one period, wave source S moves distance $v_s T$
while wavefronts advance distance cT.

arrival of two successive wavefronts and is thus equal to the distance Δx divided by the speed of the waves:

$$T_o = \frac{\Delta x}{c} = \frac{c - v_s}{c}T \quad \text{(source approaching observer, } v_s < c\text{).} \quad (17.13)$$

The frequency of the approaching source heard by the observer is thus

$$f_o \equiv \frac{1}{T_o} = \frac{c}{c - v_s}\frac{1}{T}$$

$$= \frac{c}{c - v_s}f_s \quad \text{(source approaching observer, } v_s < c\text{),} \quad (17.14)$$

where f_s is the frequency emitted by the source. Note that because v_s is positive, $[c/(c - v_s)] > 1$, so the observed frequency is higher than the emitted frequency, as expected.

Now let us consider an observer on the opposite side of Figure 17.31. To this observer, the source is receding and the distance between wavefronts is increased: $\Delta x = (c + v_s)T$. Consequently the minus sign in front of v_s becomes a plus in Eqs. 17.13 and 17.14:

$$f_o \equiv \frac{1}{T_o} = \frac{c}{c + v_s}\frac{1}{T} = \frac{c}{c + v_s}f_s \quad \text{(source receding from observer),} \quad (17.15)$$

and the observed frequency is now lower than the emitted frequency, as we expect. Contrary to the situation described by Eq. 17.14, there is no limit on the speed of the source in this case.

Example 17.8 Moving train

Standing alongside a straight section of railroad track as a train passes, you record the sound of the train's horn. By analyzing the recording, you determine that the frequency of the sound was 483 Hz as the train approached and 405 Hz after it passed. At what speed was the train moving? Use 343 m/s for the speed of sound in air.

❶ **GETTING STARTED** I am given two frequencies for one sound source, so I know this problem is about a Doppler shift. I assume the train moved at constant velocity and denote its unknown speed by v. Because the horn—that is, the sound source—was on the train, v is also the speed at which the horn moved, and I know I can use some Doppler equation to calculate this speed. The wave speed is given as $c = 343$ m/s.

❷ **DEVISE PLAN** As the train approaches, the frequency I hear is given by Eq. 17.14. After it passes, the frequency is given by Eq. 17.15. This gives me two equations with two unknowns, f_s (the frequency of the source) and v, so I can solve for v.

❸ **EXECUTE PLAN** As the train approaches, the observed frequency is given by Eq. 17.14:

$$f_1 = \frac{c}{c - v_s}f_s = \frac{c}{c - v}f_s. \quad (1)$$

After the train passes, the observed frequency is given by Eq. 17.15:

$$f_2 = \frac{c}{c + v_s}f_s = \frac{c}{c + v}f_s. \quad (2)$$

Solving Eq. 2 for f_s and substituting the result into Eq. 1, I obtain

$$f_1 = \frac{c}{c - v}\left(\frac{c + v}{c}f_2\right) = \frac{c + v}{c - v}f_2.$$

Multiplying both sides by $(c - v)$ gives

$$f_1(c - v) = f_2(c + v)$$

$$v(f_1 + f_2) = c(f_1 - f_2).$$

Therefore

$$v = \frac{f_1 - f_2}{f_1 + f_2}c = \frac{483 \text{ Hz} - 405 \text{ Hz}}{483 \text{ Hz} + 405 \text{ Hz}}(343 \text{ m/s}) = 30 \text{ m/s.} ✔$$

❹ **EVALUATE RESULT** This is about 110 km/h or 70 mi/h, not unreasonable for a train.

 17.16 In Example 17.8, what is the frequency of the sound the horn makes?

Figure 17.32 Doppler effect for an observer moving toward the source.

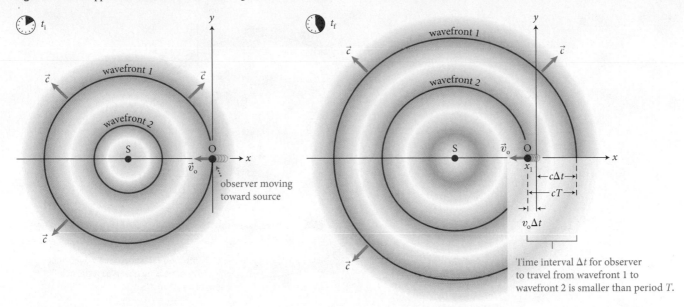

Time interval Δt for observer to travel from wavefront 1 to wavefront 2 is smaller than period T.

Applications of the Doppler effect range from measuring blood flow by reflecting a beam of ultrasound waves from red blood cells to measuring the speed of a storm using radar. The latter uses electromagnetic waves (see Chapter 30), which, like sound waves, exhibit a Doppler effect.

Any movement by an observer also affects the frequency of sound waves. When an observer is moving toward a stationary source, as in Figure 17.30c, the observer travels through the oncoming wavefronts and consequently observes more of them per unit time than if she or he were at rest. Between $t = 4T$ and $t = 6T$ in Figure 17.30c, for example, three wave cycles pass the microphone, and so the observed frequency is (3 cycles)/(6T − 4T) = (1.5 cycle)/T = 1.5f_s. Because the microphone moves toward the loudspeaker, each subsequent wavefront has to travel a shorter distance to reach the microphone, and so the observed frequency is higher than the emitted frequency.

Figure 17.32 allows us to relate the increase in frequency to the speed v_o of a observer O who is moving toward the source S. At t_i the observer is at $x = 0$ just as wavefront 1 passes her. At t_f the observer meets wavefront 2 at position x_1, and so she detects one complete cycle (that is, two wavefronts) in $\Delta t = t_f - t_i$. During that time interval, wavefronts 1 and 2 have moved a distance $c\Delta t$. From the figure we see that the sum of the distances traveled by the wavefront and the moving observer is equal to the distance between wavefronts, so $c\Delta t + v_o\Delta t = cT$. The time interval at which successive wavefronts reach the observer is thus

$$\Delta t = \frac{cT}{c + v_o}.$$ (17.16)

The frequency she observes is

$$f_o \equiv \frac{1}{\Delta t} = \frac{c + v_o}{c} \frac{1}{T} = \frac{c + v_o}{c} f_s \quad \text{(observer approaching source).}$$ (17.17)

Because $(c + v_o) > c$, the observed frequency is higher, as expected.

Let us now consider an observer who moves away from the source at a speed that is smaller than the speed of sound, $v_o < c$. (If the observer were to move

Figure 17.33 Doppler effect for an observer moving away from the source at a speed $v_o < c$.

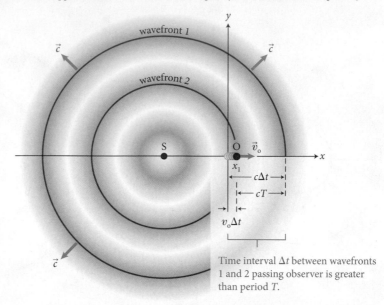

Time interval Δt between wavefronts 1 and 2 passing observer is greater than period T.

away at a greater speed, the sound would never catch up with the observer.) Again, we take the observer to be at $x = 0$ just as wavefront 1 passes him at t_i. **Figure 17.33** shows the situation at t_f when wavefront 2 catches up with the observer at position x_1. In the time interval $\Delta t = t_f - t_i$ the observer hears a complete cycle. During that time interval, wavefronts 1 and 2 have moved a distance $c\Delta t$. From the figure we see that the distance between wavefronts is equal to the difference between the distances traveled by the wavefront and the moving observer, so $c\Delta t - v_o\Delta t = cT$. The time interval at which successive wavefronts reach the observer is thus

$$\Delta t = \frac{cT}{c - v_o}. \tag{17.18}$$

Consequently the plus sign in front of v_o in Eq. 17.17 becomes a minus, and the observed frequency is thus

$$f_o \equiv \frac{1}{\Delta t} = \frac{c - v_o}{c}\frac{1}{T}$$

$$= \frac{c - v_o}{c}f_s \quad \text{(observer receding from source, } v_o < c\text{).} \tag{17.19}$$

Because $(c - v_o) < c$, the observed frequency is lower, as expected.

If both source and observer are moving, the two effects multiply—the moving source causes wavefronts to be spaced differently, giving rise to the observed frequency given in Eqs. 17.14 and 17.15, and the moving observer detects the wavefronts at a different rate, as indicated by Eqs. 17.17 and 17.19. The two effects can be combined in one equation:

$$f_o = \left(\frac{c \pm v_o}{c}\right)\left(\frac{c}{c \pm v_s}\right)f_s = \frac{c \pm v_o}{c \pm v_s}f_s, \tag{17.20}$$

which can be written in the more symmetrical form

$$\frac{f_o}{f_s} = \frac{c \pm v_o}{c \pm v_s}. \tag{17.21}$$

Figure 17.34 To use the general Doppler equation, the key thing you need to remember is that the observed frequency increases when source and observer move toward each other and decreases when they move apart.

Keep in mind that in Eqs. 17.20 and 17.21 the speeds of the observer and source are measured relative to the medium. Also, these expressions are subject to the same conditions as in Eqs. 17.14 and 17.19: when the source is approaching the observer $v_s < c$, and when the observer is receding from the source $v_o < c$.

Rather than trying to remember the correct choices for the signs in front of v_o and v_s in this expression, it is easiest to remember that the observed frequency increases when source and observer move toward each other and decreases when they move apart. For example, the top left of **Figure 17.34** shows an observer approaching a stationary source ($v_s = 0$). The observed frequency is higher and therefore you select the plus sign in front of v_o in Eq. 17.21. When the observer moves away from the stationary source (top right of Figure 17.34), the observed frequency is lower and so you select the minus sign in front of v_o in Eq. 17.21. The bottom left of Figure 17.34 shows a source moving toward an observer who is at rest relative to the medium ($v_o = 0$). The observed frequency is higher, and therefore you select the minus sign in front of v_s in Eq. 17.21. In the bottom right of Figure 17.34 the source moves away from the stationary observer; the observed frequency is now lower and you select the plus sign in front of v_s in Eq. 17.21.

17.17 (*a*) Suppose an observer moves at half the speed of sound toward a stationary source of sound waves. By what factor does the observed frequency differ from the emitted frequency? (*b*) By what factor does the observed frequency differ if, instead of the observer moving, the source moves toward the stationary observer at half the speed of sound? (*c*) Why is there a difference?

17.8 Shock waves

The observed frequency f_o given by Eq. 17.14 becomes infinite when the speed of the source approaches the speed of sound. As can be seen in **Figure 17.35a**, the wavefronts in front of a source moving at a speed $v_s < c$ crowd together. When a source moves at the speed of sound, *all* wavefronts in the forward direction travel with the source, and so the spacing between them is reduced to zero. A source traveling *faster* than the the speed of sound overtakes the wavefronts it has generated. The wavefronts then pile up to form a wavefront that is wedge-shaped in two dimensions and cone-shaped in three dimensions.

This wedge- or cone-shaped wavefront, called a **shock wave,** occurs whenever the speed of any object moving through a medium is higher than the the speed of sound in the medium, *even if the object emits no sound.* A bullet moving faster

Figure 17.35 The formation of a shock wave as the speed of a source reaches and then exceeds the speed of sound in the medium.

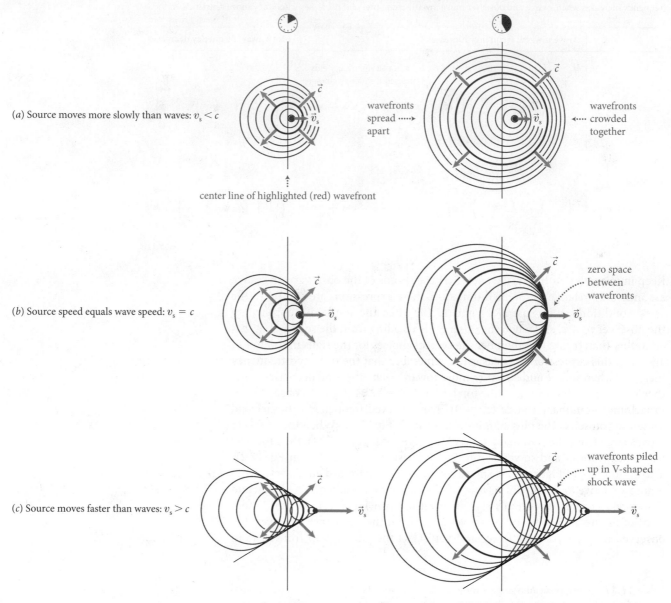

(a) Source moves more slowly than waves: $v_s < c$

wavefronts spread ⋯⋯▸ apart

wavefronts ◂⋯⋯ crowded together

center line of highlighted (red) wavefront

(b) Source speed equals wave speed: $v_s = c$

zero space ⋯ between wavefronts

(c) Source moves faster than waves: $v_s > c$

wavefronts piled ⋯ up in V-shaped shock wave

than the speed of sound in air, for example, creates a shock wave (**Figure 17.36**) even though the bullet emits no sound. Air piles up in front of the speeding bullet like snow in front of a snowplow, and this piling up of the air creates a compression in front of the bullet. This compression then moves outward at the speed of sound, just as the compression in Figure 17.8 does, and forms the wedge- or cone-shaped shock wave, which trails the bullet like a water wake trailing behind a ship.

When a shock wave sweeps over your ears, the piled-up wavefronts sound like an explosion, just as a small boat gets jolted when struck by the wake of a passing speedboat. For a small object, such as a bullet, the shock wave produces a sharp, cracking sound. The crack of a long whip is a shock wave produced when the tip of the whip is made to move faster than the speed of sound. For large objects, the shock wave sounds like a thunderous boom called a *sonic boom*. The sonic boom of a supersonic airplane reaches the pain threshold of the human ear even at a distance of 20 km. For this reason, supersonic transport is not feasible over land. The cone-shaped shock wave dragging behind the plane would break windows on the ground even at its maximum flying altitude of about 20 km.

Figure 17.36 Shock wave produced by a bullet traveling through air.

17.18 Does an observer moving at twice the speed of sound toward a stationary sound source detect a sonic boom?

As can be seen in **Figure 17.37**, the higher the source speed, the narrower the wedge or cone formed by the shock wave. From the right angle triangle PQR, we see that the angle the shock wave makes with the direction of motion is given by

$$\sin\theta = \frac{c}{v_s} \quad (v_s > c). \tag{17.22}$$

For motion through air, the ratio v_s/c is called the *Mach number*. A plane flying at Mach 1.8, for example, has a speed of 1.8 times the speed of sound.

17.19 Estimate the speed of the bullet in Figure 17.36.

Figure 17.37 The shape of a shock wave depends on the speed of the source. The higher the source speed, the smaller the angle θ and so the sharper the cone or wedge.

(a) Lower source speed v_s: wider angle θ

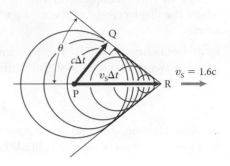

(b) Higher source speed v_s: narrower angle θ

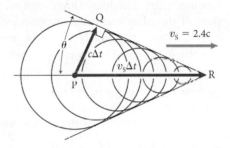

Chapter Glossary

SI units of physical quantities are given in parentheses.

Antinodal line A line in the interference pattern that is formed by the overlapping of two or more wave sources where the displacement of the medium has the maximum amplitude.

Beat frequency f_{beat} (Hz) The frequency at which beats occur between two waves of slightly different frequencies:

$$f_{beat} = |f_1 - f_2|. \qquad (17.8)$$

Beating Oscillating amplitude variation due to the superposition of two waves of equal amplitude but slightly different frequencies.

Coherent sources Two or more sources that are emitting waves that have a constant phase difference.

Decibel (dB) The logarithmic unit of measurement (not part of the SI system) that expresses the magnitude of a physical quantity (usually power or intensity) relative to a specified or implied reference level. See also *intensity level*.

Diffraction The spreading out of waves around obstacles or beyond the sides of apertures. The spreading is more pronounced when the size of the obstacle or aperture is about equal to or smaller than the wavelength of the wave.

Doppler effect A change in the observed wave frequency due to the relative motion of a wave source and an observer. The observed frequency f_o is given by

$$\frac{f_o}{f_s} = \frac{c \pm v_o}{c \pm v_s}, \qquad (17.21)$$

where v_s and v_o are the speeds relative to the medium of the source and the observer, respectively. The signs are to be chosen such that the frequency $f_o > f_s$ when source and observer approach each other and $f_o < f_s$ when they move apart.

Huygens' principle Any wavefront may be regarded as a collection of many closely spaced, coherent point sources.

Intensity I (W/m^2) For a three-dimensional wave: the energy incident per second per unit area normal to the direction of propagation:

$$I \equiv \frac{P}{A}. \qquad (17.1)$$

For a two-dimensional wave: the energy incident per second per unit *length* normal to the direction of propagation:

$$I_{surf} \equiv \frac{P}{L}. \qquad (17.3)$$

Intensity level β (dB) A quantity proportional to the logarithm of the ratio of the intensity of a sound wave to the threshold intensity for hearing ($I_{th} = 10^{-12}$ W/m^2):

$$\beta \equiv (10 \text{ dB}) \log\left(\frac{I}{I_{th}}\right). \qquad (17.5)$$

Nodal line A line in the interference pattern where the displacement of the medium is always zero.

Planar wavefront A two-dimensional, flat wavefront. All wavefronts are approximately planar when the distance to the source is large relative to the wavelength. The amplitude of a planar wavefront does not decrease as the wavefront propagates.

Point source A single identifiable source of a wave or other disturbance that can be treated as if it has no physical extent and is located at a single point in space.

Shock wave A conical or wedge-shaped disturbance caused by the piling up of wavefronts from a source moving at a speed greater than or equal to the wave speed. The higher the source speed, the narrower the angle of the shock wave:

$$\sin \theta = \frac{c}{v_s} \quad (v_s > c). \qquad (17.22)$$

Sound Longitudinal waves that propagate through a solid, liquid, or gas in the frequency range 20 Hz–20 kHz (called the *audible* frequency range).

Spherical wave A three-dimensional wave whose wavefronts are spheres. In the absence of energy dissipation, the amplitude of a spherical wave decreases with distance r to the source as $1/r$.

Surface wave A wave that spreads out in two dimensions. In the absence of energy dissipation, the amplitude of a surface wave decreases with distance r to the source as $1/\sqrt{r}$.

Wavefront A curve or surface in a medium on which all points of a propagating wave have the same phase of oscillation.

18 Fluids

18.1 Forces in a fluid
18.2 Buoyancy
18.3 Fluid flow
18.4 Surface effects

18.5 Pressure and gravity
18.6 Working with pressure
18.7 Bernoulli's equation
18.8 Viscosity and surface tension

CONCEPTS

QUANTITATIVE TOOLS

In earlier chapters we dealt with the motion and behavior of solid objects only. In the next few chapters we extend our description to include two other states of matter: liquids and gases (**Figure 18.1**). The interior forces exerted on the atoms in a solid keep each atom at a particular location in the solid. Because the atoms are not free to move relative to one another, a piece of solid material has a definite size and shape. In a liquid, the forces exerted on the particles* are not strong enough to keep them from moving relative to one another. Consequently a liquid sample has a definite volume but adjusts to the shape of its container. In a gas, the particles are far apart. They move about randomly and freely, and so a sample of gas has neither a definite volume nor a definite shape.

Liquids and gases are collectively called **fluids** because they flow.

Because fluids flow and change shape, we cannot describe their behavior in the same way we described the behavior of solids. When you look at the flow of water in a river, for example, it makes no sense to speak of "the velocity of the water" because the water may move fast in one spot and more slowly in another, or it may be flowing in one direction at one location and in another direction a bit farther downstream. Unlike a solid object, in other words, water in a river cannot be characterized by a simple set of kinematic quantities—the motion of its center of mass and rotation about that center. However, you can specify its velocity at a specific location.

In general, therefore, describing the motion of fluids requires an approach in which we associate quantities such as velocity not with a body of fluid as a whole but with a position within the body of fluid.

18.1 Forces in a fluid

The result of exerting forces on fluids is very different from the result when forces are exerted on solids. To better understand this difference, let us begin by examining how a solid object at rest responds to a set of forces whose vector sum is zero. Because the vector sum is zero, the object remains at rest, but because no solid material is perfectly rigid, the object deforms when opposing forces are exerted on it. Such opposing forces are said to cause a *stress*. A solid object that returns to its original shape when the stress is removed is said to be *elastic* (see Section 8.6). Beyond the elastic limit, the object deforms permanently, and still greater forces may cause the object to fracture. Within the elastic range, the amount of deformation caused by a given stress depends on the properties of the material and typically obeys Hooke's law (see Section 8.9) for small deformations; that is, the deformation is linearly proportional to the magnitude of the applied forces.

Because the atoms in a solid are at fixed positions, a solid object can withstand forces applied to its surface in a number of ways. A set of opposing forces along the same line of action (**Figure 18.2a**) causes either *tensile stress*, which stretches the object, or *compressive stress*, which compresses it. Under such stress, the object's dimensions perpendicular to the line of action of the forces also change to compensate for the stretching or compressing along the line of action.

Figure 18.1 States of matter.

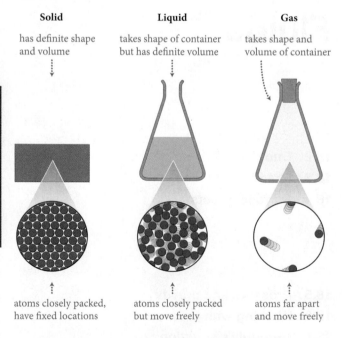

Solid	Liquid	Gas
has definite shape and volume	takes shape of container but has definite volume	takes shape and volume of container

atoms closely packed, have fixed locations · atoms closely packed but move freely · atoms far apart and move freely

Figure 18.2 Different types of stresses caused by equal forces applied in opposite directions to solid objects.

(a)
Tensile stress

Compressive stress

(b)
Bulk stress

(c)
Shear stress

*Both liquids and gases can be made up of either atoms or molecules. From now on, we'll use the generic term *particle* to refer to either atoms or molecules in a liquid or gas.

In spite of this compensating change, however, precise measurements show that the object's volume increases by a small amount when the object is stretched and decreases by a small amount when the object is compressed.

When opposing forces are exerted perpendicular to all surfaces of a solid object (Figure 18.2*b*), the atoms are pushed closer together in all directions, resulting in what is called *bulk stress*. Such a stress causes the volume of the object to decrease.

A third type of stress, *shear stress,* occurs when opposing forces are exerted tangent to the surfaces of a solid object (Figure 18.2*c*). For small forces, the object's shape changes—turning a rectangular face into a parallelogram, say—but the volume of the object does not change.

Let us now examine how a fluid responds to these same three types of stresses: tensile/compressive, bulk, and shear. If you put your hands under water parallel to each other and some distance apart and then move them toward each other, you feel resistance. Your moving hands exert a force on the water and, because forces always come in interaction pairs, the water, in turn, exerts a force on your hands. Once your hands stop moving, however, this force exerted by the water on them disappears. In addition, when you remove your hands, the water molecules don't flow back to where they were before you moved your hands. In other words, water is not elastic the way some solid materials are. If you compress an elastic solid—a foam rubber ball, say—the way you "compress" the water by bringing your hands together, you must keep exerting the force if you want to keep the ball compressed. Once you remove your hands, the ball returns to its original shape. This is not true for most liquids (water, rubbing alcohol, and gasoline, for instance) or for all gases under ordinary circumstances; these fluids are not elastic. You can easily verify that they also cannot support static tensile or shear stresses. Such fluids are said to be *nonviscous*. Liquids such as jelly or tar, which do not behave the way water does in response to a shear stress, can support a shear stress and are said to be *viscous*.

Let us next look at how fluids behave when subjected to bulk stress. If you exert forces on a fluid so as to cause a bulk stress, as in Figure 18.2*b*, the fluid resists being compressed. Imagine putting water in a cylinder fitted with a piston and pushing down on the piston (**Figure 18.3***a*). Because the water has nowhere to go and because the water molecules are already as close together as they can get, a very large force is required to change the volume of the water, and so you feel a rapidly growing resistive force exerted by the water on the piston. If, instead of water, you put a gas in the cylinder, the gas compresses easily as you push on the piston because gas particles are far apart and can easily be pushed closer together. As the gas is compressed, however, it exerts on the piston a force of increasing magnitude. Once that force is equal in magnitude to the force you exert on the piston, the system reaches mechanical equilibrium (Figure 18.3*b*). The greater the force you exert, the more the gas is compressed.

Figure 18.3 All fluids resist bulk stresses, but liquids don't compress much, whereas gases are easily compressed.

(*a*) Liquids oppose compression

Push on piston . . .

. . . causes liquid to exert opposing force on piston.

(*b*) Gases compress more easily

Push on piston . . .

. . . compresses gas until opposing force exerted by gas on piston equals push.

(*c*) Fluids exert forces on all surfaces they contact

fluid

Push on piston . . .

. . . causes fluid to exert forces on *all* surfaces of cylinder . . .

. . . so fluid pushes opposite piston out.

So, a fluid can sustain forces that are perpendicular to its surfaces, provided the forces are exerted simultaneously on *all* its surfaces. If you pushed the left piston in Figure 18.3*c* inward without also pushing the right piston inward, for example, you would simply push the water and the right piston out of the tube. Likewise, if you replaced a section of either the top or bottom wall of the cylinder in Figure 18.3*c* with a piston and again pushed on the left piston, you would also need to push both the right piston and the newly added piston inward in order to keep the water contained. From these observations we conclude that, in mechanical equilibrium, a fluid in a container exerts a (normal) force that is distributed along *all* surfaces of the container that are in contact with the fluid, and those surfaces exert on the fluid a force that is of equal magnitude but in the opposite direction.

The main difference between gases and liquids is that gases tend to compress easily, often greatly changing the volume and therefore the mass density (mass per unit volume, see Section 1.6), whereas the volume and mass density of a liquid do not change easily. For simplicity, from now on we shall assume that the liquids we deal with are *incompressible*; that is, their mass density and volume are fixed.

> **When a gas is subjected to bulk stress, its mass density and volume change easily. When a liquid is subjected to bulk stress, its mass density and volume can be considered unchanged.**

✋ **18.1** In Figure 18.3*c*, suppose you push the left piston rightward with a force of magnitude 10 N. (*a*) To keep the water in the cylinder at rest, what force must you exert on the (identical) right piston? (*b*) How does the force $\vec{F}_{wr}^c$ exerted by the water on the right piston compare to the force $\vec{F}_{pl}^c$ exerted by you on the left piston?

The two pistons in Checkpoint 18.1 are identical. Suppose we divide the right piston in Figure 18.3*c* into two pistons, each having half the surface area of the original piston. As you might expect, to keep the water in the cylinder at rest while pushing the left piston rightward with a force of magnitude 10 N, you would need to exert on each half-piston a force of magnitude 5 N, which suggests a linear proportionality between surface area and force.

To examine this relationship in more detail, consider a fluid at mechanical equilibrium in a cylinder (**Figure 18.4**). Forces are exerted on the two pistons so that the fluid is subject to a compressive stress. Now imagine a wedge-shaped volume of the fluid. Because liquids cannot sustain any shear stresses (resulting from forces tangent to the wedge surfaces) exerted on the wedge, the forces exerted by the surrounding fluid on the wedge must be perpendicular to the three wedge surfaces. Because the wedge is at rest, the vector sum of these forces must be zero. Let the three wedge surfaces have areas A_1, A_2, and A_3. Each of these areas is proportional to the length of the corresponding side of the dashed triangle in Figure 18.4*a*, and each is subject to a normal force exerted by the surrounding fluid. Let us denote these forces by $\vec{F}_1$, $\vec{F}_2$, and $\vec{F}_3$. Because these vectors add up to zero, we can arrange them in a triangle as shown in Figure 18.4*b*. Because the vectors are perpendicular

to the sides of the dashed triangle in Figure 18.4*a*, the triangle in Figure 18.4*b* is similar to the dashed triangle, and so the ratio of the force magnitudes $F_1:F_2:F_3$ is the same as the ratio of the lengths of the sides of the dashed triangle. Because the dimension of the wedge in the direction perpendicular to the plane of the drawing is fixed, the area A of each side of the wedge is proportional to its length. Therefore $F_1:F_2:F_3 = A_1:A_2:A_3$, or $F_1/A_1 = F_2/A_2 = F_3/A_3$. In other words, the ratio of the magnitude of the force exerted by the fluid on a surface and the area of that surface is constant. This ratio is called **pressure,** denoted by the symbol P. Pressure is a scalar and is taken to be positive when a fluid is under compression.

It is important to distinguish pressure from force. The two are related because forces exerted on the fluid cause the pressure in a fluid. Force, however, is a vector, while pressure is a scalar. In addition, forces of the same magnitude can cause very different pressures depending on the surface area over which these forces are exerted. Imagine, for example, exerting a force of 10 N on your skin first with the tip of a pin and then with the cover of a book. Even though the force is the same in both cases, the effect is very different. At the tip of the pin, the pressure caused by the 10-N force is very great because the surface area of the pin is small. The pressure caused by the pin is likely to cause pain, and the pin might penetrate into your skin. The book, however, spreads that same 10-N force out over a much greater surface area, and so the resulting pressure is much smaller.

Another important point to keep in mind is that because forces always come in interaction pairs, the force exerted by a container wall on a fluid (which causes the pressure in the fluid) and the force exerted by the fluid on the container wall form an interaction pair. The pressure in a fluid therefore causes the fluid to exert forces on anything that is in contact with it. Because of the mobility of the particles in a fluid, pressure is transmitted in all directions to all parts of the fluid. However, because fluids cannot sustain shear stresses, the forces exerted by the fluid on any surfaces that contain the fluid are always exerted perpendicular to the surface.

In gases, pressure can be only positive. Liquids, however, can sustain negative pressures. For example, if you hold the container of Figure 18.3*a* upside down as shown in **Figure 18.5*a*** and pull down on the piston, you feel a large resistive force, which tells you that the liquid pulls the piston inward. The water molecules exert an attractive force on one another and on the surfaces of the container, pulling them inward as you pull the piston down. So, just as a liquid under compression causes an outward push that we associate with a positive pressure, we find that a "stretched" liquid causes an inward pull that we associate with a negative pressure.

(You can easily try this yourself. Fill a glass to the top with water, place an index card on top of the glass, making sure no air is left between the water surface and the card, and then turn the glass upside down while holding the card in place with the palm of your hand. If you slowly remove your hand from the card, the water remains in the glass.)

Figure 18.4 Forces exerted on the sides of a wedge-shaped volume of fluid.

(*a*) Wedge-shaped volume in fluid at rest

area of wedge surface

(*b*) Vector sum of forces exerted on wedge is zero

····► force exerted by fluid on wedge surface A_2

Figure 18.5 Liquids can sustain negative pressures, whereas pressures in a gas can be positive only.

(*a*) Because liquid particles exert attractive forces on each other and on the container walls, liquid can hold piston up against force of gravity

(*b*) Gases expand to fill any volume and therefore cannot sustain negative pressures

Gas particles are so far apart that they interact only when they collide, and so a gas always expands to fill whatever container it is placed in. A gas can therefore not sustain negative pressure, and a piston just falls out of a gas container that is held upside down (Figure 18.5*b*).

18.2 Consider a plastic cup full of water. (*a*) Is the water exerting a force on the bottom of the cup? (*b*) On the sides of the cup? (*c*) Is the water pressure negative, zero, or positive?

The answers to Checkpoint 18.2 may have surprised you. What causes the pressure in the water if the top surface of the water is open to the environment and no piston is pushing down on that top surface? The cause is gravity. Imagine the column of water in the glass as being a stack of thin "layers" of water. Gravity exerts a force on each layer, which means that each layer pushes down on the layer underneath it, just as a book presses down on the surface of a table because of gravity. At the top of the water column, the atmosphere presses down on the surface, our imaginary top layer.

To examine the effect of gravity on the pressure in a fluid, consider again a water-filled tube fitted with identical pistons on either end, but now we orient the tube vertically (**Figure 18.6a**). Even with no force exerted on the top piston, you have to exert an upward force on the bottom piston to prevent the water from falling out of the tube. As the free-body diagram in Figure 18.6*b* shows, when you are not pressing down on the top piston, the water is subject to two forces: a downward force of gravity and an upward

Figure 18.6 Gravity exerts a downward force on a volume of fluid.

(*a*) You must exert upward force on bottom piston to keep water from falling out

(*b*) Free-body diagram for water

force of equal magnitude exerted by the bottom piston.* So the pressure at the top of the water is zero (no force exerted on the surface), whereas the pressure at the bottom of the tube is nonzero.

Now imagine dividing a liquid in a container into two equal parts, as shown in **Figure 18.7a**. Ignoring any force exerted at the top surface (we'll return to this issue in a bit), we see from the free-body diagrams in Figure 18.7*b* that the top half must be supported against the pull of gravity by the bottom half. The bottom of the container, in turn, must support both halves. Consequently the pressure at the bottom of the container is greater than the pressure at the center.

Figure 18.7 Pressure increases with distance below the surface because liquid layers at the top press down on lower layers of liquid.

(*a*)   (*b*)

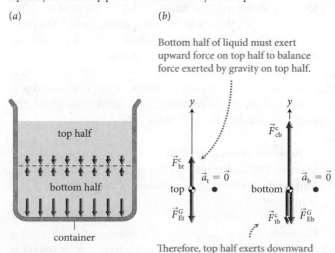

Bottom half of liquid must exert upward force on top half to balance force exerted by gravity on top half.

Therefore, top half exerts downward contact force on bottom half.

―――――

*As we shall see later, the atmosphere exerts a force on each piston, but the combined effect of these two forces is negligible. For simplicity, we also ignore the mass of the pistons, which means there is no gravitational force exerted on them and so the top piston exerts no force on the water.

18.3 How does the pressure in the liquid vary with height above the bottom of the container in Figure 18.7?

The conclusion you reached in Checkpoint 18.3 holds for any liquid that is at rest in a container of any shape:

The pressure in a liquid at rest in a container decreases linearly with height, regardless of the shape of the container

In a gas, the pressure also decreases with height, but the effect is much less pronounced because gases are much less dense than liquids. Also, because gases are compressible, gas density varies with height and so the decrease in pressure with height is not linear. Air, for example, is densest at sea level, where it is compressed by all the air above. At the cruising altitude of most airplanes (10 km), the mass density of the air is one-third of its value at sea level, and the atmospheric pressure is just one-quarter of its value at sea level.

At sea level, you are at the bottom of an "ocean" of air. The mass of a column of air that has a cross section the size of a fingernail is approximately 1 kg. In other words, at sea level the atmosphere exerts on each fingernail-sized area of your body a force that is equivalent to the force of gravity on a 1-kg object. If we were to add up the magnitudes of the forces exerted on the entire surface area of your body, you would obtain a force equal to the force of gravity exerted on 2×10^4 kg! The force with which the atmosphere pushes down on the surface of your orange juice at breakfast is more than four times the force with which this book presses down on your lap.

Given that the average atmospheric pressure at sea level is 1×10^5 N/m², it is clear that we cannot ignore the pressure at the top of the liquid in Figure 18.7. As you saw in Checkpoint 18.1, any force exerted at one surface of a liquid is transmitted to any other part of the liquid. This means that if we change the pressure in a container of liquid at any location, the change in pressure is the same throughout the liquid. This is called **Pascal's principle:**

A pressure change applied to an enclosed liquid is transmitted undiminished to every part of the liquid and to the walls of the container in contact with the liquid.

Consequently, if atmospheric pressure at the top of a column of water in a container open to the atmosphere is 1×10^5 N/m², the pressure in the water near that surface must also be 1×10^5 N/m². Below the surface, the pressure in the water increases with greater depth as more water pushes down due to gravity. The next example gives you some feel for pressure variation with height in both water and air.

CONCEPTS

Example 18.1 Water and air pressure

Consider a cylindrical container that has a radius of 30.0 mm and is filled with water to a height of 0.150 m. If the container is at sea level, what is the pressure (*a*) at the water surface and (*b*) at the bottom of the container? (*c*) How far above the water surface is the decrease in atmospheric pressure the same as the pressure decrease between the bottom and top of the water? The mass densities of air and water are 1.20 kg/m³ and 1.00×10^3 kg/m³, respectively.

❶ **GETTING STARTED** I begin by making a sketch of the situation (**Figure 18.8a**). The problem deals with the pressure at three locations: at the bottom of the container (point A), at the water surface (B), and at some location above the surface (C). Because 0.150 m is a negligible distance in the context of this problem, the pressure at B is essentially equal to the atmospheric pressure at sea level. At A the pressure should be greater than at B because of the force of gravity exerted on the water. At C the pressure should be smaller than at B because the volume of air above C pressing down on C is smaller than the volume of air above B pressing down on B.

Figure 18.8

❷ **DEVISE PLAN** The pressure at A is equal to the magnitude of the force $\vec{F}_{cw}^c$ exerted by the container bottom on the water divided by the area of the container bottom. To determine the magnitude of this force, I make a free-body diagram for the water (Figure 18.8b). The forces exerted on the water are the force of gravity $\vec{F}_{Ew}^G$, the downward force $\vec{F}_{aw}^c$ exerted by the atmosphere, and the upward force exerted by the container bottom, which I need to determine. Because the water is at rest, the vector sum of these forces must be zero, and so the magnitude of the force exerted by the container bottom on the water is $F_{cw}^c = F_{Ew}^G + F_{aw}^c$. The force $\vec{F}_{aw}^c$ is determined by atmospheric pressure. To calculate $\vec{F}_{Ew}^G$ I need to know the mass of the water, which I can obtain by multiplying the volume of the water by the mass density of water.

Because the difference in pressure between A and B is the same as that between B and C, I know that the mass of the air column between B and C must be equal to the mass of the water column between A and B. The ratio of the distances between these locations must therefore be equal to the ratio of the volumes, which is equal to the inverse of the ratio of the mass densities (assuming that the density of air is approximately constant over that column of air).

❸ EXECUTE PLAN (*a*) The pressure at B is essentially equal to atmospheric pressure at sea level, which I can look up: $P_B = 1.01325 \times 10^5 \, \text{N/m}^2$. ✔

(*b*) Dividing both sides of $F^c_{cw} = F^G_{Ew} + F^c_{aw}$ by the bottom surface area A, I get $P_A = F^G_{Ew}/A + P_{atm}$ because $P_A = F^c_{cw}/A$ and $P_{atm} = P_B = F^c_{aw}/A$. The volume of the water is $V = Ah$, and so the mass of the water is this volume times the mass density of water: $m_{water} = Ah\rho$. The magnitude of the force of gravity exerted on the water is $F^G_{Ew} = m_{water}g = Ah\rho g$, and this force is exerted over the bottom surface area A of the container. The pressure at point A is thus

$$P_A = \frac{F^G_{Ew}}{A} + P_{atm} = \frac{Ah\rho g}{A} + P_{atm} = h\rho g + P_{atm}$$

$$= (0.150 \, \text{m})(1.0 \times 10^3 \, \text{kg/m}^3)(9.8 \, \text{m/s}^2)$$

$$+ \, 1.01325 \times 10^5 \, \text{N/m}^2 = 1.03 \times 10^5 \, \text{N/m}^2. \, ✔$$

(*c*) The ratio of the distances is $\overline{AB}/\overline{BC} = \rho_{air}/\rho_{water} = (1.20 \, \text{kg/m}^3)/(1.00 \times 10^3 \, \text{kg/m}^3) = 1.20 \times 10^{-3}$. I am given that $\overline{AB} = 0.150$ m, so $\overline{BC} = (0.150 \, \text{m})/(1.20 \times 10^{-3}) = 1.25 \times 10^2$ m. ✔

❹ EVALUATE RESULT The answer I obtained in part *b* shows that the pressure difference between the top and bottom of the container is very small. That makes sense—I know from experience that my ears, which are very sensitive to pressure, don't experience any pressure difference when I swim a mere 0.15 m under the surface of water.

The answer to part *c* tells me that the distance above sea level I would have to climb in order to obtain the same pressure difference is about three orders of magnitude greater than the distance from B to A (0.15 m versus 120 m). Again, I know from experience that I don't experience any detectable pressure difference when going up 120 m in air, so my answer is not unreasonable.

18.4 How far below the surface of a deep body of water is the pressure twice what it is at the surface?

18.2 Buoyancy

The decrease in pressure with height is responsible for the **buoyant force,** an upward force experienced by objects when they are either fully or partially submerged in a fluid. The tendency of certain objects to float in air or water, called *buoyancy,* is due to this force.

If you hold a brick under water with its top surface parallel to the surface of the water, as illustrated in **Figure 18.9a,** the pressure in the water at the bottom of the brick is greater than the pressure at the top, so the upward force exerted by the water on the bottom surface of the brick is greater than the downward force the water exerts on the top surface of the brick. The free-body diagram for the brick in Figure 18.9*b* shows the forces exerted on the brick: a downward gravitational force, an upward force exerted by your hand, an upward force exerted by the water on the bottom surface, and a downward force exerted by the water on the top surface. Because the pressure is greater at the bottom of the brick than at the top, the two forces exerted by the water on the brick add up to an upward buoyant force (Figure 18.9*c*). Buoyant forces are denoted by a superscript b. (We can ignore the sideways forces exerted by the water on the brick because they cancel out.)

18.5 (*a*) What happens to the pressure difference between the top and bottom of the brick in Figure 18.9*a* when the brick is held deeper in the water? (*b*) What happens to the pressure difference when the pressure at the surface of the water is increased? (*c*) What is the effect of the pressure in the water on the vertical sides of the brick? (*d*) Consider the same brick held in the air. Does the air exert a buoyant force on the brick? If so, in which direction is this force?

Figure 18.9 Cause of the buoyant force experienced by objects that are partly or fully submerged in a fluid.

(*a*) Brick held under water

(*b*) Free-body diagram that separates force exerted by water on brick's top and bottom surfaces

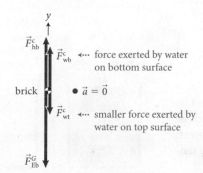

$\vec{F}^c_{wb}$ ◄···· force exerted by water on bottom surface

$\vec{F}^c_{wt}$ ◄···· smaller force exerted by water on top surface

(*c*) Free-body diagram showing buoyant force exerted by water on brick

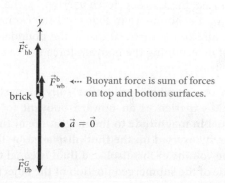

$\vec{F}^b_{wb}$ ◄···· Buoyant force is sum of forces on top and bottom surfaces.

Figure 18.10 The force exerted by gravity on the volume of liquid *displaced* by a submerged object is equal in magnitude to the buoyant force exerted by the liquid on the object.

(*a*) Submerged object   (*b*) We replace object   (*c*) Free-body diagram
                   with water it displaces   for displaced water

How large is the buoyant force that is exerted on an object submerged either fully or partially in a fluid? For an object that has a rectangular cross section, such as the brick in Figure 18.9a, we can determine the pressures at the top and bottom of the object, multiply the pressures by the surface area to get the two force magnitudes, and then take the difference of these magnitudes to obtain the buoyant force. However, many objects do not have a rectangular cross section. Consider, for example, the fully submerged object in **Figure 18.10a**. Even if we know the pressure at every location on the surface of the object, calculating the buoyant force exerted by the water on the object is a complicated matter. We know, however, that if we remove the object from the water, water fills the space previously occupied by the object (Figure 18.10b). This volume of water within the boundary defined by the object is said to be *displaced* by the object when the object is fully submerged. Figure 18.10c shows the free-body diagram for this displaced volume of water. Because all the water is at rest, we know that the vector sum of the forces exerted on the volume of water within the boundary must be zero. Two forces are exerted on this volume of water: a downward force of gravity exerted by Earth and a buoyant force exerted by the surrounding water. Given that the vector sum of these two forces is zero, we know that the buoyant force exerted on the water within the boundary must be upward and equal in magnitude to the magnitude of the force of gravity exerted by Earth on the water within the boundary.

Because the buoyant force exerted by the surrounding water on the boundary in Figure 18.10a cannot depend on the nature of the material inside the boundary, we have a way of determining the buoyant force exerted on an object of arbitrary shape:

> **An object submerged either fully or partially in a fluid experiences an upward buoyant force that is equal in magnitude to the magnitude of the force of gravity exerted on the fluid displaced by the object. The volume of the displaced fluid is equal to the volume of the submerged portion of the object.**

This statement is called **Archimedes' principle.** Note that there is no reference to the shape or composition of the submerged object: The only factor that comes into play is the volume of the displaced fluid.

18.6 If the buoyant force exerted on an object is always equal in magnitude to the force of gravity exerted on the fluid displaced by the object, why does a brick placed in a barrel of water sink?

Now that we know how to determine the buoyant force exerted on an object, we can understand why some objects float and others sink. As Checkpoint 18.6 shows, a brick sinks because the force of gravity exerted by Earth on it is greater than the force of gravity exerted by Earth on an equal volume of water (equal in magnitude to the buoyant force). Because the vector sum of these two forces is directed downward, the brick sinks unless it is held up.

When the buoyant force is greater in magnitude than the force of gravity exerted on an object fully submerged in water, the object accelerates toward the surface of the water when you release it. A block of wood released under water, for example, moves up to the surface, and so the force of gravity exerted by Earth on the block is smaller than the force of gravity exerted on an equal volume of water (**Figure 18.11a**). Once it floats at the surface, only part of the block is submerged, and so now the volume of displaced water is smaller than the volume of the block (Figure 18.11b). Because the block is at rest at the surface, the force of gravity exerted by Earth on it and the buoyant force exerted by the water must be equal in magnitude, as shown in Figure 18.11c.

Objects made out of materials that normally sink can be made to float by designing the objects in such a way that the volume of water they displace is great enough to offset the force of gravity exerted on them. For example, a steel ship floats even though a block of steel sinks. The reason

Figure 18.11 The concept of displaced volume can be used to determine the buoyant force on floating as well as submerged objects.

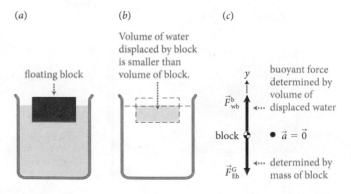

Figure 18.12 Steel ships can float even though steel sinks. The ship's hollow interior means that the volume of water displaced by the ship is larger than the volume of steel. Thus, the upward buoyant force exerted on the ship is greater than the downward gravitational force exerted on the steel.

steel hull (cross section)

Volume of water displaced by hull exceeds volume of steel.

for this is illustrated in **Figure 18.12**: As long as the force of gravity exerted on the ship is smaller than the force of gravity exerted on the volume of water displaced by the ship, the buoyant force is great enough to keep the ship floating. Because the hull of a ship is hollow, the volume of displaced water is much greater than the volume of steel.

Example 18.2 Mass densities

When a piece of cork floats in water, three-quarters of its volume is above the water surface. How does the mass density of cork compare with the mass density of water?

❶ **GETTING STARTED** I begin by making a sketch of the situation. Because one-quarter of the cork's volume is under water, I know that the cork displaces a volume of water equal to one-quarter of the volume of the cork. This also tells me that the force of gravity exerted on the whole cork $m_{cork}g$ is equal to the force of gravity exerted on the displaced water $m_{disp}g$ (**Figure 18.13**), which means that the mass of the displaced water is equal to the mass of the cork.

Figure 18.13

force of gravity on displaced water = force of gravity on cork

❷ **DEVISE PLAN** The mass density of an object is equal to the amount of mass per unit volume. Because I know how the volumes of equal masses of cork and water compare (Figure 18.13), I can compare the mass densities of cork and water.

❸ **EXECUTE PLAN** The volume of a piece of cork of a certain mass is four times greater than the volume of an equal mass of water, and so the mass density of cork is one-quarter that of water. ✔

❹ **EVALUATE RESULT** A "light" material such as cork has less mass per unit volume and therefore a smaller mass density than water, as I expect.

Figure 18.14 Checkpoint 18.7.

pan

rock

✋ **18.7** A pan with a rock in it is floating in water. Suppose you remove the rock and use a very lightweight string to suspend it from the bottom of the pan (**Figure 18.14**). If the combination still floats, is the volume of water displaced when the rock is suspended greater than, equal to, or smaller than the volume of water displaced when the rock is in the pan?

18.3 Fluid flow

We have so far restricted our study to fluids at rest. Now we turn our attention to fluids in motion; such motion is usually referred to as *fluid flow*. When the flow is such that the velocity of the fluid at any given location is constant, such as when water moves through a pipe, the flow is said to be **laminar.** Not all fluid flow is laminar, however. For example, the motion of rising smoke or the motion of water in the wake of a large ship is characterized by chaotic changes. Such flow is said to be **turbulent.**

To better understand fluid flow, we introduce the concept of **streamlines,** which are lines drawn to represent the paths taken by the particles in a fluid in motion. Streamlines can be made visible by injecting smoke into a flow of gas (**Figure 18.15**) or ink into a flow of liquid (**Figure 18.16**).

Figure 18.15 Streamline flow over a car.

Figure 18.16 Streamline flow around a cylinder.

When flow is laminar, as in Figures 18.15 and 18.16, streamlines maintain their shape and position. In turbulent flow, streamlines are erratic and often curl into whirling, circularly moving regions of fluid called *vortices* (singular *vortex*, **Figure 18.17**).

Whether a flow of fluid past a stationary object is laminar or turbulent depends on the speed of the flow, the shape of the object, and the fluid's resistance to shear stress (its *viscosity*). For a fluid that has zero viscosity and that has no friction when flowing past surfaces, streamlines just bend around a blunt object (**Figure 18.18a**). Except where the fluid has to move out of the object's

Figure 18.17 Turbulent flow around a cylinder.

way, the flow speed is the same everywhere. In such situations, the streamline pattern in regions downstream from the object is the same as the streamline pattern upstream of the object. (Although such "totally nonviscous" fluids don't exist, examining these models provides useful insights.)

Figure 18.18b shows the flow pattern for a fluid that has nonzero viscosity when that fluid is moving at a very low speed. The streamlines have the same general shape as for the nonviscous fluid of Figure 18.18a, but the pattern of speeds is very different in the two cases. At the object's surface, the viscous fluid in Figure 18.18b is stationary because of friction between the fluid and the surface. Far above and below the object, the flow is unaffected by the presence of the object. Between those two extremes, the flow speed increases from layer to layer. Because the viscosity is nonzero, adjacent layers of fluid exert shear forces on each other, with faster-moving layers trying to speed up slower-moving layers and slower-moving layers slowing down faster-moving ones. The resulting "rubbing" of layers of fluid causes energy dissipation.

As flow speed is increased, the torques caused by the forces that adjacent layers exert on each other become so

Figure 18.18 Whether the flow of fluid past a stationary object is laminar or turbulent depends on the fluid's speed and viscosity and on the object's shape.

(*a*) Low flow speed, zero viscosity

(*b*) Low flow speed, nonzero viscosity

Flow speed is zero at object's surface.

(*c*) High flow speed, turbulence

(*d*) High flow speed, streamlined object

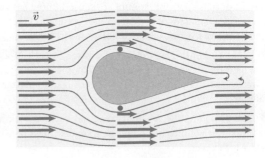

great that the flow develops vortices and becomes turbulent (Figure 18.18c). The turbulent wake alongside and downstream from the object is erratic and causes significant energy dissipation.

✋ **18.8** Instead of laminar fluid flow past a stationary object as in Figure 18.18a, consider the motion of an object moving at constant velocity through a stationary fluid. Do you expect the flow pattern surrounding the object to be the same as in Figure 18.18a or different?

To prevent turbulence and minimize energy dissipation at high flow speeds, it helps to *streamline* objects, which means to adjust their shape so as to maintain streamline flow around them. For example, when an object has a rounded upstream end and a long, tapered downstream tail, as in Figure 18.18d, the turbulent wake is very narrow and the flow pattern is similar to the low-speed flows illustrated in Figure 18.18a and b. At the surface of a streamlined object such as the one in Figure 18.18d, the fluid is still stationary, but the flow speed increases rapidly over a thin boundary layer. Outside this boundary layer, the flow resembles that of a nonviscous fluid.

Now that we have some general feeling for fluid flow, let us look at flow through a pipe. In a pipe of fixed diameter, the streamlines are all parallel to the walls of the pipe. For an (ideal) nonviscous fluid flowing through such a pipe, the flow speed is the same everywhere and the pipe offers no resistance to the flow (**Figure 18.19a**). For any viscous fluid at low flow speed, the flow speed is zero at the pipe walls and highest at the center (Figure 18.19b). At high flow speed, the speed is more constant across the diameter of the pipe, dropping off only in a boundary layer (Figure 18.19c). The higher the speed, the thinner the boundary layer.

Let us next consider flow through a constriction in a pipe (**Figure 18.20a**). To simplify matters, we ignore any turbulence or boundary-layer effects. The first thing to note is that the streamlines must crowd together in the narrow part of the pipe. (A streamline cannot have an end because that would mean a fluid particle moving along that streamline would come to a stop.) Therefore the density of streamlines is greater in the narrow part than it is in the wide part.

Figure 18.20 What happens when a fluid flows from a wider region of a pipe into a narrower region.

(a) When a pipe carrying a fluid narrows, the streamlines get closer together

(b) Where the pipe is narrower, the fluid must flow faster

These volumes must be equal (what goes in must come out), so fluid must move faster where pipe is narrow.

If the flow is laminar, the mass of the fluid passing point 1 in a given time interval in the wide part must be equal to the mass of the fluid passing point 2 in the narrow part in that time interval (Figure 18.20b). (If that were not the case, mass would accumulate between those two points and the flow would not be laminar.) Consequently, in a given time interval, the displacement Δx_2 of a fluid particle moving through the narrow part is greater than the displacement Δx_1 of a fluid particle moving through the wide part. This means that the overall fluid flows faster in the narrow part of the pipe where the density of streamlines is greater than in the wide part.

A flowing fluid speeds up when the region through which it flows narrows and slows down when the region through which it flows widens. The density of streamlines reflects the changes in flow speed: When streamlines in a laminar flow get closer together, the flow speed increases; when they get farther apart, the flow speed decreases.

This principle applies to every particle of a moving fluid. Thus each particle must accelerate as it moves along a streamline from the wide part of the pipe to the narrow part. This means that the surrounding fluid must exert a force to the right on the particle while it is in the tapered

Figure 18.19 Flow speed patterns through a pipe of fixed diameter.

(a) Nonviscous fluid   (b) Viscous fluid at low speed   (c) Viscous fluid at high speed

boundary layer

region of the tube in Figure 18.20. Because the force exerted on fluid particles is a measure of the pressure in the fluid, the pressure is greater in the wide part of the pipe than in the narrow part.

When the flow speed in a laminar flow increases, the pressure in the fluid decreases.

This effect is sometimes called the *Bernoulli effect* after the Swiss physicist who first described the pressure difference quantitatively. The pressure difference occurs along the streamlines. Because there is no flow in the direction perpendicular to a streamline, the pressure must be the same across neighboring streamlines.

There are many examples of the Bernoulli effect. During a storm, high winds blowing over the roof of a house cause the pressure above the roof to be lower than the pressure in the still air inside the house, creating an upward force on the roof. In extreme circumstances, this force can be great enough to lift the roof off the house. When a large truck speeds past a stationary car, the fast-moving air between the car and the truck has a lower pressure than the still air on the other side of the car, and consequently the car is pulled toward the truck.

Another familiar example is the curved, gravity-defying motion of a rapidly moving, spinning ball. **Figure 18.21a** shows a top view of a curveball—a baseball thrown with a counterclockwise spin. Because of friction between the surface of the ball and the air, air is dragged around with the spinning ball as the ball moves through the air. Figure 18.21*b* shows the air movement viewed from a reference frame moving along with the ball. The motion of the air caused by the spinning of the ball adds to the flow of air past the ball, causing the air behind the ball to be deflected to the right and the air on the left of the ball to move faster than the air on the right. The deflection of the air means that the direction of the momentum of the air shifts rightward, and

that change must be accompanied by an equal-magnitude leftward momentum change for the ball. Alternatively, according to the Bernoulli effect, the pressure in the air to the left of the ball is lower than the pressure to the right, causing a leftward force on the ball. Both of these effects make the ball veer to the left. Likewise a tennis ball that has "top spin" (meaning the top of the ball spins in the direction of the ball's translational motion) curves sharply downward.

The dimples on the surface of golf balls increase the friction between the air and the ball surface to enhance the effect of spin. A golf ball struck with a club is given a rapid backspin because of the slant of the club's face. The backspin forces the air behind the ball downward, causing the ball to experience a lift that carries it farther than it would travel without spin. The lift gained by the backspin more than compensates for the loss of range resulting from air drag.

Example 18.3 Magic pull

When air is blown downward into the narrow opening of a funnel (**Figure 18.22**), a lightweight ball initially positioned below the wide opening is pulled up into the funnel and held in place. Explain how the ball can be pulled upward even though the airflow and gravity are both directed downward.

Figure 18.22 Example 18.3.

When air blows ···▸
into funnel . . .

. . . ball is pulled *upward* into funnel.

❶ **GETTING STARTED** I know that if I were to blow against the ball, it would move away from me. So I reason that to pull the ball upward, there must be exerted on it an upward force that is greater than the combined effect of the downward gravitational and airflow forces. The ball is subject to an upward buoyant force, but I know this force is smaller than that of gravity alone because a ball—even a lightweight one—does not float in air. So there must be an additional force pulling the ball upward. Because this force is absent when no air flows past the ball, that flow must be causing the upward force.

❷ **DEVISE PLAN** To understand the effects of the flowing air, I should sketch the streamlines (I assume laminar flow). The density of the streamlines tells me how the speed of the flow varies, and from this information I can determine how the air pressure varies around the ball, which in turn tells me in which direction the air exerts a force on the ball.

❸ **EXECUTE PLAN Figure 18.23** shows how the streamlines must bend around the ball. In order to pass around the ball, they must be squeezed together between the ball and the sides of the funnel. At the bottom of the funnel, the diameter of the funnel is very wide and so the streamlines are spaced far apart.

Figure 18.21 Motion of a spinning ball as seen (*a*) from the Earth reference frame and (*b*) from a reference frame moving along with the ball. Because the air is dragged along with the ball surface, the air moves faster to the left of the ball and more slowly to the right of the ball.

(*a*)

(*b*)

Earth reference frame

Reference frame moving with ball

$\vec{v}_{ball}$

$\vec{p}_{air}$

high speed, low pressure

◂··· low speed, high pressure

$\vec{p}_{air}$

Air behind ball is deflected by ball's spin.

Figure 18.23

higher speed, lower pressure

lower speed, higher pressure

This tells me that the flow speed is smaller below the ball than above it and consequently that the pressure is greater below the ball than above it. This pressure difference causes an upward force on the ball. If the pressure difference is great enough, this force can exceed the combined effect of the force of gravity and the downward force of the airflow on the ball. ✔

❹ **EVALUATE RESULT** My answer is consistent with the observation given in the problem statement, even though the ball's being pulled *upward* by a downward flow of air seems nothing short of magic! I assumed the flow to be laminar, which may not be entirely correct for an object like a ball (which is not streamlined). However, because air is a gas and because gases have very low viscosity, the assumption that the flow remains laminar is not unreasonable.

✋ **18.9** The cloth roof of a convertible car often bulges at high speed, even when the top fits tightly and no wind is getting caught under it. Explain what causes the bulging.

18.4 Surface effects

A distinguishing feature between liquids and gases is that liquids have a well-defined surface but gases do not. If you put a gas in an open container, the gas escapes. A liquid, however, remains in the container it is placed in, and small quantities of liquid placed on a solid surface form drops. In each case, the liquid has a well-defined surface that separates it from the surrounding air. On a small scale—that is, for small quantities of liquid and for small objects—this surface behaves like an elastic skin, pulling small volumes of liquid into drops and supporting small objects such as dust particles or water spiders.

We can understand the behavior of liquid surfaces by considering what happens at the molecular scale. When the particles in a fluid are far apart, they exert no appreciable force on one another (**Figure 18.24**). As they get closer together, however, the interaction between particles has both an attractive and a repulsive component. At a distance of a few particle diameters, particles exert attractive forces, called *cohesive forces*, on one another. When the separation distance becomes less than a particle diameter, however, the particles strongly resist being pushed closer together, resulting in very strong *repulsive forces* between particles. In a gas, the particles move at such great speed and their

Figure 18.24 Interaction between fluid particles in a gas when the particles are far apart and in a liquid when they are closer together.

gas

liquid

Particles in gas are far apart, so exert no appreciable force on each other:

Particles in liquid are close enough to interact. When a few diameters apart, they attract:

When closer than a diameter apart, they repel strongly:

separation distances are so great that the cohesive forces are negligible. In other words, the gas particles essentially don't interact except when they collide and exert repulsive forces on one another.

Cohesive forces play an important role in liquids, however. The piston in Figure 18.5*a* stays in position because of the cohesive forces in the liquid, for instance. Likewise, if you press pure water with no air dissolved in it between two smooth plates, an enormously large force is required to separate the plates.

The cohesive forces between particles cause a liquid surface to act like a stretched elastic sheet that tends to minimize the surface area. To see why this happens, compare the forces exerted on a particle in the interior of a liquid with those exerted on a particle at the surface. The interior particle experiences attractive forces from neighbors in all directions, and the vector sum of these forces is zero. At the surface, however, there are no neighbors above the particle, and so the vector sum of the cohesive forces points into the liquid perpendicular to the surface. The surface particles cannot move into the liquid, however, because as they are pulled inward, they experience a strong repulsive outward force from neighbors.

Because of the inward pull on all surface particles, a small volume of liquid tends to arrange itself in the shape of a sphere (**Figure 18.25**). In a gas there is no attraction between neighboring particles, and therefore a collection of gas particles tends to fly apart, expanding into all available surrounding space. To keep gas particles together, you can

CONCEPTS

Figure 18.25 The cohesive forces between molecules in a liquid cause a liquid surface to act like a stretched elastic sheet. Consequently, small volumes of liquid tend to adopt a spherical shape.

(*a*) Difference between vector sum of cohesive force on molecules at the surface and in the interior of a liquid

Molecule at surface: pulled inward

$\Sigma\vec{F}$

$\Sigma\vec{F} = \vec{0}$ Molecule in interior: pulled equally in all directions

(*b*) Balloon as analogy for surface forces on liquid droplet

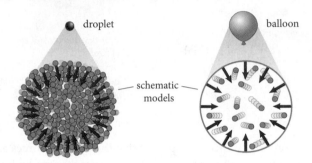

droplet

balloon

— schematic models —

Inward pull on surface molecules tends to make droplet spherical.

Stretched balloon skin exerts analogous inward force on gas.

put them inside a balloon. The stretched balloon pushes inward on the gas particles, exerting a force on them and keeping them together. The effect of the inward pull on the surface particles in a liquid is much like the force exerted by a balloon on the particles in a gas. The liquid surface thus acts like a membrane that is under tension and that pulls the liquid together in a spherical shape.

Just as an inflated balloon is said to be under tension, so do we say that a liquid surface has *surface tension*. In the absence of gravity, surface tension causes even large volumes of liquid to take on a spherical shape (**Figure 18.26**). In the presence of gravity, however, drops of liquid are not perfectly spherical, with larger drops flattening out more than small ones. The reason for the difference in how much large and small drops lose their spherical shape is that only particles on the drop surface are pulled into the spherical shape. Gravity, in contrast, pulls on all particles in a volume of liquid, not just those in the surface layer. To state it another way, surface tension is a surface effect but gravity is a volume effect. As the next exercise shows, the relative importance of these two effects changes with drop size.

Figure 18.26 Astronaut Kevin Ford watches a water bubble float freely between him and the camera aboard the International Space Station. When no large gravitational force is involved, even a large volume of liquid coalesces into a spherical shape.

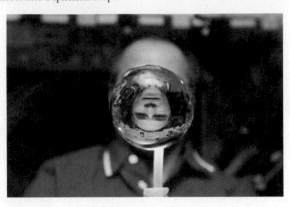

Exercise 18.4 Scaling a drop

Suppose surface tension increases in direct proportion to surface area (an oversimplification!). How does the ratio of surface tension to the force of gravity exerted on a drop change as the drop diameter increases tenfold?

SOLUTION The force of gravity is proportional to the mass of each drop, which is proportional to each drop's volume. The ratio of surface tension to the force of gravity on each drop is therefore proportional to the surface-area-to-volume ratio. For simplicity, I approximate the smaller drop as a sphere with diameter d. This means that I should compare the surface-area-to-volume ratio of this sphere with the surface-area-to-volume ratio of a sphere of diameter $10d$.

The surface area of a sphere of radius $R = \frac{1}{2}d$ is $4\pi R^2 = \pi d^2$, and its volume is $\frac{4}{3}\pi R^3 = \frac{4}{3}\pi(d/2)^3 = \frac{1}{6}\pi d^3$, and so the surface-area-to-volume ratio of a sphere is $(\pi d^2)/(\frac{1}{6}\pi d^3) = 6/d$. The surface-area-to-volume ratio thus decreases by a factor of 10 as the diameter of the drop increases by a factor of 10. ✔

The analogy between surface tension and the tension in the rubber of a balloon allows us to draw some important conclusions. Consider, for example, the air-filled balloon of **Figure 18.27**. The rubber in the uninflated end of the balloon is less stretched than the rubber in the inflated part,

Figure 18.27 A partially inflated balloon. The tension is greatest where the rubber is stretched the most.

more stretch, so more tension

little stretch, so little tension

and so there is less tension in the uninflated rubber than in the inflated rubber. (You may have noticed that balloons are softest and most easily squeezed where they are least inflated.) To understand how the tension in a balloon relates to its shape and to the pressure in the air inside the balloon, answer the following checkpoint first.

✋ 18.10 How does the air pressure in the uninflated part of the balloon in Figure 18.27 compare with the air pressure in the inflated part?

Did the answer to Checkpoint 18.10 surprise you? How can one part of the balloon be soft and another part hard if the air pressure is the same everywhere inside the balloon? The reason has to do with *radius of curvature*, which is the radius of the circle that approximates a curve at the point under consideration. As **Figure 18.28** shows, the radius of curvature is different in the two parts. The air pressure must be the same in the two parts, as you learned in Checkpoint 18.10, and the inward force exerted by the rubber surface of the balloon on the air inside is caused by the tension in the rubber. As you can see by comparing the free-body

diagrams for a small surface segment in Figure 18.28a and b, the smaller the radius of curvature, the smaller the tensile force needed to provide a given inward force. In the part of the balloon where the radius of curvature is smaller, the angle of the tensile forces is large and so smaller tensile forces add up to the same vector sum. Indeed when the radius is smaller, the rubber is stretched less and so the tensile force is smaller.

> **In an elastic membrane enclosing a gas, tension in the membrane increases with increasing radius of curvature, but the pressure is the same everywhere inside the volume enclosed by the membrane, as required by Pascal's principle.**

The situation is different with liquids because a liquid surface is not exactly like a stretched rubber skin. In particular, surface tension in a liquid is determined entirely by the cohesive forces between the liquid particles and is constant regardless of the shape of the liquid surface. So the tensile forces exerted on a given segment of the infinitesimally thin surface layer separating liquid and gas are the same no matter what the radius of curvature of the surface is. As shown in **Figure 18.29**, these constant tensile forces exerted on the surface segment of a liquid droplet cause a greater inward force when the radius of curvature is small. Because the segment is at rest, this inward force on the segment must be balanced by the forces exerted by the liquid and air on

Figure 18.28 The reason why the balloon in Figure 18.27 has an uninflated end. Because the air pressure must be the same everywhere inside a balloon, areas with a small radius of curvature must have smaller-magnitude tensile forces than areas with a larger radius of curvature.

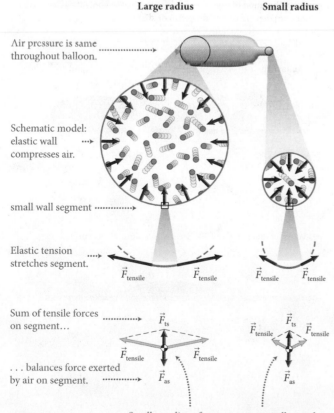

Smaller radius of curvature → smaller angle between tensile forces, so less tensile force needed to create same pressure in balloon.

Figure 18.29 Because surface tension in a liquid is independent of the shape of the liquid surface, a small liquid sphere has a greater internal pressure than a larger liquid sphere.

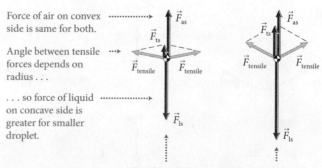

Therefore, difference in pressure across surface (due to difference between $\vec{F}_{as}$ and $\vec{F}_{ls}$) is greater for smaller radius of curvature.

CONCEPTS

either side of the surface layer. The outward force exerted by the liquid on the segment is therefore greater than the inward force exerted by the air on the segment. Because these forces result from the pressures in the fluids on either side of the surface, we can conclude that the pressure in the liquid on the concave side of the surface must be greater than the pressure in the air outside the droplet. We will refer to this difference as the *pressure difference across the surface:*

> **As the radius of curvature of a liquid surface decreases, the pressure difference across the surface increases, with the pressure being greatest on the concave side of the surface.**

This statement and the earlier boldfaced statement describing pressure in a membrane-enclosed gas are consequences of **Laplace's law,** which relates surface curvature to surface tension and to the pressure in a liquid.

Surface tension makes it possible for small insects to walk on a water surface and for small objects to float on a liquid surface. For example, if you carefully place a steel paperclip on a water surface, it stays there even though a thicker steel cylinder would sink (**Figure 18.30a**). There are two ways to explain this. The first is to invoke Laplace's law: The water surface beneath the paperclip is concave up and so the pressure above the surface is greater than the pressure just below it. The pressure just below the surface where the paperclip rests is atmospheric pressure, while the pressure above the surface where the paperclip rests is atmospheric pressure plus the pressure caused by the force exerted by the paperclip on the surface.

The second way to explain why the paperclip floats is illustrated in Figure 18.30b, which shows free-body diagrams for the segment of the surface just below the paperclip and for the paperclip. The tensile forces due to surface tension balance the downward force $\vec{F}_{ns}$ exerted by the paperclip on the surface segment. This downward force $\vec{F}_{ns}$ forms an interaction pair with the upward force $\vec{F}_{sn}$ exerted by the surface segment on the paperclip, which balances the downward force of gravity on the paperclip and makes the paperclip float.

✋ **18.11** (*a*) What is the difference between the pressure just below the water surface in a pool and the pressure in the air just above it? (*b*) Is the pressure inside a raindrop greater than, equal to, or smaller than the pressure in the surrounding air? (*c*) How does the pressure inside a small raindrop compare with the pressure inside a larger raindrop?

A liquid surface that comes in contact with a solid surface forms an angle with the solid surface (**Figure 18.31**). This angle, called the *contact angle*, is the same for a given liquid-solid combination (Figure 18.31a).* The contact angle is defined as the angle between the solid surface and the tangent to the liquid surface at the point where liquid and solid meet; the contact angle is always measured in the liquid. If the contact angle is smaller than 90°, the liquid is

Figure 18.31 Small drops are nearly spherical; larger ones flatten out. For a given combination of liquid and solid surface, the contact angle is fixed and does not depend on the drop size or shape.

(*a*)

Contact angle θ_c is fixed for given combination of liquid and solid.

Larger droplets flatten out.

(*b*)

When contact angle < 90°, we say that liquid wets surface.

Figure 18.30 Surface tension enables paperclips to float on water.

(*a*)

(*b*)

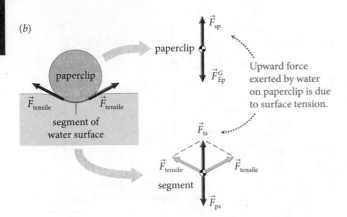

* The gas surrounding the liquid and solid also affects the contact angle. Because this effect is generally very small, we shall ignore it.

CONCEPTS

Figure 18.32 Free-body diagrams for a particle at the gas-liquid-solid junction for a liquid that (*a*) wets and (*b*) does not wet a horizontal surface.

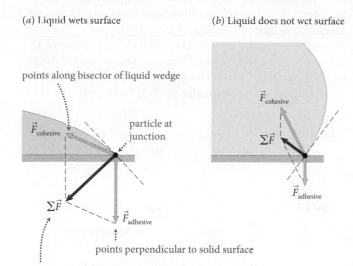

(*a*) Liquid wets surface

(*b*) Liquid does not wet surface

points along bisector of liquid wedge

$\vec{F}_{cohesive}$

particle at junction

$\vec{F}_{cohesive}$

$\Sigma \vec{F}$

$\Sigma \vec{F}$

$\vec{F}_{adhesive}$

$\vec{F}_{adhesive}$

points perpendicular to solid surface

Vector sum must point perpendicular to liquid surface (or particle would move along surface).

Figure 18.33 The concave or convex shape of the surface of a liquid in a capillary tube is determined by the contact angle.

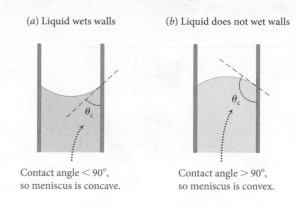

(*a*) Liquid wets walls

(*b*) Liquid does not wet walls

θ_c

θ_c

Contact angle < 90°, so meniscus is concave.

Contact angle > 90°, so meniscus is convex.

said to *wet* the solid surface (Figure 18.31*b*). If the contact angle is greater than 90°, as in Figure 18.31*a*, the liquid does not wet the surface; it forms drops instead of spreading out and wetting the surface.

The contact angle is strongly influenced by how smooth and clean the solid surface is and by the presence of impurities in the liquid. For example, water beads up into drops on a paraffin wax surface, but adding a bit of soap to the water makes the drop spread out and wet the paraffin surface.

The contact angle for a liquid on a solid surface is due to the interplay between the cohesive forces between the particles in the liquid and the *adhesive forces** between the liquid particles and the atoms in the solid. Consider, for example, a particle at the point where the surface meets the solid (**Figure 18.32**). This particle is subject to a cohesive force exerted by a wedge of liquid and an adhesive force exerted by the solid surface. Symmetry requires the cohesive force to be directed along the bisector of the wedge. Likewise, the adhesive force must be perpendicular to the solid surface. (If the adhesive force were not perpendicular to the solid surface, there would be a flow tangential to the surface in response to any tangential component of that force.) Ignoring the effects of gravity (which are very small on a single particle), we can say that the vector sum of the forces exerted on the particle is the sum of the cohesive force and the adhesive force. Because the liquid cannot sustain any shear force, the vector sum of the forces on any particle at

its surface must always be perpendicular to the surface (see Section 18.1). Given the directions of these two forces and their vector sum, their relative magnitudes are fixed. For example, for a liquid that wets a solid with a contact angle of 60° or smaller, the adhesive force is always greater than the cohesive force (Figure 18.32*a*), while for a nonwetting combination, the cohesive force is always greater than the adhesive force (Figure 18.32*b*).

The contact angle also determines the shape of the edges of a liquid surface at any container walls (**Figure 18.33**). In a very narrow tube, called a *capillary* tube (after the Latin word for *hair*), the surface of a liquid is curved. This curved surface, called a **meniscus**, is concave when the liquid wets the walls of the capillary tube (Figure 18.33*a*) and convex when the liquid is nonwetting (Figure 18.33*b*). By looking closely at the edge of the surface of a liquid in a glass, you can determine whether or not the liquid wets the glass.

The free-body diagrams for a particle at the point where the liquid surface meets the glass are shown in **Figure 18.34** for a concave meniscus and a convex meniscus. Notice the similarity with the free-body diagrams in Figure 18.32.

Figure 18.34 Free-body diagrams for a particle at the gas-liquid-solid junction for a liquid that (*a*) wets and (*b*) does not wet a vertical surface.

(*a*) Liquid wets wall

(*b*) Liquid does not wet wall

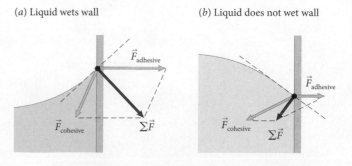

$\vec{F}_{adhesive}$

$\vec{F}_{adhesive}$

$\vec{F}_{cohesive}$

$\vec{F}_{cohesive}$

$\Sigma \vec{F}$

$\Sigma \vec{F}$

* Cohesive forces are exerted between like particles. Adhesive forces are exerted between unlike particles.

Figure 18.35 The pressure difference across the concave surface of a liquid that wets the walls of a capillary tube causes the liquid to rise in the tube, a phenomenon called *capillary rise*.

Curvature means pressure drops across surface, so $P_P < P_{atm}$.

Points Q and R are at same height, so $P_Q = P_R = P_{atm}$.

The formation of a meniscus is responsible for the rise of liquid in a capillary tube, as **Figure 18.35** shows. Because the meniscus is concave, the pressure at point P in the liquid, just below the meniscus, must be smaller than the atmospheric pressure just above the meniscus. The pressure at Q, a point directly below P and at the same height as the surface of the liquid surrounding the capillary tube, must be the same as the pressure at R (otherwise the liquid would flow so as to eliminate any horizontal pressure difference). Because the surface at R is flat, there is no pressure difference across the surface, and so we know that the pressure at R (and therefore the pressure at Q) is equal to atmospheric pressure. The pressure difference between points P and Q causes an upward buoyant force to be exerted by the liquid

in the tube between P and Q, causing a *capillary rise* until the downward force of gravity exerted on the liquid that has been raised into the tube balances the upward force due to the pressure difference. As illustrated in **Figure 18.36**, capillary rise is more pronounced in a narrow tube. The narrower the tube, the smaller the radius of curvature of the meniscus. As we know from Laplace's law, a smaller radius of curvature means a greater pressure difference across the surface and therefore a greater upward force on the liquid.

✋ **18.12** Explain why surface effects cannot support a large solid cylinder made of the same material as a needle.

Figure 18.36 The narrower the tube, the greater the capillary rise.

Smaller diameter means smaller radius of curvature R, hence . . .

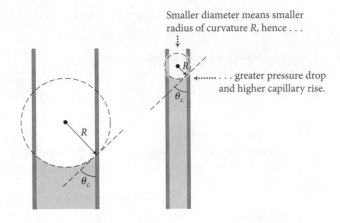

. . . greater pressure drop and higher capillary rise.

Self-quiz

1. Masons use a hose open at both ends and filled with water to ensure that the blocks they lay remain level (**Figure 18.37**). How does such a hose help them do this?

Figure 18.37

2. (*a*) Imagine a rock and a balloon of the same volume completely submerged in water. How do the buoyant forces exerted on them compare? (*b*) How do the buoyant forces compare when the balloon volume is half the rock volume? (*c*) Which object floats and which sinks in part *a* and in part *b*?

3. For a thrown ball to rise, what type of spin should the thrower place on it?

4. (*a*) Draw a free-body diagram analogous to Figure 18.32 for a gas-liquid-solid boundary at which the contact angle is 90°. Make your solid surface horizontal. (*b*) How do the magnitudes and directions of the adhesive and cohesive forces exerted on your particle compare? (*c*) How does the magnitude of the cohesive force between two liquid particles compare with the magnitude of the adhesive force between a liquid particle and an atom in the solid?

5. (*a*) Imagine a capillary tube placed in a nonwetting liquid (as opposed to the wetting-liquid situation of Figure 18.35). How does the pressure at a point P just below the now convex surface compare with atmospheric pressure? (*b*) How does the level in the tube compare with the level of the liquid outside the tube?

Answers:

1. The air pressure at both water surfaces is atmospheric pressure. Therefore the height of the water surface at the left end of the hose must be the same as the height of the water surface at the right end, in order to balance the pressure throughout the water. If the masons align the two ends of the hose with the two ends of a row of blocks and no water bubbles out of either end of the hose, the two ends of the wall are at the same height, meaning the row is level.

2. (*a*) Because the rock and balloon occupy the same volume, they displace the same volume of water, and so the surrounding water exerts equal buoyant forces on them. (*b*) The smaller volume of the balloon displaces a smaller volume of water, and so the buoyant force exerted on the balloon is half the buoyant force exerted on the rock. (*c*) In either case, the balloon rises and the rock sinks. The buoyant force on a rock is always smaller than the force of gravity exerted on it. Likewise the buoyant force on a balloon is always greater than the force of gravity exerted on it, regardless of the volume of the balloon.

3. The thrower needs to place a "backspin" on the ball, which is a spin in which the top of the ball moves toward the thrower. This direction of spin causes the speed of the air relative to the surface of the ball to be greater at the top of the ball than at the bottom. Consequently the air pressure is smaller at the top of the ball than at the bottom. As a result, the ball is subject to an upward force due to this pressure difference.

4. (*a*) See **Figure 18.38**. A contact angle of 90° means that the tangent line to the drop at the contact point is vertical. (*b*) The cohesive force makes an angle of 45° with the horizontal, and the adhesive force is directed vertically downward. The vector sum of the forces must be horizontal, perpendicular to the tangent to the drop at the contact point. The cohesive force is greater than the adhesive force because the vertical component of the cohesive force must cancel the vertically downward adhesive force. (*c*) They are equal. For a particle on the liquid-solid boundary, there are solid atoms below the boundary, liquid particles above the boundary, and liquid particles to the left and the right. The vector sum of the forces exerted on the liquid particle at the boundary is zero and so the magnitude of the cohesive forces between two liquid particles must be the same as the magnitude of the adhesive force between a liquid particle and an atom in the solid.

Figure 18.38

5. (*a*) Because the surface is convex, the pressure at P is greater than atmospheric pressure. (*b*) Because the pressure at R is still atmospheric pressure, the difference in pressure causes a downward force on the liquid in the tube and a resulting *capillary fall*.

18.5 Pressure and gravity

In the first part of this chapter we defined the ratio of the magnitude of the force $\vec{F}_{fs}^c$ exerted by a fluid on a surface and the area A of that surface as the **pressure** in a fluid:

$$P \equiv \frac{F_{fs}^c}{A}. \tag{18.1}$$

Pressure is a scalar, and the SI unit of pressure is newtons per meter-squared, N/m^2. This derived unit is called the **pascal** (Pa), in honor of the French scientist Blaise Pascal:

$$1 \text{ Pa} \equiv 1 \text{ N}/m^2. \tag{18.2}$$

This definition means that a fluid in which the pressure is 1 Pa exerts a force of magnitude 1 N on a 1-m^2 area of the container that holds the fluid. Because a pressure of 1 Pa is very small, pressures are often given in kilopascals: 1 kPa = 1000 Pa. For example, the average pressure in the atmosphere at sea level is

$$P_{atm} = 101.3 \text{ kPa}. \tag{18.3}$$

This pressure is sometimes referred to as 1 atmosphere (1 atm). *Atmosphere* is not an SI unit, however, and so any pressure given in atmospheres must be converted to an SI unit (pascals or kilopascals) before you can do most calculations.

Inside a box that contains absolutely no atoms or molecules, the pressure is zero because nothing exerts a force on the walls of the box. The box is said to contain a *perfect vacuum*. In practice, a perfect vacuum does not exist because it is impossible to remove every particle from a volume of space. Even in deep outer space, the pressure, though very small, is nonzero. In practice, a *vacuum* is any space in which the pressure is less than about 1 Pa. In such a vacuum, $P = 0$ is a very good approximation.

There are several contributions to pressure in a fluid. One contribution is from the gravitational force exerted on the fluid. The pressure in the atmosphere at sea level, for example, is due to the gravitational force exerted by Earth on all the air surrounding the planet. Other contributions are from the motion of the fluid and, when the fluid is a liquid, from the curvature of the liquid surface. A fourth contribution is from the collisions that take place between the fluid particles, and between the fluid particles and the container walls—the pressure in an inflated balloon is an example of this fourth contribution. We'll discuss this contribution to the pressure in a gas in more detail in Chapter 19. In the remainder of this chapter, we concentrate on the gravitational, motion, and surface contributions to pressure.

Let us begin by looking at a familiar type of pressure, the *atmospheric pressure* that results from the air surrounding Earth. The atmosphere can be modeled as an "ocean" of air extending from the ground up. Because gases are compressible, the distribution of gas molecules in the air is not uniform. All the molecules are attracted to the ground by Earth's gravitational pull, which means that higher-up molecules press down on lower ones, compressing the air and making the mass density high near sea level and lower at altitudes above sea level. Because gases are compressible, the relationship between atmospheric pressure and altitude is complicated by the fact that the mass density of air varies with altitude. **Figure 18.39** shows how the average atmospheric pressure varies with altitude. If the mass density of air were constant, the curve would be a straight line with a negative slope. If the extremes were as in Figure 18.39—100 kPa at sea level and essentially zero at 30 km—the atmospheric pressure at the midpoint between

Figure 18.39 Variation in atmospheric pressure with altitude above sea level.

50 kPa at 5.5-km altitude

these two altitudes, 15 km, would be half of its sea-level value. Instead we see a nonlinear relationship in Figure 18.39, with the pressure at 50 kPa, half the sea-level value, not at an altitude of 15 km but at a mere 5.5 km. This means that half of the atmosphere is below 5.5 km. At the cruising altitude of a commercial airplane (10 km), the atmospheric pressure is about one-quarter of what it is at sea level, meaning that 75% of the atmosphere is below the airplane. At an altitude of 100 km, the pressure in the atmosphere drops to about 1 Pa, close to vacuum.

Even though the changes in atmospheric pressure are considerable over large distances, they are usually negligible over small vertical distances because, even at its densest, at sea level, the mass density of air is so small. Near sea level, for example, the atmospheric pressure drops 12 Pa for every meter of altitude. The pressure difference between the air near your feet and the air near your head is therefore about 20 Pa, which is negligibly small relative to atmospheric pressure, 1×10^5 Pa.

Example 18.5 Altimeter

Airplane cabins are pressurized to prevent passengers from developing altitude sickness during flight. Your altimeter watch, which uses pressure to determine altitude, indicates a cabin altitude of 2500 m even though the captain has just announced that the airplane is flying at an altitude of 10,000 m. Armed with this information, and ignoring the motion of the airplane, you calculate the integral of the magnitude of the force exerted by the air on the fuselage of the airplane, which you estimate to be a cylinder of length 60 m and diameter 6.0 m.

❶ **GETTING STARTED** Pressure decreases with altitude as shown in Figure 18.39. Because the cabin is pressurized, the pressure inside the cabin is greater than it would be if it were allowed to equalize with the exterior atmospheric pressure at 10,000 m. That the altimeter indicates an altitude of 2500 m tells me that the cabin pressure is equal not to atmospheric pressure at sea level (about 100 kPa) but to a value somewhat lower than 100 kPa. (Because I can feel my ears "pop" as the airplane takes off and lands, I know that the cabin pressure must indeed change somewhat.)

❷ **DEVISE PLAN** The force exerted by the air on the fuselage is the vector sum of two forces: an outward force due to the pressure P_{in} inside the cabin and an inward force due to the pressure P_{out} outside the cabin. According to Eq. 18.1, the magnitude of each of these forces is PdA, where dA is the surface area of a segment of the fuselage. Because $P_{in} > P_{out}$, the air exerts on each

fuselage segment an outward force of magnitude $(P_{in} - P_{out})dA$. Figure 18.39 gives me the values for P_{out} at 10,000 m and for what the cabin pressure P_{in} must be given that it corresponds to atmospheric pressure at 2500 m. Ignoring the tiny variation in air pressure over the height of the airplane, the values of P_{in} and P_{out} are identical over the entire fuselage, and so I just need to multiply the pressure difference by the surface area $A = \int dA$ of the entire fuselage to compute the integral of the magnitude of the forces exerted on the fuselage.

❸ **EXECUTE PLAN** From Figure 18.39, I see that $P_{out} = P_{10\,km} = 24$ kPa and $P_{in} = P_{2.5\,km} = 80$ kPa, so $P_{in} - P_{out} = 80$ kPa $- 24$ kPa $= 56$ kPa. The surface area of the (assumed) cylindrical fuselage is equal to circumference times length plus the surface area of the two circular ends: $A = 2\pi R\ell + 2\pi R^2 = 2\pi(3.0 \text{ m})(60 \text{ m}) + 2\pi(3.0 \text{ m})^2 = 1.2 \times 10^3 \text{ m}^2$. The sum of the magnitudes of the forces exerted by the air on the fuselage is thus $(56 \text{ kPa})(1000 \text{ Pa}/1 \text{ kPa})(1.2 \times 10^3 \text{ m}^2) = 6.7 \times 10^7 \text{ N.}$ ✔

❹ **EVALUATE RESULT** This force magnitude is very large, corresponding to the force of gravity exerted on 6.8×10^6 kg, or 6800 metric tons! The fuselage does not rupture because the force is distributed over a very large area. For comparison, if the pressure inside the cabin were maintained at a pressure equal to the atmospheric pressure at sea level, the pressure difference across the fuselage would be $P_{in} - P_{out} = 101$ kPa $- 24$ kPa $= 77$ kPa and the force would be some 40% greater.

✋ **18.13** Consider a book lying on a table at sea level with the front cover facing up. The book is 0.28 m tall, 0.22 m wide, and 50 mm thick; its mass is 3.0 kg. How does the force exerted by the atmosphere on the front cover compare with the force of gravity exerted on the book?

The answer to Checkpoint 18.13 is astonishing. With the book under so much pressure, how can anyone lift it? The reason you can is that the air is pushing on the book from all directions. Not only does it push down on the front cover, it also pushes up on the bottom cover. Because the surface areas of the top and bottom covers are the same and because the air pressure below the book is virtually the same as that above the book, the magnitudes of the upward and downward forces exerted by the atmosphere on the book are the same, and so their vector sum is zero.

You may wonder how the atmosphere can exert an upward force on the bottom cover if the book is lying flat on a table. The reason is that there is always a tiny bit of air between the cover and the table surface, and the air pressure in this layer has to be the same as the air pressure everywhere else around the book (otherwise air would rush into or out of the space between table and cover to eliminate the pressure difference). If you were to remove the air from underneath the book—say, by putting the book on top of the opening of a chamber from which the air has been evacuated—it would be nearly impossible to lift the book off the table.

18.14 A dart that has a suction cup at one end sticks to a ceiling. Describe what force holds the dart against the ceiling.

Figure 18.40 Model for describing how the pressure in a liquid varies with height.

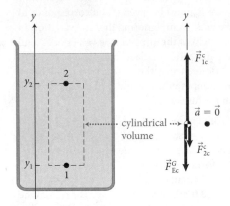

(*a*) Imaginary cylindrical volume of liquid at rest inside larger volume of same liquid

(*b*) Free-body diagram for cylinder

In contrast to gases, liquids are nearly incompressible, which means that we can take the mass density in a liquid to be uniform. Therefore we can derive a simple expression to describe how the pressure in a liquid varies with height. Consider a cylindrical volume of liquid inside a large stationary body of identical liquid (**Figure 18.40a**). The cylindrical volume has volume V and horizontal cross-sectional area A, and Figure 18.40b shows that three forces are exerted on it in the vertical direction: an upward force exerted by the column of liquid below the bottom of the cylindrical volume (point 1), a downward force exerted by the column of liquid above the top of the volume (point 2), and a downward force of gravity. Because our volume is at rest, the vector sum of the three forces must be zero, and so, with the positive y axis pointing upward, we can say for all the forces exerted on the cylindrical volume in the vertical direction,

$$\sum F_{cy} = F_{1cy}^c + F_{2cy}^c + F_{Ecy}^G = P_1A - P_2A - mg = 0, \qquad (18.4)$$

where m is the mass of the liquid in the cylindrical volume. Because the mass density ρ of the liquid is the same everywhere, we can write for the mass of the cylindrical volume $m = \rho V = \rho A(y_2 - y_1)$, and so

$$P_1A - P_2A - \rho A(y_2 - y_1)g = 0 \qquad (18.5)$$

or, dividing all terms by A and bringing terms with the same subscripts to the same side,

$$P_1 + \rho g y_1 = P_2 + \rho g y_2 \quad \text{(stationary liquid)}. \qquad (18.6)$$

Equation 18.6 tells us that the quantity $P + \rho g y$ is the same at the top and bottom of the cylindrical volume. Because the top and bottom are at arbitrary positions, the fact that $(P + \rho g y)_{\text{top}} = (P + \rho g y)_{\text{bottom}}$ means that the quantity $P + \rho g y$ is the same *everywhere* in the *entire* liquid. In other words, the pressure in a stationary liquid is the same at all points in any given horizontal plane through the liquid (that is, at some fixed value of y).

Rearranging Eq. 18.6 to bring all the terms containing y to one side $(P_1 = P_2 + \rho g y_2 - \rho g y_1)$, we see that the pressure at all points in a horizontal plane 1 located a vertical distance $d = y_2 - y_1$ below another horizontal plane 2 is given by

$$P_1 = P_2 + \rho g d \quad \text{(stationary liquid, 1 below 2)}. \qquad (18.7)$$

If we let point 2 be at the surface of the liquid (**Figure 18.41**), P_2 is the pressure at the surface, and Eq. 18.7 tells us that the pressure at a depth $d = y_2 - y_1$ below the surface is given by

$$P = P_{surface} + \rho g d \quad \text{(stationary liquid).} \tag{18.8}$$

This expression shows that the pressure P in a stationary liquid increases with depth or, put differently, P decreases linearly with the height in the liquid, just as we concluded in Section 18.2.

The term that contains g is the gravitational contribution to the pressure and is sometimes referred to as *hydrostatic pressure*.

Now consider two liquid-filled tubes, one wide and one narrow and both open at one end, connected as shown in **Figure 18.42**. In each tube, the pressure at the surface of the liquid is equal to atmospheric pressure. This means that the downward force $P_{atm}A_{wide}$ exerted by the atmosphere on the surface of the liquid in the wide tube is significantly greater than the downward force $P_{atm}A_{narrow}$ exerted by the atmosphere on the surface of the liquid in the narrow tube. How does this difference in force affect the levels of the water in each tube?

To answer this question, let's consider the pressures at points 1 and 2 in Figure 18.42. Because these points are in the same horizontal plane, the pressures must be equal, $P_1 = P_2$. Equation 18.8 tells us that these pressures are related to the (atmospheric) pressure at the surface by

$$P_1 = P_{atm} + \rho g d_1 \quad \text{and} \quad P_2 = P_{atm} + \rho g d_2. \tag{18.9}$$

Because $P_1 = P_2$, we must have $d_1 = d_2$: The liquid rises to the same height in both tubes, even though the forces exerted by the atmosphere on the surfaces of the liquid are different. The reason is that, despite the difference in these downward forces, the *pressure* at the bottom of each tube must be the same ($P_1 = P_2$). If the pressure were not the same, the pressure difference would cause the liquid to flow until the pressure difference is evened out, which occurs only when $d_1 = d_2$. The equal height of the liquid surfaces in the two tubes means that these surfaces are in the same horizontal plane. So the pressure at two points in a horizontal plane is the same as long as the two points are connected by an uninterrupted path through the liquid.

Figure 18.41 If the cylindrical volume is defined such that its top is at the liquid surface, the pressure at the top is equal to atmospheric pressure.

Figure 18.42 Liquid rises to the same level in connected tubes, regardless of their width or shape.

Example 18.6 Dam

A dam of horizontal length ℓ holds water of mass density ρ to a height h. What is the magnitude of the force exerted by the water on the dam?

❶ **GETTING STARTED** I begin with a sketch (**Figure 18.43a**). The pressure in the water behind the dam is equal to atmospheric pressure at the water surface and increases linearly with depth as given by Eq. 18.8. If I choose my y axis pointing upward, with the origin at the bottom of the dam, the pressure varies with y as shown in Figure 18.43b. For convenience, I call the water side of the dam face A and the opposite side face B.

❷ **DEVISE PLAN** Because the pressure varies with y, the magnitude of the force $\vec{F}_{wd}$ also varies with y. I therefore divide the area of face A into thin horizontal strips each of width dy (Figure 18.43a). Because I know the pressure at a given value of y, I can calculate the force dF_{wd} exerted on the strip. To calculate the force exerted by the water on the whole dam, I integrate my expression over y from $y = 0$ at the bottom of the dam to $y = h$ at the water surface.

Figure 18.43

(a)

(b)

❸ EXECUTE PLAN Because a point in the water located at some arbitrary value of y is at a depth $d = h - y$ below the water surface and because $P_{\text{surface}} = P_{\text{atm}}$, I write Eq. 18.8 in the form

$$P(y) = P_{\text{atm}} + \rho g(h - y).$$

The area of each strip is $dA = \ell\, dy$, and so the magnitude of the force exerted by the water on each strip is $dF = P(y)dA = P(y)\ell\, dy$. The magnitude of the force exerted by the water on the entire dam is then

$$F_{\text{wd}} = \int dF_{\text{ws}} = \ell \int_0^h P(y)dy = \ell\left[\, P_{\text{atm}}y + \rho ghy - \tfrac{1}{2}\rho gy^2\,\right]_0^h$$

$$= \ell h\left(P_{\text{atm}} + \tfrac{1}{2}\rho gh\right). \checkmark$$

❹ EVALUATE RESULT The product ℓh is the surface area of the dam, and so the term $\ell h P_{\text{atm}}$ is the magnitude of the force exerted by the atmosphere on the dam. Because the atmosphere exerts a force of the same magnitude on face B in the opposite direction, the first term in my answer drops out of the vector sum of the forces exerted by the water on face A of the dam and by the atmosphere on face B of the dam. The remaining term, $\ell h(\tfrac{1}{2}\rho gh)$, is the product of the area of the face of the dam and $\tfrac{1}{2}\rho gh$, which is the pressure increase halfway down in the water. Because the pressure increases linearly with depth, this term represents the average value of the pressure increase between surface and bottom, and so my answer makes sense.

Let us now turn to buoyancy. The volume of liquid in Figure 18.40 is held in place by the buoyant force $\vec{F}_{\text{lv}}^{\text{b}}$ exerted by the surrounding liquid. The vector sum of the forces exerted on the volume of liquid is thus

$$\textstyle\sum \vec{F}_{\text{v}} = \vec{F}_{\text{lv}}^{\text{b}} + \vec{F}_{\text{Ev}}^{G} = \vec{0}. \tag{18.10}$$

Because the magnitude of the force of gravity on the volume of liquid is ρVg, we obtain for the magnitude of the **buoyant force** exerted by the surrounding liquid on the volume of liquid

$$F_{\text{lv}}^{\text{b}} = \rho Vg. \tag{18.11}$$

The direction of the buoyant force is always opposite the direction of the gravitational acceleration. Because this expression holds for any object in any fluid, we can write for the buoyant force on any object o in a fluid f:

$$F_{\text{fo}}^{\text{b}} = \rho_{\text{f}} V_{\text{disp}} g, \tag{18.12}$$

where we have added a subscript to V to remind us that this volume represents the *displaced volume* of fluid and a subscript on ρ to remind us that it is the mass density of the fluid.

The vector sum of the upward buoyant force and the downward gravitational force exerted on an object in a given fluid determines whether the object sinks or floats in that fluid. When they are equal in magnitude, $F_{\text{fo}}^{\text{b}} = F_{\text{Eo}}^{G}$ or $\rho_{\text{f}} V_{\text{disp}} g = mg = \rho_{\text{o,av}} V_{\text{o}} g$, where we have written the mass of the object as the product of its average mass density $\rho_{\text{o,av}}$ and volume V_{o}. For an object that is floating, the displaced volume is less than the volume of that object:

$$V_{\text{disp}} = \frac{\rho_{\text{o,av}}}{\rho_{\text{f}}} V_{\text{o}} \quad \text{or} \quad \frac{\rho_{\text{o,av}}}{\rho_{\text{f}}} < 1. \tag{18.13}$$

Therefore we have

$$\rho_{\text{o,av}} < \rho_{\text{f}} \quad \text{(object floats)}. \tag{18.14}$$

An object placed in a fluid floats whenever the average mass density of the object is smaller than the mass density of the fluid.

Conversely, an object sinks when the magnitude of the buoyant force is smaller than that of the gravitational force. Working through the same thought sequence that got us from forces to Eq. 18.14, we see that

$$\rho_{o,av} > \rho_f \quad \text{(object sinks).} \tag{18.15}$$

An object placed in a fluid sinks whenever the average mass density of the object exceeds the mass density of the fluid.

When the object's average mass density is equal to the mass density of the fluid, $\rho_{o,av} = \rho_f$, the object is said to have *neutral buoyancy*—it can "hang" motionless anywhere in the fluid.

✋ **18.15** An object floats with 80% of its volume submerged in water. How does the average mass density of the object compare with that of water?

18.6 Working with pressure

The results in Section 18.5 allow us to understand a number of applications of pressure. Let's first consider measurements of pressure. A *pressure gauge* is used to measure pressures that are near or greater than atmospheric pressure; a *vacuum gauge* is used to measure pressures that are smaller than atmospheric pressure.

The most common pressure gauges have a flexible, sealed chamber that changes shape when the pressure inside or outside the chamber changes. The deformation of the chamber is measured electrically, optically, or mechanically. For example, in a simple mechanical pressure gauge (**Figure 18.44**), the chamber deformation is coupled via a gear to an indicating needle on a calibrated dial. The reading on a pressure gauge is the pressure in excess of atmospheric pressure. Thus when you use a pressure gauge to check the pressure in, say, a bicycle tire, the reading on the gauge, called *gauge pressure P_{gauge}*, is related to the actual pressure P in the tire by

$$P = P_{gauge} + P_{atm}. \tag{18.16}$$

For example, when a tire pressure gauge reads 2.4 atm, the pressure inside the tire is 3.4 atm. If the pressure inside a container is smaller than atmospheric pressure, the pressure gauge reading is negative.

The simplest pressure gauge is the open-tube *manometer* (**Figure 18.45**). A manometer is essentially a liquid-filled, U-shaped tube, one leg of which is connected to the container where the pressure P is to be measured and the other leg of which is open to the atmosphere. The pressure in the liquid at the bottom of the U is P_{bottom}, while that at the surface of the liquid in the right leg is atmospheric pressure. Applying Eq. 18.7 to these two points, we get $P_{bottom} = P_{atm} + \rho g y_{right}$. Applying the same procedure to the left leg, we have $P_{bottom} = P + \rho g y_{left}$, and so $P = P_{atm} + \rho g(y_{right} - y_{left})$ or, if we denote the difference in the heights of the liquid in the two legs by h, the pressure measured by the manometer is

$$P = P_{atm} + \rho g h. \tag{18.17}$$

Equation 18.17 shows that using a manometer to measure the pressure in some fluid-filled container requires knowing atmospheric pressure, which means we cannot use a manometer to measure atmospheric pressure. We can

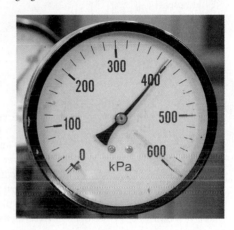

Figure 18.44 Simple mechanical pressure gauge.

Figure 18.45 An open-tube manometer. The difference in the levels in the two legs of the manometer gives the pressure P inside the bulb.

QUANTITATIVE TOOLS

Figure 18.46 A barometer. The height of the column of liquid in the tube gives the atmospheric pressure.

use another device, though, a *barometer*, illustrated in **Figure 18.46**. This device consists of a shallow reservoir; a long, thin tube closed at one end and open at the other; and a dense liquid, usually mercury. Some of the liquid sits in the reservoir. The tube is filled completely with the liquid, and its open end is covered temporarily. The tube is then inverted and its open end plunged into the liquid in the reservoir. As the temporary cover is removed, some of the liquid drains from the tube into the reservoir, leaving a vacuum above the liquid in the closed end of the tube. The level of the liquid in the tube remains above the level of the liquid in the reservoir so as to satisfy Eq. 18.7 when we define the liquid surface in the reservoir as point 1 and the liquid surface in the tube as point 2. When we let the reservoir liquid surface be at $y_1 = 0$, the left side of Eq. 18.6 becomes $P_{atm} + 0$. Because there is a vacuum above the tube liquid surface, the right side of Eq. 18.6 is $0 + \rho gh$, and so we have

$$P_{atm} = \rho gh. \tag{18.18}$$

If we know the mass density ρ of the liquid, we can determine atmospheric pressure by measuring the height h of the liquid in the tube.

Example 18.7 Liquid support

In **Figure 18.47**, the top tank, which is open to the atmosphere, contains water ($\rho_{water} = 1.0 \times 10^3 \text{ kg/m}^3$) and the bottom tank contains oil ($\rho_{oil} = 0.92 \times 10^3 \text{ kg/m}^3$) covered by a piston. The tank on the right has a freely movable partition that keeps the oil and water separate. The partition is a vertical distance 0.10 m below the open surface of the water. If the piston in the bottom tank is 0.50 m below the open surface of the water and has a surface area of $8.3 \times 10^{-3} \text{ m}^2$, what must the mass of the piston be to keep the system in mechanical equilibrium? For simplicity, ignore the mass of the partition.

Figure 18.47 Example 18.7.

$\rho_{water} = 1.0 \times 10^3 \text{ kg/m}^3$

water

oil

0.10 m

0.50 m

movable partition

area of piston = $8.3 \times 10^{-3} \text{ m}^2$

$\rho_{oil} = 0.92 \times 10^3 \text{ kg/m}^3$

❶ **GETTING STARTED** I begin by making a sketch of the arrangement and identifying points of interest (**Figure 18.48a**). Point 1 is at the water surface in the top tank, and the pressure here is atmospheric pressure. Point 2 is on the partition in the right tank separating the water from the oil. In mechanical equilibrium, the partition is not accelerating, and so, because I ignore the partition mass, the pressure must be the same on the two sides of the partition. Point 3 is at the position in the bottom tank where the oil and piston meet.

I also draw a free-body diagram for the piston, which also has zero acceleration in mechanical equilibrium (Figure 18.48b). The piston is subject to an upward force $\vec{F}^c_{op}$ exerted by the oil, a downward force $\vec{F}^c_{ap}$ exerted by the air above the piston, and a downward gravitational force $\vec{F}^G_{Ep}$.

Figure 18.48

(a)

(b)

1

water $d_1 = 0.10 \text{ m}$

2

oil

$d_2 = 0.40 \text{ m}$

$d_3 = 0.50 \text{ m}$

3

piston $\vec{a}_p = \vec{0}$

$\vec{F}^c_{op}$

$\vec{F}^c_{ap}$

$\vec{F}^G_{Ep}$

❷ **DEVISE PLAN** When the system is in mechanical equilibrium, the piston is stationary. Therefore the vector sum of the forces exerted on it must be zero. From my free-body diagram, I see that the magnitude of the upward force exerted by the oil on the piston is equal in magnitude to the sum of the downward gravitational force exerted on the piston and the downward force exerted by the air on the piston: $F^c_{op} = F^G_{Ep} + F^c_{ap} = m_p g + F^c_{ap}$.

The magnitudes F^c_{ap} and F^c_{op} are given by a rearranged form of Eq. 18.1: $F^c_{ap} = P_{air} A_{piston}$, and $F^c_{op} = P_3 A_{piston}$. The problem therefore reduces to determining the pressure P_3 at point 3, where the oil and piston meet. That point is 0.40 m below the partition in the tank on the right, where the pressure is P_2. Because points 2 and 3 are in a connected liquid (the oil), I can use Eq. 18.7 to relate P_2 and P_3. Points 1 and 2 are also in a connected liquid (the water), so I can use Eq. 18.7 to relate P_2 and $P_1 = P_{atm}$.

❸ **EXECUTE PLAN** Because the vector sum of the forces exerted on the piston is zero, I have $F^c_{op} - F^c_{ap} - F^G_{Ep} = P_3 A_{piston} - P_{air} A_{piston} - m_{piston} g = 0$, or

$$m_{piston} = \frac{(P_3 - P_{air}) A_{piston}}{g}. \tag{1}$$

To obtain P_3, I first apply Eq. 18.7 to points 1 and 2, remembering that the lower point always goes on the left side of the equation: $P_2 = P_1 + \rho_{water}gd_1 = P_{air} + \rho_{water}gd_1$. Then I apply Eq. 18.7 to points 2 and 3: $P_3 = P_2 + \rho_{oil}gd_2 = P_{air} + \rho_{water}gd_1 + \rho_{oil}gd_2$. Substituting this expression into Eq. 1, I get

$$m_{piston} = \frac{(P_{air} + \rho_{water}gd_1 + \rho_{oil}gd_2 - P_{air})A_{piston}}{g}$$

$$= (\rho_{water}d_1 + \rho_{oil}d_2)A_{piston}$$

$$= [(1.0 \times 10^3 \text{ kg/m}^3)(0.10 \text{ m}) + (0.92 \times 10^3 \text{ kg/m}^3)$$

$$\times (0.40 \text{ m})](8.3 \times 10^{-3} \text{ m}^2) = 3.9 \text{ kg.} ✔$$

④ EVALUATE RESULT The atmospheric pressure term drops out because it affects both the water surface and the piston. Points 1 and 3 are separated by 0.5 m. Because I know that the pressure difference due to 10 m of water is equal to atmospheric pressure at sea level, or about 100 kPa (see Checkpoint 18.4; these are handy numbers to remember), I know that 0.5 m of water should correspond to a pressure difference of about 5 kPa. The mass density of oil is a bit smaller than that of water, but I can ignore the difference. The surface area of the piston is about 10^{-2} m^2, and so the force giving rise to the 5-kPa pressure difference is about 50 N, which is equal to the gravitational force exerted on a mass of 5 kg, which is close to the answer I obtained.

✋ **18.16** Oil and water don't mix, and the mass density of oil is smaller than that of water. Suppose water is poured into a U-shaped tube that is open at both ends until the water surface is halfway up each leg of the tube, and then some oil is poured on top of the water in the right leg. Once the system comes to equilibrium, are the top of the oil column in the right leg and the top of the water column in the left leg at the same height? If not, which is higher?

The principles we have discussed in this section allow us to understand the working of *hydraulic systems,* which are used for lifting heavy loads or exerting large forces. The basic idea behind a hydraulic system is simple: A liquid, usually oil, is used to transmit a force applied at one point to another point. **Figure 18.49a** shows a schematic hydraulic system: two pistons fitted into two connected, oil-filled cylinders. Because the oil is incompressible, a force exerted on one piston increases the pressure everywhere in the oil, and so the force is transmitted to the other piston.

The tube that connects the two cylinders can be any length or shape, which means it can snake through tight spaces and can also fork, allowing an applied force to be distributed. In the brake system of a car, for example, the force your foot exerts on the brake pedal is transmitted to the piston in an oil-filled master cylinder. The pressure increase in the oil is transmitted through steel tubes to the four brakes in the wheels, where the oil exerts a force on the brake pads, pushing them against a disk attached to the wheel, which slows down the car (Figure 18.49b).

Another great advantage of hydraulic systems is that they permit us to "multiply" a force by varying the size of the pistons. In **Figure 18.50**, a force of magnitude F_1 is exerted on a small piston of area A_1, causing a gauge pressure

Figure 18.49 Hydraulic systems make it possible to lift heavy loads or exert large forces.

(a) Basic hydraulic system

smaller area, smaller force, greater displacement

greater area, greater force, smaller displacement

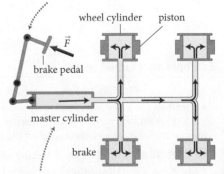

incompressible fluid

(b) Schematic model of hydraulic brake system

Mechanical lever multiplies force on brake pedal.

wheel cylinder   piston

$\vec{F}$

brake pedal

master cylinder

brake

Hydraulic system multiplies and distributes force.

Figure 18.50 Hydraulic system used to "multiply" a force.

Procedure: Working with pressure in liquids at rest

The branch of physics that deals with pressure in a liquid at rest is called *hydrostatics*. The pressure in a liquid at rest is determined by gravity and by what happens at the boundary of the liquid. To determine the pressure in such liquids:

1. Begin by making a sketch showing all the **boundaries** and identifying all the factors that affect pressure: pistons, gases at surfaces open to the atmosphere, and so on. Note the known vertical heights of liquid surfaces, the areas of these surfaces, the surface areas of pistons, and the liquid mass densities.
2. Determine the **pressure at each surface.** The pressure at a liquid surface open to the air is equal to atmospheric pressure P_{atm}. The pressure at a liquid surface bordering a vacuum is zero: $P = 0$. The pressure at a liquid surface open to a gas other than the atmosphere is equal to the pressure in the gas: $P = P_{gas}$. The pressure at a liquid surface that is in contact with a solid, such as a piston, is $P = F^c_{sl}/A$, where F^c_{sl} is the magnitude of the force exerted by the solid on the liquid and A is the area over which that force is exerted.
3. Use **horizontal planes.** The pressure is the same at all points on a horizontal plane in a connected liquid. The pressure difference between two horizontal planes 1 and 2 is given by $P_1 = P_2 + \rho gd$ (Eq. 18.7), where d is the vertical distance between the horizontal planes and 1 is below 2.

$P_1 = F_1/A_1$ in the liquid at the small piston. Because $P_3 = P_2 + \rho gh$, the gauge pressure P_2 at the large piston is then

$$P_2 = P_3 - \rho gh = P_1 - \rho gh, \tag{18.19}$$

where h is the vertical distance between the pistons. When the liquid in a hydraulic system is oil, we can ignore the term ρgh because the mass density of oil is not very great and h is generally small, so that $P_1 \approx P_2$. The gauge pressure P_2 at point 2 causes the liquid to exert a force of magnitude F_2 on the piston. If the area of that piston is A_2, we have $P_2 = F_2/A_2$, so that

$$\frac{F_1}{A_1} = \frac{F_2}{A_2} \tag{18.20}$$

or

$$F_2 = \frac{A_2}{A_1}F_1. \tag{18.21}$$

Because $A_2 > A_1$, we have $F_2 > F_1$. Therefore a small force applied to the small piston causes the liquid to exert a large force on the large piston (even though the *pressure* is the same at both points). The factor A_2/A_1 is what permits you to exert large forces on the brakes of a car even though the force your foot exerts on the brake pedal is relatively small.

Example 18.8 Liquid work

Suppose a load is placed on the large piston in Figure 18.50 and we wish to raise that load by a certain distance. How does the work done on the small piston compare with the work required to raise the load? Ignore the masses of the pistons.

❶ **GETTING STARTED** I begin by making a sketch (**Figure 18.51**). To keep my subscripts simple, I call the small piston 1 and the large piston 2. I denote the displacements of the two pistons by $\Delta\vec{x}_1$ and $\Delta\vec{x}_2$, and the forces exerted on them by $\vec{F}_1$ and $\vec{F}_2$.

❷ **DEVISE PLAN** The magnitudes F_1 and F_2 are related by Eq. 18.21, $F_2 = (A_2/A_1)F_1$. Each force does an amount of work given by the scalar product of the force and the force displacement, which is equal to the displacement of the piston on which the force is exerted. Both forces do positive work because the

Figure 18.51

direction of each force is the same as the direction of the force displacement. Because the liquid in the cylinders is incompressible, I know that the volume V_1 of liquid pushed out of the small cylinder must be equal to the volume V_2 of liquid pushed into the large cylinder: $V_1 = V_2$. This expression will help me relate the piston displacements to the piston surface areas.

❸ **EXECUTE PLAN** Raising the load a distance $d = \Delta x_2$ requires work $W_2 = \vec{F}_2 \cdot \Delta \vec{x}_2 = F_2 d$. Using Eq. 18.21, I can write for the work done on the small piston

$$W_1 = \vec{F}_1 \cdot \Delta \vec{x}_1 = F_1 \Delta x_1 = F_2 \frac{A_1}{A_2} \Delta x_1. \qquad (1)$$

The volume of liquid pushed out of the small cylinder is $V_1 = A_1 \Delta x_1$, and that pushed into the large cylinder is $V_2 = A_2 \Delta x_2 = A_2 d$. Because these two volumes are equal, I have $A_1 \Delta x_1 = A_2 d$, or $\Delta x_1 = (A_2/A_1)d$. Substituting this expression into Eq. 1, I get $W_1 = F_2 d$, telling me that the same work is done on both pistons. ✔

🖐 **18.17** In the derivation of Eq. 18.21, we ignored the effect of atmospheric pressure on the two pistons. How is the result we obtained affected by atmospheric pressure?

❹ **EVALUATE RESULT** My answer tells me that no energy is gained by using the hydraulic lift, which makes sense. The force exerted on the small piston is increased by the factor A_2/A_1 when it is transmitted to the large piston, but the displacement decreases by the inverse factor A_1/A_2, and so the work done is the same.

18.7 Bernoulli's equation

Next we turn our attention to fluids in motion. Consider the laminar flow of a nonviscous fluid through the tapered tube in **Figure 18.52**. In a time interval Δt, a thin "slice" of fluid in the wide part of the tube undergoes a displacement Δx_1. The volume of fluid that enters the tube at point 1 is thus $A_1 |\Delta x_1|$, where A_1 is the cross-sectional area of the wide part of the tube. If the mass density of the fluid at point 1 is ρ_1, the amount of mass entering the tube at point 1 is $m_1 = \rho_1 A_1 |\Delta x_1|$. Likewise, if a thin slice of fluid in the narrow part of the tube has a displacement Δx_2, and the cross-sectional area of the narrow part is A_2, then the mass of the fluid emerging at point 2 is $\rho_2 A_2 |\Delta x_2|$. If the flow is laminar, the flow speed at any location doesn't change with time. This means that no mass can accumulate in the tube, and so the mass of the fluid emerging from the narrow part at point 2 during a time interval Δt must be the same as the mass entering at point 1:

$$\rho_1 A_1 |\Delta x_1| = \rho_2 A_2 |\Delta x_2| \quad \text{(laminar flow of nonviscous fluid).} \quad (18.22)$$

If the flow speed of the fluid is v_1 at point 1 and v_2 at point 2, we have $|\Delta x_1| = v_1 \Delta t$ and $|\Delta x_2| = v_2 \Delta t$. Substituting these expressions into Eq. 18.22 and dividing both sides by Δt, we obtain

$$\rho_1 A_1 v_1 = \rho_2 A_2 v_2 \quad \text{(laminar flow of nonviscous fluid).} \quad (18.23)$$

Equation 18.23 is called the **continuity equation.** This equation quantitatively expresses the idea that the mass of the fluid emerging from the narrow part at point 2 during a time interval Δt is the same as the mass entering at point 1.

For an incompressible fluid, the mass density is the same in all parts of the tube and so

$$A_1 v_1 = A_2 v_2 \quad \text{(laminar flow of nonviscous, incompressible fluid).} \quad (18.24)$$

This equation expresses quantitatively what we concluded in Section 18.3: A fluid flows faster in a narrow part of a tube than in a wide part.

Figure 18.52 A fluid flows through a tapered tube.

cross-sectional area A_1

cross-sectional area A_2

point 1

point 2

$\Delta \vec{x}_1$

$\Delta \vec{x}_2$

volume $A_1 \Delta x_1$

volume $A_2 \Delta x_2$

We can write Eq. 18.24 in another form by introducing a quantity Q, called the **volume flow rate,** the rate at which a volume of fluid crosses a section of a tube. If a volume V crosses a section in a time interval Δt, the volume flow rate is

$$Q \equiv \frac{V}{\Delta t}. \tag{18.25}$$

The SI unit of volume flow rate is meters cubed per second (m^3/s). For a nonviscous fluid flowing at speed v through a pipe of cross-sectional area A, we have $V = A|\Delta x| = Av\Delta t$, and so the volume flow rate is

$$Q = Av. \tag{18.26}$$

Equation 18.24 thus tells us that the volume flow rate is the same at all locations in an incompressible fluid: $Q_1 = Q_2$.

We also concluded in Section 18.3 that in order for a fluid to accelerate in the region where a tube narrows, the pressure must be greater in the wide part. Let us therefore now relate pressure to flow speed. Consider the tapered tube in **Figure 18.53**. At point 1 the tube's cross-sectional area is A_1, the fluid's speed is v_1, the pressure is P_1, and the vertical height above some arbitrarily chosen origin is y_1. The corresponding quantities at point 2 are A_2, v_2, P_2, and y_2. Let us consider the system made up of Earth and the fluid initially between points 1 and 2. How does the energy of this system change?

To answer this question, let us apply the energy law (Eq. 9.1, $\Delta E = W$) to this system over a time interval Δt. As Figure 18.53 shows, during the time interval Δt the system has shifted to the right. The difference between the initial and final states of the system is a "missing" volume of fluid on the left and an "added" volume of fluid on the right. The continuity equation requires the masses of these two volumes to be the same: $m_1 = m_2 = m$. Because the mass of the fluid between points 1 and 2 doesn't change, the only forms of energy we need to consider are the kinetic and potential energies associated with m_1 and m_2. The change in kinetic energy is

$$\Delta K = \tfrac{1}{2}m_2 v_2^2 - \tfrac{1}{2}m_1 v_1^2 = \tfrac{1}{2}m(v_2^2 - v_1^2), \tag{18.27}$$

and the change in gravitational potential energy is

$$\Delta U^G = m_2 g y_2 - m_1 g y_1 = mg(y_2 - y_1). \tag{18.28}$$

Substituting Eqs. 18.27 and 18.28 into the left side of the energy law yields

$$\Delta E = \Delta K + \Delta U^G = \tfrac{1}{2}m(v_2^2 - v_1^2) + mg(y_2 - y_1). \tag{18.29}$$

Our system is not closed because the fluid that is in contact with the left and right termini of the system exerts forces $\vec{F}_1$ and $\vec{F}_2$ on the system and the points of application of these forces undergo nonzero force displacements $\Delta \vec{x}_{F1}$ and $\Delta \vec{x}_{F2}$,* respectively. So let us now evaluate the work W done on the system. We take the time interval Δt to be small enough so that we can consider the forces to be constant. Because $\vec{F}_1$ and the force displacement of $\vec{F}_1$ are in the same direction, the work done on the system at point 1 is positive:

$$W_1 = F_{1x}\Delta x_{F1} = +P_1 A_1 v_1 \Delta t. \tag{18.30}$$

*The subscript F on the displacement means we are considering the displacement of the point of application of the force (see Section 9.1).

Figure 18.53 A volume of fluid flows through a tapered tube that changes altitude.

Between these points, mass of fluid does not change.

Mass of "missing" fluid here . . .

. . . equals mass of "added" fluid here.

At point 2, negative work is done on the system because the force and force displacement point in opposite directions:

$$W_2 = F_{2x}\Delta x_{F2} = -P_2 A_2 v_2 \Delta t, \tag{18.31}$$

and so the work done on the system is

$$W = P_1 A_1 v_1 \Delta t - P_2 A_2 v_2 \Delta t. \tag{18.32}$$

Using Eq. 18.24, we can write $A_1 v_1 \Delta t = A_2 v_2 \Delta t$. The quantity $A_1 v_1 \Delta t$ is the volume of the mass of fluid m that flows into (or out of) the section of tube we are considering. From the definition of mass density, we know that $V = m/\rho$, which means that

$$\frac{m}{\rho} = A_1 v_1 \Delta t. \tag{18.33}$$

Substituting this expression into Eq. 18.32, we get

$$W = \frac{m}{\rho}(P_1 - P_2). \tag{18.34}$$

Because the work done on the system must be equal to the change in the system's energy, we have, from Eqs. 18.29 and 18.34.

$$\tfrac{1}{2}m(v_2^2 - v_1^2) + mg(y_2 - y_1) = \frac{m}{\rho}(P_1 - P_2) \tag{18.35}$$

or, dividing both sides by m, rearranging terms, and multiplying through by ρ,

$$P_1 + \rho g y_1 + \tfrac{1}{2}\rho v_1^2 = P_2 + \rho g y_2 + \tfrac{1}{2}\rho v_2^2 \quad \text{(laminar flow of incompressible, nonviscous fluid).} \tag{18.36}$$

Together with the continuity equation (Eq. 18.23), Eq. 18.36, known as **Bernoulli's equation,** forms the foundation of the hydrodynamics of incompressible fluids. Strictly speaking, Bernoulli's equation applies only to liquids because we used Eq. 18.24, which is valid only for incompressible fluids. However, for the flow of a gas at modest velocities (and for height differences $y_2 - y_1$ that are not too great), the pressure variations have little effect on the mass density and Bernoulli's equation is still a reasonable approximation.

Because the points 1 and 2 are arbitrary, Eq. 18.36 tells us that the quantity $P + \rho g y + \tfrac{1}{2}\rho v^2$ is the same at different locations in a flow stream. If the fluid is stationary, $v = 0$ everywhere, and Eq. 18.36 takes on the same form as Eq. 18.6. If points 1 and 2 are at the same height, then $y_1 = y_2$, and Eq. 18.36 becomes

$$P_1 + \tfrac{1}{2}\rho v_1^2 = P_2 + \tfrac{1}{2}\rho v_2^2 \quad \text{(horizontal laminar flow of incompressible, nonviscous fluid).} \tag{18.37}$$

This equation confirms what we concluded in Section 18.3: The pressure P is greater where the flow speed v is smaller, and vice versa.

Example 18.9 Leaky bucket

Water leaks out of a small hole in the side of a bucket. The hole is a distance d below the surface of the water, and the cross section of the hole is much smaller than the diameter of the bucket. At what speed does the water emerge from the hole?

❶ **GETTING STARTED** I begin by making a sketch of the bucket (**Figure 18.54**), defining my point 1 at the water surface and my point 2 at the hole. The bucket can be regarded as a tube open at both ends, with the top opening, cross-sectional area A_1, as one end and the hole, cross-sectional area A_2, as the other end.

Figure 18.54

❷ **DEVISE PLAN** Because $A_1 \gg A_2$, the continuity equation (Eq. 18.23, $\rho_1 A_1 v_1 = \rho_2 A_2 v_2$) tells me that the speed v_1 at which the surface of the water moves downward is much smaller than the speed v_2 at which the water emerges from the hole, $v_1 \ll v_2$. For all practical purposes, therefore, I can assume $v_1 \approx 0$. I also know that the pressure both at the water surface and at the hole is equal to atmospheric pressure. I can then use Bernoulli's equation (Eq. 18.36) to determine v_2.

❸ **EXECUTE PLAN** Because $P_1 = P_2 = P_{atm}$, Bernoulli's equation reduces to $\rho g y_1 + \frac{1}{2}\rho v_1^2 = \rho g y_2 + \frac{1}{2}\rho v_2^2$. Dividing through by $\frac{1}{2}\rho$, setting $v_1 = 0$, and bringing the terms containing y to the left side, I get $v_2^2 = 2g(y_1 - y_2) = 2gd$, and so $v_2 = \sqrt{2gd}$. ✔

❹ **EVALUATE RESULT** My answer is equal to the speed acquired over a vertical distance d by a freely falling object starting from rest. Because the Earth-object system is closed, $\Delta K + \Delta U^G = \frac{1}{2}mv^2 - mgd = 0$, and so $v^2 = 2gd$. My result makes sense: For each water drop that emerges from the hole, the water at the surface is reduced by an equal amount and the kinetic energy of the emerging drop must be equal to the decrease in potential energy.

✋ **18.18** Suppose that the diameter of the hole in Example 18.9 is 10.0 mm, the bucket diameter is 0.50 m, and the distance from the hole to the water surface is 0.30 m. At what speed does the water emerge from the hole?

18.8 Viscosity and surface tension

So far in our discussion of fluid flow we have ignored energy dissipation. As pointed out in Section 18.3, viscosity is a measure of a fluid's resistance to shear stress. Dissipation of energy occurs in both liquids and gases, and so both have a nonzero viscosity. Consider, for example, two flat plates separated by a fluid (**Figure 18.55**). The lower plate is held fixed while the upper plate is translated in the plane of the plate. Because of friction between adjacent fluid layers, a force $\vec{F}_{p,ext}$ is required to move the upper plate at constant speed v. Experiments show that the magnitude of this force is proportional to the surface area A of the upper plate and to the speed v, and inversely proportional to the distance d between the plates. Because the force is directed in the direction opposite that of the velocity of the upper plate, we can write for a plate moving in the positive x direction:

$$F_{fpx} \equiv -\eta A \frac{v_x}{d}. \tag{18.38}$$

Figure 18.55 To measure viscosity, a fluid is placed between two parallel plates. The bottom plate is held fixed while the top plate is translated. The force required to keep the top plate moving at constant speed gives the viscosity of the fluid.

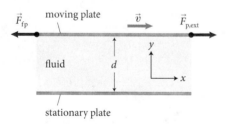

The proportionality constant η (Greek lowercase eta) is the **viscosity** of the fluid. The SI unit for viscosity is the pascal-second, with $1\ Pa \cdot s = 1\ kg/(m \cdot s)$. The greater the viscosity of a fluid, the greater the force needed to move the plate at constant speed. Because the work done by the plate on the fluid ends up as thermal energy in the fluid, a greater viscosity means more energy dissipation in the fluid as fluid layers rub past one another.

The ratio v_x/d in Eq. 18.38 can also be written as dv_x/dy because both v_x/d and dv_x/dy express the change in the x component of the velocity divided by the distance over which the change occurs. The derivative dv_x/dy, called the *velocity gradient,* is a measure of the rate at which one fluid layer moves relative to an adjacent layer. The advantage of expressing Eq. 18.38 in terms of the velocity gradient is that the resulting equation can be applied more generally:

$$F_{fpx} = -\eta A \frac{dv_x}{dy}. \tag{18.39}$$

Table 18.1 Viscosity of fluids

Fluid	Viscosity (Pa · s)	Temperature (°C)
Air	1.71×10^{-5}	0
	1.81×10^{-5}	20
	2.18×10^{-5}	100
Blood	3.0×10^{-3}	20
	2.0×10^{-3}	37
Castor oil	5.3	0
	0.986	20
	0.017	100
Water	1.79×10^{-3}	0
	1.00×10^{-3}	20
	0.282×10^{-3}	100

Because viscous forces are generally small, fluids are often used as lubricants to reduce friction between solids. **Table 18.1** lists some typical viscosities. The viscosity of gases is typically several orders of magnitude smaller than that of liquids. The viscosity of liquids typically decreases as temperature increases. Honey, for example, becomes more runny as it is heated. In contrast, gases typically get more viscous at higher temperatures.

Many instances of fluid flow, such as the velocity distribution of water through pipes or the flow of blood through arteries, involve laminar flow through cylindrical tubes. Let us therefore consider the flow of a fluid through a horizontal cylindrical pipe of length ℓ and radius R. Because the boundary layer of the fluid sticks to the interior wall of the pipe, this layer is at rest. The layer of fluid adjacent to the boundary layer moves slowly in the direction of the flow, and adjacent layers move at increasing speeds, with the fluid at the center of the pipe having the maximum speed (see Figure 18.19b).

Consider a cylinder of fluid of radius r flowing in the positive x direction through a tube of radius $R > r$. The dashed outline in **Figure 18.56** shows such a cylinder of fluid. Because of friction between the fluid in the cylinder and the more slowly moving layer of fluid adjacent to the cylinder boundary, a viscous force $\vec{F}_{fc}^{viscous}$ is exerted on the cylinder in the negative x direction. To keep the cylinder moving at constant velocity through the tube, a force of equal magnitude must be exerted on it in the positive x direction. This force requires a pressure difference ΔP between the ends of the cylinder, and so we see that for a fluid with nonzero viscosity, pressure must decrease as the fluid moves along the tube. For motion at constant speed, we have

$$\sum \vec{F}_c = \vec{F}_{fc}^{pressure} + \vec{F}_{fc}^{viscous} = 0. \tag{18.40}$$

If the pressure at the left end of the cylinder is P_1, the fluid to the left of this end exerts a force of magnitude $F_1^{pressure} = P_1(\pi r^2)$ in the positive x direction, where πr^2 is the cross-sectional area of the cylinder. If the pressure at the right end of the cylinder is P_2, the fluid to the right of this end exerts a force of magnitude $F_2^{pressure} = P_2(\pi r^2)$ in the negative x direction. The vector sum of these two forces is $(P_1 - P_2)(\pi r^2)$. The viscous force $F^{viscous}$ on

Figure 18.56 In mechanical equilibrium, the force due to the pressure on the two ends of the fluid in the cylinder defined by the dashed lines must balance the viscous force opposing the motion of the cylinder.

QUANTITATIVE TOOLS

the cylinder is given by Eq. 18.39, with A equal to the surface area $2\pi r\ell$ of the cylinder of fluid and $dv_x/dy = -dv_x/dr$.* Substituting this information into Eq. 18.40, we get

$$(P_1 - P_2)(\pi r^2) + \eta(2\pi r\ell)\frac{dv_x}{dr} = 0 \qquad (18.41)$$

or, rearranging terms,

$$-dv_x = \frac{(P_1 - P_2)(\pi r^2)}{\eta(2\pi r\ell)}dr = \frac{(P_1 - P_2)}{2\eta\ell}r\,dr. \qquad (18.42)$$

If we integrate the right side from r to R, the x component of velocity goes from v_x (the value at r) to 0 (the value at R, where the fluid is at rest because its boundary layer sticks to the tube wall):

$$-\int_{v_x}^{0} dv_x = \frac{P_1 - P_2}{2\eta\ell}\int_{r}^{R} r\,dr = \frac{P_1 - P_2}{2\eta\ell}\left[\tfrac{1}{2}r^2\right]_{r}^{R} \qquad (18.43)$$

or $\qquad v_x = \dfrac{P_1 - P_2}{4\eta\ell}(R^2 - r^2)$ (laminar flow in cylindrical tube).   (18.44)

This equation shows that the velocity varies with the square of r, and so its curve has a parabolic shape (see Figure 18.19b) with a maximum at the center of the tube, where $r = 0$.

Because the fluid velocity varies with r, the volume flow rate is no longer simply Av. To calculate the volume flow rate, we consider a thin cylindrical shell of thickness dr (**Figure 18.57**). The shell has a cross-sectional area $dA = 2\pi r\,dr$ and contributes to the overall volume flow rate an amount

$$dQ = v_x dA = v_x(2\pi r\,dr) = \frac{P_1 - P_2}{4\eta\ell}(R^2 - r^2)(2\pi r\,dr)$$

$$= \frac{\pi(P_1 - P_2)}{2\eta\ell}(R^2 r - r^3)dr, \qquad (18.45)$$

where we have substituted Eq. 18.44 for v_x. To obtain the volume flow rate Q through the tube, we must integrate this expression from $r = 0$ to $r = R$. Integrating the factor $(R^2 r - r^3)$ in Eq. 18.45 yields

$$\int_{0}^{R}(R^2 r - r^3)dr = \left[\tfrac{1}{2}R^2 r^2 - \tfrac{1}{4}r^4\right]_{0}^{R} = \tfrac{1}{2}R^4 - \tfrac{1}{4}R^4 = \tfrac{1}{4}R^4, \qquad (18.46)$$

and so the volume flow rate through a cylindrical tube is

$$Q = \frac{\pi R^4}{8\eta\ell}(P_1 - P_2) \quad \text{(laminar flow in cylindrical tube)}. \qquad (18.47)$$

Equation 18.47, called **Poiseuille's law,** shows that a high viscosity leads to a low-volume flow rate, which is reasonable. The strong dependence on the tube radius R means that a small adjustment in radius can lead to a large increase in volume flow rate. For example, increasing R by just 20% increases the volume flow rate by a factor of $(1.2)^4 = 2.1$.

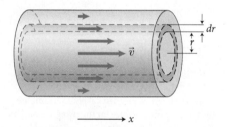

Figure 18.57 Each cylindrical shell (dashed lines) contributes an amount dQ to the volume flow rate through the tube.

---

*In Figure 18.19b v_x decreases with increasing r, and so dv_x/dr is negative. In Figure 18.55 v_x increases with increasing y, and so dv_x/dy is positive.

Example 18.10 Blood flow

Blood flows through an artery that has a radius of 3.0 mm. What is the maximum flow speed if the volume flow rate through the artery is 2.0×10^{-6} m³/s?

❶ **GETTING STARTED** I assume that the artery is cylindrical, which means I can use the results from this section.

❷ **DEVISE PLAN** I can obtain the maximum flow speed by setting $r = 0$ in Eq. 18.44. This equation contains the unknown factor $(P_1 - P_2)/(4\eta\ell)$. The expression for the volume flow rate, Eq. 18.47, however, contains the same factor, which gives me two equations with two unknowns—the maximum flow speed v and the factor $(P_1 - P_2)/(4\eta\ell)$—so I can solve for both unknowns.

❸ **EXECUTE PLAN** Setting $r = 0$ in Eq. 18.44 gives $v_{max} = (P_1 - P_2)R^2/(4\eta\ell)$. Next, I rewrite Eq. 18.47 in the form

$(P_1 - P_2)/(4\eta\ell) = 2Q/(\pi R^4)$, which I substitute into my expression for v_{max}:

$$v_{max} = \frac{(P_1 - P_2)R^2}{4\eta\ell} = \frac{2Q}{\pi R^4}R^2 = \frac{2Q}{\pi R^2}$$

$$= \frac{2(2.0 \times 10^{-6} \text{ m}^3/\text{s})}{\pi(3.0 \times 10^{-3} \text{ m})^2} = 0.14 \text{ m/s.} ✔$$

❹ **EVALUATE RESULT** I can rewrite the equality $v_{max} = (2Q)/(\pi R^2)$ from my final equation in the form $Q = \frac{1}{2}\pi R^2 v_{max} = \frac{1}{2}Av_{max}$, where A is the cross-sectional area of the artery. This equation is very similar to Eq. 18.26, the definition of volume flow rate. Indeed, $\frac{1}{2}v_{max}$ is the average flow speed. The value I obtain also appears to be reasonable—a given volume of blood travels about 1 m in 7 s.

Having dealt with forces in the bulk of a fluid, let us now turn to forces at liquid surfaces. As we saw in Section 18.4, these forces cause surface tension at the surface and are responsible for the shape of drops of liquid and capillary rise.

Figure 18.58 shows a device commonly used to measure surface tension, a length of metal bent into a U shape and attached to a loosely fitted wire to form a rectangular loop. The wire fits so loosely that it slides off when the loop is held with the U inverted. When the loop is dipped into a soap solution, however, the soap film that forms inside the loop holds the wire stationary, as Figure 18.58 shows. An upward force must be exerted on the wire to hold it in place by balancing the downward force of gravity. The only likely candidate for this upward force is the one exerted by the film, so that $F_{fw} = F_{Ew}^G$. Experiments show that F_{fw} remains constant as we move the wire up or down. Because the thickness of the film changes as the wire is moved, the observation that the force magnitude F_{fw} does not change means that the film thickness is unimportant. Therefore we must attribute the upward force exerted on the wire to the front and back surfaces of the film. Experimentally we also find that the magnitude of this force is proportional to the length ℓ of the wire. The constant of proportionality

$$\gamma \equiv \frac{F_{fw}}{2\ell} \tag{18.48}$$

is called the **surface tension** of the liquid that makes up the film. The factor 2 in the denominator accounts for the two surfaces of the film.

The SI unit for surface tension is newtons per meter. **Table 18.2** gives the surface tension for a number of liquids in contact with air.

We can also understand surface tension in terms of the energy associated with the surface of a liquid. Moving the wire in Figure 18.58 causes a force displacement Δx_F, and so work $W = F_{fwx}\Delta x_F$ is done by the film on the wire. Because $\vec{F}_{fw}$ points in the positive x direction, we have $F_{fwx} = +2\ell\gamma$, and so $W = 2\ell\gamma\Delta x_F = -2\gamma\Delta A$, where ΔA is the change in the surface area A of the film. (When the wire moves, Δx_F and ΔA have opposite algebraic signs, so $\ell\Delta x_F = -\Delta A$.) As we move the wire down, we increase the surface area A of the film, and so $\Delta A > 0$ and the work done by the film on the wire is negative. Consequently the work done by the wire on the film is positive (the energy of the film increases). Where does the energy associated with this work go? As we

Figure 18.58 The force exerted by a liquid film on a wire is due to surface tension in the film.

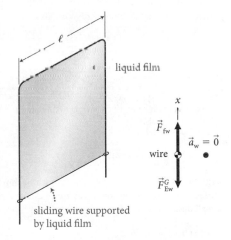

liquid film

x

$\vec{F}_{fw}$

$\vec{a}_w = \vec{0}$

wire

$\vec{F}_{Ew}^G$

sliding wire supported by liquid film

Table 18.2 Surface tensions of liquids in contact with air.

Liquid	Surface tension (N/m)	Temperature (°C)
alcohol	2.23×10^{-2}	20
copper	1.100	1130
glycerin	6.31×10^{-2}	20
gold	1.000	1070
mercury	0.465	20
neon*	5.15×10^{-3}	−247
olive oil	3.20×10^{-2}	20
oxygen*	1.57×10^{-2}	−193
silver	0.800	970
water	7.57×10^{-2}	0
	7.28×10^{-2}	20
	5.89×10^{-2}	100

*Values given for liquid in contact with vapor.

increase the surface area, more liquid particles must be brought to the surface. For each particle brought to the surface, we reduce the number of bonds between particles (see Figure 18.25), and so the energy associated with the work we do in moving the wire downward goes into breaking bonds between neighboring particles in order to bring them to the surface. So, another way of understanding surface tension is to see it as the energy required to increase the surface area of a liquid. The greater the surface tension of a liquid, the more energy required to increase the surface area of a sample of the liquid by a certain amount.

As we saw in Section 18.4, surface tension is responsible for the pressure difference across a curved liquid surface. To derive the relationship between surface tension and pressure difference, consider the spherical body of liquid in **Figure 18.59a**. The radius of the sphere is R, and the liquid has a surface tension γ. The pressure inside the liquid is P_{in}, and the pressure outside is P_{out}. Let's consider the forces exerted on one hemisphere, as illustrated in Figure 18.59b. Because the hemisphere remains at rest, the vector sum of the

Figure 18.59 Model for deriving the relationship between surface tension and pressure difference across a curved liquid surface. The surface tension forces are all directed perpendicular to the circular cross section, and the pressure-difference forces are all directed outward.

(a) Sphere of liquid

(b) Forces exerted on half of sphere due to surface tension and to pressure difference across surface

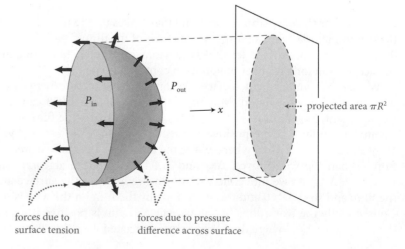

forces due to surface tension

forces due to pressure difference across surface

outward force due to the pressure difference across the surface and the inward force due the surface tension must be zero:

$$\sum F_{\text{hemi } x} = F_x^{\text{pressure}} + F_x^{\text{surf tension}} = 0. \qquad (18.49)$$

The force due to the pressure difference is perpendicular to the hemisphere surface. The components of the forces that are exerted on each segment of the surface but are not in the x direction cancel, and the x components of all these forces sum to the pressure difference $P_{\text{in}} - P_{\text{out}}$ times πR^2, which is the area of the circle projected on the screen in Figure 18.59b (see Guided Problem 18.4 in the *Practice* volume). The force due to the surface tension is exerted along the perimeter of the hemisphere, which has length $\ell = 2\pi R$. Therefore the magnitude of the force due to surface tension is $F_x^{\text{surf tension}} = 2\pi R\gamma$ (from Eq. 18.48, $\gamma = F/2\ell$; using this equation would give us $F = 2\ell\gamma = 2(2\pi R)\gamma = 4\pi R\gamma$, but we have to drop the factor 2 from Eq. 18.48 because here we are working with only one surface). Substituting these forces into Eq. 18.49 gives

$$(P_{\text{in}} - P_{\text{out}})\pi R^2 - 2\pi R\gamma = 0 \qquad (18.50)$$

or, rearranging terms,

$$P_{\text{in}} - P_{\text{out}} = \frac{2\gamma}{R} \quad \text{(spherical surface).} \qquad (18.51)$$

Equation 18.51 is a quantitative form of **Laplace's law** for a spherical surface. For a cylindrical surface, it can be shown that Eq. 18.51 takes the form

$$P_{\text{in}} - P_{\text{out}} = \frac{\gamma}{R} \quad \text{(cylindrical surface).} \qquad (18.52)$$

Example 18.11 Transmural pressure

The pressure difference across the wall of a blood vessel is called *transmural pressure*. Suppose an aorta of radius 11 mm has a transmural pressure of 12 kPa and a capillary of radius 4.0 μm has a transmural pressure of 5.0 kPa. Which blood vessel requires a greater tensile stress (tensile force per unit length) in its wall?

❶ **GETTING STARTED** I consider the aorta and the capillary to be elastic cylindrical tubes. Because the wall of a blood vessel keeps the blood confined within the tube, the tension in the wall plays the role of the surface tension γ of an unconfined liquid.

❷ **DEVISE PLAN** To determine γ for each vessel, I can use Eq. 18.52, which relates the pressure difference across the wall to the radius of the cylinder.

❸ **EXECUTE PLAN** I first rewrite Eq. 18.52 in the form $\gamma = (P_{\text{in}} - P_{\text{out}})R$. For the aorta,

$$\gamma = (12 \text{ kPa})\left(\frac{1000 \text{ Pa}}{1 \text{ kPa}}\right)(11 \text{ mm})\left(\frac{1 \text{ m}}{1000 \text{ mm}}\right)$$

$$= 1.3 \times 10^2 \text{ N/m}.$$

(You should be able to confirm that the units in this expression are indeed newtons per meter.) For the capillary,

$$\gamma = (5.0 \text{ kPa})\left(\frac{1000 \text{ Pa}}{1 \text{ kPa}}\right)(4.0 \text{ }\mu\text{m})\left(\frac{1 \text{ m}}{10^6 \text{ }\mu\text{m}}\right)$$

$$= 0.020 \text{ N/m}.$$

The tensile force per unit length in the aorta is much greater than that in the capillary. ✔

❹ **EVALUATE RESULT** The pressure differences across the aorta and capillary are of the same order of magnitude, and so less tension is required when the radius is small. This is the same situation as in Figure 18.27: The pressure difference is the same everywhere on the balloon surface, but the tension is less where the radius of curvature is smaller.

✋ **18.19** What is Laplace's law, Eq. 18.51, for a soap bubble?

Chapter Glossary

SI units of physical quantities are given in parentheses.

Archimedes' principle An object submerged either fully or partially in a fluid experiences an upward buoyant force that is equal in magnitude to the force of gravity exerted on the fluid displaced by the object. The volume of the displaced fluid is equal to the volume of the submerged portion of the object.

Bernoulli's equation The equation that relates pressure, laminar flow speed, and elevation in an incompressible fluid:

$$P_1 + \rho g y_1 + \tfrac{1}{2}\rho v_1^2 = P_2 + \rho g y_2 + \tfrac{1}{2}\rho v_2^2 \quad (18.36)$$

(laminar flow of incompressible, nonviscous fluid).

Buoyant force The upward force exerted by fluids on objects that are fully or partially submerged in a fluid. For an object that displaces a volume V_{disp} of a fluid of uniform mass density ρ_f, the magnitude of the buoyant force is

$$F_{fo}^b = \rho_f V_{disp} g. \quad (18.12)$$

Continuity equation The equation that relates the laminar flow speed of a fluid to the cross-sectional area of the tube through which it flows:

$$\rho_1 A_1 v_1 = \rho_2 A_2 v_2 \quad (18.23)$$

(laminar flow of nonviscous fluid).

Fluid Any substance that has the ability to flow; any liquid or gas.

Laminar flow The flow of a fluid for which the velocity of the fluid at any location is constant.

Laplace's law The relationship among surface curvature, surface tension, and the pressure difference across a surface. For a spherical surface,

$$P_{in} - P_{out} = \frac{2\gamma}{R} \quad \text{(spherical surface)}, \quad (18.51)$$

and for a cylindrical surface,

$$P_{in} - P_{out} = \frac{\gamma}{R} \quad \text{(cylindrical surface)}. \quad (18.52)$$

Meniscus The curved surface at the top of a liquid in a narrow tube.

Pascal (Pa) The derived SI unit of pressure, defined as $1 \text{ Pa} = 1 \text{ N/m}^2 = 1 \text{ kg}/(\text{m} \cdot \text{s}^2)$.

Pascal's principle A pressure change applied to an enclosed liquid is transmitted undiminished to every part of the liquid and to the walls of the container in contact with the liquid.

Poiseuille's law The relationship between the pressure difference across a cylindrical tube and the volume flow rate Q through the tube:

$$Q = \frac{\pi R^4}{8\eta \ell}(P_1 - P_2) \quad (18.47)$$

(laminar flow in cylindrical tube).

Pressure P (Pa) A scalar that gives the ratio of the magnitude of the force exerted by a fluid perpendicular to an area and the surface area:

$$P \equiv \frac{F_{fs}^c}{A}. \quad (18.1)$$

Streamline A path taken by particles in a fluid in motion.

Surface tension γ (N/m) A scalar that gives the magnitude of the force per unit length exerted by a liquid surface.

Turbulent flow Chaotically changing flow characterized by whirling, circularly moving regions of fluid.

Viscosity η (Pa·s) A scalar measure of the resistance of a fluid to shear deformation. For a layer of fluid between two flat plates, the viscosity is defined by the equation that relates the force required to keep the top plate moving at constant speed and the surface area A of the plate, the difference in the x components of the velocities between the two plates, $v_{top,x} - v_{bottom,x}$, and the distance $y_{top} - y_{bottom}$ between the plates:

$$F_{fpx} \equiv -\eta A \frac{v_{top,x} - v_{bottom,x}}{y_{top} - y_{bottom}}. \quad (18.38)$$

Volume flow rate Q (m³/s) A scalar that gives the rate at which a volume of fluid crosses a section of a tube:

$$Q \equiv \frac{V}{\Delta t}. \quad (18.25)$$

19

Entropy

19.1 States

19.2 Equipartition of energy

19.3 Equipartition of space

19.4 Evolution toward the most probable macrostate

19.5 Dependence of entropy on volume

19.6 Dependence of entropy on energy

19.7 Properties of a monatomic ideal gas

19.8 Entropy of a monatomic ideal gas

CONCEPTS

QUANTITATIVE TOOLS

The conservation laws allow us to analyze a broad range of phenomena, yet they cannot explain the *irreversibility* of time. Cars are damaged in a collision, a cube of ice melts when placed in a drink, and a drop of ink diffuses throughout a glass of water. These phenomena are *irreversible,* meaning they happen in one direction only. Always, no exceptions.

Yet there's nothing in the conservation laws that prohibits cars damaged in a collision to spontaneously move apart "undamaged," that prohibits an ice cube from forming in a glass of water, or that prohibits a collection of diffused ink molecules from coming together into a single drop. So why do phenomena such as these never happen? What is it that causes the irreversible flow of time toward the future?

As we shall see in this chapter, the underlying reason has to do with the randomness of the interactions at the atomic level. To help us quantify the tendency of systems to evolve in one direction only over time, I introduce a quantity, *entropy,* whose change is strongly connected to our sense of irreversibility.

19.1 States

Have you ever seen a motionless pendulum suddenly start swinging of its own accord? No; when no forces are applied, pendulums slow down and eventually come to rest. To understand why a swinging pendulum always slows down and never speeds up, let us consider a pendulum swinging back and forth inside a container. As the pendulum swings, kinetic energy gets converted to gravitational potential energy, which then gets converted to kinetic energy, which then . . . . If no energy is dissipated, the sum of these two energies remains constant and the pendulum keeps swinging forever.

Over time, however, the swings get smaller because with each swing a small part of the coherent mechanical energy of the pendulum is converted to incoherent thermal energy (see Section 7.3). This conversion is due to friction in the pendulum suspension and to collisions with the air molecules surrounding the pendulum. When the pendulum has come to rest, all of its mechanical energy has been dissipated. This energy is not gone—it still exists but now in the form of incoherent thermal energy associated with the motion of the molecules in the air surrounding the pendulum. So the universal tendency for the mechanical energy to dissipate appears to be related to the incoherent nature of the motion of atoms and molecules at the atomic scale.

Not one of the conservation laws we have studied forbids the conversion of that thermal energy back to mechanical energy. The pendulum could start swinging again if the air molecules would supply the kinetic energy. To understand why this transfer of energy from air molecules to pendulum is never observed, we need to look at molecular motion on the atomic scale. Let's begin by getting some feel for how much energy the pendulum and the air molecules have.

Exercise 19.1 Pendulum energy

Consider a 0.10-kg pendulum swinging at a maximum speed of 0.80 m/s inside a box that contains 1.0×10^{23} nitrogen molecules. The mass of a nitrogen molecule is 4.7×10^{-26} kg, and at room temperature a typical nitrogen molecule moves at 500 m/s. What are (*a*) the mechanical energy of the pendulum, (*b*) the average kinetic energy of one nitrogen molecule, and (*c*) the sum of the average kinetic energies of all the nitrogen molecules?

SOLUTION (*a*) The mechanical energy of the pendulum is equal to its maximum kinetic energy: $\frac{1}{2}mv^2 = \frac{1}{2}(0.10 \text{ kg})(0.80 \text{ m/s})^2 = 3.2 \times 10^{-2}$ J. ✔

(*b*) The average kinetic energy of a nitrogen molecule is $\frac{1}{2}(4.7 \times 10^{-26} \text{ kg})(500 \text{ m/s})^2 = 5.9 \times 10^{-21}$ J. Comparing this value with the result I obtained in part *a*, I see that the mechanical energy of the pendulum is more than 18 orders of magnitude (a billion billion times) greater than the average kinetic energy of the individual nitrogen molecules. ✔

(*c*) The sum of the average kinetic energies of all the nitrogen molecules is $(1.0 \times 10^{23})(5.9 \times 10^{-21} \text{ J}) = 5.9 \times 10^2$ J. Note that this thermal energy (the kinetic energy associated with the incoherent motion of all the nitrogen molecules) is more than four orders of magnitude greater than the mechanical energy of the pendulum. ✔

19.1 The nitrogen molecules in Exercise 19.1 move considerably faster than the pendulum and continuously bombard the pendulum from all sides. (*a*) Why does this bombardment slow the pendulum down? (*b*) When the pendulum is at rest, why don't we see the effects of this continuous bombardment?

The inertia of a pendulum at rest is so much greater than that of the surrounding air molecules that the effect of collisions between air molecules and the pendulum is hardly noticeable. To see the effect of such collisions, we would have to greatly reduce the inertia of the pendulum. In 1827 the Scottish botanist Robert Brown was the first to observe the effect of this random molecular bombardment. Using a microscope to observe grains of pollen suspended in water, Brown noticed that the grains bounced around, following a zigzag path like the one shown in **Figure 19.1**.

This random motion, called *Brownian motion,* is due to the random bombardment of the grains by the surrounding

Figure 19.1 A grain of pollen suspended in water undergoes a random zigzag motion due to collisions with surrounding water molecules.

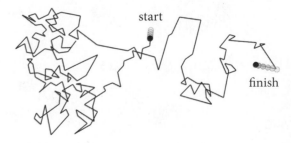

water molecules. Because the grains are small, the bombardment is not always equal on all sides, causing the grains to zigzag. The small random movements are what makes up Brownian motion.

✋ **19.2** How would Brownian motion change if the mass of the grain in Figure 19.1 were increased?

An important conclusion we can draw from the observation of Brownian motion in pollen grains suspended in water is that the bombardment is incoherent. As a result of this lack of coherence, the displacement of each grain over a long time interval is nearly zero and the grain never gains or loses any kinetic energy. If the grain were constantly kicked in the same direction, it would keep accelerating in that direction and gain kinetic energy. The same is true for a pendulum suspended in the air and hanging at rest: If it were constantly hit from one direction, it *would* start swinging.

Because it is impossible to treat the details of the incoherent atomic motion quantitatively, we need to use a very different approach to connect the atomic world of atoms and molecules to the *macroscopic* world we have described so far (*macroscopic* means "large relative to the size of a molecule"). In particular, we need to use probability theory to determine the likelihood of certain events taking place. As we shall see, the odds strongly favor slowing down a pendulum over speeding it up. To begin, let's review the essentials of probability theory using the throwing of two dice as an example.

Exercise 19.2 Throwing dice

When you throw two dice, one red and one blue, many times, what is the fraction of throws for which the dots on the two dice add to 4?

SOLUTION There are 36 combinations for the pair of dice (**Figure 19.2**), three of which add to 4. On every throw, each of the 36 combinations is equally likely to occur. If you throw the dice many times, the fraction of throws that add to 4 approaches the ratio $3/36 = 1/12$. ✔

✋ **19.3** What sum of dots are you most likely to throw with two dice?

The **probability** that a certain event will occur is the fraction of times that event occurs in a large number of repetitions. Exercise 19.2 tells you that the probability of throwing a 4 is $1/12$. If you throw two dice 12 times, you won't necessarily throw a 4 exactly once. The more times you throw the dice, however, the closer the fraction of times you throw a 4 will be to $1/12$.

If we consider the two dice as a system, there are several ways we can describe the state of this system. We can characterize it by the sum of the dots shown on the two

Figure 19.2 The 36 possible combinations for two dice.

sum of dots on both dice

dice after any given throw, or we can give a more detailed description by specifying the number of dots showing on each die. For systems with very large numbers of particles, we often care only about large-scale properties, not the detailed specifications of each particle. When we describe a system in terms of its large-scale properties, we are describing the system's **macrostate.** When we give a detailed specification of all the particles that make up the system, we are describing the system's **basic state.**[*] For a volume of gas, for example, the macrostate is described by large-scale properties that can be readily measured, such as temperature, pressure, and volume. The basic state is described by specifying the position and velocity of each individual gas particle.

Before describing a gas, let us return to the simpler system of two dice. The macrostate of the system after any throw is given by the sum thrown; the basic state is given by the number of dots shown on each die. As you can see in Figure 19.2, there are 36 basic states for the system and 11 macrostates. Because any basic state is equally likely to occur, the probability of any one basic state occurring is $1/36$. To calculate the probability of, say, the macrostate 9, we divide the number of basic states associated with this macrostate by the number of basic states associated with all the macrostates. Four out of the 36 basic states correspond to the macrostate 9. Therefore the probability of throwing a 9 is $(1/36)(4) = 4/36$. Because there are more basic states for the macrostate 7 than there are for the macrostate 9, you are more likely to throw, on average, a 7 than a 9.

---

[*]Often the term *microstate* is used instead of *basic state*. Because *microstate* and *macrostate* sound alike and are often hard to tell apart in spoken language, we'll use the term *basic state*.

Figure 19.3 As a pendulum in a box swings, it collides with three particles. The pendulum slows down as its energy is redistributed into the particles.

19.4 Suppose you are tossing four coins and decide to define the system's macrostate after any throw as the number of heads thrown. How many (*a*) macrostates and (*b*) basic states are there for this system? (*c*) What is the probability of tossing three heads? (*d*) What is the most likely macrostate after any toss?

Let us now see how all this applies to a swinging pendulum. Consider one swinging inside a box containing three gas particles (**Figure 19.3**). The particles are *distinguishable*—that is, we can tell them apart—and they collide randomly, but elastically, with one another, with the walls of the box, and with the pendulum. According to *quantum mechanics,* the energy of confined systems can only change by very small, indivisible, discrete units called *quanta* (singular: *quantum*), and many experiments confirm this discrete nature of energy units. The collisions in the box thus transfer energy units between the colliding objects.

To get a feel for how energy units are redistributed as the particles collide with the pendulum, we ignore any dissipation of energy in the pendulum's suspension and we assume that there are six identical (and therefore *indistinguishable*) energy units to be distributed among the pendulum and the three particles. (We'll drop the restriction that the energy units are indistinguishable later.) We further assume that the collisions distribute the energy units randomly throughout the system: that is, the redistribution jumbles up both the speeds of the particles and the directions in which they move. This assumption is justified not only by the observation of Brownian motion but also by the fact that the assumption leads to a behavior that accurately describes our observations.

Let us investigate how the six energy units can be distributed among the pendulum and the three gas particles. If we describe the system's macrostate by the number of energy units in the pendulum, there are seven macrostates. **Figure 19.4** shows how, for each of these seven macrostates, the energy units can be distributed over the pendulum and the three particles. Note that as the amount of energy in the particles increases, the number of basic states associated with that macrostate increases.

19.5 What are the six ways in which you can distribute three energy units over three particles such that one of the particles has two energy units?

Because collisions completely randomize the energy distribution, each basic state is equally likely to occur, and we can use statistics to determine the probability of any given macrostate. The probability of any one basic state is 1/84 (because there are 84 equally likely basic states). The probability of any macrostate is the number of basic states

Figure 19.4 The ways in which six energy units can be distributed among the pendulum and three particles of Figure 19.3. Distribution of six energy units among pendulum and three particles; each solid-colored box corresponds to one of the six units of energy. The number of basic states associated with all macrostates is 84. As the number of energy units in the pendulum decreases (left), the fraction of basic states associated with that macrostate increases (right).

Number of energy units in pendulum	Number of energy units in particles		Number of basic states	Fraction of basic states
6	0		1	$\frac{1}{84}$
5	1	three basic states having one energy unit in one particle	3	$\frac{3}{84}$
4	2		6	$\frac{6}{84}$
3	3		10	$\frac{10}{84}$
2	4		15	$\frac{15}{84}$
1	5		21	$\frac{21}{84}$
0	6		28	$\frac{28}{84}$

CONCEPTS

Figure 19.5 As the fraction of energy in the pendulum increases, the probability of that corresponding macrostate decreases.

Figure 19.7 As the number of particles increases from 3 to 100, the probability of finding a certain fraction of the system's 50 energy units in the pendulum relative to that of finding zero energy in it decreases significantly.

associated with that macrostate divided by the number of basic states associated with all macrostates, which is the number given in the last column of Figure 19.4. **Figure 19.5** shows how this probability depends on the fraction of energy in the pendulum.

19.6 What is the probability of finding (*a*) all of the energy in the pendulum and (*b*) either zero or one unit of energy in the pendulum?

We "digitized" the energy by arbitrarily dividing it into six units. However, collisions could redistribute smaller units of energy, and so the mechanical energy of the pendulum could change by smaller amounts. **Figure 19.6** shows how the probability of finding a certain fraction of energy in the pendulum relative to that of finding zero energy in it changes as we divide the energy into smaller units. Note by comparing Figures 19.5 and 19.6 that the division into finer units has little effect on the relative probabilities. In other words, the picture we obtain by dividing the energy into very coarse energy units is a remarkably good approximation of the much more realistic fine division predicted by quantum mechanics.

What happens if we increase the number of particles? **Figure 19.7** shows that as the number of particles increases, the spike in the relative probability near the origin sharpens

Figure 19.6 As the energy is divided into more units, the probability of finding a certain fraction of the system's energy in the pendulum relative to that of finding zero energy in it approaches the solid red line.

and the relative probability of all 50 energy units in the pendulum drops precipitously: With 3 particles, it is on the order of 10^{-4}; with 50 particles, it is on the order of 10^{-29}; with 100 particles, it drops to 10^{-40}.

Even with a very large number of particles, however, the relative probability of the pendulum containing all the energy is nonzero. So, if we release a pendulum in a box that contains many particles and the mechanical energy of the pendulum is gradually transferred to the particles, there is a very small but nonzero probability of the pendulum gaining all its energy back again.

We can get a feeling for how long it would take for this to happen by multiplying the average time interval between collisions by the number of basic states for the system. This gives us the length of time it would take on average to cycle randomly through all the basic states. This time interval is called the *recurrence time* of the system.

In a box of volume 1 m³ containing 3 air molecules at room temperature, the average time interval between collisions is approximately 10^{15} s. So the recurrence time is approximately $(84)(10^{15} \text{ s}) = 10^{17}$ s. If there are 10^{20} particles, the average time interval between collisions is approximately 10^{-19} s. For a large number of particles, the number of basic states is equal to the number of particles raised to the number of energy units: $(10^{20})^6 = 10^{120}$ (Section 19.6). Thus the recurrence time is approximately $(10^{120})(10^{-19} \text{ s}) = 10^{101}$ s. The age of the universe is only about 10^{18} s, so don't hold your breath waiting for the pendulum to recover all its energy!

19.7 (*a*) Averaged over a long time interval, for what fraction of the time interval does the pendulum in Figure 19.3 have more than 50% of the energy of the system? (*b*) Does this fraction increase, decrease, or stay the same as we increase the number of particles?

19.2 Equipartition of energy

In our description of a pendulum swinging among gas particles, we saw that as the number of particles increases, the probability of nonzero energy in the pendulum goes to zero (Figure 19.7). Suppose now that we have a gas of four particles instead of a pendulum and three particles. The bars for the energy units in the pendulum in Figure 19.4 then represent the energy of the fourth particle, and we see that the probability is highest for that particle to have little or no energy. We can use the same argument for each of the four particles: Each particle tends to have the smallest amount of energy possible. Because the thermal energy E_{th} associated with the incoherent motion of the particles is fixed, the system tends to distribute this energy equally over all the particles, with each particle having, on average, an amount of energy E_{th}/N, where N is the number of particles. If at any instant one of the particles has a greater fraction of the thermal energy E_{th}, this energy is rapidly redistributed over the rest of the system.

Each particle is like the pendulum. Therefore if we exchange the role of the pendulum with the role of one of the particles in Figure 19.4, we obtain the macrostates and basic states shown in **Figure 19.8**. Again, the odds are highest for that particle to have little or no energy, and as we saw in Figure 19.7, these odds become even more pronounced for large numbers of particles. Each particle tends to minimize its energy.

The situation is the same for the pendulum and the three particles. On average, each part of this system has an equal share $E/4$ of the system's energy E. If we replace either the pendulum or one of the particles with an oscillating spring, with a heavier particle, or with some other object, we can go through the same arguments and in each case we see that:

Figure 19.8 If we interchange the pendulum with one of the particles in Figure 19.4, we obtain an identical configuration of macrostates and basic states.

Number of energy units in particle 1	Number of energy units in pendulum and particles 2 and 3	Fraction of basic states
6	0	$\frac{1}{84}$
5	1	$\frac{3}{84}$
4	2	$\frac{6}{84}$
3	3	$\frac{10}{84}$
2	4	$\frac{15}{84}$
1	5	$\frac{21}{84}$
0	6	$\frac{28}{84}$

As long as the interactions between different parts of a system randomize the distribution of energy, each part of the system tends to have an equal share of the system's energy.

This equal distribution of energy among the parts of a system is called **equipartition of energy.** In Section 20.3 we shall define more precisely what "part of the system" means. For now, consider each indivisible element of the system—a particle, a pendulum, an oscillating spring, whatever—as a "container" for energy.

Example 19.3 Pendulum dissipation

Consider again the 0.10-kg pendulum of Exercise 19.1. The pendulum starts out swinging at a maximum speed of 0.80 m/s and stops swinging in 5.0 min. It is in a box that contains 1.0×10^{23} nitrogen molecules, each having a mass of 4.652×10^{-26} kg and moving at 500 m/s. The pendulum collides, on average, 1.0×10^{22} times per second with the nitrogen molecules. (a) In one collision what amount of mechanical energy is transferred on average to a nitrogen molecule, and what is the ratio of this transferred energy to the average kinetic energy of the nitrogen molecule? (b) By what fraction has the average kinetic energy of a nitrogen molecule increased when the pendulum stops swinging? (c) If the final mechanical energy of the pendulum is equal to the average kinetic energy of a nitrogen molecule, what is the pendulum's average final speed?

❶ **GETTING STARTED** The collisions gradually transfer all the pendulum's initial kinetic energy to the nitrogen molecules. For simplicity, I assume that each collision transfers the same amount of energy.

❷ **DEVISE PLAN** The number of collisions that occur during the 5.0 min it takes the pendulum to stop swinging is $(3.0 \times 10^2 \text{ s})(1.0 \times 10^{22} \text{ collisions/s}) = 3.0 \times 10^{24}$ collisions. Dividing the initial kinetic energy of the pendulum $(3.2 \times 10^{-2}$ J; Exercise 19.1a) by this number gives me the average energy transferred in each collision. I can then compare this energy with the average kinetic energy of a nitrogen molecule calculated in Exercise 19.1b $(5.9 \times 10^{-21}$ J).

When the pendulum stops, all its mechanical energy has been transferred to the molecules. In Exercise 19.1, I determined the initial mechanical energy of the pendulum $(3.2 \times 10^{-2}$ J) and the sum of the average kinetic energies of all the nitrogen molecules $(5.9 \times 10^2$ J). The ratio of these quantities gives me the fractional increase in the kinetic energy of each molecule.

The final average kinetic energy of the pendulum is half of its final mechanical energy: $\frac{1}{2} m_{pend}(v^2_{pend,f})_{av} = \frac{1}{2} E_{pend,f}$. To calculate the pendulum's average final speed, I set $E_{pend,f}$ equal to the final average kinetic energy of a nitrogen molecule from Exercise 19.1b.

❸ **EXECUTE PLAN** (a) The average amount of mechanical energy transferred from pendulum to molecule in each collision is $(3.2 \times 10^{-2}$ J$)/(3.0 \times 10^{24}$ collisions$) = 1.1 \times 10^{-26}$ J/collision. From Exercise 19.1b, the average kinetic energy of each molecule is 5.9×10^{-21} J. So the ratio of the energy transferred per collision to the average molecular kinetic energy is $(1.1 \times 10^{-26}$ J$)/(5.9 \times 10^{-21}$ J$) = 1.9 \times 10^{-6}$. ✔

(b) The fractional increase in the average kinetic energy of each nitrogen molecule is the initial kinetic energy of the pendulum (which all ends up in the molecules) divided by the combined kinetic energy of the molecules from Exercise 19.1: $(3.2 \times 10^{-2} \text{ J})/(5.9 \times 10^2 \text{ J}) = 5.4 \times 10^{-5}$. ✔

(*c*) Because the final mechanical energy of the pendulum is equal to the average kinetic energy of a nitrogen molecule, I have $\frac{1}{2} m_{\text{pend}}(v^2_{\text{pend,f}})_{\text{av}} = \frac{1}{2}(5.9 \times 10^{-21} \text{ J})$, or (0.10 kg) $(v^2_{\text{pend,f}})_{\text{av}} = 5.9 \times 10^{21} \text{ J}$. Therefore the final average speed of the pendulum is $(v_{\text{pend,f}})_{\text{av}} = [(5.9 \times 10^{-21} \text{ J})/(0.10 \text{ kg})]^{1/2} = 2.4 \times 10^{-10} \text{ m/s}$. ✔

❹ **EVALUATE RESULT** Part *a* tells me that each collision transfers only a very small fraction of the pendulum's energy. This makes sense because it takes many collisions for the pendulum to come to rest. The small value I obtained in part *b* for the fractional increase in the molecules' energy makes sense because I know from experience that the air temperature (a quantity related to the kinetic energy of the molecules in the air) in the region around a swinging pendulum does not increase appreciably as the pendulum moves. Finally, my answer to part *c* shows that, for all practical purposes, the final average speed of the pendulum indeed is zero, as I had assumed in part *a*.

As Example 19.3 illustrates, the pendulum begins with much more mechanical energy than each individual gas molecule. Each collision between the pendulum and a nitrogen molecule can increase or decrease the energy of the pendulum. On average, however, these energy exchanges gradually decrease the energy of the pendulum until all nitrogen molecules and the pendulum have roughly the same energy. The pendulum's excess energy has been dissipated over all the molecules, raising their average energy by a minuscule amount.

🤚 **19.8** Suppose a container holds a gas made up of two kinds of particles 1 and 2, with $m_2 = 2m_1$. Assume the particles interact via elastic collisions. (*a*) How do the average kinetic energies of the two kinds of particles compare? (*b*) How do their average speeds compare?

19.3 Equipartition of space

Collisions not only randomize the energy distribution in a gas, they also randomize spatial distributions. Consider, for example, a container divided into two compartments by a removable partition (**Figure 19.9**). In the left compartment is a gas, and the right compartment is empty. If we remove the partition, the gas diffuses to fill the entire volume. Likewise, if we put one type of gas on one side and another type of gas on the other side and then remove the partition, the two gases diffuse and mix. After some length of time has passed, both types of particles are evenly distributed throughout the container.

Both the diffusion of a single gas and the mixing of two different gases are irreversible processes. In Figure 19.9, for example, once the particles have expanded into the right side of the container, they do not spontaneously contract again into the left side.

Figure 19.9 (*a*) A container has gas in one half and vacuum in the other, divided by a partition. (*b*) When the partition is removed, the gas expands irreversibly into the vacuum. After the expansion is complete, there is an equal likelihood of finding a gas particle anywhere in the container.

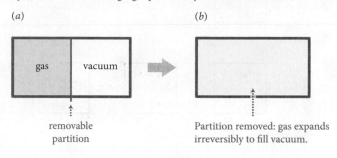

(*a*)   (*b*)

removable partition

Partition removed: gas expands irreversibly to fill vacuum.

Like dissipation of energy, this irreversible diffusion is due to the incoherent motion of particles at the atomic level. Collisions between the particles jumble up both the speeds of the particles and the directions in which they move. Consequently the likelihood at any instant of finding a particle at any given position in the container is the same as at any other position or instant—there is no "preferred" position for the particles.

🤚 **19.9** Suppose there are initially two indistinguishable particles in the left compartment of the container in Figure 19.9*a*. After the partition is removed, what is the probability at any given instant of finding one particle in each half of the container?

Checkpoint 19.9 suggests that we can use the statistical approach of Section 19.2 to determine the most likely locations of particles in a container. Consider, for example, a box that contains six indistinguishable particles. In order to count basic states, we need to "digitize" space just as we digitized energy in Section 19.2. So let's divide the container into four equal compartments as shown in **Figure 19.10** (there are no real partitions).

The basic state of this system is determined by specifying how many particles are in each of the four compartments. There are many ways to characterize the system. Let's arbitrarily define the macrostate of the system to be the number

Figure 19.10   an instant when all particles are in top left compartment

Figure 19.11

(a)

(b)

Figure 19.12 Distribution of six particles in four equal compartments of a box.

Number of particles in top left quadrant	Number of particles in other three quadrants		Fraction of basic states
6	0	A one basic state that has all six particles in top left quadrant	$\frac{1}{84}$
5	1 (3)		$\frac{3}{84}$
4	2 (3) (3)		$\frac{6}{84}$
3	3 (3) (6) (1)		$\frac{10}{84}$
2	4 (3) (6) (3) (3)		$\frac{15}{84}$
1	5 (3) (6) B(6) (3) (3)		$\frac{21}{84}$
0	6 (3) (6) (6) (3) (3) (6) (1)		$\frac{28}{84}$

└─── six basic states that have one particle in top left quadrant ───┘
and zero, two, and three particles in remaining quadrants

of particles in the upper left compartment. (An alternative macrostate would be the number of particles in the lower right compartment, say, or the number in the lower half.) In Figure 19.10, all six particles are in the upper left compartment. The basic state is thus specified by the set of numbers (6, 0, 0, 0), representing the number of particles in each compartment, and the macrostate by the number 6 (for the number of particles in the upper left compartment). To determine the probability of having this distribution rather than any other, we need to determine the number of basic states and then the probability of each macrostate.

Exercise 19.4 Spatial macrostates and basic states

In Figure 19.10, how many basic states correspond to the macrostate in which (*a*) all six particles are in the top left compartment and (*b*) five particles are in the upper left compartment?

SOLUTION (*a*) One basic state because there is only one way to put all six particles in the upper left compartment (**Figure 19.11a**). ✔

(*b*) When five particles are in the upper left compartment, the last particle can be placed in any of the three other compartments. These three basic states are shown in Figure 19.11*b*. ✔

As you may have noticed, the problem of determining the distribution of six particles in four equal compartments of a container is identical to the energy distribution problem of Section 19.2, where we distributed six indistinguishable units of energy among four distinguishable "energy containers." Here we are distributing six indistinguishable "units of matter" among four distinguishable "spatial containers." The correspondence between the two problems is summarized in **Table 19.1**.

Using the mapping from Table 19.1, we can adapt Figure 19.4 to our current discussion, as shown in **Figure 19.12**. The bar in the leftmost column, which represented the energy in the pendulum in Figure 19.4, now represents the number of particles in the top left compartment of the box. All the bars arranged in groups of three represent the number of particles in each of the other three compartments. The distribution labeled A thus represents the only basic state that corresponds to having all six particles in the top left compartment: The other three compartments are empty. The distribution labeled B represents six of the 21 basic states associated with the macrostate in which one particle is in the top left compartment. These basic states have three

Table 19.1 Two problems, one idea

	Section 19.2	Section 19.3
phenomenon	distribution of energy	distribution of particles
indistinguishable items to be distributed	units of energy	particles
over distinguishable	pendulum and particles	compartments of container
macrostate defined by	energy units in pendulum	particles in top left compartment
basic state defined by	energy units in pendulum and each particle	particles in each compartment

particles in any one of the other three compartments, two particles in another, and zero particles in the last remaining compartment.

19.10 (*a*) What is the probability of finding all six particles in one compartment? (*b*) Of finding five particles in one compartment?

Example 19.5 Particles in box

Use the data in Figure 19.12 to determine the average number of particles in the top left compartment of the four-compartment box shown there.

❶ **GETTING STARTED** The rightmost column in Figure 19.12 gives the fraction of basic states associated with each of the seven macrostates. This fraction represents the probability of finding the indicated number of particles in the top left compartment. For example, the probability of finding three particles there is $\frac{10}{84}$. In other words, if I observe the system for a long time interval, I'll see three particles in the top left compartment $\frac{10}{84}$ th of the time.

❷ **DEVISE PLAN** To calculate the average number of particles in the top left compartment, I should take the sum over all macrostates of the product of the number of particles in that compartment (leftmost column in Figure 19.12) and the probability of finding that macrostate (rightmost column).

❸ **EXECUTE PLAN** Summing the products of the values in the leftmost and rightmost columns gives $6(\frac{1}{84}) + 5(\frac{3}{84}) + 4(\frac{6}{84}) + 3(\frac{10}{84}) + 2(\frac{15}{84}) + 1(\frac{21}{84}) + 0(\frac{28}{84}) = 1.5$. So, averaged over time, there are 1.5 particles in the top left compartment. ✔

❹ **EVALUATE RESULT** My answer makes sense because there are six particles in the box to be divided over four compartments: $6/4 = 1.5$.

Example 19.5 shows that even though the most probable macrostate has no particles in the upper left compartment, the average number of particles in that compartment is nonzero. Let us generalize our result by dividing the box into a large number *M* of equal compartments and increasing the number of particles *N*. On average each compartment tends to have its "share" *N/M* of the particles, yielding a uniform distribution of all the particles over space.

This tendency to distribute particles uniformly over space is called **equipartition of space** in analogy to the concept of equipartition of energy we encountered in Section 19.2. The diffusion of ink in water or smoke in air and the uniform distribution of gas particles in a container are all manifestations of this equipartitioning of space.

19.11 Suppose the partition in Figure 19.9 is designed to slide freely to the left and right. It is positioned in the center so that the container is divided into two equal compartments and clamped in place. Then 2*N* particles of a gas are added to the left compartment and *N* particles are added to the right compartment. When the clamp on the partition is removed, does the partition move to the right, move to the left, or stay where it is?

19.4 Evolution toward the most probable macrostate

In Sections 19.2 and 19.3, we assumed that the distribution of energy and the spatial distribution of particles are entirely random, like the throw of dice. However, there is an important difference between the throwing of dice and, say, the slowing down of a pendulum.

Each time you throw two dice, the combination you get is completely independent of the combinations you threw before. After throwing a sum of 7, for example, you can throw 12, 2, another 7, or any other sum. The dissipation of the energy in a swinging pendulum, on the other hand, takes many collisions. Because a single collision redistributes only a very small portion of the system's energy, the way the energy is distributed after any given collision is only slightly different from the way it was distributed just before the collision. In other words, the energy distribution in each post-collision macrostate is not independent of the energy distribution in the pre-collision macrostate.

19.12 In the system shown in Figure 19.4, suppose each collision transfers exactly one unit of energy from one colliding object to the other. (*a*) If the system is in the macrostate that has six energy units in the pendulum, which basic state(s) can the system be in after one collision? (*b*) If the system is in the macrostate that has five energy units in the pendulum, which *macrostates* can the system be in after one collision? (*c*) How many basic states do the macrostates in part *b* correspond to?

Checkpoint 19.12 shows that only neighboring macrostates are accessible to the system after each collision. So, if we start with all the energy in the pendulum, the system can only gradually evolve to the most probable macrostate (the one with all the energy in the gas particles). It takes a minimum of six collisions to reach the most probable macrostate. The number is likely to be much greater because, as you saw in doing the checkpoint, collisions can take place between two particles, leaving the energy in the pendulum unchanged, or a collision may *add* energy to the pendulum.

19.13 Suppose the system in Figure 19.4 is in the macrostate in which two energy units are in the pendulum and one collision takes place. (*a*) What are the accessible macrostates? (*b*) What is the probability for each of these macrostates?

Note that the probability of reducing the energy in the pendulum is always higher than that of increasing the energy, and so the system gradually evolves to macrostates of increasing probability. Once the system is in the most probable macrostate, collisions continue to shuffle energy units around, but the system remains near this most probable macrostate. The system is therefore at equilibrium, and the most probable macrostate is the **equilibrium state.** If the pendulum and particles do temporarily occupy a macrostate that is less probable than the equilibrium state, then any subsequent collisions tend to move the system back toward equilibrium.

Figure 19.13 Box containing 20 particles (14 on the left, 6 on the right) and 10 units of energy. The particles in the two compartments can exchange energy with one another through collisions with the partition.

A   B

partition

As we have seen, the probability of all the energy moving from the particles to the pendulum is vanishingly small, even for a gas of just 100 particles. This one-way flow of energy from pendulum to gas particles is the essence of *irreversibility* (see Section 5.3). Irreversibility is strongly connected to our sense of time. The direction of time is clear because everything around us is evolving irreversibly toward equilibrium. Now you can see that the underlying reason for irreversibility is statistics: Any system that is in a low-probability macrostate tends to evolve toward the macrostate that has the maximum number of basic states. Once the system has reached that equilibrium state, its probability of spontaneously returning to a macrostate that has a small number of basic states is vanishingly small.

To get a better sense of this evolution toward equilibrium, let's examine the particles in the closed box of **Figure 19.13**. The box contains 20 particles and is divided into compartments A and B. The partition prevents the particles from traveling from one compartment to the other but still allows particles from the two compartments to exchange energy with one another via collisions with the partition.

The energy of the system is constant—no energy can leak out because the system is closed. Suppose A contains 14 particles, B contains six particles, and the box contains ten units of energy. **Table 19.2** shows how these ten units can be distributed among the 20 particles. Let's define the macrostate by the energy units in compartment A. The number of basic states associated with each compartment is represented by the symbol Ω (the Greek capital omega) plus a subscript identifying the compartment. For example, there is only one basic state for compartment A ($\Omega_A = 1$) for macrostate $E_A = 0$. With nine energy units in A ($E_A = 9$) and the other one in B, there are 497,420 basic states for A ($\Omega_A = 497,420$) and six basic states for B ($\Omega_B = 6$).

19.14 How many ways are there to distribute two indistinguishable energy units among six distinguishable particles?

Note in Table 19.2 that as the number of energy units in each compartment of the box increases, the number of basic states in that compartment increases rapidly. Because the number of energy units in the box is constant, the number of basic states in one compartment decreases as the number of basic states in the other compartment increases. What then is the most probable macrostate for the box as a whole?

To answer this question, consider the macrostate $E_A = 1$ in Table 19.2. There are 14 ways to distribute this 1 energy unit in A (it can go into any one of the 14 particles of A), so there are 14 basic states associated with compartment A for $E_A = 1$. One energy unit in A leaves nine energy units to be distributed in B, and as you can see from the table, there are 2002 ways to distribute these nine units over the six particles in B. For each of the 14 basic states associated with compartment A, there are 2002 basic states associated with compartment B. The number of basic states associated with the macrostate $E_A = 1$ is thus $14 \times 2002 = 28,028$. More generally, for a given macrostate, the number Ω of

Table 19.2 Number of basic states Ω associated with macrostates having 10 energy units distributed over 20 particles

E_A	E_B	Ω_A	Ω_B	$\Omega = \Omega_A\Omega_B$	$\ln \Omega$
Energy units in A	Energy units in B	Corresponding number of basic states for A	Corresponding number of basic states for B	Corresponding number of basic states for macrostate	
0	10	1	3003	3.00×10^3	8.01
1	9	14	2002	2.80×10^4	10.2
2	8	105	1287	1.35×10^5	11.8
3	7	560	792	4.44×10^5	13.0
4	6	2380	462	1.10×10^6	13.9
5	5	8568	252	2.16×10^6	14.6
6	4	27,132	126	3.42×10^6	15.0
7	3	77,520	56	4.34×10^6	15.3
8	2	203,490	21	4.27×10^6	15.3
9	1	497,420	6	2.98×10^6	14.9
10	0	1,144,066	1	1.14×10^6	14.0
Total		1,961,256	8008	$\Omega_{tot} = 2.00 \times 10^7$	

Figure 19.14 Probability of finding a given fraction of the system's energy in compartment A of the box in Figure 19.13. As the number of energy units increases from 10 to 1000, the probability distribution becomes narrower but remains centered about the mean energy.

basic states available to the system is obtained by multiplying Ω_A by Ω_B: $\Omega = \Omega_A \Omega_B$.

The probability of each macrostate is obtained by dividing Ω, the number of basic states associated with that macrostate, by Ω_{tot}, the number of basic states associated with all macrostates (2.00×10^7; see Table 19.2). The table shows you that this probability is greatest for the macrostate $E_A = 7$, as you would expect. Given that there are 14 particles in A and six in B, on average each particle has half an energy unit, and so the $E_A = 7$ macrostate corresponds to an equipartitioning of the energy. The curve labeled 10 units in **Figure 19.14** shows this probability as a function of the fraction of energy contained in A.

Example 19.6 Probability of macrostates

In Figure 19.13, after a very large number of particle-partition collisions have occurred, what is the probability of finding the system in (*a*) the macrostate $E_A = 1$ and (*b*) the macrostate $E_A = 7$?

❶ **GETTING STARTED** Because all basic states are equally likely, the probability of finding the system in macrostate E_A is equal to the fraction Ω/Ω_{tot}, where Ω is the number of basic states of the system associated with the macrostate E_A and Ω_{tot} is the number of basic states associated with all macrostates (2.00×10^7; Table 19.2).

❷ **DEVISE PLAN** To calculate the probability of a given macrostate E_A, I divide the value of Ω for that macrostate given in Table 19.2 by $\Omega_{tot} = 2.00 \times 10^7$.

❸ **EXECUTE PLAN** (*a*) For $E_A = 1$, Table 19.2 tells me that $\Omega = 2.80 \times 10^4$. The probability of macrostate $E_A = 1$ is thus $(2.80 \times 10^4)/(2.00 \times 10^7) = 1.40 \times 10^{-3}$. ✔

(*b*) For the macrostate $E_A = 7$, $\Omega = 4.34 \times 10^6$. So the probability of this macrostate occurring is $(4.34 \times 10^6)/(2.00 \times 10^7) = 2.17 \times 10^{-1}$. ✔

❹ **EVALUATE RESULT** My result shows that the macrostate $E_A = 7$ is more than 150 times more probable than the macrostate $E_A = 1$. This makes sense because, as we saw earlier, the macrostate $E_A = 7$ is the equilibrium state for which there is an equipartition of energy.

If we increase the number of energy units in the box of Figure 19.13 to 100 or 1000, the number of basic states grows exponentially, and if we plot the probability of each macrostate as a function of the fraction of energy in A, we obtain the two curves labeled 100 and 1000 in Figure 19.14. Just as we saw in Figure 19.7, the most probable macrostate doesn't change, but the probability peaks much more narrowly around this state. In other words, the most probable macrostate—the equilibrium state—is now even more likely than any other macrostate.

Note that the number of basic states is very large, even with just ten energy units and 20 particles. In a box of volume 1 m^3 containing air at atmospheric pressure and room temperature, there are on the order of 10^{25} particles and 10^{20} energy units per particle, and so the number of basic states becomes unimaginably large—on the order of ten raised to the power 10^{21}! Because the number of basic states is so large, it is more convenient to work with the natural logarithm of that number. As you can see from the rightmost column in Table 19.2, the natural logarithm of the number of basic states is indeed much more manageable.

Figure 19.15 shows how the natural logarithms of Ω_A, Ω_B, and Ω vary with the number of energy units in compartment A in Figure 19.13. As you can see, the natural logarithm of the number of basic states changes much less rapidly than the number of basic states. Note that as E_A increases, the number of basic states Ω_A increases. As E_A increases, however, E_B decreases and so Ω_B decreases. The number of basic states Ω is maximum when $E_A = 7$ and $E_B = 3$, representing an equipartition of energy. The most probable macrostate (equilibrium) is achieved when there is equipartition of energy.

19.15 What is the average energy per particle in compartments A and B in Figure 19.13 (*a*) when there is one energy unit in A and (*b*) when the system is at equilibrium?

As you can see from Table 19.2, with $E_A = 1$ the number of basic states for the system (2.80×10^4) is more than 100 times smaller than it is at equilibrium ($E_A = 7$, $\Omega = 4.34 \times 10^6$). Collisions between the particles and the partition redistribute

Figure 19.15 Natural logarithm of the number of basic states for compartment A, for compartment B, and for the two compartments in Figure 19.13 combined. The number of basic states is maximal when the energy is equipartitioned (seven energy units in A).

Figure 19.16 If the system evolves toward equilibrium from an initial macrostate with 1 energy unit in A, the number of basic states increases in A and decreases in B. The decrease for B is smaller than the increase for A and so the number of basic states still increases.

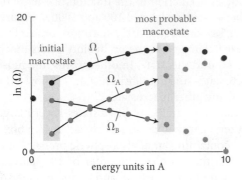

the energy among the particles, and over time the system evolves toward the most probable macrostate—the one for which each particle has its "fair share" of the system's energy $(10/20 = 0.5$ unit), just as you found in Checkpoint 19.15*b*. As the system evolves toward equilibrium from the $E_A = 1$ macrostate (**Figure 19.16**), the number of basic states in B *decreases;* that is, B moves toward a macrostate of *lower* probability. However, the rate at which Ω_A increases is greater than the rate at which Ω_B decreases, and so Ω still increases.

Example 19.7 Equilibrium

Suppose the system depicted in Figure 19.13 evolves toward equilibrium from the macrostate $E_A = 4$, $E_B = 6$. Determine the changes in (*a*) the number of energy units and (*b*) the number of basic states for compartment A, for compartment B, and for the system.

❶ **GETTING STARTED** From Table 19.2 I see that the equilibrium macrostate (the one that has the greatest number of basic states associated with it) has $E_A = 7$ and $E_B = 3$. This is the macrostate toward which the system evolves.

❷ **DEVISE PLAN** The change in the number of energy units in A is $\Delta E_A = E_{A,f} - E_{A,i}$. The change in the number of energy units in B is $\Delta E_B = E_{B,f} - E_{B,i}$. The change for this system is the sum of these two values. To determine the changes in the number of basic states, I obtain the number of basic states for the initial and final macrostates from Table 19.2 and compute the differences.

❸ **EXECUTE PLAN** (*a*)

$$\Delta E_A = E_{A,f} - E_{A,i} = 7 - 4 = +3;$$

$$\Delta E_B = E_{B,f} - E_{B,i} = 3 - 6 = -3;$$

$$\Delta E = \Delta E_A + \Delta E_B = 3 - 3 = 0. ✔$$

(*b*) $\Delta\Omega_A = \Omega_{A,f} - \Omega_{A,i} = 77{,}520 - 2380 = 75{,}140$

$\Delta\Omega_B = \Omega_{B,f} - \Omega_{B,i} = 56 - 462 = -406$

$\Delta\Omega = \Omega_f - \Omega_i = (\Omega_{A,f})(\Omega_{B,f}) - (\Omega_{A,i})(\Omega_{B,i})$

$\quad = (4.34 \times 10^6) - (1.10 \times 10^6) = 3.24 \times 10^6. ✔$

❹ **EVALUATE RESULT** My answer to part *a* shows that the change in the number of energy units in the system is zero, as I expect because the system is closed. My result in *b* shows that even though

Ω_B goes down, Ω_A increases significantly more, and so there is a gain in the number of basic states, as should happen when a system evolves toward equilibrium. Because Ω is the product of Ω_A and Ω_B, $\Delta\Omega$ is not simply the sum of $\Delta\Omega_A$ and $\Delta\Omega_B$. My result for $\Delta\Omega$, however, shows an increase in the number of basic states, as I expect.

The evolution toward equilibrium in Figure 19.13 (or in any other system) is a gradual process that seeks out the most probable macrostates through a very large number of random collisions. Once the system has reached equilibrium, the probability of returning to the macrostate $E_A = 1$ energy unit is very small—even for a system of just 20 particles. For a more realistic system, in which the number of particles is much greater, the odds favor equipartitioning so strongly that the probability of observing a system away from equilibrium is virtually zero unless the system is disturbed by outside influences.

The irreversible evolution of a system toward equilibrium can be quantified by the number of basic states Ω:

A closed system always evolves so as to maximize the number of basic states Ω. When this number has reached a maximum, the system is at equilibrium.

This irreversible tendency of closed systems to maximize Ω is called the **second law of thermodynamics.***

Often we cannot directly determine the number of basic states Ω for a system. The second law of thermodynamics, however, allows us to reach conclusions about Ω in a closed system without having to consider any details at the atomic level. Consider, for example, a closed system consisting of a drop of ink placed in a beaker of water. We know from experience that the ink diffuses until it is uniformly distributed in the water (equipartition of space). In Section 19.3 we saw that the spreading out of particles increases the number of basic states—Ω for six particles in a container is much greater at equilibrium than when all the particles are clustered in a corner. For the ink, too, Ω increases as the ink spreads out, and so we can use our intuitive sense of the direction of time to reach conclusions about the number of basic states: If a process in a closed system runs only one way (the process is irreversible), the number of basic states of that system must be increasing. Conversely, the number of basic states of a closed system undergoing a reversible process remains constant.

✋ **19.16** For which of these systems does Ω increase over time: (*a*) a thermos bottle containing warm water with an ice cube in it, (*b*) a cup of tea that is at the same temperature as the air in an insulated room, (*c*) a well-shaken bottle containing oil and water, (*d*) a seed germinating in soil inside a closed container, (*e*) the universe.

---

*Thermodynamics is the branch of physics that deals with thermal energy and engines, subjects we discuss in the next two chapters. The second law of thermodynamics was first formulated (in a different form) in the context of this branch of physics. The formulation given here represents the modern and more general view of this law.

Self-quiz

1. Figure 19.4 shows that there are 15 basic states for four energy units distributed over three particles. List all 15.

2. Suppose a container holds three types of gas. The masses of the gas particles are m, $4m$, and $9m$. How do the average speeds of the particles compare?

3. In Figure 19.12, what is the probability of finding three particles in any compartment of the box?

4. The two partitions in the container shown in **Figure 19.17** can slide freely. Where will they be positioned when the space is equipartitioned?

Figure 19.17

partitions

possible positions of partitions

5. A box with a fixed partition through which energy can be exchanged contains 50 particles, 40 on the left and 10 on the right. The system contains 250 energy units. As the system approaches equilibrium, how many energy units end up on the left? On the right?

6. If a closed system tends to change in a specific direction, such as ice melting in an insulated glass of water, what can you say about the number of basic states for this system?

Answers

1. 400, 040, 004, 310, 301, 031, 130, 013, 103, 220, 202, 022, 112, 121, 211.

2. According to the concept of equipartition of energy, the energy needs to be shared equally among all the gas particles, $\frac{1}{2}mv_1^2 = \frac{1}{2}(4m)v_2^2 = \frac{1}{2}(9m)v_3^2$, or $v_1^2 = 4v_2^2 = 9v_3^2$. Thus $v_1 = 2v_2 = 3v_3$.

3. Figure 19.12, shows that there are ten basic states with three particles in the top left compartment, regardless of the number of particles in the other compartments. When there are two particles in the top left compartment, there are six basic states with three particles in any other compartment. With one particle in the top left compartment, there are $6 + 3 = 9$ basic states with three particles in any other compartment. With no particles in the top left compartment, there are $6 + 3 = 9$ basic states with three particles in any other compartment. Therefore there are $10 + 6 + 9 + 9 = 34$ basic states with three particles in any compartment. The probability of finding three particles in any compartment is thus 34/84.

4. The partition shown at position 2 moves to position 4, and the partition shown at 4 moves to 5, so that there is 1 particle per unit length of the box.

5. Because at equilibrium the energy must be equipartitioned, the 250 units are evenly distributed across the 50 particles; with five units/per particle. The 40 particles on the left have 200 units of energy, and the 10 particles on the right have 50 units.

6. According to the second law of thermodynamics, the system evolves to the macrostate that has the maximum number of basic states. Because the process is irreversible, the final macrostate must have a greater number of basic states than the initial macrostate.

19.5 Dependence of entropy on volume

In Sections 19.2 and 19.3, we saw that the equipartition of energy and space describes the most probable macrostate of any system—that is, the state that has the greatest number of basic states. The number of *atomic parameters,* such as the position and velocity of each particle, is intractably large for any real system, and so it is generally impossible to specify the basic state of the system. The macrostate, on the other hand, is readily specified by a few measurable *macroscopic parameters,* such as volume, pressure, or temperature.

To make the connection between macroscopic and atomic parameters, we consider a gas that consists of a very large number N of particles in a container of volume V. The particles occupy a negligible fraction of the volume V and interact with one another only during collisions that randomize both the energy distribution and the spatial distribution. All collisions between the particles and the walls of the container are elastic. A gas that satisfies these conditions is called an **ideal gas.** At high temperature and low pressure, an ideal gas is a good model for a real gas.

Let us now calculate how the number of spatial basic states depends on V and N. The system is closed so that the energy of the gas remains constant. Throughout this section we shall take this energy to be equipartitioned over the gas particles. At equilibrium each particle has an equal probability of occupying any location inside the container; the space is equipartitioned and each particle has its fair share of the volume V of the container. To count basic states, we divide the container into equal-sized compartments as we did in Section 19.3. If there are M equal-sized compartments and just one particle, that particle can be placed in any one of the M compartments. Thus there are M basic states for that one particle (**Figure 19.18**). A second particle can also be placed in any of the M compartments, and so, for two particles, there are M^2 basic states. Continuing this process for N particles, we see that Ω, the number of basic states, is*

$$\Omega = M^N \quad \text{(closed system).} \tag{19.1}$$

Figure 19.18 Each of the N particles inside the container can be placed in any one of the M equal-sized compartments.

N particles in volume V

volume V divided into M compartments . . .

. . . each of which has volume δV

Exercise 19.8 Number of basic states

Suppose ten distinguishable particles are equipartitioned in a container that is divided into 100 equal-sized compartments. (*a*) How many basic states are associated with this system? (*b*) What is the natural logarithm of this number of basic states?

SOLUTION (*a*) The number of basic states is $\Omega = M^N = 100^{10} = (10^2)^{10} = 10^{20}$, an unimaginably large number. ✔

(*b*) The natural logarithm of the number of basic states is $\ln \Omega = \ln(10^{20}) = 46$, a much more manageable number. ✔

19.17 If you decrease the size of the compartments in Exercise 19.8 by a factor of 10, what is the change (*a*) in the number of basic states and (*b*) in the natural logarithm of that number?

Exercise 19.8 and Checkpoint 19.17 illustrate that the natural logarithm of the number of basic states is much more manageable and less sensitive to a change in compartment size than the number itself. The natural logarithm of the number of basic states from Eq. 19.1 is

$$\ln \Omega = \ln(M^N) = N \ln M \quad \text{(closed system at equilibrium),} \tag{19.2}$$

---

*We assume here that the particles are distinguishable from one another. In reality, the particles of an ideal gas are indistinguishable. In the case of indistinguishable particles and when $M \gg N \gg 1$, the number of basic states is found to be $M^N/N!$ instead of the result shown in Eq. 19.1. For simplicity, we shall limit the treatment in this section to systems of distinguishable particles.

where we have used the identity $\ln(a^b) = b \ln a$. If the volume of the equal-sized compartments is δV, the number of compartments is $M = V/\delta V$, and so Eq. 19.2 becomes

$$\ln \Omega = N \ln\left(\frac{V}{\delta V}\right)$$

$$= N \ln V - N \ln \delta V \quad \text{(closed system at equilibrium)}, \qquad (19.3)$$

where we have used the identify $\ln(a/b) = \ln a - \ln b$.

Because the quantity $\ln \Omega$—the natural logarithm of the number of basic states—is so important, we define a quantity called **entropy:***

$$S \equiv \ln \Omega. \qquad (19.4)$$

Entropy is a unitless quantity that is a measure of the number of basic states in a system. The greater the number of basic states, the greater the entropy. Entropy allows us to quantify the spreading out of energy or particles over space.

As we saw in Section 19.4, a closed system always evolves so as to maximize the number of basic states. As the number of basic states increases, so does the entropy: $S_f > S_i$. Therefore,

$$\Delta S > 0 \quad \text{(closed system evolving toward equilibrium)}. \qquad (19.5)$$

At equilibrium, the number of basic states reaches its maximum value Ω_{max} and the entropy of the system no longer changes:

$$\Delta S = 0 \quad \text{(closed system at equilibrium)}. \qquad (19.6)$$

Equations 19.5 and 19.6 constitute the **entropy law**, a mathematical expression of the second law of thermodynamics. The entropy law implies that the entropy of a closed system never decreases (it can only increase or remain constant).

It is important to note that Eqs. 19.5 and 19.6 apply to only closed systems. For a system that is not closed, the entropy can increase, remain the same, or decrease. Back in Figure 19.16, for example, the particles in B transfer some of their energy to the particles in A, so B does not constitute a closed system. As we saw, Ω_B decreases and so the entropy of B decreases:

For systems that are not closed, the entropy can increase, decrease, or stay the same.

For a system of N gas particles equipartitioned over a volume V, we can obtain an expression for how entropy depends on volume by substituting Eq. 19.3 into Eq. 19.4:

$$S = N \ln V - N \ln \delta V \quad \text{(closed system at equilibrium)}. \qquad (19.7)$$

This expression describes a gas that is equipartitioned over a volume V—that is, at equilibrium. The value for S given by this expression thus represents the *maximum* value for the entropy of a gas of N particles in a volume V. If the gas is not at equilibrium, its entropy is smaller than that given by Eq. 19.7.

---

*Historically, entropy has been defined as $S \equiv k_B \ln \Omega$, where k_B is a constant that makes the entropy a much smaller number and gives it units of J/K (see Eq. 19.39). In this book, however, we shall use the definition given in Eq. 19.3. This definition is called a *statistical definition* of entropy.

The first term on the right in Eq. 19.7 shows that for a fixed number of particles N, the entropy (that is, the natural logarithm of the number of basic states) increases as we increase the volume V of the container. The second term on the right depends on the size of the compartments: The smaller the compartments, the smaller this term and therefore the greater the entropy. That the entropy depends on the volume δV of the compartments may seem disturbing—after all, the partitioning is completely arbitrary. In general, however, $\delta V \ll V$, and so the second term on the right in Eq. 19.7 is much smaller than the first one and can be ignored.

In general, we shall be concerned only with *changes* in entropy, in which case the second term in Eq. 19.7 drops out entirely. Consider, for example, the expansion of a gas made up of a fixed number of particles from an initial volume V_i to a final volume $V_f > V_i$. According to Eq. 19.7, the change in entropy is

$$\Delta S = S_f - S_i = (N \ln V_f - N \ln \delta V) - (N \ln V_i - N \ln \delta V)$$

$$= N \ln V_f - N \ln V_i = N \ln\left(\frac{V_f}{V_i}\right) \quad \text{(closed system at equilibrium).} \quad (19.8)$$

Because the second term on the right in Eq. 19.7 cancels out, the entropy change does not depend on the size of the compartments. Note that because $V_f > V_i$ the change in entropy is positive.

19.18 (*a*) What does a positive entropy change in a closed system imply about the change in the number of basic states? (*b*) How does Eq. 19.8 show that a gas expands if given more room? (*c*) How does it show that the gas does not contract spontaneously into a subvolume?

Let us next examine how entropy changes when a system of two interacting gases evolves to equilibrium. Consider, for example, two gases inside a container with a partition separating the gases into two compartments, one of volume V_A containing N_A particles and the other of volume V_B containing N_B particles (**Figure 19.19a**).* If we let the partition move freely, the system evolves to the macrostate that has the maximum number of basic states. If the partition moves to the right, V_A increases, and so the number of basic states for gas A increases. As V_A increases, V_B decreases, and so the number of basic states for gas B decreases. Where does the partition come to rest? In other words, what value of V_A maximizes the number of basic states for the system as a whole?

In Section 19.4, we determined that the number of basic states for a system comprising two gases is the product of the number of basic states for the two separate gases:

$$\Omega = \Omega_A \Omega_B, \quad (19.9)$$

Using the definition of entropy (Eq. 19.4), we obtain

$$S = \ln(\Omega_A \Omega_B) = \ln \Omega_A + \ln \Omega_B = S_A + S_B, \quad (19.10)$$

where we have used the fact that $\ln(ab) = \ln a + \ln b$. Note that, unlike Ω, the natural logarithm of Ω and thus entropy are extensive properties:

The entropy of a combined system is the sum of the entropies of the individual systems.

Figure 19.19 (*a*) Two gases of unequal densities are placed on either side of a partition. (*b*) When the partition is free to move, the two gases evolve to the macrostate corresponding to the maximum number of basic states.

gases at different densities

$V_{A,i}$ $V_{B,i}$

fixed partition

When partition is free to move . . .

$V_{A,f}$ $V_{B,f}$

. . . gases evolve to macrostate corresponding to maximum number of basic states.

*We assume energy is equipartitioned over the system made up of both compartments and focus on only volume changes here. In the next section we shall examine the equipartitioning of energy.

Example 19.9 Partitioned gas

A partition divides a container into two equal compartments, A and B. Initially compartment A contains a gas of distinguishable particles and compartment B is empty. (*a*) What is the change in the entropy of the gas if the partition is removed and the gas is allowed to expand into the volume *V* of the container? (*b*) If the partition is reinserted after the gas has reached equilibrium in the volume *V*, what is the change in the entropy of the gas due to the reinsertion?

❶ **GETTING STARTED** When the partition is removed, the gas expands to fill the container, so the final volume occupied by the gas is twice the initial volume: $V_f = 2V_i$. Reinserting the partition divides the container into two equal compartments A and B again. The only difference is that now B is not empty; it contains half of the particles, and A contains the other half.

❷ **DEVISE PLAN** To obtain the change in entropy due to the removal of the partition, I substitute $V_f = 2V_i$ into Eq. 19.8. For part *b*, the entropy change due to the reinsertion is equal to the difference between the entropy of the gas after the partition is reinserted and its entropy before the partition is reinserted. To determine the entropy before the partition is reinserted, I use Eq. 19.7. Equation 19.10 tells me that after reinsertion the entropy of the gas is equal to the sum of the entropies in the two compartments. Because each compartment has half the volume of the container and contains half the gas particles, the entropies in the two compartments are equal to each other. To determine these entropies, I use Eq. 19.7 again.

❸ **EXECUTE PLAN** (*a*) Equation 19.8 gives
$\Delta S = N \ln(2V_i/V_i) = N \ln 2.$ ✔

(*b*) From Eq. 19.7, I obtain for the entropy before reinsertion of the partition: $S_i = N \ln V - N \ln \delta V$. Combining Eqs. 19.10 and 19.7, I obtain for the final entropy,

$$S_f = S_A + S_B = 2\left[\frac{N}{2}\ln\left(\frac{V/2}{\delta V}\right)\right] = N \ln \frac{V}{2} - N \ln \delta V$$
$$= N \ln V - N \ln 2 - N \ln \delta V.$$

The change in entropy is thus $\Delta S = S_f - S_i = -N \ln 2.$ ✔

❹ **EVALUATE RESULT** My answer to part *a* shows that the removal of the partition and subsequent expansion of the gas result in a positive change in entropy. This is what I expect given that the system evolves toward equilibrium. My answer to part *b* is the negative of the answer to part *a*, which tells me that the change in entropy due to the combined removal and reinsertion of the partition is zero: $\Delta S = N \ln 2 - N \ln 2 = 0$. That is surprising because the gas has expanded into a larger volume. However, the particles in this problem are distinguishable, and in reality gas particles are indistinguishable. For distinguishable particles, the reinsertion reduces the number of basic states (a particle in compartment B can no longer be in compartment A, and vice versa). If the particles are indistinguishable, reinserting the partition causes no entropy change.

Assuming that the gases on each side of the partition in Figure 19.19 remain at equilibrium, we have from Eq. 19.7

$$S_A = N_A \ln V_A - N_A \ln \delta V \qquad (19.11)$$

$$S_B = N_B \ln V_B - N_B \ln \delta V = N_B \ln(V - V_A) - N_B \ln \delta V, \qquad (19.12)$$

where $V = V_A + V_B$ is the combined (constant) volume of the system. Increasing V_A thus increases S_A but decreases S_B. **Figure 19.20** shows how the entropies of the two compartments and the entropy of the combined system depend on V_A. When the number of basic states, and thus the entropy in Eq. 19.10, are maximum, Eq. 19.6 applies, so the partition comes to rest and the combined system is at equilibrium. We therefore would like to determine for what value of V_A the system's entropy S is maximized.

At the maximum value of S, the slope of the S curve in Figure 19.20 is zero. This slope is given by the derivative of S with respect to V_A, and so at equilibrium,

$$\frac{dS}{dV_A} = \frac{dS_A}{dV_A} + \frac{dS_B}{dV_A} = 0 \quad \text{(equilibrium)} \qquad (19.13)$$

or
$$\frac{dS_A}{dV_A} = -\frac{dS_B}{dV_A} \quad \text{(equilibrium).} \qquad (19.14)$$

The quantities dS_A/dV_A and dS_B/dV_A represent the slopes of the S_A and S_B curves in Figure 19.20. Equation 19.14 thus tells us that these two curves must have opposite slopes at the equilibrium value of V_A.

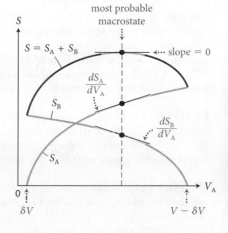

Figure 19.20 As the partition in Figure 19.19 moves to the right and V_A increases, S_A increases and S_B decreases until the entropy of the system is maximum. At this value of V_A, the partition comes to rest, and the system is at equilibrium.

We can now show that the condition expressed in Eq. 19.14 leads to equipartitioning of the space by calculating the derivatives. Because V is constant,

$$\frac{dV_B}{dV_A} = \frac{d}{dV_A}(V - V_A) = -1, \tag{19.15}$$

we have $dV_A = -dV_B$ and so can rewrite Eq. 19.14 in the form

$$\frac{dS_A}{dV_A} = -\frac{dS_B}{(-dV_B)} = \frac{dS_B}{dV_B} \quad \text{(equilibrium)}. \tag{19.16}$$

Equation 19.16 tells us that at equilibrium the quantity dS/dV evaluated on either side of the partition is the same.

Taking the derivative of Eq. 19.7 with respect to V, we get

$$\frac{dS}{dV} = \frac{d}{dV}(N \ln V - N \ln \delta V) = \frac{d}{dV}(N \ln V) \tag{19.17}$$

because $N \ln \delta V$ does not depend on V (N is fixed and δV is a constant). Recalling that

$$\frac{d}{dx}\ln x = \frac{1}{x}, \tag{19.18}$$

we get

$$\frac{dS}{dV} = \frac{N}{V}. \tag{19.19}$$

The quantity N/V represents the number of particles per unit volume and is the number density of the gas (Eq. 1.3). Substituting Eq. 19.19 into Eq. 19.16, we obtain

$$\frac{N_A}{V_A} = \frac{N_B}{V_B} \quad \text{(equilibrium)}, \tag{19.20}$$

which is exactly the requirement for the equipartition of space: At equilibrium the number densities are the same on both sides of the partition, and so each particle has the same amount of space available to it.

Example 19.10 Sliding partition

The box in Figure 19.19 contains seven gas particles in compartment A and five in compartment B, and the partition separating the compartments is free to move. Let the volume of the box be V and the initial ratio of the compartment volumes be $V_{B,i}/V_{A,i} = 3$. What is the change in the entropy of this gas as it evolves from this macrostate to equilibrium?

❶ **GETTING STARTED** Once the equilibrium state is reached, the number densities are equal on the two sides of the partition and the change in the entropy of the gas—which is my system—is the sum of the entropy changes in the two compartments.

❷ **DEVISE PLAN** Equation 19.20 gives me the volume ratio at equilibrium, which I call the final volume ratio. Knowing the initial and final ratios, I can use Eq. 19.8 to determine the entropy change in each compartment and then use Eq. 19.10 to determine the entropy change of the system.

❸ **EXECUTE PLAN** From the given initial volume ratio, I know that $V_{B,i} = 3V_{A,i}$. The volume of the box is the sum of the volumes of the compartments: $V = V_{A,i} + V_{B,i} = V_{A,i} + 3V_{A,i} = 4V_{A,i}$, and so $V_{A,i} = V/4$ and $V_{B,i} = 3V/4$. From Eq. 19.20 the ratio of the final volumes is equal to the ratio of the numbers of particles. I know that the number of particles in each compartment cannot change, so I can say that $V_{B,f}/V_{A,f} = N_B/N_A = 5/7$, which means $V_{B,f} = 5V_{A,f}/7$.

After the partition moves, the sum of the volumes is still V, and so I know $V = V_{A,f} + V_{B,f} = V_{A,f} + 5V_{A,f}/7 = 12V_{A,f}/7$.

Thus $V_{A,f} = 7V/12$ and $V_{B,f} = 5V/12$. Substituting these volumes into Eq. 19.8 gives

$$\Delta S_A = N_A \ln \frac{V_{A,f}}{V_{A,i}} = 7 \ln \frac{7V/12}{V/4} = 7 \ln \tfrac{7}{3} = 5.93$$

$$\Delta S_B = N_B \ln \frac{V_{B,f}}{V_{B,i}} = 5 \ln \frac{5V/12}{3V/4} = 5 \ln \tfrac{5}{9} = -2.94.$$

Because the entropy of the system is the sum of the entropies of the particles in the two compartments (Eq. 19.10), I have

$$\Delta S = \Delta S_A + \Delta S_B = 5.93 - 2.94 = 2.99. ✔$$

❹ **EVALUATE RESULT** The volume of compartment A increases and the volume of compartment B decreases, so I expect the entropy of the particles in A to increase and the entropy of the particles in B to decrease, as my results show. Because the magnitude of the change in entropy is greater for A than for B, the entropy change of the system is positive, as it should be for a closed system moving toward equilibrium.

✋ **19.19** Explain why the changes in entropy in Example 19.10 do not depend on the volume V of the box.

19.6 Dependence of entropy on energy

Let us now turn our attention to how entropy depends on the energy of a system. For simplicity we restrict ourselves to a *monatomic* ideal gas (that is, a gas made up of atoms for which we can ignore any internal structure), so that none of the atoms' kinetic energy can be converted to internal energy. The incoherent kinetic energy of all the atoms makes up the thermal energy of the gas. If the center of mass of the gas is at rest, the energy of the system is entirely in the form of thermal energy.

Let us now calculate how the number of basic states depends on the thermal energy E_{th} and the number of atoms N of a closed system. Throughout this section we shall take the atoms to be distributed uniformly over the (constant) volume V of the system. At equilibrium each atom has its fair share of the thermal energy E_{th} of the system. A single atom moving at speed v contributes an amount of energy $\frac{1}{2}mv^2$ to E_{th}. Because the atom is free to move in any direction, many velocities correspond to a given speed v (**Figure 19.21**) and thus to a given share of the thermal energy E_{th}. A basic state is specified by the components v_x, v_y, and v_z of all N atoms. To count the basic states, we can use the procedure from Section 19.5: We divide the available "velocity space" in Figure 19.21 into small compartments and count the number of ways we can distribute N atoms among these compartments.

What is the available velocity space? To determine this velocity space, we introduce the **root-mean-square speed,*** or *rms speed* for short:

$$v_{rms} \equiv \sqrt{(v^2)_{av}}, \tag{19.21}$$

where $(v^2)_{av}$ is the average of the squares of the speeds of all the atoms in a volume of gas. Applying the Pythagorean theorem to the two shaded triangles in Figure 19.21, we have

$$v^2 = v_x^2 + v_y^2 + v_z^2. \tag{19.22}$$

Figure 19.21 Velocity space determined by the components of velocity. All velocity vectors ending on the surface of the sphere correspond to the same speed and therefore the same kinetic energy.

one of velocity vectors contributing $\frac{1}{2}mv^2$ to E_{th}

---

*This value is obtained by taking the square *root* of the *mean* (average) of the *squares* of the speeds.

If we average over all atoms, this expression becomes

$$v_{rms}^2 = (v^2)_{av} = (v_x^2)_{av} + (v_y^2)_{av} + (v_z^2)_{av}. \qquad (19.23)$$

Given that the gas is the same in all directions, there is no difference between the x, y, and z directions, and so

$$(v_x^2)_{av} = (v_y^2)_{av} = (v_z^2)_{av} \qquad (19.24)$$

or

$$v_{rms}^2 = 3(v_x^2)_{av}. \qquad (19.25)$$

✋ **19.20** Five atoms moving along the x axis have x components of velocities +2.1 m/s, −3.2 m/s, +4.5 m/s, −0.3 m/s, and −3.1 m/s. Determine (a) the x component of the average velocity, (b) the average speed, and (c) the rms speed.

To return to determining the volume of the velocity space, let us now assume that the components of the velocities of the atoms are limited to a range of a few times the rms speed. That is, let us assume that

$$-av_{rms} \leq v_x \leq av_{rms}, \qquad (19.26)$$

Figure 19.22 Calculating the volume $\mathcal{V}$ of the velocity space.

y components of velocities lie between $\pm av_{rms}$

Cube defines "velocity space."

and likewise for the y and z components, and where a is a number between, say, 1 and 10. This may seem like a totally arbitrary restriction, but you will see in a bit that the end result is not affected by this restriction. With this simplifying assumption the velocities of all the atoms in our system lie in a cube having sides of length $2av_{rms}$ (**Figure 19.22**). The "volume" $\mathcal{V}$ of the velocity space of the atoms in a gas-filled container is then $\mathcal{V} = (2av_{rms})^3$.

We can relate this volume to the thermal energy of the gas because we know that the average kinetic energy K_{av} of one atom is equal to the thermal energy of the gas divided by the number N of gas atoms in the container:

$$K_{av} \equiv \tfrac{1}{2}m(v^2)_{av} = \tfrac{1}{2}mv_{rms}^2 = \frac{E_{th}}{N} \quad \text{(monatomic ideal gas)}, \qquad (19.27)$$

where we have used the definition of rms speed (Eq. 19.21). Now we can rewrite the rms speed as

$$v_{rms} = \left(\frac{2E_{th}}{mN}\right)^{1/2}, \qquad (19.28)$$

and so we see that the volume $\mathcal{V}$ of the velocity space is proportional to $(E_{th})^{3/2}$:

$$\mathcal{V} = (2av_{rms})^3 = \left[2a\left(\frac{2E_{th}}{mN}\right)^{1/2}\right]^3 = \left(\frac{8a^2}{mN}\right)^{3/2}(E_{th})^{3/2} = b(E_{th})^{3/2}, \qquad (19.29)$$

where $b = (8a^2/mN)^{3/2}$ is a constant.

✋ **19.21** Work out the algebra between the third and fourth terms in Eq. 19.29.

In analogy to what we did in Section 19.5, we now divide this volume $\mathcal{V}$ of the velocity space into smaller velocity-space compartments, each of volume $\delta\mathcal{V}$. The number of velocity-space compartments is

$$M_v = \frac{\mathcal{V}}{\delta\mathcal{V}} = \frac{b}{\delta\mathcal{V}}(E_{th})^{3/2}, \qquad (19.30)$$

and the number of ways we can distribute N distinguishable atoms in these M_v compartments is (see Eq. 19.1):

$$\Omega_v = (M_v)^N = \left[\frac{b}{\delta\mathcal{V}}(E_{th})^{3/2}\right]^N. \qquad (19.31)$$

For a monatomic ideal gas in which the energy is equipartitioned, the entropy is maximum and given by

$$S \equiv \ln \Omega_v = \tfrac{3}{2}N \ln E_{th} - N \ln \frac{\delta\mathcal{V}}{b} \quad \begin{array}{l}\text{(monatomic ideal gas at}\\ \text{equilibrium).}\end{array} \qquad (19.32)$$

The first term to the right of the equals sign shows that for a fixed number of atoms N, the entropy increases as we increase the thermal energy E_{th} of the gas. The factors $\delta\mathcal{V}$ and b in Eq. 19.32 tell us that the entropy depends on the size of the velocity-space compartments in which the atoms are distributed and on the restriction we imposed in Eq. 19.26. However, the term that contains these factors drops out when we consider changes in entropy:

$$\Delta S = S_f - S_i = \tfrac{3}{2}N \ln E_{th,f} - \tfrac{3}{2}N \ln E_{th,i} = \tfrac{3}{2}N \ln\left(\frac{E_{th,f}}{E_{th,i}}\right). \qquad (19.33)$$

Now we can examine how entropy changes when a system of two interacting gases initially having different amounts of thermal energy evolves toward a system-wide equilibrium state. Consider a closed system of two gases that can exchange energy with each other, as illustrated in **Figure 19.23**. The volume of each compartment and the number of atoms in each are fixed. In Section 19.4 we saw that such a system tends to evolve toward an equipartitioning of the system's thermal energy. If thermal energy is exchanged across the partition, one gas gains thermal energy and the other one loses thermal energy. Because the entropy of the gas depends on its thermal energy, the exchange of thermal energy causes the entropy to increase on one side of the partition and decrease on the other side. **Figure 19.24** shows how the entropies of the two gases and the entropy of the combined system depend on the thermal energy $E_{th,A}$ of gas A. When the number of basic states, and thus the entropy, are maximum, Eq. 19.6 applies and the exchange of thermal energy stops and the system is said to be in **thermal equilibrium.** We therefore would like to determine for what value of $E_{th,A}$ the system's entropy $S = S_A + S_B$ is maximized.

At the maximum entropy level, the slope of curve S in Figure 19.24 is zero, and so

$$\frac{dS}{dE_{th,A}} = \frac{dS_A}{dE_{th,A}} + \frac{dS_B}{dE_{th,A}} = 0 \quad \text{(closed system at thermal equilibrium)} \qquad (19.34)$$

or $\qquad \dfrac{dS_A}{dE_{th,A}} = -\dfrac{dS_B}{dE_{th,A}} \quad$ (closed system at thermal equilibrium). $\qquad (19.35)$

The quantities $dS_A/dE_{th,A}$ and $dS_B/dE_{th,A}$ represent the slopes of curves S_A and S_B in Figure 19.24. Eq. 19.35 thus tells us that these two curves must have opposite slopes at thermal equilibrium. Because E_{th} is constant,

$$\frac{dE_{th,B}}{dE_{th,A}} = \frac{d}{dE_{th,A}}[E_{th} - E_{th,A}] = -1, \qquad (19.36)$$

Figure 19.23 Container holding two gases separated by a partition. The gases can exchange energy with each other through collisions with the partition.

Figure 19.24 How the entropies of the gases in Figure 19.23 depend on the thermal energy $E_{th,A}$ of gas A.

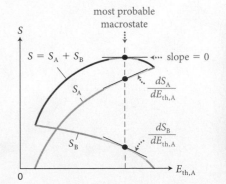

QUANTITATIVE TOOLS

we have $dE_{th,A} = -dE_{th,B}$ and so Eq. 19.35 becomes

$$\frac{dS_A}{dE_{th,A}} = -\frac{dS_B}{d(-E_{th,B})} = \frac{dS_B}{dE_{th,B}} \quad \text{(closed system at thermal equilibrium)}. \quad (19.37)$$

As you have probably noticed, there is a strong parallel between the quantity dS/dE_{th} in the above derivation and the quantity dS/dV we discussed in the preceding section (compare, also, Figures 19.20 and 19.24). In Eq. 19.19 we saw that the quantity dS/dV represents the number density of the gas and that at equilibrium the number density tends to be the same in all compartments of the system (Eq. 19.20).

To discover what physical concept dS/dE_{th} corresponds to, answer the following checkpoint.

✋ **19.22** (a) Using Figure 19.24, compare the kinetic energy of an atom in gas A with that of an atom in gas B in the thermal equilibrium state (that is, on the dashed line) and in a macrostate to the left of the dashed line. (b) In each of these two macrostates, which gas is "hotter"? (c) For the same two macrostates, compare the quantities $dS_A/dE_{th,A}$ and $dS_B/dE_{th,B}$.

As Checkpoint 19.22 suggests, the quantity dS/dE_{th} is smaller for a hot gas than for a cooler gas. We therefore define this quantity to be inversely proportional to a quantity called the **absolute temperature** T:

$$\frac{1}{k_B T} \equiv \frac{dS}{dE_{th}}, \quad (19.38)$$

The unit for absolute temperature, the **kelvin** (K), is one of the SI base units. In Section 20.2 we'll see how this unit is defined. The proportionality constant k_B, called the **Boltzmann constant,** is

$$k_B = 1.381 \times 10^{-23} \text{ J/K}. \quad (19.39)$$

The constant k_B is chosen in such a way as to reconcile the units for absolute temperature with common temperature measurements, which we shall discuss in the next chapter. For now, consider T to be a quantitative measure of the temperature obtained by adding 273.15 to the reading on a thermometer calibrated in degrees Celsius.

With this definition of absolute temperature, we see that thermal equilibrium (Eq. 19.37) implies that the absolute temperatures of the two gases are the same:

$$T_A = T_B \quad \text{(thermal equilibrium)}. \quad (19.40)$$

We can obtain another consequence of the thermal equilibrium condition by taking the derivative of Eq. 19.32 with respect to E_{th}:

$$\frac{dS}{dE_{th}} = \frac{d}{dE_{th}}\left[\tfrac{3}{2}N \ln E_{th} - N \ln \frac{\delta\mathcal{V}}{b}\right] = \frac{d}{dE_{th}}\left[\tfrac{3}{2}N \ln E_{th}\right] = \tfrac{3}{2}\frac{N}{E_{th}}, \quad (19.41)$$

where the derivative of the term $N \ln(\delta\mathcal{V}/b)$ is zero because N, $\delta\mathcal{V}$, and b are constant. Substituting Eq. 19.41 into Eq. 19.37 and inverting the result yield

$$\frac{E_{th,A}}{N_A} = \frac{E_{th,B}}{N_B} \quad \text{(thermal equilibrium)}, \quad (19.42)$$

which is exactly the requirement for equipartition of energy: At thermal equilibrium the amount of thermal energy per atom is the same on either side of the partition.

19.23 Suppose 14 atoms are in compartment A and six atoms are in compartment B, as shown in Figure 19.23. When thermal equilibrium energy is reached, what percentage of the thermal energy do you expect to find in each compartment?

19.7 Properties of a monatomic ideal gas

Let us next connect some of the atomic parameters that describe an ideal gas to its macroscopic parameters. Consider a monatomic ideal gas that consists of a very large number N of indistinguishable atoms of mass m inside a closed rigid container of volume V. The collisions between the atoms and between the atoms and the walls of the container are all elastic. **Figure 19.25** shows one atom-wall collision. Because the collision is elastic, the speed v of the atom does not change; the collision simply reverses the direction of the velocity component v_x perpendicular to the wall, leaving the velocity component v_y parallel to the wall unchanged.

What is true for the atom in Figure 19.25 is true for all the other gas atoms. Therefore the forces exerted by the wall and by the atoms are perpendicular to the wall. The collisions between the wall and the gas atoms are the origin of the pressure in the gas.

19.24 Let the system comprising the atoms and wall in Figure 19.25 be isolated. (*a*) What is the direction of the atom's change in momentum? (*b*) What is the direction of the change in momentum of the wall? (*c*) How are these momentum changes related to the forces that wall and atom exert on each other?

As we saw in Section 18.5, the pressure P in a gas is equal to the magnitude of the force $\vec{F}_{gA}^c$ exerted by the gas on a surface per unit area. Because the force exerted by the gas on the surface and the force exerted by the surface on the gas form a interaction pair, we have $F_{gA}^c = F_{Ag}^c$. Over a section of wall of area A, Eq. 18.1 then yields

$$P \equiv \frac{F_{gA}^c}{A} = \frac{F_{Ag}^c}{A}. \tag{19.43}$$

The force exerted by the wall on the gas is equal to the rate of change in the momentum of the gas (see Section 8.7), and our task is to evaluate the magnitude of this rate of change. To simplify matters, we initially assume that the x component of the velocities of all the atoms in the gas have the same magnitude $|v_x|$. (We shall see shortly that our result doesn't depend on this oversimplification.) Let's begin by evaluating the change in momentum of a single gas atom when it collides with the wall. Each collision like the one in Figure 19.25 changes the sign of the x component of the atom's velocity, and so the magnitude of the atom's change in momentum is $2m|v_x|$.

To calculate the rate at which the magnitude of the momentum of the gas changes, we need to determine how many collisions occur within a finite time interval Δt. In order for an atom, for which the x component of its velocity is v_x, to collide with the wall in a time interval Δt, the atom has to be within a distance $|v_x|\Delta t$ of the wall. So let us consider all the atoms in a cylinder of cross-sectional area A and length $|v_x|\Delta t$ (**Figure 19.26**). At equilibrium, the atoms are uniformly distributed over the volume of the container, and so the number of atoms per unit volume is N/V. The volume of the cylinder is

Figure 19.25 An atom collides elastically with a wall, reversing the perpendicular component of the incoming velocity. Its speed remains unchanged.

Figure 19.26 On average, one half of the gas atoms contained in the cylinder strike the wall during a time interval Δt.

$A|v_x|\Delta t$, and so the number of atoms in the cylinder is $N_{cyl} = (N/V)A|v_x|\Delta t$. At any given instant, there should be as many atoms moving in the $+x$ direction as there are atoms moving in the $-x$ direction, and so half of the atoms in the cylinder in Figure 19.26 collide with the wall in the time interval Δt. The magnitude of the change in momentum for all gas atoms is thus equal to the number of collisions $N_{cyl}/2$ times the magnitude of the change in momentum $2m|v_x|$ for a single collision:

$$|\Delta p| = \tfrac{1}{2}\frac{N}{V}(A|v_x|\Delta t)(2m|v_x|) = \frac{NAmv_x^2}{V}\Delta t. \qquad (19.44)$$

To calculate the magnitude of the rate of change of the momentum of the gas, we divide the left and right sides of the equation by Δt:

$$\frac{|\Delta p|}{\Delta t} = \frac{NAmv_x^2}{V}. \qquad (19.45)$$

The quantity on the left, the magnitude of the rate of change of the momentum of the gas, is equal to the magnitude of the force exerted by the wall on the gas in the cylinder in Figure 19.26, and so, substituting Eq. 19.45 into Eq. 19.43, we obtain for the pressure in the gas

$$P = \frac{|\Delta p|/\Delta t}{A} = \frac{Nmv_x^2}{V}. \qquad (19.46)$$

In deriving Eq. 19.46 we used the unlikely assumption that the x components of the velocities of all atoms have the same magnitude $|v_x|$. When we use this assumption, each atom contributes a force $(Amv_x^2)/V$, and the force in Eq. 19.45 is the sum of N such forces. If the atoms move at different speeds, we should replace v_x^2 in Eq. 19.46 by the average value $(v_x^2)_{av}$. (We can do this because N times the average value of a quantity is equal to the sum of N actual values.)

When we use the relationship between $(v_x^2)_{av}$ and v_{rms}^2 expressed in Eq. 19.25, $v_{rms}^2 = 3(v_x^2)_{av}$, Eq. 19.46 becomes

$$P = \frac{Nm\tfrac{1}{3}v_{rms}^2}{V} = \tfrac{2}{3}\frac{N(\tfrac{1}{2}mv_{rms}^2)}{V} \qquad (19.47)$$

or, substituting $N(\tfrac{1}{2}mv_{rms}^2) = E_{th}$ (see Eq. 19.27),

$$P = \tfrac{2}{3}\frac{E_{th}}{V} \qquad \text{(monatomic ideal gas).} \qquad (19.48)$$

Equation. 19.47 shows that the pressure in a monatomic ideal gas is determined by two atomic parameters: the number density N/V and the average kinetic energy $\tfrac{1}{2}mv_{rms}^2$ of an atom.

We can obtain an expression for the thermal energy of a monatomic ideal gas by substituting Eq. 19.41, $dS/dE_{th} = \tfrac{3}{2}N/E_{th}$, into Eq. 19.38, $1/k_BT = dS/dE_{th}$. Doing this we obtain

$$\frac{1}{k_BT} = \tfrac{3}{2}\frac{N}{E_{th}} \qquad (19.49)$$

or

$$E_{th} = \tfrac{3}{2}Nk_BT \qquad \text{(monatomic ideal gas).} \qquad (19.50)$$

Substituting Eq. 19.50 into Eq. 19.48, we obtain

$$P = \frac{N}{V}k_BT \quad \text{(ideal gas system at equilibrium)}. \quad (19.51)$$

This relationship among pressure, volume, temperature, and number of atoms is called the **ideal gas law.** We obtained this result among macroscopic parameters (pressure, volume, temperature) by considering what happens at the atomic scale for a monatomic ideal gas. Experiments show that, at low pressure and high temperature, the ideal gas law describes the behavior of *any* gas at equilibrium, not just monatomic gases.

Because the thermal energy of a gas is the sum of the average kinetic energies of its atoms, $E_{th} = NK_{av}$ (Eq. 19.27), we can use the Eq. 19.50 expression for E_{th} and write

$$K_{av} = \tfrac{1}{2}mv_{rms}^2 = \tfrac{3}{2}k_BT. \quad (19.52)$$

Equation 19.52 allows us to obtain an expression for the rms speed of an atom in a monatomic ideal gas:

$$v_{rms} = \sqrt{\frac{3k_BT}{m}}. \quad (19.53)$$

The rms speed of a monatomic ideal gas atom is inversely proportional to the square root of the mass of the atom and proportional to the square root of the temperature of the gas. If the temperature of a gas goes up, the rms speed of the atoms goes up, too (**Figure 19.27**).

✋ **19.25** Use the ideal gas law to express the equilibrium condition in Eq. 19.20 in terms of pressure.

Figure 19.27 When the temperature of a monatomic ideal gas in a fixed volume is increased, the rms speed of the gas atoms increases.

T_1 $T_2 > T_1$

Example 19.11 Helium speed

A sample of helium gas containing 6.02×10^{23} atoms at atmospheric pressure (1.01×10^5 Pa) occupies a volume of 22.4×10^{-3} m³. The mass of a helium atom is 6.646×10^{-27} kg. What is the rms speed of the helium atoms?

❶ **GETTING STARTED** I can treat the helium gas as a monatomic ideal gas. The rms speed of the atoms is determined by the temperature of the sample, which is not given.

❷ **DEVISE PLAN** Equation 19.53 gives the rms speed of atoms in a monatomic ideal gas. I am given the mass m of one helium atom, but not the temperature T. To determine T I can use the ideal gas law (Eq. 19.51).

❸ **EXECUTE PLAN** From Eq. 19.51, I obtain $T = PV/(Nk_B)$. Substituting this expression for the temperature into Eq. 19.53 yields

$$v_{rms} = \sqrt{\frac{3k_BPV/(Nk_B)}{m}} = \sqrt{\frac{3PV}{mN}} = 1.30 \times 10^3 \text{ m/s.} ✔$$

❹ **EVALUATE RESULT** Those helium atoms sure are zipping around fast! At 1.30×10^3 m/s, however, they are moving about ten times more slowly than the escape speed from Earth (1.12×10^4 m/s; see Checkpoint 13.22), and so my result is at least not unreasonable. I also note that using my calculated rms speed in Eq. 19.47 yields a value of 1.01×10^5 Pa for P, giving me confidence in my answer.

✋ **19.26** A certain number of helium atoms are placed in one container, and an equal number of argon atoms are placed in a separate identical container. The pressure is the same in both containers. Helium atoms have a smaller mass than argon atoms. For which gas, if either, (*a*) is the thermal energy smaller, (*b*) is the average kinetic energy of an atom smaller, (*c*) is the rms speed of an atom smaller?

19.8 Entropy of a monatomic ideal gas

Now that we have derived an expression that gives the thermal energy of a gas in terms of its temperature (Eq. 19.50), we can express the entropy in terms of temperature. Substituting Eq. 19.50 into Eq. 19.32 gives

$$S = \tfrac{3}{2}N \ln\left(\tfrac{3}{2}Nk_\mathrm{B}T\right) - N \ln\frac{\delta \mathcal{V}}{b}$$

$$= \tfrac{3}{2}N \ln T + \tfrac{3}{2}N \ln\left(\tfrac{3}{2}Nk_\mathrm{B}\right) - N \ln\frac{\delta \mathcal{V}}{b} \tag{19.54}$$

or, taking all constant terms together,

$$S = \tfrac{3}{2}N \ln T + \text{constant (monatomic ideal gas in thermal equilibrium).}$$

$$\tag{19.55}$$

This expression describes a gas for which the energy is equipartitioned over the N atoms—that is, in thermal equilibrium. As before, the constant drops out when we consider changes in entropy (Eq. 19.8). For example, if the temperature of the gas is raised from T_i to T_f while the volume is kept constant, the change in entropy is

$$\Delta S = \tfrac{3}{2}N \ln\left(\frac{T_\mathrm{f}}{T_\mathrm{i}}\right) \quad \text{(constant volume).} \tag{19.56}$$

Example 19.12 Entropy change for a cooling gas

A sample of a monatomic ideal gas consisting of 1.00×10^{23} atoms in a volume of 4.00×10^{-3} m^3 is initially at a temperature of 290 K. The gas is cooled until it reaches a pressure of 5.00×10^4 N/m^2. (*a*) What is the change in entropy for the gas and for each atom? (*b*) What is the ratio of the final rms speed of each atom to its initial rms speed? (*c*) How does the change in the entropy of the gas depend on this ratio $v_{\mathrm{rms,f}}/v_{\mathrm{rms,i}}$?

❶ GETTING STARTED Both rms speed and entropy depend on temperature. As the gas cools, its temperature decreases, and so the rms speed of the atoms and the entropy of the gas both change.

❷ DEVISE PLAN I can use the ideal gas law, Eq. 19.51, to determine the final temperature of the gas. Once I know the final temperature, I can calculate the entropy change from Eq. 19.56 and the ratio of final to initial rms speeds from Eq. 19.53. To determine how the change in entropy depends on the ratio of rms speeds, I combine Eqs. 19.53 and Eq. 19.56.

❸ EXECUTE PLAN (*a*) From Eq. 19.51, the final temperature of the gas is

$$T_\mathrm{f} = \frac{P_\mathrm{f}V}{Nk_\mathrm{B}} = \frac{(5.00 \times 10^4 \text{ N/m}^2)(4.00 \times 10^{-3} \text{ m}^3)}{(1.00 \times 10^{23})(1.38 \times 10^{-23} \text{ J/K})} = 145 \text{ K.}$$

Equation 19.56 then yields for the change in the entropy of the gas:

$$\Delta S = S_\mathrm{f} - S_\mathrm{i} = \tfrac{3}{2}N \ln\left(\frac{T_\mathrm{f}}{T_\mathrm{i}}\right) = \tfrac{3}{2}(1.00 \times 10^{23}) \ln\left(\frac{145 \text{ K}}{290 \text{ K}}\right)$$

$$= -1.04 \times 10^{23}. ✔$$

Because there are 1.00×10^{23} atoms, the change in entropy per atom is -1.04. ✔

(*b*) From Eq. 19.53 I see that the ratio of final to initial rms speeds is $v_{\mathrm{rms,f}}/v_{\mathrm{rms,i}} = (T_\mathrm{f}/T_\mathrm{i})^{1/2} = [(145 \text{ K})/(290 \text{ K})]^{1/2} = 0.707$. ✔

(*c*) Because $a \ln N = \ln N^a$, I can write Eq. 19.56 as $\Delta S = N \ln(T_\mathrm{f}/T_\mathrm{i})^{3/2}$. From part *b* I know that $v_{\mathrm{rms,f}}/v_{\mathrm{rms,i}} = (T_\mathrm{f}/T_\mathrm{i})^{1/2}$, so I can write $T_\mathrm{f}/T_\mathrm{i} = v_{\mathrm{rms,f}}^2/v_{\mathrm{rms,i}}^2$. Combining these two expressions, I see that the relationship between the entropy change of the gas and the rms speed ratio of the atoms is $\Delta S = N \ln(v_{\mathrm{rms,f}}/v_{\mathrm{rms,i}})^3$. ✔

❹ EVALUATE RESULT As the gas cools, the rms speed of the atoms decreases, as my answer to part *b* shows. As the rms speed decreases, the number of basic states possible decreases, and so the entropy should decrease, in agreement with my answer to part *a*. Because the system is not closed, there is no reason its entropy cannot decrease, as I have found here.

Equation 19.50, $E_\mathrm{th} = \tfrac{3}{2}Nk_\mathrm{B}T$, tells me that the term on the right in Eq. 19.52 is equal to E_th/N, and from this it follows that E_th is proportional to v_{rms}^2. Equation 19.32 shows that the entropy is proportional to $\tfrac{3}{2}\ln E_\mathrm{th} = \ln E_\mathrm{th}^{3/2}$ and so to $\ln(v_{\mathrm{rms}}^2)^{3/2} = \ln v_{\mathrm{rms}}^3$, in agreement with my result in part *c*.

19.27 (a) Does the negative change in entropy in Example 19.12 violate the Eq. 19.5 part of the entropy law? (b) What is the change in the thermal energy of the gas in Example 19.12?

We can combine Eq. 19.55 with Eq. 19.7 to obtain an expression that tells us how entropy depends on both volume and temperature. To do so, remember that if we consider both the basic states associated with the spatial distribution of the atoms in a gas and those associated with the velocity distribution, the number of basic states associated with both types of distributions is the product of the number of each type of basic state (Eq. 19.9):

$$\Omega = \Omega_{space}\Omega_{vel}. \tag{19.57}$$

Taking the natural logarithm of this equation, we have, from $S \equiv \ln \Omega$,

$$S = S_{space} + S_{vel}. \tag{19.58}$$

To obtain an expression for the entropy of a gas that provides the dependence on both the volume and the temperature of the gas, we must therefore substitute Eqs. 19.7 and 19.55 into Eq. 19.58:

$$S = N \ln V + \tfrac{3}{2} N \ln T + \text{constant} \quad \text{(equilibrium)}, \tag{19.59}$$

where the constant term $-N \ln \delta V$ in Eqs. 19.7 has been combined with constant terms in Eq. 19.55 to give a new constant term. Equation 19.59 can also be written as

$$S = N \ln(T^{3/2}V) + \text{constant} \quad \text{(equilibrium)}. \tag{19.60}$$

Like Eqs. 19.7 and 19.55, Eq. 19.60 describes a system at equilibrium: If different compartments of the system are not at equilibrium with each other, the entropy of the system is smaller than that given by Eq. 19.60.

Equation 19.60 is in agreement with what we saw in the conceptual part of this chapter: As we increase either the temperature or the volume, the number of basic states—and therefore the entropy—increases. If the system changes from an equilibrium state with temperature T_i and volume V_i to a new equilibrium state with temperature T_f and volume V_f, the change in entropy is

$$\Delta S = \tfrac{3}{2}N \ln\left(\frac{T_f}{T_i}\right) + N \ln\left(\frac{V_f}{V_i}\right). \tag{19.61}$$

Most important, the change in entropy is independent of *how* the system is changed: ΔS depends on only the initial and final equilibrium states of the system. Note that for a system that is not closed, there are no constraints on ΔS: It can be positive, negative, or zero.

19.28 Does the entropy of a gas whose temperature is halved and volume doubled increase, decrease, or stay the same?

Chapter Glossary

SI units of physical quantities are given in parentheses.

Absolute temperature T (K) A quantity related to the rate of change of entropy with respect to thermal energy:

$$\frac{1}{k_B T} \equiv \frac{dS}{dE_{th}}, \quad (19.38)$$

where k_B is the Boltzmann constant.

Basic state The state of a system that is described using a complete specification of all the constituent particles.

Boltzmann constant k_B (J/K) A constant of proportionality that reconciles the units for absolute temperature with common temperature measurements:

$$k_B = 1.380 \times 10^{-23} \text{ J/K}. \quad (19.39)$$

Entropy S (unitless) A quantity equal to the natural logarithm of the number of basic states Ω for a system:

$$S \equiv \ln \Omega. \quad (19.4)$$

For a system of N particles contained in a volume V at a temperature T at equilibrium, the entropy is given by

$$S = N \ln(T^{3/2} V) + \text{constant} \quad \text{(equilibrium)}. \quad (19.60)$$

Entropy law (also called the *second law of thermodynamics*) A closed system always evolves so as to maximize the number of basic states. As the number of basic states increases, so does the entropy:

$$\Delta S > 0 \quad \text{(closed system evolving toward equilibrium)}. \quad (19.5)$$

At equilibrium, the number of basic states reaches its maximum value Ω_{max} and the entropy of the system no longer changes:

$$\Delta S = 0 \quad \text{(closed system at equilibrium)}. \quad (19.6)$$

Equilibrium state The macrostate of a system that has the greatest number of basic states and therefore is the most probable macrostate.

Equipartition of energy The equal distribution of energy among all constituent parts of a system.

Equipartition of space The equal distribution of particles over all available volume.

Ideal gas A gas that consists of a very large number of particles that move incoherently, occupy a negligible fraction of the volume occupied by the gas, and interact with one another and the walls of the container only via elastic collisions.

Ideal gas law A relationship among the pressure, volume, temperature, and number of atoms in an ideal gas system at equilibrium:

$$P = \frac{N}{V} k_B T \quad \text{(ideal gas system at equilibrium)}. \quad (19.51)$$

Kelvin (K) The SI base unit of absolute temperature.

Macrostate The state of a system that is described using only quantities that can be determined by measurements made on scales much larger than molecular sizes.

Probability The fraction of times that an event occurs in a large number of repetitions.

Root-mean-square speed v_{rms} (m/s) The square root of the average of the squares of the speeds of all the atoms in a volume of gas. For an ideal gas made up of atoms of mass m at temperature T, the rms speed is

$$v_{rms} = \sqrt{\frac{3k_B T}{m}}. \quad (19.53)$$

Second law of thermodynamics See *Entropy law*.

Thermal equilibrium The condition in which all parts of a system are at the same temperature. In this condition thermal energy is equipartitioned over the system and the entropy of the system is at its maximum.

20 Energy Transferred Thermally

20.1 Thermal interactions
20.2 Temperature measurement
20.3 Heat capacity
20.4 *PV* diagrams and processes

20.5 Change in energy and work
20.6 Isochoric and isentropic ideal gas processes
20.7 Isobaric and isothermal ideal gas processes
20.8 Entropy change in ideal gas processes
20.9 Entropy change in nonideal gas processes

CONCEPTS

QUANTITATIVE TOOLS

We use terms like *hot* and *cold, heating* and *temperature* based on our everyday interpretations of these words. We know from experience that to raise the temperature of water to the boiling point for a cup of tea, we need to heat the water, which requires energy. The branch of physics that deals with these concepts, called *thermodynamics* (from the Greek *therme,* meaning "heat," and *dunamis,* meaning "power"), was developed in the early 19th century to describe the working of steam engines. The concepts of entropy and absolute temperature introduced in Chapter 19 were developed as a consequence of that work. In this chapter we connect the statistical ideas from Chapter 19 to the macroscopic concepts of temperature, pressure, and volume.

20.1 Thermal interactions

The concept of temperature is familiar: It's a measure of "hotness." According to what we saw in Chapter 19, if two objects that are not at the same temperature are placed in contact with each other, energy is transferred from the object at the higher temperature to the object at the lower temperature until the temperatures of the two are equal. We attribute this transfer of energy to a **thermal interaction** between the two objects at different temperatures. As we saw in Chapter 19, this thermal interaction is the overall effect of countless interactions at the atomic scale.

Let us begin by considering the familiar situation shown in **Figure 20.1**: heating a pot of water on a stove. As we heat the water, energy flows from the flame to the pot and then from the pot to the water. The flame, which is hotter (that is, at a higher temperature) than the pot, heats the pot, and the pot, which is hotter than the water, heats the water. If we consider the water as our system and make an energy

diagram for that system, we obtain the result shown in **Figure 20.2**. As the water gets hotter, its thermal energy increases. The burning flame provides that energy, but it is not part of the system, and so there is no change in our system's source energy. The system's kinetic energy and potential energy do not change either, and so the system's energy increases because of the increase in thermal energy.

How do we account for this increase in the energy of the system? Although there are external forces exerted on the water—the force of gravity and a normal force exerted by the pot on the water—neither force causes any displacement, and so does no work on the system.

Consequently the energy diagram of Figure 20.2 is unbalanced: The energy changes are not equal to the work done on the system. The reason for this unbalance is that this energy diagram does not account for the energy transferred into the system by the heating. To make the diagram complete, we need to add a bar that represents the energy transferred into the system by the thermal interactions among the flame, pot, and water. The amount of energy transferred by thermal interactions ("thermally") is denoted by the letter Q (**Figure 20.3**). The law of conservation of energy requires that the change in the energy of the system be equal to the energy transferred into it, so the height of the bar representing Q in Figure 20.3 has to be equal to the height of the bar representing the increase in thermal energy.

20.1 (*a*) What are the SI units of Q? (*b*) For the process depicted in Figure 20.2*a*, make an energy diagram for each of these systems: (*i*) water, pot, and flame; (*ii*) pot and flame; (*iii*) pot.

Figure 20.1 When a gas burner heats a pot of water, energy flows from higher temperature to lower temperature.

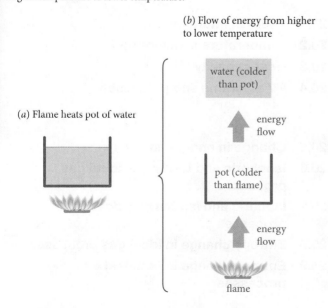

(*a*) Flame heats pot of water

(*b*) Flow of energy from higher to lower temperature

water (colder than pot)

energy flow

pot (colder than flame)

energy flow

flame

Figure 20.2 When a pot of water is heated, the energy diagram for a system comprising only the water is unbalanced.

(*a*) Initial and final states

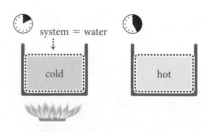

system = water

cold

hot

(*b*) Energy diagram for system

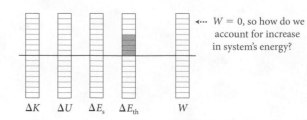

$\cdots$ $W = 0$, so how do we account for increase in system's energy?

ΔK ΔU ΔE_s ΔE_{th} W

Figure 20.3 To complete the energy diagram of Figure 20.2, we must add a bar to account for the energy transferred thermally into the system (represented by the symbol Q).

Bar accounts for energy
transferred thermally to system.

$$\Delta K \quad \Delta U \quad \Delta E_s \quad \Delta E_{th} \quad W \quad Q$$

The quantity Q is frequently called *heat*, a term we shall avoid because it is easy to confuse the verb *to heat* with the noun and to think of "heat" as a property of an object instead of a quantity of energy transferred across a boundary. When it is necessary to refer to Q by name, we shall use the term **energy transferred thermally,** reserving the verb *to heat* to refer to the process of increasing the thermal energy of a system. (For example, *I am heating a pot of water* means that I am increasing its thermal energy.)

Now consider the situation in **Figure 20.4a,** where two gases are separated by a fixed partition that is not thermally insulating. Initially gas A in the left compartment is at a lower temperature than gas B in the right compartment. Because the partition is not thermally insulating, the gases interact thermally, and energy is transferred thermally from the hotter gas to the colder one until their temperatures are the same. The energy transferred thermally is represented by the arrow labeled Q. The energy diagram for gas A in Figure 20.4b consequently shows an increase in thermal energy and the energy transferred thermally, Q, is positive.

 20.2 Make an energy diagram for gas B in Figure 20.4.

As Checkpoint 20.2 shows, the sign of Q depends on the direction of the energy transfer. Just as for work, if the transfer is into the system (that is, the energy of the system increases), Q is positive (Figure 20.4b); if the transfer is out of the system, Q is negative (Checkpoint 20.2).

Let us examine in more detail the difference between transferring energy by doing work on a system (that is, through mechanical interactions) and by transferring energy thermally to it. In **Figure 20.5a** a spring-loaded piston compresses an ideal gas into a smaller volume, doing work on the gas. We shall ignore any friction between the piston and the container walls. The ideal gas is *thermally insulated;* that is, it is not interacting thermally with its surroundings. A process that does not involve any thermal transfer of energy is called an **adiabatic process** ($Q = 0$).

Because the process depicted in Figure 20.5a is adiabatic, the amount of energy transferred to the gas is equal to the work done on the gas by the piston and is determined by the force $\vec{F}_{Pg}^c$ exerted by the piston on the gas and the force displacement $\Delta \vec{x}_F$.

How is the energy of the gas raised? There are no changes in the kinetic energy of the center of mass of the

Figure 20.4 When gases of different temperatures are placed in thermal contact, energy is transferred thermally from the hotter to the cooler gas until the temperatures of the two gases are the same.

(a) Gases at different temperatures are placed in thermal contact

partition: fixed,
not thermally insulating

low T high T same T

gas A Q gas B   gas A   gas B

energy transferred thermally

(b) Energy diagram for gas A

$$\Delta K \quad \Delta U \quad \Delta E_s \quad \Delta E_{th} \quad W \quad Q$$

Figure 20.5 A piston does work on a thermally insulated ideal gas, increasing the gas's temperature.

(a) Spring-loaded piston compresses thermally insulated ideal gas

thermal insulation   movable piston

$\vec{F}_{Pg}^c$ $\vec{F}_{Pg}^c$

gas

Gas is thermally insulated, so $Q = 0$. $\Delta \vec{x}_P$

(b) Energy diagram for gas

$Q = 0$ (process is adiabatic)

$$\Delta K \quad \Delta U \quad \Delta E_s \quad \Delta E_{th} \quad W \quad Q$$

Figure 20.6 A stationary piston does not change the speed of a gas particle that collides with it, but a moving piston does.

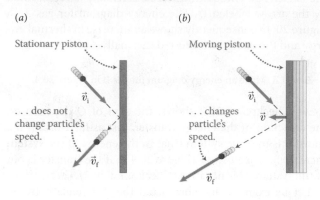

(a) Stationary piston . . .

$\vec{v}_i$

. . . does not change particle's speed.

$\vec{v}_f$

(b) Moving piston . . .

$\vec{v}_i$

$\vec{v}$

. . . changes particle's speed.

$\vec{v}_f$

gas because the gas as a whole remains at rest. There are also no changes in the potential energy of the gas because there is no potential energy associated with the interactions between particles in an ideal gas. Nor are there any changes in the source energy. Therefore the work W done on the gas must raise the thermal energy of the gas (Figure 20.5b). We can understand how this happens by considering the (elastic) collisions of the gas particles with the piston. If a particle collides with the stationary piston (**Figure 20.6a**), the particle's speed is unaltered by the collision. When the piston is moving toward the incoming particle, however, the particle gains speed because of the collision and therefore its kinetic energy increases, just as a tennis ball bounces

faster off your racquet when you swing it toward the ball. So, as the piston moves in, the particles colliding with it speed up (Figure 20.6b), increasing their incoherent kinetic energy and thus the thermal energy of the gas.

Note that in Figure 20.5a the volume decreases. During this decrease, the force exerted by the piston on the gas and the force displacement are in the same direction. Consequently the work done on the gas is positive. Had the piston moved in the opposite direction (expanding the volume), the work done on the gas would have been negative.

> **When the volume of a gas decreases, the work done on the gas is positive. When the volume increases, the work done on the gas is negative. When there is no change in volume, the work done on the gas is zero.**

Summarizing the information from Figures 20.4 and 20.5, we see that there are two ways to transfer energy to a system: mechanically (by doing work on the system) and thermally (see the box "Transferring energy to a system"). Both types of transfer can occur simultaneously. In that case the change in the energy of the system ΔE is equal to the sum of the work done on the system, W, and the energy transferred thermally to it, Q.

Let us now turn our attention to the transformation of a system from one macrostate to another. Such a transformation is called a **process**, and if the process is carried out in such a way that the system remains very close to equilibrium at all instants during the process, the process is said to be **quasistatic**.

Transferring energy to a system

	DOING WORK	TRANSFERRING ENERGY THERMALLY
Technical term:	Mechanical interaction between system and its environment	Thermal interaction between system and its environment
Mediated by:	Macroscopic pushes and pulls	Atomic collisions
Requires:	A nonzero external force $\vec{F}_{ext}$ exerted on the system and a nonzero force displacement $\Delta \vec{x}_F$	A nonzero temperature difference ΔT between the system and its environment.
Amount of energy transferred *into* system:	W ("work done on system")	Q ("energy transferred thermally to system")
Sign:	$W > 0$ when external force and force displacement are in the same direction (energy of system increases in absence of other transfers)	$Q > 0$ when environment is at a higher temperature than system (energy of system increases in absence of other transfers)
	$W < 0$ when external force and force displacement are in opposite directions (energy of system decreases in absence of other transfers)	$Q < 0$ when environment is at a lower temperature than system (energy of system decreases in absence of other transfers)
Equilibrium:	The vector sum of the external forces is zero, and the force displacement of each external force is zero (mechanical equilibrium)	System is at same temperature as its environment (thermal equilibrium)

Figure 20.7 Quasistatic versus non-quasistatic expansion of a cylinder containing a gas.

(*a*) Quasistatic expansion: piston rises gradually

— At all instants, gas fills container uniformly (is in equilibrium). —

(*b*) Non-quasistatic expansion: piston rises suddenly

— Gas catching up with piston; —   — Gas reaches
out of equilibrium.   equilibrium.

Figure 20.7a shows the expansion of a volume of gas in a cylinder. To make the expansion quasistatic, the piston is moved slowly so that the gas always uniformly fills all the available space, and each particle has its equipartition share of the thermal energy. In each frame shown in the drawing, the gas is in a different state, but each state is an equilibrium state. In a quasistatic process, therefore, the pressure may change during the process, but at any given instant the pressure has a uniform, well-defined value at all locations in the volume of gas. The same is true of the temperature: The final temperature may differ from the initial temperature, but at any given instant the temperature has a uniform, well-defined value at all locations in the volume of gas. There are no locations where the pressure is greater and no spots that are hotter than others. In Figure 20.7a, the entropy changes as the gas expands (because the entropy of an ideal gas changes with volume and temperature, Eq. 19.60), but at each instant it has the maximum value for that equilibrium state.

Suppose, however, that the piston moves at a rapid speed, as illustrated in Figure 20.7b. The motion of the piston is so fast that the gas can't keep up with it. In frame 2, for example, the gas still mostly occupies the original volume. Consequently, the pressure at the bottom of the cylinder is still nearly the same as it was in frame 1, while it is nearly zero at the top, where we still have a vacuum. Although the piston reaches its final position in frame 3, it takes the gas another three frames before it is evenly distributed and in equilibrium. In frames 2–5 of Figure 20.7b, the gas is not in equilibrium, and so the entropy is not maximum. Because

particles in a gas typically move at very great speeds, they redistribute themselves rapidly. Thus, in practice, even if a piston moves rapidly as in Figure 20.5, the resulting process can still be quasistatic.

✋ **20.3** Suppose you were to play the two film clips shown in Figure 20.7 backward. Would the resulting processes be possible?

Let us now examine how the entropy changes when energy is transferred to a system in a quasistatic process. First consider the process shown in Figure 20.4, where energy is transferred thermally between two gases. The energy transferred thermally to gas A is positive ($Q > 0$). The temperature of gas A increases. Therefore by Eq. 19.56 the entropy of the gas increases. Conversely, Q is negative for gas B, the temperature of B decreases, and so its entropy decreases. Consequently, the sign of the entropy change of a system is the same as the sign of Q for that system:

Transferring energy thermally to a system increases its entropy. Transferring energy thermally from a system decreases its entropy.

Next, let us determine what happens to the entropy of a system when work is done on it in the absence of any thermal interaction ($Q = 0$). Consider, for example, the quasistatic compression of the thermally insulated gas in Figure 20.5 again. As the piston does work on the gas, the thermal energy of the gas goes up, but at the same time the volume goes down. In Chapter 19 we saw that an increase in the thermal energy of a system raises its entropy. A decrease in the system volume, however, lowers the entropy, so we can't say offhand what happens to the entropy of the gas as it is compressed.

Let us therefore consider the closed system consisting of the contents of the box in Figure 20.5a. In contrast to the equilibration of temperatures in Figure 20.4, which is an irreversible process, the compression of the gas and the expansion of the spring are reversible. Because the process is quasistatic, the system remains in equilibrium at all instants during the compression, and therefore the entropy law tells us that the entropy of the (closed) system doesn't change: $\Delta S = 0$ (Eq. 19.6).

Because we are interested in the process (which takes place in the gas), we divide the system into two parts: the gas and the spring-loaded piston ("piston" for short). Because entropy is an extensive quantity, we can write the change in the system's entropy as $\Delta S = \Delta S_{gas} + \Delta S_{piston} = 0$.

In the spring-loaded piston, potential energy is converted to kinetic energy, both of which are coherent forms of energy (see Figure 7.10). Regardless of the speed of the piston and the configuration of the spring, there is only one way to distribute the energy and atoms such that all the energy is coherent. At any instant, therefore, the number of basic states of the spring-loaded piston is 1, and so the entropy of the spring-loaded piston does not change: $\Delta S_{piston} = 0$.

If $\Delta S_{\text{piston}} = 0$ and $\Delta S = 0$, then the entropy of the gas cannot change either: $\Delta S_{\text{gas}} = 0$. So we can conclude that in a quasistatic process during which we do work on a gas without thermally transferring any energy to it ($Q = 0$), the entropy of the gas does not change. Generalizing this idea to any type of system undergoing a quasistatic adiabatic process, we can state:

The entropy of a system undergoing a quasistatic adiabatic process does not change.

In a quasistatic adiabatic process, the temperature and volume changes are coordinated in such a way as to keep the entropy constant. This conclusion holds for only *quasistatic* adiabatic processes. For instance, in Example 19.9, a gas adiabatically expands into a larger volume, increasing the entropy of the gas. The expansion is adiabatic, but not quasistatic. Therefore the entropy of a system undergoing a non-quasistatic adiabatic process can change.

20.4 Which of the following systems undergo a quasistatic process? (*a*) A gas-containing balloon is popped inside a vacuum container. System: container, gas, and balloon. (*b*) A cup of coffee cools down. System: coffee. (*c*) A sample of compressed gas in a cylinder fitted with a heavy piston is allowed to expand, pushing the piston outward. System: gas. (*d*) An ice cube melts in a glass of hot water. System: water and ice cube.

20.2 Temperature measurement

In Chapter 19 we defined the absolute temperature as a rather abstract concept related to the rate at which entropy changes with changes in thermal energy. Entropy is a measure of the number of available basic states in a system, and thermal energy is the energy associated with the incoherent internal motion of the system. Neither of these quantities can be measured directly. We must therefore figure out some convenient way to measure the temperature of an object.

Most of the methods that have been developed to measure temperature rely on measuring some physical quantity that varies with temperature. For example, in a glass thermometer, illustrated in **Figure 20.8**, the thermal expansion of a liquid provides a means of measuring temperature. A glass tube is connected to a bulb filled with glycerine, mercury or some other liquid whose mass density decreases with rising temperature. Because the mass of the liquid is constant, its volume expands and therefore the temperature can be determined by measuring the height of the liquid in the glass tube. To calibrate this type of thermometer, it is placed in melting ice and allowed to come to thermal equilibrium. Once equilibrium is reached, a mark is made on the glass tube at the height of the liquid in the tube. The thermometer is then placed in boiling water and allowed to come to thermal equilibrium. The tube is marked at the new height of the liquid in the tube. The two marks on the tube are assigned some standard values representing the freezing

Figure 20.8 Calibrating a gas thermometer by immersing its bulb in ice water and then in boiling water.

To calibrate thermometer . . .

(*a*)
. . . we mark height of liquid when bulb is dipped in ice water . . .

(*b*)
. . . and then in boiling water.

and boiling points of water—historically 0 °C and 100 °C, respectively.

Now, if the expansion of the liquid is proportional to temperature, the temperature of any substance can be measured by immersing the thermometer in the substance and noting how far up the glass tube the enclosed liquid rises. If the thermometer is immersed in a glass of milk and the liquid in the tube rises, say, 27/100 of the distance between the 0 °C mark and the 100 °C mark, the temperature of the milk is 27 °C. Of course, in commercial thermometers there is no need to measure heights in fractions because the glass tube is marked all along its length and the temperature is read directly.

Is the expansion of a liquid proportional to the absolute temperature we defined in Chapter 19? No—as a matter of fact, the expansion of one liquid isn't even proportional to that of another liquid. For this reason, glass thermometers are accurate over only a relatively narrow range of temperatures.

How, then can we measure temperature accurately? In Section 19.7 we derived the ideal gas law, $P = Nk_{\text{B}}T/V$, which relates the absolute temperature to two macroscopic quantities that are easily measured: pressure and volume. This law is a direct consequence of our definition of absolute temperature and is valid for an ideal gas, that is, it is valid as long as the pressure, volume, and absolute temperature are such that we can ignore the internal structure of the gas particles and the interactions between particles (except for collisions between them). No gas is ideal, but many gases can approximate ideal behavior. For a dilute gas of helium atoms, for instance, the conditions for ideal behavior are satisfied down to temperatures that are quite low.

Figure 20.9 illustrates the basic principle of an **ideal gas thermometer**, which measures the pressure in a gas sample kept enclosed in a fixed volume. A bulb filled with a gas at low pressure is connected to a thin, flexible U-shaped tube that contains mercury. The end of the tube opposite

Figure 20.9 An ideal gas thermometer.

the gas-filled bulb is capped and evacuated. The difference in height between the levels of mercury in the two arms of the tube determines the pressure in the gas in the bulb (see Section 18.6). For a fixed value of V, the ideal gas law, $P = Nk_BT/V$, tells us that the pressure P is proportional to the absolute temperature T.

Suppose now that the absolute temperature of the gas in the bulb is raised. The pressure in the gas increases, pushing the mercury in the left arm down below the reference mark and increasing the volume V of the gas, as illustrated in Figure 20.10a. To restore the gas to its original volume,

we raise the right arm of the flexible U-tube until the mercury level in the left arm is back at the reference mark (Figure 20.10b).

Provided the mercury level in the left arm is always kept at the reference mark, the volume V of the gas is fixed and the height h of the mercury in the right arm measures the pressure in the gas at a constant volume. Under these conditions, the height h is a direct measure of the pressure and therefore the absolute temperature T. The ideal gas law tells us that at $T = 0$ the pressure is zero, which means there is a vacuum above both arms of the U-shaped tube. So we know that at $T = 0$ the height h should be zero.

To calibrate the thermometer and define the unit of absolute temperature, we need to find some reproducible thermal phenomenon and assign it a fixed value. The current standard of absolute temperature is based on the **triple point of water**—the unique conditions under which liquid water, solid ice, and water vapor (a gas) coexist in thermal equilibrium. To relate absolute temperature to historical definitions of temperature, the absolute temperature at the triple point of water is set at 273.16 K:*

$$T_{tp} \equiv 273.16 \text{ K.}$$

Once the height of the mercury column in an ideal gas thermometer has been measured at the triple point of water, we can draw a straight line between the origin at $T = 0$, where we know h should be zero, and the triple point. We can then determine any other absolute temperature simply by reading off the absolute temperature corresponding to the measured height (**Figure 20.11**). The important point is that the curve is linear: As long as the gas behaves like an ideal gas and is kept at constant volume, the pressure (and therefore the height of the mercury column) is directly proportional to the absolute temperature.

Figure 20.10 Using an ideal gas thermometer to measure temperature.

Figure 20.11 The height-versus-temperature graph is linear for an ideal gas thermometer. The thermometer is calibrated at the triple point of water. Any temperature can then be read from the graph.

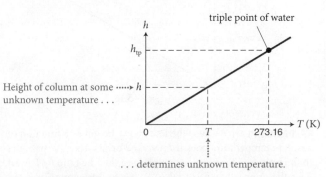

*The triple point of water occurs at a temperature of 0.01 °C (roughly 32 °F) and a pressure of 610 Pa (about one-hundredth of atmospheric pressure).

Temperature measurement scales

Methods for measuring and defining temperature were developed long before the development of the gas thermometer and the concept of absolute temperature. Starting in the early 18th century, several scales were defined for measuring temperature, two of which are still in use. The most widely used scale is the *Celsius scale*. Temperatures on this scale are measured in units that are called *degrees Celsius* (°C) and that have the same magnitude as the kelvin (a temperature change of 1 °C is the same as a temperature change of 1 K). The zero of the Celsius scale is the freezing point of water, and the boiling point of water (at a pressure of 101.325 kPa) is set at 100 °C.

We can convert between the Celsius and Kelvin scales as follows. If T_C represents the temperature expressed in degrees Celsius and T the absolute temperature expressed in kelvins, we have

$$T_C = \frac{1\,°C}{1\,K}T - 273.15\,°C. \tag{1}$$

The older *Fahrenheit scale* is used in the United States. Temperatures on this scale are measured in units called *degrees Fahrenheit* (°F). On this temperature scale, the freezing point of water is 32 °F and the boiling point is 212 °F, placing the boiling and freezing points of water exactly 180 °F apart. If T_F is the temperature expressed in degrees Fahrenheit, the relationship between the Celsius and the Fahrenheit scales is

$$T_C = \frac{5\,°C}{9\,°F}(T_F - 32\,°F). \tag{2}$$

Notice that no degree symbol, °, is used with kelvins: 13.0 °C, 55.4 °F, but 286 K. Readings in degrees Celsius or Fahrenheit can be negative, but readings in kelvins are always positive.

Example 20.1 Measuring absolute temperature

When the bulb of an ideal gas thermometer is immersed in water at the triple point, the height of the mercury column above the reference mark is 760 mm. The same thermometer is then immersed in a sample of unknown temperature, and the height of the mercury column moves to 1167 mm above the reference mark. What is the absolute temperature of the sample?

❶ **GETTING STARTED** The height of the mercury column is linearly proportional to the absolute temperature. I therefore begin by making a graph like Figure 20.11, summarizing the information given in the problem (**Figure 20.12**). I denote the unknown absolute temperature by T and the height of the mercury at this unknown temperature by $h = 1167$ mm.

Figure 20.12

❷ **DEVISE PLAN** Because the line giving height as a function of absolute temperature goes through the origin, its slope is equal to the ratio h_{tp}/T_{tp}. From my graph I see that the ratio h/T must have the same value: $h/T = h_{tp}/T_{tp}$. From this expression I can calculate the unknown temperature.

❸ **EXECUTE PLAN** Solving for T, I get $T = T_{tp}h/h_{tp} = (273.16\ \text{K})(1167\ \text{mm})/(760\ \text{mm}) = 419\ \text{K}.$ ✔

❹ **EVALUATE RESULT** The absolute temperature I obtain is about 50% higher than T_{tp}, which is what I would expect, given that the mercury height is about 50% higher than that at the triple point.

In principle, the operation of the ideal gas thermometer as described above is independent of the gas used—we can use *any* gas we want. In practice, deviations from the ideal gas law complicate matters a bit, and the science and technology of gas thermometers are more complex than presented here. Nonetheless, gas thermometers serve as the standard reference for all other types of thermometers. Commercial thermometers typically give the temperature on a different scale (see the box "Temperature measurement scales" and **Table 20.1**). In thermodynamics, and in physics in general, it makes the most sense to use absolute temperatures. For simplicity we shall henceforth refer to the absolute temperature T expressed in kelvins simply as *temperature*.

In drawing Figure 20.11 we assumed that we can extrapolate the linear relationship between pressure and temperature from the ideal gas law down to zero. In practice, it is impossible for any gas to reach this temperature because as the temperature decreases, the gas condenses into a liquid. Of all gases, helium becomes liquid at the lowest temperature (4.22 K, which corresponds to −269 °C or −452 °F), and so its useful range extends below that of any other gas. Zero temperature ($T = 0$) is called **absolute zero.** Any system at absolute zero has zero entropy (that is, it has only one available basic state), and its thermal energy is a minimum. Absolute zero therefore is the limit of low temperature.

CONCEPTS

Table 20.1 Comparison of temperature scales (defining points in bold)

Temperature	Kelvin (K)	Celsius (°C)	Fahrenheit (°F)
Absolute zero	0	−273.15	−459.67
Water freezes (at a pressure of 101.325 kPa)	273.15	**0**	**32**
Triple point of water	**273.16**	0.01	32
Room temperature	293	20	68
Average human body temperature	310	37.0	98.6
Water boils (at a pressure of 101.325 kPa)	373.12	**100**	**212**
Titanium melts	1941	1668	3034
Surface of the Sun	5778	5505	9941

Exercise 20.2 Temperature conversions

Derive an expression for converting a temperature (a) from the Celsius scale to the Fahrenheit scale, (b) from the Kelvin scale to the Fahrenheit scale, and (c) from the Fahrenheit scale to the Kelvin scale.

SOLUTION (a) To obtain an expression for the temperature T_F measured in degrees Fahrenheit in terms of the temperature T_C measured in degrees Celsius, I use Eq. 2 from the "Temperature measurement scales" box, solving this expression for T_F:

$$T_F = \frac{9\,°F}{5\,°C} T_C + 32\,°F. ✔$$

(b) Substituting the expression for converting degrees Celsius to kelvins yields

$$T_F = \frac{9\,°F}{5\,°C}\left(\frac{1\,°C}{1\,K} T - 273.15\,°C\right) + 32\,°F. ✔$$

(c) I can use the expression for T_F I obtained in part b. Solving for T yields:

$$T = \left[\frac{1\,K}{1\,°C}\frac{5\,°C}{9\,°F}(T_F - 32\,°F)\right] + 273.15\,K. ✔$$

20.5 (a) During a certain day the outdoor temperature ranges between 60 °F and 80 °F. What is the corresponding range in degrees Celsius and in kelvins? (b) The filament temperature of an incandescent light bulb is about 2800 K. What is the corresponding temperature in degrees Celsius and in degrees Fahrenheit? (Assume only two significant digits in 2800 K.)

20.3 Heat capacity

The amount of energy it takes to raise the temperature of an object depends on the amount and kind of material in the object. Indeed, we know from experience that it takes longer to heat a large pot full of water than to heat the same pot containing only a cup of water. The larger quantity of water requires more energy, and therefore more gas needs to be burned.

We can characterize how much energy it takes to raise the temperature of an object by a scalar quantity called the object's **heat capacity.** The heat capacity of an object is equal to the amount of energy transferred thermally to the object divided by the resulting change in temperature.* The SI unit of heat capacity is J/K.

20.6 Which is greater in each pair: (a) the thermal energy of a pool of water or that of a glass of water at the same temperature, (b) the heat capacity of a pool of water or that of a glass of water at the same temperature, (c) the thermal energy of a cold glass of water or that of an equal amount of warm water?

Because heat capacity is an extensive quantity (it depends on the amount of material in an object), it makes sense to introduce a related intensive quantity so that we can compare the thermal properties of different materials. Traditionally, heat capacity is turned into an intensive quantity by dividing it by the mass of the object. The resulting quantity, called **specific heat capacity** and denoted by the lowercase letter c, is a measure of how much energy is required to raise the temperature of 1 kg of a certain material by 1 K. The adjective *specific* means "per unit mass." The SI unit of specific heat capacity is J/K · kg.

Table 20.2 gives the specific heat capacities of a variety of materials. As you can see, different materials have very different specific heat capacities. For example, it takes about ten times less energy to raise the temperature of a 1-kg block of copper by 1 K (385 J) than it takes to raise the temperature of an equal mass of water by 1 K (4181 J).

Why are these values so different from one another, and what determines the specific heat capacity of a material? Remember from Chapter 19 that when an object is in thermal equilibrium, its thermal energy is equally distributed among all the parts of the object that can store energy. Clearly, different materials have different abilities to store thermal energy. To understand these differences, let us first examine the heat capacity of an ideal gas.

---

*Strictly speaking this quantity is the average heat capacity, but because the heat capacity does not depend much on temperature, we can omit the word "average".

Table 20.2 Specific heat capacities

Material	c (J/K · kg)
alcohol	2436
aluminum	897
brass	385
carbon graphite	685
copper	385
glass	837
gold	130
helium	3116
ice (268 K)	2090
iron	449
lead	130
marble	860
mercury	140
nickel	443
platinum	133
silver	235
steam (373 K)	1556
titanium	527
water	4181
wood	1700
zinc	388

All values are reported at a temperature of 298 K (unless otherwise noted) and atmospheric pressure and with the gases held at constant volume.

Table 20.3 Heat capacities per particle in units of k_B

Class	Material	C_V/k_B
Monatomic gases	helium	1.50
	argon	1.50
	krypton	1.50
	xenon	1.51
	radon	1.51
Polyatomic gases	ammonia	3.37
	hydrogen	2.47
	nitrogen	2.50
Liquids	mercury	3.38
	water	8.97
Solids	aluminum	2.91
	copper	2.94
	gold	3.08
	iron	3.02
	silver	3.05
	titanium	3.04
	zinc	3.05

All values are reported at a temperature of 298 K and atmospheric pressure and with gases held at constant volume (as indicated by the subscript V on C_V).

In Chapter 19 we found that the thermal energy of a monatomic ideal gas is given by $E_{th} = \frac{3}{2}Nk_BT$ (Eq. 19.50). Each of the N ideal gas atoms thus has an average amount of thermal energy equal to $\frac{3}{2}k_BT$, where $k_B = 1.381 \times 10^{-23}$ J/K is the Boltzmann constant. We arrived at this result by considering the kinetic energy associated with the motion of an ideal gas atom along the x, y, and z directions (see Section 19.6). The motion along each axis is called a **degree of freedom.** Because there are three independent axes for translation, there are three "translational degrees of freedom." In thermal equilibrium, the equipartition of energy provides each translational degree of freedom of each atom with an equal share of the thermal energy—the **equipartition energy share** $\frac{1}{2}k_BT$—for a total of $\frac{3}{2}k_BT$ per atom.

If we raise the temperature of an ideal gas by 1 K, the thermal energy of the gas goes up by $\frac{3}{2}Nk_B(1\text{ K})$, and that of each atom goes up by $\frac{3}{2}k_B(1\text{ K})$. If this energy is transferred thermally to the gas, we expect the heat capacity per atom to be equal to $\frac{3}{2}k_B$.

Table 20.3 lists the heat capacities per particle, denoted by the uppercase letter C, in units of k_B for a number of substances. As you can see, it is indeed $\frac{3}{2}$ for monatomic gases, such as helium and argon, but deviates from this value for polyatomic gases. For hydrogen, for example, the value is closer to $\frac{5}{2}$ than to $\frac{3}{2}$, suggesting that a hydrogen molecule has two additional degrees of freedom that can store energy.

The reason for this discrepancy is that we treated each ideal gas particle as an atom that has only kinetic energy associated with translational motion along three independent axes.

A dumbbell-shaped hydrogen molecule (**Figure 20.13a**), however, also has energy associated with rotational motion. The molecule can rotate about three independent axes (Figure 20.13b). Rotation about the z axis does not store any appreciable energy, because the rotational inertia about that axis is negligibly small.* So each hydrogen molecule has two additional "rotational degrees of freedom" for a total of five (three translational and two rotational). If each degree of freedom stores its equipartition share of $\frac{1}{2}k_BT$, we should obtain an energy per molecule of $\frac{5}{2}k_BT$. Consequently we expect a heat capacity per particle of $\frac{5}{2}k_B$, in good agreement with the experimental value of $2.47k_B$.

✋ **20.7** Consider the four-atom ammonia molecule illustrated in **Figure 20.14**. (a) Which of the three rotational degrees of freedom can store thermal energy? (b) Based on your answer to part a, what is the thermal energy per molecule? (c) What is the heat capacity per molecule? (d) Does your prediction in part c agree with the experimental value listed in Table 20.3?

---

*Although the atoms have a diameter of about 10^{-10} m and are separated by about the same distance, nearly all the mass is concentrated in the nucleus, which has a smaller diameter of about 10^{-15} m. Therefore the "bar" connecting the two atoms at the end of the H_2 dumbbell is about 10^5 times greater than the diameter of the atoms, and so the rotational inertia about the axis running through the length of the bar of the dumbbell is essentially zero (see Checkpoint 11.4).

Figure 20.13 A diatomic molecule has energy associated with rotation about two axes, as well as energy associated with translation along three axes.

(*a*) Diatomic molecule

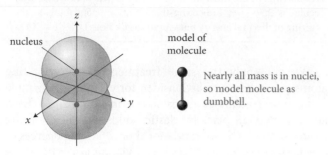

(*b*) Rotational degrees of freedom for diatomic molecule

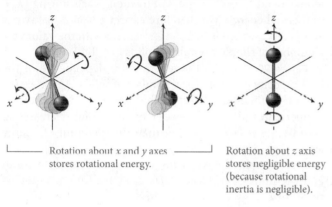

Rotation about *x* and *y* axes stores rotational energy.

Rotation about *z* axis stores negligible energy (because rotational inertia is negligible).

Figure 20.15 shows how, for a gas of diatomic hydrogen molecules, the heat capacity per particle in units of k_B varies with temperature. Notice how the heat capacity per particle in units of k_B is close to 2.5 (the value listed in Table 20.3) only around room temperature. As the temperature is lowered to about 50 K, the heat capacity per particle in units of k_B decreases to 1.5 (or $\frac{3}{2}$). Why does hydrogen gas behave like a monatomic ideal gas at low temperatures? To ask the same question another way, why doesn't the rotational-degrees-of-freedom argument presented above for hydrogen hold at low temperatures? The experimental data suggest that, at low temperatures, the rotational motions of the molecules do not contribute to their thermal energy.

Figure 20.14 Ammonia molecule.

nitrogen

hydrogen

hydrogen

hydrogen

Figure 20.15 Temperature dependence of the heat capacity per particle *C* in units of k_B for hydrogen gas molecules.

The reason for this behavior is that, according to quantum mechanics, vibrational and rotational energy comes in small fixed amounts, called quanta. Below about 100 K, the equipartition share $\frac{1}{2}k_B T$ is smaller than the quantum of energy needed to make a molecule rotate about one of the possible rotation axes. Therefore when one molecule collides with another, the amount of energy transferred during the collision is not great enough to set either molecule rotating (**Figure 20.16a**). Above 100 K, the hydrogen molecules have sufficient kinetic energy to set each other spinning (Figure 20.16b). At room temperature (about 298 K), the value $\frac{1}{2}k_B T$ is equal to several rotational quanta, and so the equipartition of energy includes the two independent rotations of the hydrogen molecules, as described in the text preceding Checkpoint 20.7.

Figure 20.16 Collisions between hydrogen molecules. (*a*) At low temperatures ($T < 100$ K), the molecules have insufficient kinetic energy to cause any changes in rotational motion. (*b*) At higher temperatures, molecules can be set into rotational motion.

(*a*)

If kinetic energy < quantum of rotational energy . . .

. . . collision cannot change rotational kinetic energy.

(*b*)

If kinetic energy > quantum of rotational energy . . .

. . . collision can change rotational kinetic energy.

Figure 20.17 At temperatures above 1000 K, diatomic molecules begin to vibrate along the axis connecting the two atoms.

Figure 20.15 shows that at temperatures above 1000 K, the heat capacity per particle increases further. At such temperatures, the equipartition share becomes comparable to the quantum associated with another type of repetitive motion: vibration of the two hydrogen atoms along the axis of the molecule (**Figure 20.17**). Although there is only one axis for this type of motion in hydrogen, this vibrational motion contributes two degrees of freedom because it involves both potential and kinetic energy, each of which can store an amount of energy $\frac{1}{2}k_BT$. So the number of degrees of freedom for hydrogen is seven (three translational, two rotational, and two vibrational). If each degree of freedom contributes $\frac{1}{2}k_BT$, we expect a thermal energy per molecule of $\frac{7}{2}k_BT$. Indeed, experiments show that the heat capacity per hydrogen molecule approaches $\frac{7}{2}k_B$ around 3000 K. To summarize:

> Only degrees of freedom for which $\frac{1}{2}k_BT$ is greater than the quantum of energy associated with that degree of freedom contribute to the heat capacity of a gas. In thermal equilibrium, each contributing degree of freedom of a particle in an ideal gas stores $\frac{1}{2}k_BT$ of thermal energy.

So, for a gas in which each particle has d contributing degrees of freedom, we expect the heat capacity per particle to be equal to $\frac{d}{2}k_B$.

Example 20.3 Energy quanta for nitrogen

At room temperature, do collisions between nitrogen molecules have enough energy to set a nitrogen molecule rotating? Enough to set it vibrating? The quantum of energy associated with rotation is $E_{rot} = 4.0 \times 10^{-23}$ J and the quantum of energy associated with vibration is $E_{vib} = 4.7 \times 10^{-20}$ J.

❶ GETTING STARTED At a given absolute temperature T each molecule stores $\frac{1}{2}k_BT$ of thermal energy per contributing degree of freedom. If the quantum of energy associated with a certain degree of freedom is greater than the energy stored per degree of freedom, then that degree of freedom cannot store any energy.

❷ DEVISE PLAN To solve this problem, I need to compare the equipartition energy share at room temperature with the energy quanta associated with rotation and vibration. I can obtain the equipartition energy share at room temperature by substituting $T = 300$ K (room temperature) into $\frac{1}{2}k_BT$.

❸ EXECUTE PLAN At 300 K the equipartition energy share is $\frac{1}{2}k_BT = \frac{1}{2}(1.38 \times 10^{-23}$ J/K$)(300$ K$) = 2.07 \times 10^{-21}$ J. This value is greater than E_{rot} but smaller than E_{vib}, which means that

at room temperature the nitrogen molecules rotate but do not vibrate. ✔

❹ EVALUATE RESULT Table 20.3 confirms my conclusion: At room temperature the heat capacity per particle of nitrogen molecules is $2.50 \approx \frac{5}{2}$, indicating that rotations contribute to the storing of thermal energy but vibrations do not.

We can apply the same treatment to the vibrating atoms in a solid crystal. Consider, for example, the simple cubic arrangements of atoms shown in **Figure 20.18**. Each atom is "tied" in place by elastic bonds with neighboring atoms, so there are no translational or rotational degrees of freedom. However, each atom can vibrate along the three independent axes of the crystal. As we have seen, each vibration contributes two degrees of freedom, and so each atom should have six degrees of freedom, each storing $\frac{1}{2}k_BT$ of thermal energy. We therefore expect a heat capacity per atom of $3k_B$, which is in good agreement with the values for a number of simple crystalline solids (see Table 20.3).

Figure 20.19 shows the temperature dependence of the heat capacity per atom for a number of solids. Again we see that quantum effects affect the heat capacity. Below certain temperatures, the heat capacity of each solid decreases to zero because $\frac{1}{2}k_BT$ is smaller than the quantum of energy associated with the vibrations.

The interplay between the various degrees of freedom and the number of basic states available for the equipartition of energy explains the heat capacities for different materials over a broad range of temperatures. For a more accurate and complete description, however, we need *quantum mechanics*—a branch of physics that accounts for the discrete nature of energy and is beyond the scope of this text.

In all of this discussion we have considered materials that do not undergo any phase transition from one state of matter to another. During a phase transition, adding energy thermally to a system does not change the temperature, but instead goes to changing the state of matter. (See the box "Phase transitions.")

Figure 20.18 Each atom in a crystal can vibrate along three independent axes.

Figure 20.19 Temperature dependence of the heat capacity per atom for a number of solids.

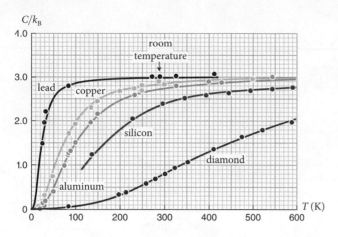

might get hotter, or expand, or the pressure might increase. In this section we examine the interplay between energy exchanges and changes in state for an ideal gas.

The equilibrium state of a gas can be completely specified by the four macroscopic measurable quantities we discussed in Chapter 19: the pressure P of the gas, its volume V, its temperature T, and the number of molecules N in that volume. Generally we shall consider samples that consist of a fixed number N of particles, so we can represent the equilibrium state of a gas by the triplet of values (P, V, T).

As we saw in Chapter 19, for an ideal gas the four macroscopic variables are related to one another by Eq. 19.51: $P = (N/V)k_B T$.* This means that if the number of particles in a gas is fixed, we need only two variables to completely specify the equilibrium state of the gas. If we choose these two variables to be P and V, then the equilibrium state of a fixed amount of ideal gas can be represented by a point on a *PV diagram* such as the ones shown in **Figure 20.20** on the next page.

We can read the corresponding pair of values (P, V) from the axes and determine the temperature from the ideal gas law (assuming we know N). Once we know the temperature, we can calculate the thermal energy and the entropy of the gas (see Eqs. 19.50 and 19.59 for monatomic ideal gases).

> Any point on a *PV* diagram represents an equilibrium state in which the gas has a well-defined temperature, thermal energy, and entropy.

*For a nonideal gas the four macroscopic variables are also related to one another, but the relationship is more complicated than that expressed by the ideal gas law.

⊛ **20.8** Two identical volumes of gases—one monatomic and the other diatomic—are at the same pressure at room temperature. The temperature of each is raised by the same amount by thermally transferring energy to each of them. Is the energy transferred to the monatomic gas smaller than, equal to, or greater than the energy transferred to the diatomic gas?

20.4 *PV* diagrams and processes

We have seen that a system can exchange energy with its surroundings in two ways: by work done on it and by a thermal transfer of energy. The exchange of energy changes the state of the system. As we saw in Section 20.1, the system

Phase transitions

Most substances occur in several *states of matter* (also called *phases*): the solid state, the liquid state, and the gaseous state. H_2O, for example, exists in the solid state as ice, in the liquid state as water, and in the gaseous state as water vapor. The transition from one state of matter to another is called a *phase transition*. During a phase transition any energy transferred thermally does not change the temperature, but instead goes toward changing the state. At a given pressure, therefore, phase transitions occur at a fixed temperature and are accompanied by a change in volume.

For example, at normal atmospheric pressure ice changes to water at a temperature of 0 °C. To melt 1 kg of ice requires a thermal transfer of energy of 3.34×10^5 J. This energy is required to break the bonds that hold the water molecules together in ice.

Because the energy transferred thermally to a substance undergoing a phase transition is an extensive quantity, we introduce an intensive quantity by dividing the energy transferred thermally by the mass of the substance undergoing the transition. The resulting quantity, $L \equiv Q/m$, is called the *specific transformation energy*

(traditionally often called *latent heat*, although the term *heat*, which is an energy and not a specific energy, is a misnomer). Because there are two phase transitions between the three states of matter, each substance has two specific transformation energies: one associated with the solid-liquid transition (*specific transformation energy for melting* L_m) and one with the liquid-gas transition (*specific transformation energy for vaporization* L_v).

Phase transitions are reversible. Energy must be added to a substance to make it undergo a transition from a lower-temperature phase to a higher-temperature phase. In the other direction, energy must be removed from the system. For example, to change 1 kg of water at 100 °C to water vapor at 100 °C at normal atmospheric pressure requires thermally transferring 2.256×10^6 J to the water. When that water vapor condenses back to water at 100 °C and normal atmospheric pressure, the same 2.256×10^6 J must be removed from the vapor.

Table 20.4 on the next page lists the specific transformation energies and associated phase transition temperatures for the melting and vaporization of a number of substances at normal atmospheric pressure.

Figure 20.20 Isotherms and isentropes in a PV diagram for an ideal gas. Points 1 and 2 represent two equilibrium states, both at $T = 300$ K. In general, on a PV diagram, the isentrope passing through a given point is steeper than the isotherm passing through that point.

(a) PV diagram showing isotherms (curves of constant temperature T) for an ideal gas

(b) Isentropes (curves of constant entropy S) superimposed on isotherms

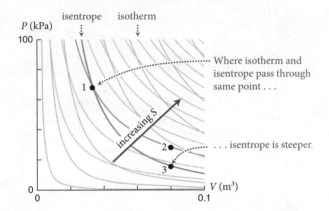

The ideal gas law implies that all equilibrium states (P, V) at a fixed temperature lie on a curve such that the product PV is constant or, to express this information another way, $P \propto 1/V$. These curves are called **isotherms**. Figure 20.20a shows a number of isotherms, each corresponding to a fixed temperature and therefore a fixed thermal energy of the gas. Isotherms that are higher on the PV diagram represent higher temperatures and greater thermal energy.

20.9 Consider the equilibrium states represented by points 1 and 2 in Figure 20.20a. Compare these quantities for an ideal gas in these two states: pressure P, volume V, temperature T, entropy S, and thermal energy E_{th}.

Another important family of curves associated with the PV diagram for an ideal gas is shown in Figure 20.20b. Each

Table 20.4 Phase transition temperatures and specific transformation energies for melting (m) and vaporization (v)

Substance	T_m (K)	L_m (10^3 J/kg)	T_v (K)	L_v (10^3 J/kg)
Helium	–	–	4.230	20.8
Hydrogen	13.84	58.6	20.37	449
Nitrogen	63.18	25.5	77.36	199
Oxygen	54.36	13.8	90.19	213
Ammonia	195	331	239.8	1369
Carbon tetrachloride	250.3	16	349.8	194
Ethanol	159	100.7	351	837
Water	273.15	334	373.12	2256
Mercury	234	11.8	630	272
Aluminum	933.6	395	2740	10,500
Lead	600.5	24.5	2023	871
Sulfur	392	38.1	717.75	326
Gold	1336.15	64.5	2933	1578
Copper	1356	134	2840	5069

curve in this family connects all points that correspond to equilibrium states that have the same entropy. Such curves are called **isentropes.**

An isentrope passing through a given point on a *PV* diagram is steeper than the isotherm passing through that point. To see why this is so, consider the isentrope and isotherm passing through point 1 in Figure 20.20*a*. As we saw in Checkpoint 20.9, the entropy of state 2 on the isotherm is greater than the entropy of state 1.* Equation 19.60, $S = N \ln(T^{3/2} V) +$ constant, tells us that in order to return the entropy to its original value, the temperature must decrease as we go at constant volume from state 2 to state 3, which lies on the isentrope. So the isentrope passing through state 1 has to be steeper than the isotherm (Figure 20.20*b*).

Isentropes that are higher on the *PV* diagram represent greater entropies. You can see this by going from state 3 to state 2 in Figure 20.20*b*. The volume is the same for both states, but the fact that you move from one isotherm to a higher isotherm means that the temperature and thus the entropy (see Eq. 19.60) increase.

Let us now turn our attention to the transformation of a system from one equilibrium state to another. If the process is quasistatic, it is a succession of near-equilibrium states. Provided these states are very close to equilibrium, we can represent them by points on a *PV* diagram, and the succession of points then constitutes a path on the *PV* diagram, such as the one shown in **Figure 20.21**.

During a quasistatic process, the system remains near equilibrium at all instants. Such a process can be represented by a continuous path on a PV diagram.

Processes that are not quasistatic cannot be represented on a *PV* diagram. For such processes we can only show the points that correspond to the initial and final equilibrium states.

There are infinitely many ways to change the state of a gas. **Figure 20.22** shows two quasistatic processes that transform a gas from the same initial state i to the same final state f. Because the two processes have the same initial and final equilibrium states and because each state has a well-defined thermal energy and entropy, the change in these two quantities is independent of the process. For an ideal gas whose center of mass is at rest, there are no changes in the kinetic, potential, or source energy. Thus the change in the energy of the gas is equal to the change in the thermal energy, and we can state:

When an ideal gas is transformed from one equilibrium state to another, the changes in the thermal energy and entropy of the gas are independent of the process.

Note that this statement holds even for non-quasistatic, irreversible processes between equilibrium states. The changes in thermal energy and entropy depend on only

Figure 20.21 A path on a *PV* diagram represents a succession of equilibrium states that takes the system from some initial state to some final state. Such a transformation is called a quasistatic process.

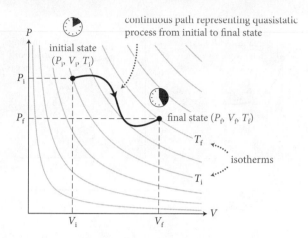

the initial and final states—what happens in between does not matter. If the change in thermal energy is independent of the process, then the energy transferred to the system ($W + Q$) must also be independent of the process. Are W and Q each independent of the process, too?

As we shall see in Section 20.5, the magnitude of the work done on a gas during any quasistatic process carried out on the gas is given by the area under the path that represents the process in a *PV* diagram. **Figure 20.23** on the next page shows a number of quasistatic processes, with the area under the path representing each process shaded; the larger the shaded area, the greater the magnitude of the work done on the gas. If the path is in the direction of increasing volume (Figure 20.23*a* and *b*), the work done on the gas is negative. If the path is in the direction of decreasing volume (Figure 20.23*c*), the work done on the gas is positive. For a vertical path (Figure 20.23*d*), the work is zero.

Comparing the sizes of the hatched areas in parts *a* and *b* of Figure 20.23 tells us that the amount of work done on the gas is different in the two graphs. These graphs represent processes A and B of Figure 20.22, telling us that the

Figure 20.22 Two quasistatic processes that transform a gas from an initial state i to a final state f.

---

*For simplicity, we shall omit the word *equilibrium* when referring to states presented by specific points on *PV* diagrams. For example, "state 1" stands for "the *equilibrium* state represented by point 1."

Figure 20.23 The work done on a gas during a quasistatic process is equal to the area under the path on the *PV* diagram representing that process.

(a)

area under *PV* curve = magnitude of work done on gas

$W < 0$

$V_f > V_i$: Gas expands, so work done on gas is negative.

(b)

hatched shading: *negative* work done on gas

$W < 0$

(c)

solid shading: *positive* work done on gas

$W > 0$

$V_f < V_i$: Gas compressed, so work done on gas is positive.

(d)

$V_i = V_f$

$V_f = V_i$: Volume does not change, so no work done on gas.

magnitude of the work needed to carry out process B is greater than the work needed to carry out process A. Unlike changes in thermal energy that occur during a process, the amount of work done does depend on the path taken.

✋ **20.10** (*a*) For which of the two quasistatic processes shown in Figure 20.22, if either, is the change in entropy greater? (*b*) Is the energy transferred thermally to the gas the same along both paths?

As Checkpoint 20.10 makes clear, the quantity of energy *Q* transferred thermally to the system, like the work *W* done on it, depends on the path taken.

Example 20.4 Different process, same change?

In quasistatic process A of **Figure 20.24**, an ideal gas is brought from an initial to a final state while its temperature is held fixed. In quasistatic process B, an identical gas is brought in two steps from the same initial state as in process A to the same final state.

Figure 20.24 States i and f are on the same isotherm.

In the first step, the gas expands at constant pressure from the initial state to an intermediate state 1, and in the second step, the gas is brought adiabatically to the final state. Is the quantity of energy transferred thermally to the gas during process B greater than, equal to, or smaller than during process A?

❶ GETTING STARTED During both processes, the gas expands, and so the work done on the gas is negative in both cases. The quantity of energy transferred thermally depends on both the work done on the gas and the change in the thermal energy of the gas.

❷ DEVISE PLAN The initial and final states lie on the same isotherm, which means the temperature of the gas is the same in the two states. Therefore the thermal energy of the gas is the same in the two states, and so the change in thermal energy is zero for both processes. This means that the quantity of energy transferred thermally to the gas is the negative of the work done on the gas.

❸ EXECUTE PLAN The area under the path for process B in Figure 20.24 is larger than the area under the path for process A, and so the magnitude of the work done on the gas is greater for process B. This means that the quantity of energy transferred thermally must be greater during process B. ✔

❹ EVALUATE RESULT I am told that the second step in process B is adiabatic, which means that $Q = 0$. The problem therefore boils down to comparing the energy transferred thermally during process A with the energy transferred thermally during the first step of process B. During process A, the change in the thermal energy is zero, and so all the energy transferred thermally to the gas can be used by the gas to do work on its environment. That state 1 is on a higher isotherm than state i tells me that the temperature of the gas increases during the first step of process B. Therefore part of the energy transferred thermally is required to raise the thermal energy of the gas. It therefore makes sense that *Q* is greater for process B.

Figure 20.25 Four types of constrained quasistatic processes.

The quasistatic processes in Example 20.4 are examples of *constrained processes*: Their path on a *PV* diagram is determined by a constraint placed on the system.

Figure 20.25 shows four important constrained quasistatic processes in ideal gases that we shall study in the second part of this chapter. When the pressure in the gas is held fixed during a quasistatic process, the path in the *PV* diagram is a horizontal line at the fixed pressure *P*; such a process is called isobaric (Greek for "same weight"). When the volume is held fixed, the path is a vertical line, and the process is called isochoric ("same volume"). Because the volume doesn't change, no work is done on (or by) the gas in an isochoric process (Figure 20.23*d*).

When the temperature is held fixed, the path lies along an isotherm, and the process is called isothermal ("same temperature"). As we saw in Chapter 19, the thermal energy of an ideal gas is proportional to the temperature of the gas,

Table 20.5 Constrained quasistatic processes

Process	Constraint	Consequence
isochoric	*V* fixed	$W = 0$
isentropic (adiabatic)	*S* fixed	$Q = 0.$
isobaric	*P* fixed	
isothermal	*T* fixed	$\Delta E_{th} = 0$

and so in an isothermal process, the thermal energy does not change.

When the entropy is constant during a process, the path lies along an isentrope and the process is called isentropic ("same entropy"). As we saw in Section 20.1, the entropy of a system remains constant during quasistatic adiabatic processes, and therefore these processes are isentropic. Paths along isentropes thus represent processes for which no energy is transferred thermally to the system ($Q = 0$). Isentropes are sometimes also called *adiabats*, and isentropic processes are also called *adiabatic processes*.*

Table 20.5 summarizes these constrained quasistatic processes and the consequences of the constraints imposed.

20.11 For each process in Figure 20.25, determine whether the following quantities are positive, negative, or zero: $W, Q, \Delta E_{th}, \Delta S$.

---

*Note, however, that an adiabatic process need not be isentropic. Only a *quasistatic* adiabatic process is isentropic.

Self-quiz

1. **Figure 20.26** shows the energy changes for a certain system over a short time interval. Describe what is happening to the system. From the diagram, what can you conclude about the temperature of the environment at the beginning of the time interval?

Figure 20.26

$$\Delta K \quad \Delta U \quad \Delta E_s \quad \Delta E_{th} \qquad W \quad Q$$

2. On a really hot day, which temperature scale (°F or °C) registers the greater number? On a really cold day, which temperature scale registers the smaller number? At what temperature do the two scales register the same number?

3. Which material in Table 20.2 has the greatest specific heat capacity? The smallest? Imagine that objects made of these materials are placed on your hand. The objects have the same mass and are initially at the same temperature. Each object equilibrates thermally with your hand, which is at a higher temperature. Describe any differences in the equilibration process.

4. What is the approximate thermal energy of a molecule that has three degrees of translational freedom, two degrees of rotational freedom, and two degrees of vibrational freedom? The molecule is in a gas at temperature T.

5. Which types of processes are represented in Figure 20.24? For each process, determine whether the following quantities are positive, negative, or zero: ΔT, ΔV, ΔP.

Answers

1. The thermal energy of the system is decreasing ($\Delta E_{th} < 0$) because energy is leaving the system ($Q < 0$) and entering the environment. That energy leaves the system means that initially the temperature of the environment must be lower than the temperature of the system.

2. The Fahrenheit scale registers the greater number on a really hot day. If the Fahrenheit temperature is 110 °F, the Celsius temperature is 43.3 °C. The Celsius scale registers the smaller number on a really cold day. If the Fahrenheit temperature is −20 °F, the Celsius temperature is −29 °C. The scales read the same temperature at −40 °C = −40 °F.

3. Water is the highest, gold and lead the lowest. Because water has such a high specific heat capacity, a large amount of energy must leave your hand and enter the water as your hand and the water equilibrate, much more than the gold or lead would. This, in part, is why it is so hard to keep warm if you are wet and why gold jewelry so quickly comes to the same temperature as your skin.

4. With seven degrees of freedom and an equipartition energy share of $\frac{1}{2}k_BT$, the molecule has roughly $\frac{7}{2}k_BT$ of thermal energy.

5. Process A in Figure 20.24 is isothermal because it follows an isotherm. $\Delta T = 0$ because the process is isothermal, $\Delta V > 0$ because $V_f > V_i$, and $\Delta P < 0$ because $P_f < P_i$. The first step of process B is isobaric because the pressure is constant. $\Delta T > 0$ because T_i is on a lower isotherm than T_1, $\Delta V > 0$ because $V_1 > V_i$, and $\Delta P = 0$ because $P_1 = P_i$. The second step of process B is isentropic because it follows an isentrope. $\Delta T < 0$ because T_f is on a lower isotherm than T_1, $\Delta V > 0$ because $V_f > V_1$, and $\Delta P < 0$ because $P_f < P_1$.

20.5 Change in energy and work

If we take into account both the transfer of mechanical energy (work) W and the energy transferred thermally Q, the energy law (Eq. 9.1) becomes

$$\Delta E = W + Q. \tag{20.1}$$

Remember that this law is a direct consequence of conservation of energy: The only way the energy of a system can change is by a transfer of some form of energy to or from the surroundings.

Let's first consider only situations where the system is an ideal gas and where the translational kinetic energy, potential energy, and source energy of the gas remain constant ($\Delta K = \Delta U = \Delta E_s = 0$). The energy law then reduces to

$$\Delta E_{th} = W + Q \quad \text{(ideal gas)}. \tag{20.2}$$

Equation 19.50 tells us that the thermal energy of a monatomic ideal gas consisting of N atoms is

$$E_{th} = \tfrac{3}{2}Nk_BT \quad \text{(monatomic ideal gas)}. \tag{20.3}$$

As we saw in Section 20.3, at thermal equilibrium each degree of freedom of an ideal gas particle contributes $\tfrac{1}{2}k_BT$ to the particle's thermal energy. For a monatomic ideal gas, each atom has three degrees of freedom, yielding the factor 3 in Eq. 20.3. Generalizing this result for an ideal gas with d contributing degrees of freedom, we have

$$E_{th} = \frac{d}{2}Nk_BT \quad \text{(ideal gas)}. \tag{20.4}$$

20.12 What is the thermal energy associated with a gas sample that contains N hydrogen molecules at room temperature ($T = 300$ K)?

When the temperature of an ideal gas sample that contains a fixed number N of particles changes, Eq. 20.4 tells us that the thermal energy of the sample changes by an amount

$$\Delta E_{th} = \frac{d}{2}Nk_B\Delta T. \tag{20.5}$$

As we noted in Section 20.4, this change in thermal energy depends on only the initial and final equilibrium states and is independent of the path taken from initial state to final state.

To calculate the work done on a gas, consider the situation shown in **Figure 20.27**: A piston with surface area A quasistatically compresses a gas in a cylinder. The x component of the force exerted by the piston on the gas is F^c_{pgx}. The work done by this external force on the gas is (Eq. 9.22)

$$W = \int_{x_i}^{x_f} F^c_{pgx}\, dx. \tag{}$$

The magnitude of the force exerted by the piston on the gas is related to the gas pressure P by Eq. 19.43:

$$P = \frac{F^c_{pg}}{A} \tag{20.7}$$

Figure 20.27 A piston that has a surface area A exerts a force on a gas, compressing it.

gas $\vec{F}^c_{pg}$ piston of surface area A

$\longrightarrow x$

Figure 20.28 Checkpoint 20.13.

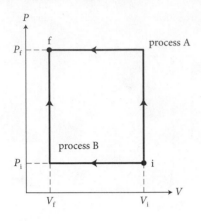

or $F_{pg}^c = PA$. If we take the positive x axis to the right as in Figure 20.27, we have $F_{pgx}^c = -F_{pg}^c = -PA$. When the piston moves a distance dx, the volume of the gas changes by an amount $dV = A\,dx$, and so the work done on the gas is

$$W = -\int_{x_i}^{x_f} PA\,dx = -\int_{V_i}^{V_f} P\,dV. \qquad (20.8)$$

The integral to the right of the minus sign in this expression represents the area under the path taken in the PV diagram, as we discussed in Section 20.4 (see Figure 20.23). If the process is in the direction of increasing volume (expansion), the integral in Eq. 20.8 is positive, making the work done on the gas negative (Figure 20.23a and b). If the process is in the direction of decreasing volume (compression), the work done on the gas is positive (Figure 20.23c).

When the pressure is constant (that is, during a quasistatic isobaric process), we can pull the pressure out of the integral, and the work done on the gas is

$$W = -P\int_{V_i}^{V_f} dV = -P(V_f - V_i) = -P\Delta V \quad \text{(quasistatic isobaric process).}$$

$$(20.9)$$

✋ **20.13** Which quasistatic process from the initial state i to the final state f in **Figure 20.28** requires more work done on the gas?

From Checkpoint 20.13 we see that the work done on a gas depends on the manner in which the gas is transformed from its initial state to its final state.

Example 20.5 Same change, different process

In Figure 20.28, an ideal gas is brought from an initial state i to a final state f by two processes. The initial volume and pressure are 0.50 m³ and 100 kPa, and the final values for these variables are 0.10 m³ and 500 kPa. How much energy is transferred thermally to the gas during (a) process A and (b) process B?

❶ GETTING STARTED Both processes are represented by a continuous path on a PV diagram and so are quasistatic. From the graph and the data given, I know that $V_i = 0.50$ m³, $V_f = 0.10$ m³, $P_i = 100$ kPa, and $P_f = 500$ kPa.

❷ DEVISE PLAN To calculate the quantity of energy transferred thermally, I can use the energy law as given in Eq. 20.2, $\Delta E_{th} = W + Q$, which gives me $Q = \Delta E_{th} - W$. From Checkpoint 20.13, I know that work is done on the gas only during the constant-pressure legs. To calculate W during these legs, I can use Eq. 20.9. The change in the thermal energy ΔE_{th} is given by Eq. 20.5, but I do not know d, N, or ΔT. The ideal gas law, however, relates pressure and volume to temperature: $PV = Nk_BT$ (Eq. 19.51). I note that the product PV is the same for the initial and final states: $P_iV_i = (100\text{ kPa})(0.50\text{ m}^3) = 50\text{ kPa}\cdot\text{m}^3$ and $P_fV_f = (500\text{ kPa})(0.10\text{ m}^3) = 50\text{ kPa}\cdot\text{m}^3$. This tells me that the

initial and final states lie on an isotherm, so $\Delta T = 0$. Therefore Eq. 20.5 becomes $\Delta E_{th} = 0$, so Eq. 20.2 yields $Q = -W$.

❸ EXECUTE PLAN The change in volume for both processes is $\Delta V = V_f - V_i = (0.10\text{ m}^3) - (0.50\text{ m}^3) = -0.40\text{ m}^3$.

(a) From Eq. 20.9, the work done on the gas for process A is $W = -P\Delta V = -(500\text{ kPa})(-0.40\text{ m}^3) = 2.0 \times 10^2$ kJ. Therefore $Q_A = -2.0 \times 10^2$ kJ. ✔

(b) $W = -P\Delta V = -(100\text{ kPa})(-0.40\text{ m}^3) = 40$ kJ, which leads to $Q_B = -40$ kJ. ✔

❹ EVALUATE RESULT The work done on the gas during process A is five times greater than the work done during process B. This is not surprising because in A the compression from V_i to V_f is done at a pressure that is five times greater than the pressure at which the compression is done in B. Because the thermal energy of the gas does not change, any energy acquired in the form of work done on the gas has to leave as energy transferred thermally out of the gas. Both Q_A and Q_B should therefore be negative, and Q_A should be greater than Q_B, which is what I found.

As we have seen, the change in thermal energy for an ideal gas undergoing some quasistatic process is independent of the process and is given by Eq. 20.5. Checkpoint 20.13 and Example 20.5, however, show that the work done on the gas and the energy transferred thermally depend on the process.

✋ **20.14** Consider the three processes shown in **Figure 20.29**. Process B is isothermal. (*a*) For which of the three processes is the energy transferred thermally greatest? (*b*) For which of the three processes is the energy transferred thermally smallest?

20.6 Isochoric and isentropic ideal gas processes

Let us now take a deeper look at what the energy law tells us about the transfers of mechanical and thermal energy that occur during constrained quasistatic processes. We begin by examining isochoric (constant volume) and isentropic (constant entropy) quasistatic processes in this section and then isobaric (constant pressure) and isothermal (constant temperature) quasistatic processes in the next section.

An example of an isochoric quasistatic process is shown in **Figure 20.30**. An ideal gas sample consisting of *N* particles enclosed in a fixed volume is heated. The energy diagram for the volume of ideal gas during this process is shown in Figure 20.30*b*. Because the gas is heated, its temperature and therefore its thermal energy increase. Because the volume is fixed, no work is done on the gas. The amount *Q* of energy transferred thermally to the gas raises the thermal energy of the gas.

Figure 20.30*c* shows the corresponding *PV* diagram. The ideal gas law, $P = Nk_BT/V$ (Eq. 19.51), tells us that if the volume is kept fixed, the pressure in the gas increases as the temperature increases. Because the volume is fixed and the pressure increases, the path that represents the heating process is straight up. The arrow representing *Q* has solid shading because energy is transferred to the gas ($Q > 0$).

Because $V_i = V_f$, the integral in Eq. 20.8 is zero, and so the work done on the gas is zero:

$$W = 0 \quad \text{(isochoric process).} \quad (20.10)$$

The energy law for an ideal gas, $\Delta E_{th} = W + Q$, then reduces to

$$\Delta E_{th} = Q \quad \text{(isochoric process).} \quad (20.11)$$

Substituting the expression given for ΔE_{th} in Eq. 20.5, we see that

$$Q = \frac{d}{2}Nk_B\Delta T \quad \text{(isochoric process).} \quad (20.12)$$

In Section 20.3, we introduced the quantity **heat capacity per particle**. Mathematically this quantity is defined as the energy transferred thermally divided by the number of particles and by the temperature change:

$$C_V \equiv \frac{Q}{N\Delta T} \quad \text{(constant volume),} \quad (20.13)$$

where here we add a subscript *V* to remind ourselves that this result is obtained at constant volume. Substituting Eq. 20.12 into this definition for C_V yields

$$C_V = \frac{d}{2}k_B \quad \text{(constant volume).} \quad (20.14)$$

Note that this result predicts that the heat capacity per particle is determined by the number of degrees of freedom, in agreement with the experimental results we discussed in Section 20.3.

Figure 20.29 Checkpoint 20.14.

Figure 20.30 An example of an isochoric quasistatic process.

(*a*) Fixed volume of gas is heated, raising *T* and *P*

(*b*) Energy diagram for gas

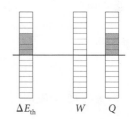

(*c*) *PV* diagram showing the isochoric process

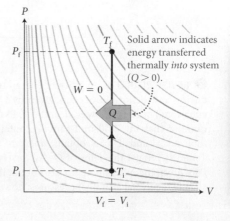

Figure 20.31 Two ideal gas processes. Process A is isochoric; process B is not.

Hatched shading: Work done on gas in process B is *negative*.

Equation 20.14 allows us to rewrite Eq. 20.5 in the form

$$\Delta E_{th} = NC_V \Delta T \quad \text{(any ideal gas process).} \quad (20.15)$$

Even though we used Eq. 20.5 to arrive at Eq. 20.15 for ΔE_{th} under isochoric conditions, Eq. 20.15 holds for all ideal gas processes, not just isochoric ones. To see why, consider two samples of N ideal gas particles undergoing the two processes in **Figure 20.31**. Both samples are initially at temperature T_i and end at temperature T_f. Process A is isochoric; process B is some arbitrary process. Because the temperature change is the same for the two processes, Eq. 20.5 tells us the thermal energy change must also be the same. This means we can use Eq. 20.15 to calculate ΔE_{th} for any process, given the change in temperature ΔT in the process and knowing C_V for the gas. In contrast to Eq. 20.5, which expresses the thermal-energy change in terms of the number of degrees of freedom of each ideal gas particle, Eq. 20.15 gives the thermal-energy change in terms of macroscopically measured quantities.

 20.15 Is Eq. 20.15 valid for an isothermal process ($\Delta T = 0$)?

Example 20.6 Energy transferred thermally

A sample of hydrogen gas that contains 1.00 mol of H_2 molecules at a temperature of 300 K and a pressure of 60.0 kPa undergoes an isochoric process. The final pressure is 80.0 kPa. How much energy is transferred thermally to the gas?

❶ **GETTING STARTED** I begin by making a PV diagram of the process, treating the hydrogen as an ideal gas (**Figure 20.32**). Because the process is isochoric, I represent it by a vertical line. Because $P_f > P_i$, I indicate that the path representing the process points upward.

Figure 20.32

❷ **DEVISE PLAN** The quantity of energy transferred thermally during an isochoric process is given by Eq. 20.12. To use this equation, I need to know N, d, and ΔT. I know from Avogadro's number that my 1.00-mol sample contains $N = 6.02 \times 10^{23}$ molecules, and I can obtain d from Eq. 20.14 if I use Table 20.3 to get the value of C_V/k_B for H_2 molecules. For ΔT, I am given the initial temperature but not the final temperature. I know the initial and final pressures, however, and because the

volume is fixed in this isochoric process, I can use the ideal gas law to determine the final temperature and so have a value for ΔT.

❸ **EXECUTE PLAN** From Table 20.3 I see that, for H_2 molecules, $C_V/k_B = 2.47$ at room temperature (about 300 K). From Figure 20.15 I see that C_V/k_B stays at that value through 700 K, and so, from Eq. 20.14, I know that $d/2 = C_V/k_B = 2.47$.

Next I rewrite the ideal gas law (Eq. 19.51) in the form $V = Nk_BT/P$. Because V, N, and k_B are constant, I know that T/P is constant, and so $T_i/P_i = T_f/P_f$. Solving for T_f, I get

$$T_f = \frac{T_i P_f}{P_i} = \frac{(300 \text{ K})(80.0 \text{ kPa})}{60.0 \text{ kPa}} = 400 \text{ K},$$

so $\Delta T = 400 \text{ K} - 300 \text{ K} = 100 \text{ K}$. Substituting my values for N, d, and ΔT in Eq. 20.12 gives me

$$Q = \frac{d}{2} Nk_B \Delta T = 2.47(6.02 \times 10^{23})(1.38 \times 10^{-23} \text{ J/K})(100 \text{ K})$$

$$= 2.05 \times 10^3 \text{ J.} ✔$$

❹ **EVALUATE RESULT** Because the temperature of the gas increases, its thermal energy must increase. The process is isochoric, so no work is done on the gas. Therefore the value of the quantity of energy transferred thermally must be positive, as my result is.

The quantity of energy transferred is significant—approximately equal to the kinetic energy of a 1-kg object moving at about 65 m/s—but I know that thermal energies tend to be large relative to kinetic energies. (See, for example, the box "Coherent versus incoherent energy" in Chapter 7.)

Next we consider a quasistatic isentropic process, a process for which the entropy remains unchanged:

$$\Delta S = 0 \quad \text{(isentropic process).} \tag{20.16}$$

As we saw in Section 20.1, no energy is transferred thermally in an isentropic quasistatic process:

$$Q = 0 \quad \text{(isentropic quasistatic process).} \tag{20.17}$$

An example of an isentropic quasistatic process is shown in **Figure 20.33a**. An ideal gas sample consisting of N particles is compressed very slowly by grains of sand dropped on the piston to ensure that the process is quasistatic. The gas is thermally insulated so that $Q = 0$. The increasing force exerted on the piston increases the pressure in the gas and decreases its volume. The corresponding energy diagram for the volume of ideal gas is shown in Figure 20.33b. The work done by the piston on the gas is positive, increasing the thermal energy of the gas. Because $Q = 0$, Eq. 20.2 becomes

$$\Delta E_{\text{th}} = W \quad \text{(isentropic quasistatic process).} \tag{20.18}$$

The increase in thermal energy means that the temperature of the gas goes up even though the gas is not being heated. During an isentropic compression, work done on the gas raises the temperature of the gas. You may have noticed this effect while using a bicycle pump: If you pump vigorously, the air in the pump—and therefore the pump and the tire tube—becomes noticeably hotter.

Figure 20.33c shows the PV diagram for the isentropic process. The shaded area under the path is the work done by the piston on the gas. As the solid shading indicates, this work is positive ($W > 0$). Because the entropy of the gas doesn't change when $Q = 0$, the path in Figure 20.33c lies along an isentrope, and because the gas is compressed, the final volume is smaller than the initial volume. As you can see from the PV diagram, the path crosses the isotherms and ends on an isotherm at a higher temperature, indicating that the process raises the temperature of the gas, as we saw before.

If we substitute Eq. 20.15 into Eq. 20.18, we obtain an expression that relates the work done on the gas W to the temperature change:

$$\Delta E_{\text{th}} = W = NC_V \Delta T \quad \text{(isentropic process).} \tag{20.19}$$

✋ **20.16** Is the product PV in the final state in Figure 20.33c greater than, equal to, or smaller than the product PV in the initial state?

20.7 Isobaric and isothermal ideal gas processes

Next we turn to an isobaric (constant pressure) quasistatic process. An example is shown in **Figure 20.34a** on the next page: An ideal gas sample consisting of N particles is heated while it is being held at constant pressure by a piston that exerts a constant force on the gas. If the piston were held in place, the heating would raise the temperature of the gas and, according to the ideal gas law, the pressure would go up. Because the piston is free to move, however, the pressure stays constant and the gas expands instead. Therefore the gas does work on its environment. The energy diagram for the volume of the ideal gas during this process is shown in Figure 20.34b. The heating transfers energy to the gas ($Q > 0$), part of which goes into raising the temperature (and therefore the thermal energy

Figure 20.33 An example of an isentropic quasistatic process.

(a) Thermally insulated volume of ideal gas is compressed slowly

(b) Energy diagram for gas

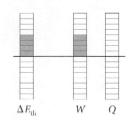

(c) PV diagram showing the isentropic process

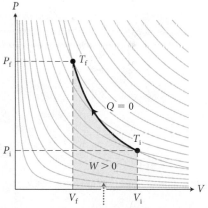

Solid shading: work done on gas is *positive*.

Figure 20.34 An example of an isobaric quasistatic process.

(a) Ideal gas heated at constant pressure

(b) Energy diagram for gas

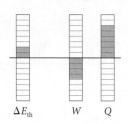

ΔE_{th} W Q

(c) PV diagram showing the isobaric process

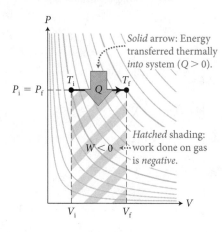

Solid arrow: Energy transferred thermally into system ($Q > 0$).

Hatched shading: $W < 0$ work done on gas is negative.

of the gas: $\Delta E_{th} > 0$), and part of which is used by the gas to do work on its environment ($W < 0$).

Figure 20.34c shows the PV diagram for the process. Because the pressure is constant, the path lies on a horizontal line. Because the gas expands, the direction of the path is to the right, toward increasing volume. The shaded area under the path is the negative of the work done on the gas ($W < 0$). (Remember our convention: A hatched area signifies that the work done *on the gas* is negative.) We draw an arrow representing Q with solid shading to represent the fact that we transfer energy thermally to the gas ($Q > 0$).

Because this process is at constant pressure, we can define heat capacity per particle at constant pressure in analogy to Eq. 20.13:

$$C_P \equiv \frac{Q}{N\Delta T} \quad \text{(constant pressure)}, \tag{20.20}$$

and so in an isobaric process the energy transferred thermally is

$$Q = NC_P\Delta T \quad \text{(isobaric process)}. \tag{20.21}$$

From the ideal gas law (Eq. 19.51), $PV = Nk_BT$, we have for the initial and final states $PV_i = Nk_BT_i$ and $PV_f = Nk_BT_f$. The change in volume is therefore $\Delta V = V_f - V_i = Nk_B\Delta T/P$, which means the work done on the gas is, from Eq. 20.9,

$$W = -P\Delta V = -Nk_B\Delta T \quad \text{(isobaric process)}. \tag{20.22}$$

Now we have all three terms in the energy law for an ideal gas, $\Delta E_{th} = W + Q$. Equation 20.15 gives the change in the thermal energy ΔE_{th}, Eq. 20.22 gives the work done on the gas W, and Eq. 20.21 gives the energy Q transferred thermally into the gas. We can use this information to obtain an expression for C_P for ideal gases. Substituting Eqs. 20.15, 20.21, and 20.22 into the energy law for an ideal gas, we obtain

$$NC_V\Delta T = -Nk_B\Delta T + NC_P\Delta T \quad \text{(ideal gas)}. \tag{20.23}$$

Dividing by $N\Delta T$, we see that for an ideal gas, the heat capacities per particle are related by the expression

$$C_P = C_V + k_B \quad \text{(ideal gas)} \tag{20.24}$$

or, substituting from Eq. 20.14 for C_V,

$$C_P = \frac{d}{2}k_B + k_B = \left(\frac{d}{2} + 1\right)k_B \quad \text{(ideal gas)}. \tag{20.25}$$

Using Eqs. 20.14 and 20.25, we can now write the **heat capacity ratio** as

$$\gamma \equiv \frac{C_P}{C_V} = \frac{\left(\dfrac{d}{2} + 1\right)k_B}{\dfrac{d}{2}k_B} = 1 + \frac{2}{d} \quad \text{(ideal gas)}. \tag{20.26}$$

For a monatomic ideal gas, for which $d = 3$, the heat capacity ratio is $\gamma = \frac{5}{3}$.

Example 20.7 Heat capacity ratio

Experimentally one obtains $C_P = 4.844 \times 10^{-23}$ J/K for nitrogen gas at room temperature. (a) Calculate the heat capacity ratio γ for a gas of nitrogen molecules, N_2, at room temperature. (b) Which degrees of freedom of the N_2 molecules contribute to the heat capacity?

❶ **GETTING STARTED** I am given the room-temperature C_P value for nitrogen gas and asked to calculate γ and then to determine which of the degrees of freedom of the N_2 molecules contribute to the heat capacity. I assume the gas behaves ideally so that I can apply the results of this section.

❷ **DEVISE PLAN** The heat capacity ratio γ is given by Eq. 20.26. To calculate this ratio I need to know d, the number of degrees of freedom of the N_2 molecules that contribute to storing energy at room temperature. Equation 20.25 relates d to C_P, which is given. Once I determine d using this relationship, I can calculate γ and establish which degrees of freedom contribute to the heat capacity.

❸ **EXECUTE PLAN** (a) From Eq. 20.25, I get $\frac{d}{2} + 1 = C_P/k_B$, or $d = 2(C_P/k_B - 1)$. Substituting the value given for C_P, I get

$$d = 2\left(\frac{4.844 \times 10^{-23}\,\text{J/K}}{1.381 \times 10^{-23}\,\text{J/K}} - 1\right) = 5.015.$$

Substituting this value for d into Eq. 20.26, I get $\gamma = 1 + \frac{2}{5.015} = 1.399.$ ✔

(b) Because the nitrogen molecule is diatomic, it has three translational, two rotational, and two vibrational degrees of freedom. I know from Section 20.3 that vibrational motion does not begin to contribute to the heat capacity until the temperature of a gas is about 1000 K. Because my sample is at room temperature, and given that my result for d is very close to 5, I conclude that the translational and rotational degrees of freedom are the ones that contribute to the heat capacity ratio. ✔

❹ **EVALUATE RESULT** I can check the reasonableness of my calculated value $\gamma = 1.399$ by using it in Eq. 20.26 to determine C_V for the nitrogen molecule and then comparing what I get with the value obtained using data from Table 20.3. From Eq. 20.26: $C_V = C_P/\gamma = (4.844 \times 10^{-23}\,\text{J/K})/1.40 = 3.46 \times 10^{-23}$ J/K; from Table 20.3: $C_V = 2.50k_B = 2.50(1.381 \times 10^{-23}\,\text{J/K}) = 3.45 \times 10^{-23}$ J/K. That these two calculations result in about the same value for C_V gives me confidence in the value I obtained for γ.

The nitrogen molecule, N_2, is similar to the hydrogen molecule, H_2. I therefore expect the contribution of the various degrees of freedom to the heat capacity of the two molecules to be similar. I know from Section 20.3 that it is translational and rotational motions that contribute in H_2, which agrees with the motion types I chose in part b.

🤚 **20.17** Suppose the isobaric process in Figure 20.34c begins and ends on the same isotherms as the isochoric process in Figure 20.30c. Which process requires a greater amount Q of energy transferred thermally?

An example of an isothermal (constant temperature) quasistatic process is shown in **Figure 20.35a** on the next page. Sand is dropped onto a piston, which then moves downward, compressing an ideal gas sample. The gas sample consists of N particles and is in thermal contact with a large volume of water. To keep the gas at constant temperature, the water volume must be large enough that adding (or removing) energy thermally to it does not noticeably change the water temperature. Such a body of water is called a thermal reservoir. The thermal reservoir is not part of the system (the gas by itself). The purpose of the thermal reservoir is to keep the temperature of our system constant by thermally exchanging energy with it.

The work done by the piston on the gas is converted to thermal energy. For the process to be isothermal, the work has to be done sufficiently slowly for the gas and the thermal reservoir to remain in thermal equilibrium. A quasistatic isothermal process is thus a slow interplay between work done on the gas and thermal transfer of energy out of the gas.

The temperature of the gas remains constant, and hence the thermal energy does not change:

$$\Delta E_{th} = 0 \quad \text{(isothermal process)}. \tag{20.27}$$

The energy diagram for the volume of ideal gas during this isothermal process is shown in Figure 20.35b. The piston is doing work on the gas ($W > 0$), and

Figure 20.35 An example of an isothermal quasistatic process.

(a) Ideal gas compressed slowly at constant temperature

thermal reservoir (*T* fixed)

(b) Energy diagram for gas

ΔE_{th} W Q

(c) PV diagram showing the isothermal process

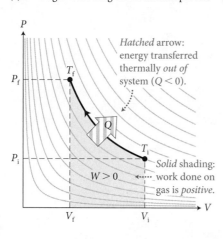

energy is transferred thermally from the gas ($Q < 0$). Because the temperature is constant, there is no change in the thermal energy. Hence the energy law for an ideal gas is $0 = W + Q$, which means

$$Q = -W \quad \text{(isothermal process).} \tag{20.28}$$

The work done on the gas can be found by substituting $P = Nk_{B}T/V$ from the ideal gas law into Eq. 20.8:

$$W = -\int_{V_i}^{V_f} \frac{Nk_{B}T}{V}dV = -Nk_{B}T\int_{V_i}^{V_f}\frac{dV}{V} \quad \text{(isothermal process),} \tag{20.29}$$

where we have pulled the (constant) temperature T out of the integral. Solving the integral, we have

$$W = -Nk_{B}T(\ln V_f - \ln V_i) = -Nk_{B}T\ln\left(\frac{V_f}{V_i}\right) \quad \text{(isothermal process).} \tag{20.30}$$

The energy transferred thermally to the gas is then, from Eq. 20.28,

$$Q = -W = Nk_{B}T\ln\left(\frac{V_f}{V_i}\right) \quad \text{(isothermal process).} \tag{20.31}$$

Figure 20.35*c* shows the *PV* diagram for the isothermal process. The path lies along an isotherm. The shading for the arrow representing Q is hatched because energy is transferred thermally out of the gas. Note that $V_f < V_i$, and so $Q < 0$, as we concluded earlier (see Checkpoint 20.11).

Table 20.6 summarizes the expressions we have obtained for the various terms in the energy law for an ideal gas for each of the four constrained ideal gas processes.

Table 20.6 Energy law for an ideal gas and constrained ideal gas processes

Process	Constraint	W	Q	ΔE_{th}	Energy law for ideal gas
isochoric	*V* fixed	0	$NC_V\Delta T$	$NC_V\Delta T$	$\Delta E_{th} = Q$
isentropic	*S* fixed		0	$NC_V\Delta T$	$W = \Delta E_{th}$
isobaric	*P* fixed	$-Nk_{B}\Delta T$	$NC_P\Delta T$	$NC_V\Delta T$	$\Delta E_{th} = W + Q$
isothermal	*T* fixed	$-Nk_{B}T\ln\left(\dfrac{V_f}{V_i}\right)$		0	$Q = -W$

Example 20.8 Isothermal compression

An ideal gas sample is compressed quasistatically at constant temperature. The initial pressure and volume are $P_i = 1.01 \times 10^5$ Pa and $V_i = 3.00 \times 10^{-2}$ m³, and the final volume is $V_f = 2.00 \times 10^{-2}$ m³. How much work is done on the gas during the compression?

❶ **GETTING STARTED** I begin by making a *PV* diagram of the process (**Figure 20.36**). The process is an isothermal compression, so it is represented by a path going up along an isotherm toward the left.

Figure 20.36

② **DEVISE PLAN** The work done on an ideal gas in an isothermal process is given by Eq. 20.30. I know the initial and final volumes, but not the factor Nk_BT. I can determine this factor from the ideal gas law, $PV = Nk_BT$; it does not matter whether I use initial values or final values in my calculation because the temperature is the same in both cases. Because I do not know the final pressure, however, I should use initial values.

③ **EXECUTE PLAN** From the ideal gas law, I have $Nk_BT = P_iV_i$. From Eq. 20.30, the work done on the gas is

$$W = -Nk_BT \ln\left(\frac{V_f}{V_i}\right) = -P_iV_i \ln\left(\frac{V_f}{V_i}\right).$$

Substituting values for the variables, I get

$$W = -(1.01 \times 10^5 \,\text{Pa})(3.00 \times 10^{-2} \,\text{m}^3) \ln\left(\frac{2.00 \times 10^{-2} \,\text{m}^3}{3.00 \times 10^{-2} \,\text{m}^3}\right)$$

$$= 1.23 \times 10^3 \,\text{J}. ✔$$

④ **EVALUATE RESULT** My answer is positive, as I expect for the work done on a gas in compressing it. To see whether the magnitude of my answer is in the right ballpark, I assume that the volume change is achieved by moving a piston of surface area $1 \times 10^{-2} \,\text{m}^2$ over a distance of 1 m. At a pressure of $1.01 \times 10^5 \,\text{Pa}$, the gas exerts on the piston a force of magnitude $(1 \times 10^{-2} \,\text{m}^2)(1.01 \times 10^5 \,\text{Pa}) \approx 10^3 \,\text{N}$. The piston exerts a force of equal magnitude on the gas. If this force were constant, the work done on the gas during a force displacement of 1 m would be $W = (10^3 \,\text{N})(1 \,\text{m}) = 10^3 \,\text{J}$, which is of the same order of magnitude as the answer I obtained. (This estimate doesn't take into account the increase in pressure and so is a bit lower than the actual value.)

✋ **20.18** Consider an ideal gas undergoing the two processes depicted in **Figure 20.37** between the same initial and final states that lie on an isotherm. In process A the gas is taken via an isochoric process to an intermediate state 1 and then via an isobaric process to the final state. In process B the gas undergoes an isentropic transformation to an intermediate state 2 and then an isobaric transformation to the final state. Which process has the greater value for (a) the work done on the gas and (b) the magnitude of the energy transferred thermally to the gas?

20.8 Entropy change in ideal gas processes

In this section we examine the entropy changes that occur for the four constrained quasistatic processes discussed in the preceding two sections. Recall from Chapter 19 that the entropy of a monatomic ideal gas is determined completely by the volume and the temperature of the gas (Eq. 19.59):

$$S = N \ln V + \tfrac{3}{2}N \ln T + \text{constant} \quad \text{(monatomic ideal gas)}. \quad (20.32)$$

We obtained this expression for a monatomic ideal gas where each atom has three degrees of freedom (Section 20.3). The factor 3 in the $\frac{3}{2}$ in this expression comes from the three dimensions of the velocity space among which we equipartitioned the energy (Eq. 19.29). In the more general case of an ideal gas with d degrees of freedom, we replace the 3 by d:

$$S = N \ln V + \frac{d}{2}N \ln T + \text{constant} \quad \text{(ideal gas)}. \quad (20.33)$$

Figure 20.37 Checkpoint 20.18.

(a) Process A: isochoric step, then isobaric step

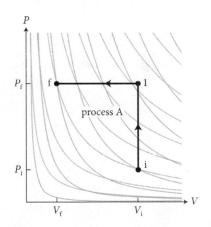

(b) Process B: isentropic step, then isobaric step

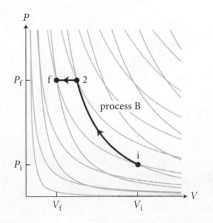

During a process in which the gas undergoes a transformation from an initial equilibrium state (V_i, T_i) to a final equilibrium state (V_f, T_f), the entropy changes by an amount (see Eqs. 19.8 and 19.56)

$$\Delta S = N \ln\left(\frac{V_f}{V_i}\right) + \frac{d}{2} N \ln\left(\frac{T_f}{T_i}\right) \quad \text{(ideal gas).} \tag{20.34}$$

For an isothermal process, $T_i = T_f$, and so the second term on the right is zero because $\ln(1) = 0$. Equation 20.34 thus becomes

$$\Delta S = N \ln\left(\frac{V_f}{V_i}\right) \quad \text{(isothermal process),} \tag{20.35}$$

a result we already obtained in Eq. 19.8. Comparing this result with Eq. 20.31, we see that we can express the entropy change for an isothermal process as

$$\Delta S = \frac{Q}{k_B T} \quad \text{(isothermal process).} \tag{20.36}$$

This expression allows us to calculate the change in entropy directly once we know the amount of energy transferred thermally, allowing us to bypass Eq. 20.34. Equation 20.36 is applicable only when the temperature is constant, however. For any other process, Eq. 20.34 provides the simplest approach for calculating the entropy change.

For an isochoric process, $V_f = V_i$, and so Eq. 20.34 reduces to

$$\Delta S = \frac{d}{2} N \ln\left(\frac{T_f}{T_i}\right) \quad \text{(isochoric process)} \tag{20.37}$$

or, substituting from Eq. 20.14,

$$\Delta S = \frac{N C_V}{k_B} \ln\left(\frac{T_f}{T_i}\right) \quad \text{(isochoric process).} \tag{20.38}$$

✋ **20.19** Can you use Eq. 20.36 to calculate the change in entropy for an isochoric process?

In an isobaric process, both V and T change, but the two are related by the ideal gas law, $PV = Nk_B T$. Because P is constant in any isobaric process, we have $V_i = (Nk_B/P)T_i$ and $V_f = (Nk_B/P)T_f$. Therefore

$$\frac{V_f}{V_i} = \frac{(Nk_B/P)T_f}{(Nk_B/P)T_i} = \frac{T_f}{T_i} \quad \text{(isobaric process).} \tag{20.39}$$

With this result, Eq. 20.34 becomes

$$\Delta S = N \ln\left(\frac{T_f}{T_i}\right) + \frac{d}{2} N \ln\left(\frac{T_f}{T_i}\right)$$

$$= N\left(1 + \frac{d}{2}\right) \ln\left(\frac{T_f}{T_i}\right) \quad \text{(isobaric process).} \tag{20.40}$$

Substituting from Eq. 20.25, we can rewrite this expression in the form

$$\Delta S = \frac{N C_P}{k_B} \ln\left(\frac{T_f}{T_i}\right) \quad \text{(isobaric process).} \tag{20.41}$$

Note the similarity between the expression for the entropy change in an isochoric process (Eq. 20.38) and the expression for the entropy change in an isobaric process (Eq. 20.41). The only difference is the type of heat capacity per particle: For the isochoric process we use C_V; for the isobaric process we use C_P.

As an example, consider the isobaric expansion shown in Figure 20.34. The final temperature is higher than the initial temperature, and so, because $\ln(T_f/T_i) > 0$, Eq. 20.41 tells us that the entropy increases. Indeed, from the PV diagram in Figure 20.34c we see that the final state must lie on a higher isentrope than the initial state, indicating that the entropy of the final state is greater than the entropy of the initial state.

In an isentropic process, the entropy doesn't change, and so

$$\Delta S = 0 \quad \text{(isentropic process).} \tag{20.42}$$

This result implies that during an isentropic process the changes in volume and temperature are such that the two terms in Eq. 20.34 cancel each other. In other words, the volume and temperature changes are correlated in such a way as to keep the entropy of the system constant.

✋ **20.20** Suppose two different combinations of constrained quasistatic processes take two identical ideal gases from the same initial equilibrium state to the same final equilibrium state. Is the change in entropy the same or different in the two cases?

Table 20.7 summarizes the entropy changes for the four constrained ideal gas processes. As you saw in Checkpoint 20.20, the value of the entropy change is independent of the process and depends on only the temperatures and volumes of the initial and final equilibrium states. For *any* process, we can use Eq. 20.34 to calculate the entropy change. The expressions summarized in Table 20.7, however, provide a quick way to obtain the entropy changes for the four basic constrained ideal gas processes. Keep in mind that in these processes the system is not closed, and so the entropy change can be positive, negative, or zero.

Equation 20.33 can be rewritten in a form that allows us to derive useful relationships among the pressure, volume and temperature of any two states, (P_i, V_i, T_i) and (P_f, V_f, T_f), that lie on an isentrope. We begin by combining the first and second terms on the right in Eq. 20.33, which gives us

$$S = N\ln(T^{d/2}V) + \text{constant.} \tag{20.43}$$

Because the entropy is constant, the quantity $T^{d/2}V$ must be constant as well for a sample that consists of a fixed number N of particles: $T_i^{d/2}V_i = T_f^{d/2}V_f$. Raising

Table 20.7 Entropy changes in ideal gas processes

Process	ΔS	Equation
isochoric	$\dfrac{NC_V}{k_B}\ln\left(\dfrac{T_f}{T_i}\right)$	20.38
isothermal	$N\ln\left(\dfrac{V_f}{V_i}\right) = \dfrac{Q}{k_B T}$	20.35, 20.36
isobaric	$\dfrac{NC_P}{k_B}\ln\left(\dfrac{T_f}{T_i}\right)$	20.41
isentropic	0	20.42

the constant quantity $T^{d/2}V$ to the power $\frac{2}{d}$, and substituting $\frac{2}{d} = \gamma - 1$ from Eq. 20.26, we see that $(T^{d/2}V)^{2/d} = TV^{\gamma-1}$, or

$$T_i V_i^{\gamma-1} = T_f V_f^{\gamma-1} \quad \text{(isentropic process)}. \tag{20.44}$$

This expression provides the relationship between volume and temperature along an isentrope. Using the ideal gas law, we can obtain expressions relating other quantities along an isentrope. Multiplying the ideal gas law, $PV = Nk_BT$, by $V^{\gamma-1}$, we obtain:

$$PV^\gamma = Nk_B T V^{\gamma-1}. \tag{20.45}$$

From Eq. 20.44 we see that the right side of Eq. 20.45 is constant for an isentropic process, and thus the quantity PV^γ must also be constant:

$$P_i V_i^\gamma = P_f V_f^\gamma \quad \text{(isentropic process)}. \tag{20.46}$$

From the ideal gas law, we know that V is proportional to T/P, which means that $PV^\gamma \propto P(T/P)^\gamma = P^{1-\gamma}T^\gamma$ is constant for an isentropic process. Raising this quantity to the power $1/\gamma$, we get $(P^{1-\gamma}T^\gamma)^{1/\gamma} = P^{(1/\gamma)-1}T$, and so in an isentropic process,

$$P_i^{(1/\gamma)-1}T_i = P_f^{(1/\gamma)-1}T_f \quad \text{(isentropic process)}. \tag{20.47}$$

Equations 20.44, 20.46 and 20.47 relate the pressure, volume, and temperature for the initial and final equilibrium states of an ideal gas sample that consists of N particles undergoing an isentropic process.

Example 20.9 Entropy changes

Figure 20.38 shows two quasistatic processes that take a sample of an ideal gas containing N particles from an initial state (P_i, V_i) to a final state (P_f, V_f). Process A is a one-step isentropic compression. Process B has two steps: an isochoric pressure increase to an intermediate state 1 followed by an isobaric decrease in volume. Express the changes in entropy for process A and process B in terms of the given quantities.

Figure 20.38

❶ **GETTING STARTED** The fact that the initial and final states are on different isotherms (red curves) in Figure 20.38 tells me

that the two are at different temperatures, which I call T_i and T_f. These temperatures are related to the initial and final volume and pressure by the ideal gas law. For the intermediate state, I can write $(P_1, V_1) = (P_f, V_i)$. I'll denote the temperature of this state by T_1.

❷ **DEVISE PLAN** Table 20.7 gives expressions for the entropy changes in the four constrained processes. I can eliminate the temperature from these expressions by using the ideal gas law, $PV = Nk_BT$, and Eq. 20.39.

❸ **EXECUTE PLAN** Process A is isentropic, which means that its entropy doesn't change: $\Delta S_A = 0$. ✔

I first obtain the entropy change for the isochoric step of process B from Eq. 20.38:

$$\Delta S_{B,\text{isochoric}} = \frac{NC_V}{k_B}\ln\left(\frac{T_1}{T_i}\right).$$

From the ideal gas law, I get for the initial and intermediate states, respectively:

$$P_i V_i = Nk_B T_i \tag{1}$$

$$P_f V_i = Nk_B T_1. \tag{2}$$

Dividing Eq. 2 by Eq. 1 gives me $T_1/T_i = P_f/P_i$, and so for the first step of process B I have

$$\Delta S_{\text{B,isochoric}} = \frac{NC_V}{k_B} \ln\left(\frac{P_f}{P_i}\right). \qquad (3)$$

The entropy change for the isobaric step of process B is given by Eq. 20.41:

$$\Delta S_{\text{B,isobaric}} = \frac{NC_P}{k_B} \ln\left(\frac{T_f}{T_1}\right).$$

Equation 20.39 yields $T_f/T_1 = V_f/V_i$, so I can write the entropy change as

$$\Delta S_{\text{B,isobaric}} = \frac{NC_P}{k_B} \ln\left(\frac{V_f}{V_i}\right). \qquad (4)$$

The entropy change for process B is the sum of the entropy changes for the two steps, so, adding Eqs. 3 and 4, I get

$$\Delta S_B = \frac{NC_V}{k_B} \ln\left(\frac{P_f}{P_i}\right) + \frac{NC_P}{k_B} \ln\left(\frac{V_f}{V_i}\right). ✔$$

4 EVALUATE RESULT The two processes connect the same initial and final states, so the entropy change should be the same for the two processes. Therefore the expression I obtained for process B should be zero: $\Delta S_B = 0$. Because the process that takes the gas from the initial to the final state is isentropic, Eq. 20.46 tells me that $P_f/P_i = (V_i/V_f)^\gamma$. Summing my expressions for $\Delta S_{\text{B,isochoric}}$ and $\Delta S_{\text{B,isobaric}}$ and making this substitution for P_f/P_i yield

$$\Delta S_B = \frac{NC_V}{k_B} \ln\left(\frac{V_i}{V_f}\right)^\gamma + \frac{NC_P}{k_B} \ln\left(\frac{V_f}{V_i}\right)$$

$$= \frac{NC_V}{k_B} \gamma \ln\left(\frac{V_i}{V_f}\right) + \frac{NC_P}{k_B} \ln\left(\frac{V_f}{V_i}\right).$$

Because $\gamma \equiv C_P/C_V$ (Eq. 20.26), I obtain, as expected

$$\Delta S_B = \frac{NC_P}{k_B} \ln\left(\frac{V_i}{V_f}\right) + \frac{NC_P}{k_B} \ln\left(\frac{V_f}{V_i}\right)$$

$$= \frac{NC_P}{k_B} \ln\left(\frac{V_i}{V_f}\right) - \frac{NC_P}{k_B} \ln\left(\frac{V_i}{V_f}\right) = 0.$$

✋ **20.21** For a quasistatic ideal gas process that ends on a higher isentrope, are W, Q, ΔE_{th}, and ΔS positive, negative, or zero when the gas is (a) expanded and (b) compressed?

20.9 Entropy change in nonideal gas processes

Let us now briefly consider what happens to the energy and entropy when the temperature of a liquid or gas changes. When we deal with a solid or liquid of given mass and constant volume, it is more convenient to work with specific heat capacity (see Section 20.3 and Table 20.2) rather than heat capacity per particle. The specific heat capacity is obtained by dividing the energy transferred thermally by the mass of the object or system and by the temperature change:*

$$c_V \equiv \frac{Q}{m\Delta T}. \qquad (20.48)$$

And so for a given change in temperature, the energy transferred thermally is

$$Q = mc_V\Delta T. \qquad (20.49)$$

Because the volume is constant, no work is done and the energy law reduces to $\Delta E_{\text{th}} = Q$, so the system's energy change is

$$\Delta E_{\text{th}} = mc_V\Delta T. \qquad (20.50)$$

*We are assuming here that the specific heat capacity does not depend on temperature. As Figure 20.15 shows, however, this is only approximately true over limited temperature ranges.

To calculate the corresponding entropy change, we rewrite the definition of absolute temperature (Eq. 19.38), which gives the relationship between changes in thermal energy and entropy, as follows:

$$dS = \frac{dE_{th}}{k_B T}. \tag{20.51}$$

For an infinitesimally small change in temperature, Eq. 20.50 becomes $dE_{th} = mc_V dT$, and so Eq. 20.51 becomes

$$dS = \frac{mc_V}{k_B} \frac{dT}{T}. \tag{20.52}$$

To determine the entropy change for a finite temperature change, we integrate this expression for a temperature change $\Delta T = T_f - T_i$:

$$\Delta S = \frac{mc_V}{k_B} \int_{T_i}^{T_f} \frac{dT}{T} = \frac{mc_V}{k_B} \ln\left(\frac{T_f}{T_i}\right). \tag{20.53}$$

We can also use Eq. 20.51 to obtain a more general expression for the entropy change in an isothermal process. Let the energy thermally transferred be Q. At constant temperature the entropy change is then

$$\Delta S = \frac{Q}{k_B T} \quad \text{(isothermal process).} \tag{20.54}$$

Note that this expression is identical to the one we obtained earlier for an ideal gas (Eq. 20.36).

Let us next determine what happens to the energy and entropy of a system during a phase transition. In Section 20.3 we defined the **specific transformation energy** as the energy transferred thermally to a substance undergoing a phase transition divided by the mass of the substance:

$$L \equiv \frac{Q}{m} \quad \text{(phase transition with } Q > 0\text{).} \tag{20.55}$$

Because the quantity L is always positive and Q can be negative or positive, Eq. 20.55 holds only for melting and vaporization. For solidification and condensation, Q is negative and so we have

$$L \equiv \frac{-Q}{m} \quad \text{(phase transition with } Q < 0\text{).} \tag{20.56}$$

Because the temperature is constant, we can use Eq. 20.54 to calculate the corresponding entropy change

$$\Delta S = \frac{Q}{k_B T} = \frac{mL}{k_B T} \quad \text{(melting or vaporization).} \tag{20.57}$$

For solidification and condensation the entropy change is of the opposite sign:

$$\Delta S = -\frac{mL}{k_B T} \quad \text{(solidification or condensation).} \tag{20.58}$$

✋ **20.22** An amount of water with a mass of 0.010 kg at a temperature of 20 °C is placed in a freezer and turns into an ice cube at 0.0 °C. What is the corresponding entropy change? Ignore any volume changes.

Chapter Glossary

SI units of physical quantities are given in parentheses.

Absolute zero The temperature at which the thermal energy of a system is minimum. A system at absolute zero has only a single microstate and zero entropy.

Adiabatic process A process that does not involve any thermal transfer of energy ($Q = 0$).

Degree of freedom Any independent way in which a particle can store energy.

Energy transferred thermally Q (J) A scalar equal to the change in the energy of a system due to thermal interactions. If the energy of the system increases, the energy transferred thermally is positive; if the energy decreases, the energy transferred thermally is negative.

Equipartition energy share In thermal equilibrium, each degree of freedom of a system at temperature T stores an amount of energy equal to $\frac{1}{2}k_BT$ per particle.

Heat capacity (J/K) A scalar defined as the amount of energy transferred thermally to an object divided by the resulting change in temperature.

Heat capacity per particle C (J/K) A scalar equal to the heat capacity of an object divided by the number of particles making up that object:

$$C \equiv \frac{Q}{N\Delta T}. \qquad (20.13, 20.20)$$

A subscript V or P is added when the heating takes place at constant volume or at constant pressure.

Heat capacity ratio γ (unitless) A scalar equal to the ratio of the heat capacity per particle at constant pressure to the heat capacity per particle at constant volume. For an ideal gas:

$$\gamma \equiv \frac{C_P}{C_V} = \frac{\left(\frac{d}{2}+1\right)k_B}{\frac{d}{2}k_B} = 1 + \frac{2}{d} \quad \text{(ideal gas)}. \quad (20.26)$$

Ideal gas thermometer A device for measuring temperature using an ideal gas.

Isentrope A curve on a PV diagram that represents states having the same entropy. These curves are sometimes called *adiabats*.

Isentropic process A process for which the entropy of the system is constant. Quasistatic adiabatic processes are isentropic. An isentropic process is an adiabatic process.

Isobaric process A process for which the pressure in the system is held constant.

Isochoric process A process for which the volume of the system is held constant.

Isotherm A curve on a PV diagram that represents states having the same temperature.

Isothermal process A process for which the temperature of the system is held constant.

Process The transformation of a system from one macrostate to another.

Quasistatic process A process for which the system always remains very close to equilibrium as the transformation takes place. A path on a PV diagram always represents a quasistatic process.

Specific heat capacity c (J/K · kg) A scalar equal to the heat capacity of an object divided by the mass of the object.

Specific transformation energy L (J/kg) The energy transferred thermally to a substance undergoing a phase transition divided by the mass of the substance:

$$L \equiv \frac{Q}{m} \quad \text{(phase transition with } Q > 0\text{)}. \quad (20.55)$$

$$L \equiv \frac{-Q}{m} \quad \text{(phase transition with } Q < 0\text{)}. \quad (20.56)$$

Thermal interaction An interaction between two objects at different temperatures that results in a thermal transfer of energy from the object at the higher temperature to the object at the lower temperature.

Thermal reservoir A body of material large enough so that its temperature does not change in a thermal interaction with the system under consideration.

Triple point of water The temperature and pressure at which the solid, liquid, and gas phases of water coexist in thermal equilibrium. By international convention, the temperature of the triple point of water is 273.16 K.

21 Degradation of Energy

CONCEPTS

21.1 Converting energy

21.2 Quality of energy

21.3 Heat engines and heat pumps

21.4 Thermodynamic cycles

QUANTITATIVE TOOLS

21.5 Entropy constraints on energy transfers

21.6 Heat engine performance

21.7 Carnot cycle

21.8 Brayton cycle

Some textbooks define energy as the *capacity to do work*. In the two preceding chapters, however, we saw that energy can do more than that. It can also be used to heat objects, and in this chapter we ask (and answer) two important questions about energy: To what extent can we use mechanical energy for heating and thermal energy for doing work? And, more specifically, to what extent can we convert energy from forms provided by nature to forms useful for technology and society?

The oceans of the world, for example, contain a very large amount of thermal energy. If we could convert just a small fraction of that energy to useful forms, we could satisfy the world's energy needs for thousands of years. Why can't a ship take in some of the thermal energy in the ocean and use it for propulsion? Such a scheme does not violate the energy law: Thermal energy would simply be converted to an equal amount of mechanical energy. As we see in this chapter, however, the entropy law imposes constraints on conversions of energy.

21.1 Converting energy

In Chapter 5 we saw that energy is a quantitative measure of the state of an object and that the law of conservation of energy implies that any change of state must be accompanied by a compensating change of state (or by a set of compensating changes of state). Whenever a pair of complementary changes of different types take place, energy is converted from one form to another. For example, burning propane gas involves two changes of state: a change in the molecular chemical bonds of the reagents (which we associate with chemical energy) and a change in the temperature of the gases (which we associate with thermal energy). The combustion is irreversible: It would be pretty startling if the hot gases would suddenly "unburn," cooling down and reconstituting the original propane and oxygen. Because the process is irreversible, we can conclude that the entropy of the gas increases in the process of burning (see Section 19.4).

A ball accelerating in free fall is another example of a complementary pair of changes of state: a change in the state of motion of the ball (which we associate with kinetic energy) and a change in the configuration of the Earth-ball system (which we associate with gravitational potential energy). This process is reversible: A movie clip of the falling ball played backward shows an upward moving ball slowing down as if it had been thrown upward (which *can* happen). We can thus conclude that the entropy of the Earth-ball system does not change.

21.1 For each system, identify the complementary changes of state and associated energies, and determine whether or not the entropy of the system increases. (*a*) A puck slides to a stop on a surface. System: puck and surface. (*b*) A compressed spring is released and accelerates a cart on a low-friction track. System: spring and cart. (*c*) A projectile is fired from a cannon. System: projectile, cannon, and explosive chemicals. (*d*) A hot object and a cold object are placed in contact and reach thermal equilibrium. System: both objects.

Figure 21.1 Energy input-output diagram.

thermal input of energy

mechanical input of energy

thermal output of energy

mechanical output of energy

To analyze the energy conversions that occur in a process, such as the ones in Checkpoint 21.1, we must choose a system and separately analyze all the energy transfers into and out of the system. As we saw in Chapter 20, energy can be transferred in two ways: mechanically and thermally. **Figure 21.1** shows for each of these two types of transfers an arrow representing the transfer of energy *into* the system (called *energy input*) and an arrow representing the transfer of energy *out of* the system (called *energy output*). Diagrams that show the energy inputs and energy outputs of a system are called **energy input-output diagrams.**

Energy inputs and energy outputs are always taken to be positive. The work done on a system is thus the difference between the **mechanical input of energy** and the **mechanical output of energy:** $W = W_{in} - W_{out}$. Likewise, the energy transferred thermally into a system is the difference between the **thermal input of energy** and the **thermal output of energy:** $Q = Q_{in} - Q_{out}$.

Figure 21.1 can represent the functioning of any device or industrial process. **Figure 21.2** shows the energy input-output diagrams for two devices: a car engine and a refrigerator. In a car, the combustion of gasoline provides a thermal input of energy to the engine (the system). The engine has two energy outputs: a mechanical output of energy to the wheels of the car and a thermal output of energy to the environment (Figure 21.2*a*). In a refrigerator there are two energy inputs (Figure 21.2*b*): a thermal input of energy from the refrigerator contents (which are part of the environment) and a mechanical input of energy from the compressor motor to the rest of the refrigerator (the system). The refrigerator also has a thermal output of energy to the environment. (You may have noticed that the back of a refrigerator gets hot.)

Each energy input or energy output in Figures 21.1 and Figure 21.2 is accompanied by changes in entropy in the environment and in the system. To gain some practice determining energy and entropy changes, let us analyze a few specific situations.

Exercise 21.1 Converting mechanical energy to thermal energy

Consider the device illustrated in **Figure 21.3**. A string is attached to a paddle wheel that is immersed in a viscous liquid in a container. As the string is pulled, the paddle wheel rotates at

Figure 21.2 Examples of energy input-output diagrams.

(*a*) Energy input-output diagram for car engine

thermal input from
fuel combustion

Q_{in}

car engine W_{out} → mechanical output
to turn wheels

Q_{out}

thermal output via exhaust
and engine cooling

(*b*) Energy input-output diagram for refrigerator

thermal input from environment
(including warm food in fridge)

Q_{in}

mechanical input
from compressor
motor W_{in} refrigerator
cooling system

Q_{out}

thermal output to environment
from cooling coils on back of fridge

constant speed, increasing the temperature of the liquid from T_i to T_f. (*a*) Draw an energy input-output diagram for the system comprising the paddle wheel and the liquid. Do the energy and entropy of the system comprising the paddle wheel and the liquid increase, decrease, or stay the same? (*b*) Assume the paddle wheel stops turning at the instant shown in Figure 21.3*b*, and we now

Figure 21.3

Hand does mechanical work on system by pulling string.

viscous
liquid

T_i

$T_f > T_i$

Mechanical work done by paddle wheel
on liquid raises temperature.

Figure 21.4

(*a*)

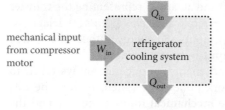

person W_{in} $\Delta E > 0$
$\Delta S > 0$

Q_{out}

environment

(*b*)

person W_{in} $\Delta E = 0$
$\Delta S = 0$

Q_{out}

environment

wait until the liquid cools back down to its initial temperature T_i. Draw an energy input-output diagram for the system, but this time over the time interval from the instant the wheel begins turning to the instant the liquid temperature is again T_i. Do the energy and entropy of the system increase, decrease, or stay the same over this new time interval?

SOLUTION (*a*) The work done on the system by pulling the string corresponds to an energy input. Because the system is not thermally insulated, energy is transferred thermally to the environment as the temperature of the system increases. My energy input-diagram therefore has one input and one output (**Figure 21.4*a***). Because the temperature of the system increases, I know that the energy of the system increases and so the energy input must be greater than the energy output. The increase in thermal energy increases the entropy of the system. ✔

(*b*) If the liquid cools back to its initial temperature, the initial and final states of the system are the same, so the energy change and the entropy change are both zero. The input of energy is the same as in part *a*, but because the energy of the system is not changing, the thermal output of energy must now be equal in magnitude to the mechanical input (Figure 21.4*b*). ✔

Note that the energy law imposes no restrictions on energy conversions: The energy law permits any form of energy to be converted entirely to any other form of energy. The device in Exercise 21.1, for example, converts mechanical energy entirely to thermal energy. Let us now look at the conversion of thermal energy to mechanical energy.

21.2 (*a*) For the situation illustrated in **Figure 21.5**, draw an energy input-output diagram for the gas. (*b*) Do the energy and entropy of the gas change? Ignore any friction in the piston and any energy transferred thermally out of the gas.

As you saw in Checkpoint 21.2, energy transferred thermally to the gas does work on the piston, and so the device converts thermal energy to mechanical energy. Because the temperature of the gas goes up, however, the thermal energy of the gas increases. Thus not all thermal energy is converted to mechanical energy in this device.

To prevent the thermal energy of the gas from increasing, we could immerse the setup in a thermal reservoir held at some fixed temperature T_R, as illustrated in **Figure 21.6**. If we then slowly remove grains of sand lying on top of the piston, the upward force exerted by the gas on the piston is

Figure 21.5 When a volume of gas is heated at constant pressure in a cylinder fitted with a movable piston, both its temperature and its volume increase.

(a)

(b)

T_i
P_i
V_i

h
$T_f > T_i$
$P_f = P_i$
$V_f > V_i$

a tiny bit greater than the downward force exerted by the remaining sand on the piston, and so the piston moves up. As the gas expands, it does work on the piston. Because the temperature of the gas remains constant, its thermal energy doesn't change, and so the energy required to raise the piston must be transferred thermally from the reservoir. Here is a situation where thermal energy is converted entirely to mechanical energy.

As a device, the setup of Figure 21.6 is not very practical because to maintain a constant gas temperature, the expansion would have to proceed *very* slowly. Moreover, in order for the gas to continue to do work on the piston, its volume would have to keep expanding.

When designing practical devices for converting energy, we usually want them to be able to operate indefinitely. If the device were to keep expanding in volume as in Figure 21.6 or keep getting hotter or building up pressure over time, it could not be operated for very long. For this reason we want the state of the device that converts energy to remain the same or to return to the same state over some repeating time interval. Such a device is called a **steady device.** When a steady device evolves from an initial state through a series of processes back to its initial state, the series of processes is called a *cycle.* During the operation of the device, this cycle is repeated continuously. For simplicity, we shall assume that all steady devices involve only quasistatic processes and that no energy is dissipated due to friction.

Figure 21.6 A gas held at constant temperature in a cylinder fitted with a movable piston expands slowly as the load on the piston is diminished.

Sand is removed slowly.

$T = T_R$
P_i
V_i

$T = T_R$
$P_f < P_i$
$V_f > V_i$

thermal reservoir at constant temperature T_R

Because the initial and final states of a steady device are the same over one cycle, there is no change in the energy of the system: $\Delta E = 0$. Over one cycle, therefore, the energy input must be equal to the energy output: $W_{in} + Q_{in} = W_{out} + Q_{out}$.

To see what constraints are imposed by the entropy law (Eq. 19.5; $\Delta S > 0$ for a closed system moving toward equilibrium) on the energy inputs and outputs of a steady device, we examine the entropy changes associated with these energy inputs and outputs. The device is not a closed system and so we cannot apply the entropy law to it. The device and its environment constitute a closed system, however, so we can write $\Delta S = \Delta S_{dev} + \Delta S_{env} \geq 0$ (Eqs. 19.5, 19.6). Because the initial and final states of the cycle are the same, we know that there cannot be any change in the entropy of the device: $\Delta S_{dev} = 0$ for one cycle. Therefore, we need to consider only entropy changes in the environment when we deal with steady devices and make sure these changes satisfy $\Delta S_{env} > 0$.

As we saw in Section 20.1, no entropy change is associated with a quasistatic adiabatic process. Because $Q = 0$ for mechanical inputs and outputs of energy and because we assume that the processes in a steady device are quasistatic, we have $\Delta S_{env} = 0$ for W_{in} and W_{out}. Therefore the only changes in the entropy of the environment we need to consider are those caused by thermal inputs and outputs of energy:

Steady devices operate under two constraints: (1) The energy input must be equal to the energy output. (2) The device's thermal inputs and outputs must increase the entropy of the environment (or leave it unaltered).

In Chapter 20, we saw that the entropy change associated with energy transferred thermally has the same sign as Q (Eq. 20.54). Therefore, a thermal output of energy increases the entropy of the environment. Conversely, a thermal input of energy decreases the entropy of the environment. **Figure 21.7** summarizes these entropy changes due to the various kinds of energy inputs and energy outputs for a steady device. We use a circular system boundary to indicate that the system is a steady device. The diagram represents the energy inputs and outputs during one complete cycle.

Figure 21.7 Energy and entropy changes associated with energy inputs and energy outputs for a steady device.

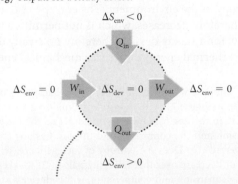

$\Delta S_{env} < 0$

Q_{in}

$\Delta S_{env} = 0$ W_{in} $\Delta S_{dev} = 0$ W_{out} $\Delta S_{env} = 0$

Q_{out}

$\Delta S_{env} > 0$

Circular system boundary indicates *steady device* ($\Delta E = 0$, $\Delta S_{dev} = 0$).

Figure 21.8 Energy input-output diagrams for two types of steady device.

(*a*) Device that converts mechanical energy to thermal energy

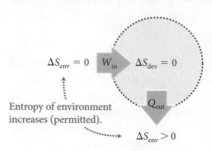

Entropy of environment increases (permitted).

(*b*) Attempt to convert thermal energy entirely to mechanical energy

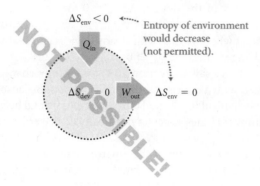

Entropy of environment would decrease (not permitted).

We are now in a position to analyze steady devices that convert energy. First consider a steady device that converts mechanical energy to thermal energy. Such a device has a mechanical input of energy and a thermal output of energy (**Figure 21.8a**). The mechanical input of energy involves no change in the entropy of the environment; the thermal output of energy causes an increase in the entropy of the environment. The entropy of the environment therefore increases, which is permitted by the entropy law. This means that a steady device can convert mechanical energy entirely to thermal energy.

Next consider a steady device that converts thermal energy to mechanical energy (Figure 21.8b). The thermal input of energy causes a decrease in the entropy of the environment; the mechanical output of energy involves no change in the entropy of the environment. The entropy of the environment therefore decreases, which is not permitted by the entropy law for a steady device. Therefore no steady device can convert thermal energy entirely to mechanical energy.

21.3 Suppose we slowly push the piston back to its original position in Figure 21.6, all the while maintaining a constant temperature in the gas. (*a*) Over the time interval that includes the expansion and the compression of the gas, has any energy been converted? (*b*) Does the entropy of the gas increase, stay the same, or decrease over that time interval? (*c*) If we keep repeating the expansion and compression, is this device a steady device?

21.2 Quality of energy

In this section we develop a graphical approach to keep track of entropy changes in the environment caused by steady devices that convert energy. Let us begin by considering the very simple situation illustrated in **Figure 21.9a**: A copper rod is in thermal contact with a high-temperature thermal reservoir on one end and a low-temperature thermal reservoir on the other end. Apart from its ends, the rod is thermally isolated from its environment. Because the temperatures of the thermal reservoirs are fixed, the rod remains in a steady state: One end remains at the temperature T_H of the high-temperature reservoir, and the other end remains at the temperature T_L of the low-temperature reservoir. (Remember that thermal reservoirs are large enough so that any energy transferred thermally to them does not change their temperature; see Section 20.7.) As a result of the temperature difference, energy is transferred thermally through the rod from the high-temperature reservoir to the low-temperature reservoir. Although the rod hardly qualifies as a device, its state doesn't change and so it satisfies the requirements that the entropy and energy of a steady device do not change over time. (The cycle for this device can be taken to be any arbitrary time interval.)

Figure 21.9b shows the energy input-output diagrams for the rod and for the two thermal reservoirs. The change in the energy of the high-temperature reservoir is equal to the thermal input of energy of the rod, $\Delta E_H = -Q_{in}$, while the change in the energy of the low-temperature reservoir is equal to the thermal output of energy of the rod, $\Delta E_L = Q_{out}$. Because the state of the rod is not changing, we know that $\Delta E_{rod} = Q_{in} - Q_{out} = 0$, so $Q_{in} = Q_{out}$ and therefore $\Delta E_H = -\Delta E_L$. The amount of energy transferred out of the high-temperature reservoir is equal to the amount of energy transferred into the low-temperature reservoir.

Figure 21.9 (*a*) A copper rod in thermal contact with a high-temperature reservoir and a low-temperature reservoir. (*b*) Energy input-output diagrams for the rod and the reservoirs.

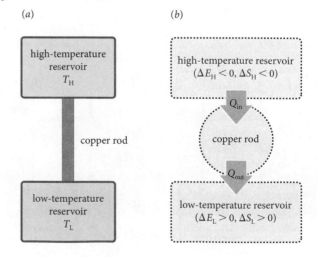

Figure 21.10 Entropy gradient. The shaded bar represents the rod's environment, which consists of the high-temperature reservoir (H) and the low-temperature reservoir (L).

Entropy gradient measures change in entropy for a given change in energy.

High-temperature reservoir has *low* entropy gradient.

Low-temperature reservoir has *high* entropy gradient.

The thermal transfer of energy through the rod causes entropy changes in the two reservoirs (both part of the rod's environment) even though their temperatures remain unchanged. Because energy is transferred out of the high-temperature reservoir, its energy decreases, and so its entropy decreases too: $\Delta S_H < 0$. The increase of energy in the low-temperature reservoir causes its entropy to increase: $\Delta S_L > 0$. Because the transfer of energy is irreversible, we know that the entropy of the environment must increase, so that $\Delta S_H + \Delta S_L > 0$.

The reason entropy increases can be understood by looking at the way we defined temperature in Chapter 19: $dS/dE \equiv 1/(k_B T)$ (Eq. 19.38).* The quantity dS/dE, called the **entropy gradient**, is a measure of the change in entropy caused by a given change in energy. Equation 19.38 tells us that the magnitude of the change in entropy caused by transferring a given amount of energy to or from a reservoir is inversely proportional to the temperature of the reservoir. The entropy change ΔS caused by a given change in energy ΔE is therefore greater in magnitude for the low-temperature reservoir than for the high-temperature reservoir. Because ΔS_L is positive and ΔS_H is negative, it follows that $\Delta S_H + \Delta S_L > 0$.

21.4 What are the signs of ΔE_R, ΔS_R, and $\Delta S_R/\Delta E_R$ for a thermal transfer of energy (*a*) to and (*b*) from a thermal reservoir?

You can view the entropy gradient as the "entropy cost of an energy change." The greater the entropy gradient (or the lower the temperature), the greater the change in entropy caused by a given energy change. As you saw in Checkpoint 21.4, the entropy gradient is always positive, regardless of the direction of the energy transfer, because ΔS and ΔE always have the same algebraic sign.

We can arrange the rod's environment by its entropy gradient. Because the high-temperature reservoir has the smaller entropy gradient, we place it to the left of the low-temperature reservoir on the entropy-gradient scale in **Figure 21.10**. If we represent the thermal transfer of energy through the rod in **Figure 21.11a**, by a curved arrow, we obtain the diagram shown in Figure 21.11b. The tail of the

*As we did in Chapter 20, we assume that the kinetic, potential, and source energies of the reservoirs remain constant, so that $\Delta E = \Delta E_{th}$.

Figure 21.11 (*a*) We rearrange the device of Figure 21.9 to separate the system (the steady device) from its environment (the thermal reservoirs). (*b*) Using this geometry, we construct an entropy diagram showing the energy conversions and transfers in the steady device. The thermal input at low dS/dE causes entropy change in the environment of smaller magnitude than thermal output at high dS/dE, so the entropy of the environment increases: $\Delta S_H + \Delta S_L > 0$.

(*a*) We separate the device (the system) from its environment

(*b*) Entropy diagram

arrow represents the thermal input of energy from the high-temperature reservoir, and the head represents the thermal output of energy to the low-temperature reservoir.

Note that we can associate the sign of the entropy changes in the reservoirs with the direction of the arrow. The tail of the arrow (the energy input) points down and $\Delta S_H < 0$; the head (the energy output) points up and $\Delta S_L > 0$. The diagram in Figure 21.11b therefore allows us to see that the transfer of energy through the rod increases the entropy of the environment: The rod takes a certain amount of energy out of the environment at low entropy cost (small dS/dE) and returns the same amount of energy to the environment at a greater entropy cost (large dS/dE). The magnitude of the entropy change caused by the output is therefore greater than the magnitude of the entropy change caused by the input. Because the input causes a decrease in entropy and the output causes an increase in entropy, the combined effect is an increase in the entropy of the environment.

Now suppose the copper rod somehow transfers energy from the low-temperature reservoir to the high-temperature reservoir, as illustrated in **Figure 21.12**. The curved arrow representing the energy transfer now points from the low-temperature reservoir to the high-temperature reservoir and, as you can readily verify, the signs of the entropy changes are the opposite of the signs in Figure 21.11. The rod takes a certain amount of energy out of the environment at large dS/dE and returns the same amount of energy to the

Figure 21.12 Entropy diagram for a thermal transfer of energy from a low-temperature reservoir (L) to a high-temperature reservoir (H), a process forbidden by the entropy law.

Input at high dS/dE would cause greater entropy change than output at low dS/dE, so entropy of environment would *decrease* — not possible!

environment at a smaller dS/dE. The entropy change of the environment in this process is thus negative, which is not allowed by the entropy law. Indeed, no one has ever observed energy being transferred thermally from a cold object to a hot object with no other changes in the system or the environment (that is, the cold object spontaneously getting colder and the hot object getting hotter).

The diagrams in Figures 21.11 and 21.12 are called **entropy diagrams.** An entropy diagram shows the energy conversions and transfers that take place in a steady device with the environment arranged according to an entropy gradient, as shown in Figure 21.10. Arrows in the diagram represent the energy transfers through the device during one complete cycle. The tails of the arrows represent energy inputs to the device, and the heads represent energy outputs. Thermal inputs of energy (tails) cause the entropy of the environment to decrease, while thermal outputs of energy (arrowheads) cause the entropy of the environment to increase.

Entropy diagrams permit us to keep track of entropy changes that result from the energy conversions by a steady device. In particular:

A transfer of energy that points to the right in an entropy diagram causes an increase in the entropy of the environment; a transfer that points to the left causes a decrease in the entropy of the environment.

As we shall see in Section 21.5, entropy diagrams can be used to derive quantitative information about entropy changes in the environment.

Let's now return to the example of a paddle wheel in a viscous liquid. This time, however, we immerse the container of viscous liquid in a large thermal reservoir that keeps the viscous liquid at a constant temperature T_R (**Figure 21.13**). The moving parts and the viscous liquid now constitute a steady device. A person does work on the device by pulling on the string and then the device transfers energy to the reservoir. The device thus converts mechanical energy to thermal energy.

To draw an entropy diagram for this energy conversion process, we must first determine where to put mechanical energy on the entropy-gradient scale. Remember that doing work—in other words, transferring energy mechanically—does not cause any change in entropy. Therefore $\Delta S = 0$

Figure 21.13 Paddle-wheel device from Exercise 21.1 is held at a constant temperature T_R by a large thermal reservoir of water.

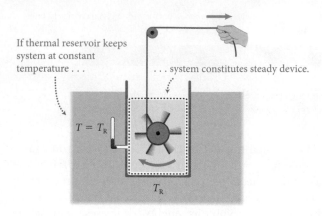

and so $\Delta S/\Delta E = 0$. The entropy gradient associated with mechanical energy is thus zero. Mechanical energy transfers therefore always appear on the far left at the origin of the dS/dE scale (**Figure 21.14**).

The only entropy change in Figure 21.14 is thus caused by the thermal output of energy. This entropy change is positive (arrow points up), and so the entropy of the environment increases.

The inverse of the process in Figure 21.14, illustrated in **Figure 21.15**—conversion of thermal energy entirely to mechanical energy by a steady device—cannot occur. In this process, the device would transfer energy thermally from the environment and mechanically to the environment. The curved arrow now points to the left, causing a decrease in the entropy of the environment, which is impossible. This process would mean that the paddle wheel in Figure 21.13 could rewind the string and pull the hand to the left by transferring energy thermally from the reservoir. The entropy law prevents this from happening.

Summarizing, we see that converting energy with a low entropy gradient to energy with a high entropy gradient with a steady device (arrow points right in entropy diagram) increases the entropy of the environment and is permitted by the entropy law. Conversely, converting energy with a high entropy gradient to energy with a low entropy gradient with a steady device (arrow points left in entropy diagram)

Figure 21.14 Entropy diagram for the process depicted in Figure 21.13.

mechanical input of
energy ($\Delta S = 0$)

mechanical
transfer

thermal reservoir

R

$dS \over dE$

thermal output
($\Delta S_R > 0$)

$\Delta S_{env} > 0$

Figure 21.15 Entropy diagram for the conversion of thermal energy entirely to mechanical energy by a steady device.

Entropy of environment would decrease: not possible.

decreases the entropy of the environment and is not permitted by the entropy law.

As energy shifts toward the right in an entropy diagram, the energy becomes less useful for, say, heating things or powering machines. You can do less with a tub of lukewarm water than with a bucket of boiling hot water that contains the same amount of thermal energy as the tub. We can therefore associate the entropy gradient with the **quality of the energy:** The smaller dS/dE, the lower the entropy cost and the higher the quality of energy (**Figure 21.16***a*). The tendency of the entropy of the environment to increase and energy to shift from higher quality to lower quality (that is, to the right in the entropy diagram) corresponds to a *degradation* of energy quality (Figure 21.16*b*). In the device of Figure 21.13, for instance, high-quality mechanical energy

Figure 21.16 Energy with a large entropy gradient is less useful and therefore of lower quality than energy with a small entropy gradient.

Relationship of entropy gradient to quality of energy

Process that degrades energy quality

Process that upgrades energy quality (not possible on its own)

(which allows us to do useful work, such as lifting or accelerating things) is irreversibly turned into less useful, lower-quality thermal energy.

A conversion of lower-quality energy to higher-quality energy (an *upgrade* in energy quality) corresponds to a left-pointing curved arrow in entropy diagrams and produces a decrease in the entropy of the environment (Figure 21.16*c*). Such upgrades cannot occur in steady devices that have a single energy input and a single energy output. For example, it's impossible to convert low-quality thermal energy entirely to high-quality mechanical energy. This is why ships can't be powered by converting thermal energy from the ocean entirely to mechanical energy.

21.5 For a steady device that has a single input of energy and a single output of energy, does the quality of the energy increase, decrease, or stay the same when the entropy change in the environment is (*a*) positive and (*b*) zero?

Example 21.2 Energy and entropy changes in a thermal reservoir

Suppose the person pulling the string in Figure 21.13 does work W on the device immersed in a thermal reservoir R at temperature T_R. (*a*) Do the energy and entropy of the reservoir increase, decrease, or stay the same? (*b*) If the same experiment is repeated with the reservoir at a lower temperature, are the changes in the energy and entropy of the reservoir greater than, the same as, or smaller than in part *a*?

❶ **GETTING STARTED** Because the device is immersed in a thermal reservoir, the state of the device doesn't change. The device is therefore a steady device, and its energy and entropy don't change. Because the reservoir temperature is lower in part *b*, the states of the device and reservoir are different from those in part *a*. In particular, a lower reservoir temperature means that the reservoir's thermal energy is smaller.

❷ **DEVISE PLAN** I can draw an energy input-output diagram for the device and determine its energy inputs and outputs. From the diagram, I can deduce whether there is any thermal transfer of energy to (or from) the reservoir. To evaluate any entropy changes in the reservoir, I draw an entropy diagram for each part of the problem.

❸ **EXECUTE PLAN** (*a*) I know that the person does work on the device and so $W_{in} = W > 0$. Because the energy of the device doesn't change, the energy law tells me that $\Delta E = W + Q = 0$, so $Q = -W < 0$, which means that energy must be transferred thermally out of the device: $Q_{out} = -Q = W$. My energy input-output diagram is shown in **Figure 21.17***a*.

The energy transferred thermally out of the device goes into the reservoir, which tells me that the energy of the reservoir increases by an amount W. ✔

To see what happens to the reservoir entropy, I need an entropy diagram. Mechanical energy initially in the device is converted to thermal energy. I represent this conversion by drawing a right-pointing arrow in my entropy diagram, running from the origin ($dS/dE = 0$ for mechanical energy) to the R representing the reservoir (Figure 21.17*b*). That the arrow points to the right tells me that the entropy of the reservoir increases. ✔

Figure 21.17

(a)

(b) warm reservoir:

(c) cool reservoir:

Figure 21.18 Entropy diagram for a process that upgrades and degrades energy.

Entropy of environment increases or stays the same:

$$\Delta S_{env} = \Delta S_{upgrade} + \Delta S_{degrade} \geq 0$$

(*b*) Even though the temperature of the reservoir is lowered, the amount of work done on the device by the person is still *W*, so the temperature change does not affect my energy input-output diagram. This tells me that the energy of the reservoir increases by the same amount *W* as in part *a*. ✔

Because the reservoir temperature is lower than in part *a*, however, on my entropy diagram for this situation (Figure 21.17*c*), I show R farther to the right than in Figure 21.17*b*. The right-pointing arrow representing the conversion is longer, meaning a greater *dS/dE* value at this temperature. A greater entropy gradient means a higher entropy cost of energy change, and so the entropy change associated with the energy change *W* must be greater than the entropy change of part *a*. ✔

❹ EVALUATE RESULT I can also evaluate the entropy changes using Eq. 20.54, $\Delta S_R = Q_R/k_B T_R$. The quantity of energy transferred thermally to the reservoir is the same for both parts of the problem: $Q_R = W$. Because the reservoir temperature T_R is lower in part *b*, the entropy change must be greater here than in part *a*.

✋ **21.6** In an entropy diagram, which of these statements are true? (*a*) The quality of the energy is proportional to the entropy gradient. (*b*) The quality of the energy is inversely proportional to the entropy gradient. (*c*) High-temperature energy is of high quality. (*d*) High-temperature energy is of low quality. (*e*) Low-temperature energy has a small entropy gradient. (*f*) Low-temperature energy has a large entropy gradient.

21.3 Heat engines and heat pumps

As we just saw, it is not possible for a steady device that has a single energy input and a single energy output to upgrade energy quality. The only way for a steady device to upgrade energy quality is to also degrade energy quality in such a way that the change in entropy of the environment that results from both processes is either positive or zero: $\Delta S_{env} = \Delta S_{upgrade} + \Delta S_{degrade} \geq 0$.

The process illustrated in **Figure 21.18** is one way to combine two compensating processes. A steady device takes in energy from a high-temperature reservoir, converts part of this energy to mechanical energy, and thermally transfers

the rest to a low-temperature reservoir. This process is allowed as long as the increase in entropy associated with the degradation of the energy (the thermal output) equals or exceeds the decrease in entropy associated with the upgrade (the mechanical output). A steady device of this type is called a **heat engine.**

One familiar heat engine that carries out the process illustrated in Figure 21.18 is the automobile engine we discussed briefly in Section 21.1. As shown in **Figure 21.19**, the thermal input of energy is provided by the combustion of gasoline at high temperature (about 2700 K). Roughly two-thirds of this input energy is discarded to the environment by the car's exhaust and cooling system, both of which are roughly at 400 K. The remaining one-third of the input energy is turned into mechanical output of energy (part of which is lost due to friction in the moving parts of the car). As you can see by the relative sizes of the Q_{out} and W_{out} arrows in Figure 21.19, in a typical car engine more energy is degraded than upgraded in order to satisfy the entropy law and keep the engine's final state the same as its initial state.

Because we arrange energy inputs and outputs on the horizontal scale of an entropy diagram according to their entropy gradient, the length of an arrow in the diagram is

Figure 21.19 Energy input-output diagram for an automobile engine, which is one type of heat engine.

fuel combustion

cooling and exhaust

Figure 21.20 Obtaining entropy changes from entropy diagrams.

(*a*) Entropy diagram

(*b*) Simplified entropy diagram

length:
quality difference ($\Delta S/\Delta E$)

height: amount of
energy transferred (ΔE)

arrowhead direction: sign of ΔS
(energy upgrade or degrade)

area (height × length):
entropy change (ΔS)

(*c*)

Q_{in} Q_{out}

$\dfrac{1}{k_B T}$

long rectangle:
large quality difference $\Delta S/\Delta E$

(*d*)

Q_{in} Q_{out}

$\dfrac{1}{k_B T}$

tall rectangle: large amount
of transferred energy ΔE

(*e*)

Q_{out} Q_{in}

$\dfrac{1}{k_B T}$

left-pointing arrowhead:
energy upgraded ($\Delta S < 0$)

same area: same entropy change ΔS

a measure of the quality difference $\Delta S/\Delta E$ between the input and output. If we take the width of each arrow to represent the amount of energy ΔE transferred, then the area of the horizontal part of the arrow (the product of the arrow's width and length) represents the magnitude of the change in entropy (**Figure 21.20a**).

Because it is difficult to draw curved arrows and determine their area, we simplify our procedure for drawing entropy diagrams, replacing the arrows with rectangles (Figure 21.20*b*). The length of the rectangle corresponds to the quality difference between the energy output and input, and the height of the rectangle corresponds to the amount of energy transferred. The area of the rectangle thus represents the entropy change in the environment caused by the energy conversion or transfer. The direction of the energy transfer is indicated by an arrow inside the rectangle. In addition we mark the energy inputs and outputs by vertical arrows: down for input and up for output. Finally, because the entropy gradient dS/dE is equal to $1/k_B T$ (Eq. 19.38), we label the axis with $1/k_B T$.

There are two ways to increase the magnitude of the entropy change. The greater the quality difference between the input and output, the greater the entropy change. For example, in Figure 21.20*c* the energy input is of higher quality than in Figure 21.20*b*. Consequently, the entropy change produced by the conversion of this higher-quality energy is greater. Shifting the input of the arrow to the left (higher quality) increases its length and therefore its area

(which represents the entropy change). As you can see from Eq. 20.54, $\Delta S = Q/k_B T$, the entropy change is also proportional to the quantity of energy Q being transferred. So, a second way to induce a greater entropy change between two fixed-temperature reservoirs is to increase the amount of energy being transferred (represented by the greater height of the rectangle in Figure 21.20*d*). Finally, if the direction of an energy transfer is reversed, the sign of the entropy change is reversed but its magnitude remains the same (compare Figure 21.20*e* with 21.20*b*). **Figure 21.21** shows the entropy diagram for a process that both upgrades and degrades energy, with rectangles used to represent the transfers.

Because thermal inputs and outputs of energy occur at different temperatures, they are separated on the dS/dE scale. Mechanical inputs and outputs of energy, however, are always located at $dS/dE = 0$, and so they overlap in an entropy

Figure 21.21 Entropy diagram for a process that upgrades and degrades energy (compare with Figure 21.18).

mechanical *output* of energy from system (*upward* arrow):
$W < 0$ because W = work done *on* system

$W < 0$ Q_{in} Q_{out}

$\dfrac{1}{k_B T}$

upgrade   degrade

Figure 21.22 For a steady device, the entropy change in the environment must be greater than or equal to zero.

(*a*) **Reversible process:**
entropy change $= 0$

upgrade area $=$ degrade area:
entropy change zero

(*b*) **Irreversible process:**
entropy change > 0

upgrade area $<$ degrade area:
entropy increases

(*c*) **Impossible process:**
entropy change < 0

upgrade area $>$ degrade area:
entropy would decrease

diagram. The end of an arrow (or rectangle) at $dS/dE = 0$ therefore does not represent W_{in} or W_{out} but rather the difference between these two, $W = W_{in} - W_{out}$, which is the work done on the system. When the arrow points up, energy is transferred mechanically from the system to the environment and hence $W < 0$ (Figure 21.21). When the arrow points down, work is done on the system, indicating a mechanical transfer of energy into the system, $W > 0$.

For a steady device, the entropy law requires the entropy change in the environment to be greater than or equal to zero, and so the area of the degrade rectangle must be larger than or equal to the area of the upgrade rectangle. **Figure 21.22a** shows a process for which the energy upgrade and energy degradation cause equal-magnitude changes in entropy. For such a process, the entropy change is zero, so the process is reversible and allowed. Figure 21.22*b* shows a process for which the magnitude of the entropy change caused by the energy upgrade is smaller than the magnitude of the entropy change caused by the energy degradation. For such a process, the entropy change is positive, so the process is irreversible and allowed. Figure 21.22*c* shows a process for which the magnitude of the entropy change caused by the energy upgrade is greater than the magnitude of the entropy change caused by the energy degradation. For such a process, the entropy change is negative, so the process is forbidden by the entropy law. The procedure for drawing entropy diagrams is shown in the Procedure box on page 573.

21.7 Draw an entropy diagram for the refrigerator in Figure 21.2*b*.

The entropy diagram for an irreversible process such as the one in Figure 21.22*b* can be treated as the entropy diagram for an irreversible degradation of energy (that is, hot to cold) superimposed on the entropy diagram for a reversible process (**Figure 21.23**). The upgrade rectangles in Figure 21.23*a* and *b* are the same, but in Figure 21.23*b* the height of the degrade rectangle has been adjusted so that the areas of the upgrade and degrade rectangles are the same. The entropy change in Figure 21.23*b* is therefore zero, and the process represented by this entropy diagram is reversible. Figure 21.23*c* shows the remainder of the energy transferred to the low-temperature reservoir. This process increases the entropy of the environment and is irreversible. The mechanical energy generated in Figure 21.23*b* is retrievable. Because the process is reversible, the mechanical energy can be converted back to thermal energy. The energy in Figure 21.23*c*, on the other hand, has been degraded and is irretrievable. It cannot be transferred back to the high-temperature reservoir without some other associated energy degradation. For now, the only processes we consider are reversible ones for which the entropy change is zero.

21.8 Why must the degrade rectangle in Figure 21.22*a* have a greater height than the upgrade rectangle?

Example 21.3 Hot or cold?

A reversible heat engine converts energy taken from a thermal reservoir at temperature T_{in} by doing work on the environment and thermally transferring energy to a thermal reservoir at temperature $T_{out} < T_{in}$. How do the thermal input and output of energy change if the temperature of the output reservoir is lowered without changing the amount of work done by the engine on the environment?

Figure 21.23 Entropy diagram for an irreversible process.

An irreversible process . . .

. . . consists of a reversible process . . .

. . . superimposed on an irreversible energy degradation.

Procedure: Drawing entropy diagrams for a steady device

1. Draw an entropy gradient axis pointing right. Add a short vertical axis to indicate the origin of the axis. Label the axis $1/k_BT$ to remind yourself of the relationship between entropy gradient and temperature.

2. Mark the positions along the axis of the thermal inputs and outputs of energy of the device. Transfers at higher temperature are on the left; transfers at lower temperature are on the right. Use downward-pointing arrows for inputs, use upward-pointing arrows for outputs, and label these Q_{in} and Q_{out}.

3. Mechanical transfers of energy are placed at the origin of the axis. Use a downward-pointing arrow when the work done on the system is positive and an upward-

pointing arrow when the work done on the system is negative. Label this arrow by W and indicate whether $W > 0$ or $W < 0$.

4. Draw rectangles to represent each energy transfer. Make the height of each rectangle proportional to the amount of energy transferred (but see point 5 below). Use an arrowhead to indicate the direction of each transfer.

5. For the operation of the device to be permitted by the entropy law, the combined area of the rectangles in which the arrows point right must be larger than the combined area of the rectangles in which the arrows point left.

❶ **GETTING STARTED** I begin by drawing an entropy diagram for the heat engine (**Figure 21.24a**). Because the engine is reversible, the area of the upgrade rectangle must equal the area of the degrade rectangle. The height of the upgrade rectangle is equal to the magnitude of W and is fixed. The height of the degrade rectangle is equal to Q_{out}.

Figure 21.24 Example 21.3.

❷ **DEVISE PLAN** To determine how the thermal input and output of energy change as the temperature of the output reservoir is lowered, I need to draw another entropy diagram (Figure 21.24b), keeping the upgrade rectangle the same as in Figure 21.24a and shifting the right side of the degrade rectangle to the right to represent the lower temperature of the output reservoir. When I make this change, I must remember that the upgrade and degrade rectangles must still have the same area, and so now my degrade rectangle is not as tall as in Figure 21.24a. Also, I know that the sum of the outputs must equal the sum of the inputs, and so $W_{out} + Q_{out} = Q_{in}$.

❸ **EXECUTE PLAN** In any entropy diagram, the height of the degrade rectangle represents Q_{out}. Because the height of the degrade rectangle is less in Figure 21.24b than in Figure 21.24a, I conclude that Q_{out} decreases when the temperature of the output reservoir is lowered. Because $W_{out} + Q_{out} = Q_{in}$ and W_{out} is not changed, Q_{in} must also decrease. ✔

❹ **EVALUATE RESULT** My result means that if the temperature difference between the reservoirs increases, I need less energy

Q_{in} to do the same amount of work on the environment. The reason is that I can compensate for the energy upgrade from thermal to mechanical with less energy: At low temperature a given amount of energy causes a greater entropy change and so my answer makes sense.

✋ **21.9** Suppose you keep W and T_{out} in the reversible process of Figure 21.24a fixed but increase T_{in}. Do the magnitudes of these quantities increase, decrease, or stay the same: (a) ΔS associated with the upgrade, (b) ΔS associated with the degradation, (c) Q_{in}?

Example 21.3 and Checkpoint 21.9 show that it is beneficial to take energy in at the highest possible temperature and discard energy at the lowest possible temperature. Doing so minimizes the thermal input of energy for a fixed amount of work done on the environment.

We can define the **efficiency** of a heat engine as follows:

The efficiency of a heat engine is the ratio of the work done by the engine on the environment to the thermal input of energy into the engine. For a heat engine operating between two fixed-temperature reservoirs, the efficiency is greatest when the thermal input of energy takes place at the highest possible temperature and the thermal output of energy takes place at the lowest possible temperature.

We see now that no heat engine—even a reversible one— can have an efficiency of 1.00 because some fraction of the thermal input of energy has to be degraded to make up for the entropy decrease that occurs in the process of upgrading the energy. The imperfect efficiency of heat engines has nothing to do with friction in the moving parts or other irreversible phenomena; rather, it is a direct consequence of the entropy law.

✋ **21.10** When the temperature of the output reservoir in Example 21.3 is lowered, does the efficiency increase, remain the same, or decrease?

Figure 21.25 Energy conversions in a heat pump.

(*a*) Entropy diagrams for energy conversions in heat pump

(*b*) Energy input-output diagram for refrigerator (a type of heat pump)

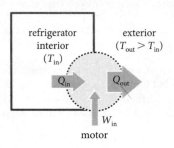

As you saw in Checkpoint 21.7, there are more ways to cause a degradation of energy that compensates for an upgrade than the one shown in Figure 21.21. For example, you can swap the roles of the upgrade and degradation shown in Figure 21.21. The resulting entropy diagram, shown in **Figure 21.25*a***, represents the operation of a **heat pump.** In a heat pump, mechanical energy is degraded in order to thermally transfer energy from a lower-temperature region of the environment to a higher-temperature region of the environment—a direction opposite the natural direction in which energy is transferred thermally. Note that work is done on the device, so $W > 0$.

The refrigerator is one familiar example of a heat pump (Figure 21.25*b*). The interior of the refrigerator constitutes the reservoir at T_{in}; the air surrounding the refrigerator is the reservoir at T_{out} (coils at the back or bottom of the refrigerator transfer the energy Q_{out} to the air).

Heat pumps are also used to heat and cool houses. In the summer, a heat pump operates as an air-conditioner and cools a house by moving energy from inside the house to outside (from cold to hot; **Figure 21.26*a***). In the winter, the same heat pump heats by moving energy from outside the house to inside (again from cold to hot, Figure 21.26*b*).

In designing a heat pump for cooling, we want to maximize the amount of energy transferred thermally from the low-temperature reservoir for a given amount of work done

Figure 21.26 A heat pump can serve as an air-conditioner in summer by removing energy from inside the house and as a heater in winter by transferring energy thermally from outside to inside the house.

(*a*) Summer　　　　　　　　　　　(*b*) Winter

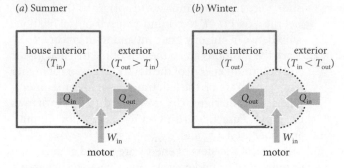

on the heat pump. The **coefficient of performance of cooling** of a heat pump is defined as the ratio of the thermal input of energy (the energy transferred thermally from the space that must be cooled) to the work done on the heat pump.

Example 21.4 Cooling performance

For a set temperature T_{in} of a refrigerator interior, does the coefficient of performance of cooling increase, decrease, or stay the same as the temperature T_{out} of the room that contains the refrigerator increases? Assume the refrigerator is a reversible heat pump.

❶ **GETTING STARTED** I begin by drawing an entropy diagram for the refrigerator (**Figure 21.27*a***). Because the refrigerator is reversible, the areas of the upgrade and degrade rectangles are equal. The coefficient of performance of cooling is the ratio of the thermal input of energy Q_{in} (the height of the upgrade rectangle) to the work W done on the refrigerator (the height of the degrade rectangle).

Figure 21.27

(*a*)　refrigerator

(*b*)　T_{out} increased

❷ **DEVISE PLAN** To determine how the coefficient of performance of cooling changes as T_{out} increases, I must draw another entropy diagram, shifting the thermal output (the point where the two rectangles meet) to the left (Figure 21.27*b*). I must still have the area of the upgrade rectangle equal the area of the degrade rectangle, so in this diagram, I increase the height of the degrade rectangle and decrease that of the upgrade rectangle.

❸ **EXECUTE PLAN** The height of the upgrade rectangle corresponds to Q_{in}, and the height of the degrade rectangle corresponds to W. Shifting Q_{out} leftward to represent the increased T_{out} made the height of the upgrade rectangle (Q_{in}) smaller and the height of the degrade rectangle (W) greater. The ratio Q_{in}/W therefore decreases, which means that the coefficient of performance of cooling decreases. ✔

❹ **EVALUATE RESULT** The fact that the coefficient of performance of cooling decreases means that more energy is required to cool the refrigerator interior when the air outside the refrigerator is at a higher temperature, which makes sense intuitively. The reason is that when the refrigerator discards energy to the environment at a higher temperature, a given amount of energy causes a smaller entropy increase than when the energy is discarded at a lower temperature. This degradation of energy therefore compensates a smaller upgrade, reducing the coefficient of performance of cooling.

In designing a heat pump for heating, we want to maximize the thermal output of energy to the high-temperature reservoir for a given amount of work done on the heat pump. The **coefficient of performance of heating** of a heat pump is defined as the ratio of the thermal output of energy (the energy delivered thermally to the space that must be heated) to the work done on the heat pump.

Ordinary heating transfers energy from a high-temperature reservoir (say, burning fuel) to a low-temperature reservoir (a room to be heated, say), and the thermal input of energy Q_{in} is equal to the thermal output of energy Q_{out} (Figure 21.11). Equivalently, in Figure 21.14, $W = W_{in} > 0$ is converted to an identical amount of energy Q_{out}. In a heat pump, however, $Q_{out} > Q_{in}$, as Figure 21.26 indicates, because $Q_{out} = Q_{in} + W$. Note that while heat engines have an efficiency less than 1, the coefficient of performance of heating always exceeds 1. A typical heat pump has a coefficient of performance of heating of 3 to 4.

🖐 **21.11** Estimate these quantities for the heat pump in Figure 21.26: (*a*) coefficient of performance of cooling and (*b*) coefficient of performance of heating.

21.4 Thermodynamic cycles

Heat engines and heat pumps are made up of three important components: a collection of moving parts, thermal reservoirs, and a *working substance* that undergoes a series of thermodynamic processes. For example, in the (heat) engine of an automobile, a mixture of air and gasoline is the working substance that produces the motion of the pistons that propels the automobile. Thermal energy generated in the combustion is transferred thermally to the environment through the engine's exhaust, and so the environment serves as a thermal reservoir. In a power plant, the working substance is water, which drives the blades of steam turbines. The steam boiler and the outside air serve as thermal reservoirs that transfer energy thermally to and from the water.

In this section we look at the thermodynamic processes that the working substance undergoes during the operation of a heat engine or heat pump. As we have seen, the engine or pump is a steady device: It must periodically return to a certain initial state. The working substance must therefore undergo a *cyclic process*—a sequence of steps in which the working substance begins and ends in the same thermal equilibrium state. Under those circumstances, the energy and the entropy of the working substance return to their initial values in one cycle.

Figure 21.28a illustrates a cyclic process that involves an expansion from state 1 to state 2 and then a compression back to state 1 via another path. We saw in Chapter 20 that during an expansion the work done on the system is

Figure 21.28 The work done on a system during a thermodynamic cyclic process is equal in magnitude to the area enclosed by the pathways making up the cycle.

CYCLE

WORK DONE ON SYSTEM DURING CYCLE

expansion:
negative work done on system

compression:
positive work done on system

complete cycle:
positive work done on system

Magnitude of work done on system is smaller during expansion than compression because expansion takes place at lower pressure.

negative and during a compression the work done on the system is positive. If the expansion takes place at a lower pressure than the compression (as it does in Figure 21.28a), the work done on the system during the expansion is smaller in magnitude than the work done during the compression. Therefore the work done on the system during a complete cycle from 1 to 2 and back to 1 is positive.

As we saw in Chapter 20, the magnitude of the negative work done on the system during the expansion $1 \rightarrow 2$ is equal to the hatched area in Figure 21.28b. The magnitude of the positive work done on the system during the compression $2 \rightarrow 1$ is equal to the shaded area in Figure 21.28c. Adding these two areas and taking their signs into account, we see that the work done on the system during a complete cycle is equal to the shaded area enclosed by the path that represents the cycle, as illustrated in 21.28d.

21.12 If you begin at state 1 again but this time go through the cycle in Figure 21.28 clockwise rather than counterclockwise, what are the magnitude and sign of (a) the work done on the system and (b) the work done on the environment?

Figure 21.28 and Checkpoint 21.12 demonstrate an important point:

The magnitude of the work done on a system during a cycle is equal to the area enclosed by the path that represents the cycle in a PV diagram. The work done on the system is negative for a clockwise cycle and positive for a counterclockwise cycle.

Because heat engines do positive work on the environment, their cycles are clockwise. Conversely, the environment does positive work on heat pumps, and so their cycles are counterclockwise.

What thermodynamic processes occur in a heat engine? To answer this question, let us consider first the thermal input of energy from the high-temperature reservoir. This process takes place at a constant temperature T_{in} and so is isothermal. The thermal output of energy at temperature $T_{out} < T_{in}$ is also isothermal. It is not possible to construct a cycle from two isotherms, so we need other processes to connect the two isotherms. Because no other thermal exchange of energy takes place, these other processes we are looking for must be isentropic. **Figure 21.29** shows a thermodynamic cycle that consists of two isothermal processes ($1 \rightarrow 2$ and $3 \rightarrow 4$) and two isentropic processes ($2 \rightarrow 3$ and $4 \rightarrow 1$). Because of its importance in thermodynamics, this cycle is called the **Carnot cycle** after the French physicist Sadi Carnot (1796–1832), who produced the first successful description of the operation of heat engines.

Beginning in state 1 in Figure 21.29, the working substance expands isothermally at a temperature T_{in} until it reaches some state 2 (at which point its volume has increased). The working substance then undergoes an isentropic expansion during which its temperature drops from T_{in} to T_{out}. From this state 3, the working substance is

Figure 21.29 *PV diagram for the thermodynamic process known as the Carnot cycle.*

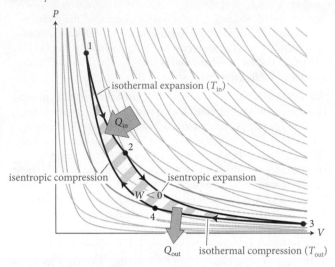

compressed isothermally to state 4, from where it undergoes an isentropic compression back to state 1, completing the cycle.

Energy is transferred thermally into and out of the system only during the two isothermal processes, but all four processes involve work. The work done on the system during the cycle is equal to the area enclosed by the cycle and has been shaded in Figure 21.29. Because W is negative, the shading is hatched. (Remember that is what we want: The heat engine must do positive work *on its environment*, and so the work done *on the system* is negative.)

The Carnot cycle has a number of deficiencies that makes it impractical for a heat engine. First of all, as you can see from the small hatched area in Figure 21.29, the amount of work done on the environment in each cycle is small. More important, the presence of the isotherms means that the cycle cannot be repeated quickly. As we saw in Section 20.7, isothermal processes are very slow, and so an engine that operates on the Carnot cycle would put out mechanical energy at a very low rate; that is, its power would be very small.

To alleviate these problems, we want to avoid isotherms and "open up" the cycle so that more work is done on the environment. If we replace the two isotherms in Figure 21.29 by isobars, we obtain the cycle shown in **Figure 21.30a**. This cycle, called the **Brayton cycle**, does substantially more work on the environment than the Carnot cycle and can be carried out fairly quickly. Gas turbines and jet engines operate on a cycle that is closely approximated by the Brayton cycle.

In the Brayton cycle, the working substance undergoes two isobaric processes ($1 \rightarrow 2$ and $3 \rightarrow 4$) and two isentropic processes ($2 \rightarrow 3$ and $4 \rightarrow 1$). Energy thermally enters and leaves the system during the isobaric processes. If we begin and end the isentropic compression in Figures 21.29 and 21.30 from the same states 4 and 1, the hatched area enclosed by the Brayton cycle is much larger than the area enclosed by the Carnot cycle. The larger hatched area means that a steady device that operates on the Brayton cycle has

Figure 21.30 The thermodynamic process known as the Brayton cycle.

(*a*) *PV* diagram for Brayton cycle

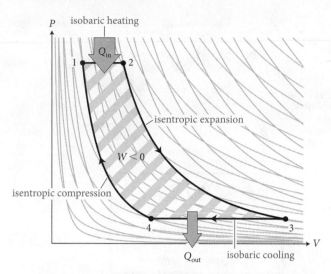

(*b*) Flow chart for gas turbine operating on Brayton cycle

a much greater mechanical output of energy than a steady device that operates on the Carnot cycle. Also, the isobaric and isentropic processes can be carried out rapidly, which means the power output in a Brayton cycle can be high.

A gas turbine engine that operates on the Brayton cycle has three main components: a gas compressor, a combustion chamber, and an expansion turbine. In practice, such an engine is an open system: Fresh air flows in at one end, and hot gases are expelled at the other end. For the purpose of thermodynamic analysis, however, we can pretend that the exhaust gases are reused in the intake.

Figure 21.30*b* shows a flow chart for a gas turbine engine. Gas—typically ambient air—is drawn into the compressor, which isentropically compresses the air to high pressure $4 \rightarrow 1$. The compressed air then flows into the combustion chamber, where it is heated to temperatures as high as 2000 K at constant pressure ($1 \rightarrow 2$). The heated, pressurized air then expands isentropically ($2 \rightarrow 3$), and the hot gases are expelled at high speed from the rear of the engine, driving the engine forward. The exhaust gases then cool

back down to the intake temperature—another constant-pressure process ($3 \rightarrow 4$)—and the cycle is complete.

To power the compressor, a turbine is placed in the expansion chamber. The expanding gases drive this turbine, which in turn feeds some energy from the expanding gases to the compressor. In a jet engine, for example, the turbine and the compressor are placed on a single drive shaft, so the turbine directly feeds the compressor (**Figure 21.31**).

Although the Brayton cycle delivers more energy and power than the Carnot cycle, it is not as efficient, which means that the work done on the environment divided by the thermal input of energy is smaller. The reason for this diminished efficiency is illustrated in **Figure 21.32a**. In the Brayton cycle, the thermal input and output of energy do not take place at fixed temperatures as in the Carnot cycle. The Brayton thermal input of energy starts at the temperature T_1 reached during compression and then moves up to

Figure 21.31 Jet engine.

Figure 21.32 Entropy diagrams for Brayton and Carnot cycles.

(a) Brayton cycle

(b) Carnot cycle

Figure 21.33 A Brayton cycle run in reverse is the cycle for a heat pump.

(a) PV diagram for Brayton cycle run in reverse

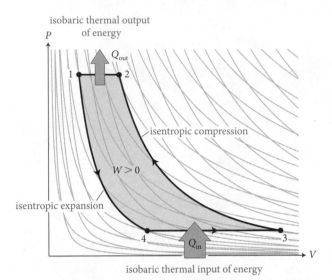

(b) Flow chart for refrigerator operating on reverse Brayton cycle

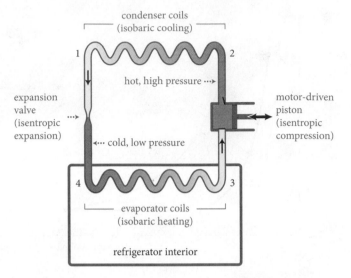

a higher temperature T_2 during combustion. The thermal output of energy starts at temperature T_3 (the temperature at the end of the isentropic expansion) and then slides down to the lower temperature T_4 (the temperature at the beginning of the isentropic compression).

As we saw in Section 21.3, the efficiency of a heat engine is highest when the thermal input of energy takes place at the highest possible temperature and the output at the lowest possible temperature. So the part of the cycle where thermal input of energy occurs at T_2 and thermal output of energy occurs at T_4 has the greatest efficiency. All other parts of the cycle have lower efficiency, which contributes to an overall efficiency that is lower than the efficiency we would see if *all* energy exchange had taken place at only the highest and lowest temperatures, T_2 and T_4, respectively. By contrast, thermal input of energy at one fixed high temperature and output at one fixed low temperature is exactly what happens in a Carnot cycle (Figure 21.32*b*).

By running the Brayton cycle in reverse (**Figure 21.33***a*), we obtain a heat pump. The cycle used in refrigerators, air-conditioners, and home heat pumps is a bit more complex because the working substance in these devices changes from liquid to vapor and back. However, if we assume the working substance is a gas, the basic thermodynamic processes are the isentropic ($3 \rightarrow 2$ and $1 \rightarrow 4$) and isobaric ($2 \rightarrow 1$ and $4 \rightarrow 3$) ones illustrated in Figure 21.33*a*.

Figure 21.33*b* shows a flow chart of the reverse Brayton cycle that takes place in a refrigerator. The working substance is first isentropically compressed by a motor-driven piston ($3 \rightarrow 2$). The compression raises both the temperature and the pressure in the working substance, which is

then cooled down at constant pressure in a long coiled tube called the *condenser* ($2 \rightarrow 1$). This tube is exposed to the ambient temperature. After passing through the condenser, the high-pressure and now somewhat cooler working substance passes through an expansion valve ($1 \rightarrow 4$) and expands isentropically. In the process of expanding, the working substance cools significantly. It then passes through a second set of coils called the *evaporator* ($4 \rightarrow 3$). Because the temperature of the space around the evaporator is higher than the temperature of the working substance in the evaporator, energy is thermally transferred from the surrounding space to the evaporator. As Figure 21.33*b* shows, this space surrounding the evaporator is the interior of the refrigerator, where food is stored and thus kept cold. After passing through the evaporator, the working substance is returned to the compressor, where the cycle repeats.

Note that a heat pump transfers energy from the interior of the refrigerator at low temperature to the room at a higher temperature. To accomplish this, it needs mechanical energy to first raise the temperature of the working substance above that of the room so that energy can be transferred thermally out of the hot working substance into the room. Then the temperature of the working substance is lowered to below that of the interior of the refrigerator so that energy can be transferred thermally from the interior of the refrigerator into the working substance.

21.13 Why doesn't the transfer of energy from the interior of the refrigerator to the room violate the entropy law?

Self-quiz

1. Describe the energy transfers in **Figure 21.34**. What is implied about the energy of the system?

Figure 21.34

2. Describe the energy conversions in **Figure 21.35**. Which are possible?

Figure 21.35

3. Write the ratios for the efficiency of a heat engine, the coefficients of performance of cooling for a refrigerator, and the coefficients of performance of heating a room using a heat pump in terms of W, Q_{in}, and Q_{out}. Make a generalization about the quantity on the top of each ratio and the quantity on the bottom of each ratio.

4. **Figure 21.36** shows an ideal gas cycle consisting of two isotherms and two isochores. Complete the table by writing the algebraic signs of each of the terms ΔE, W, and Q. If a term is zero, write zero.

Figure 21.36

	ΔE	W	Q
$1 \rightarrow 2$			
$2 \rightarrow 3$			
$3 \rightarrow 4$			
$4 \rightarrow 1$			

Answers

1. (*a*) More work is done on the system than the system does on the environment, so the energy of the system increases. (*b*) More energy is transferred thermally out of the system than into it, and work is done on the system. Depending on how the work done on the system compares to the difference between the thermal transfers of energy, the energy of the system can increase, decrease, or stay the same.

2. In both cases mechanical energy is degraded into thermal energy of a high-temperature reservoir while thermal energy of a low-temperature reservoir is upgraded to thermal energy of a high-temperature reservoir. (*a*) Because the area of the degrade rectangle is larger than the area of the upgrade rectangle, entropy is increasing, so this process is possible. (*b*) Because the area of the upgrade rectangle is larger than the area of the degrade rectangle, entropy is decreasing, so this process is not possible.

4. Efficiency $= -W/Q_{in}$, the coefficient of performance of cooling $= Q_{in}/W$, and the coefficient of performance of heating $= Q_{out}/W$. The quantities in the numerator are the desired results: work done by the engine on the environment, energy transferred thermally out of the contents of the refrigerator, and energy transferred thermally into the room to be heated. The quantities in the denominator are the energies required to obtain the desired result: the thermal transfer of energy required to run the engine and the work required to run the refrigerator or heat pump.

5. ΔE: $1 \rightarrow 2 = 0$ (isotherm); $2 \rightarrow 3 = -$ (temperature decreases); $3 \rightarrow 4 = 0$ (isotherm); $4 \rightarrow 1 = +$ (temperature increases). W: $1 \rightarrow 2 = -$ (expansion); $2 \rightarrow 3 = 0$ (isochoric process); $3 \rightarrow 4 = +$ (compression); $4 \rightarrow 1 = 0$ (isochoric process). Q (sign follows from signs of ΔE and W): $1 \rightarrow 2 = +$; $2 \rightarrow 3 = -$; $3 \rightarrow 4 = -$; $4 \rightarrow 1 = +$.

21.5 Entropy constraints on energy transfers

In the first part of this chapter, we used entropy diagrams to describe the energy conversions that occur in heat engines and pumps. We stated, without proof, that the area of the rectangle for any energy conversion or transfer represented in such a diagram is a measure of the corresponding entropy change. In this section we develop the quantitative framework for computing entropy changes from entropy diagrams.

Steady devices return to the same state after one cycle, so that

$$\Delta E = 0 \quad \text{(steady device, complete cycle).} \tag{21.1}$$

The energy law (Eq. 20.1) then tells us that for a steady device $Q + W = 0$. Because $Q = Q_{\text{in}} - Q_{\text{out}}$, we see that over one cycle the work done on a steady device must be equal to the difference in the thermal output and input of energy:

$$W = Q_{\text{out}} - Q_{\text{in}} \quad \text{(steady device, complete cycle).} \tag{21.2}$$

Because the initial and final states are the same, the entropy of a steady device doesn't change either:

$$\Delta S_{\text{dev}} = 0 \quad \text{(steady device, complete cycle).} \tag{21.3}$$

From Chapter 19 we know that only processes in which the entropy either increases or remains unchanged can occur:

$$\Delta S_{\text{dev}} + \Delta S_{\text{env}} \geq 0. \tag{21.4}$$

Equation 21.3 thus means that we must have

$$\Delta S_{\text{env}} \geq 0 \quad \text{(steady device, complete cycle).} \tag{21.5}$$

As we saw in the first part of this chapter, the entropy constraint in Equation 21.5 limits the type of energy transfers that can occur in a steady device.

✋ **21.14** What is the change in the energy of the environment in a device for which Eqs. 21.1–21.5 hold?

We begin by considering a steady device that transfers energy thermally from a reservoir at temperature T_{in} to a reservoir at a lower temperature $T_{\text{out}} < T_{\text{in}}$ (**Figure 21.37a**).

In Chapter 20 we saw that the entropy change associated with energy transferred thermally at a fixed temperature is given by (Eq. 20.54)

$$\Delta S = \frac{Q}{k_B T} \quad \text{(isothermal process).} \tag{21.6}$$

The entropy diagram in Figure 21.37a shows two thermal transfers of energy—a transfer out of the environment at the high-temperature reservoir and a transfer into the environment at the low-temperature reservoir. Let us first apply Eq. 21.6 to the high-temperature reservoir. Because energy is transferred thermally out of that reservoir, $Q_H = -Q_{\text{in}} < 0$. Equation 21.6 thus yields a negative entropy change of the high-temperature reservoir, which is at temperature T_{in}:

$$\Delta S_H = -\frac{Q_{\text{in}}}{k_B T_{\text{in}}}. \tag{21.7}$$

Figure 21.37 Entropy diagram for thermal transfer of energy (a) from a high-temperature reservoir to a low-temperature reservoir and (b) from a low-temperature reservoir to a high-temperature reservoir.

(a) Transfer to lower-temperature reservoir

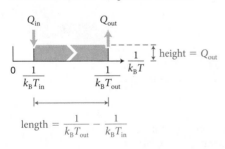

(b) Transfer to higher-temperature reservoir

Likewise, for the low-temperature reservoir, which is at temperature T_{out}, $Q_L = Q_{out} > 0$, so the entropy change is positive:

$$\Delta S_L = \frac{Q_{out}}{k_B T_{out}}. \tag{21.8}$$

Adding the entropy changes in the environment, we get for the environment entropy change during the complete cycle represented in the entropy diagram

$$\Delta S_{env} = \Delta S_H + \Delta S_L = -\frac{Q_{in}}{k_B T_{in}} + \frac{Q_{out}}{k_B T_{out}} \quad \text{(steady state).} \tag{21.9}$$

Because $\Delta E = 0$ (Eq. 21.1) and because no work is involved, the energy law tells us that $\Delta E = Q_{in} - Q_{out} = 0$, so $Q_{in} = Q_{out}$. Substituting this result in Eq. 21.9, we obtain for the entropy change in the environment

$$\Delta S_{env} = -\frac{Q_{out}}{k_B T_{in}} + \frac{Q_{out}}{k_B T_{out}} = Q_{out}\left(\frac{1}{k_B T_{out}} - \frac{1}{k_B T_{in}}\right) \quad \text{(steady state).} \tag{21.10}$$

The right side of this equation gives exactly what we have been calling the area of the rectangle representing the energy transfer in the entropy diagram. As Figure 21.37a shows, the height of this rectangle is Q_{out} (a positive quantity):

$$\text{height of rectangle} = Q_{out}. \tag{21.11}$$

If we use the quantity $1/k_B T$ to quantify the horizontal scale in the diagram, we see that the left edge of the rectangle is at $1/k_B T_{in}$ and the right edge is at $1/k_B T_{out}$. The length of the rectangle is thus

$$\text{length of rectangle} = \frac{1}{k_B T_{out}} - \frac{1}{k_B T_{in}}. \tag{21.12}$$

Because $T_{out} < T_{in}$, this quantity is positive. Note that the length is exactly equal to the term in parentheses in Eq. 21.10, so the product of the height and the length—the area—of the rectangle indeed represents the entropy change of the environment ΔS_{env} due to the transfer of energy from the high-temperature reservoir to the low-temperature reservoir.

Let us next consider the reverse process: a thermal transfer of energy from a low-temperature reservoir to a high-temperature reservoir. As we saw in Section 21.2, such an upgrade of energy is not possible. The entropy diagram for this impossible process is shown in Figure 21.37b. Note that the rectangle has the same length and height as the one in Figure 21.37a. It points to the left (from low temperature to high temperature), indicating that the entropy change is negative. Therefore we take the negative of the area of the rectangle to compute the entropy change in the environment:

$$\Delta S_{env} = -Q_{out}\left(\frac{1}{k_B T_{in}} - \frac{1}{k_B T_{out}}\right) \quad \text{(steady state).} \tag{21.13}$$

Because the entropy change in the environment must be positive (Eq. 21.5), we see that this type of transfer cannot occur by itself.

The procedure for computing the entropy change from an entropy diagram is presented in the Procedure box on page 582.

Procedure: Computing entropy changes from entropy diagrams

To determine the entropy change in the environment from an entropy diagram, compute the area of the rectangles that represent the energy transfers as follows:

1. Determine the length of the horizontal part of each rectangle by subtracting the position of the left end of the rectangle on the $1/k_BT$ scale from the position of the right end on the scale. The position of mechanical energy is always at the zero point on this scale. Verify that the result is a positive quantity. (If it isn't, you made a mistake somewhere.)
2. Express the height of each rectangle in terms of Q_{in}, Q_{out}, and W. Remember that the height must be a positive quantity; Q_{in} and Q_{out} are always positive, but W can be positive or negative. Avoid using the input or output where two rectangles meet; if necessary, you can

use Eq. 21.2, $W = Q_{out} - Q_{in}$, to express the height in terms of the quantities that are given in the problem.
3. Determine the sign of the entropy change. If the rectangle points left (energy upgrade), the entropy change is negative. If the rectangle points right (energy degradation), the entropy change is positive.
4. The entropy change for each rectangle is given by the area of the rectangle (the length multiplied by the height computed in steps 1 and 2) preceded by the algebraic sign determined in step 3:

$$\Delta S = (\text{sign}) \times (\text{length}) \times (\text{width}).$$

5. The entropy change for the process is the sum of the individual entropy changes you have calculated.

Example 21.5 Thermal transfer of energy

A steel bar transfers energy from a thermal reservoir at 750 K to one at 520 K. If the bar transfers 1.5×10^6 J of energy during a certain time interval over which the temperature distribution of the bar does not change, what is the entropy change of the environment?

❶ GETTING STARTED Because the temperature distribution does not change, the state of the bar remains constant and I can consider the bar to be a steady device. I begin by drawing an entropy diagram (**Figure 21.38**), showing a right-pointing arrow in the rectangle because the direction of the energy transfer is from the higher-temperature reservoir to the lower-temperature one. I am given $T_{in} = 750$ K, $T_{out} = 520$ K, and the amount of energy transferred $Q_{in} = Q_{out} = 1.5 \times 10^6$ J.

Figure 21.38

$T_{in} = 750$ K
$T_{out} = 520$ K
$Q_{in} = 1.5 \times 10^6$ J

❷ DEVISE PLAN To determine the entropy change of the environment, I follow the procedure shown above that tells me how to compute the entropy change from my entropy diagram.

❸ EXECUTE PLAN Because the rectangle arrow points to the right, I know that the entropy of the environment increases and thus the entropy change is positive. The height of the rectangle is Q_{in}. The length is $[1/k_BT_{out} - 1/k_BT_{in}]$. The entropy change is thus

$$\Delta S_{env} = +Q_{in}\left[\frac{1}{k_BT_{out}} - \frac{1}{k_BT_{in}}\right] = \frac{+Q_{in}}{k_B}\left[\frac{1}{T_{out}} - \frac{1}{T_{in}}\right].$$

Substituting the values given, I obtain

$$\Delta S_{env} = \frac{1.5 \times 10^6 \text{ J}}{1.38 \times 10^{-23} \text{ J/K}}\left[\frac{1}{520 \text{ K}} - \frac{1}{750 \text{ K}}\right]$$

$$= 6.4 \times 10^{25}. ✔$$

❹ EVALUATE RESULT Energy is degraded (hot to cold), so I expect a positive entropy change. The number I obtained for the magnitude of the entropy change is very large, but I know from Chapter 19 that entropy values are very large, and so my answer is not unreasonable.

21.15 Suppose the bar in Example 21.5 is disconnected from the high-temperature reservoir and allowed to thermally equilibrate with the low-temperature reservoir. (*a*) Are the changes in the energy and entropy of the bar during this process positive, negative, or zero? (*b*) Is there any change in the entropy of the environment? (*c*) Does the sum $S_{bar} + S_{env}$ change?

Next we consider a device that converts mechanical energy (work) to thermal energy. In Section 21.1 we discussed a paddle wheel immersed in water. Now we consider a somewhat different situation: a motor doing work on an electric generator that delivers electrical energy to an electric blanket, which converts the electrical energy to thermal energy (**Figure 21.39a**). We define the generator, blanket, and wires that connect the two as our system. The motor (which is part of the environment) does work on the system, and energy is transferred thermally by the blanket (part of the system) to the environment. We assume that the temperatures of the blanket and the environment remain constant. This assumption ensures that the initial and final states of the system are the same.

Figure 21.39b shows the entropy diagram for this process. Because the transfer is to the right, the entropy change is positive. The height of the rectangle is Q_{out}. (Because $W = Q_{out}$ we could also write the height of the rectangle as W.) The rectangle stretches from the origin (0 on the $1/k_B T$ scale) to $1/k_B T_{out}$, so its length is $1/k_B T_{out}$. The entropy change is thus

$$\Delta S_{env} = +Q_{out}\frac{1}{k_B T_{out}} = \frac{Q_{out}}{k_B T_{out}} \quad \text{(steady state).} \tag{21.14}$$

This is indeed the result we would expect: No entropy change is associated with the work done on the system, and the entropy change caused by the thermal transfer of energy to the environment is $Q_{out}/k_B T_{out}$, which is exactly the result we obtain in Eq. 21.14.

✋ **21.16** (a) Draw an entropy diagram for a steady device that converts thermal energy from a thermal reservoir to mechanical energy. (b) From the diagram, compute the entropy change that occurs during the process and show that such a device is impossible.

21.6 Heat engine performance

Consider a heat engine that takes in energy thermally from a high-temperature reservoir, converts part of this energy to mechanical energy by doing work on the environment ($W < 0$), and discards the remainder to a low-temperature reservoir. As we saw in Section 21.3, the entropy diagram has two rectangles: one for the energy upgrade and the other for the degradation (**Figure 21.40**). To determine the entropy change in the environment over one complete cycle, we add the entropy changes of the two rectangles:

$$\Delta S_{env} = \Delta S_{upgrade} + \Delta S_{degrade} \quad \text{(complete cycle).} \tag{21.15}$$

The entropy change for the degradation is given by Eq. 21.10, so we need only calculate the change for the upgrade. The height of the upgrade rectangle is $-W$. Because $W = Q_{out} - Q_{in}$ (Eq. 21.2), the height of the rectangle can also be written as $Q_{in} - Q_{out}$. The rectangle stretches from the origin (0 on the $1/k_B T$ scale) to $1/k_B T_{in}$, so its length is $1/k_B T_{in}$. Because the transfer is to the left, the entropy change is negative. The entropy change associated with the upgrade is thus

$$\Delta S_{upgrade} = -(Q_{in} - Q_{out})\left[\frac{1}{k_B T_{in}}\right]. \tag{21.16}$$

Figure 21.39 A setup that converts mechanical energy (from the motor) to thermal energy.

(a)

(b)

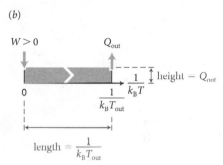

Figure 21.40 Entropy diagram for a heat engine that upgrades a portion of the thermal energy to mechanical energy and degrades the rest.

QUANTITATIVE TOOLS

Substituting Eqs. 21.16 and 21.10 into Eq. 21.15 gives

$$\Delta S_{env} = -(Q_{in} - Q_{out})\left[\frac{1}{k_B T_{in}}\right] + Q_{out}\left[\frac{1}{k_B T_{out}} - \frac{1}{k_B T_{in}}\right], \tag{21.17}$$

or

$$\Delta S_{env} = -\frac{Q_{in}}{k_B T_{in}} + \frac{Q_{out}}{k_B T_{out}} \quad \text{(complete cycle)}, \tag{21.18}$$

which is exactly Eq. 21.9, the expression we derived for the entropy change for a simple device that thermally transfers energy from a high-temperature reservoir to a low-temperature reservoir. The reason we obtain the same expression for the more complicated case of a heat engine is that no entropy change is associated with mechanical transfers of energy. Only the thermal transfers of energy to and from the thermal reservoirs contribute to the entropy change.

For a reversible heat engine, the entropy change in the environment must be equal to zero over one cycle (everything is back to what it was before), $\Delta S_{env} = 0$, so

$$-\frac{Q_{in}}{k_B T_{in}} + \frac{Q_{out}}{k_B T_{out}} = 0 \quad \text{(reversible heat engine)}. \tag{21.19}$$

Rearranging this equation, we get

$$\frac{Q_{out}}{Q_{in}} = \frac{T_{out}}{T_{in}} \quad \text{(reversible heat engine)}. \tag{21.20}$$

For a reversible heat engine that transfers energy from a thermal reservoir at T_{in}, the amount of energy discarded is proportional to T_{out}. The amount of energy discarded is independent of the type of working substance used and depends on only the temperatures of the two reservoirs. If we lower T_{out}, we decrease the amount of discarded energy, which means a greater portion of the input energy can be converted to mechanical energy. So we can maximize the work done on the environment by minimizing the temperature of the low-temperature reservoir.

✋ **21.17** Is it possible to reduce the amount of thermally discarded energy to zero by bringing T_{out} down to absolute zero?

Figure 21.41 Energy input-output diagram for a heat engine.

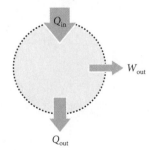

Figure 21.41 shows the energy input-output diagram for a heat engine. In Section 21.3 we defined the efficiency of such an engine as the ratio of the work done on the environment $(-W)$ to the thermal input of energy (Q_{in}). Using the symbol η (lowercase Greek eta) for efficiency, we can write

$$\eta \equiv \frac{-W}{Q_{in}}. \tag{21.21}$$

Substituting W from Eq. 21.2 yields

$$\eta = \frac{Q_{in} - Q_{out}}{Q_{in}} = 1 - \frac{Q_{out}}{Q_{in}}. \tag{21.22}$$

Equation 21.22 is a consequence of the energy law and holds for both reversible and irreversible heat engines that involve transfers of energy to and from two thermal reservoirs.

Figure 21.23 shows that for a given amount of work $-W$ done by a heat engine, Q_{in} is smallest when the engine is reversible. Therefore the efficiency of a heat engine is maximum when it is reversible. For a reversible heat engine, we can substitute Eq. 21.20 into Eq. Eq. 21.22 to obtain an expression for the maximum efficiency:

$$\eta_{\max} = 1 - \frac{T_{\text{out}}}{T_{\text{in}}} = \frac{T_{\text{in}} - T_{\text{out}}}{T_{\text{in}}} \quad \text{(reversible heat engine).} \quad (21.23)$$

In practice, the efficiency of a heat engine is always smaller than this maximum efficiency because it is impossible to completely eliminate irreversible processes. The important point to remember, however, is that even for a reversible heat engine, the efficiency is less than 1. The maximum efficiency is obtained with a minimum transfer of thermal energy to the low-temperature reservoir and has *nothing* to do with the details of the workings of the heat engine. *Only* the temperatures of the two reservoirs have any effect on the maximum efficiency: It is greatest when the ratio $T_{\text{out}}/T_{\text{in}}$ is smallest.

Example 21.6 Environmental impact of power plant

A power plant burns fossil fuel to produce steam at 650 K. The pressurized steam drives a steam turbine, where the steam condenses to water and is discarded at 310 K. What is the minimum quantity of energy discarded thermally by a 1.0-GW power plant to the environment during one day?

❶ **GETTING STARTED** Because I am interested in the minimum quantity of thermal energy discarded, I can treat the turbine as a reversible heat engine. Energy is thermally transferred to the turbine from the steam, which serves as the high-temperature reservoir at $T_{\text{in}} = 650$ K. Energy is thermally discarded along with the condensed steam at $T_{\text{out}} = 310$ K.

❷ **DEVISE PLAN** To calculate the minimum quantity of energy discarded to the environment, $Q_{\text{out,min}}$, I can use Eq. 21.2, which tells me that for a given value of W, Q_{out} is minimum when Q_{in} is minimum. No value is given for Q_{in}, but Eq. 21.21 tells me that Q_{in} is minimum when η has its maximum value, which I can calculate using Eq. 21.23. In one day, a 1.0-GW power plant delivers an amount of energy equal to $(24 \text{ h})(3600 \text{ s}/1 \text{ h})(1.0 \times 10^9 \text{ J/s}) = 8.6 \times 10^{13}$ J, and so $W = -8.6 \times 10^{13}$ J.

❸ **EXECUTE PLAN** The maximum efficiency is (Eq. 21.23)

$$\eta_{\max} = \frac{650 \text{ K} - 310 \text{ K}}{650 \text{ K}} = 0.523,$$

and so the minimum quantity of energy transferred thermally to the turbine is

$$Q_{\text{in,min}} = \frac{-W}{\eta_{\max}} = \frac{8.6 \times 10^{13} \text{ J}}{0.523} = 1.6 \times 10^{14} \text{ J}.$$

From Eq. 21.2 I thus calculate the minimum quantity of energy discarded thermally:

$$Q_{\text{out,min}} = Q_{\text{in,min}} + W = (1.6 \times 10^{14} \text{ J}) - (8.6 \times 10^{13} \text{ J})$$

$$= 7.8 \times 10^{13} \text{ J.} ✔$$

❹ **EVALUATE RESULT** The quantity of thermal energy leaving the turbine is smaller than the quantity of thermal energy entering it (as it should be) and approximately equal to the quantity of energy delivered by the plant. This makes sense because the maximum efficiency is close to $\frac{1}{2}$. I assumed the turbine to be reversible, which is unlikely. However, if the turbine is not reversible, more energy is dissipated, and so my result for the minimum amount of energy discarded still holds.

✋ **21.18** A hurricane thermally takes in energy from ocean water at 26 °C, discards some of it to the upper atmosphere at −52 °C, and converts the remainder to mechanical energy in the form of wind. (*a*) What is the maximum possible efficiency for the thermal-to-mechanical conversion? (*b*) If the temperature of the water increases by 1 °C, by what amount does the maximum efficiency increase?

If we run a heat engine in reverse, we obtain a heat pump (**Figure 21.42**). When the heat pump is used as a heater, we define the **coefficient of performance of heating** as

$$\text{COP}_{\text{heating}} = \frac{Q_{\text{out}}}{W}. \quad (21.24)$$

Figure 21.42 Energy input-output diagram for a heat pump.

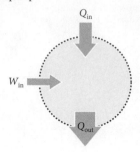

Because $W = W_{in} > 0$ and $W = Q_{out} - Q_{in}$, Q_{out} is always greater than or equal to W, and so $COP_{heating}$ for a heat pump is always greater than or equal to 1.

Substituting Eq. 21.2 into Eq. 21.24 gives

$$COP_{heating} = \frac{Q_{out}}{Q_{out} - Q_{in}} = \frac{1}{1 - Q_{in}/Q_{out}}. \qquad (21.25)$$

For a reversible heat pump that transfers energy from a lower-temperature thermal reservoir at T_{in} to a higher-temperature reservoir at T_{out}, we can substitute Eq. 21.20 into Eq. 21.25 to obtain the maximum coefficient of performance of heating:

$$COP_{heating,max} = \frac{1}{1 - T_{in}/T_{out}} = \frac{T_{out}}{T_{out} - T_{in}} \quad \text{(reversible heat pump).} \quad (21.26)$$

This expression tells us that the maximum coefficient of performance of heating is greatest when the ratio T_{in}/T_{out} is close to 1.

21.19 What is the coefficient of performance of heating for the electric blanket in Figure 21.39?

When a heat pump is used to cool (as a refrigerator or air conditioner), we define the **coefficient of performance of cooling** as

$$COP_{cooling} \equiv \frac{Q_{in}}{W}. \qquad (21.27)$$

Substituting Q_{in} from Eq. 21.2 gives

$$COP_{cooling} = \frac{Q_{out} - W}{W} = \frac{Q_{out}}{W} - 1 = COP_{heating} - 1. \qquad (21.28)$$

For a reversible heat pump, we can substitute Eq. 21.26 into Eq. 21.28 to obtain an expression for the maximum coefficient of performance of cooling:

$$COP_{cooling,max} = \frac{T_{out}}{T_{out} - T_{in}} - 1$$

$$= \frac{T_{in}}{T_{out} - T_{in}} \quad \text{(reversible heat pump).} \qquad (21.29)$$

For a refrigerator, the coefficient of performance of cooling is usually greater than 1 because the temperature of the interior T_{in} is around 255 K, and the temperature difference $T_{out} - T_{in}$ between the outside air and the interior is around 40 K.

Example 21.7 Cost of cooling off

The thermal insulation in a refrigerator is never perfect. Typically energy is transferred thermally from the room to the refrigerator interior at a rate of 60 W with the refrigerator door closed. Suppose the interior needs to be held at 4.0 °C and the temperature of the room is 20 °C. At what minimum rate must mechanical energy be delivered to the refrigerator to maintain the interior at 4.0 °C?

❶ **GETTING STARTED** Because I am interested in the minimum rate at which mechanical energy must be delivered, I can treat the refrigerator as a reversible heat pump. The room is the high-temperature reservoir, so $T_{out} = 20\,°C = 293$ K. The refrigerator interior is the low-temperature reservoir, so $T_{in} = 4.0\,°C = 277$ K. To maintain the temperature of the interior, the energy Q_{in} that leaks through the thermal insulation and moves from the room into the refrigerator must be transferred out. I am given that the rate at which this energy is transferred thermally into the refrigerator is $dQ_{in}/dt = 60$ W.

❷ DEVISE PLAN To calculate the rate at which mechanical energy must be delivered to balance a given quantity Q_{in} moving from the room to the refrigerator interior, I should first calculate how much work needs to be done to transfer that quantity of energy out of the refrigerator. To calculate the work required to transfer this quantity of energy Q_{in} I can use Eq. 21.27: $W = Q_{in}/COP_{cooling}$. This expression tells me that the amount of work needed is minimum when $COP_{cooling}$ has its maximum value, which I can determine from Eq. 21.29. To obtain the rate at which mechanical energy must be delivered, I take the time derivative of W.

❸ EXECUTE PLAN The maximum coefficient of performance of cooling is (Eq. 21.29)

$$COP_{cooling,max} = \frac{277 \text{ K}}{293 \text{ K} - 277 \text{ K}} = 17,$$

so the minimum work required is $W_{min} = Q_{in}/COP_{cooling,max}$. Taking the derivative of this expression, I obtain

$$\left(\frac{dW}{dt}\right)_{min} = \frac{dQ_{in}/dt}{COP_{cooling,max}} = \frac{60 \text{ W}}{17} = 3.5 \text{ W. ✔}$$

❹ EVALUATE RESULT My calculated value for the rate at which mechanical energy must be delivered to cancel the thermal energy that leaks from the room to the refrigerator interior is $1/17$ the rate at which that leaking occurs. This makes sense because the coefficient of performance of cooling is 17. This rate is small for what I expect for typical electrical appliances (several hundred watts), but I assumed the refrigerator was reversible. In reality, it is not reversible, and additional energy is dissipated, which means my calculated value is too low. Also, refrigerator doors are opened many times a day, thus increasing the rate of energy transferred thermally to the interior.

✋ **21.20** (*a*) If the heat pump from the refrigerator in Example 21.7 is used during the winter to heat a room to 20 °C when it's 4 °C outside, what is $COP_{heating}$? (*b*) At what rate must work be done on the heat pump if you want to heat the room at a rate of 500 W?

21.7 Carnot cycle

In Section 21.4, we identified the four processes that make up the Carnot cycle: two isothermal processes and two isentropic processes (**Figure 21.43**). Part of the energy taken in from a high-temperature reservoir is upgraded to mechanical energy, while the rest is degraded and discarded into a low-temperature reservoir (Figure 21.32*b*). The thermal transfer of energy occurs only during the isothermal processes at the two temperatures T_{in} and T_{out}.

As we study the Carnot cycle further, let us use an ideal gas as the working substance so that we can use our results for the entropy and thermal transfer of energy for each process from Tables 20.6 and 20.7, which are gathered together in **Table 21.1**.

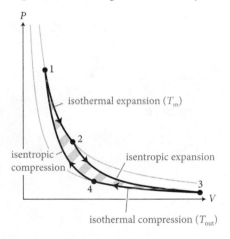

Figure 21.43 *PV* diagram for a Carnot cycle.

Table 21.1 Entropy and energy changes for the working substance in a Carnot cycle (see Tables 20.6 and 20.7)

Process	Definition	ΔS_{dev}	ΔE	W	Q
$1 \rightarrow 2$ (*isothermal*)	$\Delta T = 0$	$N \ln\left(\frac{V_2}{V_1}\right)$	0	$-Nk_B T_{in} \ln\left(\frac{V_2}{V_1}\right)$	$Nk_B T_{in} \ln\left(\frac{V_2}{V_1}\right)$
$2 \rightarrow 3$ (*isentropic*)	$Q = 0$	0	$NC_V(T_{out} - T_{in})$	$NC_V(T_{out} - T_{in})$	0
$3 \rightarrow 4$ (*isothermal*)	$\Delta T = 0$	$N \ln\left(\frac{V_4}{V_3}\right)$	0	$-Nk_B T_{out} \ln\left(\frac{V_4}{V_3}\right)$	$Nk_B T_{out} \ln\left(\frac{V_4}{V_3}\right)$
$4 \rightarrow 1$ (*isentropic*)	$Q = 0$	0	$NC_V(T_{in} - T_{out})$	$NC_V(T_{in} - T_{out})$	0
cycle	reversible	0	0	$-Nk_B(T_{in} - T_{out}) \ln\left(\frac{V_2}{V_1}\right)$	$-W$

To calculate the efficiency of a heat engine operating on this cycle from Eq. 21.21, we need to determine W and Q_{in}. We can obtain the work done on the working substance (our system) during the cycle from Table 21.1:

$$W = -Nk_BT_{in} \ln\left(\frac{V_2}{V_1}\right) - Nk_BT_{out} \ln\left(\frac{V_4}{V_3}\right) \quad \text{(Carnot cycle).} \qquad (21.30)$$

We do not need to write the two isentropic work terms because they cancel out.

For a complete cycle the entropy change must be zero, and so summing the entropy changes in Table 21.1, we get

$$N \ln\left(\frac{V_2}{V_1}\right) + N \ln\left(\frac{V_4}{V_3}\right) = 0 \qquad (21.31)$$

or

$$\ln\left(\frac{V_2}{V_1}\right) = -\ln\left(\frac{V_4}{V_3}\right), \qquad (21.32)$$

which means that

$$\frac{V_2}{V_1} = \frac{V_3}{V_4} \quad \text{(Carnot cycle).} \qquad (21.33)$$

Substituting Eq. 21.32 into Eq. 21.30, we obtain

$$W = -Nk_B(T_{in} - T_{out}) \ln\left(\frac{V_2}{V_1}\right) \quad \text{(Carnot cycle).} \qquad (21.34)$$

Because the volume ratio V_2/V_1 is greater than 1, $\ln(V_2/V_1)$ is positive. Because $T_{in} - T_{out}$ is also positive, the work done on the system is negative, which is consistent with our observation in Section 21.4: The work done on the system for a clockwise cycle is negative. Hence for a clockwise Carnot cycle, the work done on the environment is positive.

The high-temperature reservoir transfers energy thermally to the working substance during the first isothermal process (the one at T_{in}). The quantity Q_{in} is thus equal to the energy transferred thermally during the first isothermal process (see Table 21.1):

$$Q_{in} = Q_{1\to2} = Nk_BT_{in} \ln\left(\frac{V_2}{V_1}\right). \qquad (21.35)$$

Remember that not all of this energy can be converted to mechanical energy because some of it must be transferred to the low-temperature reservoir during the second isothermal process to satisfy the entropy law (Figure 21.32b).

Substituting Eqs. 21.34 and 21.35 into Eq. 21.21 thus yields

$$\eta = \frac{-W}{Q_{in}} = \frac{Nk_B(T_{in} - T_{out}) \ln\left(\frac{V_2}{V_1}\right)}{Nk_BT_{in} \ln\left(\frac{V_2}{V_1}\right)} = \frac{T_{in} - T_{out}}{T_{in}} \quad \text{(Carnot cycle),} \qquad (21.36)$$

which is exactly the maximum efficiency we obtained in Eq. 21.23 for any heat engine, regardless of the working substance.

Example 21.8 Carnot engine

In a reversible heat engine, 6.02×10^{23} molecules of nitrogen gas are used as the working substance. The gas undergoes a Carnot cycle as illustrated in Figure 21.43. The volume of the gas is 6.00×10^{-3} m^3 in state 1 and 14.0×10^{-3} m^3 in state 2. The low-temperature reservoir is at 320 K. How much energy is transferred thermally to the low-temperature reservoir during one cycle?

❶ **GETTING STARTED** The temperature of the low-temperature reservoir is $T_{out} = 320$ K. I am also given that $V_1 = 6.00 \times 10^{-3}$ m^3 and $V_2 = 14.0 \times 10^{-3}$ m^3. I need to determine Q_{out}, the amount of energy transferred thermally to the low-temperature reservoir in each cycle.

❷ **DEVISE PLAN** From Eq. 21.2 I know that $Q_{out} = W + Q_{in}$. Therefore this problem boils down to determining W and Q_{in}, which are given by Eq. 21.34 and 21.35, respectively. These equations both contain T_{in}, which is not given, but the terms containing T_{in} cancel and so T_{in} drops out.

❸ **EXECUTE PLAN** Substituting Eqs. 21.34 and 21.35 into Eq. 21.2 after solving the latter for Q_{out}, I get

$$Q_{out} = W + Q_{in} = -Nk_B(T_{in} - T_{out})\ln\left(\frac{V_2}{V_1}\right)$$

$$+ Nk_B T_{in} \ln\left(\frac{V_2}{V_1}\right) = Nk_B T_{out} \ln\left(\frac{V_2}{V_1}\right). \quad (1)$$

Substituting the values given yields

$$Q_{out} = (6.02 \times 10^{23})(1.38 \times 10^{-23}\,\text{J/K})(320\,\text{K})$$

$$\ln\left(\frac{14.0 \times 10^{-3}\,\text{m}^3}{6.00 \times 10^{-3}\,\text{m}^3}\right)$$

$$= 2.25 \times 10^3 \text{ J.} ✔$$

❹ **EVALUATE RESULT** The quantity I obtain for Q_{out} is positive, as it should be. I also note that the expression I obtain for Q_{out} in Eq. 1 can be written as $-Nk_B T_{out} \ln(V_4/V_3)$ because $\ln(V_2/V_1) = -\ln(V_4/V_3)$ (Eq. 21.32). Therefore $Q_{out} = -Q_{3\to4}$ (Table 21.1). This makes sense because energy is transferred thermally to the low-temperature reservoir only during the second isothermal process ($3 \to 4$). The minus sign in $-Q_{3\to4}$ accounts for the fact that $Q < 0$ (energy transferred out of the system) and, by definition, Q_{out} is always positive.

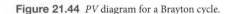 **21.21** What is the change in entropy during each of the four legs of the cycle in Example 21.8?

21.8 Brayton cycle

As we saw in Section 21.4, the Brayton cycle (**Figure 21.44**) produces more mechanical energy than the Carnot cycle. More importantly, because the Brayton cycle does not involve any isothermal processes, the rate at which work can be done is greater (yielding more power).

To determine the efficiency of the Brayton cycle, we begin by collecting the appropriate values for the entropy and energy changes from Tables 20.6 and 20.7. The result is shown in **Table 21.2** on the next page.

Figure 21.44 *PV* diagram for a Brayton cycle.

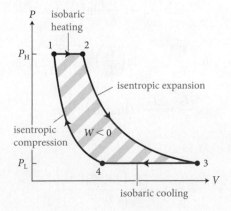

Table 21.2 Entropy and energy for the working substance in a Brayton cycle

Process	Definition	ΔS_{dev}	ΔE	W	Q
$1 \rightarrow 2$ (*isobaric*)	$\Delta P = 0$	$\dfrac{NC_P}{k_B}\ln\left(\dfrac{T_2}{T_1}\right)$	$NC_V(T_2 - T_1)$	$-Nk_B(T_2 - T_1)$	$NC_P(T_2 - T_1)$
$2 \rightarrow 3$ (*isentropic*)	$Q = 0$	0	$NC_V(T_3 - T_2)$	$NC_V(T_3 - T_2)$	0
$3 \rightarrow 4$ (*isobaric*)	$\Delta P = 0$	$\dfrac{NC_P}{k_B}\ln\left(\dfrac{T_4}{T_3}\right)$	$NC_V(T_4 - T_3)$	$-Nk_B(T_4 - T_3)$	$NC_P(T_4 - T_3)$
$4 \rightarrow 1$ (*isentropic*)	$Q = 0$	0	$NC_V(T_1 - T_4)$	$NC_V(T_1 - T_4)$	0
cycle	reversible	0	0	$-Q$	$NC_P(T_2 - T_1 + T_4 - T_3)$

Because the energy change over a cycle is zero, we have $W = -Q$. To obtain the work done during a cycle, therefore, we can sum the two terms in the right-most column of Table 21.2 (which is simpler than taking the sum of the four W terms):

$$W = -Q = -NC_P(T_2 - T_1 + T_4 - T_3) \quad \text{(Brayton cycle)}. \quad (21.37)$$

To calculate the efficiency (Eq. 21.21; $\eta = -W/Q_{\text{in}}$), we must obtain expressions for $-W$ and Q_{in}, both of which must be positive. Because $T_2 > T_1$, Q is positive during the first isobaric process ($1 \rightarrow 2$) at the high pressure P_H. Likewise, because $T_4 < T_3$, Q is negative during the second isobaric process ($3 \rightarrow 4$) at the low pressure P_L. The energy transferred thermally from the environment to the working substance is thus equal to the energy transferred thermally during the isobaric process $1 \rightarrow 2$:

$$Q_{\text{in}} = NC_P(T_2 - T_1). \quad (21.38)$$

Substituting Eqs. 21.37 and 21.38 into Eq. 21.21 and dividing out the factor NC_P, we obtain

$$\eta \equiv \frac{-W}{Q_{\text{in}}} = \frac{T_2 - T_1 + T_4 - T_3}{T_2 - T_1} = 1 - \frac{T_3 - T_4}{T_2 - T_1}. \quad (21.39)$$

We can simplify this expression for the efficiency of the Brayton cycle by using our knowledge about entropy. The entropy change for the cycle is zero (Table 21.2). This ΔS_{dev} for the cycle is the sum of the two nonzero ΔS_{dev} terms in Table 21.2, so setting the sum of these two terms equal to zero gives

$$\frac{NC_P}{k_B}\ln\left(\frac{T_2}{T_1}\right) + \frac{NC_P}{k_B}\ln\left(\frac{T_4}{T_3}\right) = 0 \quad (21.40)$$

$$\ln\left(\frac{T_2}{T_1}\right) = -\ln\left(\frac{T_4}{T_3}\right) = \ln\left(\frac{T_3}{T_4}\right), \quad (21.41)$$

which means that

$$\frac{T_2}{T_1} = \frac{T_3}{T_4} \quad \text{(Brayton cycle)}. \quad (21.42)$$

We now rewrite Eq. 21.39 as

$$\eta = 1 - \frac{T_4}{T_1}\left[\frac{(T_3/T_4) - 1}{(T_2/T_1) - 1}\right]. \quad (21.43)$$

By Eq. 21.42, the term inside the square brackets is equal to 1, so the efficiency is

$$\eta = 1 - \frac{T_4}{T_1}. \quad \text{(Brayton cycle)} \qquad (21.44)$$

The temperature T_4 is the lowest temperature in the cycle. The temperature T_1 is the temperature of the working substance at the completion of the isentropic compression, when the working substance exits the compressor (shown in Figure 21.30b).

During the isentropic compression, we have, from Eq. 20.47,

$$(P_H)^{(1/\gamma)-1}T_1 = (P_L)^{(1/\gamma)-1}T_4, \qquad (21.45)$$

where γ is the heat capacity ratio C_P/C_V given by Eq. 20.26. The temperature ratio in Eq. 21.44 then becomes

$$\frac{T_4}{T_1} = \left(\frac{P_H}{P_L}\right)^{(1/\gamma)-1}. \qquad (21.46)$$

The efficiency in Eq. 21.44 can thus be expressed in terms of the pressure increase accomplished by the compressor in the process $4 \rightarrow 1$:

$$\eta = 1 - \left(\frac{P_H}{P_L}\right)^{(1/\gamma)-1}. \quad \text{(Brayton cycle)} \qquad (21.47)$$

The ratio P_H/P_L is called the *pressure ratio*. For aircraft engines, this ratio typically is between 4 and 30. The higher the pressure ratio of an engine running on the Brayton cycle, the more efficient the engine.

Example 21.9 Performance and pressure ratio

Consider a jet engine operating on the Brayton cycle. The working substance is air, which consists primarily of diatomic molecules. The air is drawn in at atmospheric pressure, 1.01×10^5 Pa, at 288 K. In the combustion chamber, the temperature of the air is raised to 1520 K, and the engine has a pressure ratio of 30. What are the temperatures at the end of the two isentropic processes?

❶ **GETTING STARTED** Air enters the engine at point 4 in the cycle in Figure 21.44. Therefore I know that $T_4 = 288$ K. The air is compressed between state 4 and state 1 and the combustion takes place between state 1 and state 2, so I also know that $T_2 = 1520$ K. The isentropic processes end at states 1 and 3, so I need to determine T_1 and T_3.

❷ **DEVISE PLAN** To determine T_1 I can use Eq. 21.46, which relates T_1 to T_4 and the pressure ratio, both of which are given. This equation also contains the heat capacity ratio γ, which I can determine from Eq. 20.26, $\gamma = C_P/C_V = 1 + 2/d$, because I know that $d = 5$ for diatomic molecules. Once I have T_1, I can use Eq. 21.42 to determine T_3.

❸ **EXECUTE PLAN** From Eq. 20.26, I get

$$\gamma = 1 + \frac{2}{5} = \frac{7}{5},$$

so the exponent in Eq. 21.46 is $\frac{1}{\gamma} - 1 = \frac{5}{7} - 1 = -\frac{2}{7}$. I can then solve Eq. 21.46 for T_1:

$$T_1 = \frac{T_4}{(P_H/P_L)^{(1/\gamma)-1}} = \frac{288 \text{ K}}{30^{-2/7}} = 760 \text{ K.} ✔ \qquad (1)$$

Now that I have T_1 and T_2, I can get T_3 from Eq. 21.42:

$$T_3 = \frac{T_2 T_4}{T_1} = \frac{(1520 \text{ K})(288 \text{ K})}{760 \text{ K}} = 575 \text{ K.} ✔$$

❹ **EVALUATE RESULT** I know from Section 20.4 that on a given PV diagram, isentropes are steeper than isotherms, so Figure 21.44 tells me that T_1 and T_3 should lie between $T_4 = 288$ K and $T_2 = 1520$ K. The values I obtain indeed satisfy this condition.

21.22 (a) What is the efficiency of the jet engine in Example 21.9? (b) If the jet engine were to operate on a Carnot cycle between the same highest and lowest temperatures, what would its efficiency be?

Chapter Glossary

SI units of physical quantities are given in parentheses.

Brayton cycle A reversible thermodynamic cycle that consists of two isobaric processes and two isentropic processes.

Carnot cycle A reversible thermodynamic cycle that consists of two isothermal processes and two isentropic processes. This cycle operates at the maximum possible efficiency between two thermal reservoirs at fixed temperatures.

Coefficient of performance of cooling COP (unitless) The ratio of the thermal input of energy to the work done on a heat pump:

$$\text{COP}_{\text{cooling}} \equiv \frac{Q_{\text{in}}}{W}. \qquad (21.27)$$

Coefficient of performance of heating COP (unitless) The ratio of the thermal output of energy to the work done on a heat pump:

$$\text{COP}_{\text{heating}} \equiv \frac{Q_{\text{out}}}{W}. \qquad (21.24)$$

Efficiency η (unitless) The ratio of the work done by a heat engine on the environment to the thermal input of energy:

$$\eta \equiv \frac{-W}{Q_{\text{in}}}. \qquad (21.21)$$

Energy input-output diagram A diagram that shows the energy inputs and energy outputs of a system or device. Energy inputs and energy outputs can be due to mechanical interactions or thermal interactions.

Entropy diagram A diagram that shows the changes in entropy in the environment of a steady device due to the energy conversions and transfers caused by the device. See the Procedure box on page. 573.

Entropy gradient dS/dE (1/J) A scalar that represents the rate at which the entropy of a system changes with a change in thermal energy of the system. The entropy gradient is inversely proportional to the absolute temperature (Eq. 19.38).

Heat engine A steady device that does work on the environment by taking in energy thermally at a high temperature and putting out energy thermally at a lower temperature.

Heat pump A steady device that uses mechanical energy to take in energy thermally at a low temperature and put out energy thermally at a higher temperature.

Mechanical input of energy W_{in} (J) A positive scalar equal to the amount of energy transferred into a system due to a mechanical interaction.

Mechanical output of energy W_{out} (J) A positive scalar equal to the amount of energy transferred out of a system due to a mechanical interaction.

Quality of energy A measure of the ratio of energy change to entropy change. The higher the quality of the energy transferred, the smaller the associated entropy change. Mechanical energy represents the highest-quality energy.

Steady device A device that can be operated indefinitely because its state does not change more and more over time. The changes in energy and entropy of such a device must be zero either continuously or over some repeating time interval.

Thermal input of energy Q_{in} (J) A positive scalar equal to the amount of energy transferred into a system due to a thermal interaction.

Thermal output of energy Q_{out} (J) A positive scalar equal to the amount of energy transferred out of a system due to a thermal interaction.

Appendix A

Notation

Notation used in this text, listed alphabetically, Greek letters first.
For information concerning superscripts and subscripts, see the explanation at the end of this table.

Symbol	Name of Quantity	Definition	Where Defined	SI units
α (alpha)	polarizability	scalar measure of amount of charge separation occurring in material due to external electric field	Eq. 23.24	$C^2 \cdot m/N$
α	Bragg angle	in x-ray diffraction, angle between incident x rays and sample surface	Section 34.3	degree, radian, or revolution
α_ϑ	(ϑ component of) rotational acceleration	rate at which rotational velocity ω_ϑ increases	Eq. 11.12	s^{-2}
β (beta)	sound intensity level	logarithmic scale for sound intensity, proportional to $\log(I/I_{th})$	Eq. 17.5	dB (not an SI unit)
γ (gamma)	Lorentz factor	factor indicating how much relativistic values deviate from nonrelativistic ones	Eq. 14.6	unitless
γ	surface tension	force per unit length exerted parallel to surface of liquid; energy per unit area required to increase surface area of liquid	Eq. 18.48	N/m
γ	heat capacity ratio	ratio of heat capacity at constant pressure to heat capacity at constant volume	Eq. 20.26	unitless
Δ	delta	change in	Eq. 2.4	
$\Delta\vec{r}$	displacement	vector from object's initial to final position	Eq. 2.8	m
$\Delta\vec{r}_F$, Δx_F	force displacement	displacement of point of application of a force	Eq. 9.7	m
Δt	interval of time	difference between final and initial instants	Table 2.2	s
Δt_{proper}	proper time interval	time interval between two events occurring at same position	Section 14.1	s
Δt_v	interval of time	time interval measured by observer moving at speed v with respect to events	Eq. 14.13	s
Δx	x component of displacement	difference between final and initial positions along x axis	Eq. 2.4	m
δ (delta)	delta	infinitesimally small amount of	Eq. 3.24	
ϵ_0 (epsilon)	permittivity constant	constant relating units of electrical charge to mechanical units	Eq. 24.7	$C^2/(N \cdot m^2)$
η (eta)	viscosity	measure of fluid's resistance to shear deformation	Eq. 18.38	$Pa \cdot s$
η	efficiency	ratio of work done by heat engine to thermal input of energy	Eq. 21.21	unitless
θ (theta)	angular coordinate	polar coordinate measuring angle between position vector and x axis	Eq. 10.2	degree, radian, or revolution
θ_c	contact angle	angle between solid surface and tangent to liquid surface at meeting point measured within liquid	Section 18.4	degree, radian, or revolution
θ_c	critical angle	angle of incidence greater than which total internal reflection occurs	Eq. 33.9	degree, radian, or revolution
θ_i	angle of incidence	angle between incident ray of light and normal to surface	Section 33.1	degree, radian, or revolution

Symbol	Name of Quantity	Definition	Where Defined	SI units
θ_i	angle subtended by image	angle subtended by image	Section 33.6	degree, radian, or revolution
θ_o	angle subtended by object	angle subtended by object	Section 33.6	degree, radian, or revolution
θ_r	angle of reflection	angle between reflected ray of light and normal to surface	Section 33.1	degree, radian, or revolution
θ_r	minimum resolving angle	smallest angular separation between objects that can be resolved by optical instrument with given aperture	Eq. 34.30	degree, radian, or revolution
ϑ (script theta)	rotational coordinate	for object traveling along circular path, arc length traveled divided by circle radius	Eq. 11.1	unitless
κ (kappa)	torsional constant	ratio of torque required to twist object to rotational displacement	Eq. 15.25	$N \cdot m$
κ	dielectric constant	factor by which potential difference across isolated capacitor is reduced by insertion of dielectric	Eq. 26.9	unitless
λ (lambda)	inertia per unit length	for uniform one-dimensional object, amount of inertia in a given length	Eq. 11.44	kg/m
λ	wavelength	minimum distance over which periodic wave repeats itself	Eq. 16.9	m
λ	linear charge density	amount of charge per unit length	Eq. 23.16	C/m
μ (mu)	reduced mass	product of two interacting objects' inertias divided by their sum	Eq. 6.39	kg
μ	linear mass density	mass per unit length	Eq. 16.25	kg/m
$\vec{\mu}$	magnetic dipole moment	vector pointing along direction of magnetic field of current loop, with magnitude equal to current times area of loop	Section 28.3	$A \cdot m^2$
μ_0	magnetic constant	constant relating units of electric current to mechanical units	Eq. 28.1	$T \cdot m/A$
μ_k	coefficient of kinetic friction	proportionality constant relating magnitudes of force of kinetic friction and normal force between two surfaces	Eq. 10.55	unitless
μ_s	coefficient of static friction	proportionality constant relating magnitudes of force of static friction and normal force between two surfaces	Eq. 10.46	unitless
ρ (rho)	mass density	amount of mass per unit volume	Eq. 1.4	kg/m^3
ρ	inertia per unit volume	for uniform three-dimensional object, amount of inertia in a given volume divided by that volume	Eq. 11.46	kg/m^3
ρ	(volume) charge density	amount of charge per unit volume	Eq. 23.18	C/m^3
σ (sigma)	inertia per unit area	for uniform two-dimensional object, inertia divided by area	Eq. 11.45	kg/m^2
σ	surface charge density	amount of charge per unit area	Eq. 23.17	C/m^2
σ	conductivity	ratio of current density to applied electric field	Eq. 31.8	$A/(V \cdot m)$
τ (tau)	torque	magnitude of axial vector describing ability of forces to change objects' rotational motion	Eq. 12.1	$N \cdot m$
τ	time constant	for damped oscillation, time for energy of oscillator to decrease by factor e^{-1}	Eq. 15.39	s
τ_ϑ	(ϑ component of) torque	ϑ component of axial vector describing ability of forces to change objects' rotational motion	Eq. 12.3	$N \cdot m$
Φ_E (phi, upper case)	electric flux	scalar product of electric field and area through which it passes	Eq. 24.1	$N \cdot m^2/C$

Symbol	Name of Quantity	Definition	Where Defined	SI units
Φ_B	magnetic flux	scalar product of magnetic field and area through which it passes	Eq. 27.10	Wb
ϕ (phi)	phase constant	phase difference between source emf and current in circuit	Eq. 32.16	unitless
$\phi(t)$	phase	time-dependent argument of sine function describing simple harmonic motion	Eq. 15.5	unitless
Ω (omega, upper case)	number of basic states	number of basic states corresponding to macrostate	Sections 19.4, 19.1	unitless
ω (omega)	rotational speed	magnitude of rotational velocity	Eq. 11.7	s^{-1}
ω	angular frequency	for oscillation with period T, $2\pi/T$	Eq. 15.4	s^{-1}
ω_0	resonant angular frequency	angular frequency at which current in circuit is maximal	Eq. 32.47	s^{-1}
ω_ϑ	(ϑ component of) rotational velocity	rate at which rotational coordinate ϑ changes	Eq. 11.6	s^{-1}
A	area	length $\times$ width	Eq. 11.45	m^2
A	amplitude	magnitude of maximum displacement of oscillating object from equilibrium position	Eq. 15.6	m (for linear mechanical oscillation; unitless for rotational oscillation; various units for nonmechanical oscillation)
$\vec{A}$	area vector	vector with magnitude equal to area and direction normal to plane of area	Section 24.6	m^2
$\vec{a}$	acceleration	time rate of change in velocity	Section 3.1	m/s^2
$\vec{a}_{Ao}$	relative acceleration	value observer in reference frame A records for acceleration of object o in reference frame A	Eq. 6.11	m/s^2
a_c	magnitude of centripetal acceleration	acceleration required to make object follow circular trajectory	Eq. 11.15	m/s^2
a_r	radial component of acceleration	component of acceleration in radial direction	Eq. 11.16	m/s^2
a_t	tangential component of acceleration	component of acceleration tangent to trajectory; for circular motion at constant speed $a_t = 0$	Eq. 11.17	m/s^2
a_x	x component of acceleration	component of acceleration directed along x axis	Eq. 3.21	m/s^2
$\vec{B}$	magnetic field	vector field providing measure of magnetic interactions	Eq. 27.5	T
$\vec{B}_{ind}$	induced magnetic field	magnetic field produced by induced current	Section 29.4	T
b	damping coefficient	ratio of drag force on moving object to its speed	Eq. 15.34	kg/s
C	heat capacity per particle	ratio of energy transferred thermally per particle to change in temperature	Section 20.3	J/K
C	capacitance	ratio of magnitude of charge on one of a pair of oppositely charged conductors to magnitude of potential difference between them	Eq. 26.1	F
C_P	heat capacity per particle at constant pressure	ratio of energy transferred thermally per particle to change in temperature, while holding pressure constant	Eq. 20.20	J/K
C_V	heat capacity per particle at constant volume	ratio of energy transferred thermally per particle to change in temperature, while holding volume constant	Eq. 20.13	J/K
$COP_{cooling}$	coefficient of performance of cooling	ratio of thermal input of energy to work done on a heat pump	Eq. 21.27	unitless

Symbol	Name of Quantity	Definition	Where Defined	SI units
$COP_{heating}$	coefficient of performance of heating	ratio of thermal output of energy to work done on a heat pump	Eq. 21.25	unitless
c	shape factor	ratio of object's rotational inertia to mR^2; function of distribution of inertia within object	Tables 11.3, 12.25	unitless
c	wave speed	speed at which mechanical wave travels through medium	Eq. 16.3	m/s
c	specific heat capacity	ratio of energy transferred thermally per unit mass to change in temperature	Section 20.3	$J/(K \cdot kg)$
c_0	speed of light in vacuum	speed of light in vacuum	Section 14.2	m/s
c_V	specific heat capacity at constant volume	ratio of energy transferred thermally per unit mass to change in temperature, while holding volume constant	Eq. 20.48	$J/(K \cdot kg)$
$\vec{D}$	displacement (of particle in wave)	displacement of particle from its equilibrium position	Eq. 16.1	m
d	diameter	diameter	Section 1.9	m
d	distance	distance between two locations	Eq. 2.5	m
d	degrees of freedom	number of ways particle can store thermal energy	Eq. 20.4	unitless
d	lens strength	1 m divided by focal length	Eq. 33.22	diopters
E	energy of system	sum of kinetic and internal energies of system	Tables 1.1, 5.21	J
$\vec{E}$	electric field	vector field representing electric force per unit charge	Eq. 23.1	N/C
E_0	work function	minimum energy required to free electron from surface of metal	Eq. 34.35	J
E_{chem}	chemical energy	internal energy associated with object's chemical state	Eq. 5.27	J
E_{int}	internal energy of system	energy associated with an object's state	Eqs. 5.20, 14.54	J
E_{mech}	mechanical energy	sum of system's kinetic and potential energies	Eq. 7.9	J
E_s	source energy	incoherent energy used to produce other forms of energy	Eq. 7.7	J
E_{th}	thermal energy	internal energy associated with object's temperature	Eq. 5.27	J
$\mathcal{E}$	emf	in charge-separating device, nonelectrostatic work per unit charge done in separating positive and negative charge carriers	Eq. 26.7	V
$\mathcal{E}_{ind}$	induced emf	emf resulting from changing magnetic flux	Eqs. 29.3, 29.8	V
$\mathcal{E}_{max}$	amplitude of emf	amplitude of time-dependent emf produced by AC source	Sections 32.1, 32.1	V
$\mathcal{E}_{rms}$	rms emf	root-mean-square emf	Eq. 32.55	V
e	coefficient of restitution	measure of amount of initial relative speed recovered after collision	Eq. 5.18	unitless
e	eccentricity	measure of deviation of conic section from circular	Section 13.7	unitless
e	elementary charge	magnitude of charge on electron	Eq. 22.3	C
$\vec{F}$	force	time rate of change of object's momentum	Eq. 8.2	N
$\vec{F}^B$	magnetic force	force exerted on electric current or moving charged particle by magnetic field	Eqs. 27.8, 27.19	N
$\vec{F}^b$	buoyant force	upward force exerted by fluid on submerged object	Eq. 18.12	N
$\vec{F}^c$	contact force	force between objects in physical contact	Section 8.5	N

Symbol	Name of Quantity	Definition	Where Defined	SI units
$\vec{F}^d$	drag force	force exerted by medium on object moving through medium	Eq. 15.34	N
$\vec{F}^E$	electric force	force exerted between electrically charged objects or on electrically charged objects by electric field	Eq. 22.1	N
$\vec{F}^{EB}$	electromagnetic force	force exerted on electrically charged objects by electric and magnetic fields	Eq. 27.20	N
$\vec{F}^f$	frictional force	force exerted on object due to friction between it and a second object or surface	Eq. 9.26	N
$\vec{F}^G$	gravitational force	force exerted by Earth or any object having mass on any other object having mass	Eqs. 8.16, 13.1	N
$\vec{F}^k$	force of kinetic friction	frictional force between two objects in relative motion	Sections 10.4, 10.55	N
$\vec{F}^n$	normal force	force directed perpendicular to a surface	Sections 10.4, 10.46	N
$\vec{F}^s$	force of static friction	frictional force between two objects not in relative motion	Sections 10.4, 10.46	N
f	frequency	number of cycles per second of periodic motion	Eq. 15.2	Hz
f	focal length	distance from center of lens to focus	Sections 33.4, 33.16	m
f_{beat}	beat frequency	frequency at which beats occur when waves of different frequency interfere	Eq. 17.8	Hz
G	gravitational constant	proportionality constant relating gravitational force between two objects to their masses and separation	Eq. 13.1	$N \cdot m^2/kg^2$
g	magnitude of acceleration due to gravity	magnitude of acceleration of object in free fall near Earth's surface	Eq. 3.14	m/s^2
h	height	vertical distance	Eq. 10.26	m
h	Planck's constant	constant describing scale of quantum mechanics; relates photon energy to frequency and de Broglie wavelength to momentum of particle	Eq. 34.35	$J \cdot s$
I	rotational inertia	measure of object's resistance to change in its rotational velocity	Eq. 11.30	$kg \cdot m^2$
I	intensity	energy delivered by wave per unit time per unit area normal to direction of propagation	Eq. 17.1	W/m^2
I	(electric) current	rate at which charged particles cross a section of a conductor in a given direction	Eq. 27.2	A
I	amplitude of oscillating current	maximum value of oscillating current in circuit	Sections 32.1, 32.5	A
I_{cm}	rotational inertia about center of mass	object's rotational inertia about an axis through its center of mass	Eq. 11.48	$kg \cdot m^2$
I_{disp}	displacement current	current-like quantity in Ampère's law caused by changing electric flux	Eq. 30.7	A
I_{enc}	enclosed current	current enclosed by Ampèrian path	Eq. 28.1	A
I_{ind}	induced current	current in loop caused by changing magnetic flux through loop	Eq. 29.4	A
I_{int}	intercepted current	current intercepted by surface spanning Ampèrian path	Eq. 30.6	A
I_{rms}	rms current	root-mean-square current	Eq. 32.53	A
I_{th}	intensity at threshold of hearing	minimum intensity audible to human ear	Eq. 17.4	W/m^2
i	time-dependent current	time-dependent current through circuit; $I(t)$	Sections 32.1, 32.5	A
i	image distance	distance from lens to image	Sections 33.6, 33.16	m

Symbol	Name of Quantity	Definition	Where Defined	SI units
$\hat{\imath}$	unit vector ("i hat")	vector for defining direction of x axis	Eq. 2.1	unitless
$\vec{J}$	impulse	amount of momentum transferred from environment to system	Eq. 4.18	$kg \cdot m/s$
$\vec{J}$	current density	current per unit area	Eq. 31.6	A/m^2
J_ϑ	rotational impulse	amount of angular momentum transferred from environment to system	Eq. 12.15	$kg \cdot m^2/s$
$\hat{\jmath}$	unit vector	vector for defining direction of y axis	Eq. 10.4	unitless
K	kinetic energy	energy object has because of its translational motion	Eqs. 5.12, 14.51	J
K	surface current density	current per unit of sheet width	Section 28.5	A/m
K_{cm}	translational kinetic energy	kinetic energy associated with motion of center of mass of system	Eq. 6.32	J
K_{conv}	convertible kinetic energy	kinetic energy that can be converted to internal energy without changing system's momentum	Eq. 6.33	J
K_{rot}	rotational kinetic energy	energy object has due to its rotational motion	Eq. 11.31	J
k	spring constant	ratio of force exerted on spring to displacement of free end of spring	Eq. 8.18	N/m
k	wave number	number of wavelengths in 2π units of distance; for wave with wavelength λ, $2\pi/\lambda$	Eqs. 16.7, 16.11	m^{-1}
k	Coulomb's law constant	constant relating electrostatic force to charges and their separation distance	Eq. 22.5	$N \cdot m^2/C^2$
k_B	Boltzmann constant	constant relating thermal energy to absolute temperature	Eq. 19.39	J/K
L	inductance	negative of ratio of induced emf around loop to rate of change of current in loop	Eq. 29.19	H
L_ϑ	(ϑ component of) angular momentum	capacity of object to make other objects rotate	Eq. 11.34	$kg \cdot m^2/s$
L_m	specific transformation energy for melting	energy transferred thermally per unit mass required to melt substance	Eq. 20.55	J/kg
L_v	specific transformation energy for vaporization	energy transferred thermally per unit mass required to vaporize substance	Eq. 20.55	J/kg
ℓ	length	distance or extent in space	Table 1.1	m
ℓ_{proper}	proper length	length measured by observer at rest relative to object	Section 14.3	m
ℓ_v	length	measured length of object moving at speed v relative to observer	Eq. 14.28	m
M	magnification	ratio of signed image height to object height	Eq. 33.17	unitless
M_θ	angular magnification	ratio of angle subtended by image to angle subtended by object	Eq. 33.18	unitless
m	mass	amount of substance	Tables 1.1, 13.1	kg
m	inertia	measure of object's resistance to change in its velocity	Eq. 4.2	kg
m	fringe order	number indexing bright interference fringes, counting from central, zeroth-order bright fringe	Sections 34.2, 34.5	unitless
m_v	inertia	inertia of object moving at speed v relative to observer	Eq. 14.41	kg
N	number of objects	number of objects in sample	Eq. 1.3	unitless
N_A	Avogadro's number	number of particles in 1 mol of a substance	Eq. 1.2	unitless
n	number density	number of objects per unit volume	Eq. 1.3	m^{-3}

Symbol	Name of Quantity	Definition	Where Defined	SI units
n	windings per unit length	in a solenoid, number of windings per unit length	Eq. 28.4	unitless
n	index of refraction	ratio of speed of light in vacuum to speed of light in a medium	Eq. 33.1	unitless
n	fringe order	number indexing dark interference fringes, counting from central, zeroth-order bright fringe	Sections 34.2, 34.7	unitless
O	origin	origin of coordinate system	Section 10.2	
o	object distance	distance from lens to object	Sections 33.6, 33.16	m
P	power	time rate at which energy is transferred or converted	Eq. 9.30	W
P	pressure	force per unit area exerted by fluid	Eq. 18.1	Pa
P_{atm}	atmospheric pressure	average pressure in Earth's atmosphere at sea level	Eq. 18.3	Pa
P_{gauge}	gauge pressure	pressure measured as difference between absolute pressure and atmospheric pressure	Eq. 18.16	Pa
p	time-dependent power	time-dependent rate at which source delivers energy to load; $P(t)$	Eq. 32.49	W
$\vec{p}$	momentum	vector that is product of an object's inertia and velocity	Eq. 4.6	kg·m/s
$\vec{p}$	(electric) dipole moment	vector representing magnitude and direction of electric dipole, equal amounts of positive and negative charge separated by small distance	Eq. 23.9	C·m
$\vec{p}_{ind}$	induced dipole moment	dipole moment induced in material by external electric field	Eq. 23.24	C·m
p_x	x component of momentum	x component of momentum	Eq. 4.7	kg·m/s
Q	quality factor	for damped oscillation, number of cycles for energy of oscillator to decrease by factor $e^{-2\pi}$	Eq. 15.41	unitless
Q	volume flow rate	rate at which volume of fluid crosses section of tube	Eq. 18.25	m³/s
Q	energy transferred thermally	energy transferred into system by thermal interactions	Eq. 20.1	J
Q_{in}	thermal input of energy	positive amount of energy transferred into system by thermal interactions	Sections 21.1, 21.5	J
Q_{out}	thermal output of energy	positive amount of energy transferred out of system by thermal interactions	Sections 21.1, 21.5	J
q	electrical charge	attribute responsible for electromagnetic interactions	Eq. 22.1	C
q_{enc}	enclosed charge	sum of all charge within a closed surface	Eq. 24.8	C
q_p	dipole charge	charge of positively charged pole of dipole	Section 23.6	C
R	radius	radius of an object	Eq. 11.47	m
R	resistance	ratio of applied potential difference to resulting current	Eqs. 29.4, 31.10	Ω
R_{eq}	equivalent resistance	resistance that could be used to replace combination of circuit elements	Eqs. 31.26, 31.33	Ω
r	radial coordinate	polar coordinate measuring distance from origin of coordinate system	Eq. 10.1	m
$\vec{r}$	position	vector for determining position	Eqs. 2.9, 10.4	m
$\hat{r}_{12}$	unit vector ("r hat")	unit vector pointing from tip of $\vec{r}_1$ to tip of $\vec{r}_2$	Eq. 22.6	unitless
$\vec{r}_{AB}$	relative position	position of observer B in reference frame of observer A	Eq. 6.3	m
$\vec{r}_{Ae}$	relative position	value observer in reference frame A records for position at which event e occurs	Eq. 6.3	m

Symbol	Name of Quantity	Definition	Where Defined	SI units
$\vec{r}_{cm}$	position of a system's center of mass	a fixed position in a system that is independent of choice of reference frame	Eq. 6.24	m
$\vec{r}_p$	dipole separation	position of positively charged particle relative to negatively charged particle in dipole	Section 23.6	m
$r_\perp$	lever arm distance or lever arm	perpendicular distance between rotation axis and line of action of a vector	Eq. 11.36	m
$\Delta\vec{r}$	displacement	vector from object's initial to final position	Eq. 2.8	m
$\Delta\vec{r}_F$	force displacement	displacement of point of application of a force	Eq. 9.7	m
S	entropy	logarithm of number of basic states	Eq. 19.4	unitless
S	intensity	intensity of electromagnetic wave	Eq. 30.36	W/m^2
$\vec{S}$	Pointing vector	vector representing flow of energy in combined electric and magnetic fields	Eq. 30.37	W/m^2
s	arc length	distance along circular path	Eq. 11.1	m
s^2	space-time interval	invariant measure of separation of events in space-time	Eq. 14.18	m^2
T	period	time interval needed for object in circular motion to complete one revolution	Eq. 11.20	s
T	absolute temperature	quantity related to rate of change of entropy with respect to thermal energy	Eq. 19.38	K
$\mathcal{T}$	tension	stress in object subject to opposing forces stretching the object	Section 8.6	N
t	instant in time	physical quantity that allows us to determine the sequence of related events	Table 1.1	s
t_{Ae}	instant in time	value observer A measures for instant at which event e occurs	Eq. 6.1	s
Δt	interval of time	difference between final and initial instants	Table 2.2	s
Δt_{proper}	proper time interval	time interval between two events occurring at same position	Section 14.1	s
Δt_v	interval of time	time interval between two events measured by observer moving at speed v relative to an observer for whom the events occur at the same position	Eq. 14.13	s
U	potential energy	energy stored in reversible changes to system's configuration state	Eq. 7.7	J
U^B	magnetic potential energy	potential energy stored in magnetic field	Eqs. 29.25, 29.30	J
U^E	electric potential energy	potential energy due to relative position of charged objects	Eq. 25.8	J
U^G	gravitational potential energy	potential energy due to relative position of gravitationally interacting objects	Eqs. 7.13, Eq. 13.14	J
u_B	energy density of magnetic field	energy per unit volume stored in magnetic field	Eq. 29.29	J/m^3
u_E	energy density of electric field	energy per unit volume stored in electric field	Eq. 26.6	J/m^3
V	volume	amount of space occupied by an object	Table 1.1	m^3
V_{AB}	potential difference	negative of electrostatic work per unit charge done on charged particle as it is moved from point A to point B	Eq. 25.15	V
V_{batt}	battery potential difference	magnitude of potential difference between terminals of battery	Eq. 25.19	V
V_C	amplitude of oscillating potential	maximum magnitude of potential across circuit element C	Sections 32.1, 32.8	V
V_{disp}	displaced volume	volume of fluid displaced by submerged object	Eq. 18.12	m^3

Symbol	Name of Quantity	Definition	Where Defined	SI units
V_P	(electrostatic) potential	potential difference between conveniently chosen reference point of potential zero and point P	Eq. 25.30	V
V_{rms}	rms potential	root-mean-square potential difference	Eq. 32.55	V
V_{stop}	stopping potential	minimum potential difference required to stop flow of electrons from photoelectric effect	Eq. 34.34	V
$\mathcal{V}$	"volume" in velocity space	measure of range of velocities in three dimensions	Eq. 19.20	$(m/s)^3$
v	speed	magnitude of velocity	Table 1.1	m/s
$\vec{v}$	velocity	time rate of change in position	Eq. 2.23	m/s
$\vec{v}_{12}$	relative velocity	velocity of object 2 relative to object 1	Eq. 5.1	m/s
$\vec{v}_{AB}$	relative velocity	velocity of observer B in reference frame of observer A	Eq. 6.3	m/s
v_C	time-dependent potential	time-dependent potential across circuit element C; $V_C(t)$	Sections 32.1, 32.8	V
$\vec{v}_{cm}$	velocity, center of mass	velocity of the center of mass of a system, equal to the velocity of the zero-momentum reference frame of the system	Eq. 6.26	m/s
$\vec{v}_d$	drift velocity	average velocity of electrons in conductor in presence of electric field	Eq. 31.3	m/s
v_{esc}	escape speed	minimum launch speed required for object to reach infinity	Eq. 13.23	m/s
v_r	radial component of velocity	for object moving along circular path, always zero	Eq. 11.18	m/s
v_{rms}	root-mean-square speed	square root of average of square of speed	Eq. 19.21	m/s
v_t	tangential component of velocity	for object in circular motion, rate at which arc length is swept out	Eq. 11.9	m/s
v_x	x component of velocity	component of velocity directed along x axis	Eq. 2.21	m/s
W	work	change in system's energy due to external forces exerted on system	Eqs. 9.1, 10.35	J
$W_{P \to Q}$	work	work done along path from P to Q	Eq. 13.12	J
W_{in}	mechanical input of energy	positive amount of mechanical work done on system	Section 21.1	J
W_{out}	mechanical output of energy	positive amount of mechanical work done by system	Section 21.1	J
W_q	electrostatic work	work done by electrostatic field on charged particle moving through field	Sections 25.2, 25.17	J
X_C	capacitive reactance	ratio of potential difference amplitude to current amplitude for capacitor	Eq. 32.14	Ω
X_L	inductive reactance	ratio of potential difference amplitude to current amplitude for inductor	Eq. 32.26	Ω
x	position	position along x axis	Eq. 2.4	m
$x(t)$	position as function of time	position x at instant t	Section 2.3	m
Δx	x component of displacement	difference between final and initial positions along x axis	Eq. 2.4	m
Δx_F	force displacement	displacement of point of application of a force	Eq. 9.7	m
Z	impedance	(frequency-dependent) ratio of potential difference to current through circuit	Eq. 32.33	Ω
z	zero-momentum reference frame	reference frame in which system of interest has zero momentum	Eq. 6.23	

Math notation

Math notation	Name	Where introduced
$\equiv$	defined as	Eq. 1.3
$\approx$	approximately equal to	Section 1.9
Σ (sigma, upper case)	sum of	Eq. 3.25
$\int$	integral of	Eq. 3.27
$\parallel$	parallel	Section 10.2
$\perp$	perpendicular	Section 10.2
$\propto$	proportional to	Section 13.1
$\cdot$	scalar product of two vectors	Eq. 10.33
$\times$	vector product of two vectors	Eq. 12.35
$\dfrac{\partial f}{\partial x}$	partial derivative of f with respect to x	Eq. 16.47
$\vec{b}$	vector b	Eq. 2.2
$|\vec{b}|$ or b	magnitude of $\vec{b}$	Eq. 2.3
b_x	x component of $\vec{b}$	Eq. 2.2
$\vec{b}_x$	x component vector of $\vec{b}$	Eq. 10.5
$\hat{\imath}$	unit vector ("i hat")	Eq. 2.1
$\hat{r}_{12}$	unit vector ("r hat")	Eq. 22.6

Note concerning superscripts and subscripts

Superscripts are appended to forces and potential energies to indicate the type of force or energy. They may be found in the main list under F, for forces, and U, for potential energies. Uppercase superscripts are used for fundamental interactions.

Subscripts are used on many symbols to identify objects, reference frames, types (for example, of energy), and processes. Object identifiers may be numbers, letters, or groups of letters. Reference frames are indicated by capital letters. Object identifiers and reference frames can occur in pairs, indicating relative quantities. In this case, the main symbol describes a property of whatever is identified by the second subscript relative to that of the first. In the case of forces, the first subscript identifies the object that causes the force and the second identifies the object on which the force is exerted. Types and processes are identified in various ways; many are given in the main list. Here are some examples:

m_1	inertia of object 1
m_{ball}	inertia of ball
$\vec{v}_{cm}$	velocity of center of mass of system

$\vec{r}_{12}$	position of object 2 relative to object 1; $\vec{r}_{12} = \vec{r}_2 - \vec{r}_1$
$\vec{p}_1$	momentum of object 1
$\vec{p}_{Z2}$	momentum of object 2 as measured in zero-momentum reference frame
$\vec{v}_{AB}$	velocity of observer B as measured in reference frame of observer A
$\vec{v}_{Ao}$	velocity of object o as measured in reference frame A
$\vec{r}_{Ee}$	position of event e as measured in Earth reference frame
$\vec{F}^c_{pw}$	contact force exerted by person on wall
$\vec{F}^G_{Eb}$	gravitational force exerted by Earth on ball
E_{th}	thermal energy
K_{conv}	convertible kinetic energy
P_{av}	average power
a_c	centripetal acceleration
$W_{P \to Q}$	work done along path from P to Q

Initial and final conditions are identified by subscripts i and f, following other identifiers. For example:

$\vec{p}_{1i}$	initial momentum of object 1
$\vec{p}_{Zball,f}$	final momentum of ball as measured in zero-momentum reference frame

Italic subscripts are used to identify components of vectors. These include x, y, z, r (radial), t (tangential), and ϑ (angular, with respect to given axis). They are also used to enumerate collections, for example, as indices of summation, and to indicate that a subscript refers to another variable. In the context of optics (Chapter 33), the italic subscripts o and i represent object and image, respectively. Here are some examples:

r_x	x component of position
a_t	tangential component of acceleration
L_ϑ	ϑ component of angular momentum
$p_{Zball\,y,f}$	final y component of momentum of ball as measured in zero-momentum reference frame
$\delta m_n r_n^2$	contribution to rotational inertia of extended object of small segment n, with inertia δm_n at position r_n
c_P	specific heat capacity at constant pressure
W_q	electrostatic work
h_o	height of object
θ_i	angle subtended by image

Appendix B

Mathematics Review

1 Algebra

Factors

$$ax + bx + cx = (a + b + c)x$$
$$(a + b)^2 = a^2 + 2ab + b^2$$
$$(a - b)^2 = a^2 - 2ab + b^2$$
$$(a + b)(a - b) = a^2 - b^2$$

Fractions

$$\left(\frac{a}{b}\right)\left(\frac{c}{d}\right) = \frac{ac}{bd}$$
$$\left(\frac{a/b}{c/d}\right) = \frac{a}{b} \div \frac{c}{d} = \frac{a}{b} \cdot \frac{d}{c} = \frac{ad}{bc}$$
$$\left(\frac{1}{1/a}\right) - a$$

Exponents

$$a^n = \underbrace{a \times a \times a \times \cdots \times a}_{n \text{ factors}}$$

Any real number can be used as an exponent:

$$a^{-x} = \frac{1}{a^x}$$
$$a^0 = 1$$
$$a^1 = a$$
$$a^{1/2} = \sqrt{a}$$
$$a^{1/n} = \sqrt[n]{a}$$
$$a^x a^y = a^{x+y}$$
$$\frac{a^x}{a^y} = a^{x-y}$$
$$(a^x)^y = a^{x \cdot y}$$
$$a^x b^x = (ab)^x$$
$$\frac{a^x}{b^x} = \left(\frac{a}{b}\right)^x$$

Logarithms

Logarithm is the inverse function of the exponential function:

$$y = a^x \Leftrightarrow \log_a y = \log_a a^x = x \quad \text{and} \quad x = \log_a(a^x) = a^{\log_a x}$$

The two most common values for the base a are 10 (the common logarithm base) and e (the natural logarithm base).

$$y = e^x \Leftrightarrow \log_e y = \ln y = \ln e^x = x \quad \text{and} \quad x = \ln e^x = e^{\ln x}$$

Logarithm rules (valid for any base):

$$\ln(ab) = \ln(a) + \ln(b)$$
$$\ln\left(\frac{a}{b}\right) = \ln(a) - \ln(b)$$
$$\ln(a^n) = n \ln(a)$$
$$\ln 1 = 0$$

The expression $\ln(a + b)$ cannot be simplified.

Linear equations

A linear equation has the form $y = ax + b$, where a and b are constants. A graph of y versus x is a straight line. The value of a equals the slope of the line, and the value of b equals the value of y when x equals zero.

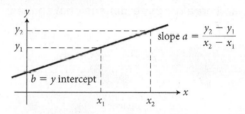

If $a = 0$, the line is horizontal. If $a > 0$, the line rises as x increases. If $a < 0$, the line falls as x increases. For any two values of x, say x_1 and x_2, the slope a can be calculated as

$$a = \frac{y_2 - y_1}{x_2 - x_1}$$

where y_1 and y_2 correspond to x_1 and x_2 (that is to say, $y_1 = ax_1 + b$ and $y_2 = ax_2 + b$).

Proportionality

If y is proportional to x (written $y \propto x$), then $y = ax$, where a is a constant. Proportionality is a subset of linearity. Because $y/x = a = $ constant for any corresponding x and y,

$$\frac{y_1}{x_1} = \frac{y_2}{x_2} \Leftrightarrow \frac{y_1}{y_2} = \frac{x_1}{x_2}.$$

Quadratic equation

The equation $ax^2 + bx + c = 0$ (the quadratic equation) has two solutions (called *roots*) for x:

$$x = \frac{-b \pm \sqrt{b^2 - 4ac}}{2a}.$$

If $b^2 \geq 4ac$, the solutions are real numbers.

2 Geometry

Area and circumference for two-dimensional shapes

rectangle:
area = ab
circumference = $2(a + b)$

paralellogram:
area = bh
circumference = $2(a + b)$

triangle:
area = $\frac{1}{2}bh$
circumference = $a + b + c$

circle:
area = πr^2
circumference = $2\pi r$

Volume and area for three-dimensional shapes

rectangular box:
volume = abc
area = $2(a^2 + b^2 + c^2)$

sphere:
volume = $\frac{4}{3}\pi r^3$
area = $4\pi r^2$

right circular cylinder:
volume = $\pi r^2 \ell$
area = $2\pi r\ell + 2\pi r^2$

right circular cone:
volume = $\frac{1}{3}\pi r^2 h$
area = $\pi r^2 + \pi r\sqrt{r^2 + h^2}$

3 Trigonometry

Angle and arc length

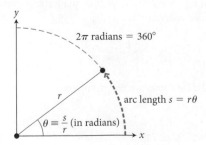

2π radians = $360°$

arc length $s = r\theta$

$\theta \equiv \dfrac{s}{r}$ (in radians)

Right triangles

A right triangle is a triangle in which one of the angles is a right angle:

hypotenuse (side opposite to right angle)

$90° = \pi/2$ radians

Pythagorean theorem: $a^2 + b^2 = c^2 \Leftrightarrow c = \sqrt{a^2 + b^2}$

Trigonometric functions:

$$\sin\theta = \frac{b}{c} = \frac{\text{opposite side}}{\text{hypotenuse}}, \quad \theta = \sin^{-1}\left(\frac{b}{c}\right) = \arcsin\left(\frac{b}{c}\right)$$

$$\cos\theta = \frac{a}{c} = \frac{\text{adjacent side}}{\text{hypotenuse}}, \quad \theta = \cos^{-1}\left(\frac{a}{c}\right) = \arccos\left(\frac{a}{c}\right)$$

$$\tan\theta = \frac{b}{a} = \frac{\text{opposite side}}{\text{adjacent side}}, \quad \theta = \tan^{-1}\left(\frac{b}{a}\right) = \arctan\left(\frac{b}{a}\right)$$

General triangles

For any triangle, the following relationships hold:

$$\alpha + \beta + \gamma = 180° = \pi \text{ rad}$$

Sine law: $\dfrac{\sin\alpha}{a} = \dfrac{\sin\beta}{b} = \dfrac{\sin\gamma}{c}$

Cosine law: $c^2 = a^2 + b^2 - 2ab\cos\gamma$

Identities

$$\tan\theta = \frac{\sin\theta}{\cos\theta}$$

$$\cot\theta = \frac{1}{\tan\theta} = \frac{\cos\theta}{\sin\theta}$$

$$\csc\theta = \frac{1}{\sin\theta}$$

$$\sec\theta = \frac{1}{\cos\theta}$$

Periodicity

$$\cos(\alpha + 2\pi) = \cos\alpha$$

$$\tan(\alpha + \pi) = \sin\alpha$$

Angle addition

$$\sin(\alpha \pm \beta) = \sin\alpha\cos\beta \pm \cos\alpha\sin\beta$$

$$\cos(\alpha \pm \beta) = \cos\alpha\cos\beta \mp \sin\alpha\sin\beta$$

Double angles

$$\sin(2\alpha) = 2\sin\alpha\cos\alpha$$

$$\cos(2\alpha) = \cos^2\alpha - \sin^2\alpha = 1 - 2\sin^2\alpha = 2\cos^2\alpha - 1$$

Other relations

$$\sin^2\alpha + \cos^2\alpha = 1$$

$$\sin(-\alpha) = -\sin\alpha$$

$$\cos(-\alpha) = \cos\alpha$$

$$\sin(\alpha \pm \pi) = -\sin\alpha$$

$$\cos(\alpha \pm \pi) = -\cos\alpha$$

$$\sin(\alpha \pm \pi/2) = \pm\cos\alpha$$

$$\cos(\alpha \pm \pi/2) = \mp\sin\alpha$$

The following graphs show $\sin\theta$, $\cos\theta$, and $\tan\theta$ as functions of θ:

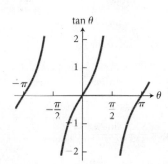

4 Calculus

In this section, x is a variable, and a and n are constants.

Derivatives

Geometrically, the derivative of a function $f(x)$ at $x = x_1$ is the slope of $f(x)$ at x_1:

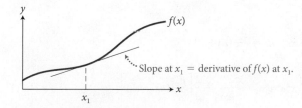

Slope at x_1 = derivative of $f(x)$ at x_1.

Derivatives of common functions

$$\frac{d}{dx}a = 0$$

$$\frac{d}{dx}x^n = nx^{n-1} \text{ (n need not be an integer)}$$

$$\frac{d}{dx}\sin x = \cos x$$

$$\frac{d}{dx}\cos x = -\sin x$$

$$\frac{d}{dx}\tan x = \frac{1}{\cos^2 x}$$

$$\frac{d}{dx}e^{ax} = ae^{ax}$$

$$\frac{d}{dx}\ln(ax) = \frac{1}{x}$$

$$\frac{d}{dx}a^x = a^x\ln a$$

Derivatives of sums, products, and functions of functions

Constant times a function: $\dfrac{d}{dx}[a \cdot f(x)] = a \cdot \dfrac{d}{dx}f(x)$

Sum of functions: $\dfrac{d}{dx}[f(x) + g(x)] = \dfrac{d}{dx}f(x) + \dfrac{d}{dx}g(x)$

Product of functions:

$$\frac{d}{dx}[f(x) \cdot g(x)] = g(x)\frac{d}{dx}f(x) + f(x)\frac{d}{dx}g(x)$$

Quotient of functions: $\dfrac{d}{dx}\left[\dfrac{f(x)}{g(x)}\right] = \dfrac{g(x)\dfrac{d}{dx}f(x) - f(x)\dfrac{d}{dx}g(x)}{[g(x)]^2}$

Functions of functions (the chain rule): If f is a function of u, and u is a function of x, then

$$\frac{d[f(u)]}{du} \cdot \frac{d[u(x)]}{dx} = \frac{d[f(x)]}{dx}$$

Second and higher derivatives The second derivative of a function f with respect to x is the derivative of the derivative:

$$\frac{d^2 f(x)}{dx^2} = \frac{d}{dx}\left(\frac{d}{dx}f(x)\right)$$

Higher derivatives are defined similarly:

$$\frac{d^n f(x)}{dx^n} = \underbrace{\cdots \frac{d}{dx}\left(\frac{d}{dx}\left(\frac{d}{dx}f(x)\right)\right)}_{n \text{ uses of } \frac{d}{dx}} \quad \text{(where n is a positive integer).}$$

Partial derivatives For functions of more than one variable, the partial derivative, written $\dfrac{\partial}{\partial x}$, is the derivative with respect to one variable; all other variables are treated as constants.

Integrals

Indefinite integrals Integration is the reverse of differentiation. An indefinite integral $\int f(x)dx$ is a function whose derivative is $f(x)$.

That is to say, $\dfrac{d}{dx}[\int f(x)dx] = f(x)$.

If $A(x)$ is an indefinite integral of $f(x)$, then so is $A(x) + C$, where C is any constant. Thus, it is customary when evaluating indefinite integrals to add a "constant of integration" C.

Definite integrals The definite integral of $f(x)$, written as $\int_{x1}^{x2} f(x)dx$, represents the sum of the area of contiguous rectangles that each intersect $f(x)$ at some point along one base and that each have another base coincident with the x axis over some part of the range between x_1 and x_2; the indefinite integral evaluates the sum in the limit of arbitrarily small rectangle bases. In other words, the indefinite integral gives the net area that lies under $f(x)$ but above the x axis between the boundaries x_1 and x_2.

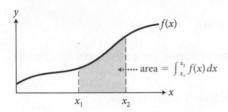

If $A(x)$ is any indefinite integral of $f(x)$, then the definite integral is given by $\int_{x1}^{x2} f(x)dx = A(x_2) - A(x_1) \equiv A(x)|_{x_1}^{x_2}$. The constant of integration C does not affect the value of definite integrals and thus can be ignored (i.e., set to zero) during evaluation.

Integration by parts $\int_a^b u\,dv$ is the area under the curve of $u(v)$. If $\int_a^b u\,dv$ is difficult to evaluate directly, it is sometimes easier to express the area under the curve as the area within part of a rectangle minus the area under the curve of $v(u)$. In other words:

$$\int_a^b u\,dv = uv\Big|_a^b - \int_a^b v\,du.$$

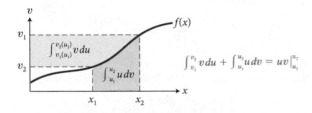

$$\int_{v_1}^{v_2} v\,du + \int_{u_1}^{u_2} u\,dv = uv\Big|_{u_1}^{u_2}$$

By choosing u and dv appropriately (both can be functions of x), this approach, called "integration by parts", can transform difficult integrals into easier ones.

Table of integrals In the following expressions, a and b are constants. An arbitrary constant of integration C can be added to the right-hand side.

$$\int x^n dx = \frac{1}{n+1} x^{n+1} \text{ (for } n \neq -1)$$

$$\int x^{-1} dx = \ln|x|$$

$$\int \frac{1}{a^2 + x^2} dx = \frac{1}{a} \tan^{-1} \frac{x}{a}$$

$$\int \frac{1}{(a^2 + x^2)^2} dx = \frac{1}{2a^3} \tan^{-1} \frac{x}{a} + \frac{x}{2a^2(x^2 + a^2)}$$

$$\int \frac{1}{\sqrt{\pm a^2 + x^2}} dx = \ln|x + \sqrt{\pm a^2 + x^2}|$$

$$\int \frac{1}{\sqrt{a^2 - x^2}} dx = \sin^{-1} \frac{x}{|a|} = \tan^{-1} \frac{x}{\sqrt{a^2 - x^2}}$$

$$\int \frac{x}{\sqrt{\pm a^2 - x^2}} dx = -\sqrt{\pm a^2 - x^2}$$

$$\int \frac{x}{\sqrt{\pm a^2 + x^2}} dx = \sqrt{\pm a^2 + x^2}$$

$$\int \frac{1}{(\pm a^2 + x^2)^{3/2}} dx = \frac{\pm x}{a^2 \sqrt{\pm a^2 + x^2}}$$

$$\int \frac{x}{(a^2 + x^2)^{3/2}} dx = -\frac{1}{\sqrt{a^2 + x^2}}$$

$$\int \frac{1}{a + bx} dx = \frac{1}{b} \ln(a + bx)$$

$$\int \frac{1}{(a + bx)^2} dx = -\frac{1}{b(a + bx)}$$

$$\int \sin(ax) dx = -\frac{1}{a} \cos(ax)$$

$$\int \cos(ax) dx = \frac{1}{a} \sin(ax)$$

$$\int \tan(ax) dx = -\frac{1}{a} \ln(\cos ax)$$

$$\int \sin^2(ax) dx = \frac{x}{2} - \frac{\sin 2ax}{4a}$$

$$\int \cos^2(ax) dx = \frac{x}{2} + \frac{\sin 2ax}{4a}$$

$$\int x \sin(ax) dx = \frac{1}{a^2} \sin ax - \frac{1}{a} x \cos ax$$

$$\int x \cos(ax) dx = \frac{1}{a^2} \cos ax + \frac{1}{a} x \sin ax$$

$$\int e^{ax} dx = \frac{1}{a} e^{ax}$$

$$\int x e^{ax} dx = \frac{e^{ax}}{a^2} (ax - 1)$$

$$\int x^2 e^{ax} dx = \frac{x^2 e^{ax}}{a} - \frac{2}{a} \left[\frac{e^{ax}}{a^2} (ax - 1) \right]$$

$$\int \ln ax\, dx = x \ln(ax) - x$$

$$\int_0^\infty x^n e^{-ax} dx = \frac{n!}{a^{n+1}}$$

$$\int_0^\infty e^{-ax^2} dx = \frac{1}{2} \sqrt{\frac{\pi}{a}}$$

5 Vector algebra

A vector $\vec{A}$ in three-dimensional space can be written in terms of magnitudes A_x, A_y, and A_z of unit vectors $\hat{\imath}$, $\hat{\jmath}$, and $\hat{k}$, which have length 1 and lie along the x, y, and z axes:

$$\vec{A} = A_x\hat{\imath} + A_y\hat{\jmath} + A_z\hat{k}$$

Dot products between vectors produce scalars:

$$\vec{A} \cdot \vec{B} = A_xB_x + A_yB_y + A_zB_z = |A||B|\cos\theta$$
$$(\theta \text{ is the angle between vectors } \vec{A} \text{ and } \vec{B})$$

Cross products between vectors produce vectors:

$$\vec{A} \times \vec{B} = (A_yB_z - A_zB_y)\hat{\imath} + (A_zB_x - A_xB_z)\hat{\jmath} + (A_xB_y - A_yB_x)\hat{k}$$

$$|\vec{A} \times \vec{B}| = |\vec{A}||\vec{B}|\sin\theta \ (\theta \text{ is the angle between vectors } \vec{A} \text{ and } \vec{B})$$

The direction of $\vec{A} \times \vec{B}$ is given by the right-hand rule (see Figure 12.44).

6 Complex numbers

A complex number $z = x + iy$ is defined in terms of its real part x and its imaginary part y. Both x and y are real numbers. i is Euler's constant, defined by the property $i^2 = -1$.

Each complex number z has a "complex conjugate" z^* which has the same real part but an imaginary part with opposite sign: $z = x + iy \Leftrightarrow z^* = x - iy$.

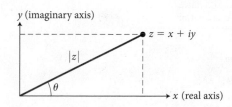

The real and imaginary parts can be expressed in terms of the complex number and its conjugate:

$$x = \tfrac{1}{2}(z + z^*)$$
$$y = \tfrac{1}{2}i(z - z^*)$$

A complex number is like a two-dimensional vector in a plane with a real axis and an imaginary axis. Thus, z can be described by a magnitude or length $|z|$ and an angle θ formed with the real axis (called the "phase angle"):

$$z = |z|(\cos\theta + i\sin\theta), \text{ where } |z| = \sqrt{zz^*} \text{ and}$$

$$\theta = \tan^{-1}\frac{y}{x} = \tan^{-1}\frac{i(z - z^*)}{(z + z^*)}.$$

Euler's formula says that $e^{i\theta} = \cos\theta + i\sin\theta$, allowing complex numbers to be written in the form $z = |z|e^{i\theta}$. This is a convenient form for expressing complex numbers. For example, it is easy to raise a complex number z to a power n: $z^n = |z|^n e^{in\theta}$.

7 Useful approximations

Binomial expansion

$$(1 + x)^n = 1 + nx + \frac{n(n - 1)}{2}x^2 + \cdots$$

If $x \ll 1$, then $(1 + x)^n \approx 1 + nx$

Trigonometric expansions

$$\sin\alpha = \alpha - \frac{\alpha^3}{3!} + \frac{\alpha^5}{5!} - \frac{\alpha^7}{7!} + \cdots \ (\alpha \text{ in rad})$$

$$\cos\alpha = 1 - \frac{\alpha^2}{2!} + \frac{\alpha^4}{4!} - \frac{\alpha^6}{6!} + \cdots \ (\alpha \text{ in rad})$$

$$\tan\alpha = \alpha + \frac{1}{3}\alpha^3 + \frac{2}{15}\alpha^5 + \frac{17}{315}\alpha^7 + \cdots \ (\alpha \text{ in rad})$$

If $\alpha \ll 1$ rad, then $\sin\alpha \approx \alpha$, $\cos\alpha \approx 1$, and $\tan\alpha \approx \alpha$.

Other useful expansions

$$\frac{1}{1 - x} = 1 + x + x^2 + x^3 + \cdots \text{ for } -1 < x < 1$$

$$e^x = 1 + x + \frac{1}{2}x^2 + \frac{1}{6}x^3 + \frac{1}{24}x^4 + \cdots$$

$$\ln(1 + x) = x - \frac{1}{2}x^2 + \frac{1}{3}x^3 - \frac{1}{4}x^4 + \cdots \quad \text{for } -1 < x < 1$$

$$\ln\left(\frac{1 + x}{1 - x}\right) = 2x + \frac{2}{3}x^3 + \frac{2}{5}x^5 - \frac{2}{7}x^7 + \cdots \text{ for } -1 < x < 1$$

Appendix C

SI Units, Useful Data, and Unit Conversion Factors

The seven base SI units

Unit	Abbreviation	Physical quantity
meter	m	length
kilogram	kg	mass
second	s	time
ampere	A	electric current
kelvin	K	thermodynamic temperature
mole	mol	amount of substance
candela	cd	luminous intensity

Some derived SI units

Unit	Abbreviation	Physical quantity	In terms of base units
newton	N	force	$kg \cdot m/s^2$
joule	J	energy	$kg \cdot m^2/s^2$
watt	W	power	$kg \cdot m^2/s^3$
pascal	Pa	pressure	$kg/m \cdot s^2$
hertz	Hz	frequency	s^{-1}
coulomb	C	electric charge	$A \cdot s$
volt	V	electric potential	$kg \cdot m^2/(A \cdot s^3)$
ohm	Ω	electric resistance	$kg \cdot m^2/(A^2 \cdot s^3)$
farad	F	capacitance	$A^2 \cdot s^4/(kg \cdot m^2)$
tesla	T	magnetic field	$kg/(A \cdot s^2)$
weber	Wb	magnetic flux	$kg \cdot m^2/(A \cdot s^2)$
henry	H	inductance	$kg \cdot m^2/(A^2 \cdot s^2)$

SI Prefixes

10^n	Prefix	Abbreviation	10^n	Prefix	Abbreviation
10^0	—	—			
10^3	kilo-	k	10^{-3}	milli-	m
10^6	mega-	M	10^{-6}	micro-	μ
10^9	giga-	G	10^{-9}	nano-	n
10^{12}	tera-	T	10^{-12}	pico-	p
10^{15}	peta-	P	10^{-15}	femto-	f
10^{18}	exa-	E	10^{-18}	atto-	a
10^{21}	zetta-	Z	10^{-21}	zepto-	z
10^{24}	yotta-	Y	10^{-24}	yocto-	y

Values of fundamental constants

Quantity	Symbol	Value
Speed of light in vacuum	c_0	3.00×10^8 m/s
Gravitational constant	G	6.6738×10^{-11} N·m²/kg²
Avogadro's number	N_A	6.0221413×10^{23} mol⁻¹
Boltzmann's constant	k_B	1.380×10^{-23} J/K
Charge on electron	e	1.60×10^{-19} C
Permittivity constant	ϵ_0	$8.85418782 \times 10^{-12}$ C²/(N·m²)
Permeability constant	μ_0	$4\pi \times 10^{-7}$ T·m/A
Planck's constant	h	6.626×10^{-34} J·s
Electron mass	m_e	9.11×10^{-31} kg
Proton mass	m_p	1.6726×10^{-27} kg
Neutron mass	m_n	1.6749×10^{-27} kg
Atomic mass unit	amu	1.6605×10^{-27} kg

Other useful numbers

Number or quantity	Value
π	3.1415927
e	2.7182818
1 radian	57.2957795°
Absolute zero ($T = 0$)	-273.15 °C
Average acceleration g due to gravity near Earth's surface	9.8 m/s²
Speed of sound in air at 20 °C	343 m/s
Density of dry air at atmospheric pressure and 20 °C	1.29 kg/m³
Earth's mass	5.97×10^{24} kg
Earth's radius (mean)	6.38×10^6 m
Earth–Moon distance (mean)	3.84×10^8 m

Unit conversion factors

Length

1 in. = 2.54 cm (defined)

1 cm = 0.3937 in.

1 ft = 30.48 cm

1 m = 39.37 in. = 3.281 ft

1 mi = 5280 ft = 1.609 km

1 km = 0.6214 mi

1 nautical mile (U.S.) = 1.151 mi = 6076 ft = 1.852 km

1 fermi = 1 femtometer (fm) = 10^{-15} m

1 angstrom (Å) = 10^{-10} m = 0.1 nm

1 light − year (ly) = 9.461×10^{15} m

1 parsec = 3.26 ly = 3.09×10^{16} m

Volume

1 liter (L) = 1000 mL = 1000 cm^3 = 1.0×10^{-3} m^3
        = 1.057 qt (U.S.) = 61.02 in.^{3}

1 gal (U.S.) = 4 qt (U.S.) = 231 in.^{3} = 3.785 L = 0.8327 gal (British)

1 quart (U.S.) = 2 pints (U.S.) = 946 mL

1 pint (British) = 1.20 pints (U.S.) = 568 mL

1 m^3 = 35.31 ft^3

Speed

1 mi/h = 1.4667 ft/s = 1.6093 km/h = 0.4470 m/s

1 km/h = 0.2778 m/s = 0.6214 mi/h

1 ft/s = 0.3048 m/s = 0.6818 mi/h = 1.0973 km/h

1 m/s = 3.281 ft/s = 3.600 km/h = 2.237 mi/h

1 knot = 1.151 mi/h = 0.5144 m/s

Angle

1 radian (rad) = 57.30° = 57°18′

1° = 0.01745 rad

1 rev/min (rpm) = 0.1047 rad/s

Time

1 day = 8.640×10^4 s

1 year = 365.242 days = 3.156×10^7 s

Mass

1 atomic mass unit (u) = 1.6605×10^{-27} kg

1 kg = 0.06852 slug

1 metric ton = 1000 kg

1 long ton = 2240 lbs = 1016 kg

1 short ton = 2000 lbs = 909.1 kg

1 kg has a weight of 2.20 lb where g = 9.80 m/s^2

Force

1 lb = 4.44822 N

1 N = 10^5 dyne = 0.2248 lb

Energy and work

1 J = 10^7 ergs = 0.7376 ft · lb

1 ft · lb = 1.356 J = 1.29×10^{-3} Btu = 3.24×10^{-4} kcal

1 kcal = 4.19×10^3 J = 3.97 Btu

1 eV = 1.6022×10^{-19} J

1 kWh = 3.600×10^6 J = 860 kcal

1 Btu = 1.056×10^3 J

Power

1 W = 1 J/s = 0.7376 ft · lb/s = 3.41 Btu/h

1 hp = 550 ft · lb/s = 746 W

1 kWh/day = 41.667 W

Pressure

1 atm = 1.01325 bar = 1.01325×10^5 N/m^2 = 14.7 lb/in.^{2} = 760 torr

1 lb/in.^{2} = 6.895×10^3 N/m^2

1 Pa = 1 N/m^2 = 1.450×10^{-4} lb/in.^{2}

Periodic Table of the Elements

Average atomic mass in g/mol.
For elements having no stable isotope, value in parentheses is approximate atomic mass of longest-lived isotope.

Number of protons → 29
Symbol for element → **Cu**
63.545

Group	1	2	3	4	5	6	7	8	9	10	11	12	13	14	15	16	17	18
Period 1	1 **H** 1.008																	2 **He** 4.003
Period 2	3 **Li** 6.941	4 **Be** 9.012											5 **B** 10.811	6 **C** 12.011	7 **N** 14.007	8 **O** 15.999	9 **F** 18.998	10 **Ne** 20.180
Period 3	11 **Na** 22.990	12 **Mg** 24.305											13 **Al** 26.982	14 **Si** 28.086	15 **P** 30.974	16 **S** 32.065	17 **Cl** 35.453	18 **Ar** 39.948
Period 4	19 **K** 39.098	20 **Ca** 40.078	21 **Sc** 44.956	22 **Ti** 47.867	23 **V** 50.942	24 **Cr** 51.996	25 **Mn** 54.938	26 **Fe** 55.845	27 **Co** 58.933	28 **Ni** 58.693	29 **Cu** 63.546	30 **Zn** 65.409	31 **Ga** 69.723	32 **Ge** 72.64	33 **As** 74.922	34 **Se** 78.96	35 **Br** 79.904	36 **Kr** 83.798
Period 5	37 **Rb** 85.468	38 **Sr** 87.62	39 **Y** 88.906	40 **Zr** 91.224	41 **Nb** 92.906	42 **Mo** 95.94	43 **Tc** (98)	44 **Ru** 101.07	45 **Rh** 102.906	46 **Pd** 106.42	47 **Ag** 107.868	48 **Cd** 112.411	49 **In** 114.818	50 **Sn** 118.710	51 **Sb** 121.760	52 **Te** 127.60	53 **I** 126.904	54 **Xe** 131.293
Period 6	55 **Cs** 132.905	56 **Ba** 137.327	71 **Lu** 174.967	72 **Hf** 178.49	73 **Ta** 180.948	74 **W** 183.84	75 **Re** 186.207	76 **Os** 190.23	77 **Ir** 192.217	78 **Pt** 195.078	79 **Au** 196.967	80 **Hg** 200.59	81 **Tl** 204.383	82 **Pb** 207.2	83 **Bi** 208.980	84 **Po** (209)	85 **At** (210)	86 **Rn** (222)
Period 7	87 **Fr** (223)	88 **Ra** (226)	103 **Lr** (262)	104 **Rf** (261)	105 **Db** (262)	106 **Sg** (266)	107 **Bh** (264)	108 **Hs** (269)	109 **Mt** (268)	110 **Ds** (271)	111 **Rg** (272)	112 **Uub** (285)	113 **Uut** (284)	114 **Uuq** (289)	115 **Uup** (288)	116 **Uuh** (292)	117 **Uus** (294)	118 **Uuo**

Lanthanoids

| 57 **La** 138.905 | 58 **Ce** 140.116 | 59 **Pr** 140.908 | 60 **Nd** 144.24 | 61 **Pm** (145) | 62 **Sm** 150.36 | 63 **Eu** 151.964 | 64 **Gd** 157.25 | 65 **Tb** 158.925 | 66 **Dy** 152.500 | 67 **Ho** 164.930 | 68 **Er** 167.259 | 69 **Tm** 168.934 | 70 **Yb** 173.04 |

Actinoids

| 89 **Ac** (227) | 90 **Th** (232) | 91 **Pa** (231) | 92 **U** (238) | 93 **Np** (237) | 94 **Pu** (244) | 95 **Am** (243) | 96 **Cm** (247) | 97 **Bk** (247) | 98 **Cf** (251) | 99 **Es** (252) | 100 **Fm** (257) | 101 **Md** (258) | 102 **No** (259) |

Appendix D

Center of Mass of Extended Objects

We can apply the concept of center of mass to extended objects. Consider, for example, the object of inertia m in **Figure D.1**. If you imagine breaking down the object into many small segments of equal inertia δm, you can use Eq. 6.24 to compute the position of the center of mass:

$$x_{cm} = \frac{\delta m_1 x_1 + \delta m_2 x_2 + \cdots}{\delta m_1 + \delta m_2 + \cdots},$$ (D.1)

object divided into segments of equal inertia δm

Figure D.1

where x_n is the position of segment δm_n. Because the sum of the inertias of all segments is equal to the inertia m of the extended object, $\delta m_1 + \delta m_2 + \cdots = m$, we can write Eq. D.1 as

$$x_{cm} = \frac{1}{m}(\delta m_1 x_1 + \delta m_2 x_2 + \cdots) = \frac{1}{m}\sum_n (\delta m_n x_n)$$ (D.2)

To evaluate this sum for the extended object, we take the limit of this expression as $\delta m \to 0$. In this limit, the sum becomes an integral:

$$x_{cm} = \frac{1}{m}\lim_{\delta m \to 0}\sum_n (\delta m_n x_n) \equiv \frac{1}{m}\int_{\text{object}} x\, dm.$$ (D.3)

To evaluate the integral we need to know how the inertia is distributed over the object. Let the *inertia per unit length* of the object be $\lambda \equiv dm/dx$. In general λ is a function of position—that is, the inertia per unit length need not be the same at different locations along the object—and so $\lambda = \lambda(x)$ and $dm = \lambda(x)dx$. Substituting this expression for dm into Eq. D.3, we obtain

$$x_{cm} = \frac{1}{m}\int_{\text{object}} x\lambda(x)dx.$$ (D.4)

In this expression, the limits of integration should be taken to be the positions of the left and right ends of the object (x_L and x_R, respectively).

For example, let the object in Figure D.1 have a uniformly distributed inertia so that $\lambda(x)$ has the same value (the inertia of the extended object divided by the length of the object) everywhere:

$$\lambda(x) = \frac{m}{x_R - x_L}.$$ (D.5)

Because $\lambda(x)$ does not depend on x, we can pull it out of the integral in Eq. D.4 and so, substituting Eq. D.5 into Eq. D.4, we get

$$x_{cm} = \frac{\lambda(x)}{m}\int_{x_L}^{x_R} x\, dx = \frac{1}{x_R - x_L}\int_{x_L}^{x_R} x\, dx = \frac{1}{x_R - x_L}\left[\tfrac{1}{2}x^2\right]_{x_L}^{x_R}$$

$$= \frac{x_R^2 - x_L^2}{2(x_R - x_L)} = \frac{x_R + x_L}{2}.$$ (D.6)

In other words, the center of mass of the object is halfway between the ends of the object (at the center of the object), as we expect.

Appendix E

Derivation of the Lorentz Transformation Equations

In this appendix we derive the Lorentz transformation equations (Eqs. 14.29–14.32), which relate position and time in two reference frames A and B. The origins of the reference frames coincide at $t_A = t_B = 0$, and the frames are moving at constant velocity $\vec{v}_{AB} = v_{ABx}\hat{\imath}$ in the x direction relative to each other (Figure E.1a).

Consider an event e that occurs at instant t_{Ae} and position x_{Ae} in reference frame A (Figure E.1b).[*] Our goal is to express t_{Be} and x_{Be}, the instant and the position at which the event occurs in reference frame B, in terms of t_{Ae} and x_{Ae}:

$$t_{Be} = f(x_{Ae}, t_{Ae}) \tag{E.1}$$

$$x_{Be} = g(x_{Ae}, t_{Ae}). \tag{E.2}$$

To obtain these relationships, we consider the space-time interval (Eq. 14.18) between the event in Figure E.1b and the event in Figure E.1a (this event being the overlapping of the two origins). The spatial separation of these two events is $\Delta x_{Ae} = x_{Ae} - 0 = x_{Ae}$ in reference frame A and $\Delta x_{Be} = x_{Be} - 0 = x_{Be}$ in reference frame B. The temporal separations are $\Delta t_{Ae} = t_{Ae} - 0 = t_{Ae}$ and $\Delta t_{Be} = t_{Be} - 0 = t_{Be}$. Because the space-time interval is an invariant, we have

$$(c_0 t_{Be})^2 - (x_{Be})^2 = (c_0 t_{Ae})^2 - (x_{Ae})^2. \tag{E.3}$$

To satisfy Eq. E.3, the relationships expressed in Eqs. E.1 and E.2 must be linear:

$$t_{Be} = D t_{Ae} + E x_{Ae} \tag{E.4}$$

$$x_{Be} = F t_{Ae} + G x_{Ae}, \tag{E.5}$$

where D, E, F, G are constants. To obtain relationships between these constants, consider the position of the origin of reference frame B at the instant illustrated in Figure E.1b. The origin of reference frame B moves at constant velocity $\vec{v}_{AB}$ relative to reference frame A, and so at t_{Ae} the position of B's origin in reference frame A is

$$x_{AB} = v_{ABx} t_{Ae}. \tag{E.6}$$

The position of B's origin in reference frame B is always zero, $x_{BB} = 0$.[†] According to Eq. E.5 we then have $x_{BB} = 0 = F t_{Ae} + G x_{AB}$, or substituting for x_{AB} from Eq. E.6, $0 = F t_{Ae} + G(v_{ABx} t_{Ae})$. Therefore

$$F = -v_{ABx} G. \tag{E.7}$$

Conversely, the origin of reference frame A is located at $x_{BA} = -v_{ABx} t_{Be}$ in reference frame B, and so, with $x_{AA} = 0$, Eqs. E.4 and E.5 become

$$t_{Be} = D t_{Ae} + 0 \tag{E.8}$$

$$-v_{ABx} t_{Be} = F t_{Ae} + 0. \tag{E.9}$$

Solving Eqs. E.8 and E.9 for F gives $F = -v_{ABx} D$, and so, from Eq. E.7,

$$D = G. \tag{E.10}$$

[*] Remember our subscript format: The capital letter refers to the reference frame; the lower case e is for "event." Thus the vector $\vec{r}_{Ae}$ represents observer **A**'s measurement of the position at which the event occurs.

[†] Do not be stymied by the unfamiliar subscript BB. It's the same format we've been using all along: The first B tells you the reference frame in which the measurement is made, the second B tells you what's being measured—in this case, the position of the origin of reference frame B.

(a)

$t_A = t_B = 0$

$z_A = z_B$

$\vec{v}_{AB}$

$x_A = x_B$

Reference frames A and B overlap at $t_A = t_B = 0$.

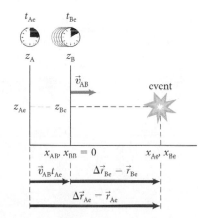

(b)

t_{Ae} t_{Be}

z_A z_B

$\vec{v}_{AB}$ event

z_{Ae} z_{Be}

$x_{AB}, x_{BB} = 0$ x_{Ae}, x_{Be}

$\vec{v}_{AB} t_{Ae}$ $\Delta\vec{r}_{Be} - \vec{r}_{Be}$

$\Delta\vec{r}_{Ae} - \vec{r}_{Ae}$

Figure E.1 Determining the space and time coordinates of an event from two reference frames that overlap at $t_A = t_B = 0$.

Equations E.4 and E.5 then become

$$t_{Be} = Gt_{Ae} + Ex_{Ae} \tag{E.11}$$

$$x_{Be} = -v_{ABx}Gt_{Ae} + Gx_{Ae}. \tag{E.12}$$

Substituting Eqs. E.11 and E.12 into the left side of Eq. E.3 and using $v_{ABx}^2 = v^2$ yields

$$c_0^2 G^2 \left(1 - \frac{v^2}{c_0^2}\right)t_{Ae}^2 + (c_0^2 EG + G^2 v_{ABx})2t_{Ae}x_{Ae} - (G^2 - c_0^2 E^2)x_{Ae}^2$$

$$= (c_0 t_{Ae})^2 - (x_{Ae})^2, \tag{E.13}$$

and then gather all the $(t_{Ae})^2$ terms, all the $x_{Ae}\,t_{Ae}$ terms, and all the $(t_{Ae})^2$ terms:

$$\left[c_0^2 G^2 \left(1 - \frac{v^2}{c_0^2}\right) - c_0^2\right]t_{Ae}^2 + 2(c_0^2 EG + G^2 v_{ABx})x_{Ae}t_{Ae}$$

$$- (G^2 - c_0^2 E^2 - 1)x_{Ae}^2 = 0. \tag{E.14}$$

Because Eq. E.14 must hold for any value of t_{Ae} and x_{Ae}, the coefficient of each term must be zero. The coefficient of the t_{Ae}^2 term yields

$$c_0^2 G^2 \left(1 - \frac{v^2}{c_0^2}\right) = c_0^2. \tag{E.15}$$

Solving Eq. E.15 for G yields

$$G = \left(1 - \frac{v^2}{c_0^2}\right)^{-1/2} \equiv \gamma, \tag{E.16}$$

and so from Eq. E.7, $F = -v_{ABx}G$, we see that $F = -\gamma v_{ABx}$.

The coefficient of the $x_{Ae}t_{Ae}$ term in Eq. E.14 must also be zero. Substituting γ for G in that coefficient gives us

$$c_0^2 E\gamma + \gamma^2 v_{ABx} = 0 \tag{E.17}$$

$$E = -\gamma v_{ABx}/c_0^2. \tag{E.18}$$

Now we are ready to substitute for D, E, F, G in Eqs. E.4 and E.5—D from Eq. E.10, E from Eq. E.18, F from Eq. E.7, G from Eq. E.16:

$$t_{Be} = \gamma\left(t_{Ae} - \frac{1}{c_0^2}v_{ABx}x_{Ae}\right) \tag{E.19}$$

$$x_{Be} = \gamma(x_{Ae} - v_{ABx}t_{Ae}). \tag{E.20}$$

Because there is no length contraction in the directions perpendicular to the relative velocity $\vec{v}_{AB}$ of the two reference frames, we have

$$y_{Be} = y_{Ae} \tag{E.21}$$

$$z_{Be} = z_{Ae}. \tag{E.22}$$

Equations E.19–E.22 are the Lorentz transformation equations we wanted to derive.

Velocities in two reference frames

We can use Eqs. E.19 and E.20 to derive Eq. 14.33, the relationship between the x components of the velocities of an object o measured in two reference frames A and B. Let the x component be $v_{Aox} = dx_{Ao}/dt_A$ in reference frame A and $v_{Box} = dx_{Bo}/dt_B$ in reference frame B. We begin by writing Eqs. E.19 and E.20 in differential form:

$$dt_B = \gamma\left(dt_A - \frac{v_{ABx}}{c_0^2}dx_{Ao}\right) \tag{E.23}$$

$$dx_{Bo} = \gamma(dx_{Ao} - v_{ABx}dt_A), \tag{E.24}$$

$$dy_{Bo} = dy_{Ao}, \tag{E.25}$$

$$dz_{Bo} = dz_{Ao}, \tag{E.26}$$

where we have replaced the subscript e by o because we are considering an object rather than an event. Dividing Eq. E.24 by Eq. E.23 yields an expression for the x component of the velocity in reference frame B:

$$v_{Box} = \frac{dx_{Bo}}{dt_B} = \frac{\gamma(dx_{Ao} - v_{ABx}dt_A)}{\gamma\left(dt_A - \dfrac{v_{ABx}}{c_0^2}dx_{Ao}\right)} = \frac{(dx_{Ao} - v_{ABx}dt_A)}{\left(dt_A - \dfrac{v_{ABx}}{c_0^2}dx_{Ao}\right)}. \tag{E.27}$$

Finally, we divide the numerator and denominator of the rightmost term by dt_A to obtain Eq. 14.33:

$$v_{Box} = \frac{\left(\dfrac{dx_{Ao}}{dt_A} - v_{ABx}\right)}{\left(1 - \dfrac{v_{ABx}}{c_0^2}\dfrac{dx_{Ao}}{dt_A}\right)} = \frac{(v_{Aox} - v_{ABx})}{\left(1 - \dfrac{v_{ABx}}{c_0^2}v_{Aox}\right)}. \tag{E.28}$$

To find the y component of the velocity in reference frame B, we divide Eq. E.25 by Eq. E.23:

$$v_{Boy} = \frac{dy_{Bo}}{dt_B} = \frac{dy_{Ao}}{\gamma\left(dt_A - \dfrac{v_{ABx}}{c_0^2}dx_{Ao}\right)}. \tag{E.29}$$

Dividing numerator and denominator by dt_A then yields

$$v_{Boy} = \frac{v_{Aoy}}{\gamma\left(1 - \dfrac{v_{ABx}v_{Aox}}{c_0^2}\right)}. \tag{E.30}$$

For the z component of the velocity we obtain a similar equation with y replaced by z

$$v_{Boz} = \frac{v_{Aoz}}{\gamma\left(1 - \dfrac{v_{ABx}v_{Aox}}{c_0^2}\right)}. \tag{E.31}$$

$$\Delta p_{sx} = +0.38 \text{ kg} \cdot \text{m/s} - 0$$

Solutions to Checkpoints

Chapter 1

1.1 A nickel and a quarter. If you had to think about this for more than a few seconds, you probably unknowingly assumed that *neither* coin could be a nickel. This is an example of a hidden assumption.

1.2 That the player works with the new batteries does not necessarily mean the old batteries are dead. They could have been inserted incorrectly, or there could have been a bad contact that got fixed when the new batteries were inserted. That the player does not work with the new batteries does not necessarily mean the player is broken. Both the new and the old batteries could be inserted incorrectly, or both the new and the old batteries could be dead.

1.3 Two valuable goals are to become a better problem solver and to learn to apply the scientific method to any type of reasoning. Either skill is useful in any type of career. If you wrote "pass physics requirement" or "get into medical school," think again. With those goals, it is going to very difficult for you to derive much satisfaction or benefit from this course.

Here are some interesting responses I have collected over the years: to become a responsible citizen of the world, to understand modern technology; to bridge the gap between the sciences and the arts/humanities, to sharpen my mind.

1.4 Likely answers are that something about the case or cap has changed. The case opening may have expanded due to the heat, or the cap may have acquired a dent that prevents it from fitting over the opening. If you answered something along these lines, you assumed symmetry with respect to translation in both time and space: If the cap fits at home, it ought to fit elsewhere now and anytime in the future.

1.5 The distance from the North Pole to the equator is one-fourth of Earth's circumference c, which means $c = 4 \times (10{,}000{,}000 \text{ m}) = 40{,}000{,}000$ m. Because $c = 2\pi R_E$, where R_E is Earth's radius, you have $R_E = c/2\pi = (40{,}000{,}000 \text{ m})/2\pi = 6{,}400{,}000$ m.

1.6 The diameter of an atom is 10^{-10} m (see Figure 1.9); the diameter of an apple is about 10^{-1} m. Therefore the required magnification factor is $(10^{-1} \text{ m})/(10^{-10} \text{ m}) = 10^9$. With this magnification, the apple's diameter would be $10^9(10^{-1} \text{ m}) = 10^8$ m, which is about 10 times Earth's diameter.

1.7 (*a*) (*i*) Somebody switches the power off; the light bulb burns out. (*ii*) Thunder; tractor trailer passing dorm; stomach growling; dorm starting to collapse. (*iii*) You spent all the money in your account; you forgot to deposit the check your parents sent you last week; the bank made a mistake. (*b*) No. All these causes occur before the event. (*c*) One emotion you almost certainly experience is anxiety. Such events tend to be unsettling—we want to know the causes of things we observe.

1.8 A typical physics class lasts about 1 h, which is 3600 s, or order of magnitude 10^4 s. The number of sequential chemical reactions is thus $(10^4 \text{ s})(1 \text{ reaction}/10^{-13} \text{ s}) = 10^{17}$ (hundred million billion!) reactions.

1.9 Because Mike Masters imposes the most constraints, you begin by placing him in seat 1 (Figure S1.9). To satisfy the constraint of having men and women alternate, placing Mike here means the odd-numbered seats are for the men. Only two arrangements avoid putting Cyndi Ahlers next to Mike: Put her in 4 or in 6. If you put Cyndi in 4, Sylvia Masters has to go in 6 to avoid being next to her husband in 1. With Sylvia in 6, John Jones cannot be in 5 or 7, and so you have to put him in 3. Mary Jones then has to go in 8. The remaining empty seats—2, 5, and 7—leave you no choice: Bob Ahlers has to go in 7 because putting him in 5 would have him next to his wife in 4, and your spouse and you get 2 and 5. (Had you put Cyndi Ahlers in 6, you would have obtained the mirror image of the arrangement shown in Figure S1.9.)

Figure S1.9

1.10 90 m. If you call the distance from the west end of the corridor to stop 1 x, the distance from stop 1 to the fountain is $2x$ (Figure S1.10). If you call the distance from stop 2 to the fountain $2y$, the distance from stop 2 to the east end of the corridor is y. Because the distance between the two stops is 60 m, you know that $2x + 2y = 60$ m. From the figure, you see that the total corridor length L is $L = x + 2x + 2y + y = 3x + 3y$. The rest is algebra: $2x + 2y = 60$ m, $x = (30 \text{ m} - y)$, $L = 3(30 \text{ m} - y) + 3y = 90$ m.

Figure S1.10

1.11 (a) $\ell = 150$ Mm (megameters) or 0.15 Gm (gigameters). (b) $t = 12$ ps (picoseconds). (c) 1.2 Mm/s. (d) 2.3 Mg.

1.12 The ratio on the left has inches in the numerator and millimeters in the denominator, meaning that the inches don't cancel out. In general, when converting from a given unit to a desired unit, you need to use a ratio that has the desired unit in the numerator and the given unit in the denominator.

1.13 (a) In 1 mol you have 6.022×10^{23} atoms, and when you pack this number of atoms into a cube, each side of the cube contains $\sqrt[3]{6.022 \times 10^{23}}$ atoms $= 8.445 \times 10^7$ atoms. The diameter of each atom is 10^{-10} m (see Figure S1.9), and so the length of each side of the cube is $(8.445 \times 10^7 \text{ atoms})(10^{-10} \text{ m/atom}) = 8.4 \times 10^{-3}$ m, which is about one-third of an inch. (b) Because 1 mol of carbon has a mass of 12×10^{-3} kg, Eq. 1.4 gives $V = m/\rho = (12 \times 10^{-3} \text{ kg})/(2.2 \times 10^3 \text{ kg/m}^3) = 5.5 \times 10^{-6}$ m^3. If you assume this value to be a cube, then the cube root of V gives the length of a side, 1.8×10^{-2} m, about twice the length for each side calculated in part a.

1.14 (a) The circumference is $2\pi R = 2\pi(27.3 \text{ mm}) = 172$ mm. You are allowed to report three significant digits because the radius R has three (the 2 in $2\pi R$ has an infinite number of significant digits, and π has as many as your calculator has digits). (b) $a + b + c = 12.3 + 3.241 + 55.74 = 71.3$ (12.3 has the fewest decimal places (one), and so the sum must be rounded to one decimal place). (c) $f = (4.00)^2/7 = 2.29$; $g = (3.00)^2/7 = 1.29$;

$f + g = (4.00)^2/7 + (3.00)^2/7 = 3.57$. Note that this result is not equal to the sum of the rounded values for f and g: $2.29 + 1.29 = 3.58$. Never use a rounded intermediate answer in a calculation!

1.15 Many answers are possible. One translation strategy would be to reason that water is like milk, and you know from experience that a quart of milk weighs about 2 lb. From Appendix [SI UNITS], you know that 1 qt $= 0.946 \times 10^{-3}$ m$^3 \approx 10^{-3}$ m^3 and that 2 lb $= 0.907$ kg ≈ 1 kg. Using Eq. 1.4, you thus obtain for the density of milk (and of water) $(1 \text{ kg})/(10^{-3} \text{ m}^3) = 10^3 \text{ kg/m}^3$.

One division strategy would be to estimate the mass and the volume of a glass of water and then use Eq. 1.4 to obtain the density. A glass of water is about 2 in. across and 4 in. tall, so $V \approx \pi[(1 \text{ in.})(2.54 \times 10^{-2} \text{ m/in.})]^2(4 \text{ in.})(2.54 \times 10^{-2} \text{ m/in.}) = 2 \times 10^{-4}$ m^3. Such a glass weighs about 0.25 lb, and so $m \approx (0.25 \text{ lb})(0.45 \text{ kg/lb}) = 0.11$ kg. Substituting V and m into Eq. 1.4 yields $\rho = m/V \approx (0.11 \text{ kg})/(2 \times 10^{-4} \text{ m}^3) = 5.5 \times 10^2 \text{ kg/m}^3$. The order of magnitude of both estimates is 10^3 kg/m^3 because $5.5 \times 10^2 \text{ kg/m}^3$ rounds to $10 \times 10^2 \text{ kg/m}^3 = 10^3 \text{ kg/m}^3$, which is the same answer we obtained before.

1.16 If we ignore the oceans, which constitute only a small layer at Earth's surface, the planet is mostly rock, which has a mass density higher than that of water—say, five times higher. As discussed in Section 1.9, the mass density of water is 1000 kg/m^3, meaning that rock should have a mass density of about 5×10^3 kg/m^3. From Checkpoint 1.5 (which you worked out, didn't you?), you know that the Earth's radius is 6.4×10^6 m. Taking Earth to be a sphere, you obtain for its volume $V = \frac{4}{3}\pi R_E^3 = 1.1 \times 10^{21}$ m^3. Rearranging Eq. 1.4 to $m = \rho V$ gives you $m = (5 \times 10^3 \text{ kg/m}^3)(1.1 \times 10^{21} \text{ m}^3) = 5 \times 10^{24}$ kg, with order of magnitude 1025 kg. (The current best measurement of Earth's mass is 5.9736×10^{24} kg.)

Chapter 2

2.1 (a) See Table 2.1. (b) See Figure 2.2.

2.2 (a) Staying the same distance from the left edge in five sequential frames means I have stopped and am standing in one spot as time passes and the camera continues to roll. (b) I am again in the same spot in two frames, but now the frames are not sequential, and the data points in between are not aligned, telling you that in the time that passed between frames 7 and 14, I walked away from the spot and then came back to it. (c) Two vertically aligned points would mean that in one frame (which means one instant in time), I was at two different distances from the origin, something that could never happen.

2.3. (a) My image is 4.5 mm tall in the film clip. Estimating my height to be 1.8 m (6 ft), you get that 4.5 mm in the photograph corresponds to 1.8 m in the real world. So 1 mm in the photograph corresponds to (1 mm in photo)(1.8 m in real world)/(4.5 mm in photo) = 0.40 m in real world. (b) In frame 1, I am 2.5 mm from the left edge of the frame; in frame 10, 12.0 mm. So the distance traveled between frames 1 and 10 is (12.0 mm in photo) − (2.5 mm in photo) = 9.5 mm in photo. This corresponds to an actual distance of (9.5 mm in photo)(0.40 m in real world)/(1 mm in photo) = 3.8 m.

2.4. (a) +3.4 m in Figure 2.3; +2.4 m in Figure 2.4. (b) +3.4 m − (+1.0 m) = +2.4 m; +2.4 m − 0 = +2.4 m.

2.5 (a) Because your final position is the same as your initial position, the x component of your displacement is zero. (b) Your distance traveled is 4 m. (c) No. In general the *distance traveled* and the *x component of the displacement* are two different quantities.

2.6 (a) A vertical line drawn from the first $x = +4.0$ m point down to the horizontal axis tells you that I was at that position at 1.7 s. The vertical line for the $x = +1$ m position is already drawn: It is the vertical axis. Therefore the length of time I took to travel this distance was (1.7 s) − (0) = 1.7 s. (b) Vertical lines through the curve at $x = +2.0$ m and $x = +3.0$ m intersect the time axis at 0.6 s and 1.2 s, and so I traveled this distance in $(1.2\text{ s}) - (0.6\text{ s}) = 0.6\text{ s}$. (c) At 0.8 s. (d) I was at $x = +2.5$ m for *zero* time (not even a split second, an infinitesimally small amount of time!) because it takes no time to move over a *point*. If this surprises you, look at your answers to parts *a* and *b*: To move from $+1.0$ m to $+4.0$ m took 1.7 s; from $+2.0$ m to $+3.0$ m it took 0.6 s. As we make the interval smaller and smaller, the time it takes to move over that interval gets smaller. If we consider just the point at $+2.5$ m, the distance shrinks to zero, and so does the time it takes to cross the point.

2.7 (a) Normal: $3.50\text{ m} - 1.00\text{ m} = 2.50$ m; slow: $2.25\text{ m} - 1.00\text{ m} = 1.25$ m (half the distance, as one would expect). (b) Normal: $(2.50\text{ m})/(1.50\text{ s}) = 1.67$ m/s; slow: $(1.25\text{ m})/(1.50\text{ s}) = 0.83$ m/s (note units of meter per second). (c) Normal: $1.50\text{ s} - 0.60\text{ s} = 0.90$ s; slow: $3.00\text{ s} - 1.20\text{ s} = 1.80$ s (twice as long, as you expect). (d) Normal: $(1.50\text{ m})/(0.90\text{ s}) = 1.67$ m/s; slow: $(1.50\text{ m})/(1.80\text{ s}) = 0.83$ m/s (same as the values you calculated in part *b*).

2.8 (a) At $t = 1.3$ s. (b) $(3.4\text{ m} - 1.0\text{ m})/(1.3\text{ s}) = 1.8$ m/s.

2.9 (a) The average speed is

$$\frac{\text{distance traveled}}{\text{time taken}} =$$

$$\frac{0.5\text{ km}}{6.0\text{ min}} \times \frac{1000\text{ m}}{1.0\text{ km}} \times \frac{1.0\text{ min}}{60\text{ s}} = 1.4\text{ m/s}.$$

(b) The average speed is

$$\frac{\text{distance traveled}}{\text{time taken}} =$$

$$\frac{0.5\text{ km}}{2.0\text{ min}} \times \frac{1000\text{ m}}{1.0\text{ km}} \times \frac{1.0\text{ min}}{60\text{ s}} = 4.2\text{ m/s}.$$

(c) $(1.4\text{ m/s} + 4.2\text{ m/s})/2 = 2.8$ m/s. This is not equal to the answer worked out in Example 2.3 because average speed is obtained not by averaging speeds over different segments of a trip but by dividing the distance traveled by the duration of the entire trip.

2.10 (a) Negative. The x component of the displacement is $-2.3\text{ m} - (-1.2\text{ m}) = -1.1$ m. Because the x component of the displacement is negative, the x component of the average velocity is negative. (b) Negative again. The x component of the displacement is $-1.2\text{ m} - (+1.2\text{ m}) = -2.4$ m, and so the x component of the average velocity is negative as well. (c) Yes. In both cases, the object moves in the direction of decreasing x and so must have a negative x component of average velocity.

2.11 (*i*) and (*iv*) are scalars because no direction is required in order to specify these quantities completely; (*ii*) and (*iii*) are vectors because direction is required to specify them completely.

2.12 (a) Because my feet in Figure 2.18 are at $x = +4.8$ m, the x coordinate of the vector pointing from the origin to my feet is $x = +4.8$ m. (b) The vector $\vec{r}$ is obtained by multiplying the unit vector by $+4.8$ m: $\vec{r} = (+4.8\text{ m})\vec{\imath}$. (c) It represents my position in the frame shown in Figure 2.18. (d) Yes. It is a vector that is 2.5 m long and points to the right (Figure S2.12). This vector could represent my position at an earlier instant, or it could be a vector representing the position of the right edge of the left garage door.

Figure S1.12

2.13 (a) $\Delta x = x_f - x_i = +4.8\text{ m} - (+2.2\text{ m}) = +2.6$ m. (b) $\Delta \vec{r} = (+2.6\text{ m})\vec{\imath}$.

2.14 (a) Positive. If the object is initially at $x_i = -2$ m and moves to $x_f = -1$ m, then the x component of the displacement is $\Delta x = -1\text{ m} - (-2\text{ m}) = +1$ m. (b) No. Imagine any case where the object moves from a negative value of x to a positive value, and the displacement is again positive. Whenever positive x values are to the right of the origin, the x component of any displacement to the right is positive, regardless of the initial and final locations.

2.15 (a) See Figure S2.15a. (b) Yes, because addition is commutative: $\vec{a} + \vec{c} = \vec{c} + \vec{a}$; see Figure S2.15b. (c) No, because subtraction is not commutative: $\vec{a} - \vec{c} \neq \vec{c} - \vec{a}$; see Figure S2.15c.

Figure S2.15

(a)

(b)   (c)

2.16 (a) The time interval between frames 6 and 17 is $\Delta t = t_f - t_i = 5.33\text{ s} - 1.67\text{ s} = 3.66$ s; the distance traveled is 2.0 m (from $x = +3.8$ m to $x = +4.8$ m and back). Average speed: $(2.0\text{ m})/(3.66\text{ s}) = 0.55$ m/s. x component of average velocity: $\Delta x = x_f - x_i = +3.8\text{ m} - (+3.8\text{ m}) = 0$, and so

$$v_{x,\text{av}} = \frac{\Delta x}{\Delta t} = \frac{0}{\Delta t} = 0.$$

Average velocity: $\vec{v}_{\text{av}} = v_{x,\text{av}}\,\vec{\imath} = (0)\vec{\imath} = \vec{0}$.

(b) The time interval between frames 1 and 17 is $\Delta t = t_f - t_i = 5.33\text{ s} - 0 = 5.33$ s; the distance traveled is 4.8 m (3.8 m from $x = +1.0$ m to $x = +4.8$ m and then 1.0 m back to $x = +3.8$). Average speed: $(4.8\text{ m})/(5.33\text{ s}) = 0.90$ m/s. x component of average velocity: $\Delta x = x_f - x_i = +3.8\text{ m} - (+1.0\text{ m}) = +2.8$ m, and so

$$v_{x,\text{av}} = \frac{\Delta x}{\Delta t} = \frac{+2.8\text{ m}}{5.33\text{ s}} = +0.53\text{ m/s}.$$

Average velocity: $\vec{v}_{\text{av}} = v_{x,\text{av}}\,\vec{\imath} = (+0.53\text{ m/s})\vec{\imath}$.

2.17 From Figure 2.30 you see that, at $t = 2.0$ s, the object is at $x = +2.8$ m. Substituting $t_i = 2.0$ s, $x_i = +2.8$ m, and $v_x = +0.60$ m/s into Eq. 2.19 yields

$$x_f = +2.8\text{ m} + (+0.60\text{ m/s})(t_f - 2.0\text{ s})$$

$$= +2.8\text{ m} + (+0.60\text{ m/s})t_f - (+0.60\text{ m/s})(2.0\text{ s})$$

$$= +2.8\text{ m} + (+0.60\text{ m/s})t_f\quad 1.2\text{ m}$$

$$= +1.6\text{ m} + (+0.60\text{ m/s})t_f,$$

which is identical to the result in Example 2.10.

2.18 (a) $x_2 = 0$, $x_9 = +0.314$ m;

$$t_2 = 2 \text{ intervals} \times \frac{0.0300 \text{ s}}{\text{interval}} = 0.0600 \text{ s}$$

$$t_9 = 9 \text{ intervals} \times \frac{0.0300 \text{ s}}{\text{interval}} = 0.2700 \text{ s}$$

$$v_{x,\text{av}} = \frac{\Delta x}{\Delta t} = \frac{+0.314 \text{ m}}{0.210 \text{ s}} = +1.50 \text{ m/s}.$$

(b) $x_8 = +0.250$ m, $t_8 = 0.240$ s, so

$$v_{x,\text{av}} = \frac{\Delta x}{\Delta t} = \frac{+0.250 \text{ m}}{0.180 \text{ s}} = +1.39 \text{ m/s}.$$

(c) See Table S2.18. (d) Decreases. Because the ball speeds up as it falls, averaging over a shorter time interval involves lower velocities, and therefore the average decreases (see also Figure 2.32). (e) See Figure S2.18. (f) Note that extrapolating the data to $\Delta t = 0$ does not yield a zero average velocity. This makes sense: The ball's velocity is nonzero before and after passing position 2, and so neither the average value nor the instantaneous value can be zero at position 2.

Table S2.18 Average velocities

Position	Δx (m)	Δt (s)	$\Delta x / \Delta t$ (m/s)
7	+0.197	0.1500	+1.31
6	+0.143	0.1200	+1.19
5	+0.102	0.0900	+1.13
4	+0.061	0.0600	+1.02
3	+0.028	0.0300	+0.93
2	0	0	–

Figure S2.18

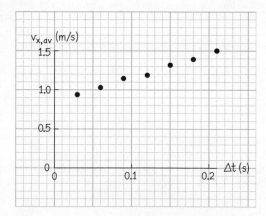

2.19 (a) Because the derivative with respect to time of a constant is zero, you have, from Eq. 2.22, $v_x = dx/dt = 0$. If the position is constant, then its x coordinate is also constant, and so Δx is always zero. Therefore $\Delta x/\Delta t = 0$ for any finite time interval Δt. Substituting $\Delta x/\Delta t = 0$ into Eq. 2.21 yields $v_x = 0$ because the limit of zero is zero. (b) If $x = ct$, then $v_x = dx/dt = d(ct)/dt = c\, dt/dt = c$. Over a finite time interval Δt, you have $x_i = ct_i$ and $x_f = c(t_i + \Delta t)$. Therefore $\Delta x = c(t_i + \Delta t) - ct_i = c\Delta t$, and so $\Delta x/\Delta t = c$. Because c does not depend on Δt, the limit in Eq. 2.21 has no effect and so $v_x = c$. This result makes sense because the relationship $x = ct$ means x changes by a constant amount c each second. Therefore the object travels the same distance in equal time intervals, and so its velocity must be constant.

Chapter 3

3.1 (a) The x component of the average acceleration is the change in the x component of the velocity divided by the time interval during which that change took place:

$$\frac{+5.0 \text{ m/s} - 0}{1.0 \text{ s}} = +5.0 \text{ m/s}^2.$$

(b)
$$\frac{+10 \text{ m/s} - (+5.0 \text{ m/s})}{2.0 \text{ s}} = +2.5 \text{ m/s}^2.$$

(c)
$$\frac{+10 \text{ m/s} - 0}{3.0 \text{ s}} = +3.3 \text{ m/s}^2.$$

3.2 (a) The minus signs on the two v_x values tell you that the car is traveling in the negative x direction. (b) $\Delta v_x = v_{x,\text{f}} - v_{x,\text{i}} = -2 \text{ m/s} - (-10 \text{ m/s}) = +8 \text{ m/s}$; because Δv_x is positive, the vector $\Delta\vec{v}$ points in the positive x direction. (c) $\vec{a}$ always points in the same direction as $\Delta\vec{v}$ and so points in the positive x direction. Consequently the x component of the acceleration is positive. (d) The acceleration points in the direction opposite the direction of the velocity, and so the car is slowing down.

3.3 (a) For both graphs, x decreases with time, which means both velocities are in the negative x direction, and so the x components of the velocities are negative. (b) The speeds are increasing in part a (more distance covered in equal time intervals as the $x(t)$ curve bends down; decreasing in part b as the curve bends up. (c) From part a you know that the velocity is always in the negative x direction; from part b you know that the speed is increasing in a and decreasing in b. Combining these results, you see that $\Delta\vec{v}$ points in the negative x direction in a and in the positive x direction in b, and so Δv_x is negative in a and positive in b. (d) The x components are negative in a and positive in b ($\vec{a}$ always points in the same direction as $\Delta\vec{v}$, and so the algebraic signs of Δv_x and a_x are the same).

3.4 (a) The car is moving in the negative x direction, and so $\vec{v}$ must point in that direction. To increase the car's speed, $\Delta\vec{v}$ must point in the negative x direction (Figure S3.4). Because $\vec{a}$ and $\Delta\vec{v}$ always point in the same direction, $\vec{a}$ also points in the negative x direction. (b) The figure shows a car slowing down in the negative x direction. Motion in the negative x direction implies a negative slope of the $x(t)$ curve, which eliminates the two graphs in Figure 3.2. Because the car slows down, it should cover increasingly smaller distances (smaller Δx for a given Δt at later instants t). This is so for Figure 3.3b.

Figure S3.4

3.5 When the book and the paper are held side by side, the book falls faster. When the paper is on top of the book, they fall at same rate. The difference is due to air resistance, which slows down the light piece of paper but not the heavier book. When the paper is on top of the book, the paper is shielded from the flow of air and so feels no air resistance.

3.6 In Figure 3.6b you can see that Δx goes from -2.2 mm at $n = 2$ to -7.0 mm at $n = 10$: The displacement increases from one exposure to the next as n increases—the ball is accelerating. Because the magnitude of the displacement is increasing with time, the magnitude of the velocity must also be increasing.

3.7 (a) The speed increases because the object covers greater and greater distances in equal time intervals. (b) The x component of the velocity is negative because the motion is in the negative x direction. From part a you know that the magnitude of the velocity increases, and so the x component of the velocity becomes increasingly negative—it *decreases*. (c) Because the object speeds up in the negative x direction, the acceleration points in the negative x direction and so a_x is negative.

3.8 The ball's speed is about 20 m/s after 1 s and 30 m/s after 2 s. All your throwing has done is change the initial speed from zero (the initial speed if the ball is released from rest) to 10 m/s. Once the ball leaves your hand at this initial speed, the only thing affecting its motion is the acceleration due to gravity, which increases the speed at the rate of about 10 m/s^2.

3.9 See Figure S3.9. Because the rock reverses its motion, the motion diagram is split into two parts: one for the upward motion and the other for the downward motion. If you take up as the positive direction, the x component of the rock's acceleration is $a_x = -9.8$ m/s^2. With the origin chosen to be at the top of the cliff, the initial conditions are $t_i = 0$, $x_i = 0$, and $v_{x,i} = +15$ m/s. At the top of its trajectory, the rock reverses direction, and so the velocity is zero at that position. You do not know its position or the instant at which it reaches the top, and so your diagram must show $t_1 = ?$, $x_1 = ?$, and $v_{x,1} = 0$. The final conditions at the instant the rock reaches the water are $t_f = ?$, $x_f - -30$ m, and $v_{x,f} = ?$

Figure S3.9

(a)

$$t_1 = ?$$
$$x_1 = ?$$
$$v_{x,1} = 0$$

$$a_x = -9.8 \text{ m/s}^2$$

$$t_i = 0$$
$$x_i = 0$$
$$v_{x,i} - +15 \text{ m/s}$$

(b)

$$t_1 = ?$$
$$x_1 = ?$$
$$v_{x,1} = 0$$

$$a_x = -9.8 \text{ m/s}^2$$

$$t_f = ?$$
$$x_f = -30 \text{ m}$$
$$v_{x,f} = ?$$

3.10 From the motion diagram in Figure 3.11 you have $t_i = 0$, $x_i = 0$, and $v_{x,i} = 0$. Substituting these values into Eq. 3.9 gives $x_f = \frac{1}{2}a_x t_f^2$ or, solving for t_f: $t_f = \sqrt{2x_f/a_x}$. Substituting the values for x_f and a_x, you get $t_f = \sqrt{2(300 \text{ m})/(9.8 \text{ m/s}^2)} = 7.8$ s. Equation 3.10 then yields $v_{x,f} = v_{x,i} + a_x t_f = 0 + (9.8 \text{ m/s}^2)(7.8 \text{ s}) = 77$ m/s. (Alternatively, you can substitute the values for a_x and Δx into Eq. 3.13 to obtain the same result.)

3.11 Figure S3.11 shows the motion diagram for the new choice of x axis. The initial conditions are as before; the final conditions are $t_f = ?$, $x_f = +h$, and $v_{x,f} = ?$. The acceleration is now positive ($a_x = +g$) because it points in the same direction as the x axis, and so Eq. 3.9 is

$$h = 0 + 0 + \tfrac{1}{2}gt_f^2,$$

which yields the same result as before for t_f. The x component of the final velocity is $v_{x,f} = +gt_f$. This x component of the velocity is equal in magnitude to the velocity in Example 3.5 but opposite in sign (because the axis has been inverted).

Figure S3.11

$$t_i = ?$$
$$x_i = ?$$
$$v_{x,i} = 0$$

$$a_x = +9.8 \text{ m/s}^2$$

$$t_f = ?$$
$$x_f = +20 \text{ m}$$
$$v_{x,f} = ?$$

3.12 Applying Eq. 3.10 to the downward part of the motion, with $v_{x,i} = 0$, $a_x = -g$, and $t = v_{x,i}/g$, you get

$$v_{x,f} = 0 - g\frac{v_{x,i}}{g} = -v_{x,i}.$$

The stone hits the ground at the same speed it had when it was launched.

3.13 Figure S3.13 shows that any angle $180° > \theta > 90°$ gives the same result you would get for an angle of $180° - \theta$. All that matters is the angle the incline makes with the floor; once you go beyond 90°, the cart faces the other way, but that is immaterial. (Compare, for example, the 60° angle with $180° - 60° = 120°$.) Note that Eq. 3.20 properly accounts for this fact because $\sin\theta = \sin(180° - \theta)$. For example,

$$a_{120°} = g\sin(120°) = g\sin(180° - 120°) = a_{60°}.$$

Figure S3.13

3.14 The first derivative, dropping the subscript f on t_f because it represents an (arbitrary) instant is,

$$\frac{dx_f}{dt} = \frac{d}{dt}(x_i + v_{x,i}t + \tfrac{1}{2}a_x t^2) = 0 + v_{x,i} + a_x t.$$

The expression on the right side is the x component of the velocity of an object moving at constant acceleration (Eq. 3.10). The second derivative yields the x component of the (constant) acceleration:

$$\frac{d^2 x_f}{dt^2} = \frac{d}{dt}\frac{dx_f}{dt} = \frac{d}{dt}(v_{x,i} + a_x t) = 0 + a_x.$$

Chapter 4

4.1 (a) Yes, because each of the $v_x(t)$ curves is a straight line (constant slope = constant acceleration). (b) The concrete, because the magnitude of the acceleration is largest when the magnitude of Δv_x for a given time interval is largest—that is, when the slope of the line is the steepest.

4.2 (a) $\Delta v_{1x} = v_{1x,f} - v_{1x,i} = +0.63 \text{ m/s} - (+0.14 \text{ m/s}) = +0.49 \text{ m/s}$. (b) $\Delta v_{2x} = v_{2x,f} - v_{2x,i} = +0.14 \text{ m/s} - (+0.63 \text{ m/s}) = -0.49 \text{ m/s}$. (c) The changes are equal in magnitude but opposite in sign, meaning that the velocity of one increases and the velocity of the other decreases.

4.3 No. The magnitude of the change in the x component of the velocity of the standard cart is always half that of the half cart. If you lower $v_{sx,i}$, the only thing that happens is that the velocity-versus-time graph shrinks in the vertical direction; the x component of the velocity of the standard cart still ends up being positive. If you increase $v_{sx,i}$, the graph expands in the vertical direction and again the x component of the final velocity of the cart is positive.

4.4 $\Delta v_{ux} = v_{ux,f} - v_{ux,i} = +0.21 \text{ m/s} - (0 \text{ m/s}) = +0.21 \text{ m/s}$; $\Delta v_{sx} = v_{sx,f} - v_{sx,i} = -0.21 \text{ m/s} - (+0.42 \text{ m/s}) = -0.63 \text{ m/s}$. Therefore $\Delta v_{ux}/\Delta v_{sx} = (+0.21 \text{ m/s})/(-0.63 \text{ m/s}) = -1/3$.

4.5 $\Delta v_{mx} = v_{mx,f} - v_{mx,i} = +0.07 \text{ m/s} - (0 \text{ m/s}) = +0.07 \text{ m/s}$; $\Delta v_{px} = v_{px,f} - v_{px,i} = -0.20 \text{ m/s} - (+0.27 \text{ m/s}) = -0.47 \text{ m/s}$; $\Delta v_{px}/\Delta v_{mx} = -6.7$.

4.6 Greater. Δv_{ux} is smaller than Δv_{sx}, which tells you that the cart of unknown inertia puts up more resistance to a change in its velocity and hence has more inertia.

4.7 (a) Extensive. The inertia of a double cart is equal to the sum of the inertias of the individual carts. (b) Intensive. The velocity of a double cart is equal to the velocity of each of the individual carts. (c) Extensive. The product of inertia and velocity of a double cart is equal to the double inertia times the velocity of the assembly: $2m_sv_d$; the sum of the product of inertia and velocity of each individual cart is equal to two times the single inertia times the velocity of the assembly: $2m_sv_d$. In general, the product of an extensive and an intensive quantity is extensive.

4.8 (a) Extensive. If I separate an amount of money into two piles, then the sum of the amounts of money in each pile equals the original sum of money. (b) Not extensive. The sum of the temperatures in each half of a room is not equal to the temperature of the entire room. (c) Not extensive. The sum of the humidities in each half of a greenhouse is not equal to the humidity of the entire greenhouse. (d) Extensive. The volume of a bathtub is equal to the sum of the volumes of each half of the bathtub.

4.9 (a) Yes. If, for example, our the new standard had only half the inertia of the French one, then the inertia in kilograms of all objects measured against the new standard would be twice as great as the values obtained with the French standard. (b) No, because we can't change the world just by choosing another standard. The only thing that matters in a collision is the *ratio* of the inertias. If we choose another standard, the numerical values of both inertias change by a certain factor, but their ratio is unchanged.

4.10 The x component of the change in momentum of the standard cart is positive, so the change in momentum $\Delta\vec{p}_s$ points in the positive x direction. The x component of the change in momentum of the red cart is negative and so $\Delta\vec{p}_r$ points in the negative x direction.

4.11 (a) Nonzero. The puck's velocity decreases, so its momentum changes. (b) Zero. The cart's velocity is constant. (c) Nonzero. The collision changes the cart's velocity. (d) Zero, see Eq. 4.9. (e) Nonzero. The cart's velocity changes.

4.12 (a) No. If you push with your legs against the sled, you are interacting with the sled and so you are not isolated. (b) Ignoring any interaction between sled and ice, however, you and the sled form an isolated system.

4.13 (a) The magnitude of the changes in momentum is $0.061 \text{ kg} \cdot \text{m/s}$, so the collision transfers $0.061 \text{ kg} \cdot \text{m/s}$. (b) Cart 1 gains that amount (Δp_{1x} is positive); cart 2 loses that same amount. So, momentum is transferred from cart 2 to cart 1.

4.14 (a) The magnitude of the impulse delivered to cart 1 is equal to the magnitude of the momentum change of cart 1, which we calculated in Checkpoint 4.13: $J = 0.061 \text{ kg} \cdot \text{m/s}$. (b) The impulse points in the same direction as the momentum change (in the positive x direction),

so $\vec{J} = (+0.061 \text{ kg} \cdot \text{m/s})\hat{\imath}$. (c) No. While momentum is conserved, the momentum of a system or object can change due to transfer of momentum.

4.15 (a) No, because the inertias are not equal: $\Delta v_{1x} = +0.17 \text{ m/s} - 0 = +0.17 \text{ m/s}$; $\Delta v_{2x} = -0.17 \text{ m/s} - (+0.34 \text{ m/s}) = -0.51 \text{ m/s}$. (b) $m_1/m_2 = (0.36 \text{ kg})/(0.12 \text{ kg}) = 3$; $\Delta v_{2x}/\Delta v_{1x} = (-0.51 \text{ m/s})/(0.17 \text{ m/s}) = -3$. (c) $p_{1x,i} = m_1v_{1x,i} = (0.36 \text{ kg})(0) = 0$; $p_{2x,i} = (0.12 \text{ kg})(+0.34 \text{ m/s}) = +0.041 \text{ kg} \cdot \text{m/s}$; $p_{1x,f} = (0.36 \text{ kg})(+0.17 \text{ m/s}) = +0.061 \text{ kg} \cdot \text{m/s}$; $p_{2x,f} = (0.12 \text{ kg})(-0.17 \text{ m/s}) = -0.020 \text{ kg} \cdot \text{m/s}$. (d) $p_{1x,i} + p_{2x,i} = 0 \text{ kg} \cdot \text{m/s} + (+0.041 \text{ kg} \cdot \text{m/s}) = +0.041 \text{ kg} \cdot \text{m/s}$. (e) $p_{1x,f} + p_{2x,f} = +0.061 \text{ kg} \cdot \text{m/s} + (-0.020 \text{ kg} \cdot \text{m/s}) = +0.041 \text{ kg} \cdot \text{m/s}$. (f) Yes. $\Delta p_{1x} = +0.061 \text{ kg} \cdot \text{m/s} - 0 = +0.061 \text{ kg} \cdot \text{m/s}$; $\Delta p_{2x} = -0.020 \text{ kg} \cdot \text{m/s} - (+0.041 \text{ kg} \cdot \text{m/s}) = -0.061 \text{ kg} \cdot \text{m/s}$. This is so because the momentum of the system does not change.

4.16 (a) Yes. Just as we do for the carts in Figure 4.3, we can ignore the interaction between the carts and the low-friction track, and so the two carts constitute an isolated system. (b) For an isolated system, the momentum law tells us that the momentum of the system cannot change.

4.17 There are two ways to solve this problem. The hard way is to apply the law of conservation of momentum to each collision separately. The easy way is to look at the momentum of the system at only two instants: before the first collision and after the final one. The system's momentum before the first collision is $mv_{x,i}$, where m is the inertia of a single railroad car. After all the cars collide, they move together at the same final velocity $v_{x,f}$. The system's final momentum is therefore $4mv_{x,f}$. Because momentum is conserved, the final momentum must equal the initial momentum. Therefore $4mv_{x,f} = mv_{x,i}$, and thus $v_{x,f} = \frac{1}{4}v_{x,i}$. The velocity of the four-car train is one-quarter the initial velocity of the first car.

Chapter 5

5.1 No. The relative speed $|\vec{v}_2 - \vec{v}_1|$ takes into account the directions of $\vec{v}_1$ and $\vec{v}_2$, but the difference in speeds $v_2 - v_1$ doesn't. For example, if $v_{1x} = +2 \text{ m/s}$ and $v_{2x} = -2 \text{ m/s}$, then $v_{12} = |v_{2x} - v_{1x}| = 4 \text{ m/s}$ but $v_2 - v_1 = 2 \text{ m/s} - 2 \text{ m/s} = 0$.

5.2 (a) Totally inelastic, because after the collision the relative speed is zero. (b) Elastic, because there is no change in the relative speed. (c) Whether or not momentum is constant depends only on whether the system is isolated, not on the type of collision. In part a, the system (ball + glove) is not isolated because the glove interacts with something outside the system (the outfielder). Thus the sum of the momenta is not constant. In part b, the system (two balls) is isolated because, if we ignore friction, neither ball interacts with any object external to the system. Therefore the sum of the momenta is constant.

5.3 Yes. Consider an object that is moving at speed v and consists of two pieces having inertias m_1 and m_2. The kinetic energy of the object, $\frac{1}{2}(m_1 + m_2)v^2$, is equal to the sum of the kinetic energies of its two parts, $\frac{1}{2}m_1v^2 + \frac{1}{2}m_2v^2$.

5.4 Denote the x component of the initial velocity of the moving cart $v_{x,i}$ and the x component of the final velocity of the combined carts $v_{x,f}$. Conservation of momentum requires that the two carts have a final momentum equal to the initial momentum, and so $mv_{x,i} = 2mv_{x,f}$. Thus $v_{x,f} = \frac{1}{2}v_{x,i}$. The initial kinetic energy is $\frac{1}{2}mv_{x,i}^2$; the final kinetic energy is $\frac{1}{2}(2m)v_{x,f}^2 = m(\frac{1}{2}v_{x,i})2 = \frac{1}{4}mv_{x,i}^2$. This is half the initial kinetic energy.

5.5 Increase. The system has some kinetic energy before the collision but zero kinetic energy after. This decrease in kinetic energy is accompanied by a change in the state of the dough (it changes shape). This change in state represents a change in the internal energy of the dough. If the sum of the internal and kinetic energies of the system is to remain constant, the internal energy must increase.

5.6 You could throw something against the cart, push it with your hand, blow against it, or ignite an explosive next to it. Changes in state or motion: The motion of the thrown object changes when it collides with the cart.

To push or blow, you have to move your muscles, which causes chemical reactions that change your chemical state. The ignition causes the chemical state of the explosive to change.

5.7 (*a*) No. The momentum of the system is zero before the spring expands and nonzero afterward. (*b*) No, because $\Delta p \neq 0$. There is an external interaction with the post that holds the left end of the spring fixed. Without this interaction, the expanding spring would not cause the cart to move.

5.8 See Figure S5.8. The car engine heats up, and so part of the chemical energy is converted to thermal energy. The sum of the changes ΔK and ΔE_{th} is equal in magnitude to the change ΔE_{chem}.

Figure S5.8

change in motion: car accelerates
changes in state: • chemical state of fuel changes
                       • engine gets warm

5.9 (*a*) No. Changing the magnitude of an object's momentum means changing the object's speed, and this automatically means changing its kinetic energy. (*b*) Yes. If the change in kinetic energy is compensated by a change in the internal energy of the object, its energy remains unchanged. (*c*) Yes, for both parts. With a system of objects, it is possible to keep the kinetic energy constant while changing the magnitude of the momentum. Imagine two identical carts on a low-friction track moving away from each other in opposite directions at speed v. The momentum of the system is zero, and the kinetic energy of the system is mv^2. If the velocity of one of the two carts is reversed by some interaction, the system's kinetic energy remains unchanged but the momentum of the system becomes $2mv$. For the energy of the system, use the same reasoning you used to answer part *b*.

5.10 For a single object, if mv_x and mv_x^2 remain constant, then the product of these two quantities must also remain constant: $(mv_x)(mv_x^2) = m^2v_x^3 =$ constant. Because m does not change for a single, isolated object, $m^2v_x^3/m = mv_x^3$ must also be constant. Therefore mv_x^3 indeed remains constant for a single object.

In an elastic collision between two objects of identical inertia m with velocities v_{1x} and v_{2x}, the system's momentum, $mv_{1x} + mv_{2x}$, remains constant. The system's kinetic energy is also constant, and so $mv_{1x}^2 + mv_{2x}^2$ is constant. The product of these two must also be constant: $m^2v_{1x}^3 + m^2v_{1x}^2v_{2x} + m^2v_{1x}v_{2x}^2 + m^2v_{2x}^3 = m(mv_{1x}^3 + mv_{2x}^3) + mv_{1x}v_{2x}(mv_{1x} + mv_{2x}) =$ constant. From this we see that $(mv_{1x}^3 + mv_{2x}^3)$ is constant if the second term, $mv_{1x}v_{2x}(mv_{1x} + mv_{2x})$, is constant. The part in parentheses is the system's momentum and is constant. The inertia m is also constant, so all we need to know is whether or not $v_{1x}v_{2x}$ is constant. Suppose $v_{1x,i}$ changes by Δv_{1x}. Conservation of momentum then requires $v_{2x,i}$ to change by $-\Delta v_{1x}$. So the product of the final velocities becomes $(v_{1x,i} + \Delta v_{1x})(v_{2x,i} - \Delta v_{1x}) = v_{1x,i}v_{2x,i} + \Delta v_{1x}(v_{2x,i} - v_{1x,i}) - (\Delta v_{1x})^2$. This can be equal to the product of the initial velocities, $v_{1x,i}v_{2x,i}$, only if the change in velocity Δv_{1x} is equal to $v_{2x,i} - v_{1x,i}$. This can indeed happen but, in general, need *not* be so. In general, therefore, mv_x^3 is not unchanged in an elastic collision.

5.11 No. If one object is initially at rest, then the other object must be moving in order for the collision to occur, and so the initial momentum of the system is nonzero. Because the system is isolated, its momentum is unchanged, and so the system's final momentum, too, is nonzero. Therefore the combination of the two objects has a nonzero velocity after the collision, which means the kinetic energy cannot be zero.

5.12 From Eq. 5.12 you know that $v = \sqrt{2K/m}$. Substituting 1.2×10^8 J for the kinetic energy K and 1200 kg for the inertia m gives $v = 4.5 \times 10^2$ m/s, which is more than 1000 mph! (Apparently it is not possible to convert all of the energy in gasoline to kinetic energy! You'll see why in Chapter 21.)

5.13 No. Cart 1 gets twice as much energy as cart 2: $K_{1f} = \frac{1}{2}m_1v_{1f}^2 = \frac{1}{2}(0.25 \text{ kg})(2.0 \text{ m/s})^2 = 0.50$ J, and $K_{2f} = \frac{1}{2}m_2v_{2f}^2 = \frac{1}{2}(0.50 \text{ kg})(1.0 \text{ m/s})^2 = 0.25$ J. The reason is that the system's final momentum needs to be zero, and so v_{1f} must be $2v_{2f}$. Because $m_2 = 2m_1$, you have $K_{2f} = \frac{1}{2}m_2v_{2f}^2 = \frac{1}{2}(2m_1)(\frac{1}{2}v_{1f})^2 = \frac{1}{4}m_1v_{1f}^2 = \frac{1}{2}K_{1f}$.

Chapter 6

6.1 Because $\vec{v}_{\text{Eo}} = \vec{v}_{\text{EM}} + \vec{v}_{\text{Mo}}$, you can write $v_{\text{Mo}x} = v_{\text{Eo}x} - v_{\text{EM}x}$. With $v_{\text{EM}x} = -3.0$ mm/frame, you have $v_{\text{M1}x} = 0 - (-3.0 \text{ mm/frame}) = +3.0$ mm/frame and $v_{\text{M2}x} = (3.6 \text{ mm/frame}) - (-3.0 \text{ mm/frame}) = +6.6$ mm/frame.

6.2 (*a*) There is no change in the state of either cart, and so the internal energy of either cart is not changing. From observer E's point of view, both velocities are constant and so both kinetic energies are constant. Observer M reaches the same conclusion: Both carts are moving at constant velocity and so their kinetic energies are constant. The observers agree that the energy of each cart is constant. (*b*) and (*c*) No state change or motion change in the environment surrounding each isolated system causes any state change or motion change inside the system, and so each system is closed.

6.3 (*a*) There is no change in the state of either cart and so no change in the internal energy. For observer E, cart 1 accelerates, and so its kinetic energy K and energy E increase; the velocity of cart 2 is constant, and so its kinetic energy K and energy E are constant. For observer M, cart 1 is at rest, and so its kinetic energy K and energy E are constant; cart 2 accelerates, and so its kinetic energy K and energy E are increasing. (*b*) For observer E, a change in state in the spring is responsible for the cart's acceleration, and so the system is not closed. For observer M, changes in both state and motion occur in the environment, but the expansion of the spring cannot account for the change in the kinetic energy of the entire environment (the universe minus cart 1), which means that the energy changes don't add to zero and so the system is not closed. (*c*) For observer E, there are no changes in state or motion in the environment that are responsible for any changes in state or motion inside the system, and so the system is closed. For observer M, there are no changes in state or motion in the environment, and so it is closed. (*d*) For observer E, the cart 1 system is not closed and its energy increases; the cart 2 system is closed, and its energy is constant. The conservation of energy law holds for both systems. For observer M, the cart 1 system is not closed, and its energy remains constant; the cart 2 system is closed, and its energy is increasing. Neither observation agrees with the law of conservation of energy.

6.4 (*a*) $v_{\text{Ec}x,i} = +0.40$ m/s, $v_{\text{Ec}x,f} = +0.80$ m/s, $\Delta K = K_{\text{Ec},f} - K_{\text{Ec},i} = \frac{1}{2}(0.12 \text{ kg})(0.80 \text{ m/s})^2 - \frac{1}{2}(0.12 \text{ kg})(0.40 \text{ m/s})^2 = 29$ mJ. (*b*) $v_{\text{Mc}x,i} = -0.20$ m/s, $v_{\text{Mc}x,f} = +0.20$ m/s, $\Delta K = \frac{1}{2}(0.12 \text{ kg})(0.20 \text{ m/s})^2 - \frac{1}{2}(0.12 \text{ kg})(-0.20 \text{ m/s})^2 = 0$. (*c*) $v_{\text{Mc}x,i} = -0.40$ m/s, $v_{\text{Mc}x,f} = 0$, $\Delta K = 0 - \frac{1}{2}(0.12 \text{ kg})(-0.40 \text{ m/s})^2 = 10$ mJ.

6.5 Because the momentum of the isolated system is not changing: $m_1v_{\text{E1}x,i} + m_2v_{\text{E2}x,i} = (m_1 + m_2)v_{\text{E}x,f}$, and so $v_{\text{E}x,f} = (m_1v_{\text{E1}x,i} + m_2v_{\text{E2}x,i})/(m_1 + m_2) = +0.20$ m/s. In the moving reference frame, $v_{\text{M}x,f} = +0.40$ m/s. See Table S6.5 on next page.

Table S6.5 Conversion of kinetic energy

Cart	Inertia (kg)	v_x (m/s) before	after	Δv_x	K $(10^{-3}$ J) before	after	ΔK
Earth reference frame							
1	0.36	0	+0.20	+0.20	0	7.2	+7.2
2	0.12	+0.80	+0.20	−0.60	38.4	2.4	−36
						$\Delta K=$	−29
Reference frame moving at −0.20 m/s relative to Earth							
1	0.36	+0.20	+0.40	+0.20	7.2	28.8	+21.6
2	0.12	+1.0	+0.40	−0.60	60	9.6	−50.4
						$\Delta K=$	−29

6.6 Because the laws of the universe are the same in all inertial reference frames, the coefficient of restitution must also be the same. Another way of seeing this: Relative velocities do not depend on the velocity of the reference frame (Figure 6.11), and so $e = v_{12f}/v_{12i}$ is also independent of the reference frame.

6.7 Less. In the Earth reference frame, $K_{E,i} = 0 + \frac{1}{2}(0.12\text{ kg}) \cdot (0.80\text{ m/s})^2 = 38\text{ mJ}$. In the zero-momentum reference frame, $K_{Z,i} = \frac{1}{2}(0.36\text{ kg})(0.20\text{ m/s})^2 + \frac{1}{2}(0.12\text{ kg})(0.60\text{ m/s})^2 = 29\text{ mJ}$.

6.8 (a) If the jogger stays in place, he must be moving at the same speed as the belt but in the opposite direction. Therefore $v_{Bjx} = -2.0$ m/s, and so $r_{Bjx} = v_{Bjx}t = (-2.0\text{ m/s})(10\text{ s}) = -20$ m. (b) Equation 6.3 yields $r_{Ejx} = r_{EBx} + r_{Bjx}$. The position of the belt relative to Earth is $r_{EBx} = v_{EBx}\Delta t$, and the position of the jogger relative to the belt is $r_{Bjx} = v_{Bjx}\Delta t$. Because $v_{Bjx} = -v_{EBx}$, you find that $r_{Ejx} = r_{EBx} + r_{Bjx} = v_{EBx}\Delta t + v_{Bjx}\Delta t = 0$.

6.9 If you define northward as the positive x direction, you have $v_{TPx} = +1.2$ m/s, $v_{ETx} = +3.1$ m/s, and $v_{Psx} = -0.5$ m/s. For the velocity of the spider relative to Earth, subscript cancellation gives $v_{Esx} = v_{EPx} + v_{Psx}$. For the velocity of the passenger relative to Earth, $v_{EPx} = v_{ETx} + v_{TPx}$, and so $v_{Esx} = (v_{ETx} + v_{TPx}) + v_{Psx} = (+3.1\text{ m/s}) + (+1.2\text{ m/s}) + (-0.5\text{ m/s}) = +3.8$ m/s. An observer standing by the side of the tracks sees the spider moving at 3.8 m/s northward.

6.10 (a) Substituting $m_1 = 3m_2 = 3m$ into Eq. 1 of Example 6.7 yields $x_{Acm} = (3mx_{A1} + mx_{A2})/(3m + m) = (3x_{A1} + x_{A2})/4$, one-quarter of the way from x_{A1} to x_{A2}. (b) $x_{Acm} = (m_1x_{A1} + m_2x_{A2} + m_3x_{A3})/(m_1 + m_2 + m_3)$. Substituting $m_1 = m_3 = 3m_2 = 3m$ and $x_{Acm} = x_{A2}$ gives $x_{A2} = (3mx_{A1} + mx_{A2} + 3mx_{A3})/(3m + m + 3m) = (3x_{A1} + x_{A2} + 3x_{A3})/7$. Then $x_{A3} = 2x_{A2} - x_{A1}$.

6.11 (a) Because $m_1 = 3m_2$, Eq. 6.26 gives: before the collision $v_{cmx} = [(m_1)(0) + (m_2)(+0.80\text{ m/s})]/(m_1 + m_2) = +0.20$ m/s; after the collision $v_{cmx} = [(3m_2)(+0.40\text{ m/s}) + m_2(-0.40\text{ m/s})]/(3m_2 + m_2) = +0.20$ m/s. This is the x component of the velocity where the two $v_x(t)$ curves intersect. (b) Yes. When two objects collide, the object that initially has greater velocity always ends up with less velocity after the collision (and vice versa). Therefore there always has to be a location at which the two objects have the same velocity. At that location $v_{1x} = v_{2x} = v_x$, and so

$$v_{cmx} = (m_1v_x + m_2v_x)/(m_1 + m_2)$$
$$= v_x(m_1 + m_2)/(m_1 + m_2) = v_x.$$

(c) From Eqs. 6.23 and 6.26, $v_{EZx} = v_{cmx} = +0.20$ m/s. From Eq. 6.8, $v_{E1x,i} = v_{EZx} + v_{Z1x,i}$, and so $v_{Z1x,i} = v_{E1x,i} - v_{EZx} = 0 - (+0.20\text{ m/s}) = -0.20$ m/s, $v_{Z2x,i} = +0.6$ m/s, $v_{Z1x,f} = +0.2$ m/s, and $v_{Z2x,f} = -0.6$ m/s. Then $p_{Zx,i} = (3m_2)(-0.20\text{ m/s}) + (m_2)(+0.60\text{ m/s}) = 0$ and $p_{Zx,f} = (3m_2)(+0.20\text{ m/s}) + (m_2)(-0.60\text{ m/s}) = 0$.

6.12

$$K_{conv} = (\tfrac{1}{2}m_1v_1^2 + \tfrac{1}{2}m_2v_2^2) - \tfrac{1}{2}(m_1 + m_2)v_{cm}^2$$

$$= (\tfrac{1}{2}m_1v_1^2 + \tfrac{1}{2}m_2v_2^2) - \tfrac{1}{2}\frac{(m_1v_{1x} + m_2v_{2x})^2}{m_1 + m_2}$$

$$= (\tfrac{1}{2}m_1v_1^2 + \tfrac{1}{2}m_2v_2^2) - \tfrac{1}{2}\frac{(m_1^2v_1^2 + 2m_1m_2v_{1x}v_{2x} + m_2^2v_2^2)}{m_1 + m_2}$$

$$= \tfrac{1}{2}\frac{(m_1v_1^2 + m_2v_2^2)(m_1 + m_2) - (m_1^2v_1^2 + 2m_1m_2v_{1x}v_{2x} + m_2^2v_2^2)}{m_1 + m_2}$$

$$= \tfrac{1}{2}\frac{(m_1m_2v_1^2 + m_1m_2v_2^2) - 2m_1m_2v_{1x}v_{2x}}{m_1 + m_2}$$

$$= \tfrac{1}{2}\frac{m_1m_2(v_1^2 - 2v_{1x}v_{2x} + v_2^2)}{m_1 + m_2} = \tfrac{1}{2}\left(\frac{m_1m_2}{m_1 + m_2}\right)(v_{2x} - v_{1x})^2$$

$$= \tfrac{1}{2}\left(\frac{m_1m_2}{m_1 + m_2}\right)v_{12}^2$$

6.13 (a) Because $\mu = m(0.5m)/(m + 0.5m) = m/3$, $K_{conv} = \frac{1}{2}(m/3)v^2$. Because $K_i = \frac{1}{2}mv^2$, the fraction that is convertible is $K_{conv}/K_i = 1/3$. (b) If it were converted, the momentum of the isolated two-object system would change.

6.14 (a) $v_{12i} = |0 - (+4.0\text{ m/s})| = 4.0$ m/s and $v_{12f} = |(+1.5\text{ m/s}) - (-0.50\text{ m/s})| = 2.0$ m/s, so $e = (2.0\text{ m/s})/(4.0\text{ m/s}) = 0.50$. (b) See Table S6.14.

Table S6.14 Conversion of kinetic energy

Object	inertia (kg)	Velocity (m/s) before	after	Δv_x	Kinetic energy (J) before	after	ΔK
Earth reference frame							
1	1.0	+4.0	−0.50	−4.5	8.0	0.13	−7.9
2	3.0	0	+1.5	+1.5	0	3.4	+3.4
						$\Delta K=$	−4.5
Reference frame moving at −1.0 m/s relative to Earth							
1	1.0	+5.0	+0.50	−4.5	12.5	0.13	−12.4
2	3.0	+1.0	+2.5	+1.5	1.5	9.4	+7.9
						$\Delta K=$	−4.5

Chapter 7

7.1 (a) The other object is Earth; this is an attractive interaction because it makes the ball and Earth accelerate toward each other. (b) Repulsive, because the interaction causes the two objects to accelerate away from each other.

7.2 (a) At $t = 30$ ms, the velocity-versus-time graph shows $v_{1x} = 0$ and $v_{2x} = +0.55$ m/s, so $p_{1x} = (0.12\text{ kg})(0) = 0$ and $p_{2x} = (0.24\text{ kg})(+0.55\text{ m/s}) = +0.13$ kg·m/s. At $t = 60$ ms, $v_{1x} = 0.37$ m/s and $v_{2x} = 0.37$ m/s, so $p_{1x} = (0.12\text{ kg})(+0.37\text{ m/s}) = +0.044$ kg·m/s and $p_{2x} = (0.24\text{ kg})(+0.37\text{ m/s}) = +0.089$ kg·m/s. At $t = 90$ ms, $v_{1x} = +0.73$ m/s and $v_{2x} = +0.18$ m/s, so $p_{1x} = +0.088$ kg·m/s and $p_{2x} = +0.043$ kg·m/s. (b) At 30 ms, $p_x = p_{1x} + p_{2x} = 0 + (+0.13\text{ kg}\cdot\text{m/s}) = +0.13$ kg·m/s. At 60 ms, $p_x = (+0.044\text{ kg}\cdot\text{m/s}) + (+0.089\text{ kg}\cdot\text{m/s}) = +0.13$ kg·m/s. At 90 ms, $p_x = (+0.088\text{ kg}\cdot\text{m/s}) + (+0.043\text{ kg}\cdot\text{m/s}) = +0.13$ kg·m/s.

7.3 (a) With the velocity values from Checkpoint 7.2 and the formula $K = \frac{1}{2}mv^2$, the kinetic energies are: at $t = 30$ ms, $K_1 = 0$ and $K_2 = 0.036$ J; at $t = 60$ m/s, $K_1 = 0.0082$ J and $K_2 = 0.016$ J; at $t = 90$ ms, $K_1 = 0.032$ J and $K_2 = 0.0039$ J. (b) At 30 ms, $K = 0.036$ J; at 60 ms, $K = 0.025$ J; at 90 ms, $K = 0.036$ J.

7.4 (a) Zero, because the ball's speed is zero. (b) The momentum of the ball is constant only when the ball is isolated—in other words, when it is not interacting with anything. Ignoring the gravitational interaction with Earth because that interaction is much, much weaker than the ball-wall interaction, you can say that the ball is not interacting with anything before and after the collision, and so its momentum remains constant during these intervals. The ball interacts with the wall during the collision, and so now momentum is not constant for the system made up of only the ball; momentum is constant, however, for the system made up of ball plus wall.

7.5 As the spring is compressed, the kinetic energy of the cart is converted to potential energy in the deformed spring. Because the sum of the kinetic and potential energies must not change, any loss in kinetic energy must be made up by a gain in potential energy. Initially, all the energy of the system is kinetic and equal to $\frac{1}{2}mv_i^2$, where m is the inertia of the cart. In the middle drawing, the kinetic energy is zero, and so the potential energy is $\frac{1}{2}mv_i^2$.

7.6 (a) Let the direction in which the puck moves be the $+x$ direction. The x component of the puck's initial velocity is then $v_x = +8.0$ m/s, and the x component of its acceleration is $a_x = -1.0$ m/s². With that acceleration, the puck's speed is reduced by 1.0 m/s each second. So, after 4 s, the speed is half of its original value. Because kinetic energy depends on v^2, the puck's kinetic energy is reduced to one-quarter of its original value after 4 s. After 6 s, the speed is one-quarter of its original value and the kinetic energy is one-sixteenth. Based on these data, your sketches should look like Figure S7.6. (b) The kinetic energy is converted to thermal energy (both puck and ice get warmer).

Figure S7.6

7.7 It should be classified as incoherent configuration energy. Chemical energy is associated with changes in the arrangement of atoms in molecules and so is configuration energy. In a chemical reaction, the orientation of the molecules and the kinetic energy given to the products are random, and so chemical energy is incoherent. It is not possible to make all products move in one direction and extract (coherent) kinetic energy. (The same arguments hold for nuclear energy, the form of incoherent configuration energy that corresponds to changes in nuclear configuration.)

7.8 Both of you, because the term *conserve* means one thing when used by physicists and another thing when used by environmentalists. To physicists, energy is always conserved, which means it is neither created out of nothing nor destroyed. When you leave the lights on, electrical energy is converted to light energy and thermal energy (lamps get hot). The sum of those forms of energy is equal to the electrical energy consumed by the lights. To environmentalists, *conserving energy* means reducing or eliminating the use of source energy. When you turn off the lights, less source energy (oil, gas, coal, or nuclear fuel) needs to be converted to electrical energy. The phrase *conserving energy* has nothing to do with the law of conservation of energy, and because Earth's supply of source energy is limited, you are right to turn off the lights.

7.9 (a) Elastic potential energy in the spring is converted to kinetic energy in the ball and in the spring as the spring expands. The interaction is non-dissipative because it can run in reverse: The ball compresses the spring. (b) The ball gains speed as it changes its position relative to the ground, which means potential energy is converted to kinetic energy. The interaction is nondissipative because it can run in reverse: The ball is launched up. (c) Kinetic energy is converted to thermal energy: The bicycle slows down because of friction, which irreversibly dissipates the kinetic energy. The interaction is dissipative because the reverse motion—the bicycle accelerates backward without the pedals moving—is not possible. (d) Chemical energy in the gasoline is converted to kinetic energy (and thermal energy). The conversion is irreversible and therefore the interaction is dissipative. (If you played this situation in reverse, you would see a car slowing down backward. This is possible, but close inspection would reveal details that are not possible: The driver pressing the gas pedal instead of the brake pedal and fuel being added to the tank.)

7.10 (a) When you throw a ball, your momentum increases in the direction opposite the direction of the ball's momentum because the momentum of the isolated system comprising you and the ball must be constant. The throwing corresponds to an explosive separation ($e > 1$). The catching corresponds to a totally inelastic collision ($e = 0$). So, when your friend catches the ball, her momentum increases in the direction in which the ball was originally moving (away from you). (Normally these momentum changes aren't noticeable because of the friction between feet and ground, which is why this checkpoint has you standing on ice.) (b) The thrower moves back ("recoils") in the direction opposite the direction of the thrown ball (away from the catcher). The catcher recoils in the direction in which the ball was originally moving (away from the thrower). Therefore, each throw or catch increases the momentum of each of you in the direction away from the other, meaning that the interaction is repulsive. The ball serves as the carrier—the "gauge particle"—of the interaction. (c) Improbable as it may seem, there actually is a mechanical model for an attractive interaction based on an exchange of particles. Imagine two people standing within arm's reach of each other and extending their arms toward each other without touching. Person A holds a ball and throws it back toward himself; person B catches it before it hits person A, and throws it back toward herself. Repeat as needed. This is perhaps not easy to implement, but the throwing back and forth does result in an attraction.

7.11 (a) Once the vehicles lock together, they have identical velocities, the center-of-mass velocity. If you take the x component of the car's initial velocity as positive, you get from Eq. 6.26 $v_{cmx} = [(1000 \text{ kg})(+25 \text{ m/s}) + (2000 \text{ kg})(-25 \text{ m/s})]/[1000 \text{ kg} + 2000 \text{ kg}] = -8.3$ m/s. Therefore $\Delta v_c = (-8.3 \text{ m/s}) - (+25 \text{ m/s}) = -33$ m/s and $\Delta v_v = (-8.3 \text{ m/s}) - (-25 \text{ m/s}) = +17$ m/s. Because it has less inertia, the car has the larger change in velocity. Because both velocity changes occur during the same time interval, the acceleration is greater for the car, in agreement with Eq. 7.6. (b) $a_{cx,av} = (-33 \text{ m/s})/(0.20 \text{ s}) = -1.7 \times 10^2$ m/s² and $a_{cx,av} = (+17 \text{ m/s})/(0.20 \text{ s}) = +83$ m/s². The ratio is not exactly -2 because of the rounding of the velocity changes in part a.

7.12

$$\Delta K_E = \frac{1}{2}m_E v_{E,f}^2 - \frac{1}{2}m_E v_{E,i}^2 = \frac{1}{2}m_E(v_{E,f}^2 - v_{E,i}^2)$$

$$= \frac{1}{2}m_E[(v_{Ex,i} + \Delta v_{Ex})^2 - v_{E,i}^2]$$

$$= m_E v_{E,i}\Delta v_{Ex} + \frac{1}{2}m_E(\Delta v_{Ex})^2.$$

Rearranging terms and substituting Δp_{Ex} for $m_E\Delta v_{Ex}$, you get

$$\Delta K_E = v_{Ex,i}(m_E\Delta v_{Ex}) + \frac{1}{2}\frac{(m_E\Delta v_{Ex})^2}{m_E}$$

$$= v_{Ex,i}\Delta p_{Ex} + \frac{(\Delta p_{Ex})^2}{2m_E}.$$

The first term on the right of the final equals sign is zero because in the reference frame of Earth, $v_{Ex,i} = 0$. The second term to the right of the final equals sign is negligibly small compared to the corresponding term for the cart because the numerators are the same (conservation of momentum requires that $\Delta p_E = -\Delta p_c$) and $m_E \gg m_c$. Therefore $\Delta K_E \approx 0$, and the only change in kinetic energy in the Earth-cart system must be that of the cart.

7.13
$$\Delta U_{12} = U(x_2) - U(x_1)$$

$$\Delta U_{21} = U(x_1) - U(x_2) = -\Delta U_{12}$$

$$\Delta U_{1 \to 2 \to 1} = \Delta U_{12} + \Delta U_{21}$$

$$= [U(x_2) - U(x_1)] + [U(x_1) - U(x_2)]$$

$$= 0.$$

The potential energy change as an object moves in one direction has a sign, and the potential energy change when the object moves back to its original position has the opposite sign and the same magnitude. Thus the change in potential energy along a round trip is zero. This statement, trivial as it may seem, is another hallmark of potential energy. No other form of energy has this property.

7.14 As the ball moves upward, it slows down, reducing its kinetic energy. Because the Earth-ball system is closed, the gravitational potential energy of the system must therefore increase as the ball moves upward. The slowing down of the upward-moving ball means that the acceleration points down—the direction in which the gravitational potential energy of the Earth-ball system decreases. When the ball moves downward, it is again accelerated downward, its kinetic energy increases, and its potential energy decreases.

7.15 (a) It increases (see Checkpoint 7.14). (b) $\Delta U^G = (3.4 \text{ kg})(9.8 \text{ m/s}^2)$ $(1.0 \text{ m}) = 33$ J. (c) Your arm muscles burn up some chemical energy as you raise the book.

7.16 No. Even though you may hear people say that the quantity expressed by Eq. 7.21 is "the gravitational potential energy of the ball," it is incorrect to do so. It is not the ball by itself that possesses the potential energy. The gravitational potential energy is a property of the configuration of the Earth-ball system. Put another way, the ball by itself is not a closed system—it does not fall by itself. Consequently, the energy of the ball by itself is not constant.

7.17 With $e = 0$, Eq. 7.26 gives $\Delta E_{th} = \frac{1}{2}\mu v_{12,i}^2$. The reduced inertia is $\mu = (1000 \text{ kg})(2000 \text{ kg})/(1000 \text{ kg} + 2000 \text{ kg}) = 667$ kg, and the initial relative speed is $v_{12,i} = 50$ m/s. Thus $\Delta E_{th} = \frac{1}{2}(667 \text{ kg})(50 \text{ m/s})^2 = 8.3 \times 10^5$ J.

Chapter 8

8.1 Because the crate's velocity is constant, its momentum is also constant. So the change in its momentum is zero, and therefore the rate of change in its momentum is also zero. Surprised? Read on.

8.2 (a) As you set the crate in motion, the acceleration and the change in momentum point in the direction of travel. Because the vector sum of the forces exerted on the crate is equal to the time rate of change in its momentum, the vector sum points in the direction of travel. This makes sense: To make the crate move faster in a certain direction, you must push it in that direction. (b) When the crate is slowing down, all the signs are reversed: The acceleration points opposite the direction of travel, and so the change in momentum and the vector sum of the forces point opposite the direction of travel. Again, this makes sense because in order to stop the crate, you have to exert a force in the direction opposite its direction of travel. (c) When the crate is at rest—whether you are pushing against it or not—the vector sum of the forces exerted on it is zero, and so there is no direction involved.

8.3 (a) Because both collisions have the same initial and final velocities, it suffices to look at must one. To see whether the momentum of the

two-cart system is constant, we calculate the change in momentum of each cart:

$$\Delta v_{1x} = v_{1x,f} - v_{1x,i} = (+0.80 \text{ m/s}) - 0 = +0.80 \text{ m/s}$$

$$\Delta v_{2x} = v_{2x,f} - v_{2x,i} = (+0.20 \text{ m/s}) - (+0.60 \text{ m/s}) = -0.40 \text{ m/s}$$

$$\Delta p_{1x} = m_1\Delta v_{1x} = (0.12 \text{ kg})(+0.80 \text{ m/s}) = +0.096 \text{ kg} \cdot \text{m/s}$$

$$\Delta p_{2x} = m_2\Delta v_{2x} = (0.24 \text{ kg})(-0.40 \text{ m/s}) = -0.096 \text{ kg} \cdot \text{m/s}.$$

The total change in momentum is therefore zero, $\Delta p_{1x} + \Delta p_{2x} = 0$, and so the momentum of the system does not change. (b) Whether or not the collision is elastic can be determined by looking at the relative speeds. Before the collision $v_{12i} = |v_{1x,i} - v_{2x,i}| = |0 - (+0.60 \text{ m/s})| = 0.60 \text{ m/s}$; after the collision $v_{12f} = |v_{1x,f} - v_{2x,f}| = |(+0.80 \text{ m/s}) - (+0.20 \text{ m/s})| = 0.60 \text{ m/s}$. Therefore the relative speed is the same before and after the collision, $v_{12i} = v_{12f}$ and so $e \equiv v_{12f}/v_{12i} = 1$, and the collisions are indeed elastic. (You can obtain the same result by verifying that the kinetic energy of the two-cart system doesn't change.)

8.4 Yes. Because two colliding objects can be considered isolated, the momentum of the system remains unchanged regardless of the type of interaction. Therefore the changes in the momentum of the objects are equal in magnitude but opposite in direction, $\Delta \vec{p}_1 = -\Delta \vec{p}_2$, and so the objects exert equal forces on each other in opposite directions.

8.5 (a) The two magnitudes are equal. If that surprises you—how can something so small exert a force on something so large?—remember that any change in the book's momentum must be made up by an equal change of opposite sign in Earth's momentum, because the Earth-book system is isolated. (b) Yes. The fact that the book exerts a force $\vec{F}_{\text{by book on Earth}} = \Delta p_E/\Delta t$ means Earth's momentum must be changing. Its velocity must therefore be changing, and so it is accelerating. Because its inertia is so great, however, the acceleration is negligible: The Earth-book system is isolated and so $\Delta \vec{p}_E + \Delta \vec{p}_b = m_E\Delta \vec{v}_E + m_b\Delta \vec{v}_b = \vec{0}$, so that

$$\Delta \vec{v}_E = \frac{m_b}{m_E}\Delta \vec{v}_b \approx \vec{0},$$

which means that Earth's acceleration during this interaction is vanishingly small.

8.6 (a) Because the collision is totally inelastic, the final velocities are the same: $v_{bx,f} = v_{mx,f}$. Because the mosquito-bus system is isolated, the final momentum of the system must be the same as the initial momentum. The x component of the initial momentum is

$$p_{x,i} = m_m v_{mx,i} + m_b v_{bx,i} = m_m(0) + m_b v_{bx,i}$$

$$= 0 + (10^4 \text{ kg})(+25 \text{ m/s}) = +2.5 \times 10^5 \text{ kg} \cdot \text{m/s}.$$

The x component of the final momentum is

$$p_{x,f} = m_m v_{mx,f} + m_b v_{bx,f} = (m_m + m_b)v_{x,f},$$

where $v_{x,f}$ is the x component of the common final velocity. Substituting inertia values gives

$$p_{x,f} = (10^{-4} \text{ kg} + 10^4 \text{ kg})v_{x,f} = p_{x,i} = +2.5 \times 10^5 \text{ kg} \cdot \text{m/s}$$

or, solving for $v_{x,f}$,

$$v_{x,f} = +25 \text{ m/s}.$$

It looks like the velocity of the bus hasn't changed at all. If you pretend that all the numerical values given are exact and keep more significant digits, however, you find that $v_{bx,f} = +24.99999975$ m/s, which means the bus velocity changes by a minuscule amount: $\Delta v_{bx} = -0.00000025$ m/s (no one in the bus notices!). The x component of the change in the mosquito's velocity is $\Delta v_{mx} = +25$ m/s.

(b) The x component of the change in the average acceleration of the bus is

$$a_{bx} = \Delta v_{bx}/\Delta t = (-0.00000025 \text{ m/s})/(0.005 \text{ s})$$

$$= -0.00005 \text{ m/s}^2.$$

That of the mosquito is

$$a_{mx} = \Delta v_{mx}/\Delta t = (+25 \text{ m/s})/(0.005 \text{ s}) = +5000 \text{ m/s}^2!$$

(*c*) The *x* component of the momentum changes are

$$\Delta p_{bx} = m_b \Delta v_{bx} = (10{,}000 \text{ kg})(-0.00000025 \text{ m/s})$$
$$= -0.0025 \text{ kg} \cdot \text{m/s}$$

and
$$\Delta p_{mx} = m_m \Delta v_{mx} = (10^{-4} \text{ kg})(+25 \text{ m/s})$$
$$= +0.0025 \text{ kg} \cdot \text{m/s}.$$

Notice that these changes in momentum are equal in magnitude and opposite in direction, so that the momentum of the isolated system doesn't change.

(*d*), (*e*)
$$(F_{\text{by bus on mos}})_x = \Delta p_{mx}/\Delta t = (+0.0025 \text{ kg} \cdot \text{m/s})/(0.005 \text{ s})$$
$$= +0.5 \text{ kg} \cdot \text{m/s}^2$$

$$(F_{\text{by mos on bus}})_x = \Delta p_{bx}/\Delta t = (-0.0025 \text{ kg} \cdot \text{m/s})/(0.005 \text{ s})$$
$$= -0.5 \text{ kg} \cdot \text{m/s}^2.$$

These two forces are equal in magnitude. Because of the large difference in inertia, however, the effect of this force on the bus is negligible, while on the mosquito the effect is enormous.

8.7 *Contact forces:* The only object in direct contact with the first magnet is the table, and so the table exerts a contact force on the magnet. There is no contact force with the other magnet because the two are not touching. Presumably the first magnet is also in contact with the surrounding air, and so there may also be a contact force exerted by the air on the magnet (in practice this force is negligible as long as the relative velocity of the magnet and the air is not too large). *Field forces:* Both gravitational and magnetic forces occur in this problem. There is a gravitational force exerted by Earth on the magnet and a magnetic force exerted by the second magnet. In principle, there is also a gravitational interaction between the two magnets and between the magnets and the table, but the forces due to these interactions are so small that we can safely ignore them.

8.8 No. Although the two forces are equal in magnitude and exerted in opposite directions, just as the two forces in an interaction pair are, they originate from different interactions and therefore are not part of the same interaction pair. The two forces in an interaction pair are exerted on different objects, whereas the two forces mentioned in this checkpoint are exerted on the same object (the book).

8.9 See Figure S8.9. During free fall, there is no contact force between the book and any other object. The only force exerted on the book is the gravitational force exerted by Earth (we ignore air resistance).

Figure S8.9

8.10 See Figure S8.10. The person is subject to one contact force: an upward force exerted by the ring (this is what keeps the person suspended). In addition, there is a downward gravitational force exerted by Earth.

Figure S8.10

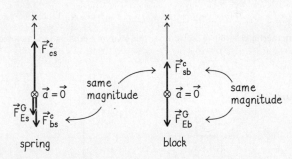

8.11 (*a*) See Figure S8.11*a*. As you accelerate the ball upward, the force exerted by your hand on the ball is larger than the force of gravity exerted by Earth on the ball. (*b*) See Figure S8.11*b*. Once the ball is released, the only force exerted on it is that exerted by Earth (ignoring air resistance). (*c*) The forces exerted on the ball are the same on all parts of the trajectory. Therefore your drawing for part *c* should look exactly like your drawing for part *b*. Although the direction of the ball's velocity reverses during flight, the force exerted by Earth always points downward.

Figure S8.11

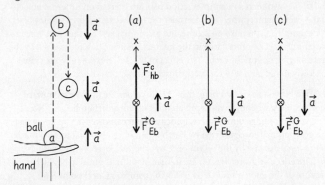

8.12 Figure S8.12 shows the free-body diagrams for the spring and the brick. The problem asks about the force exerted by the spring on the ceiling $\vec{F}_{sc}^c$, a force that forms an interaction pair with the force exerted by the ceiling on the spring. The brick is subject to a downward gravitational force exerted by Earth and an upward contact force exerted by the spring. Because the brick is at rest, we know that these two forces are equal in magnitude. The spring is subject to a downward gravitational force, a downward contact force exerted by the brick, and an upward contact force exerted by the ceiling. Because the spring is at rest we know that the forces must add up to zero and so the force exerted by the spring on the ceiling is equal to the combined gravitational forces exerted by Earth on the spring and the brick. (This result makes sense because the ceiling has to support both of them.)

Figure S8.12

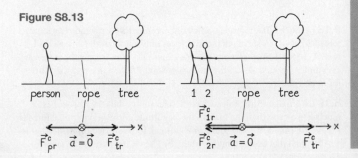

8.13 Figure S8.13 shows the free-body diagram for the rope. The tree now must exert a force of magnitude $2F$ to balance the forces exerted by the two people. This means a force of magnitude $2F$ is exerted on both ends of the rope, and so the tension is $T = 2F$—twice as large as when the two people pulled on opposite ends.

Figure S8.13

8.14 (*a*) The force you exert on your friend gives her a constant acceleration given by Eq. 8.7, where m is the inertia of your friend and her skates. Estimating m to be 60 kg (adjust for your own estimate), you have $a = (200 \text{ N})/(60 \text{ kg}) = 3.3 \text{ m/s}^2$. Her displacement in the 2.0s is $\Delta x = \frac{1}{2}a_x(\Delta t)^2 = \frac{1}{2}(+3.3 \text{ m/s}^2)(2.0 \text{ s})^2 = +6.7 \text{ m}$. (*b*) When a person jumps off a wall, he is in free fall, and so the magnitude of his acceleration is 9.8 m/s². (*c*) When you put the person's inertia at 60 kg (adjust to your liking), the magnitude of the force exerted by Earth on the person is $F_{Ep}^G = (60 \text{ kg})(9.8 \text{ m/s}^2) = 5.9 \times 10^2 \text{ N}$.

8.15 The two forces in an interaction pair are exerted on different objects and so never cancel when you consider the forces exerted on a single object. For example, if you push on a crate, the force you exert on the crate accelerates the crate. The other force in the interaction pair is a force exerted by the crate *on you*, not on the crate. The effect of this force exerted by the crate is to slow you down, not to cancel the force you exert on the crate.

8.16 (*a*) If you answered $m_E g$, think again! Does Earth have an upward acceleration g whenever you drop an object from a certain height? No; Earth doesn't budge. From the reciprocity of forces, however, you know that the gravitational force exerted by Earth on an object is equal in magnitude to the force exerted by the object on Earth. So the correct answer is $m_1 g$. (*b*) The effect this force has on Earth's acceleration is entirely negligible because of the enormous inertia of Earth (compare Checkpoint 8.6):

$$a_E = \frac{m_1}{m_E}g \approx 0.$$

If you are wondering how it is possible that the force exerted by Earth on an object and the force exerted by the object on Earth both depend on the inertia of the object only, then you are very perceptive. I shall explain this when we discuss gravity in Chapter 13.

8.17 (*a*) See Figure S8.17. Note that the $\vec{F}_{Em}^G$ vector arrow is shorter than the $\vec{F}_{fm}^c$ arrow. You drew your diagram that way, right? (*b*) Because the elevator is accelerating upward, so are you. Therefore the vector sum of all the forces acting on you must point upward. This means that the contact force exerted by the floor of the elevator on you is larger than the downward gravitational force exerted on you. From Eq. 8.8,

$$\sum F_x = ma_x = F_{fmx}^c + F_{Emx}^G$$

$$F_{fmx}^c = ma_x - F_{Emx}^G = ma_x - (-mg) = m(a_x + g).$$

For an inertia $m = 60$ kg (substitute your own inertia), this yields a force of $(60 \text{ kg})[(+1 \text{ m/s}^2) + (9.8 \text{ m/s}^2)] = 6.5 \times 10^2 \text{ N}$.

Figure S8.17

8.18 (*a*) Stiffer. If k is large, a small displacement $x - x_0$ requires a large force (Eq. 8.18). A spring that compresses only a little under a large load is stiff. (*b*) Steel. Steel compresses less (small Δx) than foam rubber (larger Δx) under equal loads. So the spring constant for steel is larger than that for foam rubber.

8.19 (*a*) Smaller. Both objects have acceleration g, but the feather has much less inertia than the brick. The magnitude of the gravitational force is $F_{Eo}^G = mg$ (Eq. 8.17), and so the gravitational force exerted on the feather is smaller than that exerted on the brick. (*b*) The momentum is the same for

both. The change in an object's momentum caused by a constant force—in other words, the impulse delivered to the object—is $\vec{F}\,\Delta t$. Because the same force is exerted on both objects for the same amount of time, $\Delta \vec{p}$ is the same for both. However the magnitude of $\Delta \vec{v}_{feather}$ is much larger than the magnitude of $\Delta \vec{v}_{brick}$ because of the difference in inertia.

8.20 (*a*) For a single object, the center-of-mass acceleration is equal to the particle's acceleration, $\vec{a}_{cm} = \vec{a}$, because the position of the center of mass coincides with the position x of the particle: $x_{cm} \equiv mx/m = x$ (Eq. 6.24). Finally for a single object there are no internal forces, so all forces are external and so $\sum \vec{F}_{ext} = \sum \vec{F}$. Consequently, Eqs. 8.46 and 8.47 are equivalent for a system made up of only one object. (*b*) Consider the motion of the system over a time interval $\Delta t = t_f - t_i$. If the center of mass initially moves at velocity $\vec{v}_{cm,i}$ at time t_i, then at the end of the time interval it has velocity

$$\vec{v}_{cm,f} = \vec{v}_{cm,i} + \vec{a}_{cm}\Delta t.$$

The change in the total momentum of the many-object system is thus

$$\Delta \vec{p} = \vec{p}_f - \vec{p}_i = m(\vec{v}_{cm,f} - \vec{v}_{cm,i})$$
$$= m(\vec{v}_{cm,i} + \vec{a}_{cm}\Delta t - \vec{v}_{cm,i}) = m\vec{a}_{cm}\Delta t.$$

After substituting Eq. 8.44 for the vector sum of the forces exerted on the system, you have your result:

$$\Delta \vec{p} = (\sum \vec{F}_{ext})\,\Delta t.$$

Chapter 9

9.1 (*a*) External, because the force is exerted from outside the system. (*b*) No, no, and no. Because the wall is hard, heavy, and anchored to the ground, it neither moves nor changes shape. Because there is no friction involved, the wall's temperature does not change. (*c*) No. Its kinetic energy doesn't change because it doesn't accelerate; its potential energy doesn't change because it doesn't change shape or deform; its thermal energy doesn't change because it doesn't heat up. (*d*) No. The energy of the wall remains the same, and so there is no transfer of energy from you to the wall, which means you do no work on the wall no matter how hard you push.

9.2 Both forces do work on the ball because for both the point of application is at the ball, and this point moves as you launch the ball.

9.3 (*a*) As the ball moves upward, its kinetic energy decreases and its internal energy doesn't change. So the change in the ball's energy (the sum of the kinetic and internal energies) is negative. This means the work done on the ball is negative. (*b*) The ball's kinetic energy now increases, causing a positive change in energy, and so the work done on the ball is positive.

9.4 The directions of the force and the force displacement are consistent with the answers obtained by analyzing energy changes. In part *a* the only force exerted on the ball (the gravitational force) is downward, but the displacement is upward, and so the work done on the ball is negative. In part *b* both vectors are directed downward, and so the work done on the ball is positive.

9.5 (*a*) Yes. There are no changes in motion or state in the environment. (*b*) Positive. As the block compresses the spring, the force exerted by the block on the spring is directed toward the wall and the point of application of that force moves toward the wall. Force and force displacement pointing in the same direction means positive work. (Also, the energy of the system increases as the spring is compressed, and so the work done on it must be positive.) (*c*) Zero. The point of contact between wall and spring is not moving, and so the force displacement is zero, meaning that the work done by the wall on the system is also zero. (Indeed, the system comprising spring and block is closed, as we concluded in part *a*.)

9.6 See Figure S9.6. The cart's kinetic energy decreases to zero, and there are no changes in the other forms of energy. The decrease in kinetic energy is the result of negative work done by the person on the cart. The force exerted by the person is directed to the left, and the force displacement is directed to the right, which is a second way of telling you that the work done by the person on the cart is negative.

Figure S9.6

9.7 See Figure S9.7. As the block comes to rest against the compressed spring, the block's kinetic energy decreases, so you must draw the kinetic energy bar below the baseline. The system has two changes in potential energy: a change in gravitational potential energy ΔU^G due to the change in the block-Earth configuration and a change in elastic potential energy ΔU_{spring} due to the compression of the spring. You should draw two potential energy bars, one for each kind. The gravitational potential energy decreases, and the potential energy of the spring increases. The thermal energy increases because of friction. The lengths of the bars add up to zero because the system is closed, so $W = 0$.

Figure S9.7

9.8 See Figure S9.8. The only energy in the system that changes is the kinetic energy, which decreases to zero. The work done on the system must therefore be negative. This negative work is the sum of the work done by the rope on the system and the work done by Earth on the system. The work done by the rope on the system is negative (force upward, force displacement downward), and the work done by Earth on the system is positive (force and force displacement both downward). The work done on the system is negative because, in order for the system to slow down, the magnitude of the force exerted by the rope must be larger than that exerted by Earth.

Figure S9.8

9.9 (*a*) See Figure S9.9. The kinetic energy remains unchanged, but energy is dissipated because of the friction between box and floor. No changes occur in potential energy. The changes in thermal energy can be attributed to work done on the system. The person exerts external forces both on the box (via the rope) and on the floor (via his feet). Only the force displacement of the force exerted on the box is nonzero. Because the force displacement and the force point in the same direction, the work done by the person on the system is positive. (*b*) Because the system now includes the person/rope, the system is closed, which means no work is done on it and the W bar in the energy diagram is blank. As in the system chosen in part *a*, you have $\Delta K = 0$, $\Delta U = 0$, and $\Delta E_{\text{th}} > 0$ (friction between box and floor increases E_{th} for the system). With the person/rope included as part of the system, the source energy bar must be filled in and it must be negative because muscle energy is used up as the person pulls.

Figure S9.9

9.10 The x component of the impulse delivered by the (constant) gravitational force is given by Eq. 8.25, $\Delta p_x = F^G_{\text{Eb}x}\Delta t = -m_{\text{b}}g\Delta t$. Because the acceleration is constant, $\Delta v_x/\Delta t = a_{x,\text{av}} = -g$, you can say that $\Delta t = -\Delta v_x/g$ and thus

$$\Delta p_x = -m_{\text{b}}g(-\Delta v_x/g) = m_{\text{b}}\Delta v_x = m_{\text{b}}(v_{x,\text{f}} - v_{x,\text{i}}).$$

9.11 Because Δx_F is larger than Δx_{cm} (see Figure 9.19), W in Eq. 9.16 is larger than ΔK_{cm} in Eq. 9.14. Because $\Delta E = W$, this means that ΔE is larger than ΔK_{cm}. This makes sense because only part of the work done on the system goes into changing K_{cm}. Another part goes into increasing the internal energy of the system. $W = \Delta E$ accounts for both the change in K_{cm} and the change in internal energy.

9.12 For a single particle, the position of the center of mass is the position of the particle (Eq. 6.24):

$$x_{cm} \equiv \frac{mx}{m} = x,$$

so the force displacement is equal to the displacement of the center of mass: $\Delta x_{cm} = \Delta x_F$. The center-of-mass translational kinetic energy is simply the particle's kinetic energy:

$$K_{cm} = \tfrac{1}{2}mv_{cm}^2 = \tfrac{1}{2}mv^2.$$

Therefore Eq. 9.14 becomes

$$\Delta K = (\textstyle\sum F_x)\Delta x_F.$$

Because a particle has only kinetic energy, Eqs. 9.1 and 9.2 give $\Delta K = \Delta E = \Delta W$, so $\Delta W = (\sum F_x)\Delta x_F$, which is Eq. 9.9, the work equation for a single particle.

Now for reducing Eq. 9.18 to Eq. 9.9. Equation 9.18 is for a many-particle system. Because you want to use this equation for a single-particle system, there is only one particle experiencing the (external) force and so only one force displacement. That means you can take the factor Δx_{Fn} out of the summation in Eq. 9.18 and drop the subscript n. The equation is then identical to Eq. 9.9.

9.13 If the force is constant—in other words, if $F_x(x) = F_x$—it can be pulled out of the integral:

$$W = \int_{x_i}^{x_f} F_x(x)\,dx = F_x \int_{x_i}^{x_f} dx = F_x(x_f - x_i) = F_x\Delta x,$$

which is identical to Eq. 9.8.

9.14 See Figure S9.14. (*a*) This system is not closed, and the brick exerts a force on the system that has a nonzero force displacement. As it moves downward, the brick does positive work on the spring. This work ends up as elastic potential energy of the spring. (The force exerted by the floor on the spring does no work on the spring.) (*b*) The system is closed, so no

work is done on it. In addition, none of the four types of energy changes! The increase in the elastic potential energy of the spring is accompanied by a decrease in the gravitational potential energy of the brick. To show this, you should draw two separate potential energy bars.

9.15 mg is the magnitude of the constant force of gravity exerted by Earth *on the brick*, not a force exerted on the spring. The contact force between brick and spring is a variable force described by Hooke's law.

If you find it surprising that the brick doesn't push down on the spring with the same force as Earth pulls down on the brick, look at the free-body diagrams for the brick in Figure S9.15. At the instant it is released just above the uncompressed spring, the brick is subject to only the downward force of gravity; the spring exerts no upward force as long as it is not compressed (Figure S9.15a). Consequently the x component of the brick's initial acceleration is $a_x = -g$. As the brick moves downward, the upward force exerted by the spring on it increases according to Hooke's law (Eq. 8.20, $F_{sbx}^c = -k(x - x_o)$). In this problem you are dealing with the situation represented by the free-body diagram in Figure S9.15b. At the instant represented in Figure S9.15b, $\vec{F}_{sb}^c$ is nonzero but still smaller in magnitude than F_{Eb}^G (because the brick has not yet come to rest against the compressed spring):

$$F_{bs}^c < F_{Eb}^G = mg.$$

Answering this checkpoint requires knowing $\vec{F}_{bs}^c$, which forms an interaction pair with $\vec{F}_{sb}^c$: $\vec{F}_{bs}^c = -\vec{F}_{sb}^c$, so

$$F_{bs}^c < F_{Eb}^G = mg.$$

The difference between the two force magnitudes F_{bs}^c and mg is what makes the brick accelerate downward. (If you wonder where I get these brain twisters, the answer is simple: As I wrote the example, I was wondering about this question myself.)

Figure S9.15

Figure S9.14

9.16 Although $\Delta x_{cm} = 0$ when the block comes to rest at its starting position, the distance it travels is nonzero: $d_{path} = 2(0.50 \text{ m}) = 1.0 \text{ m}$. All of the block's kinetic energy is converted to thermal energy, and so $\Delta E_{th} = K_i = \frac{1}{2}mv^2 = \frac{1}{2}(0.50 \text{ kg})(1.0 \text{ m/s})^2 = 0.25 \text{ J}$. From Eq. 9.28, you get $F_{sb}^f = \Delta E_{th}/d_{path} = (0.25 \text{ J})/(1.0 \text{ m}) = 0.25 \text{ N}$.

9.17 (a) Car: $(1.4 \times 10^8 \text{ J})/(1800 \text{ s}) = 78 \text{ kW}$; plane $(1.4 \times 10^8 \text{ J})/(1 \text{ s}) = 140 \text{ MW}$. (b) Equation 7.19 tells you that, to raise the load, the gravitational potential energy of the load-Earth system must be increased by $\Delta U^G = (10 \text{ kg})(10 \text{ m/s}^2)(50 \text{ m}) = 5000 \text{ J}$. The athlete can deliver 500 W = 500 J/s and so takes $(5000 \text{ J})/(500 \text{ J/s}) = 10 \text{ s}$. (c) $W_{\text{by engine}} = W_{\text{by athlete}}$ because the work done on the load does not depend on the rate at which it is done. In both cases, the work done on the load is equal to the change in the gravitational potential energy of the load-Earth system.

Chapter 10

10.1 (a) If your first reaction to this question was "In which reference frame?," you got the point! Before release, the ball is moving along with the cart, and so its initial velocity in the reference frame of the cart is zero. In the Earth reference frame, the ball's initial velocity is equal to that of the cart. (b) The speed is the magnitude of the velocity, which is the rate at which the displacement changes. Because of the cart's horizontal displacement, the ball's displacement from one frame of the film clip to the next is always greater in the Earth reference frame than in the cart's reference frame (see Figure 10.4). Therefore the ball's speed is higher in the Earth reference frame.

10.2 The ball's instantaneous velocity is the displacement over an infinitesimally small time interval. As Figure S10.2 shows, $\Delta \vec{r}$ approaches the tangent to the ball's trajectory as we make Δt smaller; $\vec{v}$ is thus tangent to the trajectory. Because of the downward curvature of the trajectory, $\vec{v}$ points above $\Delta \vec{r}$.

Figure S10.2

10.3 The suitcase is subject to a downward gravitational force and an upward contact force exerted by the belt. Because the suitcase's velocity is constant, its acceleration is zero, and so the vector sum of these forces must be zero. The two forces must therefore be equal in magnitude (Figure S10.3).

Figure S10.3

10.4 The cabinet participates in three interactions—with you, with the floor, and with Earth—and so is subject to three forces: a horizontal force due to your push $\vec{F}_{mc}^c$, a contact force $\vec{F}_{fc}^c$ exerted by the floor, and a downward force of gravity $\vec{F}_{fc}^G$. Because the cabinet remains at rest, the vector sum of these forces must be zero. You know that your force is strictly horizontal and the gravitational force is strictly vertical. With these two forces being exerted on the cabinet, the only way for the vector sum of the forces exerted on the cabinet to be zero is for $\vec{F}_{fc}^c$ to have both a horizontal component $\vec{F}_{fcx}^c$ and a vertical component $\vec{F}_{fcy}^c$. The horizontal component of $\vec{F}_{fc}^c$ is therefore equal in magnitude to $\vec{F}_{mc}^c$, and the vertical component is equal in magnitude to $\vec{F}_{Ec}^G$. The free-body diagram for the file cabinet is shown in Figure S10.4a. (Alternatively, you can draw the two components of the contact force exerted by the floor as two separate forces, as shown in Figure S10.4b.)

Figure S10.4

10.5 (a) The cabinet is subject to the same three forces as in Checkpoint 10.4. Because it moves at constant speed, the vector sum of these forces is still zero, and so the free-body diagram is as shown in Figure S10.5a. (b) The instant you stop pushing, $\vec{F}_{mc}^c$ disappears but $\vec{F}_{fcy}^c$ and $\vec{F}_{Ec}^G$ must be as before because there is no vertical motion. You know that the cabinet comes to rest when you stop pushing, and so there must be a horizontal force that slows it *after* you stop pushing. This force is $\vec{F}_{fcx}^c$. The free-body diagram for the cabinet is shown in Figure S10.5b. Once the cabinet is at rest, $\vec{F}_{fcx}^c$ vanishes.

Figure S10.5

10.6 The motion of the two surfaces in contact relative to each other determines the type of friction: static friction between two surfaces not moving relative to each other and kinetic friction between two surfaces moving relative to each other. (a) Static, (b) kinetic, (c) kinetic, (d) kinetic, (e) static (as long as you are not slipping, your feet are at rest relative to the incline each time you put them on the ground while walking).

10.7 As the person accelerates, her kinetic energy increases. As you've just seen, this increase in kinetic energy is not due to work done on her by the force of static friction. The forces in the vertical direction add up to zero and so do no work either, so the work done on her is zero. What causes her to accelerate is that chemical energy in her muscles is converted to kinetic energy (and some of it is dissipated to thermal energy). So E_{th} increases and E_s decreases; the heights of the bars add up to zero (Figure S10.7). For the package, only its kinetic energy increases. Its shape and temperature remain the same, and so its internal energy does not change. The increase in kinetic energy is entirely due to work done by the conveyor belt on the package. The point of application of the force of friction exerted by the belt surface on the package is displaced in the direction of the force, so the work done on the package is positive, as Figure S10.7 shows.

Figure S10.7

person walking   package on belt

ΔK ΔU ΔE_s ΔE_{th} W ΔK ΔU ΔE_s ΔE_{th} W

10.8 Your final displacement $\Delta \vec{r}$ is the sum of the displacements $\Delta \vec{r}_1$ and $\Delta \vec{r}_2$ in Figure S10.8. You know the length and angular coordinate of $\Delta \vec{r}_1$ and the x and y components of $\Delta \vec{r}_2$. To add the two vectors, you must first determine the x and y components of $\Delta \vec{r}_1$:

$$\Delta x_1 = \Delta r \cos \theta = (1500 \text{ m})(\cos 45°) = 1060 \text{ m}$$

$$\Delta y_1 = \Delta r \sin \theta = (1500 \text{ m})(\sin 45°) = 1060 \text{ m}.$$

Adding the components of $\Delta \vec{r}_1$ and $\Delta \vec{r}_2$ gives

$$\Delta x = \Delta x_1 + \Delta x_2 = 1060 \text{ m} + 700 \text{ m} = 1760 \text{ m}$$

$$\Delta y = \Delta y_1 + \Delta y_2 = 1060 \text{ m} - 300 \text{ m} = 760 \text{ m}.$$

The distance to the pier is thus

$$|\Delta \vec{r}| = \sqrt{\Delta x^2 + \Delta y^2} = 1.92 \times 10^3 \text{ m}.$$

Figure S10.8

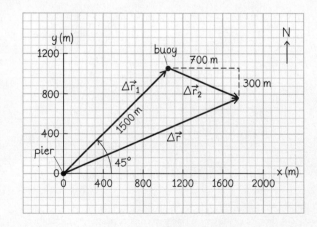

10.9 (a) According to Eqs. 10.3: $v_{x,i} = v_i \cos \theta$ and $v_{y,i} = v_i \sin \theta$. Substituting these values into the expressions we obtained in Examples 10.5 and 10.6 yields

$$x_f = \frac{2v_i^2 \sin \theta \cos \theta}{g} \text{ and } y_{top} = \frac{1}{2} \frac{v_i^2 \sin^2 \theta}{g}.$$

(b) For a given launch speed v_i, y_{top} has its greatest value when $\sin^2 \theta$ is maximal. This occurs when $\theta = 90°$, which makes sense because all of the projectile's speed goes into the upward motion when the projectile is launched straight up. (c) The greatest value of x_f is obtained when $\sin \theta \cos \theta = \frac{1}{2} \sin 2\theta$ is maximum. This occurs when $2\theta = 90°$ or $\theta = 45°$.

10.10 To answer this question, we need to compare the system's final and initial kinetic energies. Let the inertia of puck 1 be m; the inertia of puck 2 is then $2m$. The system's initial kinetic energy is $\frac{1}{2}m(1.8 \text{ m/s})^2 + \frac{1}{2} \cdot 2m(0.2 \text{ m/s})^2 = \frac{1}{2}m(3.3 \text{ m}^2/\text{s}^2)$. The final kinetic energy is $\frac{1}{2}m(0.8 \text{ m/s})^2 + \frac{1}{2} \cdot 2m(1.0 \text{ m/s})^2 = \frac{1}{2}m(2.6 \text{ m}^2/\text{s}^2)$. Because the system's final kinetic energy is not equal to the initial kinetic energy, the collision is not elastic.

10.11 To determine the sign of W, you need to know the sign of the scalar product for various relative positions of $\vec{F}$ and $\Delta \vec{r}$. To do so we choose a coordinate system that has its x axis aligned with $\Delta \vec{r}$ and then we place $\vec{F}$ in different positions (Figure S10.11). The scalar product is $F|\Delta \vec{r}| \cos \phi$, which can be written as $|\Delta \vec{r}|F \cos \phi = |\Delta \vec{r}|F_x$ and which is the product of the magnitude of $\Delta \vec{r}$ and the x component F. Because $|\Delta \vec{r}|$ is always positive, the sign of the scalar product is determined by the algebraic sign of F_x. As you can see in Figure S10.11 F_x is positive when $\vec{F}$ is in quadrants I and IV and negative when $\vec{F}$ is in quadrants II and III. So W is positive when $0 < \phi < 90°$ or $270° < \phi < 360°$. For any other angle, F_x and W are negative. According to Section 9.2, W is positive when $\vec{F}$ and $\Delta \vec{r}$ point in the same direction and negative when they point in opposite directions. So Eq. 10.40 is in complete agreement with our earlier definition of when work is positive and when it is negative.

Figure S10.11

F_x negative, Δr positive; W negative

F_x and Δr positive; W positive

10.12 (a) That the brick slides more easily on ice tells you that the force of friction is smaller in the brick-ice case than in the brick-wood case, and so μ_s is smaller for brick on ice. (b) Substituting $\mu_s = 1$ into Eq. 10.46 gives $(F_{sr}^s)_{max} = F_{sr}^c$ for the maximum force of static friction exerted by the surface on the runner. This is the maximum horizontal force the surface can exert on the runner. Because the runner is not accelerating up or down, the magnitude of the normal force must be equal to the magnitude of the force of gravity, and so $F_{sr}^c = F_{Er}^G = mg$, where m is the runner's inertia. Substituting this value into the equation of motion $\Sigma F_x = ma_x$ shows that the maximum acceleration is $a_x = +g$.

10.13 (*a*) If $\mu_s = 1$, then $\theta_{max} = 45°$ according to Eq. 10.53. (*b*) All objects start sliding well before this angle is reached, telling you that generally $\mu_s < 1$.

10.14 (*a*) The free-body diagram for the bricks is given in Figure 10.42. At the point where the bricks begin to slide, F^G_{Ebx} is equal to the maximum value of F^s_{sb}, and so $F^G_{Ebx} + (F^s_{sb})_{max} = 0$. Because both F^G_{Ebx} and $(F^s_{sb})_{max}$ are proportional to the inertia m of the bricks, the angle at which $F^G_{Ebx} + (F^s_{sb})_{max} = 0$ is independent of m. The single and double bricks therefore begin sliding at the same instant. (You can also see this directly from Eq. 10.53, which shows that θ_{max} is independent of m). (*b*) Once the bricks begin to slide, kinetic friction replaces static friction. So the vector sum of the forces exerted on the bricks in the x direction is $\sum F_x = F^G_{Ebx} + F^k_{sb} = -mg\sin\theta + F^k_{sb}$. Using Eqs. 10.43 and 10.55, you can write this as $\sum F_x = -\mu_s F^c_{sb} + \mu_k F^c_{sb} = (\mu_k - \mu_s)F^c_{sb}$. The x component of the acceleration of the bricks is thus given by

$$ma_x = \mu_k mg\cos\theta - mg\sin\theta$$

and is independent of inertia: $a_x = \mu_k g\cos\theta - g\sin\theta$. The single and double brick therefore both slide down with the same acceleration. These results can also be justified as follows: In parts *a* and *b* all forces exerted on the double brick are twice as large, but the double brick, having twice the inertia, requires twice as large a force to reach the same acceleration. Consequently there cannot be any difference between the accelerations.

Chapter 11

11.1 If $|\vec{v}_f| > |\vec{v}_i|$, the vector $\vec{v}_f$ has a greater magnitude than the vector $\vec{v}_i$. As a result, the change in velocity $\Delta\vec{v}$ and $\vec{a}_{av}$ now point not toward the center of the circle but more in the direction of motion, as shown in Figure S11.1 (compare with Figure 11.8*b*).

Figure S11.1

11.2 The centripetal acceleration is the same for both cubes, and so the force required to keep cube 1 going in a circle must be twice as large as the force required for cube 2. The maximum force of static friction, however, also scales with m—$(F^s_{tc})_{max} = \mu_s F^n_{tc} = \mu_s mg$—and so both cubes begin sliding at the same instant.

11.3 (*a*) Yes. In order to generate a vector sum of forces that points toward the center of the trajectory, the contact force exerted by the road surface on the bicycle (and that exerted by the bicycle on its rider) must be at an angle with the vertical. This can happen only when the bicycle leans into the curve. (*b*) No. The vertical component of $\vec{F}^c_{sb}$ is what prevents the bucket from falling to the ground: $F^c_{sbz} + F^G_{Eb} = 0$. If the rope is horizontal, then so is $\vec{F}^c_{sb}$ and consequently $F^c_{sbz} = 0$. Without this vertical component, the bucket cannot stay in the air.

11.4 (*a*) 3. The largest rotational inertia is obtained when the inertia of the pencil is as far as possible from the axis. For axis 3, half of the pencil is farther from the axis as for axis 2. (*b*) 1. For this axis all the inertia of the pencil is close to the axis.

11.5 (*a*) In 1.5 s the object covers an arc length of 4.5 m. Thus $\vartheta = (4.5\text{ m})/(2.0\text{ m}) = 2.3$. (*b*) The perimeter of the circle is $2\pi(2.0\text{ m})$. At 3.0 m/s, it therefore takes the object $2\pi(2.0\text{ m})/(3.0\text{ m/s}) = 4.2$ s to complete one revolution. (*c*) In 1.0 s the object moves through an arc of 3.0 m, and so the change in rotational coordinate is $(3.0\text{ m})/(2.0\text{ m}) = 1.5$. The object begins at a polar angle of 90°, which corresponds to a rotational coordinate of $(90°)(2\pi\text{ rad}/360°)/(1\text{ rad}) = \pi/2$. So the final rotational coordinate is $\pi/2 + 1.5 = 3.1$.

11.6 The faster you go, the larger the inward force required to make you go around the curve. When the maximum force $(F^s_{sp})_{max}$ is reached, $\tan\theta_{max} = \mu_s$ (Eq. 11.53) and Eq. 1 in Example 11.4 becomes

$$\mu_s mg = m\frac{v^2}{r}$$

$$v = \sqrt{\mu_s gr} = 6.6\text{ m/s},$$

where I have used the value $\mu_s \approx 1$ for the coefficient of static friction between skates and road.

11.7 (*a*) The speeds of B and C are equal, but the circumference of C's trajectory is twice as large, and so it takes C twice as long to complete one revolution. Therefore the ratio of the rotational velocities is 2. (*b*) Because of the r^2 dependence of rotational inertia (see Eq. 11.30), C's rotational inertia is four times as large as B's. Therefore the ratio of the rotational inertias is $\frac{1}{4}$.

11.8 Yes. Using Eq. 11.31, you can write for the final rotational kinetic energy:

$$\tfrac{1}{2}I_f\omega_f^2 - \tfrac{1}{2}(I_i\omega_i)\omega_f - \tfrac{1}{2}(I_i\omega_i)\omega_f > \tfrac{1}{2}(I_i\omega_i)\omega_i = \tfrac{1}{2}I_i\omega_i^2.$$

Because his arms' centripetal acceleration must increase as he pulls them in, the force required to pull them in increases, requiring physical effort. Thus internal chemical energy in his body is converted to kinetic energy.

11.9 (*a*) Suppose the dumbbell has rotational velocity ω, with each puck moving at speed $v = r\omega = (l/2)\omega$. The kinetic energy of the dumbbell is equal to the sum of the kinetic energies of the two pucks:

$$K = 2(\tfrac{1}{2}mv^2) = mv^2.$$

Substituting the Eq. 11.11 value for v, you get

$$K = m(\tfrac{1}{2}l\omega)^2 = \tfrac{1}{4}ml^2\omega^2.$$

Knowing from Eq. 11.31 that $K = \tfrac{1}{2}I\omega^2$, you can say that

$$\tfrac{1}{4}ml^2\omega^2 = \tfrac{1}{2}I\omega^2.$$

Solve this expression for I and you see that, indeed, $I = \tfrac{1}{2}ml^2$. (*b*) No. The dumbbell rotates but has no momentum. Its axis is fixed to the table, so it cannot have any translational motion. Even though v is nonzero for each puck, $v_{dumbbell} = 0$ and therefore $p_{dumbbell} = 0$. Because the axis exerts a force on the dumbbell, the puck-dumbbell system is not isolated, and so it is not necessary for its momentum to be constant.

11.10 When the axis is at the end, you should choose the origin at that end, and so the integration boundaries in Example 11.9 become $x = 0$ and $x = l$. Therefore,

$$I = \frac{m}{l}\int_0^l x^2 dx = \frac{m}{l}\left[\frac{x^3}{3}\right]_0^l = \tfrac{1}{3}ml^2.$$

11.11 No, because drilling a hole removes material and its contribution to the rotational inertia, without changing the contribution of the remaining material: $I_{solid} = I_{removed} + I_{remaining} > I_{remaining}$. The m's in the two expressions for the rotational inertia are not the same: $m_{hollow} = \rho\pi l(R_{outer}^2 - R_{inner}^2)$, while $m_{solid} = \rho\pi l R_{outer}^2$. Substituting m_{hollow} into the expression for the rotational inertia of the hollow cylinder gives $I_{hollow} = \tfrac{1}{2}m_{hollow}(R_{outer}^2 + R_{inner}^2) = \tfrac{1}{2}\rho\pi l(R_{outer}^2 - R_{inner}^2)(R_{outer}^2 + R_{inner}^2) = \tfrac{1}{2}\rho\pi l(R_{outer}^4 - R_{inner}^4)$, which is *less* than $I_{solid} = \tfrac{1}{2}m_{solid}R_{outer}^2 = \tfrac{1}{2}\rho\pi l R_{outer}^4$.

11.12 About an axis through the center of mass. I is larger about any other axis because the term md^2 in Eq. 11.53 is always positive.

Chapter 12

12.1 (*a*) The rod is subject to four forces: the force of gravity $\vec{F}_{Er}^G$ (which we can ignore because the inertia of the rod is negligible compared to m_1 and m_2), the downward contact forces $\vec{F}_1$ and $\vec{F}_2$ exerted by the two objects, and an upward force $\vec{F}_{pr}^c$ exerted by the pivot that holds the rod in place. Because the rod remains at rest, the vector sum of these forces must be zero, and so the upward force must be equal in magnitude to the sum of the downward forces (Figure S12.1). (*b*) The rod is still subject to the same forces. The rod is pinned down at the pivot, so it cannot accelerate. Therefore $\vec{a}_{cm} = \vec{0}$ as before, and the free-body diagram is unchanged. (The rod rotates to one side, pulling object 1 up and lowering object 2, but this is not reflected in the free-body diagram.) (*c*) $r_1/r_2 = m_2/m_1$. (*d*) The rod rotates so that the end where object 1 was shoots up and the end holding object 2 falls down. (*e*) The rod rotates so that the end of the rod where the object of inertia $2m_1$ is suspended goes down and object 2 is pulled up. (*f*) The end of the rod where object 1 is suspended goes down. (*g*) The difference is the speed at which the rod rotates into a vertical position: fast in part *e* and slowly in part *f*.

Figure S12.1

12.2 The seesaw remains at rest because the child causes a torque on the seesaw that is equal in magnitude to the torque you cause but tends to rotate the seesaw in the opposite direction.

12.3 (*a*) Because the torques caused by $\vec{F}_1$ and $\vec{F}_2$ cancel each other, the only way to prevent the rod from rotating is to make the torque caused by $\vec{F}_3$ zero. This can be achieved by aligning $\vec{F}_3$ along the long axis of the rod, either straight toward or straight away from the pivot. (*b*) The torque caused by $\vec{F}_1$ is $+r_{1\perp}F_1$; the torque caused by $\vec{F}_2$ is $-r_{2\perp}F_2 = -2r_{1\perp}F_2$. The lever arm distance of $\vec{F}_3$ is $r_{3\perp} = 3r_{1\perp}$, and so the torque caused by $\vec{F}_3$ is $+r_{3\perp}F_3 = +3r_{1\perp}F_1$ because $F_3 = F_1$. The sum of the torques is thus $+r_{1\perp}F_1 - 2r_{1\perp}F_2 + 3r_{1\perp}F_1$. Setting this sum to zero, I get $F_2 = 2F_1$. So, to balance the rod, you must increase the magnitude of $\vec{F}_2$ by a factor of 4.

12.4. If we neglect the very small effect of air resistance, the rotation of the wrench is steady. As you can verify by launching a stick or any other object, the object rotates in the same direction when it comes down. This shows that the rotational and translational motions are not coupled. The upward motion slows down because of the force of gravity, but this force does not affect the rotational motion because it does not cause a torque about the center of mass.

12.5. (*a*) The torque becomes greater because the lever arm distance of the force increases. See Figure S12.5a. (*b*) As the arm is raised, $\vec{F}_{mf}^c$ becomes more perpendicular to the forearm. See Figure S12.5b. This means that the torque caused by $\vec{F}_{mf}^c$ increases, and so the capacity to lift objects increases.

Figure S12.5

(*a*)

line of action $\vec{F}_{mf}^c$

$\vec{F}_{mf}^c$

$r_\perp$

(*b*)

$\vec{F}_{mf}^c$

12.6. The acceleration of the center of mass is the same regardless of where the force is exerted. The acceleration of the center of mass of a system of particles is *always* given by $\sum \vec{F}_{ext} = m\vec{a}_{cm}$. See Section 8.12.

12.7. (*a*) Because the rotation slows down, the length of $\vec{\omega}$ decreases and so $\vec{\omega}_f$ is shorter than $\vec{\omega}_i$. The vector $\Delta\vec{\omega} \equiv \vec{\omega}_f - \vec{\omega}_i$ points from the tip of $\vec{\omega}_i$ to the tip of $\vec{\omega}_f$, which means the direction of $\Delta\vec{\omega}$ is opposite the direction of $\vec{\omega}$ (Figure S12.7). (*b*) Yes, because rotational acceleration is defined as (Eq. 11.12)

$$\alpha_\vartheta \equiv \lim_{\Delta t \to 0} \frac{\Delta\omega_\vartheta}{\Delta t}.$$

Because $1/\Delta t$ is a scalar, $\vec{\alpha}$ points in the same direction as $\Delta\vec{\omega}$.

Figure S12.7

12.8. The fact that the forearm is not moving tells you that $\sum \tau_{ext} = 0$. This yields

$$\frac{\ell}{5}F_{mfy}^c - \frac{\ell}{2}F_{Ef}^G - \ell F_{bf}^c = 0.$$

Dividing both sides by $\ell/5$ and solving for F_{mfy}^c yield

$$F_{mfy}^c = \tfrac{5}{2}F_{Ef}^G + 5\,F_{bf}^c. \tag{1}$$

The condition that the vector sum of the forces exerted in the vertical direction must be zero yields

$$\sum F_y = F_{mfy}^c + F_{hfy}^c - F_{Ef}^G - F_{bf}^c = 0. \tag{2}$$

Substituting Eq. 1 into Eq. 2 and solving for F_{hfy}^c yields

$$|F_{hfy}^c| = |-\tfrac{3}{2}F_{Ef}^G - 4F_{bf}^c| = \tfrac{3}{2}F_{Ef}^G + 4F_{bf}^c.$$

Note that the magnitude of the force that needs to be supplied by the biceps muscle is *much* greater than the sum of F_{Ef}^G and F_{bf}^c: $F_{mf}^c > |F_{mfy}^c| = \tfrac{5}{2}F_{Ef}^G + 5F_{bf}^c \gg F_{Ef}^G + F_{bf}^c$. This is the price one pays for the versatility and mobility of the forearm: If a load were suspended directly from the biceps muscle, our lifting capacity would increase by at least a factor of 5! Note furthermore that the downward force exerted by the humerus on the forearm is also very great. This great downward force is necessary to counter the upward force exerted by the biceps muscle on the forearm. Without this downward force, the muscle would simply pull the forearm up rather than rotate it.

12.9. (*a*) No. A nonzero vector sum of forces would cause the disc's center of mass to accelerate, and we know that the disc remains in the same place, so $\vec{a}_{cm} = \vec{0}$. (*b*) No. Even though the *vector sum* of the forces exerted on the compact disc is zero, the individual forces cause a nonzero torque. The resulting nonzero torque is what gives the disc a rotational acceleration and increases its rotational kinetic energy.

12.10. (*a*) The cylindrical shell has greater rotational inertia than the solid cylinder (MR^2 versus $\tfrac{1}{2}MR^2$; see Table 11.3) and so, because $\tau_\vartheta = I\alpha_\vartheta$, it requires a greater torque to be accelerated rotationally. This torque is supplied by the force of static friction, so the frictional force exerted on the shell must be greater. (You can see this directly from Eq. 12.26: The shape factor c is greater for the cylindrical shell, and so F_{ro}^s is greater, too.) (*b*) The maximum value of the force of static friction is, from Eq. 10.46,

$$(F_{ro}^s)_{max} = \mu_s F_{ro}^n = \mu_s mg\cos\theta.$$

Substituting this result into Eq. 12.26 yields

$$m_s\, mg\cos\theta = \frac{mg\sin\theta}{1 + c^{-1}}.$$

Solving this expression for θ, you obtain

$$\tan\theta = \mu_s(1 + c^{-1}).$$

For the cylindrical shell, $c = 1$, and so with $\mu_s = 1$, $\tan\theta = 2$ and $\theta = 63°$. For the solid cylinder, $c = \frac{1}{2}$, and so with $\mu_s = 1$, $\tan\theta = 3$ and $\theta = 72°$. Beyond these angles the cylinders no longer can roll without slipping. Note that both angles are larger than the 45° angle above which a block would begin to slip down a ramp. (See part a of Checkpoint 10.13.)

12.11. (a) Yes, the force of static friction does cause a torque on the wheel. The direction of this torque is counterclockwise in Figure 12.40a, opposite the direction of the torque caused by the chain. (b) Because the wheel's rotational acceleration is clockwise, the sum of the torques must be clockwise. Thus the clockwise torque caused by the chain must be greater than the counterclockwise torque caused by the frictional force.

12.12. Yes. The component $\vec{F}_\perp$ does work on the cylinder because its point of application is displaced along the circular arc. The arc length displacement is $\Delta s_F = r\Delta\vartheta$, and so the work done on the cylinder is $F_\perp\Delta s_F = F_\perp r\Delta\vartheta = \tau\Delta\vartheta$. This is equal to the change in the rotational kinetic energy in Eq. 12.31. So, for a rigid object subject to a constant torque, the quantity $\tau\Delta\vartheta$ is equal to the work done on the object.

12.13. $\vec{v} = \vec{\omega} \times \vec{r}$. Because $\vec{\omega}$ and $\vec{r}$ are orthogonal, the magnitude of this product is ωr, in agreement with Eq. 11.11. You can use the right-hand rule in Figure 12.44 to verify that the vector product of $\vec{\omega}$ and $\vec{r}$ indeed gives the right direction for $\vec{v}$.

Chapter 13

13.1 (a) Rotational speed is the change in the rotational position divided by the time interval during which that change takes place, and so the object with the smaller period has the greater rotational speed. Because the Moon takes less time to complete one revolution, it has the greater rotational speed. Rotations you encounter in daily life—a spinning disc, a spinning wheel, the hands of a clock—rotate significantly faster and thus have significantly greater rotational speeds. (b) The speed is the distance traveled in 1 rev ($2\pi R$) divided by the period. Moon: $[2\pi(3.84 \times 10^8\text{ m})/(27.32\text{ days})]/(86{,}400\text{ s/day}) = 1.02 \times 10^3\text{ m/s}$. Earth: $[2\pi(1.50 \times 10^{11}\text{ m})/(365.26\text{ days})]/(86{,}400\text{ s/day}) = 2.99 \times 10^4\text{ m/s}$. Because of its much larger orbital radius, Earth's speed is considerably greater. (c) Moon: $a_c = v_M^2/R_M = (1.02 \times 10^3\text{ m/s})^2/(3.84 \times 10^8\text{ m}) = 0.00271\text{ m/s}^2$. Earth: $(2.98 \times 10^4\text{ m/s})^2/(1.50 \times 10^{11}\text{ m}) = 0.00595\text{ m/s}^2$. ($d$) These accelerations are much smaller than the acceleration due to gravity at Earth's surface: $g = 9.8\text{ m/s}^2$.

13.2 Earth's radius is about 6400 km, and so near the surface the distance to the center does not change much with altitude. For a plane 10 km above ground, the distance to the center of Earth is only $(10\text{ km})/(6400\text{ km}) = 0.16$ greater than that for an object on the ground. Because the gravitational force depends on the square of the distance, this increase results in a decrease in the strength of the force by a mere 2.4×10^{-6}!

13.3 (a) The light spreads out in a two-dimensional cone rather than a three-dimensional one, and the length of the straight line segment intersecting a two-dimensional wedge of light varies as $1/r$ (Figure S13.3), which means the force of gravity would exhibit a $1/r$ dependence. (b) The centripetal acceleration is still $a_c \propto R/T^2$. Because this acceleration is supplied by a gravitational force that is proportional to $1/r$, you have $R/T^2 \propto 1/R$ and so $T \propto R$.

Figure S13.3

13.4 For requirement (i) to hold, you must be able to interchange the indices in the expression for the gravitational force without changing the force magnitude: $F_{12}^G = F_{21}^G$. Requirement (ii) means that if you double one mass, the force exerted on the object must double. (a) No. This dependence is consistent with requirement (i) because $m_1 + m_2 = m_2 + m_1$, but not with requirement (ii) because $m_1 + 2m_2 \neq 2(m_1 + m_2)$. ($b$) Only $m_1 m_2$ satisfies both requirements simultaneously. (c) If you take a very small piece m away, leaving $M - m$ behind, the attraction is proportional to $(M - m)m = Mm - m^2 \approx Mm$ (because the term m^2 is very small compared to Mm). So, the greater m is, the greater the force is. Symmetry thus suggests that the attraction is greatest when you divide the lump into two equal pieces. Mathematically you can prove this as follows: If you divide the lump into two pieces of masses cM and $(M - cM)$, where $0 < c < 1$, then the gravitational force is proportional to $(M - cM)cM = M^2(c - c^2)$. To find the value for c at which the force is maximum, you must set the first derivative of this expression with respect to c equal to zero: $d[M^2(c - c^2)]/dc = M^2(1 - 2c) = 0$, so $1 - 2c = 0$ or $c = \frac{1}{2}$.

13.5 For the two forces to be equal in magnitude, you need

$$\frac{m_1 m_2}{r_{12}^2} = \frac{m_1 m_E}{R_E^2}.$$

You calculated the right side in Example 13.1, so

$$\frac{m_1 m_2}{r_{12}^2} = \frac{(70\text{ kg})^2}{r_{12}^2} = 1.0 \times 10^{13}\text{ kg}^2/\text{m}^2,$$

which yields

$$r_{12}^2 = \frac{(70\text{ kg})^2}{1.0 \times 10^{13}\text{ kg}^2/\text{m}^2} = 4.9 \times 10^{-10}\text{ m}^2,$$

or $r_{12} = 2.2 \times 10^{-5}$ m. This is the required separation between the *centers* of the bodies. Because the width of a human body is many orders of magnitude greater than this value, it is not possible to verify this prediction.

13.6 (a) To find the center of mass, use Eq. 6.24: $x_{cm} = (m_1 x_1 + m_2 x_2)/(m_1 + m_2)$. Let 1 be the Sun and 2 Earth. If you place the Sun at the origin, $x_1 = 0$ and x_2 equals the radius of Earth's orbit. Using the values in Table 13.1, you find

$$x_{cm} = \frac{0 + (5.97 \times 10^{24}\text{ kg})(1.50 \times 10^{11}\text{ m})}{(2.0 \times 10^{30}\text{ kg}) + (5.97 \times 10^{24}\text{ kg})}$$

$$= \frac{8.96 \times 10^{35}\text{ kg}\cdot\text{m}}{2.0 \times 10^{30}\text{ kg}} = 4.5 \times 10^5\text{ m}.$$

Compared with the radius of the Sun (7×10^8 m), this is a negligible distance: $x_{cm} = 0.00064 R_{Sun}$. (b) It speeds up because the force of gravity has a nonzero component parallel to the velocity, giving rise to an acceleration (Figure S13.6). The velocity keeps increasing until the comet reaches perihelion at the top of the ellipse. After passing that point, the comet slows down because the force of gravity causes an acceleration in the direction opposite the direction of the velocity. The slowing down continues until the comet reaches the point farthest from the Sun. At that point the velocity is a minimum.

Figure S13.6

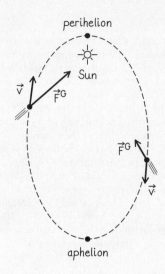

13.7 (a) The radius of Earth is about 6400 km, so the distance to Earth's center is increased by a factor of $(6400 \text{ km} + 300 \text{ km})/(6400 \text{ km}) = 1.05$. (b) Because the gravitational force changes as $1/r^2$, the force decreases by a factor of $1/(1.05)^2 = 0.91$. (c) The acceleration decreases by the same factor as the force: $0.91(9.8 \text{ m/s}^2) = 8.9 \text{ m/s}^2$. (d) The shuttle travels at such a high speed that the gravitational force exerted by Earth on it is just sufficient to provide its centripetal acceleration: $g = v^2/r$, with r the distance from the shuttle to the center of Earth.

13.8 (a) $F_{Eb}^G = mg = (1.0 \text{ kg})(9.8 \text{ m/s}^2) = 9.8 \text{ N}$. (b) The scale exerts an upward contact force of magnitude F_{sb}^c on the brick. The brick is at rest, and so you know that the vector sum of the forces exerted on it is zero. Choosing the x axis in the upward direction, we have $\sum F_x = F_{sbx}^c + F_{Ebx}^G = F_{sb}^c + (-F_{Eb}^G) = 0$, and so $F_{sb}^c = F_{Eb}^G$. Furthermore, the contact force exerted by the brick on the scale and that exerted by the scale on the brick form an interaction pair, which means they are equal in magnitude, so $F_{bs}^c = F_{sb}^c = F_{Eb}^G$. (c) Two. Step 1: $F_{sbx}^c + F_{Ebx}^G = 0$; step 2: $F_{bs}^c = F_{sb}^c$. (d) Yes, because, as you found in part b: $F_{bs}^c = F_{Eb}^G$. (If you think this question is trivial, hold off judgment until after doing Checkpoints 13.9 and 13.10.)

13.9 (a) Inside the orbiting shuttle, $g = 8.9 \text{ m/s}^2$ (see Checkpoint 13.7), and so $F_{Eb}^G = mg = (1.0 \text{ kg})(8.9 \text{ m/s}^2) = 8.9 \text{ N}$—almost the same as at the surface of Earth (see Checkpoint 13.8). (b) Zero. The brick floats: no force is necessary to support it because everything around it has the same downward acceleration. (c) No. The scale measures nothing, even though Earth pulls on the brick nearly as hard as it does on Earth's surface. (d) The answer is different because the reference frame of the shuttle is accelerating toward the Earth reference frame.

13.10 (a) The same. Because the elevator is moving at constant velocity, its acceleration (and that of the spring scale and the object) is zero. Consequently the vector sum of the forces exerted on the object is zero, as it is on the ground, and so $\sum F_x = F_{sox}^c + F_{Eox}^G = 0$. (b) To

accelerate upward, the vector sum of the forces exerted on the object must be nonzero and point upward (Figure S13.10a). If $a_x = +0.5g$, $\sum F_x = ma_x = +\frac{1}{2}mg$. Consequently $\sum F_x = F_{sox}^c + F_{Eox}^G = +\frac{1}{2}mg$, and so $F_{sox}^c = +\frac{1}{2}mg - F_{Eo}^G = +\frac{1}{2}mg - (-mg) = +\frac{3}{2}mg$. The scale reading is one and a half times what it is in a stationary elevator. (c) The object now has downward acceleration g and so is in free fall. The gravitational force exerted on it is thus the only force exerted on it (Figure S13.10b). The scale exerts no force on the object and so shows a zero reading.

Figure S13.10

13.11 (a) In Checkpoint 13.7 you found that the shuttle's downward acceleration due to gravity is $g = 8.9 \text{ m/s}^2$. The vertical distance Δh through which the shuttle falls in a time interval Δt is $\Delta h = \frac{1}{2}gt^2 = \frac{1}{2}(8.9 \text{ m/s}^2)(1.0 \text{ s})^2 = 4.5 \text{ m}$. (b) If the shuttle remains 300 km above Earth, it is in a circular orbit, and so its centripetal acceleration is given by v^2/R, where v is its speed and R the radius of its orbit. Because the shuttle's acceleration is g, you have $v^2/R = g$, $v = \sqrt{gR} = \sqrt{(8.9 \text{ m/s}^2)(6.7 \times 10^6 \text{ m})} = \sqrt{5.7 \times 10^7 \text{ m}^2/\text{s}^2} = 7.5 \times 10^3 \text{ m/s}$.

13.12 (a) For the plane to be in free fall, it must have a downward acceleration of 9.8 m/s^2 (see Checkpoint 13.2). Starting with zero vertical velocity, a freely falling object drops in 40 s a distance $\Delta x = \frac{1}{2}gt^2 = \frac{1}{2}(9.8 \text{ m/s}^2)(40 \text{ s})^2 = 7.8 \text{ km}$. (b) The magnitude of the vertical speed is given by $v = gt = (9.8 \text{ m/s}^2) \times (40 \text{ s}) = 390 \text{ m/s}$. (c) You can't tell. The instantaneous velocity of an object in free fall can be in any direction. Remember that a ball launched upward is in free fall while moving up as well as while moving down. At all times, its acceleration has the same constant downward value (see Section 3.3). The answers to parts a and b show that the plane *must* have been moving upward before going into free fall. If it had started horizontally, it would have lost almost 8 km of altitude and be dangerously close to the ground (airplanes normally fly at an altitude of about 10 km). Worse, its downward velocity at the end of the free fall would have been an amazing 1400 km/h, which is well above the maximum airspeed for most airplanes.

13.13 (a) The plane's speed is $v = (900 \text{ km/h})(1000 \text{ m/km})/(3600 \text{ s/h}) = 250 \text{ m/s}$. Because the plane remains at a fixed altitude, it must follow a circular trajectory of radius $R \approx 6400 \text{ km}$. Its centripetal acceleration is thus $v^2/R = (250 \text{ m/s})^2/(6.4 \times 10^6 \text{ m}) = 9.8 \times 10^{-3} \text{ m/s}^2$. (b) See Figure S13.13. The centripetal acceleration of the plane is so small (about 0.1% of g) that you can safely ignore it, and so the free-body diagram is identical to what it would be if the plane were sitting on the ground. The plane is subject to two forces: a downward force of gravity and an upward force exerted by the air that is equal in magnitude to the downward force. (c) Because the airplane is not in free fall, its downward acceleration is only 0.1% of what it needs to be for the people to feel weightless.

Figure S13.13

Figure S13.18

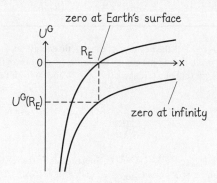

13.14 A passenger in a car that takes a right turn feels pushed outward from the turn, which means toward the left. To simulate this effect, the container should be tilted to the left.

13.15 (a) $\Delta t = \Delta x/v = (2.0 \text{ m})/(3.0 \times 10^8 \text{ m/s}) = 6.7 \times 10^{-9}$ s—just a few billionths of a second. (b) In the vertical direction you have $\Delta y = \frac{1}{2}a_y(\Delta t)^2$, $a_y = 2\Delta y/(\Delta t)^2$. To obtain a 1.0-mm deviation in the time interval obtained in part a, you need acceleration $a_y = 2(+1.0 \times 10^{-3} \text{ m})/(6.7 \times 10^{-9} \text{ s})^2 = +4.5 \times 10^{13} \text{ m/s}^2$. This is such a phenomenally large acceleration that you cannot expect to observe this effect. (c) In 0.0010 s, a light beam travels $(3.0 \times 10^8 \text{ m/s})(1.0 \times 10^{-3} \text{ s}) = 3.0 \times 10^5$ m. In that time interval, it falls like an object in free fall, and so $\Delta y = \frac{1}{2}(-9.8 \text{ m/s}^2)(1.0 \times 10^{-3} \text{ s})^2 = -4.9 \times 10^{-6}$ m—a tiny fraction of the diameter of a hair. Measuring this tiny displacement over a travel distance of 300 km is beyond current measurement accuracy.

13.16 (a) Zero. In the absence of both gravity and acceleration, the container and everything inside it are weightless. (b) The elevator moving at constant velocity has equal displacements in equal time intervals (Figure S13.16a). The path of the light pulse in the reference frame of the moving elevator is thus straight but at an angle (Figure S13.16b).

Figure S13.16

(a)

(b)

13.17 It increases because the gravitational force increases with decreasing distance r_{12}; see Eq. 13.1.

13.18 It yields values greater by an amount $|U(R_E)| = Gmm_E/R_E$. See Figure S13.18.

13.19 (a) If we let the star be at rest at the origin, then the initial kinetic energies of the star and the object are zero. The initial gravitational potential energy U^G of the closed star-object system is given by Eq. 13.14 and is negative. The initial mechanical energy of the system $E_{mech} = K + U^G$ is thus negative. If we consider the star-object system to be closed, then its mechanical energy is constant, and so it is always negative because there is no dissipation of energy. (b) Because $\vec{F}_{so}^G$ is directed toward the star's center, the object accelerates in a straight line toward that center. The minimum kinetic energy is zero (see part a). Because the object accelerates as it moves toward the star, the maximum kinetic energy is achieved when the object reaches the star's surface. Conservation of energy tells you that $E_{mech,i} = E_{mech,f}$. From part a, $E_{mech,i} = U_i^G = -GMm/r$. At the star's surface, you have $E_{mech,f} = K_f + U_f^G = K_f - GMm/R_s$. So $K_f = GMm(r - R_s)/(R_s r)$. (Because r is the distance from the object to the center of the star, you have $r > R_s$, and so $K_f > 0$, as it should be.) (c) Yes. The angular momentum is $r_\perp mv$ (Eq. 13.36). Because the motion of the object is directed straight toward the center of the star, the lever arm distance about the center of the star remains zero throughout the object's motion. The angular momentum is thus both zero and constant. (d) The answer depends on the magnitude of the launch velocity. If $K_i < |U_i^G|$, then $E_{mech} < 0$; if $K_i = |U_i^G|$, then $E_{mech} = 0$; and if $K_i > |U_i^G|$, then $E_{mech} > 0$.

13.20 (a) At r_{max}, $U^G = E_{mech}$ and so $K = 0$. This means $v = 0$ and so $\vec{L} = \vec{0}$. (b) Conservation of angular momentum requires $\vec{L}$ to remain zero. This can happen only if $\vec{r} \times m\vec{v}$ is zero (or if v remains zero, which is impossible, because then nothing holds the object in place). This vector product is zero when $\vec{r}$ and $\vec{v}$ point in the same direction—in other words, when the object's motion is restricted to a straight line. (c) No. If $\vec{L} \neq 0$, $\vec{v}$ can never point in the same direction as $\vec{r}$ and neither of these can ever become zero. This means the object can never move all the way out to r_{max}. Although moving out that far does not violate conservation of energy, it does not allow the object to keep enough angular momentum.

13.21 (a) For the planet to move in a circular trajectory of radius R at constant speed v, the star must exert a gravitational force on the planet to cause the centripetal acceleration $a_c = v^2/R$. The gravitational force is thus $GMm/R^2 = ma_c$, or

$$\frac{GMm}{R^2} = m\frac{v^2}{R}.$$

To obtain the kinetic energy $\frac{1}{2}mv^2$, multiply both sides by $\frac{1}{2}R$:

$$\frac{1}{2}\frac{GMm}{R} = \frac{1}{2}mv^2.$$

(b) The mechanical energy in the circular orbit is the sum of the kinetic energy you just determined and the gravitational potential energy from Eq. 13.11:

$$E = \tfrac{1}{2}\frac{GMm}{R} - \frac{GMm}{R} = -\tfrac{1}{2}\frac{GMm}{R}.$$

Note that this result is the negative of the kinetic energy. So, for an object in a circular orbit, the kinetic energy is half the magnitude of the system's potential energy. (c) For a circular orbit, $e = 0$, and so from Example 13.5 you know

$$\frac{2E_{\text{mech}}L^2}{G^2M^2m^3} = -1,$$

which means $E_{\text{mech}} = -\tfrac{1}{2}G^2M^2m^3/L^2$. Substituting L^2 from Example 13.5 with $e = 0$ and $a = R$ gives $E_{\text{mech}} = (-\tfrac{1}{2}G^2M^2m^3)/(GMm^2R) = -\tfrac{1}{2}GMm/R$. (d) The two results are the same.

13.22 (a) At Earth's surface, the distance to the planet's center is equal to Earth's radius: $r_i = R_E$, and so Eq. 13.23 gives

$$\tfrac{1}{2}mv_{\text{esc}}^2 = \frac{Gmm_E}{R_E}$$

or $v_{\text{esc}} = \sqrt{2Gm_E/R_E}$. (b) $v_{\text{esc}} = [2(6.6738 \times 10^{-11}\,\text{N}\cdot\text{m}^2/\text{kg}^2)(5.97 \times 10^{24}\,\text{kg})/(6.378 \times 10^6\,\text{m})]^{1/2} = 1.12 \times 10^4\,\text{m/s}$. (c) No. As long as an object is fired above the horizon (so it doesn't hit the ground), only the magnitude of the velocity matters. Once the object has enough kinetic energy to reach infinity ($E = 0$), it does so regardless of the direction in which it is fired.

13.23 (a) The integral has two parts:

$$(r^2 - R^2)\int_{r-R}^{r+R}\frac{1}{s^2}\,ds + \int_{r-R}^{r+R}ds.$$

The first term yields

$$(r^2 - R^2)\left[-\frac{1}{s}\right]_{r-R}^{r+R} = (r^2 - R^2)\left[-\frac{1}{r+R} + \frac{1}{r-R}\right].$$

Bringing both terms under a common denominator yields

$$(r^2 - R^2)\frac{(R-r) + (r+R)}{r^2 - R^2} = 2R.$$

The second term of the integral yields

$$[s]_{r-R}^{r+R} = (r+R) - (r-R) = 2R.$$

Adding both parts together yields $4R$. (b) Equations 13.24–13.27 still hold when m lies inside the shell. From Figure S13.23, we see that

$$R\cos\theta = r + s\cos(\pi - \alpha) = r - s\cos\alpha,$$

which yields the same relationship between α and θ as in Eq. 13.28. Equation 13.29 is also still valid and so we obtain the same result as in Eq. 13.33. (c) The integration boundaries are now from $R - r$ (at $\theta = 0$) to $R + r$ (at $\theta = \pi$). The first part of the integral then yields

$$(r^2 - R^2)\left[-\frac{1}{s}\right]_{R-r}^{R+r} = (r^2 - R^2)\left[-\frac{1}{R+r} + \frac{1}{R-r}\right].$$

Bringing both terms again under a common denominator gives

$$(r^2 - R^2)\frac{(r-R) + (R+r)}{R^2 - r^2} = -2r.$$

The second part of the integral yields

$$[s]_{R-r}^{R+r} = (R+r) - (R-r) = 2r.$$

Adding both parts together now yields zero. The gravitational attraction inside a uniform spherical shell is thus zero!

Figure S13.23

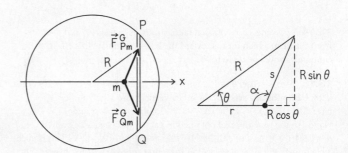

Chapter 14

14.1 (a) Because the light from event 1 reaches A before the light from event 2 reaches her, she observes event 1 first. (b) Because the light from event 1 and the light from event 2 reach B at the same instant, he observes the two events at the same instant.

14.2 (a) The light from each clock takes a finite time interval to travel from clock to observer. For clocks near the origin, this time interval is shorter than it is for clocks farther from the origin. This means (ii) is true: Nearby clocks display later time readings than distant clocks. (b) The clocks are synchronized and so by definition run at the same rate.

14.3 According to an observer moving along with the tube, the speed of the ball is l divided by Δt: $v_{\text{Mb}} = l/\Delta t$. Using the result $v_{\text{Mb}} = v_b + v_t$ from Example 14.3, you get $\Delta t = l/v_{\text{Mb}} = l/(v_b + v_t) = l/(2v)$.

14.4 (a) The observers agree that the signals do not reach the detector at the same instant because they both see that the blue light does not come on. (b) The observer at rest sees the two signals being emitted at the same instant. His reasoning for why the detector does not record simultaneity is that, because the detector is moving toward source 2 and away from source 1, signal 2 has a shorter distance to travel than signal 1. Therefore signal 2 reaches the detector first. The observer moving with the detector notes that the sources are equidistant from the detector but sees signal 2 arriving first. Because both signals travel at speed c_0 relative to him, he concludes that source 2 must have emitted its signal before source 1. The observers agree on the observation—no simultaneity—but have different explanations for it.

14.5 (a) Each signal takes $\Delta t = (5.0\,\text{m})/(3.00 \times 10^8\,\text{m/s}) = 1.7 \times 10^{-8}\,\text{s}$ to reach the detector. (b) $(20\,\text{m/s})(1.7 \times 10^{-8}\,\text{s}) = 3.3 \times 10^{-7}\,\text{m}$. (c) The travel time changes by $d/c_0 = (3.3 \times 10^{-7}\,\text{m})/(3.00 \times 10^8\,\text{m/s}) = 1.1 \times 10^{-15}\,\text{s} = 1.1\,\text{fs}$. (d) A 1.1-fs change in travel time is just barely measurable. (e) The detector moves $(1.0 \times 10^8\,\text{m/s})(1.7 \times 10^{-8}\,\text{s}) = 1.7\,\text{m}$. Light takes $(1.7\,\text{m})/(3.00 \times 10^8\,\text{m/s}) = 5.6 \times 10^{-9}\,\text{s}$ to travel this distance. Such a time interval can be measured, but note how fast the detector must be moving—$1.0 \times 10^8\,\text{m/s}$, about one-third the speed of light!—in order for the time interval to be long enough (if we can call $10^{-9}\,\text{s}$ "long") to be measurable.

14.6 (*a*) Greater than. Because the signal always travels at speed c_0, the longer distance the signal must travel according to B increases the duration of the cycle and therefore the period. (*b*) Increase. The faster the clock moves relative to B, the farther the mirror moves away from its initial position above the location where the signal was emitted in one period of a clock at rest and so the period increases.

14.7 (*a*) Slow, because the mechanical watch takes longer to complete 1 minute. (*b*) Fast.

14.8 Yes and no. By moving at high speed, you could slow down your biological clock and therefore slow down the rate at which your body ages, but *only as measured by an observer who is not in your reference frame.* From your perspective, you see your biological clock running at its "regular" rate (that is, a rate that is the same as what you would measure if you remained at rest on Earth). To you, there is no slowing down of your biological clock, regardless of your motion relative to any observer. So, although you could lengthen your life in the eyes of an observer, it would be impossible to do so from your own point of view.

14.9 Figure S14.9*a* shows the situation viewed from B's reference frame. B starts accelerating relative to A when her clocks read 3 o'clock. Figure S14.9*b* shows the situation viewed from A's reference frame. Because the unit is moving, the rear clock is ahead of the front clock, and so A sees the rear clock accelerate before the front clock, which means A sees B's unit getting shorter.

14.10 No. See Figure S14.10. To the observer on the ground, the front end of the pole reaches the exit (event 1) at 3 o'clock and the rear end reaches the entrance (event 2) at the same instant. To the observer moving along with the pole, these two events do not occur simultaneously. To this observer, the tunnel is in motion, and so clocks at the two ends are desynchronized, with the clock at the exit ahead of the clock at the entrance. Consequently, this observer sees the front end of the pole exit the tunnel before the rear end enters and concludes that the pole is longer than the tunnel.

Is this disagreement a problem (like the problem of the clock fitting between the pegs in Figure 14.19)? Suppose the tunnel is equipped with doors that can close or open instantly. Initially the entrance is open and the exit is closed. When the front of the pole reaches the exit, the exit door opens. When the rear of the pole reaches the entrance, the entrance door closes. According to the observer on the ground, these two events occur at the same instant, and at that instant the pole fits exactly between the two doors. For the observer moving along with the pole, the front of the pole

is at the exit before the rear is at the entrance, and so the exit door opens before the entrance door closes. The pole doesn't need to fit (and *can't* fit) in the tunnel.

Figure S14.10

14.11 No, because the two observers measure different speeds for the object, and inertia depends on speed.

14.12 (*a*) When the spring is compressed, its internal energy increases, and so its mass increases. (*b*) When the coffee cools down, its internal energy decreases, and so its mass decreases.

14.13 (*a*) Because a particle has no internal energy, the mass is constant. Because the particle is accelerated, its kinetic energy increases. Therefore the energy of the system increases, and so the inertia increases. (*b*) As with any collision, we can consider the system of colliding objects to be closed, and so neither the energy nor the inertia can change. The internal energy must increase as the particle comes to rest in the target, and kinetic energy is converted to internal energy. Therefore the mass of the system increases.

Figure S14.9

14.14 If you use Eq. 14.6, your calculator will round the result to 1 for all but d. A better approach is to use Eq. 14.11 to calculate $\frac{1}{2}v^2/c_o^2$ and then add 1. (a) $\frac{1}{2}(30 \text{ m/s})^2/(3.00 \times 10^8 \text{ m/s})^2 = 5.0 \times 10^{-15}$, $\gamma = 1 + 5.0 \times 10^{-15}$. ($b$) $\gamma = 1 + (3.5 \times 10^{-13})$. ($c$) $\gamma = 1 + (5.6 \times 10^{-10})$. ($d$) For this part you cannot use Eq. 14.11 because the speed is not small. Equation 14.6 gives $\gamma = 1/\sqrt{1 - (0.60)^2} = 1.25$.

14.15 From Eq. 14.17 you obtain $s^2 = [(3.00 \times 10^8 \text{ m/s})(5.0 \times 10^{-7} \text{ s})]^2 - (120 \text{ m})^2 = 8.1 \times 10^3 \text{ m}^2$. This value equals $(c_o \Delta t_{proper})^2$. So $(\Delta t_{proper})^2 = (8.1 \times 10^3 \text{ m}^2)/(3.00 \times 10^8 \text{ m/s})^2$ and $\Delta t_{proper} = 3.0 \times 10^{-7} \text{ s}$.

14.16 According to an observer in the car, the 1-km length of road travels past the car at $100 \text{ km/h} = 28 \text{ m/s}$. According to this observer, the measured length l_v is l_{proper}/γ (Eq. 14.28). The amount by which the length contracts is $l_{proper} - l_{proper}/\gamma = l_{proper}(1 - 1/\gamma) = l_{proper}(\gamma - 1)/\gamma$. For low velocities, γ is close to 1. According to Eq. 14.11, $\gamma - 1 \approx \frac{1}{2}v^2/c_o^2$, and so $(\gamma - 1)/\gamma \approx \frac{1}{2}v^2/c_o^2$. The difference in length is thus $l_{proper}(\frac{1}{2}v^2/c_o^2) = (1.0 \times 10^3 \text{ m})\frac{1}{2}[(28 \text{ m/s})/(3.00 \times 10^8 \text{ m/s})]^2 = 4.3 \times 10^{-12} \text{ m}$, which is a few orders of magnitude less than the smallest distance that can be measured. For all practical purposes, the road is still 1.0 km long.

14.17 Because of symmetry, the collision seen by A is identical to that seen by B. The time interval measured by A between the throw and catch of particle 1 is therefore equal to the time interval measured by B between the throw and catch of particle 2.

14.18 (a) Because $\vec{v}_2$ has a nonzero component along the x axis, A sees $v_2 > v_1$. (b) According to Eq. 14.40, $m_{v2} > m_{v1}$. Hence A concludes that inertia increases with speed. (c) From the perspective of B, $v_1 > v_2$. In going from reference frame A to reference frame B, the roles of particles 1 and 2 are interchanged, and so in reference frame B, Eq. 14.40 reads $m_{v1} = \gamma m_{v2}$. According to B, $m_{v1} > m_{v2}$, and so B, too, concludes that inertia increases with speed.

14.19 You know that for the electron at rest, m_v and m in Eq. 14.41 are identical, and so you want to know what speed v yields $\gamma = 1000$. Substituting this value into Eq. 14.9 yields:

$$v^2/c_o^2 = 1 - 10^{-6}$$

$$v = \sqrt{1 - 10^{-6}}\, c_0 = 0.9999995 c_0.$$

14.20 (a) Because the final relative speed is zero, the collision is totally inelastic. (b) Using $\vec{p} = m\vec{v}$, you find $m_p v_{px,i} + m_e v_{ex,i} = 0$, $v_{e,i} = (m_p/m_e)v_{p,i} = (1836)(0.6c_0) = 1102c_0!$

14.21 $K = (\gamma - 1)mc_o^2 \approx (\frac{1}{2}v^2/c_o^2)mc_o^2 = \frac{1}{2}mv^2$.

14.22 (a) See Figure S14.22. The collision converts kinetic energy to internal energy. (b) Kinetic energy is not constant because the final kinetic energy is zero. Mass is not constant because the increase in internal energy corresponds to an increase in mass. Energy is constant because the system is closed.

Figure S14.22

14.23 (a) See Figure S14.23. (b) The internal energy of the atom decreases because of the radiation emitted by it. The equivalence of mass and internal energy tells you that the mass of the atom decreases. (c) Because the atom is at rest, its inertia is equal to its mass. Because the mass decreases, the inertia also decreases.

Figure S14.23

14.24 If you denote the initial energies as $E_{1i} = E_{2i} = E$, the energy law yields $E_{1i} + E_{2i} = 2E$. Because the momentum of the system is zero, we have from Eq. 14.57 $(2E)^2 = (300 m_p c_o^2)^2$, or $E = 150 m_p c_o^2$. From Eqs. 14.52 and 14.54, $K_{1i} = E - m_p c_o^2 = 149 m_p c_o^2 = 2.2 \times 10^{-8} \text{ J}$, which is much less than the energy obtained in Example 14.13. (For this reason particle colliders use colliding beams rather than stationary targets.)

Chapter 15

15.1 (a) Two forces are exerted on the spring: one by the cart and the other by the post, and three forces are exerted on the cart: one by the spring, one by Earth, and one by the track. Figure S15.1 shows the free-body diagrams during compression (when the spring is stretched, the direction is reversed for the three horizontal forces in the diagrams). (b) None. The only forces that have a nonzero displacement along their line of action are the contact forces between the spring and the cart, but these are internal forces and so do no work on the system. (c) The contact force exerted by the cart on the spring points in the same direction as the force displacement, so the work done by this force on the spring is positive. This makes sense because, as the spring is compressed, its elastic potential energy increases. (d) The force exerted by the spring on the cart is directed in the direction opposite the force displacement, so the work done by this force on the cart is negative. Because $\vec{F}_{cs}^c = -\vec{F}_{sc}^c$ and the force displacement is the same for both forces, the work done by the spring on the cart is the negative of the work done by the cart on the spring.

Figure S15.1

15.2 (*a*) Negative. Just before reaching the position where the spring is maximally stretched, the velocity is positive (points right), and just afterward, it is negative (points left). So the change in velocity and the acceleration are both negative. (*b*) It is greatest where the curvature of the $x(t)$ curve is greatest, when the spring is maximally stretched or compressed at the instants represented in Figure 15.2*a*, Figure 15.2*e*, and Figure 15.2*i*. It is smallest (zero) when the cart is at the equilibrium position at the instants represented in Figure 15.2*c* and 15.2*g*.

15.3 (*a*) *a*: tangential component of gravitational force, *b*: vertical component of elastic force in ruler, *c*: tangential component of gravitational force, *d*: vertical component of elastic force in string. (*b*) Gravitational potential energy in *a* and *c*, elastic potential energy in *b* and *d*.

15.4 (*a*) Factor of 4. From Chapter 9 you know that the potential energy of a spring is proportional to the square of the displacement from the equilibrium position. So, if the spring is compressed twice as much, the initial potential energy is four times as much. The initial kinetic energy is zero, so the energy is four times greater. (*b*) The initial compression determines the amplitude, and so the energy in the oscillator is proportional to the square of the amplitude.

15.5 (*a*) Upward, see Figure S15.5. (*b*) Downward. The two shaded regions in Figure S15.5 indicate that the shadow moves over increasingly smaller distances Δx during a given time interval Δt until it reaches the top. In other words, the shadow slows down. This means that the direction of the acceleration vector is opposite to that of the velocity vector.

Figure S15.5

15.6 (*a*) A pure sinusoidal function requires just a single term in the Fourier series, so the spectrum consists of a single peak at frequency $f = 1/T$. The peak height A is the square of the amplitude of the function. (*b*) As T increases, $f = 1/T$ decreases, and the single peak in the spectrum shifts to a lower frequency.

15.7 (*a*) At $x = x_0$ and for large x, $\Sigma F_x = 0$, and so these are equilibrium positions. Only the position at x_0 is a stable equilibrium position. (At very large x, the equilibrium is unstable because the object will tend to accelerate in the negative x direction.) (*b*) The shape of the curve tells you that the magnitude of the restoring force is greater for a negative displacement from x_0 than for a equal positive displacement.

15.8 If you did not set your calculator to work with radians before getting the five values, you might have concluded that the small-angle approximation $\sin \theta \approx \theta$ is not correct! Because radians measure ratios of arc lengths and radii (see Section 11.4), $\sin \theta \approx \theta$ applies only if θ is expressed in radians. Thus your first step is to convert each angle from degrees to radians, and then (with your calculator set at "rad") get the sine values. As Table S15.8 shows, the approximation is correct to better than 1% up to rotational positions corresponding to polar angles of 10°.

Table S15.8 Small-angle approximation

polar angle θ in degrees	polar angle θ in radians	sin θ	error (%)
1	0.0174533	0.0174524	0.0051
5	0.0872665	0.0871557	0.1270
10	0.1745329	0.1736482	0.5095
20	0.3490659	0.3420201	2.0600

15.9 (*a*) If the length of the pendulum is increased, the displacement of the pendulum bob for a given angle increases, but the restoring force remains the same. So the restoring force for a given displacement is smaller and thus the period is longer (for a mathematical proof see Example 15.6). (*b*) The smaller acceleration of gravity on the Moon decreases the restoring force exerted on the pendulum, and so the period is increased. (*c*) Neither the mass nor the spring constant is affected by the smaller gravitational attraction on the Moon, and so the object's period is the same on the Moon and on Earth.

15.10 (*a*) x positive, v_x positive, a_x negative. (*b*) x negative, v_x negative, a_x positive.

15.11 (*a*) Substituting the maximum displacement $x = A$ into Eq. 15.15, you get $U = \frac{1}{2} m\omega^2 A^2$. (*b*) Yes. At maximum displacement, $K = 0$ and $E = U$.

15.12 (*a*) Yes. The velocity is given by the derivative of Eq. 15.6, as Eq. 15.7 shows. Because $\phi_i = \pi/2$, at $t = 0$, $v_x \propto \cos \pi/2 = 0$. (*b*) No. In Figure 15.26, for example, the cart moves to the left (negative x component of the velocity) even after crossing the position $x = 0$. Only after reaching $x = -A$ does the cart turn around and the x component of the velocity become positive.

15.13 (*a*) Because cart 2 remains in place after the first collision, the carts collide again when cart 1 returns to its initial position at $x = -15$ mm. Because the sine function is symmetrical about the maximum, this occurs after a time interval twice as long as that required to reach maximum compression. So $t = 2(0.17 \text{ s}) = 0.34$ s. (*b*) Immediately after the second collision, cart 1 has zero velocity and then begins a new oscillation with an amplitude of 15 mm. Cart 2 moves away to the right at a constant speed of 0.10 m/s.

15.14 If the block is lifted above x_{eq}, Eq. 2 remains valid—the only difference now is that $x - x_{eq}$ is negative because x is on the other side of x_{eq}. The vector sum of the forces is then positive, reflecting the fact that the restoring force is now downward.

15.15 Decreasing the radius of the disk reduces its rotational inertia (which means it rotates more easily). Decreasing I increases ω (Eq. 15.29), and hence f increases (Eq. 15.4).

15.16 No. The oscillating rod experiment determines the acceleration due to gravity g, not G. The two are related (Eq. 13.4, $g = Gm_E/R_E^2$), but the relationship contains Earth's mass, which must be determined independently. [As you may remember, Earth's mass is determined from G, which is measured in the Cavendish experiment (see Section 13.5), not the other way around, see Example 13.3.]

15.17 Greater. The upward acceleration effectively increases g, which means that an object in your hand feels heavier. If g increases, the frequency of the pendulum increases too (see Example 15.6). An alternative way to see that f increases is to look at the free-body diagrams for the pendulum bob in an elevator at rest (Figure S15.17*a*) and in an elevator that is accelerating upward (Figure S15.17*b*). For the elevator at rest (or moving at constant velocity), the upward vertical component of the tensile force exerted by the string on the bob and the downward force of gravity add approximately to zero (ignoring the small vertical acceleration due to the pendulum motion). When the elevator accelerates upward, the tensile force exerted by the string on the bob must increase so that the vertical component of $\vec{F}^c_{sb}$ becomes greater than the gravitational force. This causes the pendulum bob to accelerate along with the elevator. If $\vec{F}^c_{sb}$ becomes greater, however, the horizontal component also increases, and so the restoring force for a given displacement increases, which increases f.

Figure S15.17

15.18 (*a*) The time-varying amplitude is given by $x_{max} = Ae^{-t/2\tau}$, where A is the initial amplitude. If the amplitude decreases by a factor of 3, $x_{max}/A = 1/3$, so $e^{-(4.0\,s)/2\tau} = 1/3$. Taking the natural logarithm (see Appendix B) of both sides, you get $-(4.0\,s)/2\tau = \ln(1/3) = /1.1$, $\tau = (-2.0\,s)/(-1.1) = 1.8\,s$. (*b*) $Q = \omega t = 2\pi f \tau = 2\pi(262\,Hz)(1.8\,s) = 3.0 \times 10^3$.

Chapter 16

16.1 (*a*) See Figure S16.1. (*b*) The x component of the bead's velocity is always zero because the bead moves in only the y direction. The y component of the bead's velocity is positive on the leading edge of the pulse and negative on the trailing edge.

Figure S16.1

16.2 (*a*) Yes. Using a ruler, you can verify that the displacement of the pulse from one frame to the next is constant. (*b*) Between $t = 0$ and $t = 0.36\,s$, the peak of the pulse moves over 16 beads, which corresponds to a displacement $\Delta x = (15)(5.0\,mm) = 75\,mm$, and so the wave speed is $c = (75\,mm)/(0.36\,s) = 0.21\,m/s$.

16.3 (*a*) 0.4 m. (*b*) 0.1 m. (*c*) 0. (*d*) Greater, because the pulse moves to the right and so the 1.5-m point on the string is about to be pulled upward.

16.4 (*a*) The point at $x = 0$ reaches its maximum height at $t = 0.50\,s$; the point at $x = 1.0\,m$ reaches its maximum height at $t = 1.0\,s$. So it takes the pulse 0.50 s to move 1.0 m. (*b*) $c = (1.0\,m)/(0.50\,s) = 2.0\,m/s$.

16.5 (*a*) Figure 16.16*b* plots the horizontal displacement of each coil on the spring from its *equilibrium* position. The coils between $x = 0.20\,m$ and $x = 0.40\,m$ are displaced from their equilibrium position and so $x = 0.30\,m$ is the midpoint of the pulse. The coil originally at $x = 0.30\,m$ is displaced 0.05 m to the right, as shown by the slanted line in Figure 16.6*a*. So, even though this coil appears at $x = 0.35\,m$ in Figure 16.6*a*, it really is at the midpoint of the pulse. (*b*) Yes, but the displacement is now negative. See Figure S16.5.

Figure S16.5

16.6 (*a*) At t_1, the free-body diagram for each bead to the right of bead 3 is identical to the one for bead 3. Because the accelerations of all these beads are zero, the forces exerted on each bead by its two neighboring beads are equal in magnitude and opposite in direction. In addition, you know that any two adjacent beads exert reciprocal forces on each other, and so at t_1 all the forces exerted on each other by the beads to the right of bead 3 must be equal in magnitude to F^c_{43} (5 N). To hold the right end of the string in place, some object must therefore be exerting a horizontal force of 5 N on that bead. (*b*) All beads move in only the vertical direction, and so their acceleration in the horizontal direction is always zero. You can thus use the same argument as in part *a* to show that the magnitudes of the horizontal components of all forces along the string are equal to 5 N. (*c*) The direction of the force exerted by the hand is tangent to the direction of the string: up and to the left. (*d*) As you found in part *b*, the magnitude of the horizontal component is 5 N. Because the vertical component is nonzero, the magnitude of the force exerted by the hand must be greater than 5 N. (*e*) The horizontal component keeps the string taut; together with the force exerted by the wall at the right end, it provides the tension in the string. The vertical component accelerates the first bead vertically upward.

16.7 (*a*) The shape of the pulse does not change as it propagates along the string, and so each bead executes the same motion as the pulse passes through it. This means that each bead has velocity $\vec{v}_{peak}$ and acceleration

$\vec{a}_{\text{peak}}$ when it is at its highest point, velocity $\vec{v}_{\text{half}}$ and acceleration $\vec{a}_{\text{half}}$ when it is halfway up to its highest point, and so on. Because the position of bead 4 at t_4 is the same as the position of bead 3 at t_3, $\vec{v}_4(t_4) = \vec{v}_3(t_3)$ and $\vec{a}_4(t_4) = \vec{a}_3(t_3)$. (b) They are the same. For each string, the motion of each point along the string is identical to the motion of the end you moved (provided the pulse doesn't change shape as it travels along the string). Because the end of A and the end of B move in identical fashion, all particles of *both* strings execute the same motion and so have equal velocities at equal displacements. (c) See Figure S16.7a. When the pulse on B has a displacement of $\Delta \vec{x}_B$, the displacement $\Delta \vec{x}_A$ of the pulse on A is twice as large because of the greater wave speed on string A. In addition—make sure you have not overlooked this—the pulse on A is twice as wide, for this reason: If, during the time interval it took your hand to move from initial position to maximum displacement, the pulse on A advanced a distance $\frac{1}{2}w_A$ (half the *width* of the pulse), then the pulse on B advanced only half as much: $\frac{1}{2}w_B = \frac{1}{2}(\frac{1}{2}w_A)$. (d) See Figure S16.7b. Each point carries out the same motion, taking the same amount of time to go up and then back down, and so the curves have the same shape. Because the pulse on B travels more slowly, the particle of B executes its motion at an instant t_B that is later than the instant t_A at which the particle of A executes its motion.

Figure S16.7

(a)

(b)

16.8 Because the tension in A is greater than that in B, the pulse travels faster on A than on B. This is the same as in Checkpoint 16.7, and so the sketches are the same. (a) See Figure S16.7a. (b) See Figure S16.7b.

16.9 See Figure S16.9. From the motion of the hand in Figure 16.9, you see that the end of the string first moved up, then down, and so on. Similarities: Your graph and the snapshot of the wave have identical shapes. Differences: In Figure S16.9, the beginning of the wave motion is on the left at $t = 0$; in the snapshots in Figure 16.9, however, the leading edge of the wave is on the right. So, in addition to your curve having a different scale, it is a mirror image of the wave of Figure 16.9.

Figure S16.9

16.10 (a) Source: All particles of the string follow the motion of the source. (b) Properties of the string. (c) Both: The wavelength is determined by the wave speed and the period (see Figure 16.9). The wave speed is determined by the properties of the string, and the period is determined by the source. (d) Source: Because each string particle executes the same up-and-down motion as the source, the maximum speed is determined by the source.

16.11 Yes. Imagine putting some object in the path of the pulse. When the pulse displaces the string so that the string hits the object, the object is set in motion, and so the string has transferred momentum to the object.

16.12 (a) No. To see why, assume for simplicity that the pulses overlap at the midpoint of each string. In Figure 16.12, the maximum displacement at points away from the midpoint where the two pulses overlap is the peak displacement of the larger pulse. In the region of overlap near the midpoint, however, the maximum displacement is greater. In Figure 16.13, the maximum displacement at every point except where the pulses overlap is again the peak displacement of the larger pulse, but the maximum displacement at the midpoint is smaller than this. (b) See Figure S16.12a and b. In Figure S16.12a, the left peak shows how the point near the string's left end is displaced (just after $t = 0$) as the right-moving pulse in Figure 16.12 passes through the point. The right peak shows how, at some later instant, this same point is displaced by the left-moving pulse in Figure 16.12.

Figure S16.12

(a) Point near left end in Figure 16.12

(b) Point near left end in Figure 16.13

(c) String midpoint in Figure 16.12

(d) String midpoint in Figure 16.13

Figure S16.12*b* shows the same thing for the two pulses in Figure 16.13. (*c*) See Figure S16.12*c* and *d*. Assuming, as in part *a*, that the two pulses overlap at the string midpoint, the Figure S16.12*c* peak is the algebraic sum of the two peaks in Figure 16.12, and the Figure S16.12*d* peak is the algebraic sum of the two peaks in Figure 16.13. (*d*) Comparing Figure S16.12*a* and *c* tells you that a point near the string's left end is displaced twice but the midpoint is displaced only once, justifying the answer no for Figure 16.12. Comparing Figure S16.12*b* and *d* tells you the same thing for Figure 16.13.

16.13 (*a*) See Figure S16.13. At the midpoint, the two pulses always cause displacements of equal magnitude in opposite directions. (*b*) The velocity of a point along the string is equal to the derivative of the displacement of that point with respect to time. If the displacement is in the *y* direction, the *y* component of the velocity is $v_y = dD_y/dt$. Because the displacement is the sum of the individual displacements, the velocity is the sum of the individual velocities.

Figure S16.13

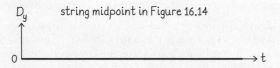

16.14 Because the string is straight, its elastic potential energy is zero, which means all the energy is kinetic energy. As Figure 16.16 shows, the pulse is in the process of inverting itself and, although the string is straight, every particle within the wave pulse is in motion.

16.15 (*a*) To see what happens, we construct the pulse shape by the superposition of the incident pulse and an imagined noninverted reflected pulse (Figure S16.15). At t_5 the peaks of both pulses have just reached the free end, and the leading edge of the reflected pulse overlaps the trailing end of the incident pulse. The velocities of particles of the leading edge of the reflected pulse are upward and those on the trailing edge of the incident pulse are downward, so the velocities of particles of the combined pulse are zero (see Checkpoint 16.13). The kinetic energy is zero. (*b*) Let the original pulse have elastic potential energy *U*; then $K = U$ (see Section 16.3) and $E = 2U$. If the string obeys Hooke's law, the potential energy is proportional to the square of the displacement. At t_5, when the displacement at the free end is equal to the sum of the amplitudes of the two pulses (that is, twice as great), the potential energy is four times as great. However, at t_5 the pulse is only half its original width, and so the potential energy is $2U$. (*c*) Yes, $E_1 = E_5 = 2U$.

Figure S16.15

(a) String at instant t_5

$\vec{v}_{string} = \vec{0}$ free end

boundary

(b) Incident pulse

$\vec{c}$

$\vec{v}_{string}$

(c) Reflected pulse

$\vec{v}_{string}$ $\vec{c}$

16.16 (*a*) With $\mu_2 = 0$, the boundary becomes a free end, and so the reflected pulse has the same amplitude as the incident pulse and nothing is transmitted to string 2. (*b*) With $\mu_2 = \infty$, the boundary becomes fixed. Again the (inverted) reflected pulse has the same amplitude as the incident pulse and nothing is transmitted to string 2. (*c*) When $\mu_2 = \mu_1$, the strings become one: There is no boundary and so no reflection. The pulse travels unchanged from string 1 to string 2. (*d*) Because the wave speed is greater in string 2, the transmitted pulse is spread out more than the incident pulse (see Section 16.2).

16.17 (*a*) All but (*iii*), which cannot represent a traveling wave because the exponential factor e^{-x} is not a function of $(x \pm ct)$. (*b*) All three, by substituting $(x \pm ct)$ for each *x*.

16.18 (*a*) At $t = 0$, the string has zero velocity and so $K = 0$ and all the energy is stored as elastic potential energy. At $t = \frac{1}{8}T$, the string is moving vertically and is not in the equilibrium position, so the energy is distributed between kinetic and elastic potential. At $t = \frac{1}{4}T$, the string is horizontal, so $U = 0$. All the energy is kinetic. (*b*) Yes. Each particle of the string executes simple harmonic motion about its equilibrium position (but different points have different amplitudes—zero at the nodes, maximum at the antinodes). Because the energy of a simple harmonic oscillator is constant, the energy of any particle or any length of string is also constant. (*c*) No. The amount of energy f_1 carries rightward is equal to the amount f_2 carries leftward, so the combined flow of energy is zero.

16.19 (*a*) No. Suppose one amplitude is twice as large as the other. Half of the large-amplitude wave forms a standing wave with the other wave, but the remaining half remains a traveling wave. The superposition of a standing and a traveling wave is not a standing wave. (*b*) No. Because the wavelengths are not the same, the interference at any position is constructive at some instants and destructive at other instants, unlike the interference illustrated in Figure 16.37, which for a given position is the same at all instants.

16.20 (*a*) See Figure S16.20. Two contact forces act on A: F_{hA}^c and F_{BA}^c. If the gravitational force exerted on A is much smaller than these contact forces, we can ignore it: $\Sigma F_A = 0$. (*b*) The momentum does not change, which makes sense because A moves upward at constant velocity $\vec{v}$. (*c*) Yes, because the scalar product of the force and the force displacement is nonzero and positive: $dW = \vec{F} \cdot d\vec{r}_F$. (*d*) The energy increases because an increasing amount of string moves upward at velocity $\vec{v}$.

Figure S16.20

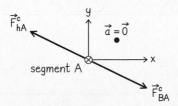

16.21 Greater (twice as great to be precise) because *two* waves travel away from the point you are shaking, one in each direction along the string. Another way to see this is by looking at the force you must exert to move the string. For a point in the middle, this force is twice as great as the force you must exert on an end because the pieces of string on either side of your hand each exert the same force as one end of the string. So the amount of work you do on the string increases by a factor of 2.

16.22 The frequency *f* (and therefore the angular frequency ω) is determined by the source that causes the wave. The wave number *k* is equal to ω divided by the wave speed *c*, which is determined by the tension and linear mass density of the string.

Chapter 17

17.1 (*a*) Because the wave speed c is constant, $R_2 = 2R_1$. (*b*) The circumference at R_1 is $2\pi R_1$, making the energy per unit length $E/2\pi R_1$; at R_2 this becomes $E/2\pi R_2 = E/4\pi R_1$. (*c*) The energy varies as $1/r$ because the wavefront circumference increases with r.

17.2 By reducing the amplitude of the source as time passes so that it always matches the decrease in amplitude of the outward traveling wave. Consequently the amplitude of the wave in Figure 17.1, though uniform over *space*, is not constant in time; it uniformly decreases over the entire wave pattern.

17.3 (*a*) Increase. The greater the spring constant, the faster any disturbance is passed from one bead to the next. The effect is the same as when the tension in a string carrying a transverse wave is increased (see Section 16.2). (*b*) Decrease. The greater mass slows down the transmission of the wave just as it does for a transverse pulse on a string of beads.

17.4 (*a*) Just as for a transverse wave, the x component of the velocity of each bead is dD_x/dt. If D_x is a sine function, the x component of the velocity is a cosine function. This means that the velocity wave is always one-quarter wavelength ahead of the displacement wave, as shown in Figure S17.14a. (*b*) By comparing Figure 17.9b and Figure S17.4a, you can see that the linear density is greatest where the velocity is maximum and smallest where the velocity is minimum. Figure S17.4b shows a plot of the linear density versus position.

17.5 Spherical. The shape of the wavefront is determined by the distance traveled by the wavefront. Because the wave speed is the same in all directions, a given wavefront reaches the same distance from the loudspeaker in all directions. (The sound is louder in the front than in the back because of differences in the wave amplitude, which is greater in front because of the way speakers are designed.)

Figure S17.4

17.6 (*a*) Zero, because the displacement caused by each wavefront is zero. (*b*) The displacement at that point does not remain zero, however. A quarter period later, two crests (or troughs) meet at that point, and so the displacement at that point varies sinusoidally with an amplitude of $2A$ (Figure S17.6a). (*c*) Along the line that connects the half-filled circles, the waves generated by the two sources are 180° out of phase. Two

Figure S17.6

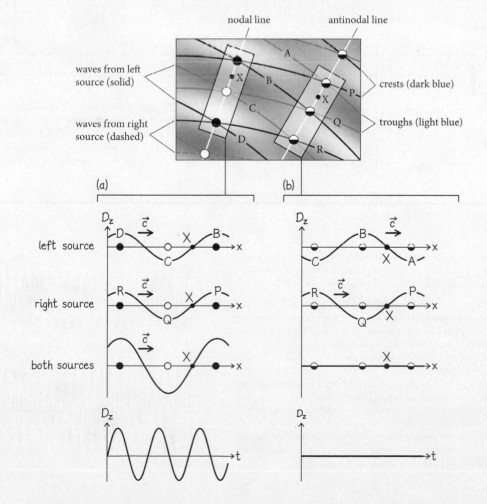

equal-amplitude sine waves that are 180° out of phase cancel, and so the medium displacement is zero at *all* points along the nodal line, not just the ones marked with half-filled circles. (*d*) See Figure S17.6*b*.

17.7 No, because the displacement at this point doesn't remain zero. See Checkpoint 17.6.

17.8 (*a*) $A + A = 2A$ in Figure 17.16*a*; A in Figure 17.16*b*. (*b*) Increase, for two reasons: There is now twice as much energy (two sources), and instead of radiating outward uniformly, the wave energy travels in only certain directions (between nodal lines). (*c*) $E \propto A^2$, and so the energy that passes P increases by a factor of 4. The energy delivered by the sources increases by a factor of 2, while the area over which the energy is spread out is reduced by a factor of 2 (there are just as many antinodal lines as there are nodal lines). These two effects multiply to produce a fourfold increase in the flow of energy at P.

17.9 There are six nodal lines above the horizontal straight line through S_1 and S_2 (and six below also, of course). So $2(d/\lambda) = 6$, $d/\lambda = 3$, $d = 3\lambda$; the distance between the sources is three wavelengths.

17.10 Because along this line, the two waves travel in the same direction and are in phase, which means they reinforce each other everywhere.

17.11 It does not change. Except for a little spreading at the edges, the wavefronts remain straight and parallel. What reaches a 10λ-wide line segment parallel to the row of sources at a distance R also reaches a similar segment at a distance $2R$.

17.12 See Figure S17.12. A narrow gap causes diffraction regardless of the orientation of the incident wavefronts because the incident waves cause the gap to become a point source. (For simplicity the reflections of the planar wavefronts from the back surface of the barrier have been omitted from the drawing.)

Figure S17.12

17.13 10 dB corresponds to 1 bel or one order of magnitude (because $\log 10 = 1$). So the intensity must be increased by a factor of 10, which means that ten clarinets must play at the same time.

17.14 (*a*) Three. The A and B lines fall exactly on top of each other at P, but as you move down they get out of step until you reach Q, where they match again. So each band has a whole number of lines between P and Q, but A has one more line. (If they had the same number of lines, each A line would fall on top of a B line. If A had more than one extra line between P and Q, the lines of A would catch up with those of B before Q.) Between Q and S the bands line up twice more, so band A has three additional lines between P and S. (*b*) Points P, Q, R, and S become dark (because the lines of the two patterns now fall right between each other), while the dark bands turn bright (because the lines now line up; Figure S17.14). Note that the moiré pattern moves down a considerable distance (half the distance between P and Q) even though B moved down only half a line spacing. This effect can be used to measure small displacements.

Figure S17.14

original placement   band B moved down by half the spacing between its lines

band A   band B

P –

Q –

R –

S –

17.15 Yes, but the beats are less pronounced than when the two amplitudes are equal. Let one wave have amplitude A and the other amplitude $2A$. The first wave produces beats with half of the second wave. The other half adds to the beat pattern, resulting in a oscillating wave with a varying amplitude (Figure S17.15), but the amplitude never goes all the way to zero.

Figure S17.15

17.16 Equation 1 in Example 17.8 gives $f_s = f_1(c - v)/c$. Substituting the values for f_1, c, and v yields $f_s = 441$ Hz.

17.17 (a) With $v_o = \frac{1}{2}c$ and $v_s = 0$, Eq. 17.20 yields $f_o = \left[(c + \frac{1}{2}c)/(c - 0)\right]f_s = \frac{3}{2}f_s$. (b) With $v_o = 0$ and $v_s = \frac{1}{2}c$, $f_o = (c - 0)/(c - \frac{1}{2}c)f_s = 2f_s$. (c) The answers are different because there is a physical difference in the two situations. When the source moves, the wavefronts bunch up or spread out, changing the wavelength. When the observer moves, the wavelength, which is fixed by the wave speed in the stationary medium, does not change. Instead, the moving observer intercepts a different number of wavefronts per unit time. So it is not just the relative motion of source and observer that matters; the fact that their speeds are measured relative to the medium that transmits the wave also matters.

17.18 No. Shock waves are due to the piling up of wavefronts. When the source is stationary and the observer moves, the wavelength is unchanged. Setting $v_o = 2c$ with $v_s = 0$ in Eq. 17.20 yields $f_o = 3f_s$. This reflects the fact that the moving observer intercepts three times as many wavefronts per unit time as an observer at rest.

17.19 The cone angle is about 35°, and sin 35° = 0.57. From Eq. 17.22, you have $c/v_s = 0.57$, $v_s = 1.7c \approx 600$ m/s.

Chapter 18

18.1 (a) If the water is to remain at rest, the vector sum of the forces exerted on it must be zero. Because you initially exert a rightward 10-N force on the left piston, you must also exert a leftward 10-N force on the right piston. (b) Figure S18.1 shows free-body diagrams for the two pistons and the water. Because of the two interaction pairs marked in the figure, all six forces are equal in magnitude, so $\vec{F}^c_{pl} = \vec{F}^c_{wr}$. In other words, the force you exert on the left piston is transmitted by the water to the right piston.

Figure S18.1

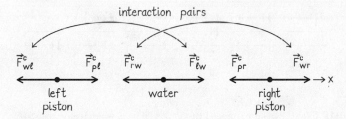

18.2 (a) Yes. The water is at rest, which means the downward force of gravity exerted on it must be balanced by an upward contact force exerted by the bottom of the cup. That the bottom exerts a force on the water tells you that the water must exert a force on the bottom. (b) Yes. If the sides of the cup were to disappear, the water would move radially outward. That the water remains in the cup tells you that the sides must exert a force on the water, and consequently the water must exert a force of equal magnitude on the cup in the opposite direction. (c) Positive. Because the water pushes outward on the surfaces of the cup, the surfaces must push inward on the water, putting it under compression. By definition, compression means positive pressure.

18.3 If you divide the liquid into three equal layers, each layer is subject to an identical force of gravity. The bottom layer supports the upper two, the middle layer supports only the top one, and the top one supports no other layer. If you make the division even finer, you can see that the pressure decreases linearly with height.

18.4 10 m. The pressure at the surface is 1.0×10^5 N/m², and that pressure doubles when the force of gravity exerted on a column of water of height h and cross-sectional area $A = 1$ m² has magnitude $F^G = mg = 1.0 \times 10^5$ N. The volume of this column is $V = hA$, its

mass is $m = \rho_{water}V = \rho_{water}\,hA$, and the magnitude of the force of gravity exerted on it is $mg = \rho_{water}\,hAg$. Thus $h = mg/(\rho_{water}\,Ag) = (1.0 \times 10^5$ N$)/[(1.0 \times 10^3$ kg/m³$)(1$ m²$)(9.8$ m/s²$)] = 10$ m.

18.5 (a) Nothing. Because the pressure in a liquid at rest decreases linearly with height, the pressure difference between the top and bottom of the brick is the same at every water depth. (b) Nothing. Pascal's principle tells you that a pressure change applied to a liquid is transmitted undiminished to every part of the liquid. So, increasing the pressure at the water surface increases the pressure at the top and at the bottom of the brick by the same amount, leaving the difference unchanged. (c) There is no effect because this pressure at the sides causes equal forces in opposite directions. (d) Yes, because the pressure in the atmosphere also decreases with height, although much less than in water. This force is upward.

18.6 The magnitude of the buoyant force exerted on the brick by the water is equal to the magnitude of the force of gravity exerted by Earth on the water displaced by the brick. Because the density of the brick is greater than the density of the water, the mass of the brick must be greater than the mass of the displaced water. Therefore the magnitude $m_{brick}g$ of the force of gravity on the brick is greater than the magnitude $m_{water}g$ of the force of gravity on the displaced water. The magnitude of the upward buoyant force exerted by the water on the brick is thus smaller than the magnitude of the downward force of gravity exerted on it, and so the brick sinks.

18.7 Equal. Because the pan-rock combination floats in both cases, the buoyant force exerted in both cases must be equal to the force of gravity exerted on the displaced water. You also know that the upward buoyant force on the combination must be equal to the downward force of gravity on the combination because the combination remains at rest. The mass of the pan-rock combination doesn't change when the rock is suspended (you can ignore the mass of the string), so the volume of water displaced doesn't change.

18.8 The same. The principle of relativity tells you that the laws of the universe are the same in all inertial reference frames. So, if you view the motion of an object moving at constant velocity through a stationary fluid from the reference frame of the object, you obtain the same situation—a laminar flow of fluid past a stationary object—as in Figure 18.18a.

18.9 As you can see in Figure 18.15, streamlines that pass over the roof of the car get closer together, indicating a higher flow speed and therefore lower pressure just above the roof. The air pressure inside the car, however, is unchanged and therefore greater than that outside, making the cloth roof bulge outward.

18.10 According to Pascal's principle, the pressure in the air in the balloon must be the same everywhere.

18.11 (a) Zero. The tensile forces due to surface tension are in the plane of the surface and therefore unable to compensate for any pressure difference across the surface when the surface is level. (b) Greater. The vector sum of the tensile forces exerted on a segment of the surface points toward the center of the drop. (c) It is higher. According to Laplace's law, the smaller radius of curvature of the small drop causes a greater pressure difference across the surface. Because both drops are surrounded by air at atmospheric pressure, the pressure must be greater inside the small drop.

18.12 Because the cylinder has a radius of curvature larger than that of the needle, the upward force exerted by the curved liquid surface on the cylinder is smaller than the upward force exerted on the needle. This smaller upward force is unable to support the (greater) downward force exerted by the cylinder on the surface.

18.13 The magnitude of the force exerted by the air on the cover is $F^c_{ac} = P_{atm}A = (101$ kPa$)(1000$ Pa$/1$ kPa$)(0.28$ m$)(0.22$ m$) = 6.2 \times 10^3$ N. The force of gravity exerted on the book is $F^G_{Eb} = (3.0$ kg$)(9.8$ m/s²$) = 29$ N. The force exerted by the atmosphere on the cover is more than 200 times greater than the gravitational force exerted by Earth on the book.

18.14 As the suction cup hits the ceiling, the bowl of the cup collapses, forcing out the air that was initially in the bowl. Consequently, the pressure in the space between the cup and the ceiling is lower than atmospheric pressure. As long as the seal between the cup edge and the ceiling is maintained, the air in the room underneath the cup exerts an upward force greater than the downward force exerted by the air inside the cup that holds the dart up against the ceiling.

18.15 That the object floats tells you that the buoyant force exerted on it must equal the force of gravity exerted on it, and so equating Eqs. 18.11 and 18.12 gives you $\rho_{o,av}V_o g = \rho_{water}V_{disp}g$. You are given that $V_{disp} = 0.80V_o$, and so $\rho_{o,av} = (\rho_{water}V_{disp})/V_o = 0.80\rho_{water}$ (see Example 18.2).

18.16 No. The pressure at the oil-water interface in the right leg must be the same as the pressure at a point that is at the same height in the left leg (Figure S18.16). Because the mass density of oil is smaller than that of water, the height of a column of oil required to cause a certain pressure difference is greater than the height of a column of water required to cause the same pressure difference. Therefore the top of the oil column must be higher than the top of the water column.

Figure S18.16

same pressure

oil

water

18.17 Because the atmosphere exerts a force on both pistons, it increases the pressure below them. When you add the effect of atmospheric pressure, the pressure in the liquid at the small piston is $P_1 = P_{atm} + F_1/A_1$ and the pressure at the large piston is $P_2 = P_{atm} + F_2/A_2$. Ignoring the term ρgh in Eq. 18.19 again, you have $P_1 \approx P_2$, and so $P_{atm} + F_1/A_1 = P_{atm} + F_2/A_2$. The atmospheric pressure cancels out, and you obtain the same result as in Eq. 18.21.

18.18 The continuity equation for an incompressible fluid (which means $\rho_1 = \rho_2$) gives $A_1v_1 = A_2v_2$ or $v_1 = v_2A_2/A_1 = v_2R_2^2/R_1^2$. Squaring all terms, subtracting v_2^2 from both sides, and dividing through by -1 give you $v_2^2 - v_1^2 = v_2^2(1 - R_2^4/R_1^4)$. With $R_1 = \frac{1}{2}(0.50\text{ m})$ and $R_2 = \frac{1}{2}(10.0\text{ mm})$, you have $(R_2/R_1)^4 = 1.6 \times 10^{-7}$, which is so small that you can ignore this term to get the result $v_2^2 - v_1^2 = v_2^2(1 - R_2^4/R_1^4) \approx v_2^2$. Thus the assumption that $v_1 \approx 0$ in Example 18.9 is excellent, and you can use the result in that example: $v_2 = \sqrt{2g\bar{d}} = 2.4$ m/s.

18.19 A soap bubble consists of a thin film of soap solution surrounding a volume of air. Because the film has two surfaces, the force due to surface tension gains an additional factor 2. Thus Eq. 18.51 becomes $P_{in} - P_{out} = 4\gamma/R$.

Chapter 19

19.1 (a) Collisions with the leading edge of the pendulum slow it down, and collisions with the trailing edge speed it up. Because of the motion of the pendulum, nitrogen molecules that collide with the leading edge move faster relative to the pendulum than nitrogen molecules that collide with the trailing edge. Therefore there are more collisions with the leading edge than with the trailing edge, and the pendulum slows down. (b) When the pendulum is at rest, the average speed of the nitrogen molecules that hit the left edge is the same as the average speed of the molecules that hit the right edge, which means that the momentum transfers due to the collisions tend to balance out.

19.2 Each segment of the zigzag path would decrease in length, so the Brownian motion would be less pronounced and the maximum displacement of the grain from the initial position would be smaller.

19.3 7.

19.4 See Figure S19.4. (a) Five macrostates. (b) 16 basic states. (c) $4/16 = 1/4$. (d) The most likely macrostate is two heads because there are six basic states associated with this macrostate.

Figure S19.4

macrostate:
no. heads
per 4 tosses

microstates

19.5 See Figure S19.5.

Figure S19.5

energy unit

particle

19.6 (a) $1/84$, which is around 1%. (b) $\frac{28}{84} + \frac{21}{84} = \frac{49}{84}$, which is more than 50%.

19.7 (a) The pendulum has more than 50% of the energy when it has four, five, or six units of energy. There are $6 + 3 + 1 = 10$ basic states associated with these macrostates. The probability that the pendulum has more than 50% of the energy is then $10/84 = 0.12$. (b) Figure 19.7 shows that as the number of particles increases, the relative probability of any given fraction of energy being in the pendulum decreases.

19.8 (a) The average kinetic energies are equal because the energy of the gas is equally distributed among all the particles. (b) Because the two particles have the same average kinetic energy, $\frac{1}{2}m_1v_1^2 = \frac{1}{2}m_2v_2^2$. Therefore $v_1 = (m_2/m_1)^{1/2}v_2 = 2^{1/2}v_2$. Particle 1 has a greater average speed by a factor of $2^{1/2}$.

19.9. There are three ways of placing the two indistinguishable particles in the two compartments (Figure S19.9). The probability of finding one particle in each side is $1/3$.

Figure S19.9

19.10. (*a*) Four basic states have all six particles in one compartment. They originate from different macrostates. Distribution A in Figure S19.10 has six particles in the top left compartment and is a macrostate. Distribution D is part of a different macrostate: no particles in the top left compartment. The three basic states in distribution D correspond to six particles in any of the other three compartments. There are 84 basic states, all equally probable, and so the probability of finding six particles in any compartment is $4/84 = 0.048$. (*b*) There are 12 basic states in which one compartment contains five particles: three for distribution B in Figure S19.10, three for distribution C, and six for distribution E. The probability of finding five particles in any compartment is thus $12/84 = 0.143$. Note that distribution E has six associated basic states, corresponding to the six ways one particle can be placed in one of three containers and five particles can be placed in another of the three containers.

Figure S19.10

Number of particles in top left quadrant	Number of particles in other three quadrants							Fraction of basic states
6 ▮▮▮▮▮▮	0 **A** ① one basic state having all six particles in top left quadrant							$\frac{1}{84}$
5 ▮▮▮▮▮	1 **B** 3							$\frac{3}{84}$
4 ▮▮▮▮	2 ▮▮ 3 ▮ 3							$\frac{6}{84}$
3 ▮▮▮	3 ▮▮▮ 3 ▮▮ 6 ▮ 1							$\frac{10}{84}$
2 ▮▮	4 ▮▮▮▮ 3 ▮▮▮ 6 ▮▮ 3 ▮▮ 3							$\frac{15}{84}$
1 ▮	5 **C** 3 ▮ 6 ▮▮ 6 ▮▮ 3 ▮▮ 3							$\frac{21}{84}$
0	6 **D** ③ **E** 6 ▮ 6 ▮▮ 3 ▮▮ 3 ▮▮ 6 ▮▮ 1							$\frac{28}{84}$

three basic states having no particles in top left quadrant and all other particles in a single quadrant

19.11. The partition moves until the particles are uniformly distributed over the space enclosed by the two compartments. Because there are twice the number of particles in the left compartment, the partition moves to the right until the volume of the left compartment is twice the volume of the right compartment.

19.12. (*a*) All six energy units are initially in the pendulum, which means each collision moves one energy unit from the pendulum to one of the particles. The system then is in one of the three basic states depicted in the second of row of Figure 19.4. (*b*) Now there are three possibilities for how energy is transferred in any given collision: from the particle that initially has the one unit to either of the two other particles, from the particle that initially has the one unit to the pendulum, or from the pendulum to any one of the particles. When a unit is transferred from one particle to another, the amount of energy in the pendulum does not change, and so the macrostate does not change (that macrostate is represented in the second row of Figure 19.4). In a collision between the pendulum and a particle, the pendulum can either gain or lose a unit of energy, and so the

system ends up in the macrostates represented by the top and third rows in Figure 19.4. So, after one collision the system can be in any one of the top three macrostates in Figure 19.4. (*c*) The number of basic states in the top three macrostates is $1 + 3 + 6 = 10$.

19.13. (*a*) There are three accessible macrostates: three units in pendulum, two units in pendulum, one unit in pendulum. (*b*) To find the probability for each macrostate, you need to consider the number of basic states representing each: 10, 15, and 21, respectively, for a total of 46. The probabilities are thus $10/46$, $15/46$, and $21/46$.

19.14. (*a*) There are 21 ways that two energy units can be distributed among the six particles. Label the particles 1 through 6. Place one energy unit in particle 1. The second energy unit can be placed in any of the six particles, resulting in six basic states. Now place one energy unit in particle 2. The second energy unit can be placed in the five particles 2 through 6 but not in particle 1 because we already counted that basic state. Repeat this process for particles 3 through 6. The number of basic states is then $6 + 5 + 4 + 3 + 2 + 1 = 21$.

19.15. (*a*) There are 14 particles in A, so the average energy per particle in A is $1/14 = 0.07$ energy unit. The average energy per particle in B is $9/6 = 1.5$ energy units. (*b*) At equilibrium there are seven energy units in A, corresponding to an average energy per particle of $7/14 = 0.5$ energy unit. The average energy per particle in B is $3/6 = 0.5$ energy unit.

19.16. (*a*) Over time the ice cube heats up and melts, and the water cools. Because the system irreversibly evolves toward equilibrium, Ω must be increasing. (*b*) Because everything—cup, tea, air—is in equilibrium, Ω is at its maximum value and not changing. (*c*) Over time the oil separates and floats to the top. Because this separation constitutes an irreversible process (the oil doesn't spontaneously mix back into the water), Ω must be increasing. (*d*) Germination is an irreversible process, so Ω is increasing. (*e*) As far as we know, the universe evolves irreversibly, so Ω is increasing.

19.17. (*a*) The compartment size decreasing by a factor of 10 means that $M = 1000$. The number of basic states is then $\Omega_f = M^N = 1000^{10} = 10^{30}$. The initial value is $\Omega_i = 10^{20}$ (see Example 19.8), so the change in the number of basic states is $10^{30} - 10^{20}$, which for all practical purposes is equal to 10^{30}. This represents an enormous increase in the number of basic states. (*b*) $\ln \Omega_f = \ln (10^{30}) = 69$. The initial value is $\ln \Omega_i = 46$ (see Example 19.8), so the change is $69 - 46 = 23$.

19.18. (*a*) According to Eq. 19.4, an increase in entropy means the number of basic states has increased. (*b*) For an expanding gas, $V_f > V_i$, and so the $N \ln (V_f/V_i)$ term in Eq. 19.8 is positive, as expected for a system evolving toward equilibrium. (*c*) If the gas were to contract into a subvolume, $V_f < V_i$, and so the $N \ln (V_f/V_i)$ term is negative, meaning a decrease in entropy. Such a decrease would violate the entropy law.

19.19. Even though entropy depends on volume, the entropy change depends on a ratio of volumes (Eq. 19.8). Because the volume of a compartment is a fraction of the volume V of the box, V cancels when we take the ratio of volumes for each compartment.

19.20. (*a*) Adding up the x components of the velocities and dividing by 5 gives an x component of the average velocity of 0. (*b*) Adding up the speeds (the absolute values of the x components of the velocities) and dividing by 5 gives an average speed of 2.6 m/s. (*c*) Adding up the squares of the speeds, dividing by 5, and then taking the square root gives a rms speed of 3.0 m/s. Note that the rms speed is not equal to the average speed of the atoms: in a gas, the former is typically about 10% greater than the latter.

19.21. Putting all the numerical factors in the third term of Eq. 19.29 together gives

$$\left[2a\left(\frac{2E_{th}}{mN}\right)^{1/2}\right]^3 = \left[\left(\frac{8a^2E_{th}}{mN}\right)^{1/2}\right]^3 = \left(\frac{8a^2}{mN}\right)^{3/2}(E_{th})^{3/2}.$$

19.22. (a) At thermal equilibrium there is equipartition of energy, and so, on average, the kinetic energy of all the atoms is the same. To the left of the dashed line, S_A is smaller and S_B is greater than at thermal equilibrium. According to Eq. 19.32, $E_{th,A}$ is therefore smaller than the equilibrium value and $E_{th,B}$ is greater than the equilibrium value. Consequently, to the left of the dashed line the average kinetic energy of the atoms in A is smaller than that in B. (b) At thermal equilibrium, both gases are equally hot. To the left of the dashed line gas B is hotter because the average kinetic energy of the atoms is greater. (c) At thermal equilibrium, $dS_A/dE_{th,A} = dS_B/dE_{th,B} = -dS_B/dE_{th,A}$ (Eq. 19.37). Figure 19.24 shows that the magnitude of the slope of curve S_A increases and the magnitude of the slope of curve S_B decreases when going left from the equilibrium point. Therefore, to the left of the equilibrium point $dS_A/dE_{th,A} > dS_B/dE_{th,B}$.

19.23. From Eq. 19.42 we have $E_{th,B}/E_{th,A} = N_B/N_A = 6/14 = 3/7$, and so 30% of the energy is in compartment B and 70% is in compartment A.

19.24. (a) Only the component of the momentum perpendicular to the wall changes. The atom's final momentum is away from the wall, and so the change in momentum is perpendicular to the wall and directed toward the interior of the container. (b) Because the system is isolated, the direction of the wall's change in momentum is opposite the direction of the atom's change in momentum. (c) As you saw in Section 8.7, the force exerted on an object is proportional to the object's change in momentum. The force exerted by the wall on the atom is therefore perpendicular to the wall and directed toward the interior of the container. The force exerted by the atom on the wall points in the opposite direction.

19.25. In deriving Eq. 19.20 we assumed that the system is in thermal equilibrium (see the beginning of Section 19.5), and so $T_A = T_B$. Multiplying the left and right sides of Eq. 19.20 by $k_B T_A$ gives $N_A k_B T_A / V_A = N_B k_B T_B / V_B$, or using the ideal gas law, $P_A = P_B$. In equilibrium, the pressure is the same on both sides of the partition, as we would expect.

19.26. (a) Neither. Because the pressures and volumes are equal, the thermal energies of the two gases are equal. (b) Neither. Because the two containers have the same number of atoms, the average kinetic energy is the same for all atoms. (c) Argon. The rms speed is proportional to the square root of the average kinetic energy divided by the mass (Eq. 19.53). Although the average kinetic energies of the two gases are equal, a helium atom has a smaller mass than an argon atom, so the rms speed of a helium atom is greater than that of an argon atom.

19.27. (a) No, because the system is not closed; as the gas cools, thermal energy leaves the system. The entropy law applies only to closed systems. (b) From Example 19.12a, we have $T_f = 145$ K, so $\Delta T = 145$ K $-$ 290 K $= -145$ K, and so, from Eq. 19.50:
$\Delta E_{th} = \frac{3}{2} N k_B \Delta T = \frac{3}{2}(10^{23})(1.38 \times 10^{-23} \text{ J/K})$
$(-145 \text{ K}) = -300$ J.

19.28. Decrease. From Eq. 19.61, because $T_f = T_i/2$ and $V_f = 2V_i$, we have

$$\Delta S = \frac{3}{2} N \ln \frac{1}{2} + N \ln 2.$$

Because $\ln \frac{1}{2} = -\ln 2$, this can be written as

$$\Delta S = -\frac{3}{2} N \ln 2 + N \ln 2 = -\frac{1}{2} N \ln 2 < 0,$$

and so the entropy decreases. When the temperature of the system is halved, the energy of the system decreases, and so the system is not closed.

Chapter 20

20.1. (a) Joules. (b) See Figure S20.1.

Figure S20.1

(i) system: water, pot, flame
thermal energy of pot and water

(ii) system: pot, flame
thermal energy of pot

(iii) system: pot
thermal energy of pot

20.2. See Figure S20.2.

Figure S20.2

20.3. See Figure S20.3. The quasistatic process is possible because it depicts a succession of equilibrium states, all of which show an equipartition of space. The non-quasistatic process is not possible: As the first four frames show, it would require the gas molecules to "pull away" spontaneously from the piston, before the piston begins moving down in frame 2.

Figure S20.3

(a) Reverse quasistatic process

(b) Reverse non-quasistatic process

20.4. During a quasistatic process the system must remain near equilibrium at all instants during the process. (a) Not quasistatic; just after the balloon is popped, the pressure inside the container is not the same everywhere and so the system is not in equilibrium. (b) Quasistatic; even though the temperature of the coffee changes, the change is slow. The coffee therefore has a well-defined uniform temperature and is in equilibrium throughout the cooling process. (c) Quasistatic; as the gas pushes the piston outward, the pressure in the gas remains uniform and so the gas is in equilibrium. (d) Not quasistatic; the temperature of the ice cube and the hot water are different, and so the system is not in equilibrium.

20.5. (a) Using Eq. 2 from the "Temperature measurement scales" box, you find for $T_F = 60\ °F$:

$$T_C = \frac{5\ °C}{9\ °F}(60\ °F - 32\ °F) = 16\ °C.$$

Likewise, for $T_F = 80\ °F$, you obtain $T_C = 27\ °C$, making the range 16 °C to 27 °C. By adding 273.15 to these values, you get the corresponding range in kelvins: 289 K to 300 K.

(b) Equation 1 from the box gives you

$$T_C = \frac{1\ °C}{1\ K}(2800\ K) - 273.15\ °C = 2500\ °C.$$

The expression I used in the solution to Exercise 20.2b gives

$$T_F = \frac{9\ °C}{5\ °F}\left[\frac{1\ °C}{1\ K}(2800\ K) - 273.15\ °C\right] + 32\ °F = 4600\ °F.$$

20.6. (a) There are many more water molecules in the pool than in the glass. Thermal energy is proportional to number of molecules, and so the pool has greater thermal energy. (b) The heat capacity of the pool is greater

because the amount of thermal energy needed to increase the temperature of all the water in the pool by 1 K is greater than the amount needed to increase the temperature of all the water in the glass by 1 K. (c) The glass of warm water because thermal energy is proportional to temperature.

20.7. (a) All three. Unlike a hydrogen molecule, an ammonia molecule is not linear, so its rotational inertia is nonzero along the three orthogonal axes. (b) Because there are six degrees of freedom, three translational and three rotational, the thermal energy per molecule is $6(\frac{1}{2}k_BT) = 3k_BT$. (c) If you raise the temperature by $\Delta T = 1$ K, the increase in thermal energy per molecule is $\Delta E_{th} = 3k_B\Delta T$. The heat capacity per molecule is thus $\Delta E_{th}/\Delta T = 3k_B$. (d) It's within 10%. The experimental value listed in Table 20.3 is $3.37 kB$.

20.8. Less than. More energy must be transferred to the diatomic gas because it has more degrees of freedom, and so its heat capacity per particle is greater.

20.9. $P_1 > P_2$, $V_1 < V_2$, and $T_1 = T_2$ because the two states are on an isotherm. The entropy dependence on temperature and volume is given by Eq. 19.60, $S \propto \ln T^{3/2}V$. The temperatures are the same in the two states, and so the differences in entropy depend only on volumes. That $V_1 < V_2$ tells you that $S_1 < S_2$. Because $E_{th} \propto T$, the thermal energies of the two states are the same.

20.10. (a) The change in entropy is the same for the two processes (the same initial and final states and therefore the same initial and final temperatures and volumes). (b) No. Because the two processes have the same initial and final states, the change in temperature is the same for both. Hence the change in thermal energy ΔE_{th} is the same. This change is the sum of the work done on the gas and the energy transferred thermally to it: $\Delta E_{th} = W + Q$. Because the work done on the gas (the area under the path) is different for the two processes, the amount of energy transferred thermally must also be different.

20.11. See Table S20.11. The work done on the gas is positive during compression, negative during expansion, and zero for any isochoric process.

The thermal energy is proportional to the temperature (see Eq. 19.50). As you can see from Figure 20.25, the isentropic expansion brings the system to a lower isotherm, and so the thermal energy decreases; in the isochoric process, the temperature increases, and so $\Delta E_{th} > 0$; the isobaric process decreases the temperature, and so $\Delta E_{th} < 0$; and the isothermal compression doesn't change the temperature, so $\Delta E_{th} = 0$.

The isentropic process is adiabatic, so $Q = 0$. For the other processes, the sign of Q can be determined from ΔE_{th} and W, because the sum of the work done on the gas and the energy transferred thermally to it equals the change in thermal energy.

For the isentropic process the change in entropy is zero by definition. As you can see from Figure 20.25, the isochoric process brings the system to a higher isentrope and so $\Delta S > 0$. The isobaric and isothermal compressions bring the system to a lower isentrope, so $\Delta S < 0$. (Because the system is not closed, the entropy can decrease.)

20.12. Table 20.3 and Figure 20.15 tell you that at $T = 300$ K, the heat capacity per particle for hydrogen is $2.5k_B$ and so it has five degrees of freedom (three translational and two rotational). So, if we assume the gas can be treated as ideal, the thermal energy is $E_{th} = \frac{5}{2}Nk_BT$ (approximately N times 10^{-20} J).

Table S20.11 Checkpoint 20.11

Process	ΔE_{th}	W	Q	ΔS
isentropic expansion	negative	negative	0	0
isochoric pressure increase	positive	0	positive	positive
isobaric volume decrease	negative	positive	negative	negative
isothermal compression	0	positive	negative	negative

20.13. Process A. The vertical legs for both A and B are at constant volume, and Eq. 20.9 tells you that no work is done on the gas. In process A, the gas undergoes an isobaric decrease in volume at a higher pressure than process B. The volume change is the same in both cases. So, by Eq. 20.9 (which has ΔV no longer equal to zero), the work done on the gas during the isobaric process in process A is greater than in process B. (Note that the area under path A in Figure 20.28 is larger than the area under path B and the work done on the gas is positive, thus confirming our answer.)

20.14. (a) Process C. Because the initial and final states lie on an isotherm, $\Delta E_{th} = 0$ for all three processes. The work done on the system in each process is negative and equal in magnitude to the area under the path. Because $\Delta E_{th} = 0$, $Q = -W$ and so Q is equal to the area under the path, which is largest for process C and (b) smallest for process A.

20.15. Yes. If $\Delta T = 0$, then the temperature doesn't change, and if the temperature doesn't change, then Eq. 20.5 tells us that E_{th} doesn't change either, so $\Delta E_{th} = 0$.

20.16. Greater. Because $PV = Nk_BT$ and Nk_B is constant, the product PV is proportional to the temperature T of the state. The final temperature T_f is greater than the initial temperature T_i, and so $P_fV_f > P_iV_i$.

20.17. The isobaric process. Both processes have the same ΔE_{th} because the temperature change is the same. No work is done on the gas during the isochoric process, which means that in this process the energy transferred thermally goes entirely into raising the temperature. During the isobaric process, more energy must be transferred thermally into the gas during the expansion because the work done on the gas is negative.

20.18. Because the initial and final states lie on the same isotherm, the thermal energy of the gas doesn't change. From this you know that $\Delta E_{th} = W + Q = 0$ and so $W = -Q$. The work done on the gas is positive for both processes ($V_f < V_i$), and so the energy transferred thermally must be negative. (a) The work done on the gas is equal to the area under the path. From the paths in Figure 20.37 you see that the rectangular area under path A is larger than the area under path B, which means that the work done on the gas in process A is greater than the work done on the gas in process B. (b) Because W is greater for process A, the magnitude of Q must be greater for process A.

20.19. No. Equation 20.36 gives the change in entropy between two equilibrium states that are at the same temperature. During an isochoric process, the temperature changes, so we cannot use Eq. 20.36.

20.20. The same. Equation 20.34 is independent of the process. The entropy change depends on only the temperatures and volumes of the initial and final states. If the two combinations of processes have the same initial and final states, the change in entropy is the same in the two cases.

20.21. See Table S20.21. ΔS is positive when a process ends on a higher isentrope. To determine the sign of Q, we approximate the ideal gas process by a series of infinitesimal isentropic and isothermal segments. (We can do this for any process.) Along the isentropic segments, $Q = 0$. Along the isothermal segments, Q has the same sign as ΔS, which is positive. Therefore for any process for which $\Delta S > 0$, we know that Q must be positive too. The change in the thermal energy is the sum $Q + W$. Because isentropes

Table S20.21 Checkpoint 20.21

	Expansion	Compression
W	negative	positive
Q	positive	positive
ΔE_{th}	positive, negative, or zero	positive
ΔS	positive	positive

are steeper than isotherms, ending on a higher isentrope while compressing the gas means ending on a higher isotherm, and so the temperature T and the thermal energy both have to increase ($\Delta E_{th} > 0$). When the gas expands, its entropy can increase while its temperature and thermal energy increase, decrease, or stay the same. (a) $W < 0$ for expansion. (b) $W > 0$ for compression.

20.22. We have to calculate entropy changes associated with two processes: the cooling down of the water from 20 °C to 0.0 °C and the phase transition from water to ice. The entropy change during the cooling is given by Eq. 20.53. Substituting the specific heat capacity for water from Table 20.2, we obtain

$$\Delta S = \frac{(0.010 \text{ kg})(4181 \text{ J/kg} \cdot \text{K})}{1.38 \times 10^{-23} \text{ J/K}} \ln\left(\frac{273}{293}\right) = -2.1 \times 10^{23}.$$

For the phase transition, we use Eq. 20.58 and substitute the specific transformation energy for water from Table 20.4:

$$\Delta S = -\frac{(0.010 \text{ kg})(3.34 \times 10^5 \text{ J/kg})}{(1.38 \times 10^{-23} \text{ J/K})(273 \text{ K})} = -8.9 \times 10^{23}.$$

The total entropy change is thus -11×10^{23}.

Chapter 21

21.1. (a) There is a change in the state of motion of the puck, which decreases its kinetic energy. Because the temperature of the puck and surface increases, their thermal energy increases. This is an irreversible process, so the entropy increases. (b) The spring relaxes from the compressed state, and the cart changes its state of motion. The configurational potential energy of the spring-cart system decreases, and the kinetic energy of the cart increases. The process is reversible, so the entropy does not change. (c) A chemical reaction changes the state of the explosives, releasing source energy. The projectile changes its state of motion, increasing its kinetic energy. The temperature and thermal energy of the cannon and projectile increase. Because the process is irreversible, the entropy increases. (d) The temperature of the hot object decreases, and therefore its thermal energy decreases. The temperature of the cold object increases, and therefore its thermal energy increases. This process is irreversible, so the entropy increases.

21.2. (a) See Figure S21.2. Energy is transferred thermally to the gas. This results in an increase in both the temperature and the volume of the gas. The expanding gas does work on the piston. (b) Both change. The temperature of the gas increases, so its thermal energy increases. The entropy increases because both the temperature and volume of the gas increase (Eq. 19.61).

Figure S21.2

21.3. (a) Pushing the piston back to its original position requires us to do as much work on the device as the device has delivered to us (Eq. 20.30). Therefore once the piston is back to its original position $W = 0$, and because $\Delta E = 0$, $Q = 0$ too. No energy has been converted. (b) The volume and temperature of the gas are the same before expansion and after compression, so by Eq. 19.61 the entropy stays the same. (c) Yes, because the device keeps returning to its initial state.

21.4. (a) $\Delta E_R > 0$ (energy increases), $\Delta S_R > 0$ (entropy increases with energy), $\Delta S_R / \Delta F_R > 0$. (b) $\Delta E_R < 0$, $\Delta S_R < 0$, $\Delta S_R / \Delta E_R > 0$.

21.5. (a) Energy quality decreases because $\Delta S > 0$ means that energy is transferred to the right on the dS/dE axis, as in Figure 21.16b. (b) Energy quality remains the same because it remains at the same value of dS/dE.

21.6. (b), (c), and (f).

21.7. See Figure S21.7.

Figure S21.7

21.8. Because the process depicted in Figure 21.22a is reversible, $\Delta S_{env} = 0$, and so the two rectangles must have equal areas. The rectangle on the right is less long and therefore must have a greater height.

21.9. (a) Because you increase T_{in}, the label Q_{in} and the point where the two rectangles meet both move to the left. The length of the upgrade rectangle decreases, which means the magnitude of ΔS corresponding to the upgrade decreases. (b) Because the process is reversible, the magnitude of ΔS associated with the degradation also decreases. (c) Because the length of the degrade rectangle increases, the height must decrease; therefore Q_{out} decreases. That means, because $W = Q_{out} - Q_{in}$ and W is constant, Q_{in} decreases.

21.10. Lowering T_{out} requires a smaller thermal input of energy for the same work done on the environment, so the efficiency increases.

21.11. (a) In Figure 21.26, the Q_{in} arrow is roughly twice as wide as the W_{in} arrow. Because $W = W_{in}$, the coefficient of performance of cooling is $Q_{in}/W = 2$. (b) Because $Q_{out} = Q_{in} + W_{in} = 3W_{in} = 3W$, the coefficient of performance of heating is $Q_{out}/W = 3W/W = 3$.

21.12. (a) Now the area under the expansion path $1 \to 2$ is greater in magnitude than the area under the compression path $2 \to 1$, which means the negative work done on the system is greater than the positive work done on the system. So the work done on the system during the cycle is negative, and the magnitude is equal to the shaded area in Figure 21.28d. (b) The sign of the work done on the environment is the opposite of the sign of the work done on the system and so is positive. The magnitude is the same as in part a.

21.13. Although the transfer from low temperature to high temperature is an upgrade of the energy and therefore a decrease in entropy, the entropy increase from the degradation of the mechanical energy input is greater than the decrease.

21.14. Zero. The law of energy conservation requires that the energy of the closed system comprising the device and its environment cannot change. Because the energy of the steady device is not changing, $\Delta E = 0$ (Eq. 21.1), the energy of the environment cannot change either.

21.15. (a) Both negative. Because energy is transferred thermally out of the bar, the energy of the bar decreases and so its entropy decreases. (b) Energy is transferred thermally to the environment, and S_{env} increases. (c) The equilibration is irreversible, so ΔS_{env} must be greater than ΔS_{bar}, which means $S_{bar} + S_{env}$ increases.

21.16. (a) See Figure S21.16. (b) Because the transfer is to the left, the entropy change is negative. The height of the rectangle is Q_{in}. (Because

$W = -Q_{in}$ you could also write the height of the rectangle as $-W > 0$.) The rectangle stretches from the origin (0 on the $1/k_B T$ scale) to $1/k_B T_{in}$, so its length is $1/k_B T_{in}$. The entropy change is thus

$$\Delta S_{env} = -(Q_{in})\left(\frac{1}{k_B T_{in}}\right) = \frac{-Q_{in}}{k_B T_{in}}.$$

This process not allowed by the entropy law because $\Delta S_{env} < 0$.

Figure S21.16

21.17. Yes, in theory. According to Eq. 21.20, Q_{out} goes to zero if T_{out} goes to zero. As T_{out} goes to zero, the length of the degrade rectangle becomes infinite, but the area of the rectangle can remain constant. Unfortunately there are no thermal reservoirs at $T = 0$.

21.18. (a) $\eta_{max} = (299 \text{ K} - 221 \text{ K})/299 \text{ K} = 0.261$. (b) $\eta_{max} = (300 \text{ K} - 221 \text{ K})/300 = 0.263$, so the efficiency increases by 0.002.

21.19. The blanket converts mechanical energy entirely to thermal energy, and so from Eq. 21.24, $COP_{heating} = Q_{out}/W = 1$, which is the smallest possible value.

21.20. (a) Equation 21.28 gives $COP_{heating} = COP_{cooling} + 1$. You know from Example 21.7 that $COP_{cooling}$ is 17. Therefore $COP_{heating}$ is 18. (b) You can use Eq. 21.24 to get the delivery rate: $dW/dt = (dQ_{out}/dt)/COP_{heating} = (500 \text{ W})/18 = 28 \text{ W}$.

21.21. As the gas goes from state 1 to state 2 the entropy change of the gas is (Table 21.1):

$$\Delta S_{1 \to 2} = N \ln\left(\frac{V_2}{V_1}\right).$$

Substituting the values given then yields

$$\Delta S_{1 \to 2} = 5.10 \times 10^{23}.$$

During the two isentropic legs, the entropy doesn't change:

$$\Delta S_{2 \to 3} = 0$$
$$\Delta S_{4 \to 1} = 0.$$

The entropy change over the entire cycle is zero, so the entropy change as the gas goes from state 3 to state 4 must be the negative of the entropy change as the gas goes from state 1 to state 2:

$$\Delta S_{3 \to 4} = -\Delta S_{1 \to 2} = -5.10 \times 10^{23}.$$

21.22. (a) The efficiency of the jet engine is given by Eq. 21.44. Substituting T_1 and T_4 from Example 21.9, we get $\eta = 1 - (T_4/T_1) = 1 - (288 \text{ K})/(760 \text{ K}) = 0.62$. (b) Equation 21.36 gives the Carnot efficiency: $\eta = (1520 \text{ K} - 288 \text{ K})/(1520 \text{ K}) = 0.81$, which is significantly greater than the 0.62 efficiency of the engine running on the Brayton cycle. (Remember, however, that the Carnot cycle operates very slowly, which means the power is very low.)

Credits

COVER PHOTO Franklin Kappa

CHAPTER 1 P. 1 Ted Kinsman/Science Source; **p. 5 left** Eric Schrader/Fundamental Photographs; **right** Leonardo DaVinci/Public Domain; **p. 7 left** Wilson Ho, University of California, Irvine; **right, from top to bottom** Wilson Ho, University of California, Irvine; José Antonio Peña/Science Source; Torsten Wittmann/Science Source; John Woodcock /© Dorling Kindersley; NASA; NASA/GSFC/SDO; Bobboz/Fotolia; NASA; NASA/ESA; NASA; **p. 9 from top to bottom** Edelweiss/Fotolia; Waddell Images/Shutterstock; swisshippo/Fotolia; Bombacrt Patrick/Fotolia; NASA; **p. 10** dziewul/Fotolia.

CHAPTER 2 P. 28 Tomohiro Ohsumi/Bloomberg/Getty Images; **p. 29** Eric Mazur; **p. 31 both** Eric Mazur; **p. 33** Eric Mazur **p. 35** Eric Mazur; **p. 41 both** Eric Mazur; **p. 43** Eric Mazur.

CHAPTER 3 P. 53 Fahad Shadeed/Reuters; **p. 56** Igor Kovalchuk/Fotolia; **p. 57** David T. Sandwell and Walter H. F. Smith/NOAA.

CHAPTER 4 P. 75 Astronaut-EVA/NASA; **p. 76** PASCO scientific; **p. 77** Eric Mazur; **p. 79** Accent Alaska/Alamy; **p. 86** National Meteorology Institute of Japan (NMIJ); **p. 98** Eric Mazur.

CHAPTER 5 P. 101 Gemasolar solar thermal plant, owned by Torresol Energy ©SENER; **p. 105 left** Evgeny Murtola/Shutterstock; **right** Stephen Rudolph/Shutterstock.

CHAPTER 6 P. 121 Simon McComb/Getty Images; **p. 135** Denis Doyle/Bloomberg/Getty Images.

CHAPTER 7 P. 148 Todd Taulman/Shutterstock; **p. 152** Ted Kinsman/ScienceSource; **p. 161** NASA; **p. 162 behind** NASA; **inset** Steve Heap/Shutterstock.

CHAPTER 8 P. 176 Claus Mikosch/Shutterstock.

CHAPTER 9 P. 202 Jonathan Blair/Corbis.

CHAPTER 10 P. 226 Patrick Eden/Alamy; **p. 227** Eric Mazur; **p. 229** NASA Earth Observatory; **p. 240** Eric Mazur.

CHAPTER 11 P. 254 David Samuel Robbins/Corbis; **p. 268** Eric Schrader/Pearson Education; **p. 273** Toby Melville/Reuters.

CHAPTER 12 P. 281 Jack Fields/Corbis; **p. 286** Richard Megna/Fundamental Photographs.

CHAPTER 13 P. 308 NASA/HubbleSite; **p. 317** NASA; **p. 320 left** NASA Earth Observatory; **right** NASA; **p. 322** European Pressphoto Agency b.v./Alamy.

CHAPTER 14 P. 337 Erich Lessing/Art Resource.

CHAPTER 15 P. 374 Tom Wang/Shutterstock; **p. 380** Klaus Sailer/Shutterstock.

CHAPTER 16 P. 400 Peo Quick/Matton Collection/Corbis; **p. 401** AFP/Getty Images.

CHAPTER 17 P. 433 Josef Hanus/Shutterstock; **p. 439** Reprinted with the permission of Alcatel-Lucent USA, Inc.; **p. 441** Berenice Abbott/Science Source; **p. 446** Mikael Damkier/Shutterstock; **p. 461** Omikron/Science Source.

CHAPTER 18 P. 463 Sharon Day/Shutterstock; **p. 471 top** culture-images GmbH/Alamy; **bottom** Science Source; **p. 472** Science Source; **p. 476 top** NASA; **bottom** Eric Shrader/Pearson Education; **p. 478** Andrei Kuzmik/Shutterstock; **p. 487** xtrekx/Shutterstock.

CHAPTER 19 P. 501 David Hare /Alamy.

CHAPTER 20 P. 529 CCat82/Shutterstock.

CHAPTER 21 P. 562 David Gould/Getty Images; **p. 577** Colin Salmon © Dorling Kindersley.

Index

A

Absolute temperature, 522
Absolute time, 8
Absolute zero, 536, 537
Acceleration, 53–74
  average, 54, 71
  center-of-mass
    in many-object systems, 199–200
    in rolling motion, 299–300
    in two-object systems, 197–198, 329–330
    work and, 216–217
  centripetal, 258, 266
    gravitational force and, 309–311
  changes in velocity and, 54–55
  in circular motion, 257–258
  constant, 63–66
  definition of, 54
  direction of, 54
  displacement and, 63–64, 71–73
  due to gravity, 55–57, 66–67, 191–192
  in fluid flow, 473–474
  on inclined plane, 69–70
  instantaneous, 70–73
  in interactions, 149, 164, 1167
  magnitude of, 54
  of object in free fall, 55–57
  in one vs. two dimensions, 230–231
  of projectile, 57–59
  radial, 267, 268
  rotational, 265–266, 268
    in rolling motion, 299–300
    vs. centripetal acceleration, 266
    vs. tangential acceleration, 267
  in simple harmonic motion, 386
  spring-scale measurement and, 319, 320
  symbol for, 54
  tangential, 266–267, 268
  in two reference frames, 135
  unit of, 54
  vs. gravity, 320–323
  in wave propagation, 406
  x component of, 54–55, 59, 71–73, 268
Acceleration vectors, 54
  in one vs. two dimensions, 230–231
Acceleration vs. time graphs, 71
Acceleration-gravity equivalence, 320–323
Addition
  significant digits in, 19
  of vectors, 44
    decomposition and, 239
    in one vs. two dimensions, 228–229
Adhesive forces, 479
Adiabat, 545
Adiabatic (isentropic) processes, 531, 534, 545, 551
  entropy and, 557–558
Air pressure, 468
Air resistance, for falling object, 56
Algebra, vector, 238–240
Altitude, atmospheric pressure and, 482–483
Amplitude
  of oscillation, 376, 386, 389
  wave

    in one dimension, 407
    in two dimensions, 436
Angular coordinates, 238
Angular frequency
  of oscillation, 385–386
  of wave, 420
Angular momentum, 269–274
  around center of mass, 314–315
  central force and, 314–317
  circular motion and, 316
  conservation of, 271, 293–297
    galaxy shape and, 317
  definition of, 271
  elliptical motion and, 316
  gravity and, 314–317
  lever arm of, 271
  line of action of, 271
  motion at constant velocity and, 316
  orbital motion and, 314–317
  symbol for, 271
  torque and, 282–285
  units of, 271
Angular momentum law, 295
Antinodal lines, 441–444
Antinodes, 421
Aphelion, 312
Apparent weight, 320
Area, 46
  surface
    conservation of, 83
    pressure and, 466
Atmosphere, 482
Atmospheric pressure, 468, 482–484. *See also*
    Fluid pressure
  measurement of, 488
Atoms, 6
  incoherent motion of, 503
Audible frequency range, 438
Average acceleration, 54, 71
Average power, 427–428
Average velocity, 35–37, 50
  rotational, 265
Avogadro constant, 15
Axial vectors, 291
Axis of rotation, 255
  center of mass as, 286
  fixed, 285
  orientation of, 289–290
  rotational inertia and, 262

B

Balance scale, 318
Bar diagrams, 104–105
Barometers, 488
Basic states, 503–505
  number of, entropy and, 514–516
Beat frequency, 453
Beating, 451–453
Bernoulli effect, 473–474
Boltzmann constant, 522
Bonds, energy used in breaking, 156, 158
Bosons, vector, 161
Boundary effects, 411–414

Brayton cycle, 576–578, 589–591
Brown, Robert, 502
Brownian motion, 502–503
Bulk stress, 465, 466
Buoyancy, 469–471, 486–487

C

Calculators, significant digits and, 18–20
Candela, 15
Capillary rise, 480
Capillary tube, meniscus in, 479–480
Carnot cycle, 576–578, 587–589
Cartesian coordinate system, 229, 238
Causality, principle of, 8
Cavendish, Henry, 325
Celestial mechanics, 309–313, 329–334. *See also*
    Orbital motion
Celsius scale, 537
Center of inertia, 138
Center of mass, 137–141
  angular momentum around, 314–315
  central force and, 314–315
  equation of motion for, 199–200
  kinetic energy and, 142–145
  rotation around, 286
  in two-object systems, 198–199, 329–330
Center-of-mass acceleration
  in many-object systems, 199–200
  in rolling motion, 299–300
  in two-object systems, 197–198, 329–330
  work and, 216–217
Center-of-mass velocity, 139–141
  in many-object systems, 199
  in two-object systems, 197–198
Central force
  angular momentum and, 314–317
  center of mass and, 314–315
  definition of, 314
  gravity as, 314–315
Centripetal acceleration, 258, 266
  gravitational force and, 309–311
Charge, electric, 161
Chemical bonds, energy used in breaking, 156, 158
Chemical energy, 108, 109, 156–158, 198
Circular motion. *See also under* Rotational
  acceleration and, 257–258, 265–267
  angular momentum and, 316
  at constant speed, 255
    simple harmonic motion and, 378, 385–388
  definition of, 255
  forces and, 259–262
  kinematics of, 264–269
  rotating reference frame and, 259
  speed and, 265–266
  velocity and, 256, 265, 270
Classical mechanics, 3
Clocks, 338
  light, 345
  reference, 340
  synchronized, 338, 339, 347–348
Closed paths, 329

Closed systems, 108–110
    conservation of energy in, 116–118
    entropy in, 514–518
Coefficient(s)
    damping, 397
    of friction, 248–253
    of performance of cooling, 574, 586
    of performance of heating, 574, 585–586
    of restitution, 115
Coherent deformation, 153–154
Coherent energy. *See* Mechanical energy
Coherent motion, 503
Coherent sources, 440–444
Cohesive forces, 475–476
Collisions. *See also* Interaction(s)
    center-of-mass velocity in, 137–141
    changes of state in, 105
    classification of, 102–103
    coefficient of restitution of, 115
    elastic, 102, 112–114, 115. *See also* Elastic
        collisions
    entropy and, 504–505
    equipartition of energy and, 505–507
    equipartition of space and, 507–509, 518
    friction and, 80–81
    inelastic, 102, 115–116. *See also* Inelastic
        collisions
    internal energy in, 105–108
    in isolated systems, 92
    kinetic energy in, 103–108, 151–152
    momentum changes in, 88–89, 149
    pendulum motion and, 502–505
    as process, 105
    relative speed and, 102, 112, 115
    relative velocity and, 102, 112
    reversible vs. irreversible, 154
    totally inelastic, 102, 115
    in two dimensions, 242–243
    velocity changes in, 76–81
Combustion, energy conversion in, 157
Component vectors, 229–231, 238–239
Compression, in longitudinal waves, 436
Compressional waves, 437
Compressive stress, 464–465
Condition for rolling motion without slipping,
    298
Conic sections, 330–331
Conservation, 8
    of angular momentum, 271, 293–297
        galaxy shape and, 317
    of energy, 108, 116–118, 156, 213, 547
        in elastic vs. inelastic collisions, 128–129
        in inertial reference frames, 128
        in interactions, 151–152
        special relativity and, 368–372
        work and, 214
    of momentum, 94–99, 214
        in interactions, 164
        special relativity and, 364–368, 372
    relativity and, 145–147
    of surface area, 83
Conservation laws, 8, 502
    relativity and, 145–147
Conserved quantities, 82–84
Constrained processes, 545
Constructive interference, 410
Contact angle, 478–479

Contact forces, 180
    springs and, 184
Continuity equation, 491
Convertible kinetic energy, 142–145
Cooling. *See also* Thermal energy transfer
    coefficient of performance of, 574, 586
    by heat pumps, 574–575, 586
Coordinates
    angular, 238
    Cartesian (rectangular), 229, 238
    polar, 238
    radial, 238, 264–265
    rotational, 256–257, 264–265, 268
    selection of, 233
Counting numbers, 19
Cylindrical volume, fluid pressure and, 484–485

D

Damped oscillations, 396–398
Damping coefficient, 397
Decibels, 449
Decimal places, 18
Decomposition
    of forces, 231–234
    of vectors, 229–231, 238–239
Deductive reasoning, 4
Deformable objects, center-of-mass acceleration
    of, 200
Deformation, 464
    coherent vs. incoherent, 153–154
    stresses causing, 464–465
Degrees of freedom, 538, 540
Density
    definition of, 15
    mass, 15–16
        linear, 414
    number, 15
Derivatives, 49, 50, 71
Destructive interference, 410
Desynchronized twins, 347
Diagrams
    bar, 104–105
    energy, 206–211
        input-output, 563–564
        unbalanced, 530
    entropy, 568–573, 570–572
        computing entropy change from, 582
    free-body, 182–184
        extended, 286–288
    motion, 59–61
    PV, 541–545
    system, 82
Diffraction, wave, 445–446
Displacement, 31–32, 41–45, 228
    acceleration and, 63–64, 71–73
    definition of, 31
    fluid, buoyant force and, 470, 486–487
    force, 214, 218, 219
    in motion in a plane, 227–228, 230–231
    of particle in wave, 402–403, 416–421
    rotational, 290–291
        in rolling motion, 298
        in simple harmonic motion, 393–394
    work and, 243–247
    x component of, 31–32, 35, 41, 268
        for acceleration, 71–73
        for velocity, 46–47, 73

Displacement curve, 403
Displacement vectors, 41–45, 50
    commutation of, 290–291
    sum of, 290
    in two dimensions, 230–231
Dissipated energy, 153–157
    in fluids, 494–499
    friction and, 235
Dissipative forces, 219
Dissipative interactions, 157, 171–174
Distance. *See also* Length
    definition of, 41
    lever arm, 271
    relativity of, 348–349, 360–364
Distance traveled, 32, 35, 41
Division, significant digits in, 19
Doppler effect, 350, 454–459
Drag forces, 397
Drawings. *See* Diagrams

E

Ear. *See also* Sound
    sensitivity of, 438, 449–450
Earth, gravitational force of, 309–313, 318
    satellite orbits and, 329–334
Earth reference frame, 122, 124, 125, 130
    straight-line motion in, 227–228
Effective weight, 320
Efficiency
    definition of, 573
    of heat engine, 573, 583–585
Einstein, Albert, 122, 338
Elastic collisions, 102, 114–116. *See also*
        Collisions
    coefficient of restitution of, 115
    conservation of energy in, 128–129
    definition of, 102
    kinetic energy in, 102–105, 113–114, 151–152
    relative speed in, 112, 115
    relative velocity in, 112
Elastic force, 185
Elastic limit, 185, 464
Elastic potential energy, 153
Elastic range, 184–185
Elastic restoring forces, 382, 389
Elasticity, 464
Electric charge, 161
Electric force, 180
Electromagnetic interactions, 161
    forces in, 180
    weak interactions and, 162
Electrons, 6
Electroweak interactions, 162
Elliptical motion, angular momentum and, 316
Elliptical orbits, 330–334
Energy, 102–120
    in breaking chemical bonds, 156, 158
    chemical, 108, 109, 156–158, 198
    classification of, 154, 156, 158
    coherent. *See* Mechanical energy
    of configuration, 154–156
    conservation of, 108, 116–118, 156, 213, 547
        in elastic vs. inelastic collisions, 128–129
        in inertial reference frames, 128
        in interactions, 151–152
        special relativity and, 368–372
        work and, 214

dissipated, 153–157
  in fluids, 494–499
  friction and, 235
entropy dependence on, 519–525
equipartition of, 505–507, 538–540
explosive separations and, 115, 118–119, 173
incoherent, 153–156, 158
in interactions, 151–158
internal, 105–108, 154–156. *See also* Internal
  energy
kinetic, 103–105. *See also* Kinetic energy
matter and, 350–353, 370–372
mechanical input/output of, 563. *See also*
  Mechanical energy
of motion, 154–155
nuclear, 156–158, 351
potential, 152–153, 158. *See also* Potential energy
quality of, 569
radiation, 351
solar, 156–158
source, 156–158
specific transformation, 541, 560
of systems, 105–108
  distribution of, 502–507
thermal input/output of, 563. *See also*
  Thermal energy
transfer of, 109
wave, 410–411, 426–428
work and, 203, 213
Energy consumption, 157
Energy conversion, 109, 156–158, 563–566
  energy law and, 564
  energy quality and, 569
  entropy and, 565–570, 580–583
    entropy diagrams and, 568–569, 570–572
    entropy gradient and, 567–569
  by heat engines, 570–573
  by heat pumps, 574–575
  irreversible, 157, 502, 510
  by steady devices, 565–566
Energy degradation
  energy conversion and, 563–566. *See also*
    Energy conversion
  energy quality and, 566–570
  entropy constraints and, 580–583
  heat engines and, 570–573, 583–585
  heat pumps and, 574–575, 585–587
  thermodynamic cycles and, 575–580
    Brayton, 576–578, 589–591
    Carnot, 576–578, 587–589
Energy diagrams, 206–211
  choice of, 208–211
  input-output, 563–564, 584
  unbalanced, 530
Energy law, 213, 214
  energy conversions and, 564
  for ideal gas, 547, 554
  for nonideal gas, 559–560
  for single particle vs. system of particles, 219
  work and, 547
Energy transfer. *See* Energy conversion
Energy transferred thermally, 531
Engines
  gas turbine, Brayton cycle in, 577, 589–591
  heat. *See* Heat engines
Entropy, 501–528
  adiabatic processes and, 531, 534, 545

changes in, 515–516, 521
  in energy conversion, 580–583
    energy diagrams for, 582
in closed systems, 514–5185
collisions and, 504–505
of combined system, 516–517
definition of, 515
dependence on energy, 519–527
dependence on volume, 514–519, 526–527
energy conversion and, 565–570, 580–583.
  See also Energy conversion
energy distribution and, 502–507
equipartition of energy and, 505–507
equipartition of space and, 507–509, 518
irreversibility and, 502, 510
macrostates and, 503
of monoatomic ideal gas, 526–527, 555–559
of nonideal gas, 559–560
number of basic states and, 514–515, 516
in phase transitions, 559–560
probability and, 503
quasistatic processes and, 532, 534, 543–545
  entropy changes in, 555–560
system states and, 502–505
temperature and, 526–527
thermal energy transfer and, 533–534
work and, 533
Entropy diagrams, 568–573, 570–572
  computing entropy change from, 582
Entropy gradient, 567
Entropy law, 515
  energy conversion and, 565, 568
Environment, systems and, 81
Equation of motion, 188–191
  for center of mass, 199–200
  for single particle vs. system of particles, 219
  vector sum of forces and, 188–189, 190
Equilibrium
  evolution toward, 509–512
  mechanical, 295, 318
  rotational, 295
  thermal, 521–523
    heat capacity and, 537–540
  translational, 181, 196, 295
Equilibrium state, 509
Equipartition energy share, 538–540
Equipartition of energy, 505–507
  in thermal equilibrium, 538–540
Equipartition of space, 507–509, 518
Escape speed, 334
Event, 338
Explosive separations, 115, 118–119, 173
Extended free-body diagrams, 286–288
Extensive quantities, 82–84
External forces
  in many-object systems, 198–200
  in two-object systems, 196–198
  work done by, 203. *See also* Work
External interactions, 91
External torque, 294

F

Fahrenheit scale, 537
Falling object, air resistance for, 56
Field, 159–160
Field forces, 180
First harmonic, 379

Floating, 470–471, 486–487. *See also* Buoyancy
Flow. *See* Fluid flow
Fluid(s), 464–500. *See also* Gas(es); Liquid(s)
  Archimedes' principle and, 470
  Bernoulli's equation and, 491–494
  buoyancy and, 469–471, 486–487
  compression of, 464–468
  energy dissipation in, 494–499
  forces in, 464–469
  hydrostatics and, 490
  Laplace's law and, 478, 499
  Pascal's principle and, 468
  Poiseuille's law and, 496
  surface effects and, 475–480. *See also* Liquid
    surfaces
  viscosity of, 465, 472, 494–497
Fluid flow, 471–474
  Bernoulli effect and, 473–474
  fluid pressure and, 473–474
  friction and, 472, 474
  laminar, 471–472
  speed of, 473–474
  streamlines and, 471–474
  through pipes, 473
  torque and, 472–473
  turbulent, 471–472
  volume flow rate and, 492
Fluid pressure, 466–469, 482–491
  atmospheric, 468, 482–484
  cylindrical volume and, 484–485
  definition of, 482
  flow speed and, 473–774
  gravity and, 467, 484–485
  height and, 484–485
  Pascal's principle and, 468
  unit of, 482
Fluid volume, buoyancy and, 486–487
Force(s), 176–201
  adhesive, 479
  buoyant, 469–471, 486–487
  central, 314. *See also* Central force
  circular motion and, 259–262
  cohesive, 475–476
  components of
    normal, 232, 234
    tangential, 232–233, 234
  contact, 180
  damping, 396–398
  decomposition of, 229–234
  definition of, 177
  dissipative, 219
  drag, 397
  elastic, 185
    restoring, 382
  electric, 180
  external
    in many-object systems, 198
    in two-object systems, 196–198
    work done by, 203
  field, 180
  in fluids, 464–469
  free-body diagrams and, 182–184
  frictional, 177, 248–250; Frictional force.
    See also Friction
  gravitational, 180, 191–192, 308–336. *See also*
    Gravitational force; Gravity
  identifying, 180–181

impulse and, 194–196
internal
   cancellation of, 199
   in many-object systems, 198
   in two-object systems, 196–197
magnetic, 180
on many-object systems, 198–200
momentum and, 177–178
net, 177
normal, 234–235
opposing, 464–465. *See also* Stress
paired, 178–179, 190–191, 466. *See also*
      Interaction(s)
pulling, 184
reciprocity of, 178–180, 190
repulsive, 475–476
restoring, 184, 193, 381–382, 388, 389, 391.
      See also Restoring forces
superposition of, 178, 189
support, 184, 185
tangential, in rotational motion, 282
tensile, 186
translational equilibrium and, 181
in two-object systems, 196–198
   celestial, 329–334
as vector, 177
vector sum of, 178, 188–189
viscous, 465, 472, 494–49
vs. pressure, 466
vs. torque, 283
work and, 243–247
Force displacement, 214, 218, 219
drag and, 397
for variable forces, 220–222
Force of friction, 234–235
work and, 222
Fourier analysis, 380
Fourier series, 380
Fourier synthesis, 380
Fourier's theorem, 379–381, 421
Free fall, 228
definition of, 56
equations for, 66–69
of projectile, 57–59
from rest, 56–57
weightlessness and, 320
Free rotation, 285–286
Free-body diagrams, 182–184
extended, 286–288
Frequency
angular, 385–386
audible, 438
beat, 453
fundamental, 379
of oscillation, 376, 385–386
unit of, 385
wave, 407
   Doppler effect and, 454–459
Friction, 76
coefficients of, 248–253
collisions and, 80–81
energy diagrams and, 210–211
energy dissipation and, 155–156
fluid flow and, 472, 474
force of, 177, 234–235
kinetic, 235, 252
   coefficient of, 252
static, 234–236, 248–252, 299

thermal energy from, 157, 222
work and, 222, 235–236
Frictional forces, 177, 248–250
definition of, 253
magnitude of, 250
maximum value of, 248–250
working with, 250
Fundamental frequency, 379
Fundamental interactions, 160–163

G

Galaxy shape, angular momentum and, 317
Galilean relativity, 133–137
Galilean transformation equations, 134
Galileo Galilei, 56, 69, 320
Gas(es), 464, 541. *See also* Fluid(s)
compression of, 464–468
equilibrium state of, 541
ideal. *See* Ideal gas
nonideal, entropy of, 559–560
work done on, 547–548
Gas pressure, 523–525, 541
Gas thermometers, 534–536
Gas turbine engine, Brayton cycle in, 577, 589–591
Gauge particles, 160, 161
Gauge pressure, 487
General relativity. *See* Relativity
Gluons, 162
Graphs, 11
calibration of, 30–31
position-vs.-frame, 123
position-vs.-time, 31, 32–34
slope of curve in, 35
x component in, 31–32, 35–37, 41, 46–47, 47
Gravitational acceleration, principle of
      equivalence and, 320–323
Gravitational constant, 325–326
in Newton's law of gravity, 312, 325
Gravitational force, 180, 191–192, 308–336.
      See also Gravity
buoyancy and, 469–471, 486–487
centripetal acceleration and, 309–311
direction of, 191
of Earth, 308–313, 318
exerted by sphere, 334–336
fluid pressure and, 467
magnitude of, 192, 325–326
mass and, 311–313
mass-inertia equivalence and, 311–312
of Moon, 308–309, 312, 318
orbital motion and, 309–313
weight and, 317–320
work done by, 210, 213–216
Gravitational interactions, 161, 168–169, 180
Gravitational potential energy, 153, 326–329
of paired celestial objects, 329–334
Gravitational restoring forces, 382
Gravitons, 161
Gravity, 308–336. *See also* Gravitational force
acceleration due to, 55–57, 66–67, 191–192
angular momentum and, 314–317
as central force, 314
Newton's law of, 312, 325
   Kepler's laws and, 315, 316
principle of equivalence and, 320–323
universal, 309–313
vs. acceleration, 321–323
Gravity-acceleration equivalence, 320–323

H

Hair cells, 438
Harmonic waves, 407
   wave function of, 419–421
Harmonics, 379–380
   sound, 438
Hearing. *See also* Sound
   sound perception and, 438
   sound waves and, 448–450
Heat, 530–531. *See also* Thermal energy transfer
   latent, 541
Heat capacity, 537–541
   definition, 537
   degrees of freedom and, 538, 540
   equipartition energy share and, 538
   in phase transitions, 559–560
   rotational energy and, 538–539
   specific, 537
   temperature and, 539
   vibrational energy and, 539–540
Heat capacity per particle, 538–540, 549
Heat capacity ratio, 552
Heat engines, 570–573
   efficiency of, 573, 583–585
   energy input-output diagram for, 584
   performance of, 583–587
   reversible, 584–585
   as steady devices, 573
   thermodynamic processes in, 575–578
Heat pumps, 574–575
   coefficient of performance of cooling for,
      574, 586
   coefficient of performance of heating for, 574,
      585–586
   efficiency of, 585–586
   thermodynamic processes in, 578
Heating
   coefficient of performance of, 574, 585–586
   heat engines for, 570–573
   heat pumps for, 574–575, 585–586
Height, fluid pressure and, 484–485
Hertz, 385
Hertz, Heinrich, 385
Hidden assumptions, 3
Higher harmonics, 379–380
Hooke, Robert, 193
Hooke's law, 192–194, 464
Hour, 16
Huygen's principle, 445
Hydraulics, 489–491
Hydrodynamics, 493–494
Hydrogen, heat capacity of, 539–540
Hydrostatics, 490
Hyperbolic orbits, 331
Hypothesis, 2
   formulation and testing of, 3–4

I

Ideal gas. *See also under* Gas
   definition of, 514
   equilibrium states for, 541–545
   momentum of, 523–524
   monoatomic, 519
      entropy of, 526–527, 555–559
      properties of, 523–525
   number of particles in, 514, 519, 541
   pressure of, 523–525, 541
   PV diagram for, 541–545

quasistatic processes in, 532, 534, 543–545
  isentropic (adiabatic), 531, 534, 543, 545,
    551, 557–558
  isobaric, 545, 551–552, 554, 556–557
  isochoric, 545, 549–550, 554, 556, 557
  isothermal, 545, 553–554, 556, 557
root-mean-square (rms) speed of, 519, 525
temperature of, 524–525, 541
  entropy and, 526–527
thermal energy of, 524–525, 541, 547–548
volume of, 525–526, 541–545
  entropy and, 514–519
  equilibrium and, 541
Ideal gas law, 525
Ideal gas thermometers, 534–536
Impulse, 96–97
  force and, 194–196
  rotational, 295
Impulse equation, 195
Incident pulse, 411–412
Inclined plane, acceleration on, 69–70
Incoherent deformation, 153–154
Incoherent energy, 153–156, 158
Incoherent motion, 503
Inductive reasoning, 4
Inelastic collisions, 102, 115–116. *See also*
    Collisions
  coefficient of restitution of, 115
  conservation of energy in, 128–129
  definition of, 102
  kinetic energy in, 152
  relative speed in, 115
Inertia, 76–81, 367
  center of, 138
  definition of, 79
  determinants of, 80–81
  determination of, 86–87
  kinetic energy and, 350–353
  momentum and, 76–81, 87–89, 364–368
  of moving particle, 367
  ratio of, 79, 86
  reduced, 143
  restoring forces and, 383
  rotational. *See* Rotational inertia
  as scalar, 86
  special relativity and, 350–351, 364–368
  symbol for, 86
  unit of, 86
  velocity and, 76–80
Inertial reference frames, 124–126
  center of mass in, 137–141
  comparison of, 130
  conservation of energy in, 128–129
  kinetic energy in, 127–128, 145–146
  measurement in, 130
  momentum in, 127, 129, 137–141, 145
  velocity in, 130
Inertial standard, 86
Inertia-mass equivalence, 311–312, 320–321, 367
Instantaneous acceleration, 70–73
Instantaneous power, 223
Instantaneous speed, 48
Instantaneous velocity, 48–49, 50
Integers, 19
Integrals, 72
Intensity, 448–450
  of sound, 449–450
Intensive quantities, 82

Interaction(s), 148–175. *See also* Collisions
  acceleration in, 149, 164, 167
  attractive, 149
  coherent vs. incoherent deformation in,
    153–154
  conservation of energy in, 151–152
  definition of, 91, 149
  dissipative, 153–157, 171–174
  effects of, 149–152
  electromagnetic, 161, 162, 180
  electroweak, 162
  external vs. internal, 91–92
  fields and, 159–160
  forces in, 178–180, 190. *See also* Force(s)
  fundamental, 160–163
  gravitational, 161, 168–169, 180
  internal energy in, 151–152
  irreversible, 105, 154, 157, 171, 502, 510
  kinetic energy in, 151–152
  long-range, 159–160
  momentum in, 149, 152
  nondissipative, 157, 165–168
  notation for, 168
  physical contact in, 159
  potential energy in, 152–153, 165–168
  repulsive, 149
  residual, 161, 162
  reversible, 154, 157, 165
  short-range, 159
  strength of, 159
  strong, 162
  thermal, 529–561
  weak, 161–162
Interaction pairs, 178–179, 190–191, 466
Interaction range, 158–160
Interactions, momentum in, 149, 152, 164
Interference, 409–410
  in two or three dimensions, 439–444
Interference patterns, 440–444
Internal energy, 105–108, 154–156. *See also*
    Energy
  changes of state and, 105–108
  conservation of energy and, 116–118
  definition of, 105, 155
  in explosive separations, 116–118
  in interactions, 151–152
  as invariant, 31
  mass and, 351–353
  potential, 152–153
  special relativity and, 370–372
Internal forces
  cancellation of, 199
  in many-object systems, 198
  in two-object systems, 196–197
Internal interactions, 91
Internal torque, 294
Invariants, 342, 350
Irreversible processes, 105, 502, 510
  interactions as, 154, 157, 171
Isentropes, 543, 545
Isentropic (adiabatic) processes, 531, 534, 543,
    545, 551
  entropy and, 557–558
Isobaric processes, 545, 551–552, 554
  entropy and, 556–557
Isochoric processes, 545, 549–550, 554
  entropy and, 556, 557
Isolated systems, 89–94, 203

definition of, 91
momentum of, 91–94
selection of, 92, 93
Isotherm, 542
Isothermal processes, 545, 553–554
  entropy and, 556, 557

J

Joule (kinetic energy), 114
Joule (work), 203
Joule, James Prescott, 114

K

Kelvin, 522
Kelvin scale, 537
Kepler, Johannes, 309, 315, 316
Kepler's laws of planetary motion, 315, 316
Kilogram, 86, 311
Kinematics, 29. *See also* Motion
  rotational, 264–269
  translational, 268
Kinetic energy, 103–105, 154–155, 158. *See also*
    Energy
  in collisions, 102–105, 113–114, 151
  conservation of energy and, 116–118
  conversion to internal energy, 151–152
  convertible, 142–145
  definition of, 103, 113
  dissipated, 153–157
  in explosive separations, 116–118, 173
  inertia and, 350–353
  in inertial reference frames, 127–128,
    145–146
  in interactions, 151–152
  internal energy and, 105–108
  in nondissipative interactions, 165–167
  relativity of, 350–351
  rotational, 269
    of extended objects, 274–275
    torque and, 302–304
  as scalar, 103
  in simple harmonic motion, 388
  for single-particle vs. system of particles, 219
  special relativity and, 369–372
  of spring, 375
  translational, 142
    in many-particle system, 217
  unit of, 114
  wave, 410–411, 426–428
  work done on single particle and, 213–216
  work done on system of particles and, 216–219
Kinetic friction, 235, 252
  coefficient of, 252

L

Laminar flow, 471–472
Laplace's law, 478, 480, 499
Latent heat, 541
Law(s), 2
  angular momentum, 295
  conservation, 8, 502. *See also* Conservation
    relativity and, 145–147
  energy. *See* Energy law
  entropy, 515, 565–568
  Hooke's, 192–194, 464
  ideal gas, 525
  Kepler's planetary motion, 315, 316
  Laplace's, 478, 480

momentum, 96–99
Newton's. *See* Newton's laws
Poiseuille's, 496
second law of thermodynamics, 512
Leading zeroes, 17–18
Length, 6. *See also* Distance
    measurement at high speeds, 360–364
    proper, 349
Length contraction, 348–349, 350, 360–364
Lever arm distance, 271
Light, speed of. *See* Speed, of light
Light clocks, 345
Linear mass density, 414
Linear restoring force, 193, 381–382, 388
Liquid(s), 464, 541. *See also* Fluid(s)
    Bernoulli's equation for, 491–494
    compression of, 464–468
    hydrodynamics of, 493–494
    pressure in. *See also* Fluid pressure
        cylindrical volume and, 484–485
Liquid surfaces, 475–480
    adhesive forces and, 479
    capillary rise and, 480
    cohesive forces and, 475
    contact angle and, 478–479
    Laplace's law and, 478, 480
    meniscus and, 479–480
    surface tension and, 476–477, 497–499
Liter, 16
Longitudinal waves, 404
    compression and rarefaction in, 436–437
    sound, 436–439
Lorentz factor, 356
Lorentz transformation equations, 356
Loudness, 438

M

Mach number, 461
Macrostates, 503–505
    probability of, 509–514
Magnetic force, 180
Manometers, 487–488
Mass
    center of. *See* Center of mass
    definition of, 311
    gravitational force and, 311–312
    internal energy and, 351–353
    as invariant, 350
    reduced, 143
    unit of, 311
Mass density, 15–16
    linear, 414
Mass-inertia equivalence, 311–312, 320–321, 367
Mathematics
    in physics, 11
    significant digits and, 17–20
Matter, 6–7
    clustering of, 7
    energy and, 350–353, 370–372
    relative size of, 6–7
    states of, 464. *See also* Phase transitions
Measurement. *See* Units of measure
Mechanical energy, 153–156, 158
    conversion to thermal energy, 563–566.
        See also Energy conversion
    generation of, 156–157

in simple harmonic motion, 388
from thermal energy, 563–566. *See also*
    Energy conversion
work and, 532
Mechanical energy transfer. *See also* Work
    in entropy diagrams, 568
    in quasistatic processes, 549–559. *See also*
        Quasistatic processes
    vs. thermal energy transfer, 531–534
Mechanical equilibrium, 295, 318
Mechanical input of energy, 563
Mechanical output of energy, 563
Mechanical waves, 401. *See also* Wave(s)
    longitudinal, 404
    transverse, 403
Meniscus, 479–480
Meter, 6
Metric ton, 16
Michelson, A. A., 342
Microstate, 503
Minute, 16
Models, 3, 30
Moiré pattern, 440, 451
Mole, 15
Momentum, 76–81, 87–89
    angular. *See* Angular momentum
    change in, 188
    in collisions, 88–89, 149
    conservation of, 94–99, 214
        in interactions, 164
        special relativity and, 364–368, 372
    definition of, 87
    equation of motion and, 188–191
    force and, 177–178
    of ideal gas, 523–524
    impulse and, 96–97, 194–196
    inertia and, 76–81, 87–89, 364–368
    in inertial reference frames, 127,
        129, 137–141, 145, 364–368
    in interactions, 149, 152, 164
    in many-object systems, 198
    symbol for, 87
    of systems, 89–94
    translational equilibrium and, 181, 196
    in two dimensions, 242–243
    in two-object systems, 197
    units of, 87
    as vector, 87
    vector sum of forces and, 203
    velocity and, 87–89
    vs. inertia, 87
    x component of, 87
Momentum law, 96–99
Moon
    gravitational force of, 308–309, 312, 318
    orbit of, 309–310
Morley, E. W., 342
Motion, 28–52
    average speed and, 34–36
    average velocity and, 35–37
    Brownian, 502–503
    circular, 254–280, 316. *See also* Circular
        motion
    coherent, 503
    with constant acceleration, 63–66
    at constant velocity, 46–48, 64–66
        angular momentum and, 316

displacement and, 31–32, 41–45, 228
distance traveled and, 32, 35
elliptical, 316
energy of, 154–155
equation of, 188–191, 199–200, 219
horizontal component of, 228
incoherent, 503
Newton's laws of, 190, 191
of object at rest, 29, 65
in one dimension, 28–52
in one direction, 39
orbital, 309–317, 329–334. *See also* Orbital
    motion
periodic, 374–399. *See also* Periodic motion
position and, 30–32
projectile, 57–59, 240–242
representations of, 29–30, 32–34
rolling. *See* Rolling motion
rotational, 255–261. *See also* Rotational
    motion
straight-line, 227–228
translational, 255
    rotational motion and, 267–268, 297–299,
        306
in two dimensions, 227–253. *See also* Motion
    in a plane
vertical component of, 228
wave, 402
Motion analysis
    displacement in, 31–32
    film clips in, 29, 30, 36
    graphs in, 29–30, 32–34, 36–37
    position in, 30–32
Motion diagrams, 59–61
Motion in a plane, 227–253
    acceleration and, 230–231
    collisions and, 242–243
    displacement and, 227–228, 230, 243–247
    in Earth reference frame, 227–228
    force decomposition in, 231–234
    friction and, 234–236
        coefficients of, 248–252
    horizontal component of, 228
    momentum and, 242–243
    projectile, 240–242
    vectors and, 228–231
        decomposition of, 229–231, 238–239
        scalar product of, 245–247
    velocity in, 230
    vertical component of, 228
    work and, 243–247
        friction and, 235–236
        as scalar product, 246–247
Multiplication
    significant digits in, 19
    of vectors, 45
Muons, half-life of, 348

N

Natural philosophy, 2
Negative work, 204–206
Net force, 177
Neutrons, 6
Newton, 188–189
Newton, Isaac, 8, 188, 309, 310
Newton's law of gravity, 312, 325
    Kepler's laws and, 315, 316

Newton's laws of motion
  first, 190
  second, 190
  third, 190, 191
Nodal lines, 440–444
Nodes, 410, 421–423
Nondissipative interactions, 157, 165–168
  energy conversions in, 165–167
  kinetic energy in, 165–167
  potential energy in, 165–170
    determination of, 168–170
  reversibility of, 165
Noninertial reference frames, 125–126,
    259
Nonviscous fluids, 465, 472
Normal components, 232, 234
Normal force, 234–235
Notation, scientific, 6
  significant digits and, 18
Nuclear energy, 156–158, 351
Number density, 15

O

Observer, 122
Opposing forces, 464–465. *See also* Stress
Orbit(s)
  elliptical, 330–334
  escape speed and, 334
  hyperbolic, 331
  parabolic, 331
  planetary, 315, 316
  satellite, 329–334
Orbital motion, 309–313
  angular momentum and, 314–317
  gravitational potential energy and,
    329–334
  Kepler's laws of, 315, 316
Order of magnitude, 6
Order-of-magnitude estimates, 23–26
Oscillation(s), 375. *See also* Periodic motion;
    Simple harmonic motion
  damped, 396–398
  quality factor for, 398
  thermal energy and, 539–540
  translational, 393
Oscillator, simple harmonic, 377, 385–388.
    See also Simple harmonic motion
  definition of, 377
  energy of, 385–388, 398
  rotational, 393–394
  torsional, 393

P

Pain threshold, 448, 450
Paired forces, 178–179, 190–191, 466. *See also*
    Interaction(s)
Parabolic orbits, 331
Parallel-axis theorem, 279
Particles
  definition of, 213
  subatomic, 6, 7, 161, 162, 370
Pascal, 482
Pascal's principle, 468
Pascal-second, 494
Pendulum
  energy distribution and, 502–505
  period of, 383

restoring forces for, 382–383
  as rotational oscillator, 393–394
Perfect vacuum, 482
Perihelion, 312
Period, 257, 376
Periodic function
  shape of, 379
  spectrum of, 380
Periodic motion, 374–399. *See also* Oscillation;
    Simple harmonic motion
  amplitude of, 376
  definition of, 374
  energy and, 375–376
  frequency of, 376
  harmonic components of, 379–381
  kinetic energy and, 375–376
  period of, 376
  potential energy and, 375–376
  simple harmonic, 377–379. *See also* Simple
    harmonic motion
Periodic waves, 407–408
Phase transitions, 464, 465, 540, 541, 542
  entropy change in, 559–560
  specific heat capacity in, 559–560
  specific transformation energy in, 541, 560
  thermal energy transfer in, 540, 541, 542,
    559–560
Phasor, 385
Photons, 161
Physical quantities, 6
  symbols for, 14, 50
  units of measure for, 14–17. *See also* Units of
    measure
Physics
  definition of, 2
  mathematics in, 11, 17–20
  reasons for studying, 2, 4
  reflective, 5
  rotational, 5
Pitch, 438
Planar wavefront, 436
Planetary motion, 309–317, 329–334. *See also*
    Orbital motion
  Kepler's laws of, 315, 316
Point source, 434
Poiseuille's law, 496
Polar angle, 256
  rotational coordinate and, 264
  units of, 264
Polar coordinates, 238
Polar vectors, 291
Position vectors, 41, 43–45, 50
Position-vs.-frame graphs, 123
Position-vs.-time graphs, 31, 32–34
Positive work, 204–206
Potential energy, 152–153, 158
  dissipation of, 154–155
  elastic, 153
  gravitational, 153, 326–329
    of paired celestial objects, 329–334
  in interactions, 152–153
    nondissipative, 165–170
  near Earth's surface, 168–169
  position and, 165–167
  in simple harmonic motion, 388
  of spring, 221–222, 375
  wave, 410–411, 427–428

Power, 223–224
  average, 427–428
  definition of, 223
  instantaneous, 223
  symbol for, 223
  unit of, 223
Pressure
  air, 468
  atmospheric, 468, 482–484
    measurement of, 488
  definition of, 466
  fluid, 466–469, 482–491. *See also* Fluid
    pressure
  gas, 523–525, 541
  hydraulics and, 489–491
  measurement of, 487–488
  surface area and, 466
  vs. force, 466
  water, 468
Pressure gauge, 487
Principle of causality, 8
Principle of equivalence, 320–323
Principle of relativity, 129–130. *See also*
    Relativity
Principle of superposition. *See* Superposition
    principle
Probability, 503
Problem solving, steps in, 20–24
Processes
  constrained, 545
  definition of, 105, 531
  irreversible, 105, 154, 157, 171, 501, 502
  quasistatic, 532, 534, 543–545
  reversible, 105, 154, 157, 165
Projectile
  acceleration due to gravity of, 58
  definition of, 57
  trajectory of, 57
Projectile motion, 57–59
  in two dimensions, 240–242
Proper length, 349
Proper time interval, 339
Protons, 6, 370
Pulling, 184
  by spring, 184
  tension and, 186
Pulse. *See* Wave pulse
PV diagrams, 541–545
  isentropes in, 543
  isotherms in, 542

Q

Quality factor, 398
Quanta, 504
  equipartition energy share for, 539–540
Quantum mechanics, 3, 504, 540
Quarks, 162, 370
Quasistatic processes, 532, 534, 541–545,
    549–559
  constrained, 545
  entropy and, 555–560
  isentropic (adiabatic), 531, 534, 543, 545, 551,
    557–558
  isobaric, 545, 551–552, 554, 556–557
  isochoric, 545, 549–550, 554, 556, 557
  isothermal, 545, 553–554, 556, 557
  in *PV* diagrams, 541–545

R

Radial acceleration, 267, 268
Radial axis, 258
Radial coordinates, 238
Radians, 264
Radiation energy, 351
Radius of curvature, surface tension and, 477–478
Rarefaction, in longitudinal waves, 436–437
Rectangular (Cartesian) coordinates, 229, 238
Recurrence time, 505
Reduced inertia (mass), 143
Reference circle, 385
Reference clock, 340
Reference frames. *See also* Relativity
    conservation in, 145–147
        of energy, 368–372
        of momentum, 364–368
    definition of, 122
    Earth, 122, 124, 125, 130
        straight-line motion in, 227–228
    in Galilean relativity, 133–137
    inertial, 124–126. *See also* Inertial reference
        frames
    invariants and, 342–343, 350
    for motion in a plane, 227–228
    noninertial, 125–126, 259
    principle of equivalence and, 320–323
    rotating, 259
    simultaneous events in, 340–344
    subscript operations for, 136
    time measurement in, 340–344
    zero-momentum, 130–131, 138–139, 142,
        365–366
Reflected pulse, 411–414
Reflective physics, 5
Reflective symmetry, 5
Refrigerators, Brayton cycle in, 578, 589–591
Relative speed, 102
    in elastic collisions, 112, 115
    in inelastic collisions, 115
    kinetic energy and, 103–104, 105
    ratio of, 115
Relative velocity, 102
    in elastic collisions, 112
Relativity, 122–147. *See also* Reference frames
    conservation laws and, 145–147
    convertible kinetic energy and, 142–145
    Doppler effect and, 350
    Galilean, 133–137
    motion of observer and, 122
    principle of, 129–130
    principle of equivalence and, 320–323
    reference frames and, 122–126. *See also*
        Reference frames
    of simultaneity, 340–344, 345, 349–350
    special, 3, 337–373
Repulsive forces, 475
Residual interactions, 161, 162
Restitution, coefficient of, 115
Restoring forces, 184
    elastic, 382, 389
    gravitational, 382
    linear, 193, 381–382, 388
    in simple harmonic motion, 381–383
Restoring torques, 393–396
Reversible processes, 105
    interactions, 154, 157, 165

Revolutions, 264
    period of, 267
Right-hand rule, 289–290
Rigid objects, center-of-mass acceleration
    of, 200
rms speed, 519, 525
Rolling motion, 297–302
    acceleration in, 299–300
    dynamics of, 299–300
    rotational inertia and, 274–276
    static friction and, 299–300
    velocity in, 298–299
    without slipping, 298
Root-mean-square (rms) speed, 519, 525
Rotating reference frame, 259
Rotation. *See also* Rotational motion
    axis of, 255
        center of mass as, 286
        fixed, 285
        orientation of, 289–290
        rotational inertia and, 262
    direction of, 288–291
    free, 285–286
    right-hand rule for, 289–290
    vectorial nature of, 288, 304–306
Rotational acceleration, 265–266, 268
    in rolling motion, 299–300
    vs. centripetal acceleration, 266
    vs. tangential acceleration, 267
Rotational coordinates, 256–257, 264–265, 268
Rotational degrees of freedom, 538
Rotational displacement, 290–291
    in rolling motion, 298
    in simple harmonic motion, 393–394
Rotational equilibrium, 295
Rotational impulse, 295
Rotational inertia, 262, 269–270
    axis of rotation and, 262
    definition of, 262, 269
    of extended objects, 274–279
    rolling motion and, 274–276
    unit of, 269
Rotational kinematics, 264–269
Rotational kinetic energy, 269
    of extended objects, 274–275
    torque and, 302–304
Rotational motion, 255. *See also* Rotation
    angular momentum and, 269–274
    circular, 255–261. *See also* Circular motion
    definition of, 255
    heat capacity and, 538–539
    orbital, 309–313
    point of application in, 282–285
    rolling, 297–302. *See also* Rolling motion
    shape factors in, 275, 300
    tangential force in, 282
    torque in, 281–307
    translational motion and, 267–268, 297–299,
        306
Rotational oscillators, 393–394
Rotational physics, 5
Rotational speed, 265
Rotational symmetry, 5, 6
Rotational velocity, 257–258, 268, 270
    average, 265
Rotational velocity vectors, 257, 291
Rounding, 18–20

S

Satellite orbits, 329–334. *See also* Orbital motion
Scalar, 39
Scalar product
    definition of, 245
    work as, 246–247
Scales
    balance, 318
    spring, 318–320
Scientific method, 2–4
Scientific notation, 6
    significant digits and, 18
Scientific principles, application of, 4
Second, 8
Second law of thermodynamics, 512
    entropy law and, 515
Shape factors, in rolling motion, 275, 300
Shear stress, fluid viscosity and, 472
Shock waves, 459–461
SI units, 14–17. *See also* Units of measure
Signal delay, 339
Significant digits, 17–20
Simple harmonic motion, 377–399
    acceleration in, 386
    amplitude of, 386, 389
    basic kinematic equations for, 387
    circular motion at constant speed and, 378,
        385–388
    damped oscillations and, 396–398
    definition of, 377
    Fourier's theorem and, 379–381
    frequency of, 385
    kinetic energy in, 388
    linear restoring force for, 378
    of pendulum, 382–383
    periodic motion and, 379–381
    phase of, 386, 389
    restoring forces in, 381–383
    of springs, 389–392
    velocity in, 386
    wave equation and, 429–431
Simple harmonic oscillator
    definition of, 377
    energy of, 385–388, 398
    rotational, 393–394
    torsional, 393
Simple harmonic oscillator equation, 387
Simultaneity
    definition of, 340, 373
    relativity of, 340–344, 345, 349–350
Simultaneity detector, 341
Sinusoidal functions, in Fourier's theorem,
    379–380
Sketches. *See* Diagrams
Solar energy, 156–158
Solids, 541
Sonic boom, 460
Sound, 436–439
    beating and, 451–453
    Doppler effect and, 350, 454–459
    intensity of, 448–450
    loudness of, 438
    perception of, 438
    pitch of, 438
    shock waves and, 459–460
    speed of, 460
    threshold of hearing and, 448, 450

threshold of pain and, 448, 450
timbre of, 438
tonal quality of, 438
Sound waves, 436–439
    subsonic, 438
    ultrasonic, 438
Source energy, 156–158
    renewable, 157
Space, equipartition of, 507–509, 518
Space-time, 345–350
Space-time interval, 350, 359–360
Special relativity, 3, 337–373
    conservation of energy and, 368–372
    conservation of momentum and, 364–368, 372
    inertia and, 350–351, 364–368
    invariants and, 342–343, 350
    length contraction and, 348–349, 350, 360–364
    simultaneous events and, 340–344, 349–350
    space-time interval and, 350, 359–360
    time dilation and, 345–348, 350, 355–360
    time measurements and, 338–344
Specific heat capacity, 537. See also Heat capacity
    in phase transitions, 559–560
Specific transformation energy, 541, 560
Spectrum, of periodic function, 380
Speed
    average, 34–36
    definition of, 48, 49
    escape, 334
    of fluid flow, 473–474
    instantaneous, 48
    of light
        as invariant, 342–343
        measurement of, 342–344
        in time measurement, 338–339
        in vacuum, 342
    relative, 102
        in elastic collisions, 112, 115
        in inelastic collisions, 115
        kinetic energy and, 103–104, 105
        ratio of, 115
    relativistic vs. nonrelativistic, 356
    root-mean-square (rms), 519
    rotational, 265–266
    rotational velocity and, 257
    of sound, 460
    in two dimensions, 231
    wave, 402, 406–408, 424–426
Sphere, gravitational force exerted by, 334–336
Spherical waves, 435–436
Spring(s), 184–186
    compression of, 184, 185, 192–193
    elastic limit of, 185
    elastic range of, 184–185
    elastic restoring force and, 389
    forces exerted on/by, 184–185, 192–193, 220–222
    Hooke's law and, 192–194
    kinetic energy of, 375–376
    periodic motion of, 375–376. See also Periodic motion
    potential energy of, 221–222, 375–376
    relaxed length of, 184
    simple harmonic motion of, 389–392. See also Simple harmonic motion

stretching of, 184, 185, 192–193
work done on, 205
Spring constant, 192–193
Spring scales, 318–320
Standing waves, 421–424
States
    basic, 503–505
    changes in, 105
        internal energy and, 105–108
    definition of, 105
    equilibrium, 509
    macrostates, 503–505
        probability of, 503–505
States of matter, 464. See also Phase transitions
Static friction, 234–236, 248–252
    coefficient of, 249
    maximum force of, 248–250
    rolling motion and, 299–300
    torque and, 299
    work and, 235–236
Steady devices
    energy conversion by, 565–566
    heat engines as, 570–573
Stored solar energy, 156–158
Straight-line motion, 227–228
Streamlines, 471–474
Stress, 464
    bulk, 465, 466
    compressive, 464–465
    deformation from, 464–465
    shear, fluid viscosity and, 472
    tensile, 464–465
Strong interactions, 162
Subatomic particles, 6, 7, 161, 162, 370
Subscript operations, 136
Subsonic waves, 438
Subtraction
    significant digits in, 19
    of vectors, 44–45
        decomposition and, 239
        in one vs. two dimensions, 229
Superposition principle, 178, 189
    waves and, 409–411, 439, 451–453
        beating and, 451–453
        in two or three dimensions, 439
Support force, 184, 185
Surface area
    conservation of, 83
    pressure and, 466
Surface effects, 475–480. See also Liquid surfaces
Surface tension, 476–477, 497–499
    Laplace's law and, 478, 480
Surface waves, 434
Symmetry, 4–6
    definition of, 4
    reflective, 5
    rotational, 5, 6
    translational, 5
Synchronized clocks, 338, 339, 347–348
System(s), 81–84
    atomic parameters of, 514
    basic state of, 503–505
    boundaries of, 81
    closed, 108–110
        conservation of energy in, 116–118
        entropy in, 514–518

configuration state of, 152
constraints on, 82–83
definition of, 81
energy of, 105–108. See also Internal energy
    distribution of, 502–507
entropy of. See Entropy
environment and, 81
equilibrium in, 509–512
equipartition of energy in, 505–507
equipartition of space in, 507–509, 518
extensive quantities in, 82–83
external vs. internal interactions and, 91–92
intensive quantities in, 82
isolated, 89–94, 203. See also Isolated systems
macroscopic parameters of, 514
macrostate of, 503–505
    probability of, 509–514
of many interacting objects, 198–200
momentum of, 89–94
nonisolated, 203
recurrence time of, 505
selection of, 81–82
states in, 503
of two interacting objects, 196–198
System diagrams, 82

T

Tables, 11
Tangential acceleration, 266–267, 268
Tangential axis, 258
Tangential components, of force, 232–233, 234
Tangential force, in rotational motion, 282
Temperature
    absolute, 522, 536
    heat capacity and, 539
    of ideal gas, 524–525, 541
        entropy and, 526–527
        measurement of, 534–537
Temperature scales, 536, 537
Tensile forces, 186
Tensile stress, 464–465
Tension, 184–186, 186
    surface, 476–477, 497–499
        Laplace's law and, 478, 480
Theories, 2
Thermal energy, 108, 154, 155, 158
    conversion to mechanical energy, 157, 563–566. See also Energy conversion
    equipartition energy share and, 538–540
    from friction, 157, 222
    generation of, 157
    of ideal gas, 524–525, 526, 541, 547–548
        entropy and, 525–526
        work and, 547–548
    from mechanical energy, 563–566. See also Energy conversion
Thermal energy transfer, 531–534
    entropy and, 533–534
    heat capacity and, 537–541
    heating in, 530–531
    in nonideal gas, 559–560
    in phase transitions, 540, 541, 542, 559–560
    PV diagrams and, 541–545
    in quasistatic processes, 532, 534, 541–545, 549–559. See also Quasistatic processes
    specific transformation energy and, 541, 560

thermal interactions and, 530–534
  vs. mechanical energy transfer, 531–534
  work and, 531–534, 547–548
Thermal equilibrium, 521–523
  heat capacity and, 537–540
Thermal input of energy, 563
Thermal interactions, 529–561
Thermal output of energy, 563
Thermal reservoir, 553
Thermodynamic cycles
  Brayton, 576–578, 589–591
  Carnot, 576, 577, 578, 587–589
  in heat engines, 575–578
  in heat pumps, 578
Thermodynamics, 530
  second law of, 512
    entropy law and, 515
Thermometers, 534–536
Threshold
  of hearing, 448, 450
  of sound, 448, 450
Timbre, 438
Time, 8
  absolute, 8
  change and, 8
  definition of, 8
  direction of, 8
  irreversibility of, 502, 510
  recurrence, 505
  units of, 8
Time constant, 398
Time dilation, 345–348, 350, 355–360
Time interval, proper, 339–340
Time measurement, 8, 338–344
  at high speeds, 355–360
  proper time interval and, 339
  reference frames in, 340–344
  signal delay in, 339
  simultaneous events and, 340–344
  speed of light in, 338. *See also* Speed,
    of light
  synchronized clocks in, 339
Time scales, 8
Tonal quality, 438
Torque, 281–307
  472–473
  angular momentum and, 282–285, 293–297
  definition of, 283
  extended free-body diagrams for, 286–288
  external, 294
  free rotation and, 285–286
  internal, 294
  notation for, 284
  restoring, 393–396
  rotational kinetic energy and, 302–304
  sign of, 284
  static friction and, 299
  sum of, 284
  vs. force, 283
Torsional constant, 393
Torsional oscillators, 393
Totally inelastic collisions, 102
  relative speed in, 115
Trailing zeroes, 18
Trajectory, 57
Translational equilibrium, 181, 196, 295
Translational kinematics, 268

Translational kinetic energy, 142
  in many-particle system, 217
Translational motion, 255
  rotational motion and, 267–268, 297–299, 306
Translational oscillation, 393
Translational physics, 5, 6
Translational symmetry, 5
Transverse waves, 403
Traveling waves, 416–421
Triple point of water, 535
Turbulent flow, 471–472
Twin paradox, 347
Two-dimensional motion. *See* Motion in a plane
Two-object systems
  celestial, 329–334
  forces in, 196–198

U

Ultrasonic waves, 438
Ultrasound, 446
Unit vector, 40
Unit vector notation, 40, 50
Units of measure, 6, 14–17
  abbreviations for, 14
  conversion table for, 16–17
  non-SI, 16–17
  prefixes for, 14
  SI, 14–17
  significant digits and, 17–20
Universal gravity, 309–313
Universe
  definition of, 6
  size scales of, 6

V

Vacuum
  definition of, 482
  perfect, 482
Vacuum gauge, 487
Variable forces, work done by, 220–222
Vector(s), 39
  acceleration, 54
    in one vs. two dimensions, 230–231
  addition of, 44
    decomposition and, 239
    in one vs. two dimensions, 228–229
  axial, 291
  component, 229–231, 238–239
  decomposition of, 229–231, 238–239
  definition of, 39
  direction of, 39
  displacement, 41–45, 50
    commutation of, 290–291
    sum of, 290
    in two dimensions, 230–231
  impulse, 96
  magnitude of, 40, 50
  momentum, 87
  multiplication of, 45
  notation for, 39, 40, 50
  in a plane, 228–231
  polar, 291
  position, 41, 43–45, 50
  representation of
    graphical, 40
    mathematical, 40–41
  right-hand rule for, 289–290

rotational velocity, 257, 291
scalar product of, 245
  work as, 246–247
subtraction of, 44–45
  decomposition and, 239
  in one vs. two dimensions, 229
tangential component, 232–233, 234
in two dimensions, 228–231
unit, 40
velocity, 45–46, 50
  in two dimensions, 230–231
vs. scalars, 39
x component of, 41, 46–47, 50
zero, 42
Vector algebra, 238–240
Vector bosons, 161
Vector product, 304
Vector sum of forces, 178
  equation of motion and, 188–189, 190
  momentum and, 203
Velocity
  average, 35–37, 50
    rotational, 265
  center-of-mass, 139–141
    in many-object systems, 199
    in two-object systems, 197–198
  changes in, 54–55. *See also* Acceleration
    in collisions, 76–81
    in two reference frames, 135
  in circular motion, 256
  constant, 46–48, 64–66
  definition of, 35, 48
  in Galilean relativity, 133–137
  inertia and, 76–80
  in inertial reference frames, 130
  instantaneous, 48–49, 50
  momentum and, 87–89
  relative, 102
    in elastic collisions, 112
  in rolling motion, 298–299
  rotational, 257–258, 265, 268, 270
  in simple harmonic motion, 386
  in wave propagation, 406
  wave speed and, 408
  x component of, 46–47, 73, 268
  of zero-momentum reference frame, 130–131
Velocity space, 519–520
Velocity vectors, 45–46, 50
  in two dimensions, 230–231
VENUS mnemonic, 21–22
Vibration. *See* Oscillation(s)
Viscosity, 465, 494–497
  definition of, 494
  fluid flow and, 472
  Poiseuille's law and, 496
  unit of, 494
Visual representations, 9–11. *See also* Diagrams;
    Graphs
Volume, of ideal gas, 525–526, 541–545
  entropy and, 514–519
Volume flow rate, 492
Vortices, 472

W

Water. *See also* Fluid(s); Liquid(s)
  triple point of, 535
Water pressure, 468. *See also* Fluid pressure

Watt, 223
Wave(s)
  amplitude of, 407
  antinodes of, 421, 424
  average power and, 427–428
  beats and, 451–453
  boundary effects and, 411–414
  coherent sources of, 440–444
  compressional, 437
  definition of, 401
  displacement and, 402–403, 416–421
  energy transport in, 410–411, 426–428
  frequency of, 407
    Doppler effect and, 454–459
  graphic representations of, 401–404
  harmonic, 407, 419–421
  intensity of, 448–450
  longitudinal, 404
    compression and rarefaction in, 436–437
    sound, 436–439
  mechanical, 401
  medium for, 401
  motion of, 402
  nodes of, 410, 421–423
  nonmechanical, 401
  in one dimension, 400–432
  periodic, 407–408
  point source of, 434
  propagation of, 401–402, 404–409
    in two dimensions, 434–436
  shock, 459–461
  sound, 436–439. *See also* Sound
  spherical, 435–436
  standing, 421–424
  subsonic, 438
  superposition of, 409–411, 439, 451–453
    beating and, 451–453
    in two or three dimensions, 439
  surface, 434
  transverse, 403

  traveling, 416–421
  in two and three dimensions, 433–462
  ultrasonic, 446
Wave diffraction, 445–446
Wave equation, 429–431
Wave functions, 416–421, 434
  sound, 437–438
  time-dependent, 416–417
  time-independent, 416
Wave interference, 409–410
  in two or three dimensions, 439–444
Wave number, 419
Wave pulse, 401–404
  incident, 411–412
  reflected, 411–414
Wave speed, 402, 406–408, 424–426
Wavefronts
  Huygen's principle and, 445
  planar, 436
  sound, 438–439
  spherical, 435–436
  in three dimensions, 436
  in two dimensions, 434–436
Wavelength, 407–408
  unit of, 419
Weak interactions, 161–162
Weight
  apparent (effective), 320
  definition of, 320
  gravitational force and, 317–320
  measurement of, 318–320
    with balance, 318
    with spring scale, 318–320
  vs. gravitational force, 320
Weightlessness, 318, 320
Work, 202–225, 532
  center-of-mass acceleration and, 216–217
  definition of, 203–225
  done by gravitational force, 210, 213–216
  done by thermodynamic cycles, 576

  done by variable forces, 220–222
  done on ideal gas, 547–548
  done on many-particle system, 216–219
  done on single particle, 213–216, 219
  efficiency and, 573
  energy and, 203, 213, 547–548
  energy diagrams for, 206–208
  in energy law, 213
  entropy and, 533
  force displacement and, 203–204, 214,
    218, 219
  friction and, 222, 235–236
  motion in a plane and, 235–236, 243–247
  negative, 204–206
  positive, 204–206
  potential energy and, 221–222
  power and, 223–224
  as scalar product, 246–247
  symbol for, 213
  thermal energy transfer and, 531–534, 547–548
  unit of, 203
Work equation, 214
  for single particle vs. system of particles, 219

X

x component
  in graphs, 31–32, 35–37, 41, 46–47
  of vectors, 36–37, 40–41, 50

Z

Zero(es)
  absolute, 536, 537
  leading, 17
  in significant digits, 17–20
  trailing, 18
Zero vector, 42
Zero-momentum reference frames, 130–131, 142
  kinetic energy in, 142
  momentum in, 365–366
  velocity of, 138–139

... = 3.281 ft

... = 5280 ft = 1.609 km

1 km = 0.6214 mi

1 nautical mile (U.S.) = 1.151 mi = 6076 ft = 1.852 km

1 fermi = 1 femtometer (fm) = 10^{-15} m

1 angstrom (Å) = 10^{-10} m = 0.1 nm

1 light $-$ year (ly) = 9.461×10^{15} m

1 parsec = 3.26 ly = 3.09×10^{16} m

Volume

1 liter (L) = 1000 mL = 1000 cm^3 = 1.0×10^{-3} m^3
        = 1.057 qt (U.S.) = 61.02 in.^{3}

1 gal (U.S.) = 4 qt (U.S.) = 231 in.^{3} = 3.785 L = 0.8327 gal (British)

1 quart (U.S.) = 2 pints (U.S.) = 946 mL

1 pint (British) = 1.20 pints (U.S.) = 568 mL

1 m^3 = 35.31 ft^3

Speed

1 mi/h = 1.4667 ft/s = 1.6093 km/h = 0.4470 m/s

1 km/h = 0.2778 m/s = 0.6214 mi/h

1 ft/s = 0.3048 m/s = 0.6818 mi/h = 1.0973 km/h

1 m/s = 3.281 ft/s = 3.600 km/h = 2.237 mi/h

1 knot = 1.151 mi/h = 0.5144 m/s

Angle

1 radian (rad) = 57.30° = 57°18'

1° = 0.01745 rad

1 rev/min (rpm) = 0.1047 rad/s

Time

1 day = 8.640×10^4 s

1 year = 365.242 days = 3.156×10^7 s

Mass

1 atomic mass unit (u) = 1.6605×10^{-27} kg

1 kg = 0.06852 slug

1 metric ton = 1000 kg

1 long ton = 2240 lbs = 1016 kg

1 short ton = 2000 lbs = 909.1 kg

1 kg has a weight of 2.20 lb where $g = 9.80$ m/s^2

Force

1 lb = 4.44822 N

1 N = 10^5 dyne = 0.2248 lb

Energy and work

1 J = 10^7 ergs = 0.7376 ft $\cdot$ lb

1 ft $\cdot$ lb = 1.356 J = 1.29×10^{-3} Btu = 3.24×10^{-4} kcal

1 kcal = 4.19×10^3 J = 3.97 Btu

1 eV = 1.6022×10^{-19} J

1 kWh = 3.600×10^6 J = 860 kcal

1 Btu = 1.056×10^3 J

Power

1 W = 1 J/s = 0.7376 ft $\cdot$ lb/s = 3.41 Btu/h

1 hp = 550 ft $\cdot$ lb/s = 746 W

1 kWh/day = 41.667 W

Pressure

1 atm = 1.01325 bar = 1.01325×10^5 N/m^2 = 14.7 lb/in.^{2} = 760 torr

1 lb/in.^{2} = 6.895×10^3 N/m^2

1 Pa = 1 N/m^2 = 1.450×10^{-4} lb/in.^{2}